D1685955

35 [illegible]

A TEXT-BOOK

of

PATHOLOGY

By

W. G. MacCALLUM

Professor of Pathology and Bacteriology
In The Johns Hopkins University
Formerly Professor of Pathology
At Columbia University

With 575 Illustrations, Chiefly from Drawings

By

ALFRED FEINBERG

PHILADELPHIA AND LONDON

W. B. SAUNDERS COMPANY

1918

Reprinted March, 1917

Reprinted February, 1918

PRINTED IN AMERICA

PRESS OF
W. B. SAUNDERS COMPANY
PHILADELPHIA

To

G. A. MacCallum, M.D.

My Father

With Gratitude and Affection

PREFACE

In this book, which represents in its order and contents the course in Pathology given in the second year to the students of the College of Physicians and Surgeons, an effort has been made to discuss the general principles of Pathology as illustrated by a study of the commoner and more important diseases.

It is therefore in no sense intended as a book of reference. No attempt has been made to describe systematically all the diseased conditions which may occur in each organ, and for that reason there is no division into general and special pathology. Instead the whole is constructed upon the idea that all pathological disturbances are the result of some form of injury, or of the immediate or more remote reactions of the body to injury. It has been found possible to carry out this conception quite logically except when, as in the case of tumors, we are quite ignorant of the causes of the disease. For that reason, after a few chapters devoted to the general working principles with illustrations from the most common conditions, the rest of the book is divided into chapters which deal with various types of, injury and their immediate and remote effects. The discussion of tumors necessarily forms a separate part, since they seem to be so little controlled by the laws which govern other pathological processes.

The whole book is planned therefore to discuss disease as far as possible upon the basis of etiology, and the usual subdivision of the material according to its anatomical distribution has not been employed. Nevertheless the index is so arranged as to facilitate reference to lesions of the heart, lungs, etc.

Partly because of lack of space, but chiefly because they are admirably treated in great detail in books easily accessible to students, several whole sections usually included in books on pathology have been omitted. This is true of the relations of heredity to disease, of the biology of bacteria and other parasites, of malformations, and of many diseases of the nervous system. The whole subject of resistance and immunity is touched upon only in the briefest way. Nevertheless, even though such subjects are intentionally omitted, it is realized that criticism may well be offered when it is found that the diseases chosen to illustrate the principles of pathology do not include many important affections, such as multiple sclerosis, progressive muscular atrophy, rabies, yellow fever, and a host of others.

In discussing the prominent types of injury an attempt has been made to give an impression of the far-reaching interdependence of pathological conditions by making a continuous story of the whole with numerous digressions for the description of special lesions or their causes. Several chapters are devoted to the results of obstruction of the flow of contents of hollow organs, and while it may seem that this is a rather forced arrangement the type of injury is one whose effects depend in each instance upon certain common principles.

A constant effort has been made to speak of the disturbances of function and of chemical interchange in the course of disease, as far as that was possible, and even to describe symptoms. If this makes the book seem like a treatise on clinical medicine, it is only because pathology and clinical medicine are, after all, the same thing viewed from slightly different angles.

References to the literature given with each chapter have been chosen, as far as possible, to direct the student to readable and comprehensive papers which review the subject and give further and more complete references.

The illustrations are almost entirely from specimens which we have studied in this laboratory, but I have to thank many friends in other laboratories for their kindness in sending me material or for allowing me use of photographs. The drawings with very few exceptions have been made by Mr. Alfred Feinberg.

I am indebted to my assistants for much help, and especially to Dr. A. M. Pappenheimer, who furnished the material for the section on the thymus and aided me in reading the proof, and to Dr. R. A. Lambert who made the index.

W. G. MacCALLUM.

981 Madison Ave., New York City

CONTENTS

CHAPTER XXXI

CHAPTER XXXII

CHAPTER XXXIII

CHAPTER XXXIV

CHAPTER XXXV

CHAPTER XXXVI

CHAPTER XXXVII

TEXT-BOOK OF PATHOLOGY

CHAPTER I

DISTURBANCES OF THE FLUIDS OF THE BODY

Relation of fluids to tissues; blood, lymph, tissue fluids. The blood: variations in quality and quantity. Readjustment. Plethora and oligæmia. Clotting. Thrombosis.

Relation of Fluids to Tissues.—The cells of the tissues are, like other living beings, dependent for their life and activity upon a constant and abundant supply of food and oxygen and an equally adequate removal of their waste-products. This service is rendered them by the circulation of the various fluids through every part, propelled by a mechanical arrangement, the perfection of which we shall have frequent occasion to admire. There are three main types into which we may divide these circulating fluids, the blood, the tissue fluids, and the lymph.

The blood is practically everywhere separated from actual contact with the cells of the tissues by a semi-permeable membrane composed of other cells, the endothelium. It flows through the whole body, giving off certain substances and withdrawing others, always through this membrane. Between the cells outside the blood-vessels there are spaces, or at least potential spaces, in which a small amount of fluid collects which directly bathes the cells and directly receives their waste. This tissue fluid is constantly being changed too, by interaction with the blood. But it also stands in exactly the same relation to the lymph, which, like the blood, flows inside channels with semi-permeable walls composed of endothelial cells and goes to empty into the vein. We do not believe now that there are open communications between the lymphatic channels and the tissue crevices. That idea, it seems, has been thoroughly disproved by the recent work which shows the completeness of the endothelial lining of these channels.

It will be realized, then, that there must be qualitative differences at all times between these three fluids, although by processes of diffusion and osmosis there is constantly going on an attempt to establish a balance between them. Uniformity is never reached, though, on account of the metabolic activity of the tissue-cells and the immediate removal of the blood and lymph before equilibrium is established. These qualitative differences and, indeed, the question of the chemical composition of the fluids need not arrest us here. Materials pass from the arterial side of the capillaries into the tissue spaces, and from there either into the lymphatics or into the veins, and it is obvious that, according to the character of the cells which make up the tissue, the nature of the lymph and of the venous blood produced in this way must vary greatly in different parts of the body. The portal blood is filled with materials which could not be found in any such quantities in the blood of the femoral vein, and the hepatic vein contains blood which is altogether changed by passing through the liver. The degree of activity of the organs plays a great part also, so that during digestion portal blood undoubtedly differs very greatly from the blood of the same vein at other times.

THE QUANTITY OF BLOOD IN THE BODY

Normally the quantity of blood in the body bears a fairly definite relation to the weight of the body. Until recently the determinations of this quantity were notoriously inaccurate, and even yet little is known about the possible variations. But with the method of Haldane-Smith, which consists essentially in administering a known amount of carbon monoxide and estimating its concentration in a sample of the blood, the quantity has been shown to be from 5 to 5.3 per cent. of the body weight.

Experimental efforts to increase or decrease the amount of blood in proportion to the tissues fail except for very short periods, because the excess of fluid introduced is immediately excreted, and that which is removed from the blood-vessels by bleeding is quickly made up by the filtration of fluid from the tissues into the capillaries. Blood-pressure is scarcely changed by any such measures because the vasomotor mechanism immediately adapts the capacity of the stream-bed as nearly as possible to its new contents.

The adjustment is especially rapid and effective when an excess of fluid is introduced, and if it does not enter the veins too abruptly and rapidly the excretion by the kidneys keeps pace with it almost perfectly. In the other case, the removal of blood, there are naturally limits to the power of the tissues to give up fluid to restore its bulk. Even under the best circumstances this is a slower process than the removal of fluid by excretion. The terms *plethora* and *anæmia* or *oligæmia* have long been in use to imply an excess of blood, on the one hand, and a poverty of blood, on the other, but with this extraordinary compensatory power of the body in view, it seems that we must use them with some caution. Nevertheless it is perfectly obvious at autopsy, if not during life, that in some persons the vessels are distended with an enormous quantity of blood, while in others not only do the vessels seem collapsed, but all the tissues are shrunken and dry looking. Especially is the latter true in old persons and those who have long suffered from a wasting disease.

Plethora.—Apparently the existence of actual changes in the amount of blood which last for any time is dependent chiefly upon qualitative changes in the blood itself and in the tissues. A true plethora, in which the blood is increased without change in its composition, probably occurs with defects in the action of the heart which then allows a part of the blood to remain practically stagnant in the veins and propels an abnormally small part of it into the arteries. The compensation for this diminution of the arterial circulation by introduction of more fluid may restore the normal amount in active circulation, but increases the total amount in the body. Hydræmic or serous plethora is spoken of as a condition in which the quantity of blood is increased by a relative increase in its watery part. As has been said, it is impossible to maintain this for any length of time experimentally because the kidneys promptly excrete the excess of water, but it is conceivable, though not proven, that it may arise when the excretory power of the kidneys is lowered by disease.

Oligæmia.—Practically the same things may be said of oligæmia or anæmia. The simplest type of general anæmia is undoubtedly that which is produced when a considerable amount of blood is lost through the opening of a blood-vessel. The person becomes blanched, makes forced respirations, and may become unconscious on account of the poor supply of nutrition to the brain. He becomes very weak and thirsty, and his pulse is low and scarcely perceptible, but often very rapid. An immediate attempt is made by the tissues to pour back again into the vessels enough fluid to fill them again and to raise the blood-pressure, and consequently, for some time, on account of this adding of fluid both from the tissues and from water taken in by mouth, the blood becomes dilute. The proportion of red corpuscles, which can be determined by counting, sinks for two or three days, at which time the inflow of fluid ceases and the reproduction of corpuscles by the blood-forming organs begins to make itself evident. From that time onward there is a steady increase in the number of corpuscles to each cubic millimetre until the blood reaches its normal state. There seems to be also the other form of oligæmia in which the quantity is reduced by loss of water. Naturally this will be compensated as quickly as possible, too, but in such diseases as cholera the loss is so rapid that the tissues become desiccated as well. It is quite possible, therefore, that the decrease in the quantity of blood is merely proportional to the desiccation of all the tissues.

CLOTTING, THROMBOSIS, ETC.

Clotting.—We are not well informed as to the nature of the process through which an injury to a single cell or a unicellular animal is healed. The wound is closed very rapidly, and apparently by a process rather more complex than the mere flowing together of the protoplasm. We do know, however, that in such animals as the crustacea and in the higher types, where there is a circulation of blood and other body juices, these fluids possess the peculiar property of clotting, or coagulating as soon as they are exposed to contact with anything which has not the character of the living vessel-wall. It is through this property that the loss of blood from every trifling wound is checked, although otherwise it might well prove fatal. In this sense the clotting is distinctly a protective process, probably developed from the time of the first appearance of animal life as a factor indispensable to the preservation of the animal. The same process appears again and again under the greatest variety of circumstances in pathological conditions, but it will be seen that in all—in spite of many imperfections in the mechanism—it has a protective significance.

Clotting, even in its simplest form, is a complex process which has been diligently studied for many years, but even yet there are many important parts of it which are not at all well understood. The names of Alexander Schmidt, Arthus, Hammarsten, Pekelharing, Loeb, Fuld, Spiro, and Morawitz are especially prominent in this connection, and the following may be regarded as the most generally accepted results of their work, which have been clearly stated by Morawitz.

When blood and lymph are allowed to escape into a glass dish they clot, usually in a very short time. If the blood is continually stirred, the clot adheres to the stirring rod, leaving a permanently fluid blood (defibrinated blood). If it is not stirred, the clot forms uniformly throughout the whole quantity of blood, converting it into a solid, rather dry, firm mass, often so tenacious that the dish, if it be not too wide and shallow, may be inverted without spilling. Such a clot is of a uniform dark-red color. If it be squeezed, a red fluid is forced out which is identical with defibrinated blood. If the spongy mass be washed in running water, all the red blood-corpuscles may be washed away, leaving a stringy, yellowish white, elastic mass of fibrin. If the fresh blood be kept very cold, or if it be received into an oiled dish, it will not clot so quickly, and since the red corpuscles are heavier than the plasma, there may be time for them to sink to the bottom in a very thick layer. The leucocytes are lighter and rest in a layer on top of the red corpuscles, while above there is some plasma almost free from cells. By this time clotting occurs throughout, the clot differing from the uniform red one formed by rapid coagulation, in the presence of a grayish-yellow upper layer which contains most of the leucocytes and platelets. This was called the "buffy coat" by the old bloodletters, and its thickness was, in their hands, an index of the rapidity with which the blood clotted, and of the number of leucocytes contained, although their deductions usually took various other turns.

This slow clotting showing the effects of gravity is seen very commonly in the heart at autopsy, for the intact endothelial lining of the heart keeps its contents a long time without clotting. There the deep-red portion of the clot ("cruor clot") is in the dependent part, while the tough, elastic, translucent, yellowish substance (chicken-fat or turtle-fat clot) occupies the uppermost part of the heart as the body lies on the table (Fig. 1). The homogeneous elasticity of this kind of clot and the fact that it is readily removed from the heart-wall, leaving it unaltered, make it quite easy to distinguish it from the thrombus formed on injured areas of the heart-wall during life, although extraordinary mistakes have been made and the postmortem clot held to be the cause of death.

At first—and especially when it is rapidly formed—the clot is quite dry. Indeed, it is this which confers the dryness and firmness upon the lung in the early stages of pneumonia, where a fresh clot occupies each air-cell. Later, however, through its own elasticity, the clot contracts away from the wall of the glass and shrinks together. In this way it expresses from its meshes a clear fluid, the serum, in which it is finally bathed. If we examine the clot microscopically, we shall find it to be composed of a delicate network of fine fibrils, among which there are entangled the cells of the blood. In the rapidly formed clot these are perfectly homogeneously distributed in the proportions in which they existed in the circulating

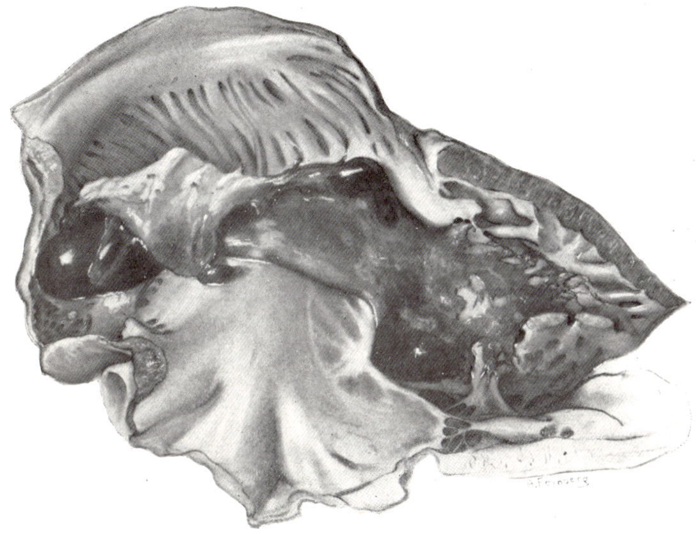

Fig. 1.—Postmortem clot in the cavity of the heart.

blood, but in the layered clot which has slowly formed there are red corpuscles, but fewer leucocytes in the lower red part of the clot, while in the upper layer there are numerous leucocytes with platelets, but no red cells; there may even be a layer in which there are very few cells of any kind (Fig. 2).

Throughout the clot one may sometimes recognize minute centres about which the fibrin radiates, or if the corpuscles are not too much crowded, it may be possible to see star-like radiations of filaments of fibrin about single cells. One sometimes sees these radial arrangements of fibrin about bacteria in the blood, and this may be especially striking in cases of anthrax or other such infection in which the blood contains many foreign cells. Besides these, in clots which are formed after death in the heart or large blood-vessels, it is generally possible to find in sections pale, pink-staining clumps to which a number of leucocytes adhere buried deeply and irregularly among the red corpuscles. These have been described by Rost and others and seem to consist chiefly of groups of blood-platelets. Nevertheless, the distinctive character of the clot formed after death in the stagnant blood is its general homogeneity of structure, in which respect it differs so sharply from the clots formed during life in the streaming blood.

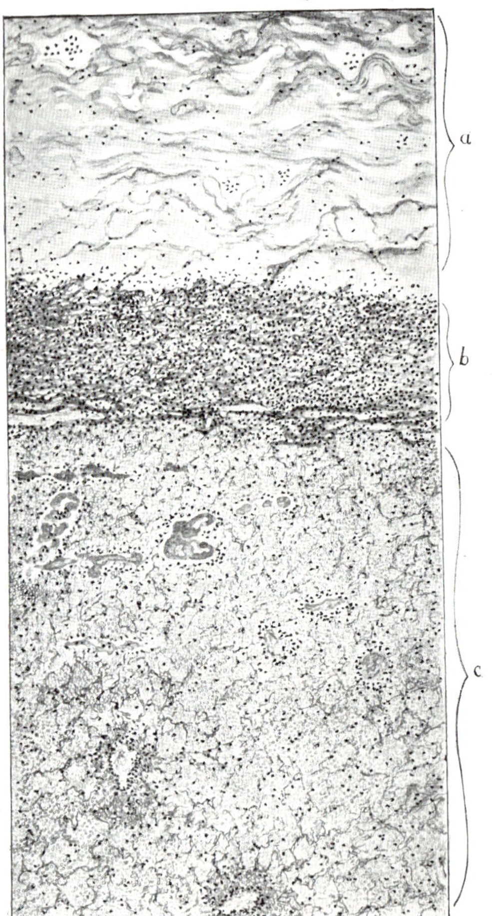

Fig. 2.—Postmortem clot: *a*, Fibrin; *b*, layer of leucocytes; *c*, cruor clot with red corpuscles and platelets in clumps.

As to the mechanism of the clotting, it is generally agreed that the fibrin is formed by the action of a ferment-like substance called by Morawitz *thrombin*, upon a proteid substance, fibrinogen, which occurs in the plasma. The thrombin is in itself, according to this theory, a complex result of the interaction of two substances. The first is a material called *thrombokinase*, which is derived from the formed elements of the blood (leucocytes or platelets) or from any tissue with which the blood may come into contact. It does not seem necessary that these cells should be actually destroyed, but merely altered in some particular which we cannot recognize. The second constituent occurs in the plasma and is called *prothrombin*. What the character of the union or interaction of thrombokinase with prothrombin is we do not know, but it is known that the presence of a soluble salt of calcium is required to complete it and bring about the formation of thrombin. After the thrombin is formed, the calcium is no longer necessary to carry out the second phase of the clotting, although it accelerates it. This second phase consists in the interaction between the thrombin and fibrinogen, which is present in the plasma with the formation of a fine fibrillary network of fibrin.

The blood ordinarily remains fluid in the vessels because the leucocytes and other cells are not injured enough to liberate thrombokinase—whatever small amounts are set free are neutralized by the *antithrombin* which has been shown to exist in the plasma. The conversion of fibrinogen to fibrin is irreversible, but the nature of the change is not known—possibly one is a hydrosol, the other a hydrogel. Howell states that thrombin may be obtained in a pure form, that it is of the nature of a protein, and that it probably does not act as a ferment, although a minimal amount will combine quantitatively with 215 times its bulk of fibrinogen. He proposes a very different theory of clotting, which is based largely upon the fact that a sort of balance is maintained between the antithrombin and the prothrombin which neutralize each other. The injured cells or tissues give off a substance which he calls thromboplastin or thromboplastic substance, and which he recognizes as a lipoid identical with kephalin. The antithrombin present in normal plasma is sufficient to bind the prothrombin, but the thromboplastin neutralizes the antithrombin. The free prothrombin now forms thrombin with the aid of calcium, and at once coagulates the fibrinogen, forming the clot.

The part played by particular cells in producing the thromboplastin or thrombokinase has been discussed, and special attention has been directed to the platelets, but without resulting in the proof that they are more active in this respect than other cells. Duke thinks their absence may account for the prolonged bleeding in purpura. There are some conditions, particularly such infectious processes as pneumonia, in which clotting occurs very rapidly, and shortly after death complete moulds of the vessel may be pulled out from the large vascular trunks. In such instances the clots are tough and dry and uniformly deep red throughout. On the other hand, there are other conditions, such as hæmophilia, icterus, etc., in which coagulation is greatly delayed and serious hæmorrhage may occur during and after the slightest surgical operation. Whipple thinks that the delay in clotting of blood in disease of the liver with jaundice is due to an excess of antithrombin in the blood, while Howell shows that in hæmophilia the blood is deficient in prothrombin. On the other hand, spontaneous clotting of the blood in the veins during life may be due to a deficiency in antithrombin.

Thrombosis.—On the basis of either theory of clotting it is easy to understand that a coagulum might form about any mass of cells which, after suffering some injury, had become clumped together or agglutinated in the blood, and, indeed, Loeb and others have observed that an agglutination of formed elements always precedes the formation of the fibrin. The part played by the platelets is perhaps important in postmortem or extracorporeal clotting, but it becomes especially prominent in the inception of thrombi, which are peculiar clots formed during life in the streaming blood.

The character of these thrombi is very different in some respects from that of the postmortem clots, although the principles concerned in their formation are the same, except that the single mechanical factor of the streaming movement of the blood disturbs the ordinary process of clotting and brings into prominence the feature of preliminary agglutination of the platelets.

A thrombus begins by the deposition, on the wall of the blood-channel, of a minute, pearly, translucent mass of platelets which grows by the adhesion of other platelets as they come by. These produce curious upstanding laminæ or walls running transversely to the blood-stream and anastomosing freely with one another; the platelets are so welded together that their outlines can no longer be seen, and in section these laminæ appear as faintly pink-staining, finely granular bands in the substance of the thrombus (Fig. 3).

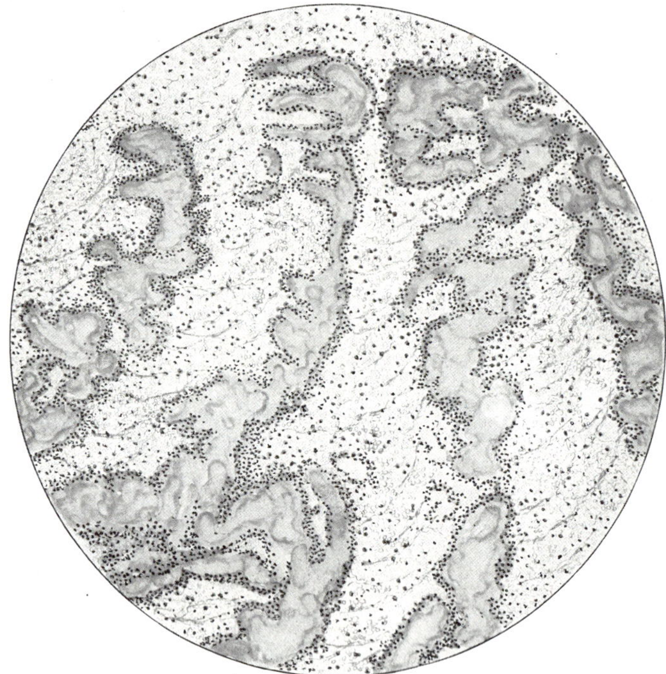

Fig. 3.—Thrombus: coral-like laminæ of platelets with marginal leucocytes and intervening red corpuscles and fibrin.

However, it must not be supposed that they rise up alone and unsupported in the current. Instead of that, they quickly catch the passing leucocytes and hold them all along their surfaces (borders in the section), like flies on sheets of sticky fly-paper; and at the same time they seem to liberate thromboplastic substance, so that filaments of fibrin spread out from them on all sides, and, meeting with filaments from the next lamella, hang in festoons between them. In this way the branching and anastomosing lamellæ are guyed and braced together by fibrin, which, needless to say, entangles quantities of red corpuscles so that finally the whole is a solid mass of peculiarly constructed clot. At first, of course, this thrombus

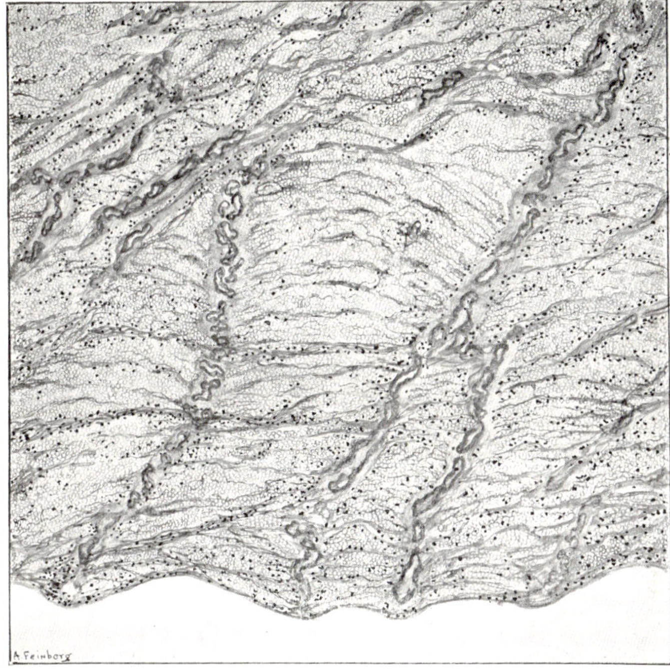

Fig. 4.—Thrombus: the strands of platelets form superficial corrugations.

is predominantly a red mass, although the grayish-white lamellæ of platelets can be seen in a cross-section forming a web all through the red. On the free surface of the thrombus these same lamellæ project slightly above

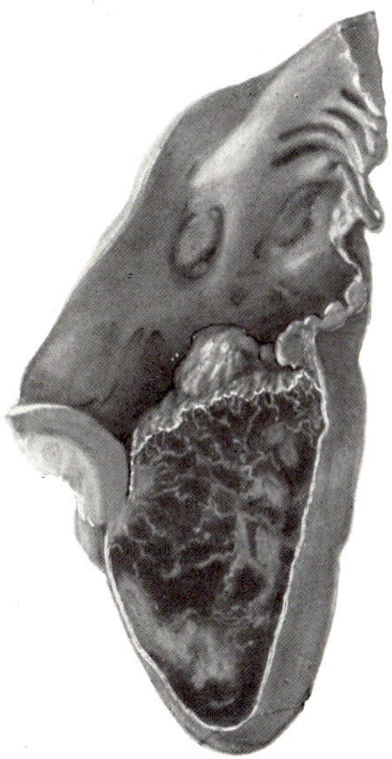

Fig. 5.—Thrombus in auricular appendage.

the red part of the clot, and these corrugations are known as the "lines of Zahn" (Fig. 4). Red corpuscles, under such circumstances, soon die, lose their hæmoglobin, and finally disappear into a formless débris which in time assumes a semitranslucent appearance. A thrombus, therefore, which is largely red at first, becomes yellowish gray after a time, and the

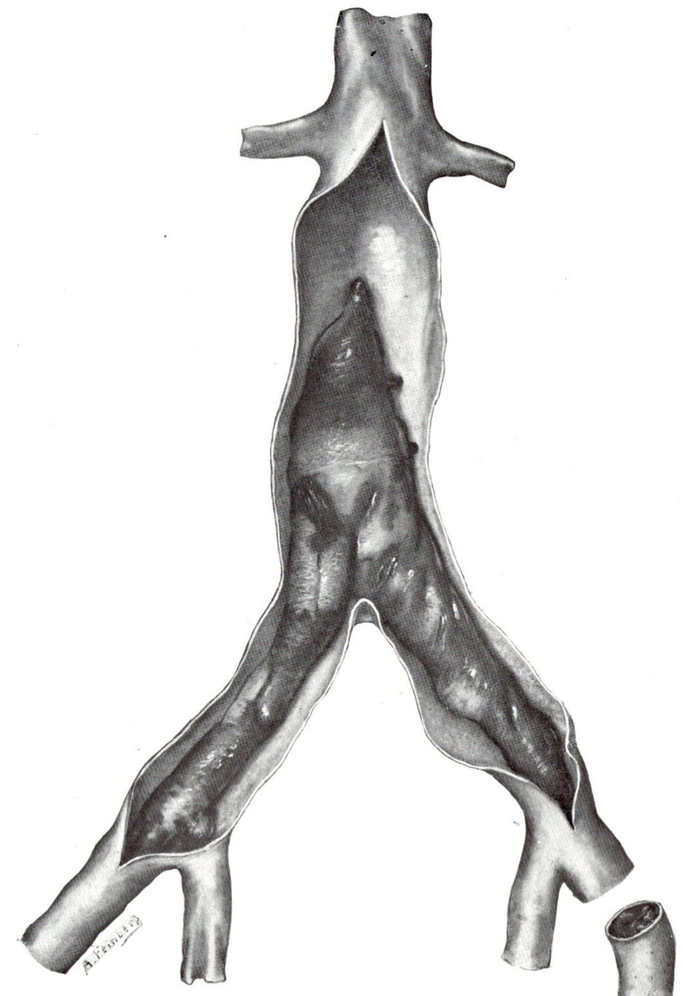

Fig. 6.—Thrombus in vena cava.

contrasting color of the platelet sheets is lost in the homogeneous mass. Nevertheless, since a thrombus continually tends to grow by accretion, the parts of different ages show differences in color. Indeed, when a thrombus forms in a vein, occluding it, there is left a perfectly stagnant column of blood reaching to the next affluent of the vein, and in this an ordinary homogeneous clot is formed, just as it would be in a test-tube—

not exactly, however, for there is some motion communicated to this column of blood and clumps of platelets are found. At the inflow of the next branch the clotting may stop or begin once more to assume the character of the thrombus. Thus, as Aschoff says, a thrombus has a head, and then, perhaps, extending both ways in the vein, a propagated part or tail, which differs from it, being more like a postmortem clot.

Thrombi may be formed anywhere in the blood-stream, even in the walls of the aorta, where it might seem that the pulsating torrent of blood would allow no chance for the deposition of the pioneer platelets. But most commonly they appear in the veins or in the auricular appendages or intertrabecular spaces of the heart or upon the valves of the heart. In the veins they seem to start from the region of a valve, where the slight obstruction gives rise to eddies. In the heart (Fig. 5) they bulge forward from the recess as pinkish yellow, distinctly corrugated masses, generally coated with an adherent red clot—sometimes they are quite smooth and globular, and these, which seem to be old ones, are frequently found to be softened into a semifluid or fluid material in their central parts. In the veins (Fig. 6) the lumen is usually, though not always, obliterated, and at the lower end the vein is plugged for a long way with a soft red clot. The thrombus itself differs from a postmortem clot in being inelastic, friable, and granular, and in adhering to the wall of the vein so that when it is removed the lining of the vein is left roughened and dull looking. In the propagated clot one may find for some distance indications of the general characters of the thrombus, and such freshly formed thrombi are hard to tell from postmortem clots. Any part of the thrombus may break off and be swept along in the blood-stream to plug some distant vessel.

The question as to the cause of the formation of thrombi has been answered in various ways. The wall of the vessel underlying them is always injured, but whether by the presence of the thrombus or by something which in that way provoked the formation of the thrombus is hard to say. Most of the older writers assumed a primary injury of the wall (Eberth and Schimmelbusch, Welch) which allowed the production of thrombokinase or thromboplastin. This seems especially true of those instances in which thrombi are formed in the aorta upon ragged, arteriosclerotic patches or in the venous sinuses of the dura at a point where an abscess extending from the middle ear encroaches upon them. For a time there was great enthusiasm over the idea that thrombi occurring in general infections and after surgical operations were due to the presence of bacteria which injured the vessel-wall. Perhaps this was going too far, but now the pendulum has swung the other way, and Aschoff and his colleagues contend that thrombi are essentially produced by some mechanical obstruction or slowing of the stream, and that the bacteria which are found in them are brought to the thrombus after it is well formed. Aschoff has made elaborate studies to show that, in a stream of water with obstructions of various forms, sawdust or sand floating in the stream will accumulate according to definite laws in a certain relation to the obstructions, and especially where eddies are formed and where consequently the stream is slowed. The distribution of little sand-banks in the course of a crooked stream with many obstructions is familiar enough to every one, and it is easily credible that such mechanical factors are of great importance in determining where the thrombus shall start and how the deposition shall proceed. Indeed, the difficulty is confined to the explanation of the first deposit of platelets—after that the growth of the thrombus is easily explained by the ordinary principles of clotting and by the obstruction produced by the thrombus itself. But I must still believe that many thrombi arise because an injured or dead surface is exposed to the coagulable circulating blood, as in the sclerotic patches of the aorta, the infected cranial sinus in otitis media, the uterine veins in puerperal sepsis, or the portal branches leading away from an appendix abscess. No one thinks of the thrombus formed upon a heart valve as caused by mechanical slowing of the stream with secondary deposit of bacteria. Why, therefore, is there any difficulty in believing that bacteria may lodge on the endothelium of a valve in a vein where the current is vastly slower, and there, by injuring the endothelium, make possible the first step in the formation of the thrombus. As a predisposing and later as a guiding factor controlling the architecture of the thrombus, modifications of the velocity and direction of the current are undoubtedly of great importance, but for the first step in the lodgment of platelets injury to the endothelium seems to me to be of prime significance. Mechanical injury to the vessel quite naturally brings about thrombus formation. If a vessel be ligated very gently in two places, so that the endothelium is not injured, but merely gently pressed together, clotting of the contained blood will not occur for a long time, but if the vessel-walls are crushed and torn, it ensues almost at once. Cut vessels of small size close themselves partly by contraction but partly by the formation of a thrombus at the bleeding end.

Aschoff, in his classification, describes three other forms of thrombi: Agglutination thrombi, which occur in capillaries such as those of the glomeruli of the kidney and are really formless masses of agglutinated red corpuscles (Flexner). Precipitation thrombi, which are produced in the capillaries of exposed tissue, like the mucosa of the stomach, by strong chemical poisons which coagulate or precipitate the whole protein-rich blood, and, third, thrombi which are composed of the débris of red corpuscles and other cells which may appear in quantities after some hæmolytic process.

LITERATURE

Welch: Allbutt's System of Medicine, 1899, vi, 155.

Eberth and Schimmelbusch: Thrombose, Stuttgart, 1888.

Aschoff, Beck, de la Camp, and Krönig: Beiträge zur Thrombosefrage, Leipzig, 1912.

Whipple: Arch. Int. Med., 1913, xii, 637.

Howell: Amer. Jour. Physiol., 1910, xxvi, 453; Arch. Int. Med., 1914, xiii, 76; Amer. Jour. Physiol., 1912, xxxi, 1; 1913, xxxii, 264.

Morawitz: Oppenheimer's Handb. der Biochemie, 1909, ii, 40.

Aschoff: Arch. Int. Med., 1913, xii, 503.

CHAPTER II

LOCAL DISTURBANCES IN THE CIRCULATION OF THE BLOOD

Hyperæmia; anæmia. Postmortem changes in distribution; active and passive hyperæmia. Local anæmia. Embolism. Infarction. Gangrene.

THE circulation through the tissues is dependent upon three main factors: the activity of the heart, the changes in the calibre of the blood-vessels, and the amount of blood. Of these, the changes in the calibre of the blood-vessels are of special importance as far as the local conditions are concerned. The muscular walls of the arteries, and to a less extent the veins, are controlled, as is well known, by the vasomotor nerves, so that the amount of blood which passes through any given tissue depends largely on the activity of these nerves. Quite aside, therefore, from any pathological conditions, there are remarkable changes from time to time in the amount of blood which passes through the different tissues, the arterial blood supply generally increasing with the activity of that particular tissue.*

* **Postmortem Changes.**—During life the distribution of the blood in any organ or tissue is a very uniform one, as a rule, but on the cessation of the action of the heart numerous alterations take place, so that in the tissues, as observed in the dead body, the distribution of the blood is very much changed, and it is necessary to be familiar with these changes in order to appreciate those which are actually the results of pathological conditions which have existed during life. The contractility of the arterial walls is dependent not only upon their muscular structures, which aid, by a sort of peristaltic movement, the action of the heart, but also upon the large amount of elastic tissue which exists in their walls. The combined effect of the contraction of these two tissues, as soon as the heart stops beating, is to drive the blood out of the arterial side into the venous side of the circulation in each organ, in that way immediately producing a change in the appearance of the organ.

The liver, which is in life of a uniform red color, shows at once on cessation of the heart-beat the lobulation with its darker blood-filled central portion and paler periphery, a mottling being produced by the collection of blood in the central portion of each lobule, while the periphery is left pale. In the same way the great veins in the abdomen become filled with blood, whereas the arteries everywhere are found collapsed and nearly empty.

Other influences are brought to bear also, and especially that of gravity, so that all dependent portions, as the body lies, become overfilled with blood and assume a dark purplish hue, while the upper portions are relatively pale. This is true even of the different parts of the internal organs, so that the loops of intestine which lie in the pelvis and in the lower part of the peritoneal cavity show a great distension of the veins, although the upper portions of the loops are pale. When the intestine is opened and stretched out, these areas appear as patches of congestion, the nature of which is not always recognized by the beginner.

The purplish discoloration of the skin of the back is not seen in those parts upon which the body has lain; thus, for example, the backs of the shoulders, the buttocks, and heels usually appear quite white, because, owing to the pressure of the weight of the body, the blood has not been allowed to sink into them. Firm pressure of the fingers upon the purple area is sufficient to drive the blood out of those veins and to leave white marks. This overdistension of the veins through gravity is spoken of as *livor mortis*, and it must be distinguished from accumulations of blood in the tissues themselves—hæmorrhage. This distinction is readily made because in livor mortis (hypostasis) the blood is still

An increase in the amount of blood to any part is spoken of as *hyperæmia;* and such hyperæmia may be active, when there is an actual increase in the amount of arterial blood, or passive when, through any obstruction, the outflow of venous blood is retarded. On the other hand, decrease of the supply of blood in any area is known as partial or complete *anæmia* and results from obstruction of the arterial flow.

HYPERÆMIA

Active hyperæmia is usually the result of vasomotor effects upon the vessels, and is essentially a physiological process, being concerned so largely with the supply of increased nutritive fluid to tissues which are assuming for the time a heightened activity. It, however, appears in certain nervous disturbances, and also may be brought about by the direct application of heat and irritants, which cause the blood-vessels to dilate. It is probably in just this way that the irritant, which is sufficiently intense to bring about an inflammatory reaction, causes the active hyperæmia which forms so striking a feature of that process. The tissues through which such a rapid stream of arterial blood is passing are usually somewhat swollen and red and warmer than the surrounding tissue.

Passive hyperæmia is more commonly a pathological or abnormal process, inasmuch as it is the result of interference with the outflow of blood. It is usually a very wide-spread obstruction, due to some inability on the part of the heart which dams back blood into the whole venous tract, but occasionally it may be quite local. This is especially due to the fact that the veins are more easily compressed than the arteries, so that pressure from without which will occlude the veins can still allow the blood to be poured in from the more resistant arteries, congesting and distending the tissues with stagnant blood.

It is by no means uncommon to find a loop of intestine pushed through an aperture in the abdominal wall, thus constituting a hernia. Such a loop may, in most cases, be pushed back into the peritoneum; but sometimes, when it has escaped habitually through this newly formed aperture into the sac which is formed outside, it may become so enlarged by an increase of its

---

within the veins, while in hæmorrhage it has escaped from the blood-vessels and can no longer be pressed away with the fingers.

If the body has lain for some time, and especially if the temperature of the surrounding air has been high, there may appear other discolorations which are due not particularly to the distribution of blood nor to its escape from the vessels, but to the disintegration of the red corpuscles by a physico-chemical process which we shall discuss later under the name of hæmolysis. This sets free into the fluid the red staining matter of the blood (hæmoglobin), which tinges diffusely all dead tissues with which it comes into contact; the lining of the aorta, for example, and of the heart itself may assume a dull red color which is in sharp contrast to the normal. Such blood staining of the tissues may appear with great rapidity in persons who have died from infection with one of those bacteria which have the property of destroying the red corpuscles rapidly by the poison which they produce. In such infections, notably the streptococcus infections, the blood in the vessels stains the surrounding tissues to such an extent that the course of the subcutaneous veins may be seen in the form of a network of purplish lines through the skin.

contents that it can no longer be returned, and indeed so large that its blood-vessels, which, of course, stretch through the aperture, also become constricted there, and the circulation is brought to a full stop, not because blood cannot get in through the artery, but because it cannot escape through the more readily compressed vein. This is a condition which is known as "strangulated hernia."

A local congestion of not quite so extreme a degree may often be seen in the liver when a tumor nodule embedded in the liver substance presses on the efferent vein and causes that portion of the liver ordinarily drained by the vein to become congested. The process is put to therapeutic use in Bier's treatment of various local infections in which a stagnation of blood is produced for a time in the inflamed area by the application of a tight bandage which obstructs the veins and leaves the arteries open.

Ordinarily, the communications between veins are very abundant, so that the obstruction of any one vein is hardly likely to cause such congestion. Nevertheless, the surgeon must be careful in operating to leave the tissues not only with a sufficient arterial supply, but also with an adequate venous outflow if they are to remain alive; for the stoppage of the stream from the venous side is just as important as the obstruction of the arterial side. In the case of mesenteric veins, renal veins, etc., ligation or occlusion may readily lead to the death of the tissue which they drain. In other places where anastomosis is free there may be no effect, but if the obstruction, as in the case of a long thrombus of the femoral vein, is extensive enough to plug the communicating branches, the accessory channels are also closed and the circulation is greatly disturbed. In such a case great pain is experienced, the leg becomes swollen and livid, or later pale, with purplish blotches, and, because of the malnutrition and œdema, it can scarcely be moved (milk-leg). Œdema or oozing of the fluid of the blood into the tissue-spaces is characteristic of all instances of marked passive hyperæmia, and in extreme cases, with great disturbance of the nutrition of tissues, hæmorrhage may also occur.

Passive hyperæmia may be the effect also of nervous disturbances which render immobile for a long time the muscles of an extremity. The same result follows to a slight extent if disease of the joints with ankylosis makes them immovable. In both these cases the passive hyperæmia is relatively slight, and is essentially the effect of gravity. In this respect it resembles the condition which is found in the dependent portions of organs in persons who are constrained to lie in bed for a long time in one position. It is spoken of as *hypostasis*, and becomes particularly striking in the lungs, where it may so lower the nutrition, and consequently the power of resistance, of the tissues as to allow bacteria to take root there and produce the so-called hypostatic pneumonia.

LOCAL ANÆMIA

In a general anæmia, such as has been mentioned, each individual tissue may, of course, suffer somewhat, but the most intense effects of this type may be brought about locally without regard to the general condition of the circulation. Such local anæmia must always result from an obstruction opposed to the inflow of arterial blood. This may be an effect of the active contraction of the blood-vessels through the intermediation of the vasomotors, or it may be due to pressure on these vessels from without, or to thickening of the walls of the vessels with narrowing of their lumen, or, finally, and most commonly, to a complete obstruction or plugging of the artery by some foreign material which is lodged there. Combinations of all these things very commonly occur. The vasomotor narrowing of the vessel is ordinarily a normal process, aimed at the withholding of blood from a vessel which does not need it at that particular stage of its activity, but sometimes it may become pathological, as in the so-called *Raynaud's disease,* which consists in such a constriction of the vessels of the fingers and toes as to cause even the death of those tissues. Apparently the familiar *chilblains* depend upon such excessive narrowing of the vessels when the hands or feet are exposed to cold. That seems to happen in particularly susceptible persons, and probably especially in those whose habits are sedentary and in whom the circulation is ordinarily not very active.

Pressure from without might cause the closure of an artery if it were directly enough applied. It is difficult, however, to obstruct the arteries by pressure from without, because they are so protected by other tissues; and it is well known that a ligature tied tightly around an extremity will cause rather an increase of blood in the ligated part, because it obstructs the outflow through the veins long before it can obstruct the artery. In order to render a limb bloodless for the purpose of carrying on an operation in a clean field, as in the method of Esmarch, a rubber bandage must be applied with great force.

The pressure of tumor-nodules and of aneurysms upon arteries may sometimes cause their obstruction in such a way as to cut off completely the supply of blood from the part. The pedicle of a tumor or the long mesentery of a loop of intestine may become twisted so as to shut the lumen of the artery and cause the death of the tissue supplied by it; but usually, as we have stated in speaking of strangulated hernia, this first results in the obstruction of the vein, so that the tissue becomes engorged with stagnant blood and the final effect of shutting off the artery masked.

The walls of the arteries themselves may undergo structural changes which finally lead to such narrowing of the lumen as to prevent the further flow of blood. This usually occurs when an organ has passed its stage of usefulness, and such an abundant blood supply is no longer necessary. It is somewhat difficult to draw a line between this more or less physiological process of narrowing the artery and that which comes from actual disease of the artery wall. Still, in extreme cases, the pathological character of the process is very evident. There are various forms of disease of the artery wall, roughly classed under the general name of *arteriosclerosis*, which bring about this effect, and so completely may the vessel be obstructed that all the tissue ordinarily supplied by it dies. When, in the legs, for example, this extreme is not reached, the narrowing of the artery may be only sufficient to so cut down the blood supply that the person is able to walk perfectly well for a short distance, when his muscles fail him solely on account of their insufficient nutrition. After a rest he is able to go on again for a time. This is often spoken of as *intermittent claudication*. Harmful in some cases, this shutting-off of the blood-stream by thickening of the vessel-walls is useful in others—it is the physiological method by which the ductus Botalli is closed; it appears in organs such as the senile uterus and breast, which have outlived their usefulness, and it forms a safeguard against hæmorrhage from the erosion of arteries in the lung by advancing tuberculosis: as the cavity extends and cuts across these arteries it finds them reduced to bloodless cords. Nevertheless in the kidney the same sort of narrowing of the small vessels produces local anæmia and destruction of patches of tissue which can only be replaced by scars (Fig. 7). Arteries thus narrowed by changes in their walls are very often finally and completely closed by the formation of a thrombus throughout the narrowed portion.

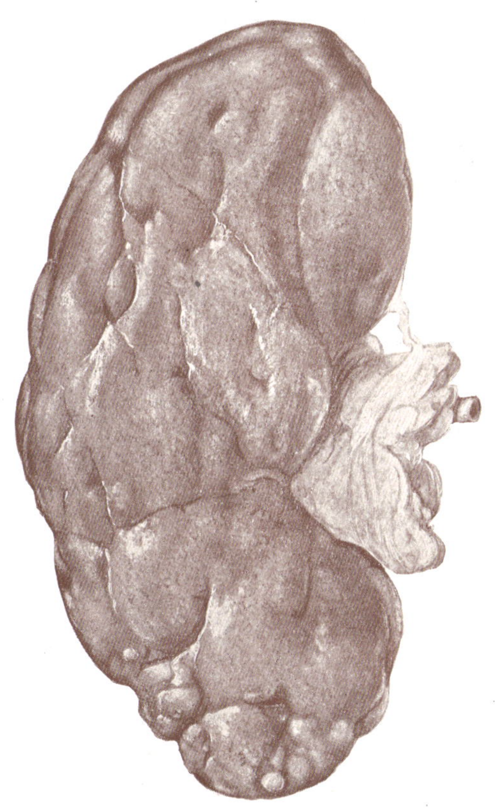

Fig. 7.—Arteriosclerotic scarring of kidney.

EMBOLISM

Local anæmia of extreme degree is produced most commonly by some sort of plug which obstructs the artery supplying blood to the part. Such a plug is known as an embolus, and embolism is defined by W. H. Welch as the impaction in some part of the vascular system of any undissolved

3

material brought there by the blood-current. Naturally, the number of kinds of material that can get into the blood-stream is limited, but there is, nevertheless, a surprising variety. The commonest are thrombi or fragments of thrombi, but tumor cells, tissue fragments, clumps of bacteria, protozoan and worm parasites, as well as oil-globules and gas-bubbles, may play the same rôle. Of these, only the thrombi are from the first within the blood-vessels: the others must first gain access to the stream before they can act as emboli.

It has been shown that thrombi form most commonly on the venous side of the circulation, although they are occasionally found in the arteries, and are common enough upon the heart-valves. Their rather intimate adhesion to the underlying vessel-wall was mentioned, though not the fact that, after they remain in position for a time, they become firmly fixed to the wall by blood-vessels and connective-tissue cells which grow into them and ultimately replace them completely with fibrous tissue. Before this so-called *organization* begins they can be dislodged by violent movements or by manipulation, and then arises at once the condition which makes embolism of some distant part of the blood-channel inevitable. A loose mould of the vein or a fragment of it caught in the current of the blood-stream must move along toward the heart because the vein becomes larger and larger. Sometimes the whole thrombus, with its long adherent propagated clot, is then dislodged; sometimes only a fragment, the original situation of which might perhaps be recognized by fitting together the surfaces of fracture. When the crumbly thrombi which form on the heart-valves are the source of such emboli, the dislodged fragments may be large enough to plug the aorta, or at the other extreme sifted off as fine particles which go on to the smaller arterioles. It must be remembered that a long narrow thrombus may become folded and doubled on itself and thus occlude a much larger cavity than that in which it formed. This is the case when dislodged clots from the femoral vein are swept into the pulmonary artery, blocking it completely. This whole process may occupy only a few seconds after the loosening of the thrombus, and death may follow instantly.

Such an embolus when formed from a part of an old thrombus can usually be recognized easily enough by its evident age, although in its new lodging-place it is almost at once surrounded by propagated clots.

Seats of Embolism.—Given its size and its point of origin, the site at which the embolus will lodge may be foretold with some accuracy, although the actual distribution of multiple small emboli has been learned only by experiment. It was found, for example, that the great majority of a large number of recognizable particles introduced into the blood-stream of the aorta were hurried past the mouths of arteries supplying the viscera into the vessels of the muscles of the legs. After that only came the embolism of the brain, liver, kidney, spleen, skin, etc.

Briefly, one may say that an embolus set free in any of the systemic veins, and caught in the current entering from the next branch above the part of the vein which had been completely occluded, is swept through the vena cava into the right side of the heart, and thence thrown violently into the pulmonary artery. Only the exceptional chance of its passing through a wide-open foramen ovale will allow it to reach the systemic arteries unless it is a particle so minute that it can pass through the capillaries of the lung. The same course is followed by a thrombus mass originating in the right auricle or in the intertrabecular spaces of the right ventricle, and obviously this holds true also for vegetations dislodged from the tricuspid or pulmonary valves. Thrombi set free in any of the veins which go to form the portal trunk are caught in the branches of that channel in the liver. Those arising in the pulmonary veins, left auricle, or left ventricle, vegetations from the mitral and aortic valves or thrombi formed on the walls of the aorta, are hurried into the aorta and distributed as described above. Naturally a thrombus formed in any smaller artery and dislodged is merely pushed further into the branches of that artery. Since emboli are most easily traced by the effects they produce, the impression is likely to arise that they lodge most often in such organs as the brain, the kidneys, or the spleen, but from what has been said it will be clear that even though no effects become visible, the actual number is greatest for the lungs, the body musculature, and perhaps the liver, which is menaced through both the portal vein and the hepatic artery.

With regard to the size of the embolus, a few more words may be said. The mass travels until it comes to a pass too narrow to admit it, and there it lodges like a cork. Naturally, since the branches are smaller than the main trunk in a bifurcating vessel, the plug is often found riding or balanced upon the point of bifurcation. Still, most arteries become narrower as they advance, and the majority of emboli stick on this account. In a case of vegetative endocarditis seen at autopsy recently there were two masses of thrombus material successively lodged in the common iliac artery, and one much larger mass riding at the bifurcation of the aorta. Each was surrounded by a propagated clot formed in the blood rendered stagnant by its advent.

The **other things which can act as emboli** do so rarely and are of far less importance as emboli than are thrombi, although in their other effects they may be of great significance. *Air-bubbles* may act as emboli of a rather temporary character, because the gas is so readily dissolved in the circulating blood. If, however, a great amount of gas is introduced into the circulation at any one time, the obstruction may be sufficient to cause death either by passing into the vessels of the brain, or, much more commonly, by filling up the heart and yielding to its churning action, so as to exclude the inflow of blood. A considerable amount of air or other gas is necessary to produce this result—probably much more than is generally supposed. It is in operations and injuries which involve the accidental opening of the veins of the neck that this is likely to take place. The pressure in these veins is so lowered by the inspiratory enlargement of the chest that the air enters with a hissing sound, and the death of the individual may take place very rapidly. Probably its entrance into the coronary arteries is of great importance.

For a time the appearance of gas in bubbles in the organs of the body was regarded as evidence of air embolism, especially in the case of women who had died after childbirth when it was thought that the air had entered the large open sinuses in the uterine wall. Welch has pointed out that these were cases of infection with the Bacillus aërogenes capsulatus, which produced after death bubbles of hydrogen gas everywhere throughout the organs, so that they became distended like bread that is rising and full of holes. The liver assumes the appearance of a red rubber bath sponge, and on incision bubbles of gas appear which burn with a blue flame when a match is applied. Similar cavities may be formed all through the brain, where they have somewhat the appearance of the holes in a Swiss cheese. In the intestine or stomach the mucosa may be lifted up into blebs.

At other times emboli may be constituted of *droplets of fat* which are set free into the blood-stream from the adipose tissue. Such globules lodge, as a rule, in the capillaries of the lung, and are pressed into a sausage shape by the blood of the pulmonary artery. They can be recognized in the frozen section of such a lung by their highly refractive character, and also by the fact that they readily stain with those stains which are soluble in fat, such as Sudan III. They produce no obvious change in the appearance of the lung, and indeed must be searched for in this way. They are commonly introduced by some mechanical injury to the bones, such as fracture; but even a severe blow seems sufficient to cause such a commotion in the marrow as to introduce some of the abundant fat into the venous channels. Fat embolism also occurs in a number of convulsive diseases, and particularly in such conditions as delirium tremens, in which probably the violent exertions of the individual play a part in the process.

Injury or crushing of the tissues of cellular organs sometimes introduces *fragments or groups of cells* into the blood-stream, where they act as emboli. Most commonly this is observed in connection with the cells of the bone-marrow and the syncytial structures which arise in pregnancy. There is little evidence, however, of their producing any mechanical effect where they lodge in the capillaries.

Bacteria may enter the blood-stream by growing through the walls of capillaries or by being discharged from infected thrombi, and can, as is well known, circulate with the corpuscles of the blood through any capillaries. That they often lodge and grow into colonies which produce characteristic effects on the surrounding tissue is shown in cases of generalized miliary tuberculosis and in general pyæmia, but they can be said to act as emboli only when they circulate in clumps large enough to obstruct the capillaries. Protozoan parasites in the same way usually circulate through the capillaries, but certain worms, such as the Schistosomum, can behave as actual mechanical emboli, plugging and obstructing the vessels.

In the case of *malignant tumors*, the transportation of cells foreign to the blood is of particular importance, although these cells rarely act as gross emboli. It is perfectly clear, from a study of the gross anatomy of such invading tumors, that they frequently extend their growth through the wall of a vein and hang loosely in the blood-stream, so that fragments can be broken off and swept on by the stream. It is, however, by no means always possible to recognize the mode of entrance, and it seems likely that in many cases individual cells gain entrance into the thin-walled veins of the tumor itself, possibly as a result of mechanical trauma. The cultivation of these cells on the glass slide, however, has shown them to be endowed with a remarkable power of amœboid movement, so that Hanes and Lambert have advanced the idea that the separate cells of the tumor may actively push their way through the endothelial lining of the vein and thus enter the venous blood-stream. The cells appear to be able to pass through such capillaries as those of the lung, and to set up their growth in more distant organs, where they find a suitable environment.

Results of Embolism.—The degree of anæmia produced by the occlusion of any artery will depend upon the relation of its branches to those of the surrounding arteries and to the other branches of its own trunk, because, just as in the case of the veins, such connections dilate to accommodate blood whenever it finds its way blocked through its ordinary channel. If these branches anastomose widely with the terminal twigs of the adjacent artery, a sufficient supply of blood may be maintained in its area of tissue. Indeed, this communication between the end-twigs of the arterial branches is so wide in some tissues, such as the muscles, skin, lungs, etc., that even a large artery can be closed off without causing a moment's delay or diminution in the supply of blood to the tissue. It can be seen, then, that the advent of an embolus in one of these arterial branches will cause no particular disturbance in such tissue as muscle or lung, or even in the stomach-wall.

This compensation for lost arterial supply can be seen most vividly if one injects a quantity of ultramarine blue in suspension into one of the gastric arteries. This fills the artery, with all its branches, with blue fluid, but the moment the stream of blue fluid is interrupted or its pressure lowered, the inflow of blood from the neighboring vessels replaces the blue material in that artery. In this case, however, the connections are between the larger branches and it is found that the minute twigs of the gastric artery thus injected remain permanently plugged with the blue granules and the tissue which they supply suffers.

In other places the communications are not nearly so free, so that if it becomes impossible for the blood to go through one branch, the connections with the adjacent branches may indeed be sufficient to keep the tissue living by furnishing blood to the terminal twigs, but they can do this only by actually increasing their own calibre; so that in such a case the anatomical development of a collateral circulation is much more plainly seen. Sometimes these connections are so minute as to be invisible under ordinary circumstances, but become quite conspicuous after they are dilated in this way.

Extraordinary examples of the development of such a collateral circulation are seen in connection with the larger arteries of the body. So when the aorta is tied, as in the experiments of Halsted and Porta, there appears

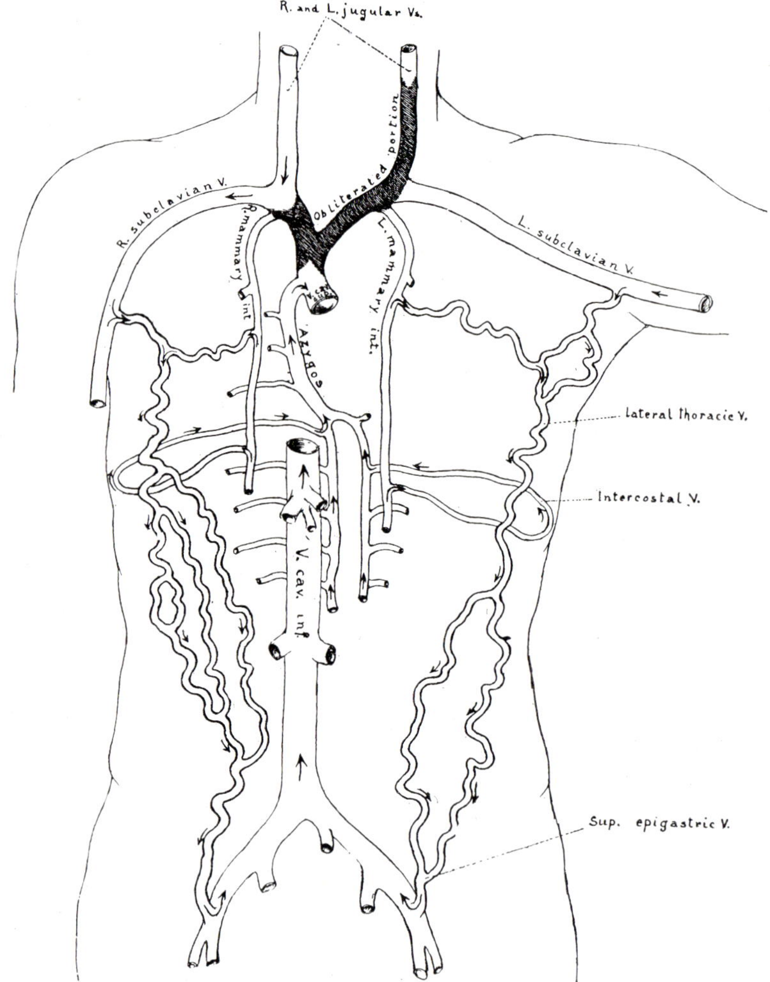

Fig. 8.—Collateral circulation after obstruction of vena cava superior (Osler).

after a time a whole brush of vessels which anastomose with branches below the point at which the ligature is applied and which reëstablish the circulation. I have recently seen two cases in which there had occurred obstruction of the large abdominal arteries. In one instance it was the trunk of the cœliac axis which had been gradually obstructed by an arteriosclerotic thickening of its wall, supplemented finally by the formation of a thrombus; and in the other it was the superior mesenteric artery which had been gradually but completely pressed together by the growth of a small aneurysm developed from a point very near its orifice in the wall of the aorta. In neither of these cases was there the slightest disturbance in the appearance of the abdominal organs, for in both the pancreatico-duodenal artery had dilated and had assumed the burden of transmitting the whole supply of blood for those organs which would otherwise have been deprived of it—in one case in one direction and in the other case in the other. It is not merely in the case of the arteries that such a collateral circulation can be developed, for the same thing may be observed in the case of an obstruction of one of the great veins. In one case studied not long ago the superior vena cava had been completely occluded, and the venous circulation from the head took place through the enormously dilated veins of the abdomen* (Fig. 8).

In certain situations the tissues are entirely dependent upon receiving their supply of blood from a single artery. In these cases there is practically no chance for compensation through the pouring-in of blood from adjacent arteries, for there are no adequate anastomoses, and such arteries have been referred to by Cohnheim as "end arteries," and such a circulation as "terminal" circulation. The propulsion of an embolus into such an artery as this will inevitably cause complete anæmia of the portion of tissue which had hitherto been supplied by that artery (Fig. 9).

The effect of the diminution of the supply of blood to any part by way of the artery thus depends upon the degree to which the function of that artery can be replaced by the formation of channels connecting its region of distribution with other arterial supplies. The time which is occupied in this reëstablishment of the blood-stream is of the greatest importance, for if the obstruction be gradually produced, it may reach a very advanced degree without there having appeared at any time an insufficiency in the blood supply to the tissues; whereas if the cut-off be sudden, the tissue is likely to suffer.

Finally, there are some organs, such as the liver and lung, which enjoy a double circulation, both arterial and venous blood being poured into the tissues and escaping by way of a common efferent channel. In both these instances the flood of venous blood is far more profuse than the small stream of arterial blood, and doubtless contributes very largely to the nutrition of the tissues, although that is perhaps the main function of the arterial supply. In such cases the life of the tissue is somewhat more secure as far as its food supply is concerned than in the case of those organs which are supplied solely from the artery; and, indeed, it is actually found that a very much more extensive disturbance is necessary to produce anatomical changes in these organs than in many others.

---

* Osler: Johns Hopkins Hospital Bulletin, July, 1903, xiv, 172.

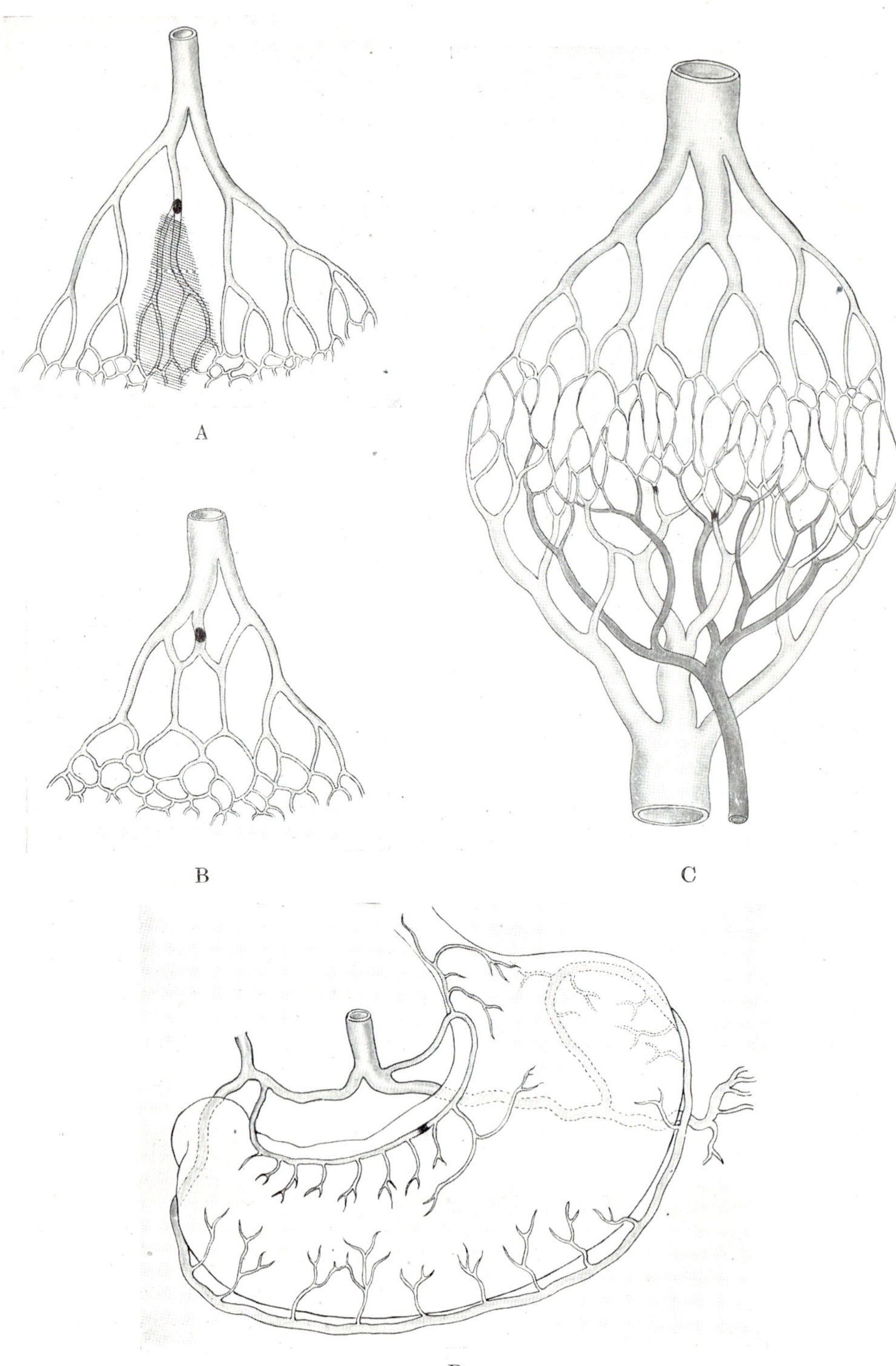

Fig. 9.—Diagram showing circulation after plugging of arteries: A, Terminal circulation; B, circulation with rich anastomoses; C, double blood supply, as in the liver; D, circulation of the stomach with abundant large anastomoses.

Quite aside from the patency of the arteries themselves or of the veins, a condition of local anæmia which is very effective in disturbing the nutrition of the tissues can be brought about by muscular contraction in those tissues which are largely made up of smooth muscle. Welch and Mall have pointed out that this violent spasmodic contraction of the intestinal wall which arises from a sufficient interference with the entrance of the blood, results in the complete exclusion of the blood from that part of the intestine, and in that way takes a great part in the final destruction of the tissue. It is really this which renders the circulation of the mesentery and of the intestine, which is, from an anatomical point of view, so rich in anastomoses, comparable to a terminal circulation.

INFARCTION

The effect of local anæmia upon the tissue is found to vary with the degree of deprivation to which the tissue is subjected and with the nature of the tissue itself. As has already been indicated, the more complex the structure of the cell, and the more highly developed its specialization of function, the more delicate and susceptible to injury it becomes. This is well seen in the case of the nerve-cell, whose function becomes impossible if its nutritive supply is withheld even for a few moments, and is irremediably destroyed in a very short time.

On the other hand, there is a long series of tissues with gradually decreasing susceptibility until we reach the least highly organized and consequently the most resistant among the connective-tissue structures which can withstand removal from any connection with the circulation for hours or even days, and still resume their functions as soon as they are placed in proper surroundings or grow again when transplanted into another animal of the same kind.

The injurious effects of anæmia become more severe the more complete it is and the longer it lasts, and they reach their climax in the death of the tissues. Slighter grades of anæmia may become evident in their effect only when great effort is demanded of the organ involved, as, for example, in the intermittent claudication spoken of above.

More complete anæmia, whether caused by the inability of the blood to reach the tissues or to give place to new blood, commonly causes the death of the affected part, and this is the all-important feature in the production of the so-called *infarction.* Other changes subsequent to this may alter very strikingly the appearance of the tissues, but they are of secondary importance. As in the clotting of blood and the formation of a thrombus, the death, or even the severe injury, of the cells is immediately followed by the setting free of some sort of ferment which causes the coagulation of the blood, and the intracellular as well as the intercellular fluids. The nuclei either fade or break up into small, deeply staining fragments, and in every other respect the cells lose the aspect which they possessed during life. They are dead cells entangled and held in a coagulum which involves the whole area of tissue, and the process is described by Weigert and called by Cohnheim "coagulative necrosis."

The area occupied by these changes is that to which the blood supply becomes insufficient. It need not correspond exactly, therefore, with the distribution of the plugged artery, because there is almost always some compensation from the branches of adjacent arteries. Its form is generally stated to be pyramidal, but is not really so in most cases, although it may approach that traditional form. This is because the vessels in most organs really assume a rather fan-shaped arrangement, as is almost inevitable in any vessel which branches out regularly. Still in some, such as the kidney, there are blood-vessels which spring up almost at right angles from the main trunk, and which reach through the organ, so that we may readily

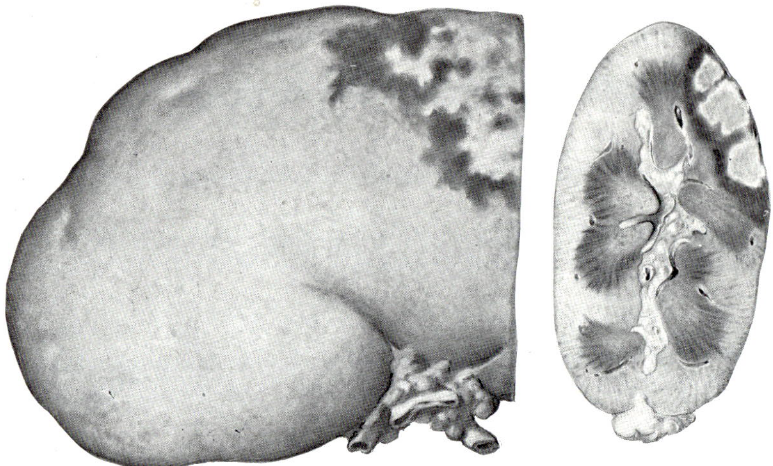

Fig. 10.—Anæmic infarction of kidney.

find an infarct of a more or less cubical form in its cortex (Fig. 10). There is nothing typical about the form of the infarct in the intestine which merely occupies the whole wall of a certain length of the intestine. So, too, in the heart, the area of infarction is irregular in form. The pyramidal form is most nearly approached by the infarct of the lung, but even this is frequently quite irregular in its shape.

In all instances the infarcted area seems at first swollen and firm, and projects above the surrounding surface of the tissue. This is true even in the brain in the beginning, although after a short time has elapsed the infarcts of the brain become soft and are commonly spoken of as areas of softening. Their resemblance to other infarcts in the early stages was pointed out by Marchand, who appreciated the fact that they too at the beginning present the appearance of a firm coagulum, although later the liquefaction of the myeline substance proves more than sufficient to overcome the firmness contributed by the fibrin and to make the whole area soft. The swelling and firmness of an infarct are due to the accumulation of a coagulum produced from the coagulable fluids which diffuse into the dead area from the surrounding tissue. In a short time the mass becomes dense and hard and may be appreciated immediately by the finger passed over the surface of the organ. There is no other disturbance in the architecture of the tissue at this stage, and the outlines of the cells may still be seen quite clearly. Even the outlines of the nuclei may still be seen, and as for the supporting structural framework, it is usually quite well preserved, at least in its outlines; but the whole area is dead and reminds one, on viewing it through the microscope, of the appearance of charcoal as contrasted with that of living wood, or of the streets of Pompeii as contrasted with those of a modern town.

The death with coagulation of the tissues converts them into a white or yellowish white, perfectly opaque, dull-looking mass so long as there is no infiltration of red corpuscles. We must recognize, however, two kinds of infarcts, in both of which the principles just described affect the result in an identical manner, but one is spoken of as a *hæmorrhagic infarct* because, on account of the laxity of the tissue and the richness of the adjacent capillary circulation, red corpuscles ooze into the dead area. The other kind, which remains pale and opaque, is commonly spoken of as an *anæmic infarct,* although it is plain enough that anæmia is the cause of the death of the tissue in both. The arrangement of the circulation and the density of the tissue seem to be the deciding factors as to whether an infarct shall remain anæmic looking and white, or, by being flooded with stagnating red corpuscles, assume a deep red color. So, in the kidney, we practically never observe a hæmorrhagic infarction, whereas in the lung and in the intestine the reverse is the case, and it is only with the greatest difficulty that we can produce experimentally an infarction which remains anæmic looking. In other organs, such as the heart, the spleen, the liver, we may have sometimes anæmic, sometimes hæmorrhagic, types.

Kidney.—In the kidney, infarctions are likely to be quite small. They seem to arise as the result of the entrance of the embolus into one of the arcuate arteries, or even into one of the branches, passing thence into the cortex. One can nearly always find this plug on careful search and observe that the propagated thrombus extends both ways from it. The infarcts commonly occupy especially the cortex, but they may sometimes extend down into the pyramid of the kidney. One occasionally sees a ramifying, anastomosing area of infarction which occupies a great portion of the kidney, and such, indeed, was the result in a peculiar instance observed recently. In this case a stab wound had passed through a branch of the renal artery which happened to begin its branching outside of the kidney, and a hæmorrhage occurred, which continued slowly for two or three days, being restrained apparently in part by the surrounding tissue. At the end of that time the kidney was removed at operation, together with the mass of blood which had been extravasated. It was found that there was an extensive infarction occupying a portion of the kidney which should have been supplied by the injured artery. This was an instance of local anæmia, but not caused by the presence of a plug in the vessel.

On inspection of such a kidney containing infarcts it is possible to determine readily enough the position of the infarct even through the capsule,

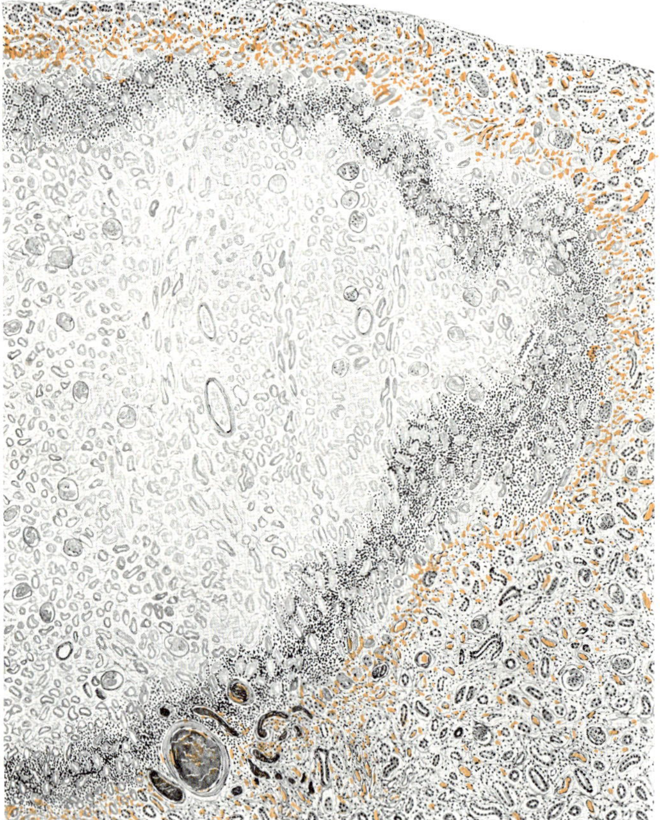

Fig. 11.—Margin of renal infarction showing necrosis of tissue with zones of hæmorrhage and leucocytic invasion.

for the opaque yellow color shines through, but this opacity does not quite reach the surface, being covered by a layer of living and very hyperæmic kidney tissue, which receives its blood supply from the capillaries which extend to it from the capsule. On incision one finds the infarct surrounded by at least two distinct zones, which differ in color from the opaque yellowish-white central portion. These zones are first a translucent gray line of varying thickness, and then an irregular band of deep red which borders the infarct and marks it out from the surrounding normal tissue.

the gray zone is found, on careful examination, to be produced by an accumulation of the white cells of the blood which have wandered in there and have become more or less broken up. The zone of hæmorrhage is partly within the necrotic area and partly in the living area, and although it may, like the accumulation of leucocytes, be explained in part as due to the inflammatory reaction about the dead tissue, it seems probable that the anæmic changes in the endothelium of the capillaries play a part too in allowing the escape of red cells (Fig. 11).

Spleen.—Almost the same descriptions might be applied to the anæmic infarctions in the spleen, except that they are usually much larger and more irregular in form (Fig. 12). They, however, differ from the infarctions in the kidney inasmuch as there is no capsular circulation, which is necessary to keep alive any superficial layer of the spleen, so that the death of the tissue extends quite out to the peritoneal surface. There the dead tissue exerts the same influence upon the peritoneal fluid as it does upon

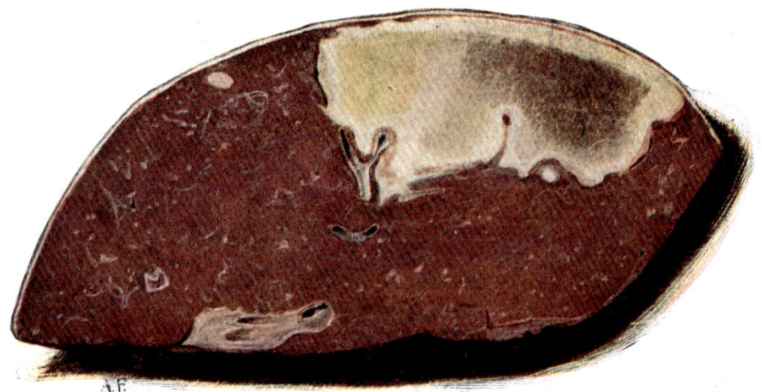

Fig. 12.—Infarction of spleen.

the passing lymph, and there is deposited over the surface of an infarct in the spleen a layer of fibrin which roughens the surface. Sometimes one can make the diagnosis of the existence of an infarct of the spleen from pain which comes from the rubbing of this roughened surface against that of the adjacent peritoneum when a deep breath is taken.

Heart.—Exactly the same thing is true of infarcts of the lung, and even those of the heart wall; but in the kidney there is no opportunity for such an occurrence. The infarcts of the heart are particularly interesting because of their great importance with regard to the function of the heart. The coronary arteries present some anastomoses one with the other, but, as has been pointed out recently by Spalteholz, these are insufficient to supply the really enormously active circulation which is necessary for such an organ as the heart. So, therefore, the arteriosclerotic narrowing of the coronaries often leaves traces of malnutrition of the tissues when even there is no actual infarct formed; but when to this there is added a thrombus formation, or when a vegetation from the valve sweeps into the mouth of the coronary artery, as has happened so frequently, the nutrition of the heart muscle is intolerably limited and the muscle dies. In one such instance recently observed there had been an aortic endocarditis with vegetations, and a plug, like a cork, still projected from the mouth of the left coronary artery. The whole of the septum between the ventricles, together with the anterior portion of the walls of the right and left ventricles, formed a necrotic mass. The heart had become abnormally slowed from involvement of the auriculoventricular bundle, but still continued to beat until a sudden effort caused the rupture of the wall of the left ventricle with a fatal hæmorrhage.

Other instances, however, have not so immediately led to death, but rather to recovery, with replacement of the dead tissue by scar. In that case a patch in the heart wall may be markedly thinned and comes to be composed of a fibrous tissue which has by no means the power of resistance or the strength of the muscular wall, and one frequently sees such an area bulged out into a sac which in time may rupture. Such an event is, however, by no means always the outcome of an infarction, but may depend on the gradual loss of the muscle substance from a partial anæmia.

Liver.—In the liver infarcts are very rare because of the extremely abundant blood supply from two sources. It is stated that complete closure of the main trunk of the hepatic artery will produce complete necrosis of the liver, whereas closure of any of its branches has no special result. Obstruction to the main portal vein is said to diminish the production of bile, as has been shown recently by Voegtlin and Bernheim, but it does not interfere with the nutrition of the tissue. This is especially well seen in the numerous instances in which experimentally the whole of the blood of the portal vein has been diverted into the inferior vena cava by the so-called Eck's fistula. In that case undoubtedly the whole of the tissue of the liver must be supplied by the hepatic artery, but the animals live, and after a time show no very obvious change in the tissue of the liver, although it is stated that sometimes the liver decreases in bulk. Obstruction of the whole portal vein is not very uncommon, arising from the thrombosis of the branches from some point of infection or injury in the alimentary tract, and extending into the main trunk; or as the result of compression from without by gall-stones or tumor-masses in the vicinity. Closure of branches of the portal vein may be followed by the formation of hæmorrhagic infarctions when there is some disturbance or enfeeblement of the general circulation, so that the hepatic artery does not succeed in making up the nutrition which is lost by the shutting-off of the portal.

Lung.—In the lung also there is a double vascular supply, the bronchial arteries really furnishing nutriment only to the bronchi and the immediately adjacent lung tissue. It is, therefore, not to be wondered at that if we tie a branch of the pulmonary artery which has no connections with other branches, as, for example, in one of the isolated lobules of a dog's lung, all the tissue dies except the bronchial walls. The pulmonary arteries anastomose with extraordinary freedom in the lung, probably largely by means of the extremely wide capillaries. On this account it proves to be impossible to produce an infarction in the lung of a healthy animal by throwing emboli into the pulmonary stream, because the nutrition of the obstructed area is immediately assumed by adjacent branches. Virchow did succeed in producing such infarctions, and this was the basis of his great work on embolism. But apparently he succeeded because the emboli which he used carried bacteria, and he caused, in that way, a far more extensive injury to the lung tissue than could be produced by sterile plugs. It is only when there is some other circumstance which causes a general slowing of the circulation in the lungs, a high pressure in the pulmonary veins, and such malnutrition of the lung tissue as leaves it susceptible to injury, that a plug in a branch of the pulmonary artery will cause the formation of an infarct. This is the condition which we find in the so-called chronic passive congestion which results from the obstruction of the

Fig. 13.—Hæmorrhagic infarction in lung, the seat of chronic passive congestion.

mitral valve or from the regurgitation of blood through the mitral valve backward into the lung. Other causes may, of course, produce the damming back of blood into the lungs and slowing of their circulation, but the changes in the heart, and especially those which we have just mentioned, are the most prominent. Under such circumstances, when emboli are dislodged from some point on the venous side of the circulation and thrown into the branches of the pulmonary artery, there arise hæmorrhagic infarctions in the lungs (Fig. 13). Sometimes one can recognize by symptoms the beginnings of such infarcts from the sudden pain and the spitting-up of blood, and possibly even from the change in the percussion-note, which becomes dull over the region of the infarct. When the lung is inspected, it is found possible to recognize these infarcts at once because they are solid, hard masses, often present in numbers and extending to the surface of the lung. The pleura over them is roughened by a layer of fibrin which destroys its gloss and causes the pain of which we have spoken by scratching against the opposite pleural surface in respiratory movement. The infarcts vary greatly in size, from a diameter of about 1 cm. to such a size as to occupy almost the whole of the lobe. They have a tendency to a somewhat triangular or pyramidal form, but their margins are usually round, and they bulge out on the surface of the lung. They are very dark red,—almost black in color,—and on cutting through them this is found to be true also of their interior portion. They are dry and sometimes of a remarkable hardness.

It is nearly always quite easy to see the embolus which has caused their formation lying in the pulmonary artery which forms the apex of the triangle. Usually such a plug is prolonged both ways by the clot which is formed about it, but sometimes this may not have happened, and cases are even recorded in which the embolus lay at a point somewhat separated from the actual region of infarction by an empty stretch of vessel. This is important because there has been so much dispute as to whether these infarctions were really caused by emboli or whether the clot in the vessel was the result of the infarction. It seems perfectly clear, however, that the weight of evidence is entirely in favor of the embolic origin of the infarcts. Von Recklinghausen lays a great deal of stress upon the formation of hyaline thrombi in the smaller branches of the pulmonary artery, but these, it seems to me, might be secondary. There is often a question as to whether we are dealing with a real infarction or with a mere hæmorrhage into the lung substance. Such hæmorrhages occur frequently from all kinds of causes, but they are never really comparable in appearance to infarctions—first of all, because they are almost never hard and dry, but rather soft and loose, and usually very irregular in outline, occupying any part of the lung without regard to any special arrangement and without necessarily approaching the surface of the lung. From such hæmorrhages absorption of the blood takes place with extreme rapidity, and this may possibly account for their remaining so soft. On the other hand, it is quite difficult to understand why the hæmorrhagic infarction should be so extremely hard unless it be that the coagulation of the red corpuscles is also brought about in the general coagulation of the necrotic lung tissue. Close examination of the area involved in the infarction shows that it is overfilled in every part with blood. Not only are the alveoli themselves full of red corpuscles in even greater concentration than in the circulating blood, but these corpuscles are found also in the substance of the tissue.

The epithelial cells which line the alveoli disappear rather rapidly, but the framework of the lung is very resistant, and it may not appear to have been injured very markedly by the local anæmia. There are those who speak of resolution of infarctions of the lung, stating that there is no real necrosis, but that later the contents of the alveoli may be absorbed as in a simple hæmorrhage, and the lung resume its function. This, however, seems very doubtful, and one may feel sure that when the effect of the anæmia is such as has been described, much more complicated changes than a mere resolution or restoration to normal will take place. The difficulty in deciding this consists chiefly in the fact that when hæmorrhagic infarctions are formed in the lungs the person is so ill as to die before any great length of time has been allowed for alterations to take place in the

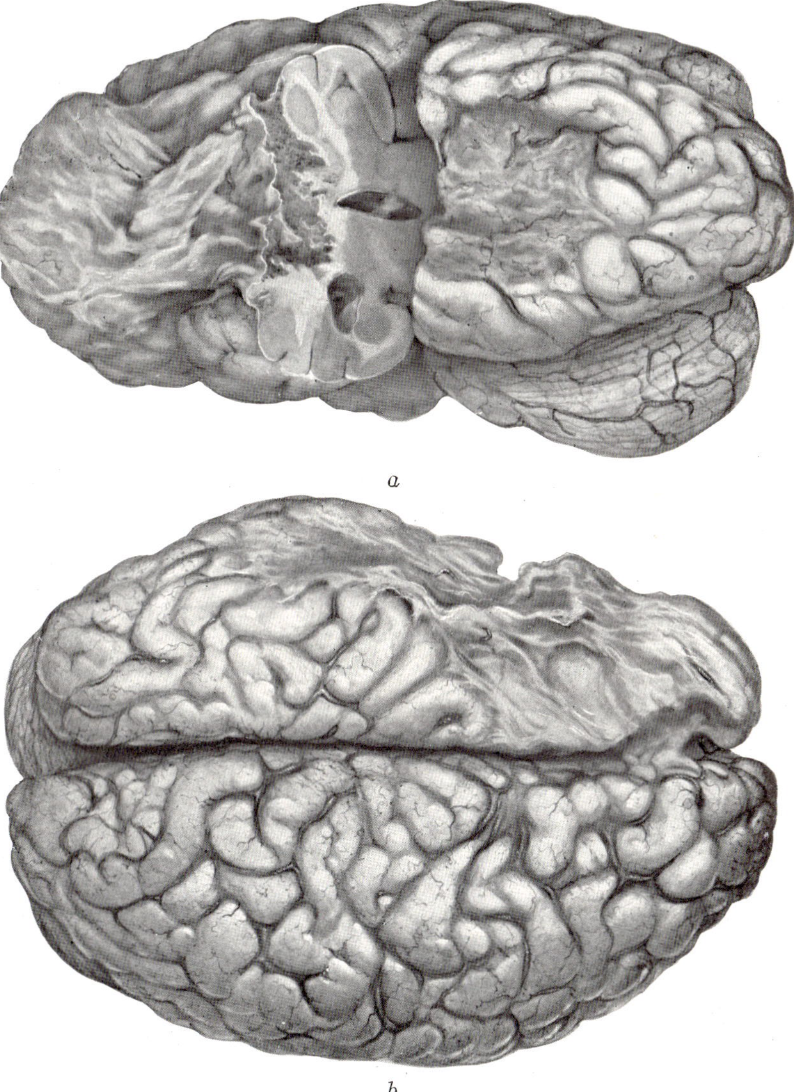

Fig. 14.—Extensive old infarction of brain.

infarctions, and so it is that we commonly see at autopsy fresh hæmorrhagic infarctions and only rarely find areas of infarction which have lasted for a long time. When we do there is no evidence of resolution, but rather of a great shrinkage of the tissue, a loss of the red color, a deep yellow pigmentation from the débris of the red corpuscle, and the formation of dense,

4

hard scar tissue in the place once occupied by the infarct. In this respect the hæmorrhagic infarctions of the lung are quite similar to the anæmic and other infarctions in the spleen and in the kidney. Even in the fresh infarctions of the lung one finds always a good deal of the yellow pigment which comes from the disintegration of red corpuscles. This is not a part of the fresh process, but rather a result of the long-continued stagnation of blood in the capillaries of the lung, which is the essential feature of a chronic passive congestion, and which, as we have said, constitutes the requisite basis for the formation of an infarct there.

Brain.—The formation of infarctions in the brain is an extremely common occurrence, and leads to more or less serious results. It is naturally most likely to occur when thrombi are formed in the left side of the heart in such a way as to be dislodged and thrown into the cerebral circulation. The mechanical results of such embolism will again depend upon the position reached by the embolus, and if the obstruction produced is in the meninges, it may happen that no obvious result will follow. If, however, the plug enters one of the arteries actually on its way to supply the brain, there is inevitably an infarct formed because they are terminal arteries (Fig. 14).

The symptoms will depend upon the particular tissue thus destroyed, but if a large branch is occluded, there may be general symptoms in many respects like those of apoplexy; that is, the patient becomes unconscious. There may be a flaccid paralysis from which, however, he recovers later with the exception of some limited paralysis, which corresponds with the portion of the brain destroyed.

The writer has recently seen an instance in which practically a whole cerebral hemisphere was thus converted into a necrotic mass through rather extensive embolism of the arteries at the base of the brain. In other instances where smaller plugs reached this circulation there may be only temporary lapses from consciousness, or not even that. There may or may not be narrowly localized paralysis. Indeed, it is not infrequent to discover at the autopsy, in a person who has long suffered from a cardiac affection, very numerous yellowish patches scattered all over the surface of the brain and sunken below its surface. These are merely the pigmented scars which have resulted from the formation of the infarcts time after time without any history of symptoms. When these infarcts are perfectly fresh they are, as stated above, swollen, project above the surface, and are somewhat firm, but they very quickly soften into a semifluid mass because the greater portion of the brain is composed of lipoid substances (myelines) which become converted into a more fluid form in the process leading to necrosis of the tissue. At this stage of softening phagocytic cells wander in to such an area and load themselves with fat-globules, which they carry away (Fig. 15).

Intestine.—The infarctions of the intestine are usually hæmorrhagic. They are perhaps most commonly produced, as in strangulated hernias, where the blood supply is impeded by the crowding into the aperture, of the mesentery as well as the intestine itself. Other instances are seen in the so-called volvulus, in which a lobe of intestine with long loose mesentery becomes twisted completely round on itself so that the blood-vessels in the mesentery are closed. Almost the same effect can be produced by bands of fibrous tissue such as arise in the form of adhesions between various abdominal organs and can be pulled tight over the vessels running to some portion of the intestine. The other type of artificial obstruction

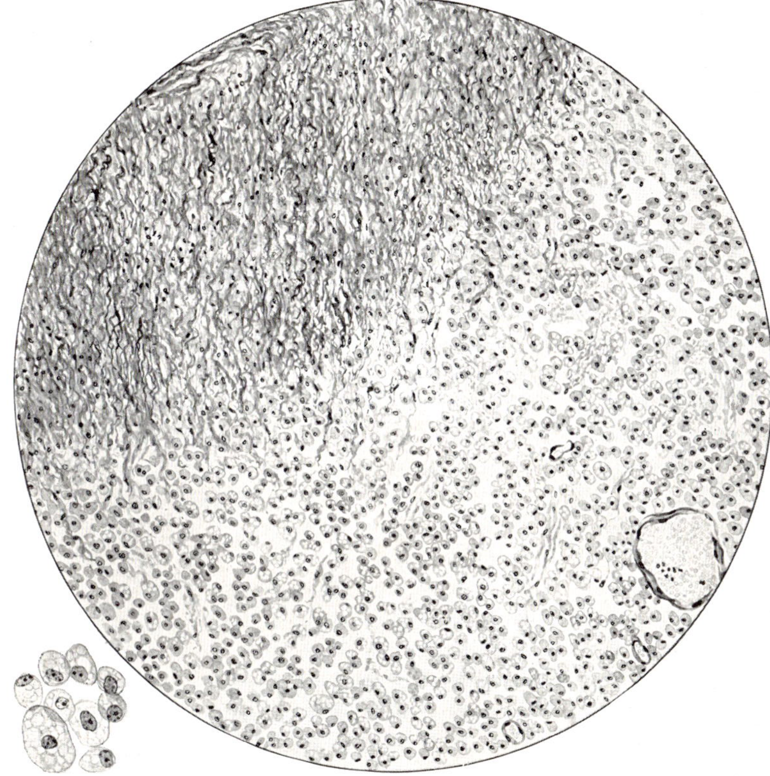

Fig. 15.—Margin of fresher infarct of brain showing fat-laden phagocytes. Several of these are shown enlarged below.

is, as in the infarction just described, produced by an embolus or thrombus. As has been pointed out, the intestines are peculiarly susceptible to withdrawal of their blood supply because they add to the anæmia by their violent contractions. The intestinal wall at first becomes absolutely pale with this contraction, but later on, with the death and relaxation of the tissue, it swells enormously and is infiltrated with blood. The swelling is particularly intense in the submucosa, which may attain the thickness of a centimetre, and the blood oozes through the mucosa into the lumen of the intestine and is passed in great quantities, giving the diagnostic sign of intestinal infarction.

The surgeon sometimes meets with this condition of swelling and hæmorrhage before the complete death of the cells has occurred, and occasionally he may replace the enlarged loop from the hernial sac or liberate it from its constriction and see restoration to normal condition follow his operation. It is a matter for his judgment, however, to determine whether the injury has passed the point at which this is still possible. Welch and Mall, in their experiments, have found that there is relatively little compensation for the cutting-off of the arterial supply through the mesenteric

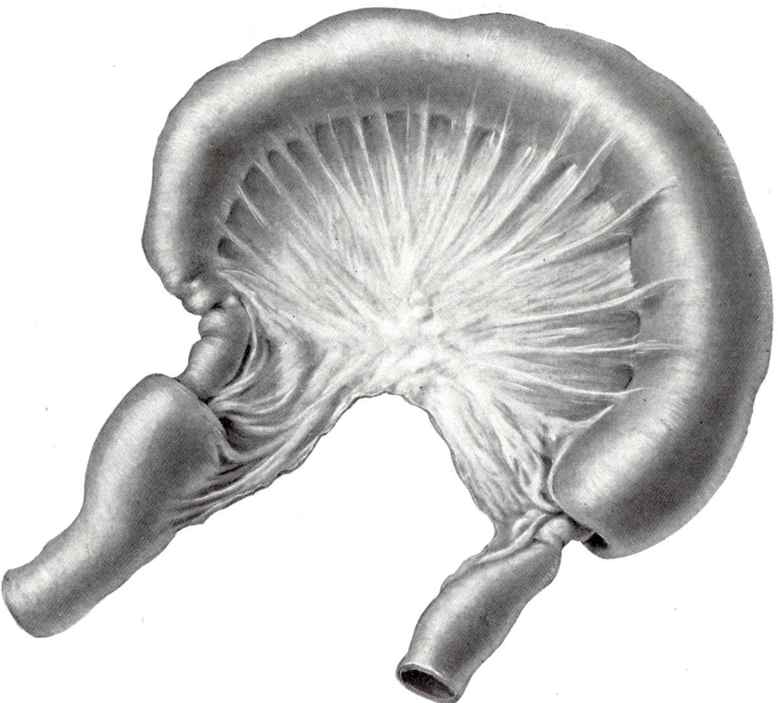

Fig. 16.—Intussusception in child's intestine.

arteries, so that if even such a short length of intestine as five centimetres be separated from its blood-vessels, it will undergo necrosis because the supply from the adjacent portion is insufficient.

One of the commonest causes of infarctions is the so-called *intussusception*, which occurs most commonly in children (Fig. 16). It may apparently be spontaneous, and indeed it seems to be produced by irregular peristalsis in the intestine, so that one portion not answering to the peristaltic wave is dragged by it into the next portion, to which the wave has actually leaped. At any rate such intussusceptions are found very commonly in the intestine of infants, where they have been produced postmortem, by the peristaltic action of the partially quiescent intestine. The portion which is telescoped into a receiving part below draws with it, of course, its mesenteric blood supply. If the intestine be pulled out again at this moment, no harm is done; but if it remain thus imprisoned for any considerable time, there arises a moderate interference with the outflow of the venous blood from the enfolded part, which soon makes it swell to such an extent as to cause a very much more intense interference with the blood supply. This circle of events continues to intensify itself, so that very soon the intestine acts as a constricting band to prevent the inflow or outflow of blood, and brings about the hæmorrhagic infarction of the interior portion.

The question as to whether an infarct shall become hæmorrhagic or not seems to depend upon a variety of things. Experimental studies have been made with regard to the infarction in the intestine, particularly by Welch and Mall, by Niedstein and Marek. The results of these experiments may be summed up in the following conclusions:

If a branch of the mesenteric artery or the mesenteric vein alone be obstructed, a hæmorrhagic infarction results. If, however, the arterial channels leading to any portion of the intestine be absolutely blocked by plugging or tying every possible anastomosis, an anæmic infarction appears, even though the veins be left widely open. It is evident, therefore, that the hæmorrhagic infiltration of the tissue which forms the peculiar feature of hæmorrhagic infarction does not come, as Cohnheim thought, from regurgitation of the blood from the veins, but is the result of the oozing of blood through the walls of the enlarged capillaries and from the adjacent arterioles.

The laxity of the tissue which is found in the lungs and in the intestines aids in this, whereas the sudden complete consolidation of the infarcted areas of the kidney and spleen makes it almost impossible. It is for this reason that the infarcts in the last-named places are commonly pale. This is true in the case of the spleen, particularly when the intervascular and vascular spaces are densely filled with foreign cells, as in the case of acute splenic tumor and leucæmic changes in the spleen.

Infected Emboli.—Secondary changes are produced in infarctions by the invasion of bacteria. Thus an embolus may carry with it a quantity of bacteria when it originates from an already infected source, and is spoken of then as a *septic embolus*. It gives rise at first to the ordinary mechanical effects of plugging the blood-stream, but later there become evident the effects of the poisons produced by the bacteria, and the infarcted area becomes the seat of an intense acute inflammatory process, with all the softening and disintegration which follow upon the development of liquefying ferments both from the bacteria and from the leucocytes, which hurry to the spot as a part of the inflammatory reaction. The infarct may actually assume the appearance of an abscess, and it is sometimes difficult to say whether it started as an infarct or not. In most cases, though one sees distinctly the form and general character of the infarct, he finds that its central part is softened down into a grayish pulp while the periphery still retains something of its firmness. This softening is quite different from that which we have mentioned in the case of the infarcts of the brain, and probably seldom ends in healing and scar formation.

Healing.—Healing of the uninfected infarcts is by no means uncommon in such organs as the spleen and kidney, and it has been described already in the heart and brain. It consists in the replacement of the dead tissue by a scar tissue which constantly tends to contract, so that finally, in either the spleen or in the kidney, one finds, as a sign of where the infarct was, a sunken, hard, scar-like area, usually rather opaque and colored yellow here and there from the remains of pigment derived from the dead cells. In such a scar there may remain some traces of the most resistant of the structures previously occupying that place, such as obliterated glomeruli in the kidney; but usually these are scarcely recognizable, although, on account of the contraction of the scar, they may be concentrated together in considerable numbers.

GANGRENE

All of these instances of anæmic necrosis which we have described under the name of infarcts have been in tissues somewhere in the interior of the body, completely surrounded by other tissues from which there could be derived by infiltration the ever-increasing supply of fluid which might undergo coagulation. This it was which formed the basis of the so-called coagulative necrosis. If, however, the anæmia affects an extremity or any such tissue as is not thus accessible to the adjacent coagulable fluids, a different appearance results. The necrosis of the tissue is effected in just the same way, but there is no opportunity for it to assume the character of a coagulative necrosis. At least the amount of fluid which undergoes coagulation is relatively small, and the extremity does not become rigid and hard as the result of this process. Such death of an extremity is called *gangrene*, and it is commonly brought about in the same way as is the death of the tissue in infarctions, that is, by any one of the various processes which lead to diminution in the blood supply of the part, often aided by more general disturbances of circulation or by decreased vitality of the tissues from other causes, as, for example, in the case of diabetes, where gangrene of the feet is so common. It may assume one of two forms—the so-called "moist" gangrene or "dry" gangrene. In the former case the tissues remain moist, infiltrated with blood. They become opaque, dull looking, and livid in color. But the color does not remain as it is in the beginning, but rapidly changes through a series of shades to deep purple or greenish black (Fig. 17). The epidermis becomes loosened when rubbed, often leaving a raw, damp surface, which may readily become infected and undergo putrefaction. Such death of the tissues usually occupies a portion of the extremity which is sharply demarcated from the remainder by a line which separates the dead from the living tissue; but commonly this line moves upward with the advance of the necrosis until it reaches the point at which the blood supply becomes sufficient to maintain constantly the life of the part above. Unless the leg be amputated at some point conveniently above this line, there may be a good deal of absorption of the poisonous products of putrefaction, and the tissue itself may fall away so as to expose the bone.

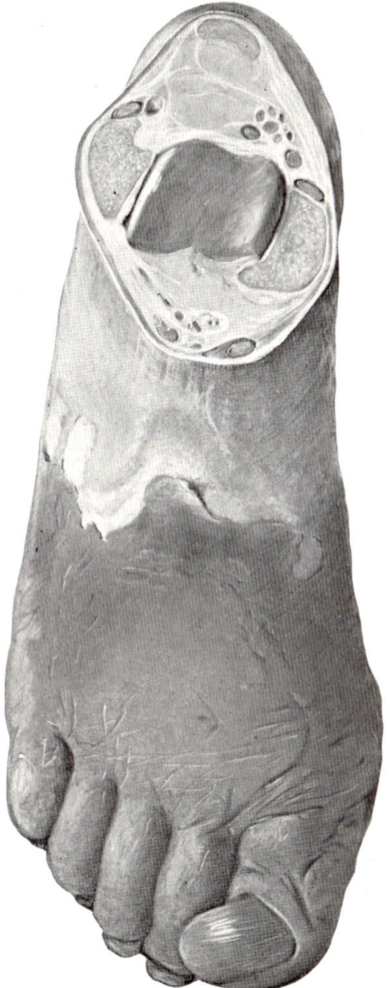

Fig. 17.—Gangrene of foot. Case of diabetes with arteriosclerosis.

The other kind, the *dry gangrene,* occurs when all possible advent of fluid is shut off from the living tissue and mummification or gradual drying up of the extremity takes place. The writer studied one instance in an old man in whom some infection of the axillary glands had led to their scarring and calcification in such a way as to constrict the axillary artery and adjacent nerves. The pain from this constriction was such that an operation was performed in which the artery was ligated and removed with the constricting mass. Almost immediately there began the evidence of death of the fingers and of the hand and wrist, which assumed the dry form, and resulted in a few days in almost complete desiccation, so that his hand came to look like horn or some such transparent material, plastered over the bones.

Gangrene of the extremities occurs in connection with diabetes, as has been mentioned, and also with certain infectious and toxic processes. Perhaps the most striking is that which has been observed in epidemic form as a result of ergot poisoning. It was known in the middle ages as St. Anthony's fire, and relief was sought for it in a pilgrimage to Paris, which at least acted as a preventive. The truth of the matter was, although it was by no means recognized, that the peasants of France ate bread which was contaminated with the ergot smut, and consequently suffered from that peculiar poisoning which brings about an intense constriction of the arterioles. Death of the extremities was not infrequent, and in those pre-surgical days, from the ninth to the fourteenth century, it was no uncommon thing to have part of a hand or a foot torn off, after such necrosis, with a glove or boot. At the church in Paris the pilgrims were fed with bread from the monks' kitchen and most of them recovered.

There is one other important instance of the production of gangrene through anæmia, which is extremely common and which occurs in those persons whose general powers of resistance have been lowered and who have been constrained to lie in one position in bed for a long time. This is the so-called bed-sore or decubitus ulcer, to which we have referred before. The term gangrene is used most loosely in referring to the death of tissues produced by bacteria or by other means when associated with putrefaction. Thus we shall meet with gangrene of the lungs, which is by no means necessarily caused by mechanically produced anæmia, but is dependent upon the destruction of the pulmonary tissue by various forms of bacteria associated later with the ordinary bacteria of putrefaction. Another instance is seen in the so-called noma, or cancrum oris, and in the hospital gangrene, which used to cause such mortality in the wards of the larger hospitals. In all these cases it appears, from recent studies, that a combination of fusiform bacilli and spirilla plays an important part.

LITERATURE

Karsner: Jour. Med. Research, 1912, xxvii, 205. (Literature.) Jour. Amer. Med. Assoc., 1911, lvii, 951. (Infarctions.)

Umber: Mitth. a. d. Grenz. d. Med. u. Chir., 1901, vii, 487.

Versé: Ziegler's Beit., 1910, xlviii, 526. (Obstruction of portal vein.)

Welch: Allbutt's System of Medicine, 1899, vi, 228. (Literature.) Trans. Assoc. Amer. Phys., 1887, ii, 211.

Winternitz: Johns Hopkins Hospital Bulletin, 1911, xxii, 396.

Voegtlin and Bernheim: Jour. Pharm. and Exp. Therap., 1910, ii, 455.

Whipple and Hooper: Jour. Exp. Med., 1913, xvii, 593.

Niedstein: Deutsch. Zeitschr. f. Chir., 1909, xcviii, 188.

J. Marek: Arch. f. wiss. u. prakt. Tierheilk., 1907, xxxiii, 225.

CHAPTER III

DISTURBANCES OF INTERCELLULAR FLUIDS AND LYMPH

Their movement, character, and excessive accumulation. Œdema, ascites, etc.

ŒDEMA, ASCITES, ETC.

It is apparent from what has been said that the well-being of the tissues is dependent upon the continuous and unobstructed circulation of the blood through them from the arteries and the veins; but the conditions are even more complicated, for there is a constant circulation of fluids with dissolved materials from the blood, from the arterioles and capillaries, out into the crevices of the tissue and into a position where they can come into immediate contact with the cells. In this process almost all the cells are left behind, but a certain number of them undoubtedly take part in this wandering-out from the blood-vessels. This type of circulation is completed by the reëntrance of the transuded fluid into the veins or into the lymphatic channels, and in every case the fluid must pass again a complete, continuous, and semipermeable membrane composed of endothelial cells.

The idea formerly held that these tissue spaces are in open communication with the lumen of the lymphatics must be abandoned in the light of recent anatomical work (MacCallum and Sabin), and it becomes necessary to regard the tissue fluid as having its own peculiar characteristics. It is with the tissue fluid that the cells have immediate relations, and this circulation must be quite active. Up to the present no method has been found by which this particular fluid can be drained away and studied, so that the statements are, to a certain extent, based on hypothesis.

The distribution of the fluids of the blood into the tissues, and the drainage of these tissues, proceed in such a way that no matter how rapid the circulation may be, there is at no time an excessive quantity of fluid among the cells. There are conditions, though, in which a disproportion in the rate of inflow and outflow occurs, and there arises an accumulation in the crevices of the tissue (*œdema*) or in the body cavities which are in a sense analogous to the tissue spaces. When this concerns the peritoneal cavity, we speak of it as *ascites;* collections of fluid in the pleural cavity constitute *hydrothorax;* in the pericardial cavity, *hydropericardium.*

Œdematous tissues are swollen, ooze fluid on incision, and are inelastic on account of the spreading apart of the cells so that they retain the impress of one's fingers on pressure. Any organ may become so, but the most striking examples are seen in the subcutaneous tissues, especially in the extremities, and in such places as the external genitalia or in the soft parts below the eyes, where the tissues are loose. When the water-logged condition of the subcutaneous tissue is very general, it is spoken of as *anasarca*.

In those cases which generally result from diseases of the heart or kidneys the accumulation of fluid is often such that the skin becomes tense and shiny, and may even crack and allow the escape of some of the fluid. The tissues lose much of their opacity, and become almost agate-like in appearance, because the opaque cells are widely separated by the clear yellowish fluid. This is especially true of the lungs, and of such fibrous and muscular tissues as make up the wall of the intestine and gall-bladder.

Causes.—There are many things which seem capable of causing such damming-up in tissues, and, indeed, in spite of long study and experimentation we are not yet precisely informed as to the part played by each. Pathologists have proposed a great many widely different theories to explain this occurrence, and probably all of them contain some part of the truth. Ludwig's school contented itself chiefly with the mechanical increase in infiltrative pressure which seemed to them sufficient explanation, although it is obvious that there are many instances of œdema which can by no means be explained in this way. For that reason Heidenhain, Hamburger, and others introduced the conception of the vital secretory activities of the endothelial cells which were thought to pour the fluid from the vessels into the tissues. This idea involves a mystery which may, of course, be unavoidable, but which does not seem to help us further toward a satisfactory understanding of the condition. This is true, in fact, of all the theories which attempt to bridge over the difficult places by resorting to such vague terms as "vital activity," which, while they may express a present conception of the process, shed no new light upon it. In general, stress is laid upon the mechanical obstruction to the outflow of fluids, malnutrition, and poisoning of the tissues and endothelial cells which increase their permeability, disturbances of trophic, vasomotor, and motor nerves, and, more recently, alterations in the metabolism and in the state of nutrition of the tissues themselves, which may change their power of actively attracting and retaining water within themselves.

The first of these four general factors, the *obstruction to the outflow of fluids*, concerns both lymphatic and venous outflow, which are apparently in a sense compensatory to each other, for it has been observed that if the veins of an extremity are tied, the flow of lymph from the lymphatic trunk becomes greatly increased. No such observations appear to have been made upon the venous outflow when the lymphatics are obstructed. Mechanical obstruction of the flow in both veins and lymphatics arises when the heart fails in its duty of propelling the blood, and it becomes difficult for more blood to enter it. But such venous stagnation is felt by all the tissues, not only through the obstruction to the escape of fluids, but through the consequent obstruction to the entrance of new nutritive arterial blood. Consequently there arise at once several factors which might favor œdema. Filtration pressure, increased permeability of the endothelium from malnutrition, and, for the same reason, heightened osmotic pressure on the part of the tissues occur, and it is difficult to determine which of these is the most important. All are removed if the heart is supported to increased activity, when, with the improved circulation, the œdema disappears.

Local venous obstruction may bring about the same chain of events as in the so-called *milk-leg*, which is an œdema produced by the obstruction of the femoral vein by a clot. This kind of local œdema seems to be based on precisely the same principles as exist in the case of the general disablement of the circulation. It depends, to a certain extent, upon the suddenness with which the obstruction has been produced, and in any case disappears later if there be established a collateral circulation which allows the proper drainage.

Those types of œdema which are ascribed to *alterations in nervous activity* rest on a very vague and indefinite foundation, and even such so-called angioneurotic œdemas as have been long known and quite helplessly ascribed to nervous interferences are gradually revealing themselves as effects of chemical disturbances of a complicated character. Naturally, those diseases of the nervous system which are followed by prolonged inactivity of the limbs result in œdema of these immovable extremities in just the same way as ankylosis of the joint or contractures of the tendons might produce it. In all such cases the circulation is impaired, the kneading action of the muscles which ordinarily propels the fluids in the limb is lost, and the tissues are badly nourished. Almost exactly the same factors exist in the various forms of anæmia and cachexia with œdema.

The deterioration in the nutritive qualities of the blood in general anæmias, and the absorption of some indefinite poisonous material in the so-called cachexias, bring about the important factor of tissue malnutrition regardless of pressure relations. Poisonous substances, indeed, are very commonly responsible for the appearance of œdema, and certain things seem especially capable of producing it. Such substances as morphine, the juice of grapes and of various fruits, etc., are always spoken of in the text-books as capable of producing such œdema, possibly by injuring the endothelial wall of the vessel, and the same explanation is offered for the œdema which arises as a response to all the manifold effects of injury which give rise to the complex inflammation. In every case we probably do have just such an injury to the vessel-walls, but we can never exclude an injury of the surrounding tissues, which may be an equally important factor.

It is only because the fluid which exudes in the course of an inflammation differs quite markedly in its chemical composition from that which we find in other instances of œdema that we seem to have especially good proof of the existence of an injury to the endothelial walls which makes them more permeable for the albuminous material of the blood.

Œdema of the Lungs.—In spite of much study the mechanism of œdema of the lungs is not yet clear. Welch, who produced it experimentally by compressing the left ventricle and thus producing an enormous disproportion in the work of the two sides of the heart, thought that it might result from such a disproportion arising spontaneously. It can be produced by adrenalin injections, and some have thought it of toxic origin. The fluid of the blood exudes into the alveolar walls, and especially into the alveoli, so that the air is expelled by the coagulable liquid. In the extreme examples of this agonal condition frothy fluid may run away from the nostrils and the patient die practically drowned (Fig. 18).

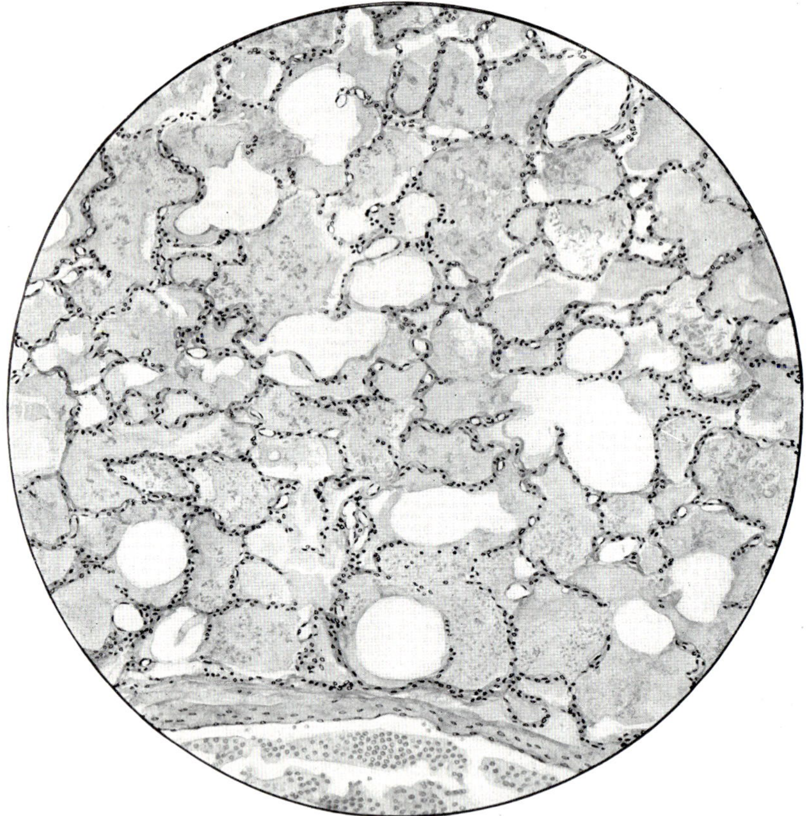

Fig. 18.—Œdema of the lung. Alveoli filled with fluid coagulated by fixing agent.

The œdema which so frequently accompanies nephritis of various types is apparently clearly shown to be due to the inability of the kidney to excrete water and salt. It appears that in most instances the power to excrete salt is at fault, its retention causing the retention of water in order to maintain the normal tonicity of the tissue fluids. Withdrawal of salt from the diet has generally the remarkable effect of increasing for a time the excretion of salt, and consequently the excretion of water, so that the œdema disappears as though by magic, and the swollen patient shrinks visibly day by day. At a certain point the relations of salt and water excretion approach the normal in proportion to the intake and the patient remains œdema-free, but an indiscretion in the consumption of salt may again suddenly close the exit, so that with its retention water again accumulates in the tissues.

LITERATURE

Cohnheim and Lichtheim: Virchow's Arch., 1876, lxix, 106.
Meltzer: "Œdema," American Medicine, 1904, viii, 19, 59, 151, 191.
Muller, F.: Verh. Dtsch. Path. Gesellsch., 1906, ix, 75.
Welch: Virchow's Archiv, 1878, lxxii, 375.

CHAPTER IV

THE STRUCTURE AND METABOLISM OF CELLS

Cellular doctrine; ultimate unit of life. Nucleus and cytoplasm. Mitochondria, plasmosomes, paraplasmic substances, intercellular substances. Tissues and motile cells. Variations in the appearance of cell. Necrosis, coagulation, and autolysis. Death.

WITH the establishment of the cellular nature of the tissues, and Virchow's epochal revelation that disease may be referred to alterations in the cell, it may well have seemed that the ultimate unit of life had been reached and that no minuter element need be considered. Indeed, our doctrine of pathology is essentially a cellular one, although we realize that the cell is in all cases a vastly complicated structure, within which there are elaborate mechanisms developed in almost infinite variety, and within which, too, we can discern evidences of the accomplishment of chemical processes which, in complexity and ingenuity of combination, surpass anything which can be carried out in the best of chemical laboratories. Within one cell there may occur at once and side by side synthetic processes and decompositions which, in the laboratory, would require, if they were possible at all, the most elaborate apparatus and the most extravagant expenditure of energy. Therefore it is not surprising that many have sought for a still simpler unit of living matter.

But even though we can recognize minuter organ-like structures within the cells, we realize that they are merely coördinate parts in building up the cell, which is the ultimate mechanism which seems complete enough to live independently. The smaller parts may be specialized instruments for some particular function, but they cannot exist or carry on this work apart from the cell. Indeed, it seems that it is upon the nice adjustment and coordination of all the parts of the mechanism in the cell that life depends; when food and temperature conditions are favorable, the precisely adjusted mechanism begins to move as though by spontaneous combustion under the boiler of an engine all prepared.

While the modern studies of immunity seem to ascribe wonderful properties to the fluids of the body, and changes almost intelligent in their purposefulness in these fluids in response to noxious substances, all the chemical characters are controlled by the cells and there is little prospect of a return to the humoral theories of long ago.

It would serve no good purpose here to enter into the details of the various conflicting theories as to the nature of the substances which make up the body of the cell and its nucleus—all this may be read in the work of M. Heidenhain, the recent review of Benda and Ernst, and in other places.

So little is firmly established that it will suffice here to mention those points which we seem to know most surely.

THE STRUCTURE OF CELLS

In spite of the great variety in form and size and in special modifications of the cell-body for different functions, we may recognize the following parts:

(1) The nucleus.
(2) The centrioles or centrosomes.
(3) The attraction-sphere or archoplasm. (Golgi's reticular apparatus.)
(4) The cytoplasm, in which are found—
(5) The mitochondria.
(6) The plasmosomes.
(7) Various paraplasmic substances.

(1) The *nucleus* differs from the general protoplasm in its density, its chemical nature, and its inner structure.

How it is separated from the rest of the cell is a matter still disputed, but it is clear than an active interchange of materials goes on between the nucleus and the protoplasm, and that the nucleus presides over the activities of the cell, and especially over its reproduction by division, in which it is itself so intimately concerned. In the absence of a nucleus the protoplasm can remain alive a short time and carry on sluggish assimilation, but it soon dies. The minute structure of the nucleus is as much disputed as that of the cytoplasm. In most cases there is a homogeneous nucleolus, and in our fixed preparations there are various condensations of deeply staining chromatin material. Kite states that, from dissection of the living nucleus, he can show that the chromatin is not in definite masses in the resting cell, and that only the nucleolus is recognizable as a colloid material of different density from the rest. In the process of mitosis, however, the clumping of the chromatin into tangible masses, the chromosomes, is familiar to every one. Their longitudinal division into equal parts, and the separation of these parts by the action of the fibrils of the achromatic spindle into the so-called daughter stars, which later form two separate nuclei, is abundantly described in all books on histology.*

(2) The *centrioles* or *centrosomes* are minute bodies, occurring in pairs outside the nucleus, and surrounded by modified protoplasm. They occupy varying positions in the resting cell, being often at the roots of the cilia in ciliated epithelium, in other cells often embedded in a dell in the nucleus. In mitosis they become active, separating to opposite poles of the cell and surrounding themselves with radiating, contractile fibrillæ (achromatic spindle), which exercise a mechanical influence upon the chromosomes.

* For a discussion of the peculiar extra chromosomes which have to do with the determination of sex the reader is referred to Morgan's book, Heredity and Sex, 1913.

(3) The *attraction-sphere*, or *archoplasm*, is a little understood structure in the cytoplasm, usually near the centrioles, and affected by them in mitosis, during which it also divides and passes to each half of the cell. It is composed of a net-like or basket-like arrangement of fibrils, the nature and purpose of which are unknown.

(4) *The Cytoplasm.*—The divergent theories as to the nature of the protoplasm may be read elsewhere. It seems that the more recent study of the granular structures which are embedded in it has removed much of the support for the earlier theories, and the outcome seems to be that the cytoplasm is essentially colloid in its composition, obeying the physical laws which govern colloids in their various phases. Possibly a mixture of colloids of various densities, it has varying powers of water absorption and swelling. The admixture of fat-like substances alters its physical character somewhat. With regard to the surface of the cell, it has been suggested that some such condensation through the aid of cholesterin or lecithin admixture may exist. Overton's theory that there is an actual thin lipoid membrane which acts as a semipermeable sheath to each cell is well known, and serves in the explanation of the action of anæsthetics, but it still admits of criticism.

E. Albrecht held a view of the constitution of the cytoplasm which was long regarded as plausible, although now being abandoned. He taught that the fluids of less density in the protoplasm might resolve themselves into droplets, which became separated from the rest by a lipoid membrane (tröpfige Entmischung).

Anitschkow seems to have shown that this idea is untenable, since the droplets are actually modifications of the various granules in the protoplasm.

(5) *The Mitochondria.*—Altmann, in 1894, devised staining methods which made visible certain granules in the cell protoplasm which he regarded as elementary organisms, or the only living constituents of the cytoplasm. While this view cannot be maintained, there is much that is exact in his observations. Benda recognized by other stains granules, rods, and threads in the protoplasm which he called mitochondria, and which have been shown by many workers (Meves, Duesberg, and others) to be a very constant constituent of the cell-body.

Many names have been proposed indicating differences in form, such as *chondriocont* for the longer filamentous forms, *chondriomita* for those resembling a string of beads, etc., but the original term, *mitochondria*, may well be used in a collective sense. The greatest variety of functions has been ascribed to them by different writers. Meves claims that they furnish the connective-tissue fibrillæ, that they transmit the hereditary characters of the cell-body, etc. Champy, in studying absorption and secretion in the intestinal epithelium, states that they accumulate at both poles of the cell and are converted into secretory granules.

It is clear that we must as yet be careful in interpreting their function, and while it seems probable that they play some important rôle, it is possible that already too many different duties have been assigned to them.

(6) *The Plasmosomes.*—Benda distinguishes sharply from the mitochondria these granules, which he speaks of as concerned with the housekeeping of the cell, with the assimilation of nutritive materials, with the formation of secretory products as the result of their specific metabolism, and with the excretion of waste.

They are not to be recognized in themselves by any of the staining methods which we know now, but are readily enough made visible by the substances which they store or secrete or by their power to store vital stains. That they are really distinct from the mitochondria is shown by their different position in the cell, by the fact that the mitochondria are recognizable as thin filaments in a cell in which, side by side with them, the plasmosomes are swollen with some absorbed material, or with a stainable secretion, and by the fact that in mitosis, mitochondria, and plasmosomes separately divide and continue their existence in the daughter-cells.

It is in connection with these that fats and carbohydrates are stored in the cell. It is probably they that swell and become conspicuous in "cloudy swelling" or "parenchymatous degeneration." They in their varieties constitute the specific granulations of the leucocytes and other cells. To this class too belong, no doubt, the zymogen granules in many glands, even though in such a gland as the pancreas we can distinguish so easily the coarse, deeply staining zymogen granules in the acinar cells from the very minute granules of two types in the cells of the islands of Langerhans.

It is clear that the construction of the cell is highly specialized in most cases for the function which it is to carry out, and that it is supplied with the most perfect mechanisms for these purposes. Some of these are evident in the form of contractile bands in the protoplasm, or in long nerve processes like electric wires carefully insulated by sheaths of fatty material, or in mobile cilia which mechanically perform duties in the transportation of foreign particles. In others the tools of their trade are recognizable in the form of the granules which seem to prepare ferments by which the chemical processes which the cells effect are carried out. While these are visible in many cases, there are others in which, even when we know that the most multifarious chemical reactions are being carried on, nothing of the mechanism is recognizable to our eyes.

(7) *Paraplasmic Substances.*—While the actual instruments of metabolism are thus often invisible, the materials which are being worked up by the cells, and more especially those which the cell is unable to dispose of, often remain conspicuous in the cell-body. Such "paraplasmic" particles, which may consist of fat-globules (Fig. 19), glycogen granules (Fig. 20), vacuoles filled with fluid, granules of pigment or calcium, often form an index of the activity of the metabolism of the cell, and are useful in determining its condition, although it must be remembered that there are doubtless many other substances equally burdensome to the cell, and accumulated in

its protoplasm, because its metabolism is so sluggish as to make it unable to dispose of them, and these, because of their solubility or because they are inaccessible to our stains, are invisible. Certainly these substances are not to be thought of as alive, at any rate until they become, through assimilation, integral constituents of the chemical structure of the protoplasm.

TISSUES AND MOTILE CELLS

It is, of course, clear in connection with this that the higher animals, at least, exist as communities of cells in which each district is made up of

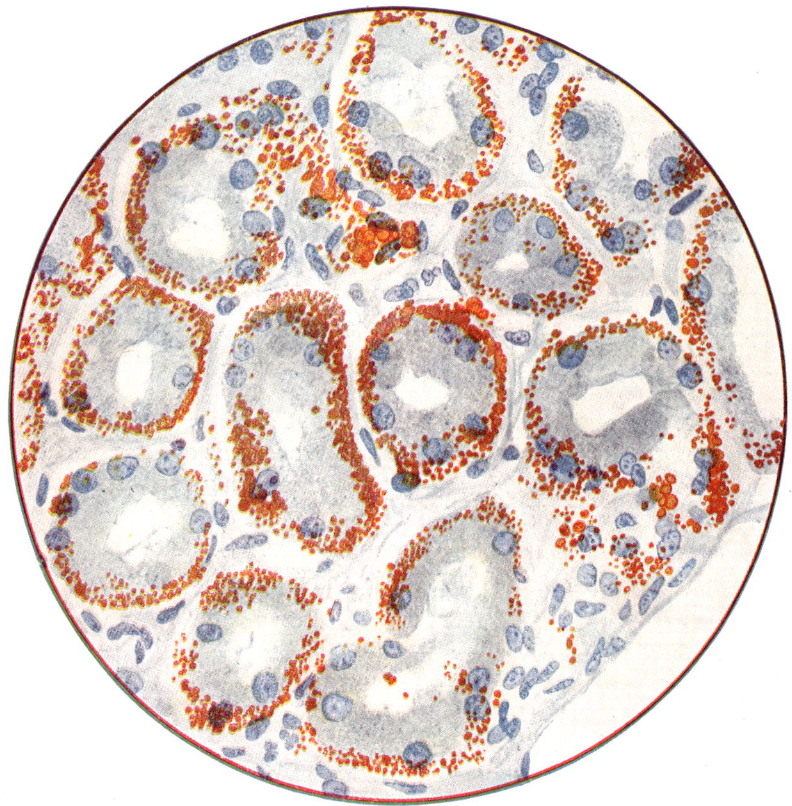

Fig. 19.—Fat-globules in the epithelium of the renal tubules. Sudan stain.

individuals which have specialized in some form of activity which is contributed to the good of the whole, and that in such a community there are many things in common, such as the blood supply, the gaseous interchange, and the removal of waste. Just as in a town the water supply, the air, and the sewerage are of common interest, so we have seen that in the body whole districts may suffer from the failure of one of these common necessities.

Communities of this character, inasmuch as they hold together in a coherent grouping, we easily recognize as "tissues." It is not so easy to think of a constantly moving and changing group of cells like the blood as a tissue, although in every other respect it deserves the same dignity as the community of liver-cells or kidney-cells. And so it is with those free lances, the wandering phagocytic cells, which straggle about in the tissues everywhere, but are ready on call to assemble at a point where they are needed. Intimately related to the mobile cells of the blood, they have the same claim to the honors of a community, although it must be remembered that they

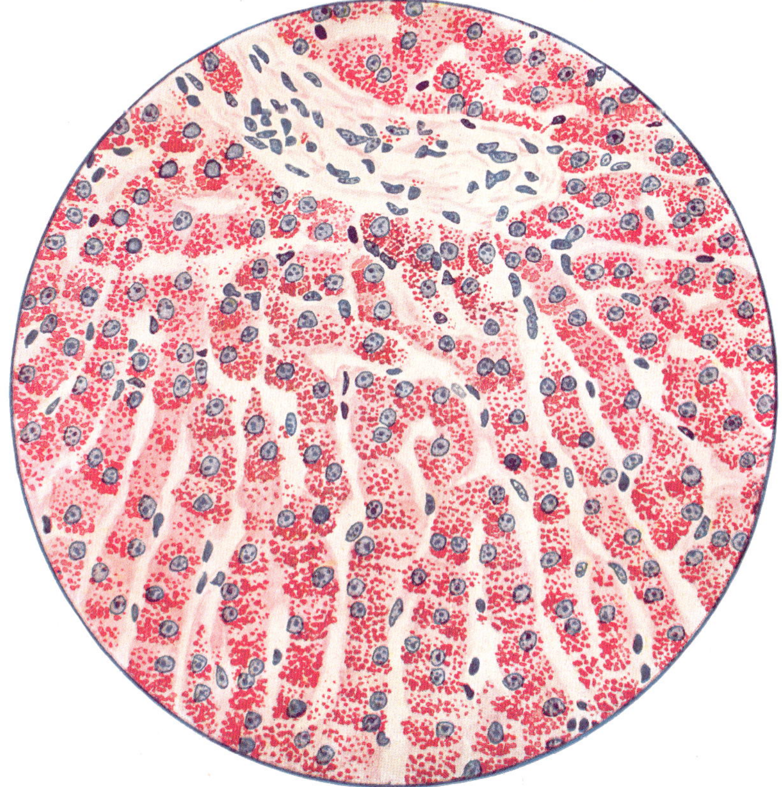

Fig. 20.—Liver of a normal well-fed dog showing glycogen in cells. Best's carmine stain.

differ from the "fixed tissue" elements in refusing to hold together into a solid structure or to adopt any particular place as a permanent site.

The whole body is not composed of cells. Were the cells all removed, there would still remain a framework so complete that although we might see through it as through a basket, the whole form of the body in all its parts would be represented and much of its solidity would remain. This is the intercellular substance, which varies greatly in character in different places, being almost the whole of the skeleton and the bulkier part of all the connective tissues which permeate all tissues and organs. Whether this material is alive has been long discussed. Certainly the fibres of connective tissue, the matrix of cartilage, and the calcified substance of bone could not remain alive alone; but in the body all these things undergo constant change, being broken down and reconstructed, and there seems no doubt that they carry on a sluggish interchange of chemical materials—a slow metabolism.

VARIATIONS IN APPEARANCE OF CELLS

Alterations in the appearance of the cell arise constantly from variations in its activity, and one must be familiar with such physiological transformation in order to interpret correctly what might otherwise be looked upon as the effects of pathological processes. This presupposes that we are able to view the cells as they are in the height of their activity, but in truth this is seldom the case, since most studies of human tissue are made after the individual has been dead for some time, or after the tissue has been removed from the body at operation. Naturally, changes must be expected to occur in this interval, and it is easily realized that the more quickly the cells can be studied after their removal from the living body, the more nearly they will approach to their living condition. Naturally, too, there are great advantages to be gained by studying such cells at once without the application of any chemical reagent, a method once universal, but now far too little used. But it is realized that while much may be learned in this way, such tissues change rapidly, and we, therefore, preserve them by suddenly stopping all ferment action and coagulating the protein substances by the application of some fluid, such as alcohol or formalin. Advantage is taken of the fact that nuclei, protoplasm, etc., react differently to various stains, and in the end our microscopical preparations show us the cells sharply brought into relief by being coagulated, and by having each of its elements differently colored. We are accustomed to the appearance in the stained preparations of what was a normal cell and interpret diseased conditions of the cell by its divergence from this standard, but at the same time we know that the cell is really greatly changed from its appearance while alive. It resembles the living cell about as a boiled egg resembles a fresh laid one. In an autopsy upon a man who had swallowed a large amount of pure carbolic acid, which is an excellent "fixing fluid," the gastric mucosa was obviously dead and coagulated into a white layer long before the man died, but although it looked so abnormal, the microscopical section showed the most perfectly preserved normal gastric mucosa.

If, then, these are all dead cells which constitute our standard of the appearance of live cells, how shall we recognize injured or dead cells among living ones? It is very easy, because what we recognize is not the death of the cell, but the changes to which it is exposed, after death, *while still surrounded by living tissues and their fluids*, and which result partly from the action of ferments and partly from the formation of a clot in the substance of the dead cell and the coagulable fluids which may permeate it.

If only a portion of the gastric mucosa had been killed, so that the man remained alive for a time, it would soon have been liquefied by the gastric juice. Exactly so a dead cell in the substance of the liver becomes the seat of clotting, and then is liquefied by the ferments of the passing fluids and mobile cells, and it is in some stage of this process that we recognize the necrotic cell. A cell which had just died would look quite like its living neighbor.

NECROSIS AND NECROBIOTIC CHANGES

It is important, then, to consider briefly these evidences of the effects of necrobiotic changes, a matter which is simplified since they are the same

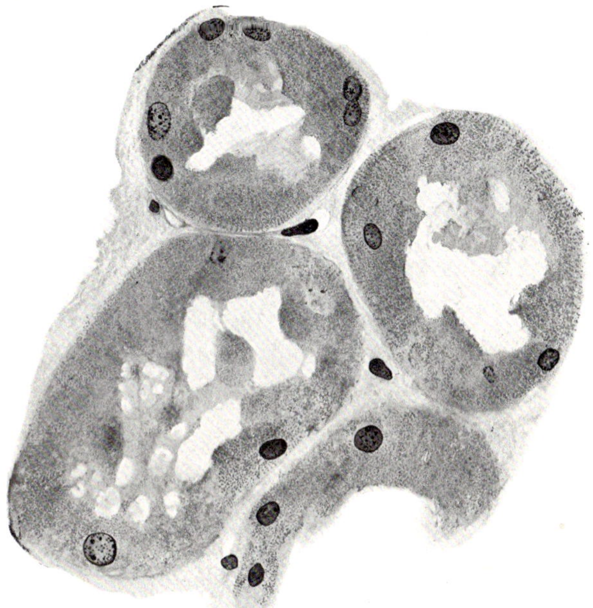

Fig. 21.—Renal epithelium showing pyknosis in several nuclei, with disappearance of others.

throughout, whether the injury be caused by a poison, by starvation, or in any other way unless, of course, the poison or mechanical injury should in itself produce some peculiar change in the cell. With the cessation of life in the cell there is a short pause, during which the dead cell has every appearance of being alive, and then its protoplasm sets in a clot. The thromboplastic substance, or thrombokinase, which the dead cell radiates causes the coagulation of the fibrinogen in the blood plasma which filters into it, and in the end the body of the dead cell becomes a swollen mass, much denser and heavier than the body of the original live cell. All this is not done without changes in the appearance of the cell—changes which probably begin before the actual death and continue after clotting has

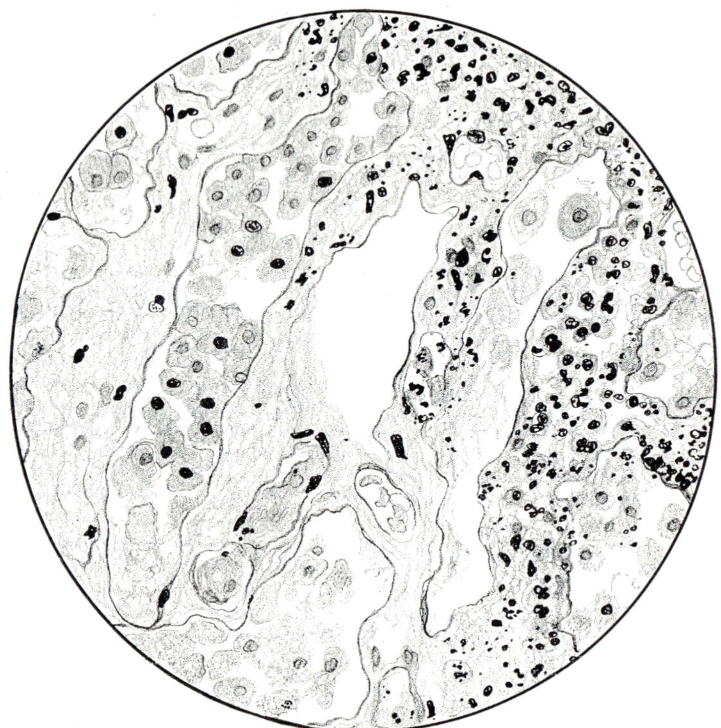

Fig. 22.—Karyorrhexis. Edge of infarct of kidney.

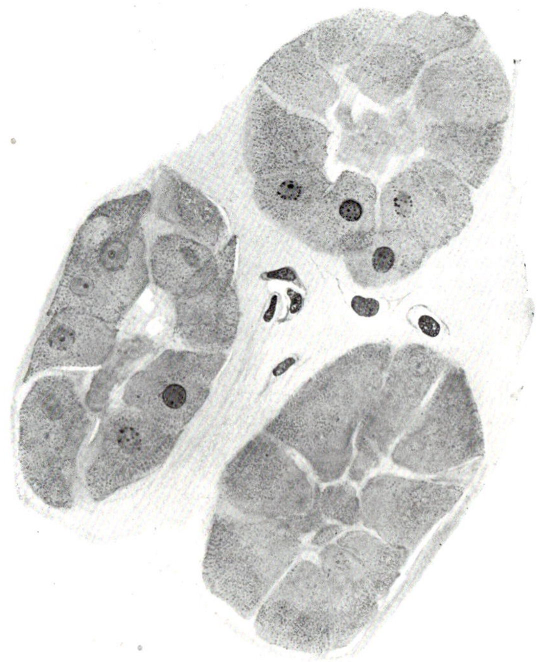

Fig. 23.—Karyolysis in renal epithelium.

occurred. The most conspicuous are alterations in the nucleus which may cause it to shrink and stain more deeply (*pyknosis*) (Fig. 21). Portions of its substance may be extruded beyond its original outline in bizarre forms, or it may break up into several irregular, solid-looking, and deeply stained fragments, or even into a fine dust of black grains (*karyorrhexis*) (Fig. 22). On the other hand, it sometimes retains its form for a long time, but gradually fades until only the faintest rim takes the stain and in turn finally disappears (*karyolysis*) (Figs. 23 and 24). At the same time the structural details of the cytoplasm are lost, and merge into a dense, granular or vitreous mass, which assumes a deep pink stain with eosin. Later changes caused by proteolytic ferments lead to the erosion, disintegration, and final liquefaction and disappearance of the whole cell remnant. Frequently

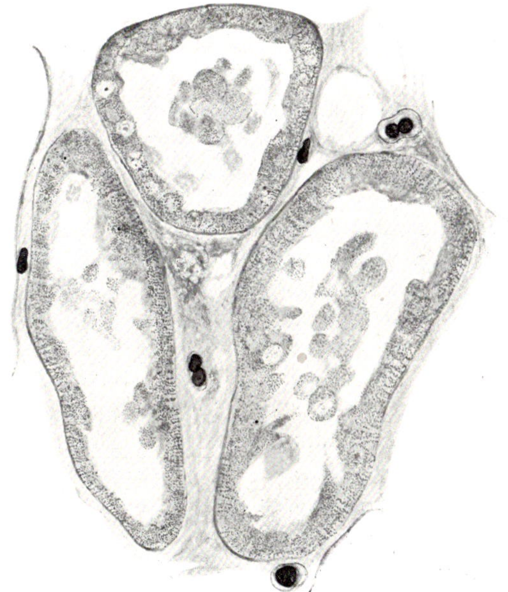

Fig. 24.—Death of renal epithelium with fading nuclei.

the boundaries of many adjacent necrotic cells are lost before liquefaction occurs, and a granular mass remains in which nuclear fragments or the fine dust of them is scattered, but even then it is often possible to make out the positions of the original cells because the more resistant connective-tissue framework of the tissue persists.

Much of the disintegration and removal of the débris of such dead cells is effected mechanically by phagocytic cells, usually of the mononuclear type, which engulf particles in their protoplasm in addition to their activity in furnishing the proteolytic ferment. They in the end wander away with these partly digested fragments, the liquefied material is absorbed, and the area of cell death collapses or is partly filled by a growth of scar tissue. Sometimes, as in large infarctions or in tuberculous foci, the dead material may remain undissolved for a long time, and is walled off by a capsule of fibrous tissue.

Autolysis.—This liquefaction by means of a proteolytic ferment is exactly the process known as autolysis, except that it is recognized in that process that all tissues can liberate in varying degrees of intensity the proteolytic ferment necessary to dissolve their own cell-bodies. Even a piece of lung or liver kept sterile in a warm place will soften and finally liquefy, while tissues, such as spleen, which contain large numbers of specialized phagocytic cells which are particularly active in producing such ferments will dissolve into a turbid fluid rich in amino-acids far more quickly. Undoubtedly this mechanism is well adapted to rid the body of useless dead and crippled cell material, and it will be seen that it plays a great part in the restoration, to an untrammeled working condition, of all injured organs, and throughout life is the constantly active method of housecleaning which keeps the machinery in order.

Death.—Death of cells is thus a relatively complicated matter, but the whole body is a community of tissues which is not entirely disabled, even by the loss of many cells. As in the cell where the controlling nucleus is destroyed the protoplasm also dies, so in the body life is the expression of the working of a delicate machine which works because it is marvelously attuned to the environment. Because it has elaborate regulators, controllers, and safety-valves, it can compensate for many injuries, but when the limit of the influence of these is passed, the machine stops. Therefore there are many ways in which the balance can be made impossible at one point or another—points important enough to involve finally the all-important circulation and respiration. When they cease, all the tissues soon die, although for some time after the main machine has stopped working, the various accessory machines are still in good working order, and need only the current of clean blood through their vessels to make them begin once more to work. Of course, the central nervous system is the great regulator, and one might say the master engineer, but life can go on without it if only some one will assume its rôle and arrange that the circulation should continue properly. So, though it is so familiar, it is difficult to define precisely what a person's death means or to say at just what moment the most important part of death occurred.

LITERATURE

Albrecht, E.: Ergebn. d. allg. Path., i_3, vi, vii, xi_2.
Altmann: Die Elementarorganismen, Leipzig, 1894.
Benda: Ergebn. d. Anat. u. Entwickl., 1903, xii, 743.
Benda: Verh. Dtsch. Path. Gesell., 1914, xvii, 5.
Champy: Arch. d'anat. Microsc., 1911, xiii, 55.
Ernst: Verh. Dtsch. Path. Gesell., 1914, xvii, 43.
Heidenhain, M.: Plasma u. Zelle, 1907, i.
Meves: Arch. f. mikr. Anat., lxxi, lxxii, lxxv, lxxvi, etc. Anat. Anzeiger, xxxi, xxxiv.
Morgan, T. H.: Heredity and Sex, Columbia University Press, 1913.

CHAPTER V

DISTURBANCES IN THE NUTRITION AND METABOLISM OF CELLS

Nature of metabolism. Disturbances resulting from slight injuries. Degenerations. Atrophy: its causes.

Ordinarily the normal and abnormal metabolism of animals is studied by chemical investigation of the materials taken into the body in comparison with those excreted, taking into account the energy liberated in the form of heat, and the changes in the weight of the body. This gives a fairly accurate idea of the whole material interchange in the body, and when the normal balance is much disturbed, it is usually easy to recognize the effects anatomically.

It is known to every one that in early life the anabolic, or building-up, processes should be in excess of the katabolic, or destructive, processes, so that growth proceeds through the assimilation and permanent retention of much of the food materials in the form of body tissue. In mature life such an exquisite balance is maintained that little change in the body weight occurs, while in the declining years the organs waste and the body shrinks because the katabolic outstrip the anabolic processes.

Substances taken in as food may be used directly for the building up of tissue, whereupon they become a relatively stable part of the body structure, or they may be burnt to produce energy, or stored for future burning. Such stores are essentially labile constituents of the body, ready at any time to be moved about or to undergo rapid chemical change. They thus constitute the ready fuel, and it is only after they are exhausted that the actual cell substance is consumed. It is like Palissy's furnace, into which, when the supreme effort was being made and fuel was finally exhausted, he cast his furniture.

Naturally, if the activities of the cells are restricted, the fuel will tend to accumulate—even if the cell is slightly injured, so that it can no longer make use of all the materials brought to it, we may expect them to collect in its body.

Under these circumstances we can often see the accumulated materials, although we can detect no evidence of injury to the structure of the cell, and it must be a matter of long experience to ascertain how much real injury corresponds with the heaping-up of such materials.

This is the basis of the so-called "degenerations," of which so much has been written. When it was thought that the globules of fat in a cell were the direct product of the decomposition of its protoplasm, this naturally indicated a great injury, but now if we think the fat merely a part of that which is transported from place to place, finally sidetracked in these cells, we cannot be so readily convinced of the injury to the cell, especially since we know that the same appearances can arise in perfectly normal persons. It is almost as though we were to attempt to tell the condition of a flour mill which we suspect of being out of order by estimating the amount of wheat in its hopper at any given moment. It might be better to estimate the flour it has ground or to look for broken wheels in its machinery.

The situation is difficult for the following reasons: Of all the substances which enter into the material interchange of the cells, we can see only a few, such as fat. As shown by chemical studies, great disturbances of metabolic activity may occur without our being able to see the substances concerned, and, on the other hand, great variations in the quantity of the visible materials in the cell need not indicate an injury to the cell. Functional disability of the cell may exist without any obvious anatomical alteration, and yet cause this stagnation of food materials, while perfectly obvious anatomical demolition of the cell machinery may occur in such a way that no heap of fuel material collects to indicate the change. So we must interpret what we find with extreme care.

It is the aim of this chapter to discuss the anatomical changes in the tissues produced by injuries, which are accompanied by disturbances of metabolism. These changes may be so slight as to be invisible, and indicated only by the accumulation of materials which should have been used up, or they may be so intense as to have destroyed the structure of the cell.

The term *degeneration* is usually employed to indicate the effect of an injury sufficient not to cause the death of the cell, but to disturb its metabolism to such a degree that the raw materials or the products of its activities accumulate in it. It is loosely used in other senses, as in the case of hyaline degeneration, in which the cells die and are merged into a homogeneous mass, or amyloid degeneration, in which an abnormal substance is deposited in the crevices of the tissue.

It would seem desirable, if possible, to abandon the term degeneration entirely and to use others which refer more accurately to the disturbances of metabolism or to the actual injury of the cell. But even if we attempted this, it would probably be unsuccessful, for the words are so deeply rooted and express so concisely a complex and obscure idea.

It must be observed that a rather limited number of raw materials are normally concerned in the chemical processes of the body, although they are presented in an almost infinite number of combinations, and pass through many further changes in the cells, but the body can deal with other things which are not good food or drink or air to breathe, in ways which are sometimes surprising and always more or less definitely adapted to its protection.

Normally we take in water, air, protein, carbohydrates, and fats, together with smaller but continuous supplies of the salts of sodium, potassium, magnesium, and calcium, combinations of iron, phosphorus, sulphur, iodine, chlorine, and minimal amounts of various other substances. The lack of any one of these will be severely felt, and may produce an astounding upset of the whole machinery of the body.

At other times, when the facilities for dealing with one or other of these substances are disarranged, it may become necessary to eliminate them from the food if life is to be prolonged—carbohydrates are withheld from the diabetic and salt from the waterlogged sufferer from Bright's disease.

ATROPHY

In order that growth should occur, or even that the tissue should maintain its status, the machinery of the cell must be in working order. We may imagine that, by reason of age, this machinery might deteriorate or that in other ways it might be incapacitated.

Evidently when this deterioration appears, the oxidizing or katabolic processes go on, although the more difficult building up proceeds but haltingly until the cell is hopelessly in arrears and wastes away.

The cell laboratory does not start up into activity merely because food is presented—rather it is controlled in its synthetic and analytic processes by influences from without—from the nervous system, perhaps indirectly through the organs of internal secretion. They set the pace and determine the rate of work. Without them tissue-cells will grow a little in such a culture as has lately become possible, but this growth is so meagre that their importance has become more than ever clear. When the cell does nothing, we might perhaps, at first thought, expect it to remain unchanged, and so it would if we assured its complete inactivity by putting it in formalin, but the inactivity of a cell is more like a household in which the breadwinner stops work.

Of course, grosser influences may have the same effect—hunger may deprive the tissues of nutrition, pressure may so constrict the cell that nourishment is impeded, or poisons may wreck the machinery. The atrophy of tissues is, therefore, not a simple matter, and perhaps were the effects as different in appearance as the causes, we might have many words to describe it. And even though we may discover the primary reason for the great change, we cannot always be sure of the immediate cause because a vicious circle is started each time, any part of which may be responsible for the end result. Can we be sure, when the muscles of a limb atrophy from disuse, whether the inactivity of the muscle-cell directly halts its metabolism, or whether the cell wastes because but little blood comes to it now, either because it fails to assist the circulation, or since the vasomotors adjust the supply to its needs as an inactive, rather than an active cell?

Wasting of the tissue may be caused by starvation, by old age, by mental disease, by derangement of the internal secretions, by infections and intoxications, especially when associated with fever, by inactivity, especially when caused by paralysis, by mechanical pressure, and by various other causes.

Hunger.—According to the state of nourishment with which it starts, the animal body can survive the complete withdrawal of food for varying periods. If water is available, the length of time that elapses before serious symptoms or death results may be several weeks, especially in certain persons who have trained themselves to fast. It is even longer in dogs. Aside from the sensations of hunger (which soon decrease) and weakness, there are usually no particular symptoms until rather late, when phenomena of intoxication with nervous symptoms arise on account of the irregular decomposition of fats into β-oxybutyric acid and acetone, with related substances. This acid intoxication, which may bring on coma, is not, as a rule, seen in fasting dogs.

In a starving person the absorption of oxygen and exhalation of carbon dioxide continue, the excretion of urine goes on, although the fæces disappear. Wasting occurs first in the stored substances, such as fat, glycogen, etc., then in the tissues themselves, beginning with those which are least called into use. Of the muscles, the active ones retain their bulk longer than the idle ones. The liver shrinks, and the parts which retain their full size for a long time are the central nervous system, the heart, and the bones, although the last probably become rarefied.

While complete deprivation in this way brings about the rapid wasting of the body, there are many mechanical and other conditions which lead to the same result more slowly. Any obstruction to the passage of food through the mouth and œsophagus to the stomach may gradually starve the sufferer, and so may an obstruction at the pylorus, since nourishment is not sufficiently absorbed from the stomach and is usually vomited after a long stay there. Beside this, there are various nervous disturbances, which result in inability to take food (anorexia nervosa) or to retain and digest it, and lead to extreme emaciation.

Senility.—With the advance of age, wasting becomes evident in many organs, if not in all, although the inconstancy with which it appears leads one to wonder whether other factors do not also play a part. The skin becomes thin and satiny, and the disappearance of fat and muscle tissue beneath it throws it into wrinkles. The hair, after becoming white, falls out, the teeth loosen and decay and fall out. The muscles waste away and grow weak, and the ligaments which bind together the bones stretch and weaken. Deprived of its strong muscular and ligamentous support, the back bends forward. The bones become rarefied, so that they break more easily and heal with greater difficulty than in a young person.

The internal organs decrease in size and turn brown, and every cell, through its shrinkage and the accumulation of pigment, can be recognized as that of a senile organ. The liver becomes a flabby, shrunken organ, of a dark-brown color, made up of lobules far smaller than the normal; often whole layers of liver tissue disappear, so that on the surface of the organ blood-vessels, bile-ducts, and the fibrous skeleton of the liver lie exposed (Fig. 25). The heart becomes small and brown, with tortuous coronary arteries showing through the watery, brownish fat. The fat of the epicardium has disappeared, and its cells are separated by fluid which gives the gelatinous appearance to the tissue. The heart decreasing in size is too small for the coronary vessels, which must take a tortuous course. Each heart muscle cell greatly reduced in thickness shows at the poles of its nucleus great quantities of a yellowish brown, granular pigment, which stains a little with Sudan III (*brown atrophy*) (Fig. 26). This is one of the little known group of lipochrome pigments which seem to arise everywhere with the wasting of the cell-body. The formation of a pigmented ring about the margin of the cornea (*arcus senilis*) is another analogous process—there, too, the pigment is probably of the group of lipochromes. The brain withstands this shrinkage for a long time—at least so far as its external appearance goes, though in the end the convolutions become narrower and separated by wide sulci in which fluid collects. Long before this the mental deterioration may have given an index of the disappearance of association-tracts and the disabling of the cells.

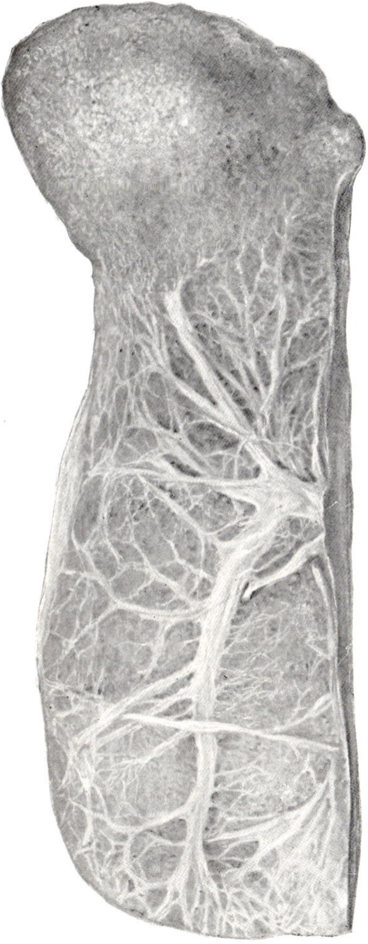

Fig. 25.—Superficial atrophy in a senile liver, exposing the vessels and the framework of the organ.

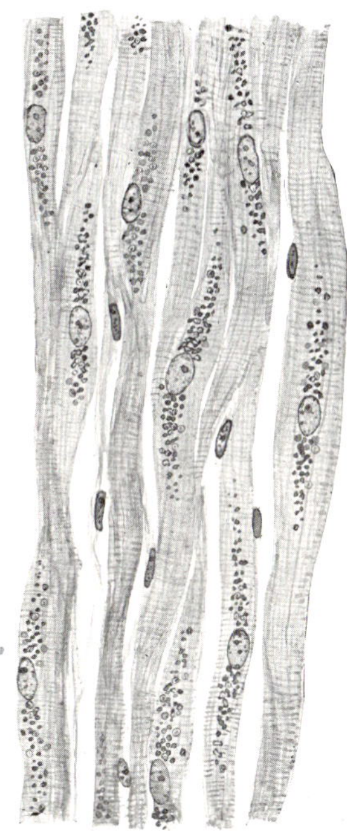

Fig. 26.—Brown atrophy of the heart. Pigment-granules at the poles of the nuclei of the wasted fibres.

In the skeleton, aside from the general rarefaction of bony tissue, conspicuous deformities may occur, such as the gradual erosion or hollowing away of the outer table of the skull over the parietal regions until deep grooves are formed over these regions—sometimes so deep as to penetrate the inner table and leave the brain covered only by a soft tissue.

Mental Disease.—We know very little about the control of metabolism from the central nervous system, but every one is familiar enough with the lean and hungry looks of the fanatic and the sleek plumpness of such as are content and sleep "o'nights." Possibly it is the constant activity of the one and the folding of the hands of the other that cause these differences, but mere muscular activity seems not quite sufficient to account for it all.

In some mental diseases the influence of excitation or apathy is very striking—in the manic depressive insanity, or *folie circulaire*, the patients pass through periods of the wildest maniacal excitement, which alternate with others of apathy and depression. In the maniacal periods they become emaciated in the extreme, only to grow fat when they pass into the state of depression.

Deranged Internal Secretions.—These are intimately related with the mental condition, and it is possible that it is in some way through them that the mental disturbance acts to affect metabolism. Psychic disturbances change the secretion of the adrenal (Cannon), and possibly they do the same with the thyroid in such a disease as exophthalmic goitre. Wasting characterizes that disease, while in the absence of the thyroid, in deficiency of the hypophysis or of the ovary or testis, fat accumulates. Evidently these organs have the most intimate relations with the general metabolism, and are in most direct control of it, for their integrity affects not only the disposition that is made of the labile substances, but also the growth of the tissues.

Febrile Disease and Tumors.—In infections and intoxications accompanied by fever the whole metabolism is so adjusted that the katabolic processes are in excess, and it is thought that in time the tissues themselves are attacked and oxidized. It is, therefore, not surprising that extreme degrees of emaciation are found in cases of protracted infections with fever—the long-standing cases of pulmonary and bone tuberculosis or typhoid fever are examples.

But the same appearances sometimes accompany the ravages of certain tumors, even when there is no bacterial infection, no ulceration, and no fever. Not all tumors can do it, nor are the emaciation and evidence of poisoning dependent altogether upon the size of the new-growth—instead, such symptoms as weakness, pallor, loss of weight, lowered resistance to infection, and all the other signs of what has long been called "*cachexia*," may be the first indication of the existence of any tumor. For this reason, although one might imagine that much food and body substance would be used up or diverted to the formation of a large new-growth, it is necessary to believe, when the tumor is very small, that it disturbs metabolism through some poison which it distils or whose formation it favors.

In such emaciated people the fat from the wasted subcutaneous tissue seems to be lodged in the liver and other internal organs whose cells are unable to dispose of it.

Inactivity.—More local in its effects, and scarcely capable of causing anything resembling the general emaciation which is seen under the foregoing conditions, inactivity may stop the growth of the tissues of the young and lead to the wasting of those of adults. In such organs as muscles the forced repose which follows the rigid splinting of an extremity or the unbending fixation of a joint is quickly followed by a decrease in the size of the muscle which can be seen to be the effect of wasting of the separate

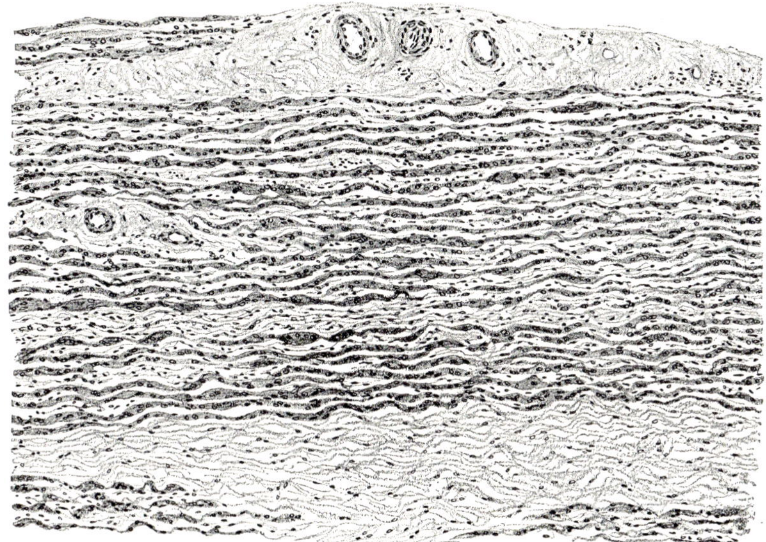

Fig. 27.—Atrophy of muscle with pigmentation and concentration of sarcolemma nuclei.

fibres until, with the loss of fibril after fibril, they are reduced to remnants of thread-like thinness or disappear entirely (Fig. 27). Generally, the sarcolemma nuclei remain and collect together until they form long beaded rows in the collapsed sheath. But they disappear also in time, and their place is taken by a little fat or by fibrous tissue which contracts so as to pull the joint into a fixed position.

When the inaction follows the cutting of the nerves or destruction of the motor nerve-cell in the anterior horn of the spinal cord (as in the so-called progressive muscular atrophy), the wasting is even more rapid and complete. It seems that even when the normal muscle is perfectly quiescent there are impulses reaching it constantly through the nerve which maintain its tension or tone. A kind of tremulous, tuned-up state is kept up which prevents its complete inertness, and this involves a certain metabolic activity.

When the nerve is cut, all these impulses cease and the muscle sags down quite flaccid—compared with the oxygen and carbon dioxide exchange of the intact resting muscle the metabolism of this paralyzed muscle is almost nothing, and hence, no doubt, its rapid wasting. Doubtless, as was suggested before, the decreased blood supply to a paralyzed limb adds to the tendency to waste, although it cannot be regarded as the most important factor.

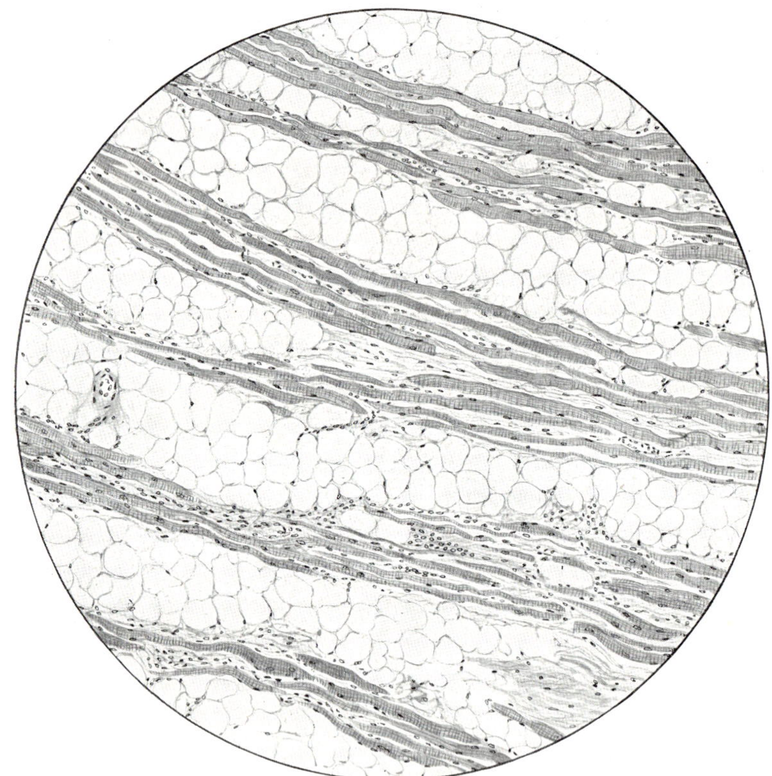

Fig. 27A.—Atrophy of muscle-fibres. Juvenile muscular dystrophy.

Other things than muscle waste in these same circumstances—the bone, the ligaments, even the skin, become atrophic in a paralyzed extremity.

We have little experience with changes that might occur in internal organs deprived of their nerve supply, but they are rendered inactive in other ways, and chiefly, perhaps, by the occlusion of their ducts or by compression. Examples of the former are discussed elsewhere (hydronephrosis, pancreatic duct occlusion, etc.).

The secretion accumulates and distends the duct, finally compressing the gland tissue so that the nutrition of the cells is interfered with. The whole gland may be converted into a thin-walled sac containing the secretion under high tension. The other factors which play a part in completing the destruction of the tissue are no doubt the compression of the blood-vessels, which now run in the tense wall of the sac, and the stoppage of the function of the secreting cells.

We know little about the actual mechanism of secretion, but it seems probable that if the concentration of any element of the secretion in the sac becomes very high, it will be impossible for the cell to continue to pour more of that substance into the solution. That part of the cell's metabolism will come to a standstill, although it is shown that if the sac be emptied, secretion will begin again at once. It is possibly somewhat as though two salts were in solution. If from these a new salt can be formed which alone of the four possible combinations is capable of escaping by osmosis from the solution, that salt will be formed and escape until all its constituents are gone. Not so if it cannot be removed—it will be formed until a balance is reached and then all interaction will cease.

This is different from the cessation of metabolism which follows section of the nerve, but it is equally capable of exposing the cell to continued, if gradual, breaking-down processes.

Pressure.—Continuous pressure, if applied to sensitive tissues firmly enough, may cut off the entrance of blood completely so that the tissue dies. This is the fate of the skin and underlying tissues in the formation of bedsores or "decubitus ulcers" in bedridden and emaciated persons whose tissues are already poorly nourished. Where their prominent bones touch the bed, the skin is kept pressed bloodless and quickly dies. But if the pressure is less violent, the cells of the tissue dwindle away slowly. This is once more a question of inadequate nourishment, for not only are the blood-vessels partly closed, but the cells themselves are compressed, so that absorption of nutriment and the carrying on of their functions sink to a low ebb.

This is seen particularly well about a tumor-nodule growing in such an organ as the liver—all the surrounding cells and capillaries are flattened and gradually disappear.

One might expect the accumulated food-stuffs, such as fat-globules, to disappear first, and after that the cell-body itself, but it appears that if the cell is caught with fat-globules in it, it may be unable to use them up before it itself is quite disabled, perhaps by lack of oxygen. Therefore the liver-cells immediately next to the advancing tumor-nodule may be loaded with fat, though most exposed to pressure (Fig. 28).

The effect of pressure in distorting and perverting the growth of tissue is seen in the misshapen heads of some French peasants and certain Indians, in the crippled feet of the Chinese women, and the constricted livers of the fashionable white women of past generations. Numerous other instances are found in the compressed and distorted organs, and limbs found in malformed infants as the result of amniotic adhesions in intra-uterine life.

Another example commonly adduced is the effect of aneurysms upon the tissues upon which they impinge. Soft tissues yield in front of them—

hard tissues, like bone, are hollowed out before them. But I cannot believe that this is merely a pressure atrophy, for one finds the bone actually comminuted, as though with a hammer, and the fragments bathed in blood and attacked by great phagocytic giant-cells (osteoclasts). In the vertebral column the centra of the vertebræ are thus excavated, while the intervertebral discs project unchanged (Fig. 29).

Decreased blood supply is commonly held to be a prominent cause of

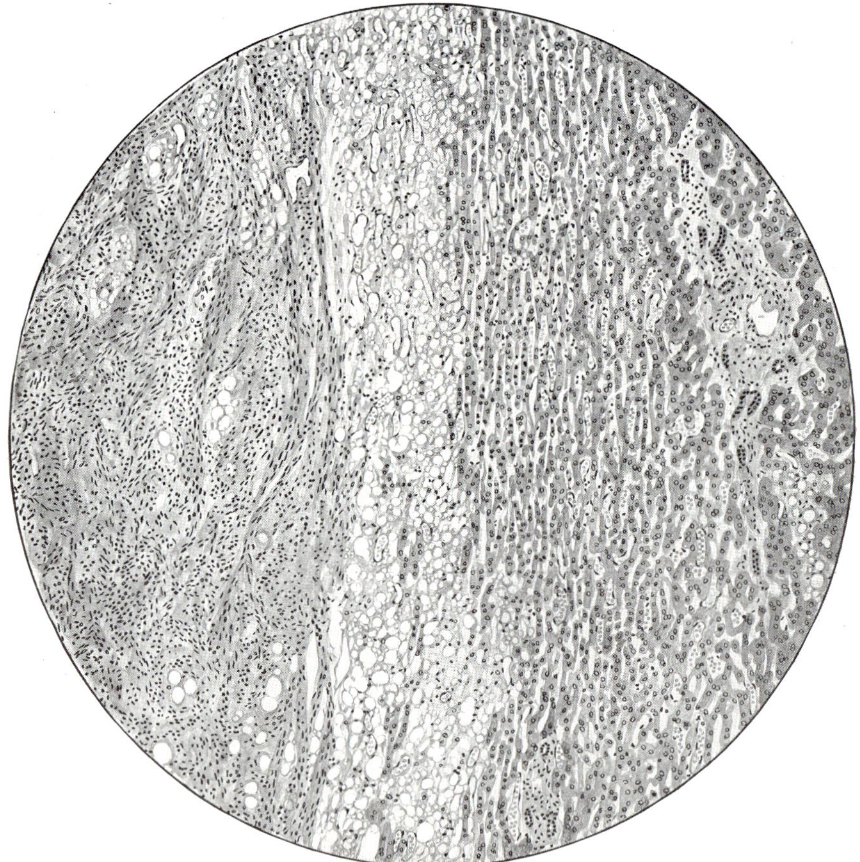

Fig. 28.—Compression of liver-cells about a metastatic tumor-nodule.

atrophy without questioning more closely the nature of the examples that are always presented. Decreased blood supply does occur in regions or organs which we find in a state of atrophy, but it must be asked whether it is cause or effect. The blood supply may be decreased by pressure on the supplying artery, or by contraction of the vessel or the narrowing of its lumen by abnormal thickening of its wall.

If effective occlusion of the vessels occurs rapidly, the tissue dies—if gradually, a collateral or roundabout circulation is developed and no effect is produced.

Probably such a situation as is found in the kidney in which arteriosclerotic narrowing of the blood-vessels limits the blood supply without recourse, could be most satisfactorily given as an example of atrophy of

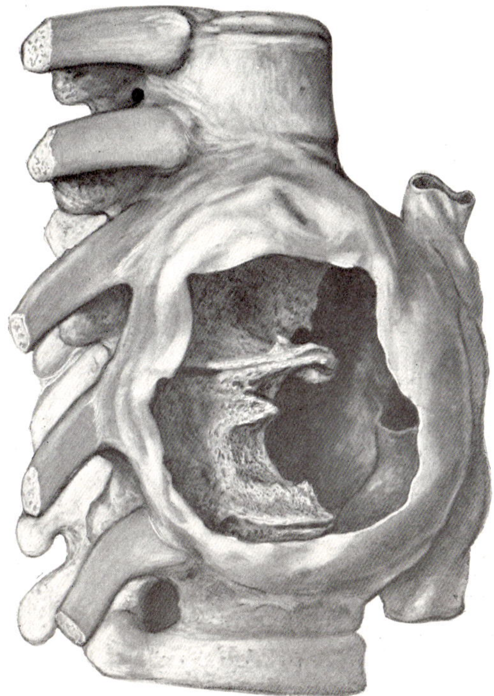

Fig. 29.—Destruction of vertebræ by aneurysm. Dried specimen with aneurysmal sac *in situ*.

the tissue from this cause, although, as in the senile ovary or uterus, in which the arteries become gradually obliterated, the wasting of the kidney might be explained otherwise.

In a kidney recently observed there were two supplying arteries, one of which had long been occluded by a thrombus. That half of the kidney was shrunken, in sharp contrast with the other half.

CHAPTER VI

DISTURBANCES OF FAT METABOLISM

Neutral fats and lipoids. Their source, absorption, distribution, and functions. Pathological disturbances.

If we attempt to discuss the disturbances of metabolism in their relation to pathology, we must remember that the methods of pathological anatomy which show alterations in the tissues consisting of destructive changes of the cell structure, on the one hand, and accumulation of the materials concerned in metabolism, on the other, must give us only the most incomplete and even misleading idea of what is taking place. Many of the protein or albuminous materials are in solution and invisible, and even when we make them visible by coagulation, it is impossible to recognize them definitely. The same thing is true of the carbohydrates, since glycogen is the only form that we can demonstrate histologically. Sometimes we can see fats and lipoid substances, but rarely when they are in the form in which they take part in the actual function of the cell—rather it is when they are stored and inactive, or when they are thrown out of the current of the life of the cell as stagnant material, that they can be seen. Indeed, we are doubtless wrong even in trying to consider proteins, fats, and carbohydrates separately, for in their relation to the processes of life they seem to combine into the really important substances with which we are only indirectly acquainted. Fat we know as it appears in adipose tissue or in globules in other cells, but fat in what may be a lipoid proteid combination as it exists invisible in the cell and recoverable from it only after the cell is reduced to débris by digestion, we scarcely know, although it is probably in that form that it is most important.

It seems that in these combinations, varied as they are, we may find the agents of many of the extraordinarily efficient chemical processes that go on in the body. This should be the ground for discussion in pathology. It should form one of the principal chapters, if we only knew enough to bring it into the field; on the other hand, it seems hardly worth while to describe in detail the various places where abnormal accumulations of some of the inert separated constituents of these specialized expert bodies are laid up so that we can see them.

If we could do more than guess at the nature of most of the disturbances that wreck the machinery and heap up the raw material or the slag, it would be something, but even that is commonly obscure. Nevertheless, we must tell what we can with our surmises about the true inwardness of the actions which have left these traces.

Of all these substances, as long as we have been in the habit of separating them into three great classes it has been the custom to regard the proteins as the most important, the real basis of life, the substance of protoplasm, while the fats and lipoids or fat-like materials were looked upon as fuel and as useful in other vaguely understood ways, possibly as insulating materials in the nervous system or even as padding underneath the skin to keep the body warm. Carbohydrates seemed essentially fuel for rapid burning; now, however, in Ivar Bang's phrase, the lipoids are beginning to be recognized as actors of extreme importance, with rôles of unsuspected delicacy and complexity. Even yet the carbohydrates have not met with what may be a deserved recognition, but it is becoming clearer that it is the ensemble action, and not the part played by the isolated fragments, which we salt out or extract with ether, that brings about the wonders of life.

FATS AND LIPOID SUBSTANCES

The fat-like bodies soluble in organic solvents, such as ether, alcohol, chloroform, or benzol, are defined by Bang as lipoids. It is perhaps common, however, to speak of the neutral fats as fats, and of the rest as lipoids, since that must have been the origin of the word.

Of this great group there are almost innumerable examples, and the series may perhaps be extended to forms as yet unsuspected, but in human physiology and pathology comparatively few concern us.

These are as follows, according to Bang:

1. Fats—lipoids of the aliphatic series containing only C, H, and O, without N or P.
2. Cholesterines—lipoids of the aromatic series containing only C, H, and O, without N or P.
3. Phosphatides—lipoids containing N and P in addition to C, H, and O.
4. Cerebrosides—lipoids containing N but not P, together with C, H, and O.
5. Other important but little understood lipoid substances, which include the lipochromes.

The details of what is known chemically of these substances must be read in such works as those of Leathes, Bang, Jolles, and others, and only the barest outline can be given here.

Fats.—These, which form the great bulk of the subcutaneous and other depot fat, are esters of glycerin with fatty acids. For the most part those which occur in the animal body are triglycerides of stearic, palmitic, and oleic acids, but in certain secretions, as in milk, butyric, caproic, and other fatty acids occur.

A typical formula is as follows:

$$\begin{array}{l} CH_2\text{—O—OC—}C_{17}H_{33} \\ | \\ CH\ \text{—O—OC—}C_{17}H_{33} \\ | \\ CH_2\text{—O—OC—}C_{17}H_{33} \end{array}$$

which is triolein.

The difference in their melting-points and other characters, and in the proportions in which they occur in the fat of different animals, are all well known, and one realizes that if sheep-fat is more solid at room temperature than human or dog fat, it is because it contains more tristearin and tripalmitin and less triolein.

Such fats may be saponified or broken up by the action of alkalies into glycerol and soaps, or combinations of the alkalies with the fatty acids. In another way they may be separated into their constituents, glycerol and fatty acid, by the action of a ferment (lipase), and this action is reversible.

The *cholesterines* occur in wide distribution throughout the body as constant constituents of the cells and body fluid, either free or in combination with fatty acids (cholesterine esters), often in solution, but sometimes, as in the adrenal cortex, in the form of globules. Crystals of free cholesterine are found under pathological conditions. The formula for the cholesterine found in the human body is given as $C_{27}H_{46}O$. It is a complex terpene, bearing no relation to fats, carbohydrates, or proteins, but consisting probably of a saturated cyclic system with the character of a secondary alcohol, since it can form ketones, and also with fatty acids, esters. It crystallizes in flat, rhombic plates which often show broken or reëntrant angles.

The *phosphatides* are of the very greatest biological importance, and enter extensively into the structure and function of many organs. They fall into the following groups (Bang, Thudichum, Aschoff):

1. Monoaminomonophosphatides (lecithines, kephaline) (glycerophosphoric acid esters of two fatty acids and choline).
2. Monoaminodiphosphatides (cuorine, etc.).
3. Triaminodiphosphatides (sahidine, etc.).

All of these contain unsaturated acids. Of the phosphatides containing saturated fatty acids we have:

4. Diaminomonophosphatides (sphingomyeline, etc.).
5. Triaminomonophosphatides.

Of these substances, the knowledge is essentially vague, since practically none of them can be obtained in a pure state, partly on account of their labile character. The best known are probably the lecithines and kephalines, although they too are enveloped in a haze of uncertainty, and one cannot say whether these fragile substances which are strained out of the brain and other organs ever existed there in the form in which they come to light.

Lecithine, which forms sticky, waxy white or orange masses, is given the formula:

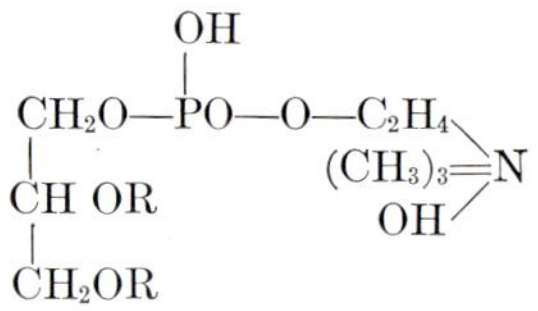

$$\begin{array}{llll}
 & \quad OH & & \\
 & \quad | & & \\
CH_2O - & PO - O - C_2H_4 & \diagdown & \\
| & & (CH_3)_3 = & N \\
CH\ OR & & OH \diagup & \\
| & & & \\
CH_2OR & & &
\end{array}$$

That is a glycerophosphoric acid ester of two fatty acid radicles (one of which is unsaturated) in combination with choline. It is soluble in alcohol and other lipoid solvents except cold acetone; it unites with acids and bases, with carbohydrates and with proteins (vitelline, lecithoalbumin).

Kephaline is a resin-like, crumbling, hygroscopic substance, soluble in ether, etc., but not in alcohol or acetone. It is the chief phosphatide of the brain, and is otherwise widely distributed. Bang gives the following probable constitution:

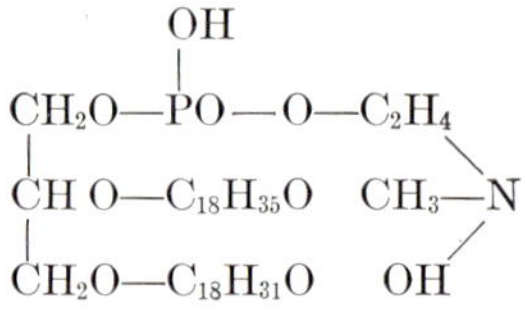

$$\begin{array}{lll}
 & \quad OH & \\
 & \quad | & \\
CH_2O - & PO - O - C_2H_4 & \\
| & & \diagdown \\
CH\ O - C_{18}H_{35}O & & CH_3 - N \\
| & & \diagup \\
CH_2O - C_{18}H_{31}O & & OH
\end{array}$$

which is a glycerophosphoric ester of stearic and linoleic acids with a monomethylcholine.

The Cerebrosides.—These are glucosides, and being disintegrated, yield a sugar, galactose, fatty acids, and a nitrogenous substance, but no phosphoric acid. They occur in the white substance of the brain, the blood, spermatozoa, etc. The most important are perhaps the phrenosin and kerasin of Thudichum.

The other little understood lipoid substances, which include the pigmented fatty granules found in wasting cells (lipochromes), and probably various substances concerned in immunity, remain to be investigated.

It has been said that these substances are sometimes recognizable as such (neutral fats, cholesterine esters, etc.), but most of them are extracted from the organs by the aid of various solvents, and freed from impurities by different chemical manœuvres. It is, therefore, hard to feel sure that in the living organs they exist in the form in which they are finally studied and not rather in some easily disturbed combination with proteins or other substances. Some of them are readily dissolved out of the cells, in which they can be seen as globules of pure fat; others appear to be loosely adherent or adsorbed in fine, invisible layers about other substances in the cells. They can be extracted too without great difficulty, although they cannot be seen with the microscope in the cell. Still others are so firmly held that they seem to be in chemical combination with the materials of the cell, and these, naturally invisible in the cell, can be extracted only after the tissue is digested or hydrolyzed so that its chemical compounds are disintegrated. That there is constant change in their relations is indicated by the way in which the simpler fats undergo lipolytic decomposition into glycerin and fatty acids, followed by the formation of soaps, their decomposition, and the reconstruction of fats.

As Aschoff says, the pathological anatomist is most interested in determining in what form these lipoid substances become morphologically visible, and by what means their specific composition can be recognized. The chemist, on the contrary, must be content with analyzing the lipoids which remain to him after his tortuous methods of extraction, separated thus by a gulf from their original relations, and perhaps even entirely changed in their characters. It is the biologist who must try to combine these two sets of information and attempt to learn the functional rôle which the lipoids play in the body.

The anatomist applies with success certain methods to the study of fats in the tissues. There are stains which color all lipoids, such as sudan, others which stain neutral fats red, phosphatides blue, such as Nile-blue sulphate; osmic acid is blackened by fats of unsaturated acids; cholesterine esters are doubly refractive. Phosphatides and soaps form bizarre myeline figures, and so on. Great ingenuity has been applied to the recognition and distinction of fatty bodies by these methods (which must be read in the works of Aschoff, Kawamura, Versé, and others), but they are still very imperfect and unreliable, except in the simplest situations.

SOURCE, ABSORPTION, TRANSFORMATION, AND DEPOSITION OF FATS

Since similar substances occur in the tissues of other animals, it is probable that a great source of the fats in the human body is to be found in animal food. Some are derived from vegetable foods, and others are produced in the body from carbohydrates, and since carbohydrates can be formed from the decomposition products (amino-acids) of proteins, no doubt fats are thus indirectly derived from proteins. Cholesterine comes to us in animal food—how it is produced in the bodies of herbivorous animals is not perfectly clear, but it probably arises from the phytosterines which are found in plants.

Taken into the intestine, the absorption of fats occurs by the action of lipolytic ferments, which produce glycerin and soluble soaps, which are reconstituted into fats in the intestinal wall, or by direct passage of unchanged fats, perhaps with the aid of the bile. Whether in the reconstitution in the intestinal wall the foreign fats are remoulded into human fats is uncertain. Undoubtedly, some foreign fats go through unchanged to the tissues, but since the fats of animals are characteristic, the remoulding must take place somewhere, possibly in the course of numerous decompositions and reconstitutions which accompany the wanderings of fat in the body. How cholesterine and its esters enter is not investigated. Cholesterine fed to rabbits is lodged in the tissues largely in the form of cholesterine esters. The advent and transformation of phosphatides and cerebrosides are even more obscure.

Distribution in the Body.—Neutral fats are, as every one knows, lodged, sometimes in enormous quantities, in what are roughly known as fat depots, among which the subcutaneous and intermuscular tissues, the bone-marrow, the mesentery, omentum, and retroperitoneal tissues, the epicardium, the tissue about the kidneys, and the tissues of the orbit furnish examples. In very obese persons the fat, after filling these places to their utmost, seems to overflow into the most unexpected localities—adipose tissue extends through the wall of the heart and appears under the endocardium; it pushes apart the lobules of the pancreas, and even spreads round to the free surface of the intestines. In every case the fat is inclosed in cells. In the infant one may readily observe that the adipose tissue falls into lobules which are easily separated. These are seen to be sharply outlined, gland-like structures, provided with an extremely rich capillary circulation, and composed of polygonal cells with very granular protoplasm which contains only the beginnings of the accumulation of oil-globules which will ultimately distend them (Fig. 30). Such lobules are quite distinct from the surrounding loose connective tissue, which contains no fat, and are very conspicuous in any section which passes through adrenal or thyroid since a comparison with those glands is at once suggested. They have even been described by Pende as organs of internal secretion, and perhaps the specificity of the adipose tissue is almost sufficient to justify him in such an idea. In later life they disappear because so much fat gathers in their cells that the protoplasm becomes a mere film about the great oil-globule—the separate lobules of this tissue swell until they touch one another, the intervening fibrous tissue is lost to view, and we seem to have a homogeneous adipose tissue.

It would be interesting to be able to show that all adipose tissue is of this nature, but probably in obesity fat accumulates in other connective-tissue cells which have no specific relation to its metabolism.

Neutral fat occurs in the blood plasma and in the lymph and chyle, and thus indicates the mode of transport from one part of the body to another,

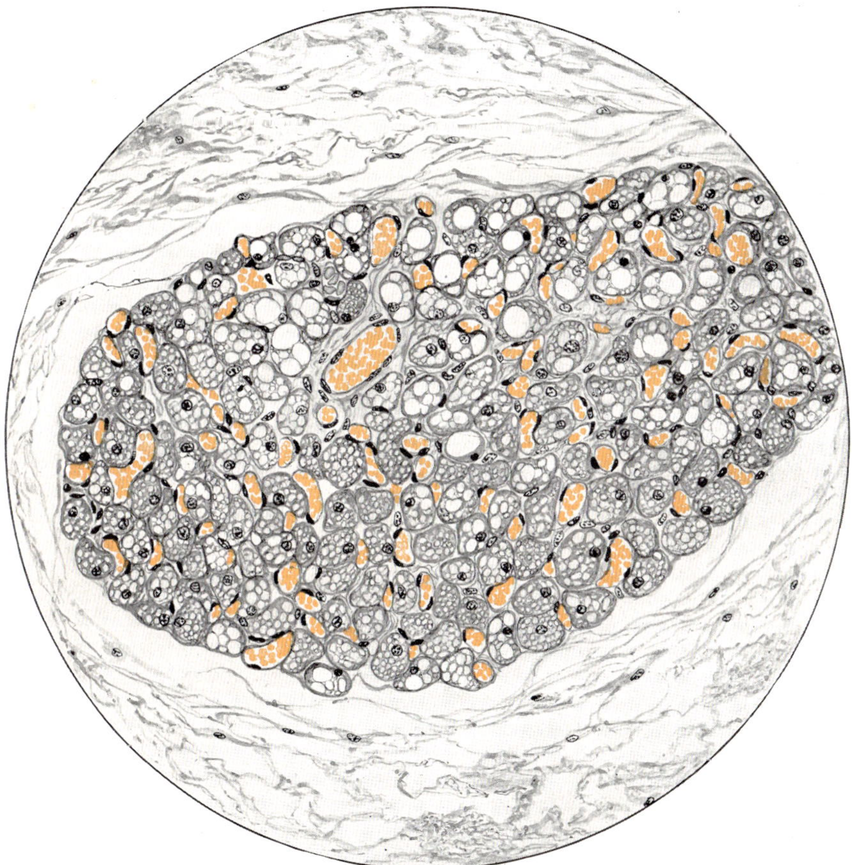

Fig. 30.—Adipose tissue of fœtus. Lobule of specialized connective tissue in which fat accumulates.

and from the digestive tract to the tissues. It is found in the cells of many parenchymatous organs, such as the liver, adrenals, and others, where it may be merely stored, or where its presence may be explained in other ways which shall be discussed later.

There seems to be little evidence to show that such neutral fats, aside from being foods and the source of energy, play any very complex part in the life of the cell. On the contrary, although we do not know exactly how they are distributed in the tissues, we cannot escape the impression that the phosphatides, the cholesterine compounds, and cerebrosides are absolutely essential elements in most of the important functions of the cells. Each new investigation reveals their silent and unsuspected participation in the most fundamental processes.

It is known that even when the microscope, aided by the most effective staining methods, reveals no trace of fat in the tissues, a large quantity can be extracted by chemical methods. A perfectly normal human kidney which shows no recognizable fat yields 10 to 20 per cent. of its weight upon digestion and extraction. This fat must have been in some extremely fine state of division, or else in chemical combination, such that it failed to give the usual staining reactions.

None of the hypotheses about this disposition of lipoids in the cell has up to now been satisfactorily proved, and they are the subject of much dispute. It is Overton's idea that each cell is bounded by a very thin lipoid membrane which controls the entrance and exit of the substances which reach the cell. According to this idea, drugs like narcotics, which are usually soluble in fats, gain easy access to the cell, although it does not appear quite easy to understand how these substances leave the lipoid membrane to enter the watery cell-body. On the other hand, the passage of salts in and out becomes difficult, and the theory is forced to resort to the vital activity of the cell to explain these things. Nevertheless, the idea of a lipoid enveloping membrane for cell and nucleus is very generally held.

Within the cell similar lipoid membranes are supposed to line vacuoles and perhaps to cover some of the specific granules—at any rate, there is much to show that the fine globules of fat which appear in the cell protoplasm do so in relation with mitochondria, or, as Benda claims, rather with the vegetative granules, the plasmosomes. These granules accumulating fat about them finally take on the form of globules. But even with these explanations it is evident that there must be much lipoid material in the cell in an invisible form.

FUNCTIONS OF FATS AND LIPOIDS

The most obvious and best known function of the fats lies in their acting as food-stuffs. In their oxidation to set free energy in the form of heat or work, they require more oxygen than do carbohydrates, so that the respiratory quotient or ratio, $\frac{CO_2}{O}$, is about .795. They form, of course, since they can be conveniently stored, the ideal material for the accumulation of a source of energy. Nevertheless, we must suppose that they also take part in aiding the growth of the tissues through furnishing material for their constructive processes.

If it be true that they form lipoid membranes about each cell, each nucleus, and each vacuole, it must be agreed that they are primarily instrumental in regulating the assimilation of the cell and in permitting it to control in a way the substances which present themselves for absorption.

The part played by lipoid substances, especially the phosphatides and cerebrosides, in the construction of the nervous system, must be of prime importance, although we approach its contemplation so awkwardly by extracting them from the ground-up brain. From their arrangement in the myeline sheaths of the nerve-fibres it would appear that they may act as insulating substances which insure the passage of the nervous impulse to the correct end-organ; in other words, that they serve a purpose analogous to that of the rubber and shellac in a complex electric cable, or even in the brain, to that of the more elaborate insulation in the interior of the dynamo.

In their relation to enzyme action the neutral fats are played upon by lipases which occur everywhere in the organs and fluids of the body, as well as in the digestive juices. Anti-lipases which inhibit this reversible action exist also. The lipases which must exist to control the decomposition of cholesterine esters and of the phosphatides (lecithinase, cholesterase, etc.) are not yet even certainly demonstrated. Bang objects that experiments carried out to show that such lipoid substances may influence the action of other ferments are inconclusive, but Jobling has shown that the decomposition products of some fats—unsaturated fatty acids and their soaps—have the most decisive inhibiting action upon proteolytic ferments, their power being in a sense porportional to the degree of unsaturation of the fatty acid. So universally is it true that such unsaturated fatty acids can impede the action of proteolytic ferments that many pathological conditions (such as the persistence of caseous tuberculous material in its solid form) can be shown to be due to their presence. If they are rendered impotent by saturation of their unsaturated group with iodine, the proteolysis goes on rapidly and the caseous tubercle or gumma rapidly softens.

In the complex process which occurs in the clotting of blood Howell has shown that the thromboplastic substance derived from the tissue is a lipoid, kephaline. It has been shown that certain lipoid substances, especially cholesterine, can act as inhibiting or neutralizing agents toward such hæmolytic poisons as saponin, cobra poison, etc., through forming with them an innocuous compound. By some (Takaki) it was thought that lipoids of the nervous system, phrenosin, cerebron, etc., could neutralize the tetanus toxin, but this is contradicted by others and is uncertain. In the so-called "Wassermann reaction" lipoid substances act in a somewhat similar way to combine with or absorb the complement and withdraw it from combination with the blood-corpuscles.

Our knowledge in this direction is very slight; nevertheless it is enough to suggest the possibility that lipoid substances may sometimes accumulate in an organ for the protection of the cells of that organ from toxic injury. On the other hand, lipoids may act as toxic substances or as activators of toxins. Of these, the toxic ones are foreign lipoids, such as may be extracted from bacteria. The fats from the tubercle bacillus may produce lesions somewhat resembling those caused by the organisms themselves. It is in connection with hæmolytic poisons, such as cobra venom, that lipoids (lecithin) are found to behave as activators. Regarded at first as representing the complement according to Ehrlich's theory (Kyes), it now seems more probable that the lipoids may aid in transferring the poison to the cell, since the "lecithid" is apparently only a solution of the venom in lecithin (Bang). The direct production of immunity against lipoid substances used as antigens has given some vague results, but the matter still remains to be investigated.

Undoubtedly the lipoids fill an important position in many ways, in relation to the processes of immunity, but for the further discussion of the matter reference must be made to works upon that subject.

Cholesterine compounds are known to exist in the circulating blood and in the adrenal cortex, as well as in other tissues. What must be a significant index of their importance is found in the course of pregnancy, when there comes a gradual but great increase in the quantity found in the blood, a great storing in the corpora lutea, and, with the end of pregnancy and beginning of lactation, an outpouring of cholesterine esters with the first milk. After that the proportion decreases in the milk, and in the blood sinks back to normal. Why this should be is not known, but the flooding with cholesterine esters seems to have a protective influence of some kind, since under those circumstances animals will survive the loss of the adrenal gland far longer than non-pregnant controls, and, indeed, the injection of cholesterine esters seems to have the same influence (Stewart).

PATHOLOGICAL DISTURBANCES OF FAT

So far we have attempted to review the normal relations of the lipoid substances in the body, and finding our knowledge so woefully incomplete there, we turn not very hopefully to their study under pathological conditions.

Obesity.—From what was said of the normal use of fats as food we may judge that a certain balance is maintained in the storehouse of the body. Nevertheless, the consumption of a great excess, especially an excess of fats and oils and of carbohydrates, tends, in persons who lead an inactive, sedentary life, to cause the accumulation of excessive fat in all possible depots in the body. Even the secreting cells of parenchymatous organs, such as the liver, become somewhat richer in fat than normal, although it is by no means in obese people that one finds the great collection of fat in the liver-cells. The storing-up of fat can be prevented and the fat made to disappear by active exercise, massage, etc., or even by hot baths, which seem to hasten its consumption. But every one has noticed that the obesity which comes from mere sedentary habits and overeating is in most persons a mild kind of disability; other people, even with the greatest abuse of these things, remain quite thin, while there are certain unfortunates who, in spite of efforts to limit their diet strictly and to take abundant exercise, grow enormously fat. It seems possible that in these cases there may exist some defect in such organs of internal secretion as the thyroid or the hypophysis, whose secretion appears to enhance the activity of metabolism in general. In known cases of hypophysis defect in young persons great obesity arises with retardation of sexual development, and in cases in which the thyroid has been destroyed a similar, if less extreme, obesity may arise.

Diabetes.—In pancreatic diabetes another disturbance of internal secretion in which the consumption of carbohydrates is made difficult, an abnormally violent attack is made upon the fats, which are turned into the blood-stream for transportation in such a way as to give the serum a milky appearance (diabetic lipæmia). The irregular consumption of these fats leads to the production of the poisonous acetone bodies. (See Diabetes.)

Degeneration of Nerves.—It has been pointed out that lipoid bodies form the coatings of nerve-fibres, as though to insulate the axis-cylinders within these myeline sheaths. When the nerve dies through being cut through or from the destruction of its cell-body, the lipoids of the myeline sheath about the dead axis-cylinder disintegrate, leaving globules of the decomposition products which now blacken with osmic acid in a way foreign to the myeline itself (Figs. 31A and 31B). Saponine attacks and combines with the lipoid sheath of the nerve and causes paralysis. Many other substances, most of which have certain affinities for lipoid materials, cause injuries to the nerves, followed by inflammation or by paralysis. Lead palsy, arsenical and alcoholic neuritis, the neuritis occurring in the intoxication associated with pregnancy and in diabetes, are examples of this vague connection. Beriberi, a form of multiple neuritis, is supposed to result from the lack of a lipoid constituent belonging to the covering of the rice grain, since it occurs in persons fed on polished rice. This is not yet satisfactorily proven, but all these things point to the possibility of a common character in the affection of nerves due to disturbances in their medullary sheaths.

Anæmias.—The same vagueness and uncertainty prevail with regard to the part played by the lipoids in the production of some forms of anæmia. Faust and Tallquist thought that the pernicious type of anæmia caused by the bothriocephalus was due to a lipoid which they later stated to be oleic acid, but this is scarcely probable. On the other hand, many of the toxic materials which produce anæmia, such as benzole, are solvents of lipoids or soluble in them, and it may be through this relation that the lipoid constituents of the red cells are attacked. The whole question of hæmolysis has intimate dependence upon the lipoid content of the cells.

Abnormal Accumulations of Fats and Lipoids in Organ Cells.—One type of evidence as to the rôle of the lipoids in pathological conditions which has scarcely been touched upon is found in the anatomical recognition of abnormal accumulations of these bodies in the cells of the organs. This, which has always formed the chief interest of pathological anatomists, is, after all, at most only an indication of the disability or injury of those cells, and has relatively little bearing upon those functions of the lipoids which are beginning to show themselves as of fundamental importance.

Both neutral fats and globules or granules of other lipoids, especially the

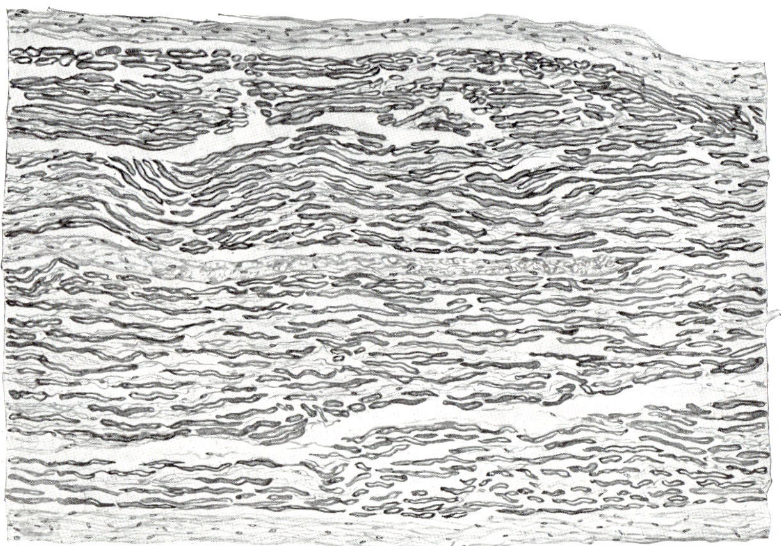

Fig. 31A.—Normal nerve. Osmic acid (Marchi) tinges the myeline sheaths gray.

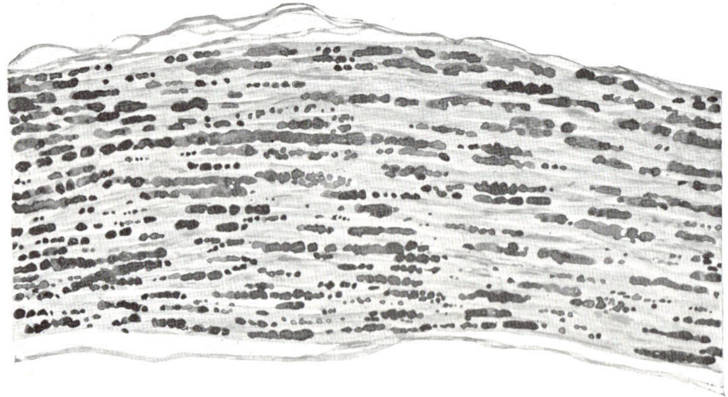

Fig. 31B.—Degenerated nerve (Marchi). Lipoid medullary sheath reduced to fat-like globules which stain black with osmic acid.

cholesterine esters, and probably also the phosphatides, may appear in abnormal situations. Since they are normally present in some organs, we recognize their abnormal character by their unwonted situation or sometimes by their quantity.

The source of these fats has long been the subject of dispute, the main question being whether they are derived from the substance of the cell in which they are found, or transported thither from some depot of fat or other source. This problem has lost much of its interest, since we have learned that much of the fat is transported, while some is made visible (fat phanerosis) by being liberated from its invisible combinations in the cell. The old question as to the production of the fat-globules at the expense of the protoplasm of the cell is now hardly discussed in that form.

A few examples of such fat accumulation may be mentioned before considering further the nature of the process.

In the *heart* one may find, in cases of long-standing anæmia, or chronic infection, or intoxication, or in disturbances of the coronary circulation, especially in the inner layers of its muscle, a yellowish pallor which, on close inspection, is found to be due to innumerable minute streaks and patches of opaque yellow which shine through the endocardium and give the checkered appearance which has long been called tigering or the faded-leaf appearance (Fig. 32). Ribbert thinks that the patches correspond with minute irregularities in the distribution of the capillary blood supply, and that local anæmia produces them. Microscopically it is found that the yellow patches show heart muscle-fibres in which myriads of minute globules, ranged in transverse and longitudinal rows, lie in the sarcoplasmic discs (Fig. 33).

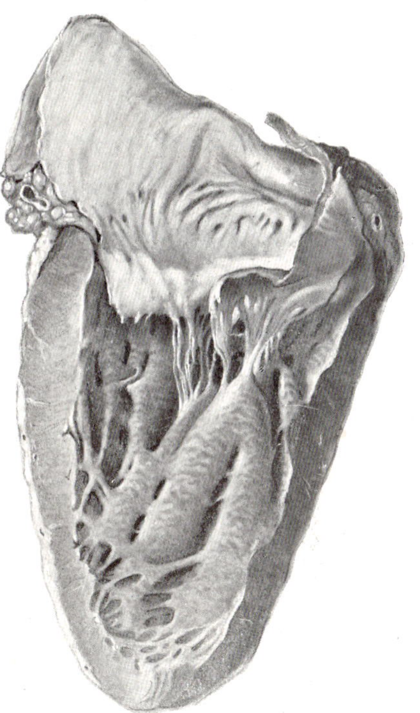

Fig. 32.—Fatty heart, showing mottling of myocardium.

In the *liver*, where there is normally some fat in the cells, various conditions can arise. The whole organ may be enormously enlarged, yellowish white, with swollen round edges, and on section greasy to the touch, rigid, and inelastic. In such a liver almost every cell is found stretched with one or more globules of fat, so that the nucleus is flattened to one side and only a thin film of protoplasm remains. In others fat is found about the efferent vein, in the middle zone, or about the portal veins, but not with such sharp consistency that one can well associate these forms of distribution with different ætiological factors. Whenever there is a destructive lesion of the liver-cell, as in chronic passive congestion or focal necrosis involving part of each lobule, fat generally accumulates in the cells just adjacent to the injured cell, and therefore usually between them and the portal vein radicle. Sometimes the fat is in large droplets, sometimes in small ones or granule-like particles. Probably these arise differently, but they can surely not be made the basis for declaring, as Virchow did, that the first indicate a physiological infiltration, the second a "fatty degeneration," in which the fat is produced at the expense of the cell-body.

In the *kidney* fat-globules collect in the epithelium of the tubules, most often in the convoluted portions and in the glomerular epithelium, but

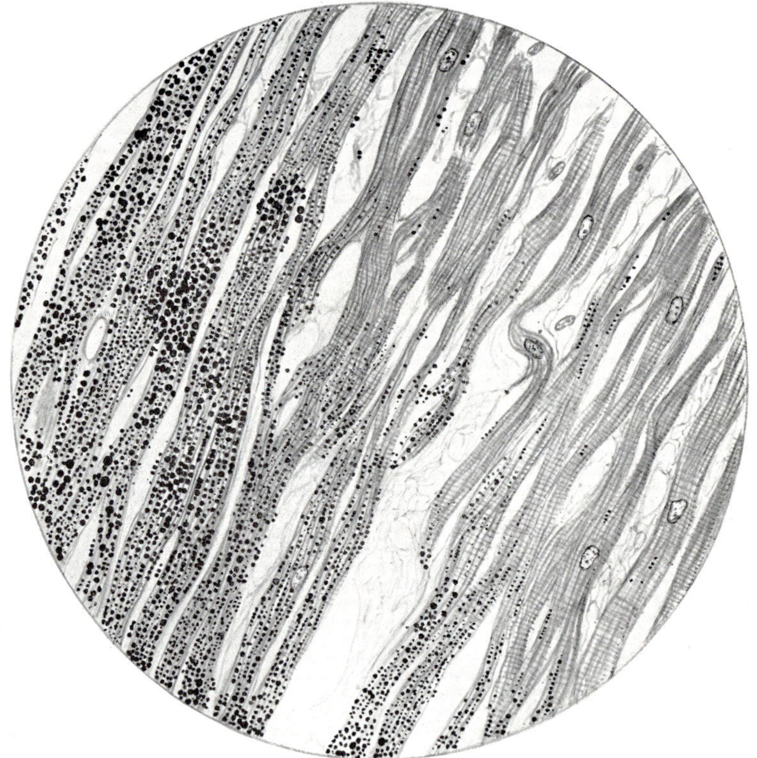

Fig. 33.—Fatty heart muscle. Fat-globules in fibres stained with osmic acid.

appearing also in the conducting tubules (*cf.* Fig. 19). They lie usually near the base of the epithelial cells at first, but later, when the quantity is greater, they may occupy most of the protoplasm. Such fat is sufficient to give a very opaque yellow color to the labyrinthine portions of the renal cortex, and in much scarred and distorted kidneys it is seen in patches where the tubular tissue is best preserved.

In the *aorta and smaller arteries* which are the seat of arteriosclerotic processes fats accumulate in the intimal thickenings and give them their opaque yellow color.

But it is impossible to refer to all the situations in which the cells may thus be the lodging-place of abnormal fats. Somewhat different in principle are those collections of fat which form in the living tissues around foci of necrosis in the brain, in which multitudes of phagocytic cells are found loaded with globules of fat derived from the disintegrating brain substance. These are analogous to the fat-laden zones of tissue about infarctions or abscesses or in the neighborhood of tuberculous lesions which have destroyed much tissue. The cells bordering upon a growing tumor are laden with fat, and so are those whose nutrition is affected in any other mechanical way by the cutting off of the blood supply. Even the malnutrition which comes in company with general anæmia, such as pernicious anæmia, brings with it extensive stagnation of fat in all the organs.

Not all this fat is alike chemically or physically. Nearly always there are globules of neutral fats, but in the kidney the sclerotic plaques of the aorta, in the desquamated epithelial cells of the alveoli adjoining tuberculous lesions in the lungs, in the phagocytic cells about infarcts of the brain, and in a thousand other places, many of the globules have a different nature. They shine dully; under the polarizing microscope they show a brilliant outline; on heating they disappear; on cooling again they start back into view suddenly as brilliant, round, doubly refractive globules, showing a Maltese cross of light. These are cholesterine esters and have the characters of the *myeline bodies* described by Virchow (Adami). Cholesterine crystals are often associated with them, and probably various soaps, although these must be of a rather evanescent character. Whether combinations of phosphatides and cerebrosides occur in these places too, our present technical methods do not reveal clearly, but it seems inevitable that they should be there especially when the lesion affects nervous tissue. But without paying too much attention to that probability, Aschoff and others emphasize the occurrence of degenerative changes in the cells, accompanied by the lodgment of two distinct types of fatty substances, glycerin esters and cholesterine esters.

What explanation can we offer for the accumulation of these fatty bodies in the cells? Briefly, the results of the long discussion are about as follows: Virchow's idea that the fat might reach the cell from elsewhere and appear there as an infiltration in the case of normal cells, or be produced at the expense of the protoplasm, when it was to be spoken of as a fatty degeneration, held sway for long years. These two types were distinguished by the large size of the globules of fat in the infiltration, their very small size in degeneration. But Rosenfeld showed, in a long series of investigations, that the cells of the liver received fat from distant depots when the animal was poisoned with phosphorus. He starved dogs and then fed them on mutton fat until it was stored in quantities in their subcutaneous tissues—phosphorus poisoning then loaded the liver with mutton fat. If the dog was so starved as to have no subcutaneous fat, none appeared in the liver after phosphorus. It seemed to Rosenfeld that all the fat came from outside. But an organ with abundant fat-globules in the cells need contain no more fat on chemical analysis than one which shows none microscopically—the production of a fatty degeneration need not increase the total quantity of fat in the organ. Beside the fats found, there are often cholesterine esters which are not to be obtained from the subcutaneous tissue, although they may well be transported from other sources, such as the adrenal, where they have been stored.

In view of these and other facts the following explanations of the appearance of fat in the tissue-cell seem possible:

1. An excess of fat may be brought to the normal cell.
2. A normal amount of fat may be brought to a cell which is injured, and therefore incapable of using up its fat with normal rapidity. Such injury may or may not be anatomically obvious. Impaired circulation, impaired oxygen supply from general anæmia, or toxic injury to the cell in the course of infection are among the causes which might give occasion for the condition. Fat would accumulate because it was not properly consumed.
3. Injury of many types might disintegrate the physical or chemical combinations of lipoids which are known to exist in invisible form in the cells, and thus make the lipoids visible as such in the cell-body (fat phanerosis).
4. Tissues in the neighborhood of areas of cell destruction may absorb or engulf by phagocytic activity the fats set free from those disintegrating tissues, as in the case of an infarct of the brain or other organ.

That fats are redistributed in the body in cases of infection and intoxication is shown not only by the demonstration of the fats in transit in the blood, but by the enormous accumulation of fat in the liver in certain cases in which the rest of the body is greatly emaciated.

LITERATURE

Anitschkow: Ziegler's Beiträge, 1913, lvi, 379; 1914, lvii, 201.

Aschoff: Ziegler's Beiträge, 1910, xlvii, 1.

Bang, Ivar: Ergebn. d. innere Med., 1909, iii, 447. Chemie u. Biochemie der Lipoide, Wiesbaden, 1911. XVII. Internat. Cong. of Med., London, 1913, Sect. III, i, 151.

Dietrich: Ergebn. d. allg. Path., 1909, $xiii_2$, 283.

Herxheimer: Ergebn. d. allg. Path., 1904, $viii_1$, 625.

Kraus, Ribbert, Albrecht, Rosenfeld: Verh. Dtsch. Path. Gesellsch., 1904, vi, 37–73.

Kawamura: Cholesterinesterverfettung, Jena, 1911.

Landau: Ber. Naturf. Gesellsch., Freiburg, 1913, xx, 69.

Leathes: The Fats, Monographs on Biochemistry, 1910.

Lubarsch: Ergebn. d. allg. Path., 1897, iii_1, 631.

Rothschild: Ziegler's Beiträge, 1914, lx, 39, 66, Lit.

Stewart: XVII. Internat. Cong., London, 1913, iii_2, 173.

Versé: Ziegler's Beiträge, 1912, lii, 1.

CHAPTER VII

DISTURBANCES OF PROTEIN AND CARBOHYDRATE METABOLISM

General character of protein metabolism. The purine bodies. Gout. Cloudy swelling. Hyaline metamorphosis. Amyloid infiltration. Carbohydrate metabolism. Glycogen.

Protein Metabolism.—It is somewhat surprising, in view of the great importance of protein materials in the constitution of the body and in the composition of our food, to find ourselves able to say so little with regard to the pathological alterations of the metabolism of these substances.

Doubtless it is altogether the result of our inability to see or make recognizable the abnormalities that may arise. We cannot tell, as we can in the case of fats and carbohydrates, whether a tissue is loaded with an excess of protein material. Indeed, we know rather little about the relation of labile or food protein to tissue protein. But one may recognize the abnormal loss of protein in the urine in renal disease, the passage of albumoses into the urine in disease of the bones (myeloma, etc.), and the occurrence of various amino-acids there when the liver has been extensively destroyed (leucine and tyrosine in acute yellow atrophy of the liver). Under other circumstances there occur cystinuria and alkaptonuria, both resulting from disturbances of protein metabolism, and producing, in the one case, urinary concretions of yellow crystals, in the other, a pigmentation of the cartilage.

Disturbances in Purine Metabolism.—Variations occur also in the quantities of urea, uric acid, ammonia compounds, etc., in the urine, and these naturally have a direct relation to the protein metabolism. Nevertheless, it is rarely possible to gather any real clue as to the protein metabolism from their variations. The disproportion in this regard is seen especially well in the case of uric acid, a substance playing an important rôle in gout. From the variations in its reaction it would never be possible to diagnose gout, because even greater variations occur in a healthy person.

GOUT

This is a disease the cause of which is unknown. It may even be said that the essential nature of the disease is quite unknown, since the disturbance of a part of the protein metabolism, which is accompanied by striking symptoms, is evidently only the effect of some underlying disarrangement of the machinery of intermediary metabolism, which is obscure.

Profound alterations arise in the metabolism of the purine substances, such that uric acid, the common end-product of fermentative decompositions and oxidations of these complex bodies, is retained in the tissues in the form of salts of soda and calcium, and lodges itself in cartilages and elsewhere, causing great pain to the sufferer.

Chemistry of Purine Bodies.—The investigation of the chemical nature of the complex bodies which finally yield uric acid has been made by Kossel, Fischer, Brugsch and Schittenhelm, Burian, Jones, Levene, and others, and may be read in Jones' monograph (Nucleic Acids).

It appears that compounds containing nitrogen and phosphorus, which have long been known as nucleins or nucleoproteins, can be extracted from the tissues, and in special abundance from those such as thymus, lymph-glands, or materials like pus or spermatozoa, in which cell nuclei form a large proportion of the mass. These names are being abandoned since it has been shown that they mean nothing definite, and that the characteristic constituent is a *nucleic acid.* It is from the nucleic acids that the peculiar and important alloxuric bodies are derived by the action of ferments. These, in so far as they interest us, are guanine, adenine, hypoxanthine, xanthine, and uric acid. All are chemical derivatives of purine.

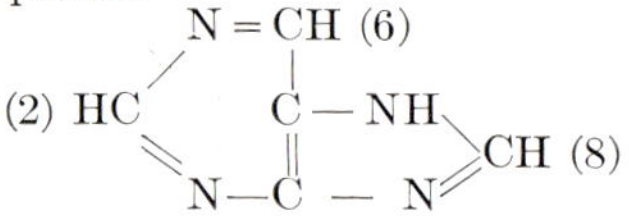

```
          N = CH (6)
        /     |
(2) HC        C — NH
        \\    ||       \
          N — C  —  N  // CH (8)
```

Representing the purine ring, with its three replaceable hydrogen atoms, by the abbreviated expression, $P \begin{cases} H\ (2) \\ H\ (6) \\ H\ (8) \end{cases}$, the relation of the five purine compounds to one another is seen in the following diagram (Jones):

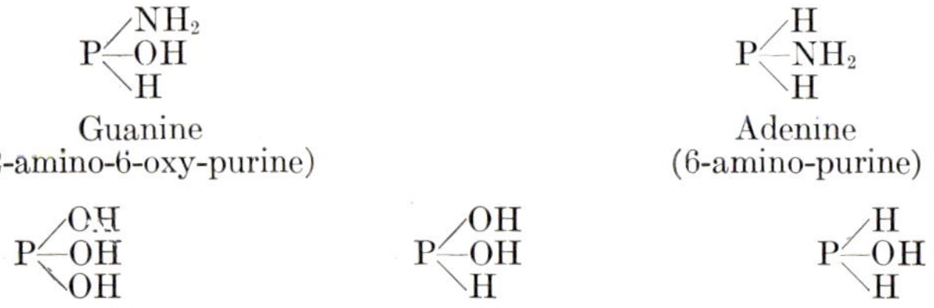

$P \begin{cases} NH_2 \\ OH \\ H \end{cases}$

Guanine
(2-amino-6-oxy-purine)

$P \begin{cases} H \\ NH_2 \\ H \end{cases}$

Adenine
(6-amino-purine)

$P \begin{cases} OH \\ OH \\ OH \end{cases}$

Uric acid
(2-6-8-trioxy-purine)

$P \begin{cases} OH \\ OH \\ H \end{cases}$

Xanthine
(2-6-dioxy-purine)

$P \begin{cases} H \\ OH \\ H \end{cases}$

Hypoxanthine
(6-oxy-purine)

Uric acid can be formed from the amino-purine by deaminization and subsequent oxidation—from the oxypurines by oxidation. The deaminization is brought about by special ferments, guanase and adenase, which are distinct and vary greatly in their localization with animal species. The lack of guanase in the pig's tissue seems to be the explanation of the deposition of guanine which sometimes occurs there (guanine gout).

As a brief indication of what precedes this, the following may be quoted from Jones' monograph:

Thymus nucleic acid, according to Levene, is a combination of four mononucleotides, each of which is a nucleoside united with phosphoric acid. Hexose, joined to the nitrogenous ring compound or purine group, is a nucleoside. From this point of view the nucleic acid is a tetranucleoside, made up of four mononucleotides. Levene and Jacobs give the following formula for animal nucleic acid:

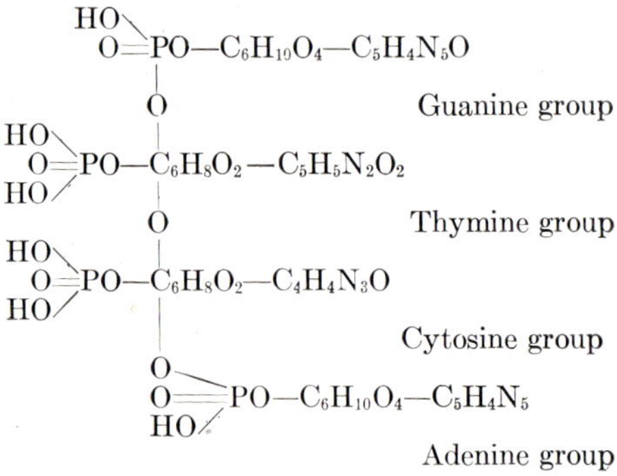

```
         HO\
          O=PO—C6H10O4—C5H4N5O
               |
               O                 Guanine group
     HO\       |
      O=PO—C6H8O2—C5H5N2O2
     HO/       |
               O                 Thymine group
     HO\       |
      O=PO—C6H8O2—C4H4N3O
     HO/       |
               |                 Cytosine group
               O\
               O=PO—C6H10O4—C5H4N5
              HO/
                                 Adenine group
```

The disruption of this complex takes place by the action of two ferments, which first split the tetranucleotide into two dinucleotides, after which they in turn are split into mononucleotides. These ferments are phosphonuclease and purine nuclease. Levene and Medigreceanu find that nucleotidases split the nucleotides to nucleosides, which further separate into carbohydrate and purine base under the action of a nucleosidase.

The liberation of the guanine and adenine is well in the line of uric-acid formation; the fate of the pyrimidine groups, thymine and cytosine, is still uncertain. Dr. Levene tells me that he has been unable to find an enzyme which will decompose the nucleoside in which they occur, and that since they cannot form uric acid, they are possibly excreted as urea or in other forms. Only 50 per cent. of the nucleic acid nitrogen can be counted on for the production of uric acid, namely, that in the guanine and adenine groups.

The tissues of the lower animals contain a ferment, uricase, which can decompose uric acid, but no such ferment exists in human tissues, and uric acid is excreted as such.

Uric acid is derived from the food or from the waste of the tissues. It occurs in the blood in small amounts, and is excreted in the urine in quantities up to one gram daily. The amount excreted is increased by the feeding of substances rich in nucleic acid. The solubilities of uric acid are interesting and important, since it has been stated by Gudzent that the monosodium urate exists in the blood in two forms—one, the easily soluble, unstable lactam form, the other the isomeric, stable, relatively insoluble lactim urate. The change from one of these forms to the other may, according to him, account for the precipitation of the urates in the tissues. More important seems the more recent work of Schade, who shows that uric acid or its salts may, through the influence of alkalies (hydrates), pass into a condition in which it is far more soluble than usual, and that, in reaching the crystalline form from this oversaturated solution, it passes through a colloid stage in which it is relatively stable. Materials which protect this colloid stage and antagonize precipitation occur, such as glycerin, urea, albumen of the serum, nucleic acids, etc. The application of this knowledge has not yet been made.

Gout is a hereditary affection most common in men, often transmitted by women who have themselves shown no symptoms. It is common in those who overeat, and yet it occurs as well in the poor. It is often associated with lead-poisoning, on which account a type, "saturnine gout," has been spoken of. Renal disease is a frequent but not constant accompaniment or sequel, and some writers, thinking that the gout might depend on renal disease, have specified another form, "renal gout." But for these separate forms there is little good evidence.

There seems to be an underlying hereditary tendency to develop the actual disease in these persons, although much may be done to ward off its appearance by careful avoidance of foods rich in purine. Whether it can be prevented in this way remains uncertain. Alcohol has always been thought an important cause of gout, although its actual influence is not clearly defined.

Acute attacks are characteristic, with remissions in which the condition is fairly good. Chronic forms also occur in which acute attacks appear as exacerbations of the more continuous process. The acute attack begins with violent nocturnal pain in a joint, followed by fever and chills and evidences of inflammation in the joint.

Before the attack the excretion of uric acid in the urine is diminished; during the attack it is much increased. It is clear from this that there is no real inability on the part of the kidneys to excrete uric acid. Between attacks it is about normal, although it may be diminished (Umber). Throughout there is a marked increase in the amount of uric acid in the circulating blood, and this is true in chronic gout.

Although Garrod and others held that the decreased excretion was due to the disability of the kidneys, Umber puts forward the more plausible suggestion that the uric acid is actively retained by the tissues.

Anatomically, the most prominent feature of the disease is the extraordinary deposition of needle-shaped crystals of monosodium urate in the substance of the cartilages. Such opaque, white, chalky deposits are very conspicuous when an affected toe-joint or knee-joint is opened (Fig. 34); they lie a little beneath the free surface, and extend only about one-third of the way through the cartilage, rarely entering the bone. Microscopically in sections of the joint, sheaves of these fine crystals are found em-

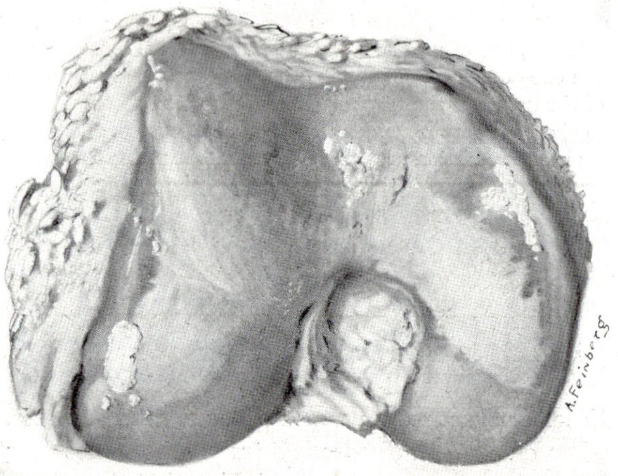

Fig. 34.—Knee-joint with white deposits of urates. Gout.

bedded in the matrix of the cartilage, often surrounded by an area of hyaline, pink-staining altered cartilage. Ebstein thinks that necrosis of the cartilage is the necessary forerunner of their deposit, but in this he is not supported by the other writers, who feel that the changes in the cartilage may be secondary to the crystalline deposit.

Besides the joint cartilages, the neighboring ligaments, tendons, and synovial membranes may occasionally be subjected to the precipitation. Other sites are the edges of the cartilages of the ear, the eyelids, the larynx, the kidneys, especially the pyramidal portion, where masses of crystals may form in or between the tubules, and many other situations. But the cartilages of the joints, especially of the great toe, the fingers, and the knees form the site of predilection. Such accumulations of crystals, when they become bulky, are called *tophi*, and in the course of chronic gout tophi of great size may form in and about the joints, causing their great deformity and disability (Fig. 35). They become encapsulated, cause a persistent mild inflammation, and may sometimes, through stretching the skin to atrophy, break through and appear as chalky concretions exposed to the air.

Digestive and nervous disturbances, arteriosclerosis with myocardial disease, and circulatory disabilities, chronic nephritis with scarring of the kidney are common accompaniments of the disease. The patients finally die from some intercurrent affection.

From the present knowledge no clear idea of the underlying fault is to

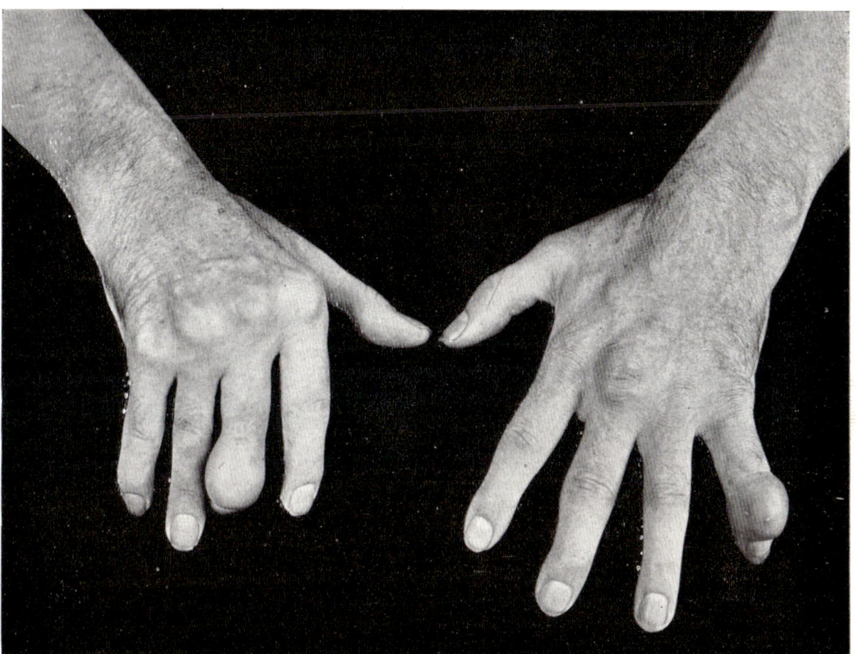

Fig. 35.—Gout. Uratic tophi about the finger-joints.

be gained, but it seems as though it might be elucidated by further study of the ferments concerned in the production of uric acid and in the influences which modify the solubilities of that substance. It seems a mere evasion to say that it may perhaps be controlled by some organ of internal secretion.

LITERATURE

Ebstein: Gicht, Wiesbaden, 1906, II. Aufl.
Jones: Nucleic Acids, Longmans, Green & Co., 1914.
Levene and Jacobs: Jour. Biol. Chem., 1912, xii, 411.
Magnus Levy: Harvey lectures, 1909–10, 251.
Minkowski: "Gicht," Nothnagel's Handb., vii, 2.
Schade: Zeitsch. f. phys. Chem., 1913, lxxxiii, 347; lxxxvi, 238.
Umber: Ernährung u. Stoffwechselkrankheiten, 1914, 335.

CLOUDY SWELLING OR PARENCHYMATOUS DEGENERATION

When the liver and kidneys and some other organs are inspected in the body of a person who has died of typhoid fever, pneumonia, diphtheria, or any one of many other acute infections or intoxications, they are commonly found swollen, inelastic, or pasty, and on section very dull and opaque in appearance. It is often said that the liver looks as though it had been boiled. In frozen sections the epithelial cells are seen to be much enlarged and very granular. In the renal epithelium the free edge of the

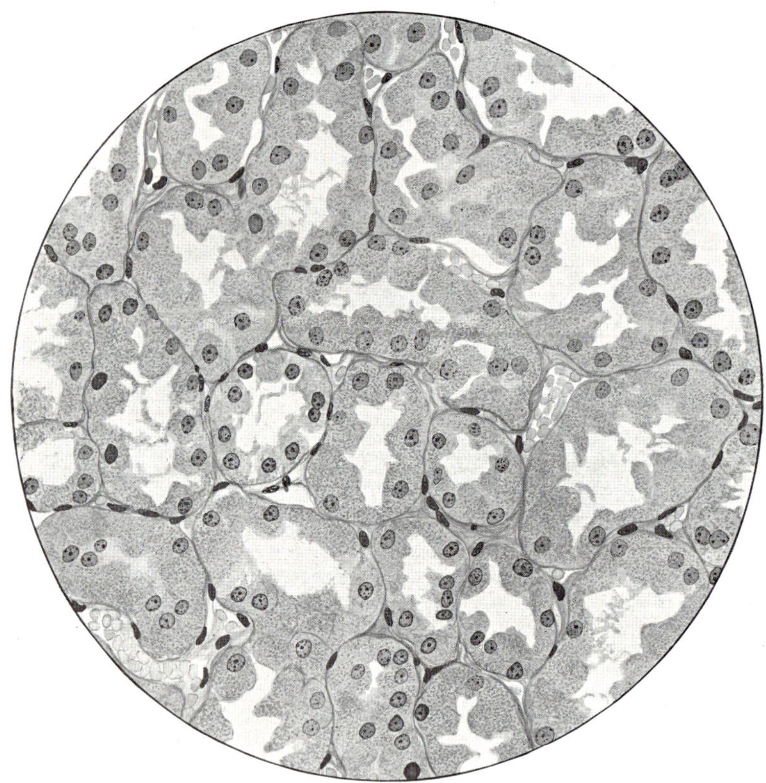

Fig. 36.—Cloudy swelling of epithelium of renal tubules.

cell is ragged and irregular, projecting far out into the lining of the tubule—even far enough, sometimes, to meet the opposite cells and greatly narrow the cavity of the tubule (Fig. 36). The same appearance is found in the kidney if the work of both is suddenly put upon it by the removal of the other. This cloudy opacity of the cells with swelling has long been known, but even yet its nature is not clear. Virchow thought it the expression of a nutritive stimulus and increased absorption of food material. Cohnheim, on the contrary, thought it a kind of localized coagulation process. It is known that the altered appearance is not necessarily indicative of an irrevocable change in the cell, for after the acute infection is past, the cells recover their normal appearance. This was, therefore, regarded as one of the mildest forms of "degeneration" of the cell.

The protein nature of the abundant granules which crowd the body of the swollen cell has been generally accepted and proven by their solubility in alkalies and acetic acid, and by their positive xanthoprotein reaction, as well as by other tests, and the problem remains as to their origin and their relation to the essential structures of the cell.

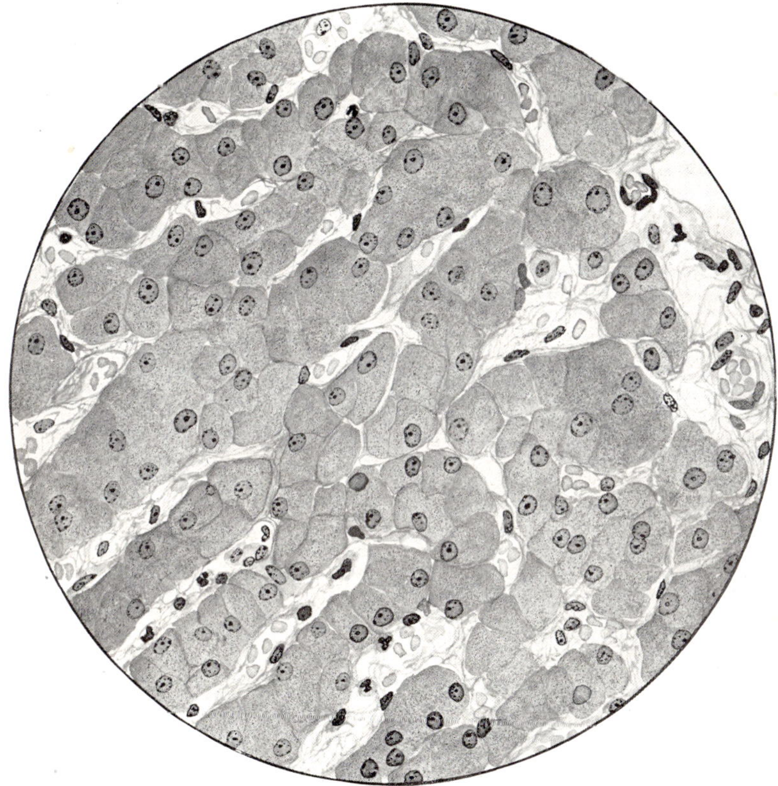

Fig. 37.—Cloudy swelling of epithelium of liver.

The confused literature is reviewed by Ernst in his recent paper without arriving at any definite conclusion as to the nature of the granules, although he raises the question as to their relation to the preëxisting granules, and states that the weight of evidence is in favor of their being derived from the mitochondria and their variations.

In the renal epithelial cells there are found, especially in the more chronic forms of nephritis, but occasionally in the acuter form, globules of much larger size than any of the granules ordinarily seen, globules of a density and high refractive index to make them at once conspicuous objects (Fig.

38). These, it is true, vary greatly in size, and are thought by some writers (Pfister) to show gradual transitions into the ordinary granules. Fahr objects to this since, as is well known, the large droplets stain sharply with the Weigert fibrin stain. They probably play a prominent part in the formation of hyaline casts in the tubules.

Anitschkoff has tried to determine the relation of the granules in cloudy swelling to the mitochondria by experiment, and finds that, by the application of hypotonic solutions to the cells, the mitochondria swell up into droplets, which, after a time, take the specific stain only at their margins. The production of cloudy swelling is, he thinks, a complex process, consisting of a series of changes in the mitochondria which begins by their decomposition into smaller granules, which then swell into droplets sometimes large enough to touch one another and give the whole cell a web-like appearance. This is analogous to the swelling of colloid, which is intensified by acids, as shown by M. Fisher, and corresponds with the observation of Orgler upon the increase in the water contents of the altered tissues. Naturally, this process is reversible under experimental conditions, but it is not so easy to assume that this is true in the body, where the granules may burst, or, as in the kidney cells, be discharged into the tubule. Further, a distinction must be maintained between the increase in the mitochondria in cells undergoing hypertrophy, and the swelling and disorganization of those structures in injured cells, where the change can be regarded as the effect of excessive function only in the beginning, if at all. Dibbelt, in studying the effect of diphtheria toxin in the kidney, finds in the same way that the first effect consists in a stimulation of the mitochondria to activity, followed by a molecular disintegration, with the liberation of lipoid substances. Fahr, on the other hand, in discussing the hyaline droplets in the kidney cells, makes a sharp distinction between mitochondria and secretory granules. Normally, droplets distinguishable from the mitochondria by their staining reaction exist in the epithelium of parts of the tubule. Pathological droplets staining intensely by Weigert's fibrin stain occur, however, in different situations in the tubules, and are thought to be not merely evidences of the activity of secretory granules, but new formed globules, indicating the disintegration of the cell.

All this is very contradictory and confused, but at least one may see that it is scarcely believed any longer that the granular opacity of the organ cells in infections and intoxications is due to the accumulation of protein food materials, but that it is intimately related to changes in the specific granules of the cell. More study is necessary to make the matter quite clear.

LITERATURE

Anitschkoff: Verh. Dtsch. Path. Gesellsch., 1914, xvii, 103.
Dibbelt: Verh. Dtsch. Path. Gesellsch., 1914, xvii, 114.
Ernst: Verh. Dtsch. Path. Gesellsch., 1914, xvii, 81.
Fahr: Verh. Dtsch. Path. Gesellsch., 1914, xvii, 119.
Landsteiner: Ziegler's Beiträge, 1903, xxxiii, 237.

HYALINE DEGENERATION

This expression is loosely employed to class together, in the present state of our ignorance, a great many unrelated substances, usually recognizable only with the microscope, which have in common, besides their protein nature, only their translucent clear or hyaline appearance and their tendency to stain brightly with such acid dyes as eosin.

Naturally, there can be nothing chemically specific about such a heterogeneous group, and it is easy to withdraw from it such a constant and sharply characterized substance as amyloid, which, although it is hyaline and stains with eosin, is easily recognized by special microchemical reaction as well as by its peculiar distribution.

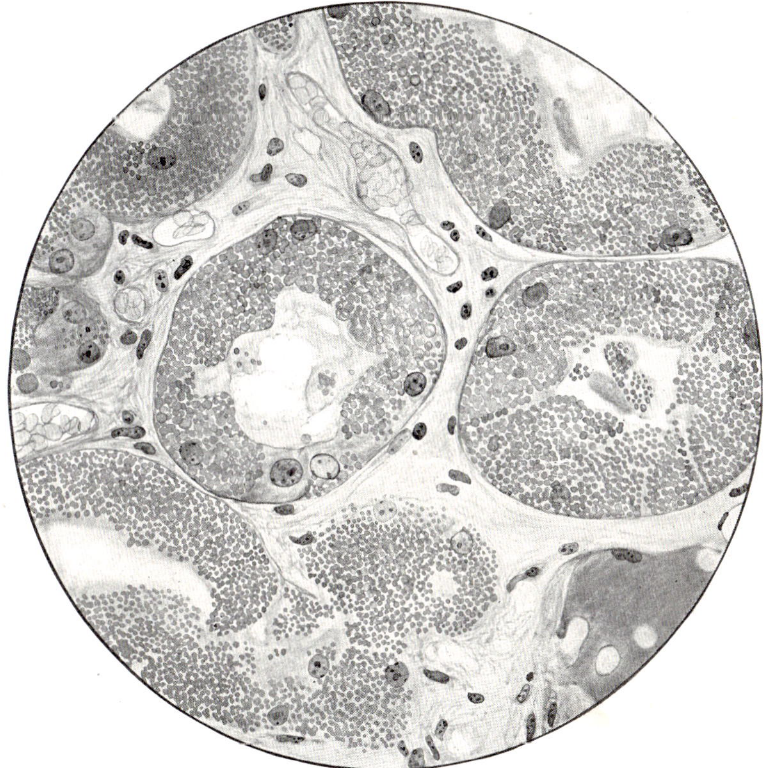

Fig. 38.—Colloid or hyaline droplets in the epithelium of renal tubules.

Ernst has pointed out the possibility of dividing these substances into two groups, according to whether the hyaline material is derived from the metamorphosis of epithelial and other cells or from connective tissue. This rough subdivision, which is open to many criticisms, is based on the reaction to the van Gieson stain with which epithelial hyaline stains yellowish brown, while connective-tissue hyaline takes the red fuchsin stain.

Since we know so little of the chemical nature of the various substances, nothing remains but to describe their appearance. In all cases the death of the tissue precedes its conversion into a hyaline material, so that we are dealing with necrotic and usually coagulated cells which have undergone even further change in assuming the hyaline aspect.

Epithelial Hyaline.—In areas of necrosis in such organs as the liver or kidney or skeletal or cardiac muscle, the protoplasm of the dead cell coagulates, of course, with the aid of coagulable fluid, which filters in from ad-

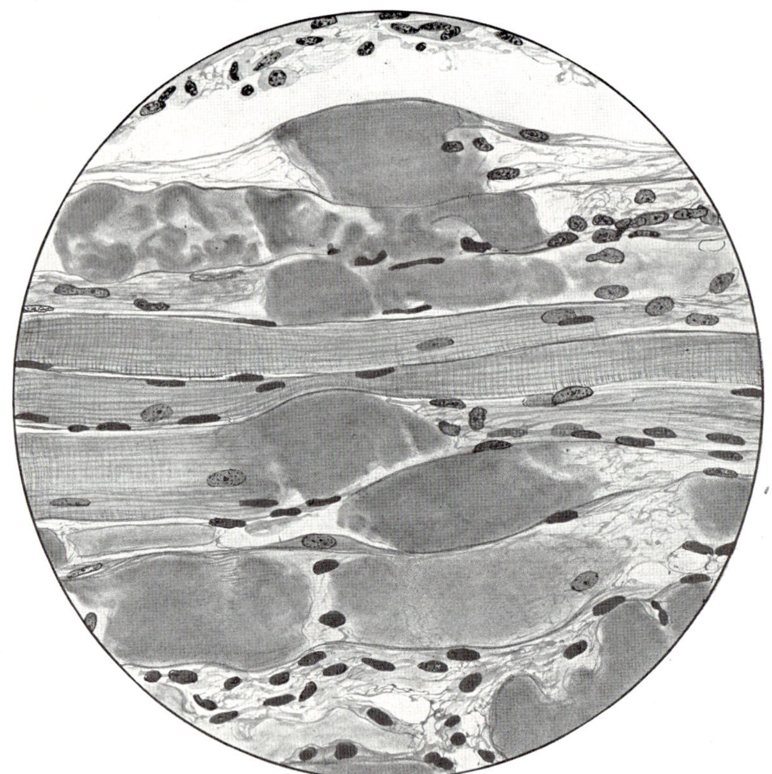

Fig. 39.—Hyaline changes in muscle. Typhoid fever.

jacent capillaries and tissue spaces. But it does not at once become glossy or hyaline. Instead, it seems to require time and perhaps compression or the infiltration of more coagulable fluid before the details of the structure of the cells are quite lost and fused into a homogeneous, shining mass. A good example is found in the clumps of hyaline material sometimes found shrunken in the interior of the sarcolemma sheath of the fibres of the rectus abdominis and other muscles in typhoid fever (Fig. 39). Many other instances will be referred to in other places.

This, which involves the whole cell, must be very different from the process which gives origin to the globules or droplets of hyaline appearance so often seen in the renal epithelium (Fig. 38). Other hyaline droplets which seem to be formed in some analogous way are the so-called Russel's fuchsinophile bodies, which may be found in tumors or in old granulation tissue. Perhaps the "corpora amylacea" which occur in the alveoli of the lung and in the prostate may be regarded as similarly formed by the stratified accretion of the hyaline débris of cells, or the secretion of epithelial cells around some nucleus which itself may be a dead cell.

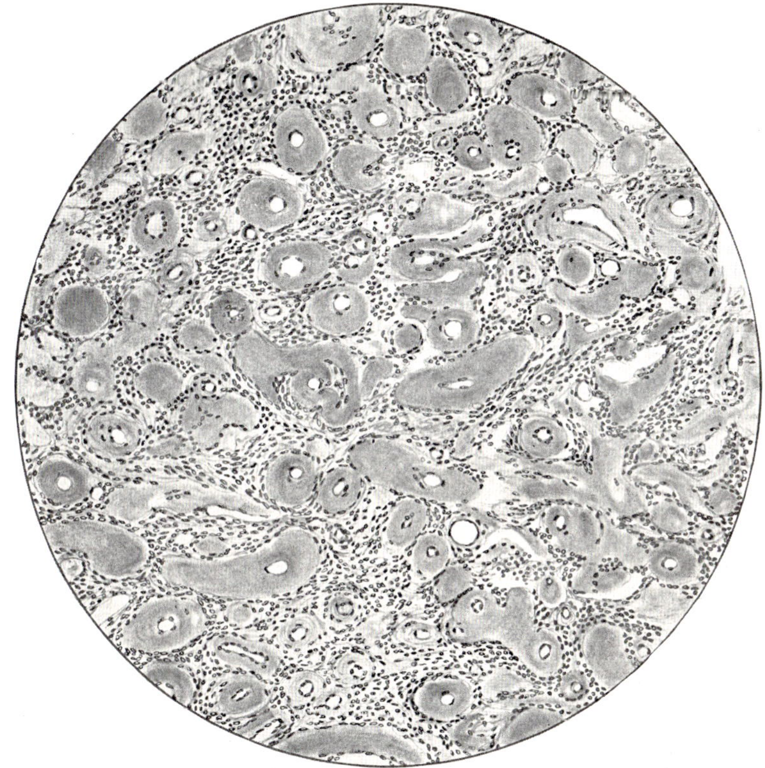

Fig. 40.—Hyaline vessel-walls in a tumor of the uterus.

The globules of hyaline material seen in diseased renal epithelium are sometimes spoken of as colloid droplets, and the condition is called colloid degeneration. This is confusing, and it is obviously wrong to speak of the accumulation of the colloid of the thyroid even when excessive, as a colloid degeneration, since it is only the normal secretion of the gland.

The hyaline casts found in the renal tubules which have in themselves the general character of hyaline material must be derived from disintegrated and amalgamated epithelial cells, together with their secretions, and they are found to stain in a corresponding way.

Connective-tissue Hyaline.—In the framework of lymph-glands draining malignant tumors or tuberculous lesions, hyaline material was first described. But the same appearance can be found in scar tissue or in the compact fibrous tissue which underlies old granulation tissue in the walls of thickened and diseased blood-vessels (Fig. 40). Especially in the walls of the vessels of the uterus or ovaries when they shrink and become obliterated in old age does one see the vitreous or hyaline change take place in the connective tissue that narrows the lumen. In the ovary every corpus luteum, when it loses its specific cells, is finally reduced to a cell-free, hyaline, shining mass, the corpus albicans or candicans.

We must, one supposes, regard such hyaline fibrous tissue as dead, and frequently there are evidences of coagulative processes which have occurred all through it, after which it has become more compact and glistening. Often calcium is deposited in such dead tissue. But while it is hyaline, it takes, with greater or less brilliancy, the fuchsin red of van Gieson's stain, because its inherent chemical value is not quite lost by its becoming melted down into hyaline.

Thrombi, after long standing, fuse in the same way into a formless, homogeneous mass in which fibrin, platelets, nuclei of leucocytes, and red corpuscles lose their identity in the uniform hyaline mass. This is especially true in the lower strata of the thrombi that occupy old aneurysmal sacs, where one may no longer be able to distinguish the hyaline thrombus from the hyaline fibrous wall of the sac.

More rapidly produced are the hyaline thrombi which appear in the capillaries, especially in the renal glomeruli in some infectious diseases (diphtheria, hog cholera, plague). They fill the capillaries like a homogeneous injection mass, and can usually be stained by the Weigert fibrin stain, so that they veritably look like a colored injection. It was thought that they too were composed of fibrin, but Flexner has shown that they consist largely of agglutinated red blood-corpuscles.

Unsatisfactory as it is, this general conception of nondescript hyaline materials derived by necrobiotic processes from the cells and tissues is useful so long as we are quite unable to define their nature any more closely.

LITERATURE

Lubarsch: "Hyaline and Amyloid Degeneration," Ergebn. d. allg. Path., 1897, iv, 449.

AMYLOID INFILTRATION

There was observed long ago, by Rokitansky and the Viennese school, a curious material lodged in the substance of various organs, and this was later studied in greater detail by Virchow. This *amyloid* was so called because of its fancied resemblance to starch and its fancied resemblance to cellulose. It is a translucent, glistening substance, usually so firm and often so abundant as to enlarge and render rigid the organs in which it occurs.

It is in persons who have passed through a long wasting illness that it is found. In the organs of those who have died after suffering for months or years from some exhausting suppurative process, such as an old osteomyelitis, some chronic destructive infection, such as tuberculosis or actinomycosis, or from such protracted intoxication as may accompany syphilis, chronic nephritis, or cancer, this substance is not uncommonly discovered at autopsy. With the improvement in surgical technique, which eliminates much of such chronic suppurative and tuberculous disease, it is less common than formerly, but it is still frequent enough in homes for the incurable and such places.

The spleen, liver, and kidneys are perhaps the commonest sites for its deposit, but it occurs in every other organ at times, not even excepting the brain.

In the spleen it appears in two forms, in one of which it is confined to the Malpighian bodies, and stands out as clear, rounded globules against the

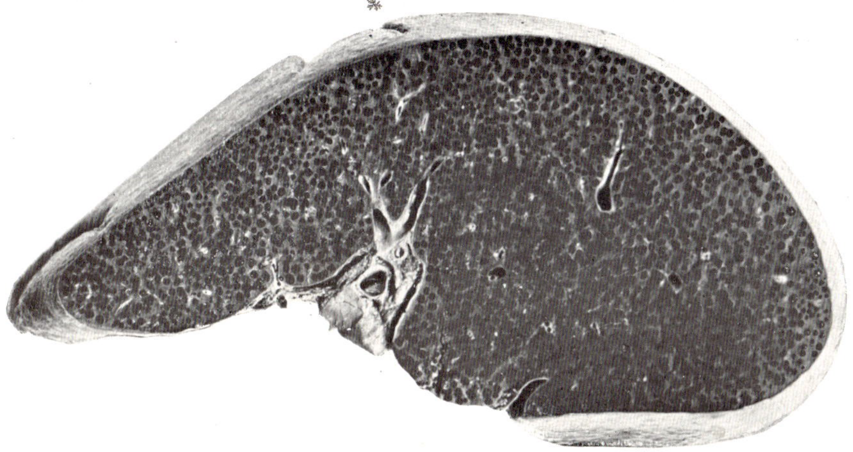

Fig. 41.—Amyloid infiltration; sago spleen.

red background of the splenic pulp (Fig. 41). Virchow, recalling a favorite red-wine soup with sago, named it very appropriately *sago spleen*. In the other form the amyloid is diffusely spread through the splenic pulp, and being everywhere mixed with the tissue, it is less translucent and glistening.

In the liver it may be very inconspicuous, but if abundant, the liver is greatly enlarged and firm, and on section the lobulation is rendered invisible by the diffuse infiltration of translucent amyloid. Minute streaks of yellowish, opaque liver tissue stretch through it, and there are usually patches of liver which are practically free from any admixture of it.

The kidneys are often pale, large, smooth, and firm, but on the other hand they may show any stage of the distortion which follows the extreme scarring of the organ and still be found to contain amyloid. This is lodged in the glomeruli and in the walls of the arterioles and straight conducting tubules, and occasionally one may discern it with the naked eye, although usually it is too finely divided for that.

The adrenals may contain much or little. In extreme cases the organ is greatly enlarged and composed almost entirely of translucent amyloid, almost like an enlarged mould of the normal structure. In the intestinal wall it is sometimes possible to recognize its presence by the pallor and rigidity of the mucous membrane, but this is rare.

In lymph-glands it is not commonly abundant, but in a recent case in which it was widely distributed the cervical lymph-glands were greatly enlarged and were found to be composed of almost solid masses of amyloid.

While the condition of the spleen, liver, and adrenals is easy to recognize, one might overlook its existence in the kidneys and in other organs. In its detection great help is afforded by the peculiar microchemical reactions which can be applied to the fresh organs. They are as follows:

1. A solution of iodine stains the tissues in general yellow, but makes the amyloid stand out sharply in deep brown. This is especially striking if the tissue is made acid in reaction with acetic acid. If strong sulphuric acid is used instead, the amyloid turns blue or black with iodine, and hence its supposed resemblance to cellulose.

2. Various aniline dyes, such as methyl-violet, methyl-green, thionin, etc., cause the amyloid to show a metachromatic stain; that is, it stains red while the tissue takes the obvious blue or green color of the dye.

These stains can be applied to frozen sections in which the amyloid also shows its acidophilic character, staining intensely pink with eosin, and brownish with van Gieson's stain.

When thus brought into distinct relief by specific stains, it becomes quite clear that the amyloid substance is merely poured into the crevices of the tissue, and not situated in any of the cells. It is a true infiltration, as though melted paraffin had been forced into the tissue-spaces and allowed to solidify. In the spleen it crowds the cells of the Malpighian body, between which it lies until most or all of them atrophy and disappear (Fig. 42). Everywhere it appears in the substance of the walls of the smallest blood-vessels, sometimes between the muscle-cells of the media, sometimes in the intima. The vessels of capillary calibre are most commonly chosen for such a coating of amyloid.

In the liver it is found in only one situation, and that is about the endothelium of the capillaries, and hence between those cells and the liver-cells. The amyloid becomes so bulky in that situation that it presses on the capillary and liver-cells, and causes the latter to melt away into thin threads of protoplasm and finally to disappear (Fig. 43).

The same crowding is apparent to an extreme degree in the adrenal, where the tissue is practically reduced to nothing in advanced cases. In the intestinal mucosa amyloid accompanies the minute blood-vessels in the villi. Application of iodine makes each one brown separately, so that the mucosa assumes the appearance of brown velvet.

In the kidney it lodges in the glomerulus, between the endothelium of the capillaries and their epithelial covering, and consequently soon narrows the capillary to a very minute calibre or obliterates it. Elsewhere it is found as a mantle for the tiny arterioles and venules in the cortex and pyramids, and also for the conducting tubules. It is easy to understand that the application of iodine to the cut surface of such a kidney would reveal the glomeruli as brilliant, chestnut-brown points in a tissue everywhere very finely streaked with brown (Fig. 142).

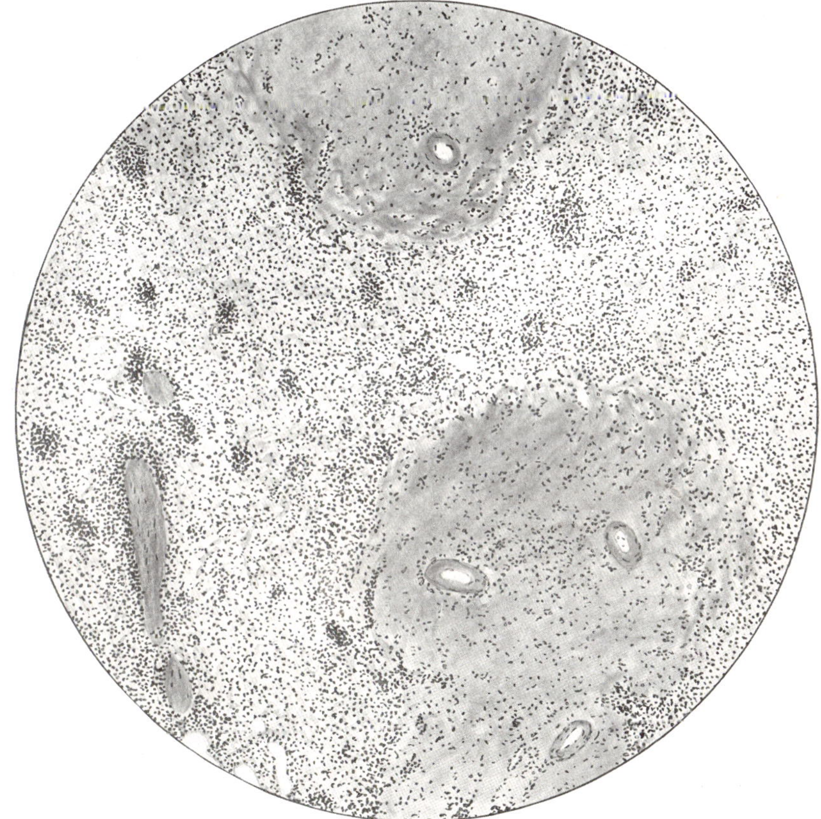

Fig. 42.—Amyloid infiltration of Malpighian bodies of spleen. Attempted regeneration of lymphoid tissue.

It is unnecessary to describe in detail the distribution in other organs, where it follows the same principle of infiltrating between capillary endothelium and the adjacent cells. Wherever it is present in abundance it causes atrophy of the preëxisting tissues. Its distribution is usually sufficient to distinguish it, even if specific stains cannot be applied, from other hyaline materials which stain with eosin but have not the peculiar chemical character of amyloid.

Chemical Nature.—Amyloid is a very resistant substance, which apparently persists, when once formed, although some experiments tend to show that when it is produced in animals it will disappear after a time if the animal is allowed to recover from the injections of bacteria or toxin which are used to produce it. It was thought not to be attacked even by digestive ferments, but now it has been shown that it can be digested slowly by artificial gastric juice. In the attempt to determine its chemical nature

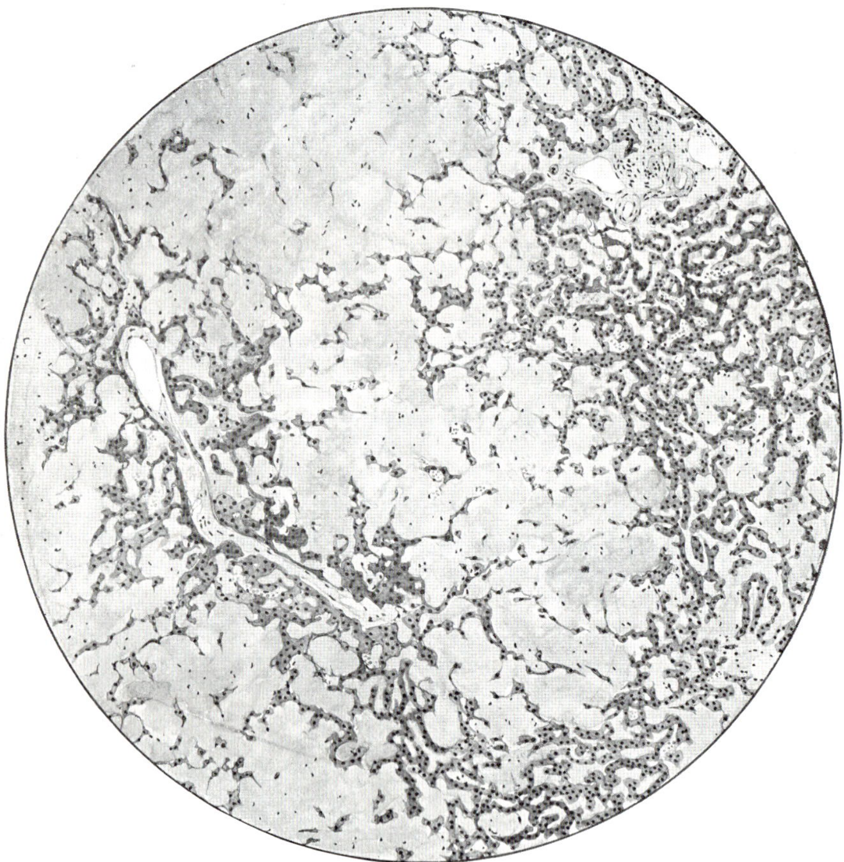

Fig. 43.—Amyloid infiltration of liver. Compression and atrophy of liver-cells.

it was first extracted in a fairly pure form by taking advantage of its solubility in baryta water. Oddi then discovered that while different specimens vary widely in composition, all sorts of amyloid contain chondroitin-sulphuric acid, a substance found normally in cartilage, but whose structure is still unknown. Amyloid, however, is of protein nature, and is apparently a compound of chondroitin-sulphuric acid with a histone. Details of the rather fruitless attempts to determine its composition may be read in Neuberg's paper.

Davidsohn has speculated on the way in which it is formed. Since it cannot be transported in the blood-stream, it must be formed *in situ*, and this he thinks is accomplished by a ferment formed in the spleen, since amyloid is not to be produced in an animal without a spleen.

Much has been said of its experimental production. Krawkow succeeded in this by repeated injections of bouillon cultures of Staphylococcus aureus, but others have found that turpentine or other pus-producing poison or cultures of various other bacteria or their toxins will also cause its appearance. The horses used for the manufacture of diphtheria antitoxin often show amyloid changes in their organs, and so do mice and rats inoculated with transplantable tumors.

A point of peculiar interest is that amyloid seems to go through several stages in its formation—at first it will not stain with iodine, although giving a metachromatic stain with methyl-violet. It is only in the latest stages that it will give the blue or black color with sulphuric acid and iodine. The early stage of non-stainable amyloid recognized by Davidsohn was called *achroöamyloid.* Quite recently we observed an instance in a young man with advanced pulmonary tuberculosis in whom a typical sago spleen, enormous, bacon-like liver, and advanced renal amyloid were found. Nevertheless, although the diagnosis was unmistakable to the naked eye, none of the amyloid would stain with iodine.

Besides the general amyloid infiltration, there occur localized amyloid deposits, sometimes in the form of tumor-like masses, usually in connection with cartilage-containing structures, such as the bronchi (Herxheimer, Schilder).

LITERATURE

Davidsohn: Ergebn. d. wiss. Medizin, 1910, i, 330; Virch. Arch., 1907, clxxxviii, 395; 1908, cxcii, 245.

Herxheimer: Virch. Arch., 1903, clxxiv, 130.

Schmidt: Verh. Dtsch. Path. Gesellsch., 1904, vii, 2.

Neuberg: *Ibid.*, 1904, vii, 19.

Schilder: Ziegler's Beiträge, 1909, xlvi, 602.

CARBOHYDRATE METABOLISM—GLYCOGEN

Carbohydrates as they appear in the body are, for the most part, practically inaccessible to our staining methods and do not appear in our microscopical studies of the tissues except in the form of glycogen, which we can make evident by certain stains. Nevertheless we can study accurately by chemical methods the various phases of the carbohydrate metabolism, and recognize quantitatively the presence of sugars, etc., in different fluids and tissues.

It has been shown that carbohydrates can be formed in the liver from many of the amino-acids which form the constituents of proteins, and therefore from the proteins themselves. The evidence is, on the whole, against their formation from fats. Most of the carbohydrate is, however, absorbed in a soluble form in the intestine and conveyed to the liver and to the general circulation in turn. In the liver it is probable that, through the activities of the cells, the soluble sugar which has already passed the intestinal wall, chiefly in the form of dextrose, is polymerized and becomes glycogen (Fig. 20). Apparently the liver-cells are not the only ones which can carry out this function, for glycogen is found lodged in many other tissues. In the epithelial cells, in cartilage, etc., there is constantly glycogen present, while it is normally lacking in the nervous system, pancreas, salivary glands, breasts, thyroid, hypophysis, adrenals, bone-marrow, etc. Its amount varies in the muscles and liver according to the activity of those organs, the state of nutrition, etc. In the heart muscle it is usually more abundant than in the skeletal muscles. In the embryo it is in general more abundant than in the adult, but its presence is by no means characteristic of embryonic tissue, and we are not justified in speaking of pathological new-growths as composed of embryonic tissue merely because they contain much glycogen. It is, nevertheless, true that many rapidly growing tumors are especially rich in this substance.

For its redistribution glycogen must be again converted into diffusible sugar, which may be brought to the muscles to act as a store of energy. In the blood—especially in the leucocytes—some glycogen may be demonstrated under varying circumstances, but this cannot be regarded as the mode of transport, and the dissolved sugar escapes our microchemical tests. In order to bring this about certain diastatic ferments must be brought into play—the process of mobilizing the carbohydrate. This is easy enough in such organs as the liver and muscles, which, with respect to glycogen, act largely as storehouses, but in others, like the cartilages and epithelial layers, the glycogen seems to form an integral part of the cell-body and is not readily mobilized.

The diastatic ferment converts the glycogen into the more readily soluble dextrose, which then enters the blood and is carried to the muscles or other places, where it is required to furnish energy or heat, and there, by the aid of other ferments, undergoes the process of glycolysis, with final oxidation to carbon dioxide and water. This diastatic ferment may continue to act after death, so that haste is necessary and proper fixation in substances such as strong alcohol, if we wish to demonstrate glycogen in the tissues. Solution of the glycogen in the fluids of the cell may also occur postmortem, so that estimates of the glycogen content of the cells after death become uncertain unless carried out with care.

Glycogen may be stained brown with iodine or bright red by Best's carmine method, and is usually in rounded masses in the cell protoplasm or in the interstitial tissue, but not in the nucleus (Fig. 20); if it has been dissolved postmortem in the cell protoplasm, it does not quickly pass the cell boundaries, but is precipitated in granular masses by the alcohol or other fixing fluid.

In pathological conditions produced by intoxications, disturbances of circulation, inflammation, etc., glycogen may appear in tissues ordinarily devoid of it or containing very little. The cells about areas of necrosis or inflammation may be especially rich in it. This is due to the impairment of their function, which does not readily allow them to get rid of the carbohydrate mass, exactly as is true in the case of fat accumulations. In many rapidly growing tumors, especially those of teratomatous character and the more malignant growths, it is likely that glycogen may be found, although there are many exceptions to this rule, especially in those derived from cells whose functions are directed rather to the production of mucin, glycoproteids, milk-sugar, etc., where glycogen is not likely to appear.

In *diabetes mellitus* the glycogen content of most of the tissues is found to be decreased, although for some reason the cells of part of the convoluted tubules of the kidney, the heart muscle, and the leucocytes become loaded with it. No good explanation for this is known. It is thought that it may be due to their inability to get rid of the glycogen, which is brought to them by the sugar-rich blood—or that, in the case of the kidney cells, they reabsorb carbohydrate from the urine in the tubule. Diabetes seems to rest, in part at least, on such a disturbance in carbohydrate metabolism that the dextrose is not stored up as polymerized sugar (glycogen) in the liver and elsewhere, or else on the extraordinarily active mobilization of the sugar in the organs—in either case proper glycolysis and consumption of the sugar thus thrown into the blood are lacking, and the sugar is lost by being excreted through the kidney. Probably this disturbance of glycolysis is in many instances due to the loss, through disease, of the ferment-like internal secretion of the pancreas, which ordinarily takes part in glycolysis. Much difference of opinion prevails as to this latter point, and it is impossible as yet to make any definite statement.

Glycogen, then, must be regarded as a normal constituent of many organs—absent in others and present in a third group in both a stabile and a labile form, the latter of which is most easily mobilized to furnish soluble sugar to the blood. Under pathological conditions where nourishment and functional activity of cells are depressed, there may appear unaccustomed accumulations of glycogen simply because the cell is no longer able to make use of this material, and by depolymerization set it free into the circulation. Removal of the disabling agency soon leaves such cells free to resume their ordinary metabolism, and the glycogen disappears.

LITERATURE

Gierke: Lubarsch and Ostertag, Ergebnisse, 1907, xi_2, 871.

Klestadt: Lubarsch and Ostertag, Ergebnisse, 1912, xv_2, 349.

Macleod: Diabetes—its Pathological Physiology, London, 1913.

CHAPTER VIII

DISTURBANCES OF MINERAL AND PIGMENT METABOLISM

Calcium. Its source, distribution, deposition in necrotic and other tissues. Its relation to various functions of the body. Iron: its distribution and functional importance. Disturbances in its quantitative relations. Chlorosis. Hæmochromatosis. Pigment: function and distribution. Endogenous and exogenous pigmentation. Jaundice. Dust diseases.

METABOLISM OF CALCIUM

CALCIUM, which in various combinations plays many important rôles in the animal body, is absorbed in the intestinal tract, and in very considerable quantity reëxcreted into the intestine, although the excretion is also carried on to a less extent in the urine. Its most obvious application in the body is in the formation of the rigid tissues of the skeleton, but it seems to have a very important influence upon the activity of the heart, the excitability of nerves, the clotting of blood, etc., and is found to form a constant constituent of the blood and tissues.

The pathological disturbances in calcium metabolism might readily fall into two groups: those in which there is an inadequate supply or excessive withdrawal of calcium, and those in which the reverse occurs and the tissues become the seat of abnormal accumulations of lime salts. In both instances the disturbance may be local or general, and indeed it seems possible that calcium may be removed from one place, only to be deposited again at another place in the body.

Calcium Deficiency.—Experimentally one may, by feeding a diet poor in calcium, reduce the consistence of the bones so that they are easily cut or broken. The ordinary process of ossification (Fig. 44) is distorted, and new-formed bone is calcified only at the expense of the old. Similarly in certain diseased conditions whose causation is obscure (rickets and osteomalacia) we find changes which are very similar to the osteoporosis produced by withdrawal of lime salts from the food; but different also, in many respects, especially in the production of much osteoid tissue—which is bone tissue morphologically but uncalcified. In both rickets and osteomalacia there appears to be an active withdrawal of lime from the already formed bone (halisteresis), but this is perhaps more obvious in osteomalacia. In these diseases we find extraordinary, complicated histological changes which appear, however, to depend upon chemical alterations, and to arise in response to changes in the available amount of calcium or to disturbances in the power of the tissue thus freshly produced to seize upon the dissolved calcium and fix it in solid form.

The processes of building up and breaking down of bone go on constantly through life, and it is apparently the result of a disproportion between these that the constructive processes are in old age overshadowed by the otherwise normal destructive processes. The osteoclasts or giant-cells, whose function is to erode away and dissolve the old bone, continue their work, while the osteoblasts, whose function it is to rebuild, slacken in their new bone production. The result is the senile osteoporosis which attenuates the bony structures until the bone becomes very much rarefied and easily broken. Whether this depends upon changes in the available quantity of

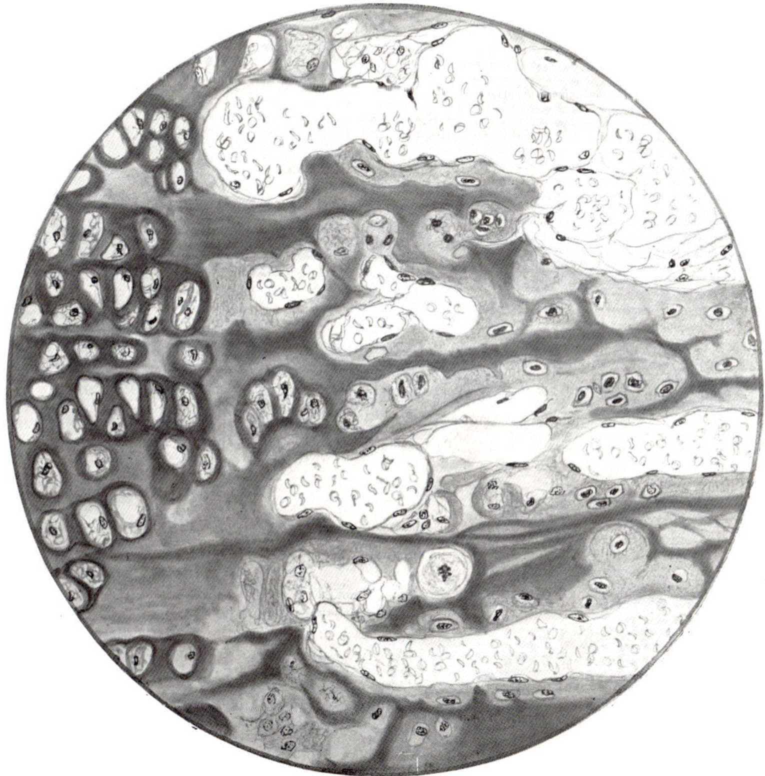

Fig. 44.—Process of calcification in normal line of ossification in fetal bone. Blood-vessels with osteoblasts depositing bone on remaining matrix.

calcium it is difficult to say. So, too, in the so-called arthritis deformans, which is accompanied by great irregularity in ossification and rarefaction in the bones, the excessive excretion of phosphorus seems to point to a general chemical disturbance which is associated with the destruction of the bone.

The effects of withdrawal of calcium upon the other tissues are far less evident, but it has been shown experimentally that this substance, when injected, diminishes the excitability of the nervous system. Conversely, it might be supposed that in such conditions of nervous hyperexcitability as tetany, a symptom-complex which follows upon the destruction of the parathyroid glands, there might be an active withdrawal of calcium from the tissues; and, indeed, a great many observations have been made which support this. Erdheim has shown that the destruction of the parathyroids results in an extreme decrease in the process of ossification and in the normal calcification of the dentine, so that fractured bones heal very poorly and the teeth become so softened as to break. After actual removal of calcium from the blood by dialysis the nerves of extremities perfused with such blood become electrically hyperexcitable.

Calcium Excess.—In the other group of conditions, in which the deposition of calcium in unusual situations takes place, we meet with many difficulties in finding an explanation for each step. Aside from the modification in the density and in the quantity of the calcified tissues of the bones, we may find gritty or mortar-like, or even compact, hard, stone-like concretions of lime salts in various parts of the body in positions where they can have no direct relation to the skeleton. Thus nothing is commoner than the finding of necrotic or caseous tubercles in the lung or elsewhere which have become encapsulated with a dense connective tissue, and in the central parts of which rough granules of lime have appeared in the cheesy substance. These may become so abundant and so compactly placed that it is impossible to cut through the stony mass. The lymph-glands of the mesentery undergo the same changes after tuberculous infection, and may be finally converted into rough white masses like pebbles. The walls of the aorta and other large arteries are found to contain plaques of calcified material which conform with the curve of the wall, and are usually smoothly covered internally with endothelium. Such plaques are formed in the necrotic patches of thickened intima in the course of the disease arteriosclerosis, and when fully formed resemble bits of eggshell embedded in the vessel-walls (Figs. 171). In the smaller vessels such areas of calcification are found in the muscular coat (Figs. 177, 178). Adami points out the fact that during life these calcified vessels are soft and yielding, the lime-holding material being mortar like and setting after death and on exposure to the air.

With advancing age, and probably in association with such conditions as bring about calcification of the blood-vessels, we find the calcification of such cartilages as the costal and tracheal, which ordinarily remain free from this substance.

Sublimate poisoning and anæmic necrosis in the kidneys are frequently followed by an abundant precipitation of calcium in the form of casts in the tubules or in the necrotic cells themselves (Fig. 45), and similarly it is extremely common to find calcified plates or spicules or even great, stone-like masses developed in tumors whose circulation has become deficient, so that necrosis of the tissues has resulted. This is analogous to the deposition of such granules in any necrotic tissue or about the bodies of dead parasites, such as trichinæ, which have been long embedded in the muscles. We find no difficulty in understanding that tumors which spring from the bone themselves produce actual bone in sheets and spicules, because we are accustomed to ascribe to the osteoblasts the power of forming bone. In some other tumors, such as the so-called psammomata, tumors which often arise from the coats of the brain or the pineal gland, etc., there appear

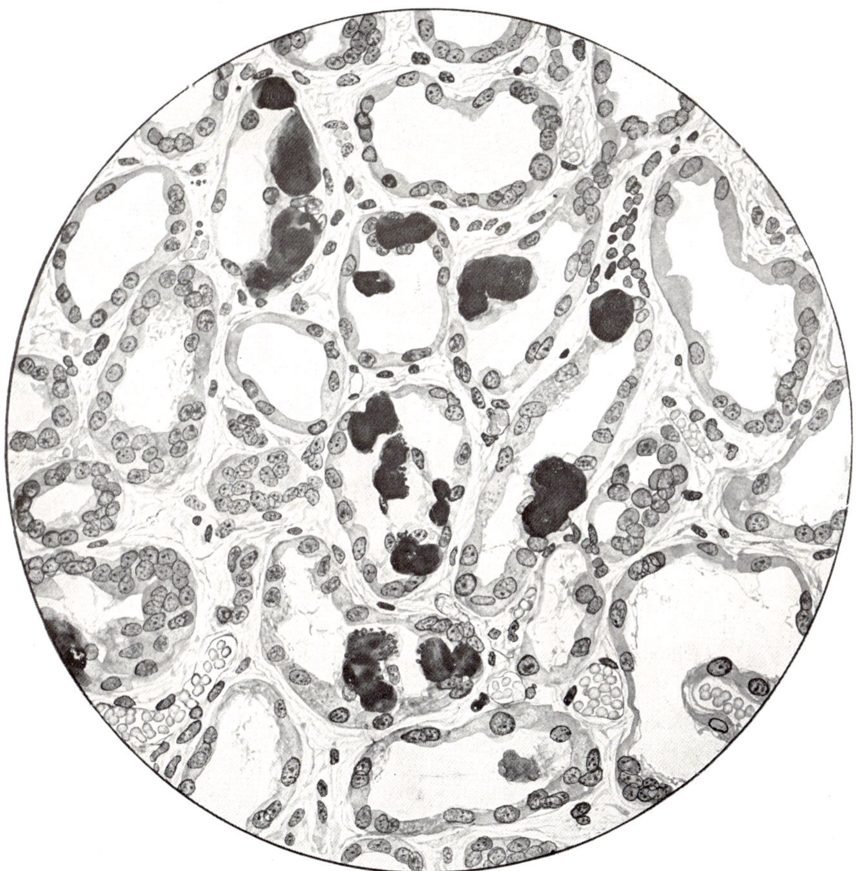

Fig. 45.—Calcification of necrotic renal epithelium. Sublimate poisoning.

small calcified grains which are often closely surrounded by the tumor-cells and may even replace groups of them.

Except in the case of the growing bone, the osteosarcomata, and other tumors springing from the bone, those tissues which become incrusted or impregnated with gritty particles of lime are usually dead. They have generally assumed the vitreous, glistening appearance which we are accustomed to associate with the descriptive term hyaline. Even in the case of elastic fibres and other substances which are homogeneous in the normal state, it seems probable that we shall find that those which become calcified are, after all, dead. We may confidently look for dead tissues as the basis for such precipitation when we find, for example, a cuirass-like shell of lime about the heart in an old case of pericarditis, or a stony plug in the veins of the spleen or of the pelvic plexuses where thrombi have lain for weeks or months (*phleboliths*).

The reason for this process has been sought with eagerness in recent years, because simple explanations which once seemed satisfactory are found to be baseless. There seems to be something peculiar about these tissues, living or dead, which gives them the power to catch up the calcium from the circulating fluids and hold it finally in solid form; and the Germans have called such tissues "*Kalkfänger.*" But so far no precise and satisfactory chemical explanation has been found. It is shown that the lime salts deposited in dead tissues are generally the same and in the same proportion as those in bone—about 87 per cent. of calcium phosphate and 10–15 per cent. of calcium carbonate. Some authors, however, have found only one of these salts in pathological calcification. Magnesium salts seem to play a subordinate part in both situations, and although some observers have found them present in the proportions found in the bones, we are still imperfectly informed with regard to the precipitation of these salts. When calcium is present in great quantities in the blood, as in the rabbit, calcification of dead tissue takes place very rapidly, so that the rabbit is an especially favorable animal for the study of this process. If we ligate the blood-vessels of the rabbit's kidney, the tissue becomes quite densely calcified within a few days.

Necrotic fat tissue seems very prone to calcification, and this has given origin to the theory, expressed by Klotz, that, in general, calcification is preceded by an accumulation of fat with decomposition of the fat into fatty acids and another component. This is followed by the formation, by a process of double decomposition, of insoluble calcium soaps, and later completed by the conversion of these soaps into calcium phosphate and carbonate, with the liberation once more of the fatty acid. Unfortunately, although the theory is tempting, it has been shown that Klotz's methods were inadequate to prove his point, and it has not been possible to show, except perhaps in the necrosis and calcification of fat itself, that there is more than a trace of calcium soap in any such area—not sufficient to justify us in assuming that it plays an important part. Nevertheless, the investigations have been concerned chiefly with finished calcium deposits, and it may well prove that the calcium soaps have a transitory existence in leading to this result. Wells, who has offered these criticisms, has no equally simple explanation in its place, but finds that certain substances, when introduced in the tissue fluids of an animal like the rabbit, have far greater powers of absorbing calcium salts and retaining them than have others. Thus, while pieces of fat, spleen, thymus, etc., are found to contain, after a stay of fourteen weeks in the peritoneum of a rabbit, only about 12 mgm. of calcium, a similar piece of cartilage has absorbed 154 mgm. And this is true even if the cartilage be boiled, so that there can be no question of vital activity. Different forms of cartilage differ in this respect, and while the above is true of epiphyseal cartilage, that which ordinarily does not become ossified, such as the rings of the trachea, will take up hardly more than the spleen. Wells thinks, therefore, that the beginning of calcification is based upon a simple physical adsorption of these hyaline substances; that the process in the calcification of pathological or dead tissues is identical with that in ossification. Calcium is carried in the blood in amounts not far from saturation point, held in solution by the colloids and the carbon dioxide. This unstable double salt of calcium bicarbonate and dicalcium phosphate is adsorbed in the hyaline matrix and precipitated by a reduction in the quantity of carbon dioxide. Calcium deposition, according to him, seems to depend, alike in normal and most pathological conditions, rather on physico-chemical processes than on chemical reactions.

Another type of calcification has been described in the so-called *metastasis of lime salts,* which is said to depend usually upon the saturation of the circulating fluids with those salts as the result of extensive breaking down and solution of the bony tissues in some part of the body. Then the calcium is deposited elsewhere where the carbon dioxide content of the fluid is least, as in the mucosa of the stomach and sometimes in the vessel-walls. The existence of this process has been called into question by some writers, and at least it must be quite rare.

Occasionally, as in the tuberculous lung or in the walls of the sclerotic aorta, the stony, calcified material may in time be replaced by a formation of true bone with Haversian systems, and a marrow cavity in which all the characteristic cells of the bone-marrow appear. This seems to occur only upon the immediate foundation of a mass of formless calcium which has itself occupied the place of the dead tissue, and is perhaps to be regarded as a kind of reparative process.

LITERATURE

Aschoff: Lubarsch-Ostertag Ergeb., 1902, viii, 561.
MacCallum, Lambert, and Vogel: Jour. Exp. Med., 1914, xx, 149.
Ricker: Lubarsch-Ostertag Ergeb., 1896, iii_1, 643.
Schultze: *Ibid.*, 1910, xiv_1, 706.
Wells: "Calcification and Ossification," Archives Internal Med., 1911, vii, 721. Harvey Lectures, New York, 1910–11, 102.

DISTURBANCES IN THE METABOLISM OF IRON

Distribution of Iron in the Body.—The whole nature of the interchange of iron in the body is very imperfectly understood, although it is known to be of profound vital significance.

Iron exists in the body of an adult in the hæmoglobin of the red corpuscles and in all the cells of other tissues. The amount contained in the blood is about 3 gm. That contained in invisible form in other cells has been estimated roughly at 1 to 3 gm.

It is similarly a constituent of the blood and tissues of other animals and of vegetable cells, being present in chlorophyll in combinations somewhat allied to that found in hæmoglobin. Hence it enters into the human body in animal and vegetable food. The complex organic compounds are decomposed in the intestine in such a way that the iron is absorbed in the ionic form. Bunge's statement that it could be absorbed only when presented in the form of the higher organic combination is rendered improbable by this fact, and further disproved by the familiar clinical experience of the effect of administering inorganic compounds in anæmias, and by the results of direct experiments which show the absorption of these compounds.

The ingested iron is absorbed in the duodenum and the upper part of the small intestine. As has been shown in cases of intestinal fistula, the chyme of the lower part of the ileum contains none. On the other hand, the excess is excreted into the colon and leaves the body with the fæces. By microchemical methods it may be demonstrated in the walls of the duodenum, and again in those of the colon, but not in the walls of the lower ileum.

The exact mechanism of absorption is not clearly known. Some is directly received by the epithelial cells and transferred later. Some appears to be carried into the tissues by leucocytes, or may possibly enter in association with lipoid droplets (A. B. Macallum). Part of it is thought to pass by way of the thoracic duct, but it may be assumed that the greater part enters by way of the portal vein and reaches the liver. We are equally ignorant of the exact mechanism of excretion, but in this respect iron seems to show analogies with calcium.

In the blood, iron is found in the *hæmoglobin*, a combination of a very complex protein, globin, with hæmochromogen or its oxidation product, hæmatin. Hæmatin ($C_{34}H_{34}N_4O_5Fe$, Abderhalden) may be decomposed into hæmatoporphyrin through the loss of its iron, and this in itself is a complex carbon compound containing pyrrol derivatives, and related to an analogous decomposition product of chlorophyll. Abderhalden points out that the formation of hæmoglobin involves, therefore, the process of formation of hæmatin and its subsequent union with the highly specific globin, which, since all must start with the simplest building-stones which can pass the intestinal wall, leaves several points at which the production of the hæmoglobin may be deranged.

The intermediary exchange of iron is beset with difficulties of interpretation. Red blood-corpuscles are destroyed in the body, probably very largely by the spleen. The hæmoglobin thus set free passes intact or partly decomposed from the spleen to the liver. Doubtless most of the iron absorbed from the intestine passes in the same way directly to the liver.

From the hæmatin separated from the globin iron is liberated in the liver, and the iron-free residue constitutes the bile-pigment, *bilirubin,* which is an isomer of hæmatoidin.

W. H. Brown criticizes this statement because powdered hæmatin injected into the peritoneum does not produce hæmatoidin or hæmosiderin. It seems, however, that the appropriate conditions are imperfectly reproduced in this experiment.

The fate of the iron thus set free in the liver, and of that brought there from the intestines, has not been traced, but it is clear enough that it is somehow worked up into hæmoglobin.

The iron of the tissues which is largely a constituent of the chromatin is tenaciously held by the cells and shared with the blood only in conditions of grave anæmia.

At birth the fœtus is rich in iron which was stored in its body from the mother, but during suckling very little iron is absorbed with the milk, which is extremely poor in that substance. Therefore, the iron content is low at the end of the period of suckling, but rises rapidly when the infant begins to take other food than milk. M. B. Schmidt found that if the iron-free diet were continued in growing mice after the termination of suckling, they gradually became anæmic and were stunted in their growth. The offspring of such mice were studied through several generations, throughout which the feeding was continuously "iron free." If, now, iron were given to one of a litter of such meagre, anæmic mice, it quickly outgrew the control brother, and as quickly acquired a high percentage of hæmoglobin and a nearly normal blood count, showing that the manufacture of hæmoglobin had been halted by the failure of the tissues to acquire and then set free sufficient iron, and that this matter was quickly set aright by the supply of inorganic iron. The rapid growth that ensues indicates the fundamental importance of iron. The spleen appears to be the organ in which blood-corpuscles, destroyed there or elsewhere, give up their iron to be carried to the liver. But this idea of the function of the spleen, which is regarded by Chevallier also as an organ of assimilation of iron, preserving and transferring it for the manufacture of hæmoglobin, must be made to accord with the fact that the spleen is a great site of blood destruction, and the further fact that its extirpation has a beneficial effect in such severe anæmias as pernicious anæmia.

The function of iron in the body is at least to be definitely associated with the transfer of oxygen, and probably more generally with the processes of oxidation of the tissues. Its rôle in connection with its presence in the chromatin of the cells is not so clear, but it seems to affect directly or indirectly the process of growth. As in the case of fats and lipoids, it is evident that the forms in which iron is active in carrying out its important functions are those in which it is invisible even with the aid of most microchemical reactions. When it becomes visible, it is because it is cast out of functional activity and lies scattered in the tissues in pigmented granules.

Much has been written recently concerning its relation to the process of calcification. It appeared from the work of Gierke and others that substances about to become the seat of a deposit of lime salts first absorbed a quantity of iron. Hueck opposed this on the ground that the microchemical reactions showing the presence of iron in calcified areas were due to impurities of fixing fluids, etc. He even suggested the test for iron in tissues soaked in a weak iron solution as a means of demonstrating the distribution of calcium. Noesske found that, while perfectly fresh bones and calcified tissues showed no iron, it was to be demonstrated in those situations if the body had lain for some time. He, therefore, thought that in this interval iron had been absorbed from the adjacent tissues.

Sumita, Eliascheff, and others return to the original idea that iron is actually to be found as a forerunner of the deposition of calcium in tissues examined when perfectly fresh after every precaution has been observed to avoid the objection that calcified material eagerly absorbs iron from the most dilute solution. Sprunt found an incrustation of elastic tissue fibres with calcium and with iron, while Gigon, in studying a lung supposed to contain a similar combination of lime and iron, as shown by microchemical methods, found by analysis no calcium, but much iron in association with sodium salts. The results are very contradictory, but there is, at least, much evidence that iron and calcium are deposited together, although it is not so clear as to which is the pioneer.

Two definite affections may be mentioned here as examples of disturbances in the metabolism of iron, the others, which appear to be rather more incidental processes, leading to local accumulations of iron-containing pigment, being discussed elsewhere.

Chlorosis.—Young girls frequently develop a peculiar greenish pallor with great weakness, perversion of appetite, digestive disturbances, and constipation. The blood shows a nearly normal number of red corpuscles, which, however, are very pale, so that the hæmoglobin index may be extremely low. The disease is readily cured or even passes away itself with improvement in the state of the digestive organs, so that little is known with regard to its pathological anatomy. It is influenced by purgatives, and in a most remarkable way by the administration of iron in any form. Whether the inorganic iron thus given actually forms the material for the new production of hæmoglobin, or stimulates its production by liberating the supply of combined iron from the tissues, remains uncertain. Nor do we know whether the defect in the formation of hæmoglobin is due to the inadequate absorption of iron or to some difficulty in its combination with hæmatoporphyrin to form hæmatin, or finally to lack of the necessary globin. One might imagine that if these combinations are formed under the influence of ferments, the digestive disturbances could explain their absence.

Hæmochromatosis.—A disease described by Hanot and Chauffard, and named by v. Recklinghausen, in which an extraordinary deposition of iron-

Fig. 46.—Hæmochromatosis. Pigmentation of liver.

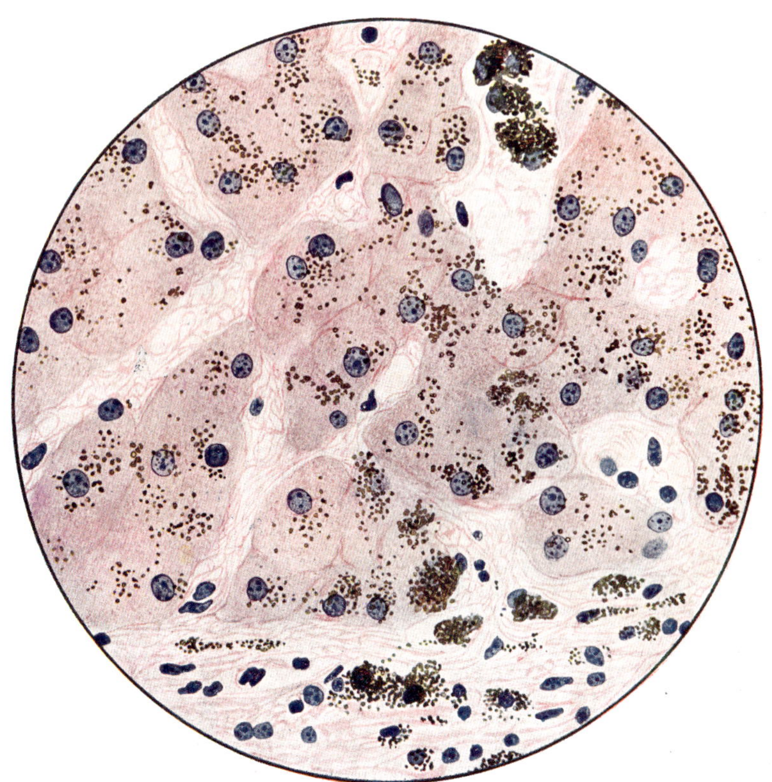

Fig. 47.—Hæmochromatosis. Pigment deposit in tissues of the liver.

containing pigment (hæmosiderin), together with other pigment (hæmofuscin) which contains no iron, is found in practically all the organs, including the skin. It is often associated with cirrhosis of the liver and pancreas and with diabetes, hence the name, "bronzed diabetes," which is appropriate in many cases.

The skin is of a dusky bronze hue, and in sections the pigment may be demonstrated by its giving the Prussian-blue reaction. The liver, pancreas, kidneys, lymph-glands, heart muscle, etc., are found to be of a bright, chestnut-brown color, and show microscopically astounding collections of pigment in clumps and granules (Fig. 46). The pigment lies chiefly in phagocytic cells, such as Kupffer's cells of the endothelium of the liver, but it is also lodged in the connective tissue and in the liver-cells themselves (Fig. 47). In the other organs it has a corresponding position—apparently its presence as a foreign body leads to much new-growth of encapsulating fibrous tissue. Most of it can be stained blue with ferrocyanide and hydrochloric acid, but part of it remains brown and responds to no tests for iron (hæmofuscin).

There is no obvious anæmia, no especial evidence of wide-spread blood destruction, and no especial activity of the blood-forming organs to repair a destruction of blood which would, of course, occur to any one as the probable source of so much iron-containing pigment.

Here the disturbance of iron metabolism must occur at some other point. In sharp contrast with chlorosis, in which it appears that absorption of iron or its combination into hæmoglobin is deranged, there is found an adequate hæmoglobin production, little or no blood destruction, but at the same time an overwhelming accumulation of hæmosiderin. In lack of definite information one may make the surmise that it may prove that the normal excretion of the excess of iron through the mucosa of the colon is defective, and that the pigment represents a retention. But this is far from standing as a satisfactory explanation, and hæmochromatosis remains a problem.

LITERATURE

Abderhalden: Lehrb. d. physiol. Chemie, 1909, 491.
Bunge: Lehrb. d. physiol. Chemie, 1889, 84.
Chevallier: Virch. Arch., 1914, ccxvii, 358.
Eliascheff: Ziegler's Beitr., 1911, l, 143.
Gierke: Virch. Arch., 1902, clxvii, 318.
Hueck: Centralbl. f. allg. Path., 1908, xix, 774.
Macallum, A. B.: Jour. of Physiol., 1894, xvi, 268. Proc. Roy. Soc., 1891, l, 277.
Noesske: Centralbl. f. allg. Path., 1909, xx, 56.
Opie: Jour. Exp. Med., 1899, iv, 279.
Schmidt, M. B.: Verh. Dtsch. Path. Gesellsch., 1912, xv, 91.
Sprunt, T. P.: "Hæmochromatosis," Archives of Inter. Med., 1911, viii, 75.

DISTURBANCES OF PIGMENT METABOLISM

Pathological disturbances of metabolism are by no means limited to proteins, carbohydrates, and fats, but involve irregularities in the formation and distribution of many other substances which ordinarily serve a normal function. Were we better informed, it would be most logical to discuss each of these according to its chemical nature and relations, but we know so little that we can hardly escape from the temptation to group them according to some striking peculiar feature. It is for this reason alone that we discuss in one chapter pigments which are often hardly related, except through the fact that they are colored.

Most of these pigments serve important purposes, and very little of their history concerns pathology except when, like the slag heap that indicates the activity of a smelter, they show by their accumulation the presence of some unusual activity in the body. Ordinarily, enough of the coloring-matter of the skin or hair is produced to confer on the animal those colors which are the beauty of the animate world, and which serve so well in the protection and even in the propagation of each individual's life. Or they are concerned in the interior of the body with the mechanisms for carrying oxygen to the tissues and in the production of bile, and an exquisite economy is observed in their use and the maintenance of their proper proportions. Only when something disturbs these mechanisms do we find the pigments or disjointed by-products in their formation accumulated somewhere in excess, or, on the other hand, lost to the body to such a degree that it lacks its normal colors.

Certain colored substances are formed in the body and elaborated to typical forms, although we may meet, too, with less complex materials which are destined to be built up into these type forms or are the results of their decomposition. These are endogenous pigments. Beside these there are foreign materials—colored particles breathed into the lungs or taken into the stomach or through the skin, or fluids which impregnate the body with colored deposits, and these are called exogenous pigments.

Endogenous Pigments

Of these, several kinds are met with, the principal ones being those which are specially produced to color the skin, and hair and eyes, usually grouped as the melanins, those which are directly or indirectly derived from the hæmoglobin of the blood, and those which are somehow associated with fat-like substances and come from the wear and tear and breaking down of the tissue-cells.

Melanins.—The melanins may assume various colors, but are usually dark brownish or black. Their enormous variety and the ways in which they normally occur more abundantly in those races exposed to sun and wind, their abundance largely dependent upon hereditary powers of the cells, their rapid appearance in the form of tan and freckles in response to exposure—all these things are hardly our concern, but belong to the field of physiology. Still the study of their abnormal production and distribution may throw some light upon their normal origin. Melanins are complex substances containing no iron, but rich in sulphur. Much discussion has arisen as to their origin and as to their chemical nature, but since no two of them seem to have the same composition, the latter point still remains obscure. In general, it is found that such substances may be produced by the action of oxidizing ferments, such as tyrosinase, upon materials like tyrosin, ornithin, etc., which contain the groups pyrrol, pyridine, skatol, or indol, but that it is hardly possible that melanin should be produced from hæmatin unless some other, sulphur-containing substance be brought into the reaction. The evidence seems to be entirely against the origin of melanins from the constituents of the blood. On the contrary, it was shown by Wieting and Hamdi and others that these granules are formed in the epithelial cells apparently especially as products of the nucleus, and although they may be held for a little in these "melanoblasts," they may also be given over to other wandering cells of connective-tissue origin, the chromatophores. Thus the pigment of the eye is thought to be formed in the retina and secondarily transferred to the cells of the choroid.

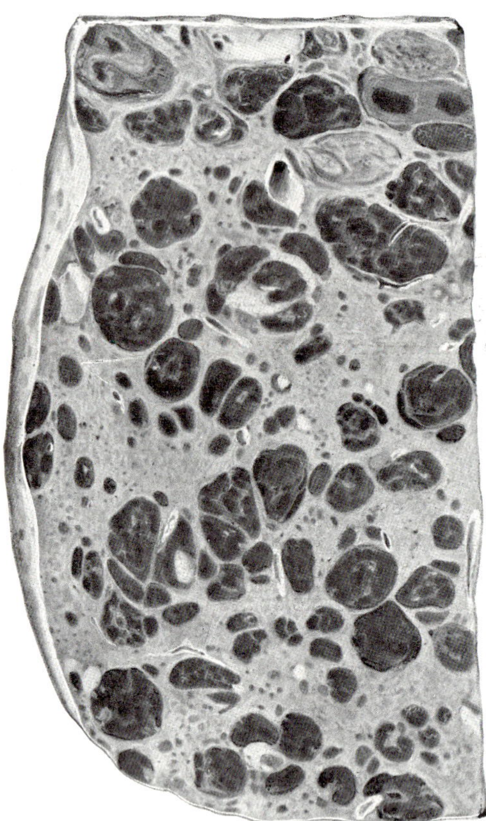

Fig. 48.—Melanotic sarcoma. Secondary nodules in liver.

Except in a few cases, we are not at all well informed with regard to the abnormal development of melanins in the skin. There are pigmentations which are doubtless only accentuations of the normal, and occur chiefly in the most pigmented areas of the body, such as the chloasma of tuberculosis and of pregnancy, in which brownish flecks appear on the face and body, and the areolæ of the nipples, axillæ, etc., become more deeply colored. Probably, too, in the healing of many destructive skin diseases, and in the area about an old healing ulcer, increase of melanin produces part of the brown coloration, although, especially in the latter instance, blood-pigment plays a part. In Addison's disease, which results from the destruction of the adrenal glands, the skin gradually assumes a darker hue until finally it is like that of old bronze. Whence this pigment comes we do not know, nor are we well informed as to its nature.

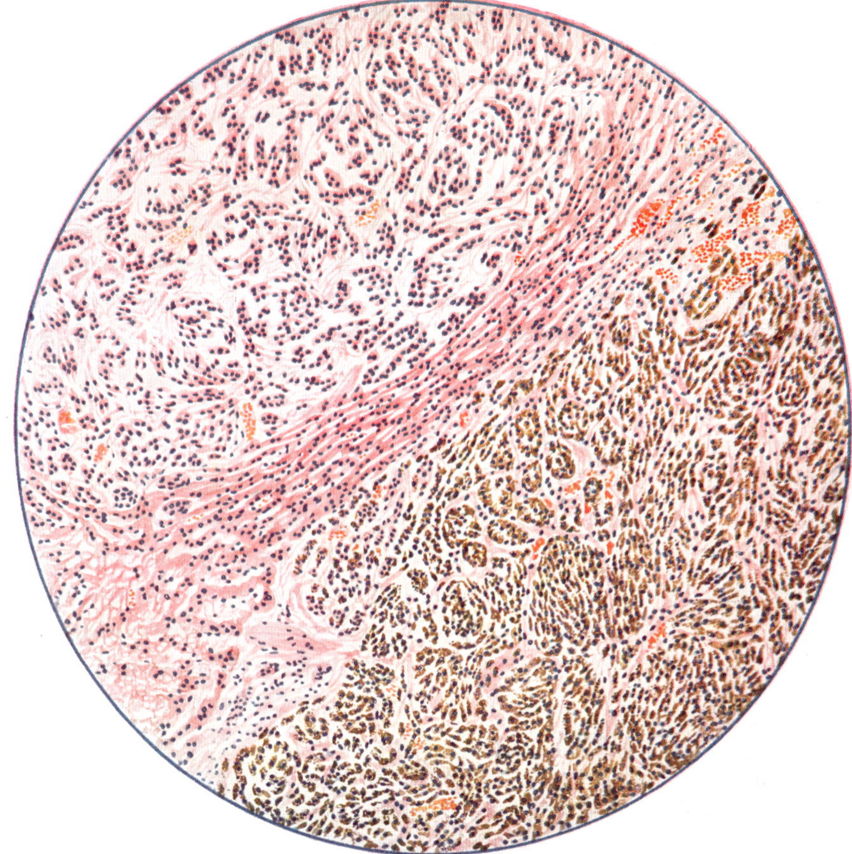

Fig. 49.—Pigmented cells of melanotic sarcoma in contrast with others not pigmented. Pressure atrophy of the liver.

The most striking example of the massive production of melanin is seen in the so-called *melanotic tumors*, which usually spring from the skin or from the pigmented tissues of the eye. Such tumors, which in their early and apparently innocent stages are known as moles or pigmented nævi (Fig. 504), seem to be derived from the melanoblasts, inasmuch as their metastatic nodules continue to form melanin, which could not be expected of mere pigment-carrying cells, the chromatophores. The weight of evidence in the prolonged strife as to their sarcomatous or carcinomatous nature is apparently with those who hold that they are really of epithelial origin. Growing with extreme rapidity and invading the most distant parts of the body arid of pigment, these tumor-cells continue to manufacture such quantities of coloring-matter that not only is the mass itself coal black (Figs. 48, 507), but the pigment is carried away and appears in the urine either as such or in a modified, colorless form, which turns again on exposure, or when an oxidizing substance is added, to pigment which stains the urine black. No one seems to have followed very precisely the wandering of this pigment, although it is known that melanins injected into the circulation of an animal become decolorized by the reducing action of the tissues, only to blacken again when they are oxidized.

Ochronosis is a rather rare condition in which a brown or blackish pigment, probably allied to the melanins, is deposited especially in the cartilages and ligaments, but also in the aorta and sometimes in the kidneys. The patient becomes conspicuous on account of the bluish color that shimmers through the skin, where, as on the nose and ears, the pigmented cartilages are near the surface. It is due to metabolic disturbances often accompanied by alkaptonuria, or to the introduction of small quantities of such a substance as carbolic acid, as in the prolonged treatment of an ulcer with that antiseptic. Poulsen thinks that the pigment is produced by the action of such a ferment as tyrosinase upon tyrosin or homogentisinic acid, or upon derivatives of the phenol introduced by the surgical dressings.

The *malarial parasite,* while still within the red blood-corpuscle, produces particles of a shining, brownish-black pigment at the expense of the hæmoglobin-containing cell. This is probably derived directly from the hæmoglobin, although it is iron free and by most authors regarded as a form of melanin. The remainder of the hæmoglobin dissipated in the plasma after the parasite breaks out of the cell forms an iron-containing pigment. Spleen, liver, and other organs become so laden with a combination of these pigments as to be quite blackened (Figs. 383 and 384).

Of the second group of endogenous pigments, **those derived from the blood,** we may distinguish several forms. The source of all is hæmatin, which, in combination with a globin, forms hæmoglobin, and it is after the hæmoglobin has been set free from its suspension in the corpuscle that the decomposition may take place. Many things, ranging from distilled water through a series of organic or inorganic poisons to the most subtly modified blood-sera, may act as hæmolytic substances capable of disintegrating the red corpuscles and setting free the hæmoglobin. If it be thus set free in large amounts in the general circulation, it may be excreted through the kidneys, producing the so-called hæmoglobinuria. This is not an uncommon accompaniment of malaria in some countries (blackwater fever), and there has been much discussion as to whether it is caused by the malaria or the quinine given to cure it.

Another form occurs in paroxysmal attacks in certain predisposed persons whose red corpuscles seem very fragile and liberate the hæmoglobin on the slightest injury. Even the mere exposure to cold produces an excretion of hæmoglobin, and it has been found that this is because the hæmolytic substances present can combine and act only at a low temperature. The kidneys become loaded with clumps of a yellowish material which seems to have come through the glomeruli and lodged in the tubules. In a similar way poisoning with chlorates produces the excretion of a modified hæmoglobin, methæmoglobin, and that with sulphonal and allied poisons causes the appearance of iron-free hæmatoporphyrin.

Some bacteria have the power of causing hæmolysis, and in general infections, where the blood becomes filled with these bacteria, there is much destruction of red corpuscles. After death the laked blood stains the tissues so that at autopsy the walls of the heart and the linings of the blood-vessels are of a dull red color. Through the walls of the superficial veins this color may diffuse to such an extent that one sees a network of purplish bands shimmering through the skin. Nor is this cadaveric staining exclusively the effect of such general infections, for in any body which has lain some time after death the tissues which are in contact with large accumulations of blood are stained deep red. It is not particularly a pathological phenomenon, but one which might confuse the unwary.

Pigments Arising From the Decomposition of Hæmoglobin.—Ordinarily, although, as we know, the red corpuscles circulate intact only a relatively short time, so that in every hour millions of them fall to pieces, there is no noticeable coloring of the blood-plasma with hæmoglobin. Nor is the hæmoglobin excreted from the body in the urine—instead, it is taken up by various cells and converted into different sorts of yellowish-brown pigment. Just here our knowledge of the process proves somewhat incomplete, but it is generally accepted that the liver-cells form *bilirubin* from such raw material, while if the blood is laked in a mass, as, for example, in some cavity of the body, so that it is not, except at its edges, in contact with living cells, a red-brown pigment, called *hæmatoidin*, is formed, which most authors think is identical, or at least isomeric, with bilirubin. When, however, the hæmatin or the whole hæmoglobin is taken up by living cells, even including the liver-cells at times, there may be formed another yellowish-brown, granular pigment—*hæmosiderin*. These are the main types, although there are others of less importance. Of bilirubin we shall speak in connection with jaundice. Like it, hæmatoidin is an iron-free substance ($C_{16}H_{18}N_2O_3$) which occurs in amorphous or crystalline form, or sometimes as a diffuse staining of tissue. It is often recognizable in the central portions of large hæmorrhagic infarcts, in thrombi or old hæmorrhages, sometimes in cysts in which hæmorrhages have occurred, as in the thyroid, or in the brain in healing apoplectic hæmorrhages.

It is probably of relatively uncommon occurrence as contrasted with the third of these colored materials, the *hæmosiderin*. To this we can give no formula, for it is merely a mixture of pigments in which iron exists in a most accessible form, so that its presence may be readily shown by the application of the Prussian-blue reaction. Hæmosiderin is the common blood-pigment which results upon any small extravasation of blood into the tissues, in so far as that blood is not immediately reabsorbed as such. Thus in every sort of wound and bruise, in every sort of inflammation in which red corpuscles escape from the vessels, in purpura, in scurvy, and in every other disease where there are ecchymoses or more extensive hæmorrhages into the tissues, or about the stings of insects or reptiles, it may be found after some days. When the poison is of a hæmolytic character, and in fact in any condition in which blood or the coloring-matter of blood escapes into direct contact with the tissues, there may be formed in the

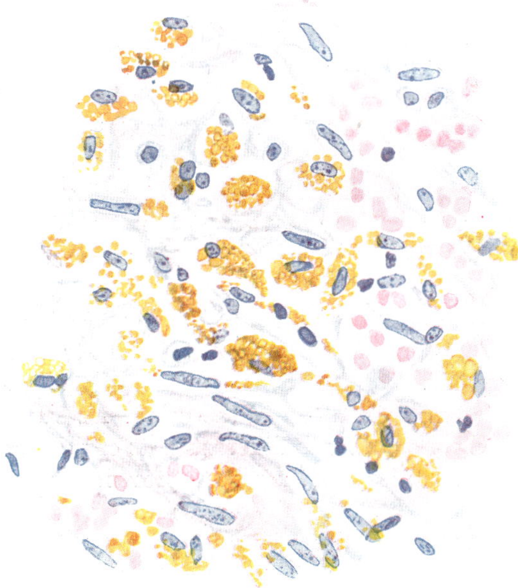

Fig. 50.—Hæmosiderin in phagocytic cells near an organizing thrombus.

phagocytic cells yellow or yellowish-brown, shapeless granules of hæmosiderin (Fig. 50).

A few common examples may illustrate the mode of occurrence of this pigment. In old insane persons, especially, perhaps, those forms of insanity arising from syphilis and chronic alcoholism with arteriosclerosis, one may find lining the dura mater a thick, blood-stained membrane which will peel off in thin layers and which, on being washed free of blood, proves to have an ochre or orange-yellow color. This so-called *chronic hæmorrhagic pachymeningitis* may be the result of a single hæmorrhage, but is usually produced by something, perhaps itself a small hæmorrhage, which causes the formation of a thin layer of vascular granulation tissue from the capillaries of which new hæmorrhages occur and cause the growth of a new layer of tissue. In the wandering phagocytic cells which pervade this tissue hæmosiderin appears in granules which give the yellow color to the whole. A quite similar rusty-brown membrane may be found in hæmorrhagic hydrocele sacs where the tunica vaginalis testis has long been inflamed. Sometimes a hæmorrhagic infarction of the lung may heal, and the area, once turgid with crumbling red corpuscles, is found shrunken and firm with scar tissue and of the color of a mass of iron rust. In the interior much of the pigment may be the iron-free hæmatoidin, but that in the more marginal portions is found to stain blue with ferrocyanide and hydrochloric acid, and to be made up of amorphous granules inclosed in cells which are often fairly bursting with their load of pigment. Again, when the mitral valve is contracted so that blood does not readily escape from the lungs, we may find them distinctly brown on section. A piece of such a lung washed free of blood and dipped in ferrocyanide of potassium and then in weak hydrochloric acid becomes bright blue, and we find that this is because blood-corpuscles have for months oozed into the alveolar cavities, and have there given up their hæmoglobin, to have it converted in the alveolar epithelial cells into hæmosiderin. Microscopically, these cells are seen, swollen with yellow granules, lying in the alveoli or in the sputum which has been coughed up from the lung. Their dependence upon this chain of events has given them the name "heart-failure cells" (Fig. 51).

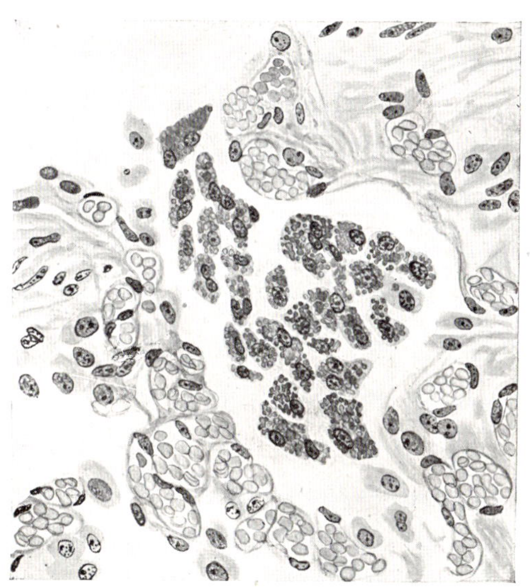

Fig. 51.—Heart-failure cells in the lung. Chronic passive congestion.

Arnold finds that many of the iron-staining granules are due to the assimilation of fluid iron-holding material by the specific granules of the cell protoplasm, and not to mere engulfing of hæmosiderin granules by phagocytic cells, and Neumann states, too, that in the heart-failure cells the pigment masses often have a coal-black central point and are really formed by the incrustation of particles of soot by the iron-containing hæmosiderin.

Not in all cases is the formation of hæmosiderin such a local process, however, for there are many forms of general anæmia in which the destruction of the red corpuscles, usually by some unrecognized agency, sets free continuously a great excess of hæmoglobin into the circulating blood. This may cause the production of an excess of bile-pigment or it may result in a wide-spread deposition of hæmosiderin in the cells of many organs. In the so-called pernicious anæmia, of whose true nature we are ignorant, the cells of the liver and often of the cortex of the kidney, spleen, etc., become laden with hæmosiderin in fine granules (Fig. 52).

In hæmochromatosis, a disease of which mention has already been made, there is an even greater deposition of hæmosiderin and of another iron-free pigment, hæmofuscin, without any extensive destruction of red corpuscles.

We know that such pigment is transported from one part of the body to the other, and transferred from cell to cell, and that much of it reaches the bone-marrow, where it must be thought of as furnishing, according to the economical scheme, the iron-rich material for the formation of new hæmoglobin by the erythroblasts, but that step in the process is far from

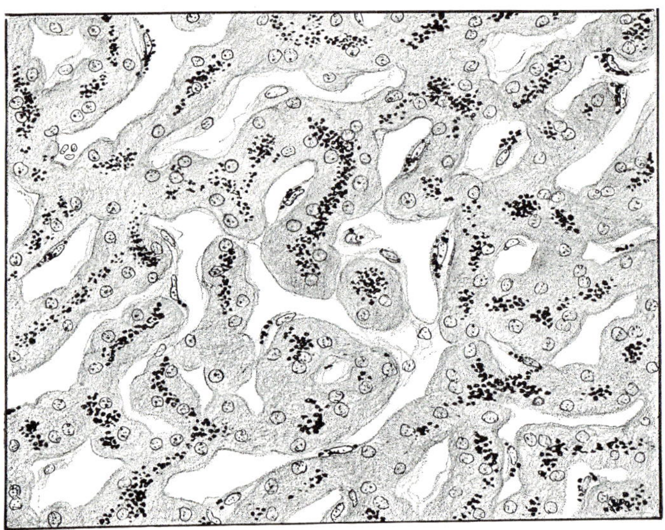

Fig. 52.—Hæmosiderin granules in the liver-cells and endothelium. Pernicious anæmia.

clear. When there has arisen in any way a deposit of hæmosiderin in the tissue of the intestinal wall or in the liver and spleen, decomposition of the body after death or even the excessive formation of hydrogen sulphide in the intestine or in the infected peritoneum may give rise to the formation of black iron sulphide throughout the superficial layers of the tissue. This is pseudomelanosis.

The **third group of endogenous pigments** may be more briefly dismissed, since we know little to tell of them. Nevertheless, we may probably look forward to learning some day that their significance is greater than we have thought. These are the yellowish granules which are found in many organs, such as the seminal vesicles, heart muscle, ganglion-cells, and probably also the interstitial cells of the testes and the cells of the corpus luteum and adrenal. They give something of the characteristic color to the organ, and in some cases this color is intensified when the cells of the organ waste away. It seems that the pigments are in some instances produced from the cell protoplasm in the process of wasting, wherefore Lubarsch and Sehrt call them "wear and tear pigments." Others have loosely called them lipochromes, but they do not give the reactions which have been set forth for the "true" lipochromes, such as have been found in plants and are found in fats, and perhaps in the lutein cells of animals. Their distinctive feature is that they are in a sense colored lipoids and stain brightly with sudan and other fat stains. Perhaps the best example of their accumulation in gross is seen in the wasted, shrunken heart of old or cachectic people (brown atrophy of the heart). There the muscle has a chestnut-brown color, and microscopically the spaces at the ends of the nucleus in the narrow, thread-like muscle-fibre are filled with brown granules which are shining and red after staining with sudan. Of course, they are normally there, but they are vastly more abundant in the brown, atrophic heart (Fig. 26).

Jaundice.—Jaundice or icterus results from the diffusion of bile-pigment throughout the body, with imbibition of the tissues. There has been and still exists an active dispute as to whether this pigment is necessarily the bilirubin formed by the liver-cells, or whether from the laked blood the same pigment can be formed by other tissues. This question appeared to be settled by the experiments of Minkowski and Mering, Moleschott, and others who rather crudely destroyed the liver in geese and were then unable to produce jaundice. But recently evidence has appeared in favor of the opposite view, and Dr. Whipple even tells me that, after completely extirpating the liver in a dog or after ligating off all connection between the thorax and the abdomen, so that the heart of the dog pumped blood only through the head and thorax, the introduction of laked blood was quickly followed by the staining of the tissues with unquestionable bile-pigment.

Still, even if this is true, it is without doubt the liver which usually produces bilirubin, and in nearly all cases it is from some disturbance in the liver and its ducts that we have jaundice. Since the yellow color appears over the whole body, and is easily shown to be due to the presence of bile in the circulating blood, the bile, on being formed by the liver-cell, must pass into the circulation instead of the intestine by way of the ducts. According to most observers this takes place by way of the lymphatic channels, but there are those who believe that it passes directly into the veins. With the appearance of jaundice the patient is usually depressed, his pulse is slowed, and his skin itches. The bile-pigments and acids appear in the urine, which, when the jaundice is intense enough, becomes brownish green and gives a green froth. The coagulation of the blood becomes slowed, and surgeons hesitate to operate upon jaundiced persons lest they bleed to death.

Minkowski held that jaundice might result from the secretion by the liver-cell of its product through the outer side directly into the lymph-sheath of the liver-cell cord. Evidence seems to be rapidly accumulating, however, to show that probably all forms of jaundice are due to mechanical obstruction at some point or other to the outflow of bile. Eppinger, in his recent monograph, ascribes many forms to the plugging of the bile capillaries by solid, thrombus-like masses, which seem to result from the passage into the capillary of an albuminous, coagulable substance. Just as in the kidney injury of the renal epithelium allows the passage of albumin-containing urine, so injury to the liver-cells has a similar result. Such plugging is quickly followed by the bursting of the capillary and the liberation of the dammed-up bile into the neighboring lymphatic canal. On a grosser scale, he thinks the same ruptures occur when the obstruction is far down in the common duct.

Certainly it seems clear enough that when a gall-stone lodges in the common duct, or even when several gall-stones lodge in branches of the hepatic ducts, we have cause for jaundice (not so, of course, when the cystic duct is obstructed nor when the gall-bladder is full of gall-stones, for that whole apparatus serves only as a reservoir). So, too, when a tumor fills up the common duct or, growing outside, compresses it. A tumor of the pancreas or of the stomach may do this, and secondary nodules or metastases from such tumors growing in the liver may compress the branches of the hepatic ducts (*cf.* Fig. 548), and, by producing local areas of obstruction, cause nearly as intense jaundice.

One sometimes sees the most profound jaundice as the result of an ascending growth of bacteria along the mucosa of the gall-ducts, with the production of abscesses about their terminations (cholangitic abscesses). This seems rather due to the occlusion of the ducts themselves than to any pressure on the ducts leading from other parts of the liver, for one may have numerous large abscesses produced by amœbæ or by bacteria brought in through the portal vein without any appreciable jaundice.

In the cases in which obstruction is produced far down in the common duct by the pressure of a tumor, the gall-ducts are found dilated and thinned out, and the gall-bladder is dilated to its extreme capacity with bile. In those cases, however, in which the obstruction arises from the impaction of gall-stones which have lain in the gall-bladder or in the branches of the hepatic ducts, one usually finds the ducts roughened and thickened and the gall-bladder likewise contracted and thick-walled (Courvoisier's law).

Such is the jaundice from obvious mechanical obstruction. Slightly different only is the common form, in which an inflammation of the mucosa of the gall-duct, with abundant mucus formation, may be sufficient to cause transient jaundice. This may reach the deepest bronze if the inflammation is intense enough and involves the minuter ducts in the liver, as it is supposed to do in the so-called biliary cirrhosis.

Other forms of jaundice are harder to explain. Thus in acute yellow atrophy of the liver, which is undoubtedly only a name applied to the widespread necrosis of the liver which might result from the action of many different poisons, there may be the deepest jaundice, although there is no obvious obstruction to the gall-ducts, and most of the liver-cells are incapacitated for producing bile. Still, those which remain are probably disconnected from their ordinary outlet by the destruction of the liver-cells which formed the walls of the intervening portion of the bile capillary, and hence their secretion escapes finally into the blood. So it must be in cirrhosis of the liver, which we may look upon as the healing of repeated slight injuries of a similar type, with eventual reëstablishment of interrupted connections betweeen the liver-cell cords and the bile-ducts, or in the cell cords themselves. In those cases in which a massive destruction of whole lobules occurs, we are perhaps less likely to find jaundice than in those in which minuter lesions destroy merely a few cells here and there but none the less interrupt the continuity of the bile capillary. Still the reëstablishment of these connections is very rapid and effective, and, after all, jaundice occurs in cirrhosis chiefly in those cases in which there are infection and swelling of the mucosa of the gall-ducts.

The jaundice which is produced by toxins and hæmolytic substances has much in common with that seen in such infectious diseases as pneumonia and general septicæmias. Stadelmann produced icterus experimentally with injections of toluylene-diamine, arseniuretted hydrogen, etc., and found not only hæmolysis, but the production of quantities of bile so thick that it practically blocked the gall-ducts. In this sense he regards it as an obstructive jaundice, and Eppinger supports him by finding his bile thrombi plugging in these cases the bile-capillaries. In the infectious forms no such obstruction could be found by Eppinger or Abramow, who have studied the subject. The pathogenesis in these cases is still in question, and they, with the toxic hæmolytic forms, constitute the chief material for the support of the idea of a true hæmatogenous jaundice without the intervention of the liver.

Jaundice of the newborn is also obscure, although, of course, the types caused by syphilis or by congenital atresia of the duct, etc., are clear enough. The common form, which lasts about two weeks and is peculiar in showing no tinting of the scleræ nor any bile in the urine, seems to be definitely not an obstructive process. Another type of jaundice has been studied recently which shows many peculiarities. This is a congenital hereditary affection, thus often occurring in several members of a family, and is associated with a marked anæmia and enlargement of the spleen. Iron therapy, which improves the anæmia, seems to cure some of them, and in one case which I saw splenectomy produced a complete cure.

Microscopically, in advanced jaundice, one finds a diffuse staining of the tissues, but in the liver especially there are masses of green bile-pigment forming casts of the bile-canals, and especially branching moulds in the intercellular bile canaliculi, which are dilated and distorted and often ruptured by these accumulations. It is the denser portions of these moulds that Eppinger regards as bile thrombi, formed with the addition of some coagulable material, and causing evident obstruction of the canal (Fig. 53).

The liver tissue is seen to be rather disorganized and broken where this occurs, and there is a diffuse staining of the liver-cells about the plugs of green material. Beside this one may see that the endothelial cells of the blood-capillaries are stained green, and that there are many large phagocytic cells with clear cytoplasm, but loaded with fragments of the

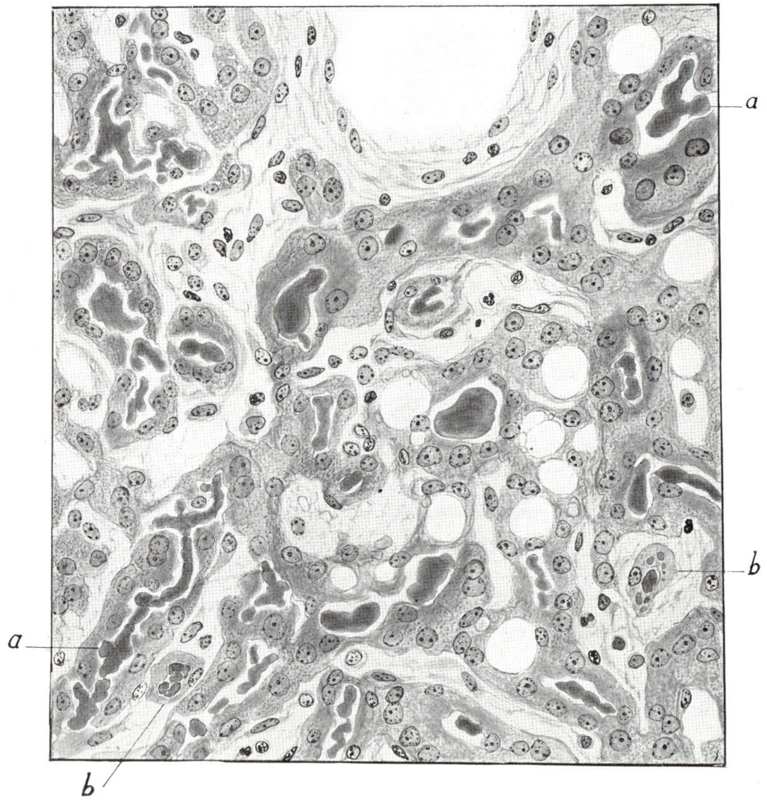

Fig. 53.—Bile-canaliculi in jaundice plugged with bile-pigment (*a*, *a*). Phagocytic cells in capillaries containing similar plugs of bile-pigment (*b*, *b*).

green plugs, lying in the capillaries. These have a single nucleus, although they are often accompanied by many leucocytes and are probably to be regarded as the phagocytic cells of the endothelium, which in the liver are known to be so active.

Exogenous Pigments

These are nearly always relatively simple substances, which get into the body in some way and color the tissues. Most common are those found in the various dust diseases, or konioses, in which the lungs become loaded with the particles which are breathed in by those who ply a dusty trade. The miller fills his lungs with flour, the smoker with soot, the coal-miner with coal-dust (*anthracosis*), the grinder with metallic dust (*siderosis*) or with the dust from cut stone (*chalicosis*), and so on. These should be called *pneumonokonioses*, and their variety is as the variety of dusts. The most common is the ordinary, practically universal anthracosis, which is found in every one and every animal of sufficiently advanced age, especially if they live in a city. The pigment is sometimes in discrete patches, collected along the interlobular septa, but when it is very abundant, as in the coal-miner, it fills all the tissues of the lung. Such lungs are often very hard on

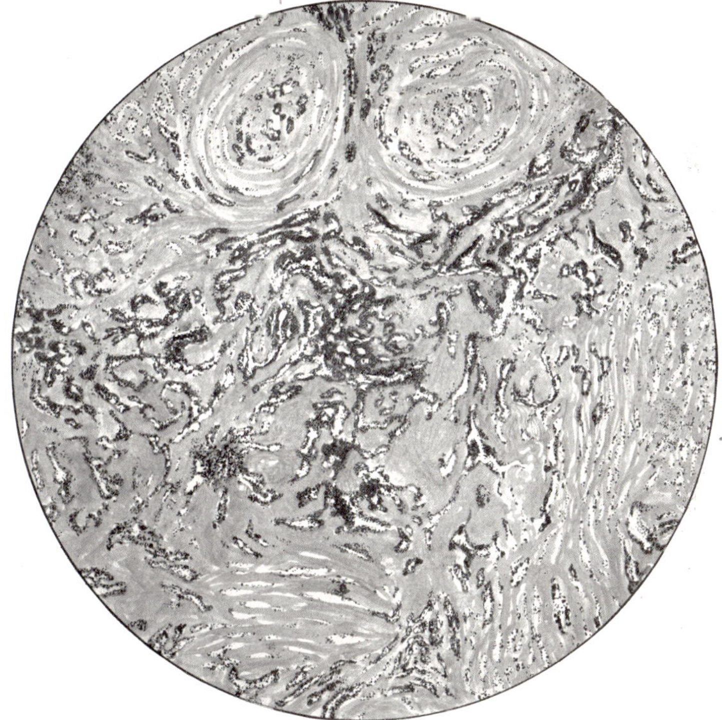

Fig. 54.—Anthracosis of bronchial lymph-gland. Hyaline alteration of gland tissue.

account of the constant attempt at encapsulation of the pigment in scar tissue, and some pigments are so irritating and require so dense a capsule that the lung tissue becomes almost stony (Fig. 54).

The nature of the coal-pigment has been disputed, and it probably is a mixture of soot and a great variety of insoluble particles, but Traube was able to show in some lungs, doubtless those of actual coal-miners, that the granules were really fragments of carbonized coniferous plants, as could be seen from the characteristic bordered pits of the cells which had persisted throughout. Engulfed by phagocytic cells in the alveoli, or even in the free state, these particles gain entrance to the lymphatics of the lungs, and are carried, probably with frequent interruptions and transfers, to other phagocytic cells, to the bronchial lymph-glands, which are blackened and indurated by their presence. These glands are often found adherent to the pulmonary veins in such an intimate way that there may arise an actual transfer of pigment to the vein-wall, or even a hole in the wall through which pigment is swept into the blood-stream. This may explain the occasional presence of coal-pigment in the abdominal lymph-glands or in the spleen and liver, for it has been found that little if any of the dirt and colored matter taken into the intestine passes through the walls into the lymph-glands.

Metallic dust may be inhaled, and colored substances derived from it distributed in the tissues. Most striking is the rusty pigmentation of phagocytic cells about a needle or any other iron particle which has long been embedded in the tissue. These cells look almost as if they had actually gnawed off particles of the metal and carried it away. The same thing is true of the silver sutures used by some surgeons and left in the tissues. Years afterward they may be recognized by a gray cloud about them, which is found to be due to the presence of swarms of branching cells loaded with fine particles of blackish silver. The long-continued administration of any silver salt by mouth, as was once the habit in the treatment of epilepsy, gastric disturbances, etc., often led insidiously to the production of *argyria*, in which the skin, connective tissues, and the framework of various organs assumed a leaden color from the fine deposit of what is probably a silver albuminate. Any one who has ever seen one of these victims can never forget the ghastly gray-blue color of his face and hands.

The **lack of normal pigments** is, of course, quite as important a divergence from the normal as their unusual accumulation. Hereditarily some persons possess very little pigment anywhere in the skin, hair, or eyes. These are albinos, who, although their melanins are scant, have a normal store of hæmoglobin. They suffer from the dazzling effect of the light in their unpigmented eyes, in which the ordinary effect of the camera obscura is much impaired. Localized absence of pigment in patches which are often surrounded by skin of denser pigmentation is not uncommon (leucoderma, vitiligo), and is a characteristic of some deep scars, in the formation of which the melanoblasts seem not to have wandered in.

LITERATURE

Eppinger: Ergeb. d. inn. Med. u. Kinderh., 1908, i, 107
Hueck: Ziegler's Beitr., 1912, liv, 68.
Lubarsch and Sehrt: Virch. Arch., 1904, clxxvii, 248.
Poulsen: Ziegler's Beitr., 1910, xlviii, 348.
Stadelmann: Ikterus, Stuttgart, 1891.
Wieting and Hamdi: Ziegler's Beitr., 1907, xlii, 23.
Whipple: Jour. Exp. Med., 1913, xvii, 612.

CHAPTER IX

DEFENCES OF THE BODY AGAINST INJURY

Immediate and late reactions to injury. Inflammation, fever, immunity production, and repair. Inflammation an elaborate mechanism to combat injury. Details of vascular and phagocytic phenomena. The wandering cells.

Reactions to Injury.—We may say without hesitation, except perhaps in the case of tumors of whose origin we are ignorant, that the underlying cause of every abnormal change in the body is some sort of injury. Often we may see the direct effects of such injuries, but in many cases they are confused with the efforts of the body to annul or repair the hurt.

In the course of ages, through the action of external agencies, the human body has been elaborated to its present form, which is marvelous in its perfect adaptation in every detail to its uses. Variations from this standard in some respects are compatible with life so long as they are not too extreme, although they may handicap the individual in his struggle for existence. Why such a form should have been developed involves broader questions than we can consider here. The same questions arise in connection with every other species, and it is a matter of interest to the palæontologist and the general biologist that, once established, such creatures should go on transmitting through ages all the details of their structure to their offspring, and that individuals should possess the inherent tendency to maintain that form and to return to it as they recover from maiming and distorting injuries. So great is this tendency in the lower orders of animals and in plants that if only a fragment of the body is left it can reconstruct the whole. Even in man, such is the tenacity with which the standard is adhered to that within the life of the individual great strides are made to return to the normal when tissues and organs have been disarranged.

It seems, however, that there are two distinct chains of events, the first being the perfection of a structure and form adapted to the environment, but subject to extremely slow variations, which maintain this adaptation and are hereditary and stamp the species. The second group of phenomena is subservient or auxiliary to this, and consists in the development of protective mechanisms which guard the life of the individual. But one cannot so sharply classify and divide these things, for they overlap. Mechanisms which protect the individual, form some of the characters of the species, and the repairing of a wound in the individual is in great degree guided by the hereditary tendency toward the form characteristic of the species and independent of the momentary action of the environment.

It is this group of hereditary and gradually perfected mechanisms for defence that we must discuss. Of these, some are quite simple and obvious in their character. The body is covered with a relatively impervious skin, further protected in places by hair and nails. It is true that, compared with a turtle or a rhinoceros, we are defenceless in that regard, but ordinarily our need is perhaps not so great. Our respiratory tract is lined with cilia, which keep dust out of the lungs, aided by sneezing or coughing when necessary. Irritating substances are ejected from the stomach by vomiting. Wounds are warded off by all sorts of reflex muscular movements, and so on. All these, in so far as they are functional, have become or were always involuntary processes tending toward the protection of the body from injury.

But still injuries occur from mechanical, physical, or chemical causes, and from the invasion of living plant or animal parasites, and these injuries, which generally imply the destruction of some of the tissue, call into activity several kinds of reactions or responses which have been elaborated through ages of natural selection and bequeathed to their offspring by those whom they have helped to survive. They are of several types, and appear to be rather independent of one another, for some injuries call out one, some another, but most often they all come in combination or in succession. They are: Inflammation, fever, immunity production, repair.

Inflammation is a complicated vascular and cellular response, which follows almost immediately upon the injury, and is adapted, by bringing much blood to the spot and pouring out its elements upon the injured tissues, to prevent the extension of the injury, hold in check the injurious agent, or even destroy it. Through the agency of some of the cells which are brought in, and in other more purely mechanical ways, it is also important in clearing away the débris of injured or dead tissue and preparing the way for the process of repair.

Fever is another complex response through which, by certain changes in the heat-regulating mechanisms, the temperature of the body is raised chiefly through the saving of heat. It is thought that this is bound up with—

Immunity production, is a response to certain types of injury which quietly and slowly forms substances specifically adapted to annul and prevent the inroads of that particular injurious agent. Sometimes this power remains inherent in the tissues for life.

Repair is the new-formation of tissue to replace that which was destroyed. It may be local, in which case the repair is often a kind of patching with tissue of a different sort. Or it may occur in addition at a distance from the point of injury, and consist in the new-formation of the sort of tissue which was destroyed in such a way as to make up for the deficiency which its loss occasioned. Then it is often called compensatory hyperplasia.

Repair must therefore not be confused with inflammation nor regarded as a part of it. It is true that the result of the local tissue growth is not always what we should regard as the ideal outcome of an attempt at healing. Awkward scars or an altogether excessive mass of fibrous tissue may be produced which may even interfere seriously with the function of the organ and be entirely out of proportion with what would seem necessary for the repair of the actual gap first produced by the injury. Usually this is because the injurious agent persists and repeatedly frustrates healing by injuring the repairing tissue itself, so that layer after layer of this new tissue is laid down and consolidated into a firm scar. Possibly this might not be so to such an extent were it not for the inflammatory outpouring of fibrin which it has become the habit of this mechanism to replace by fibrous tissue, rather than to remove in any other way.

It is a mechanism like the others which seems to have been perfected through long generations toward a rather complex end, for not only does it repair gaps in the tissue, but it is protective in the sense that it brings about the encapsulation of any noxious material and prevents its further influence upon the neighboring tissues. While we are familiar with its ordinary course, and can even prophesy what will happen in a given case, we are not so well informed as to the exact mechanism which impels these cells to grow. If, therefore, we speak of the impulse to repair, or disturbance in the equilibrium of tissues, or, on the other hand, of chemical or mechanical stimuli acting directly upon the cell and causing its proliferation, we are using vague terms, all of which may possibly have the same meaning.

This reaction, like the others, is imperfect, and may produce unsatisfactory or even harmful results; but if the person survives, there is set at work a remodeling process through which, in time, much is done toward restoring the tissues to the normal standard. This involves other mechanisms which obliterate blood-vessels in one place and form them in another, rarefy and fret away tissue at one point or strengthen it at another. Seldom does any one live long enough to have this completed, but we find evidence at autopsy that it has been at work.

INFLAMMATION

According to the definition of inflammation given above, it seems preferable to use this name for the immediate protective and defensive reaction to an injury. It is a complex phenomenon, elaborated to a certain degree of perfection in which the blood-vessels with their contents and the wandering cells from adjoining regions play the greatest parts. Its aim seems to be the prevention of further injury by antagonizing the injurious agent, and this must be thought to include the solution and removal of foreign materials (which may be the dead cells themselves) because such material is in itself a cause of injury.

The removal of foreign material or of cellular débris may take place, as in the desquamation of the epidermis or the bursting of an abscess by mechanical means, which hardly form part of the inflammatory reaction, so that perhaps this process of cleaning up the field so that repair may occur may be regarded as incidental to the main aim of combating the injury. At any rate, the reaction seems to be quite distinct from the process of repair. It is confusing, however, that inflammation, cleansing of the site of injury, and repair commonly overlap and proceed together inextricably mingled in the same area. One might construct a simile in which the fire department, hurrying to a burning house, represents the inflammation, although often long before the fire is extinguished workmen are found carrying away the charred timbers and enthusiastic carpenters are rebuilding wherever they can approach near enough. If this combination of activities be carried on for a long time, it is easy to foretell a curious distorted building as the result of the carpenters' efforts. But would any one say that it was the fire that had directly stirred the carpenters to work?

We must discriminate between the direct effect of the injurious agent upon the tissues and the inflammatory reaction. This direct effect may be the killing of some of the cells, with further injury not sufficient to cause death, diminishing as one passes away from the point at which the destructive agent impinged upon the tissue. Sometimes the injury is hardly visible, although it stirs up an intense inflammation, but generally it is necessary that at least a few cells be killed, that this may result. Extensive injuries which cause metabolic disturbances in the cells may arouse no inflammatory reaction at all; cells may gradually waste away from disease or malnutrition or from pressure, as in a hydronephrotic kidney, and there is little or no inflammation; but let a few cells die and coagulate into what is virtually a foreign body, or introduce any foreign body, and an inflammatory reaction appears at once. This reaction is not attuned to all sorts of injuries, nor even necessarily to the most severe, for a man may have his leg cut off by the surgeon and the wound will heal with evidences of an inflammation which is directed toward the annihilation of the few dying cells which happen to have been cut in two in the line of incision, quite regardless of the more serious catastrophe that the man had lost his leg. Or a vein may be opened aseptically and an animal bled nearly to death; wonderful reparatory processes will occur in the distant bone-marrow to restore the blood, and fluid will pour from the tissues into the blood-vessels, but there will be no inflammation. Cauterize the wound, however, with a hot iron or with boiling oil, as they did in the time of Paré, and the inflammatory reaction will appear in its full force. We are tempted to ask whether, after all, inflammation as a reaction responds only to the presence of dead cells, and their diffusible decomposition products, and whether, in the course of the development and elaboration of the reaction, this has evolved itself as the general signal for inflammation, but we know that we may greatly intensify the reaction by the use of some other more irritating substance to kill the cells.

Given the adequate injury, the inflammatory reaction begins with a red flush. It can be followed in any place near the skin, perhaps especially well, as Samuel pointed out, in such an object as the rabbit's ear, where the blood-vessels can be seen, but for the minute details it is best to study with the microscope such transparent tissue as the mesentery or tongue of the frog or the wing of the bat. If the tip of the rabbit's ear be painted with croton oil or dipped in hot water, the whole process comes on with a rush. First, after a momentary contraction, there is the widening of the arteries

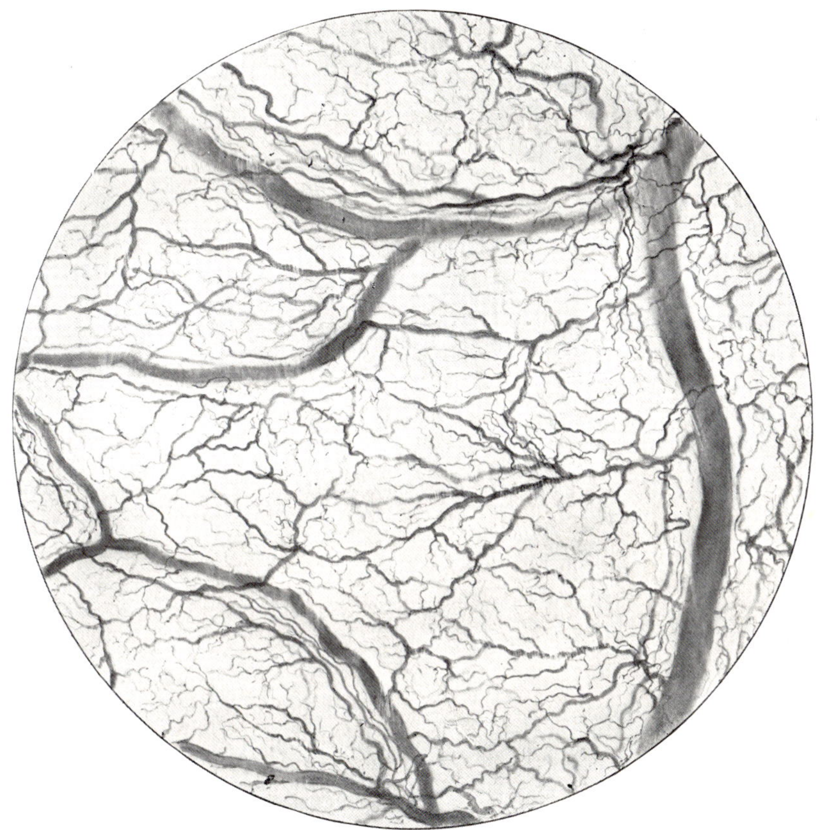

Fig. 55A.—Portion of inflamed diaphragm cleared by Spalteholtz's method to show the abundant dilated blood-channels.

and veins, so that the blood courses through them very rapidly, and simultaneously the widening of all the minute arterioles and venules in the affected area, so that channels come into view which were evidently completely collapsed before (Figs. 55A and B). This much is commonly attained if, by compressing the veins or by cutting the sympathetic nerves, we cause the dilation of the vessels. But, in addition, in the inflamed ear, all the spaces between these visible widened channels become uniformly red. A needle passed through one of these spaces in the mechanically congested ear will draw no blood; but in the inflamed ear there is free bleeding from the puncture. Evidently, then, the capillaries are uniformly distended with blood. While this change takes place at first in the actually injured area, it soon spreads to the adjacent part of the ear, and finally even to its root or over the side of the head. The ear is much warmer than the other, because blood rushes through it so fast that it has the temperature of the interior of the body, and it is gone again before there is time to cool off.

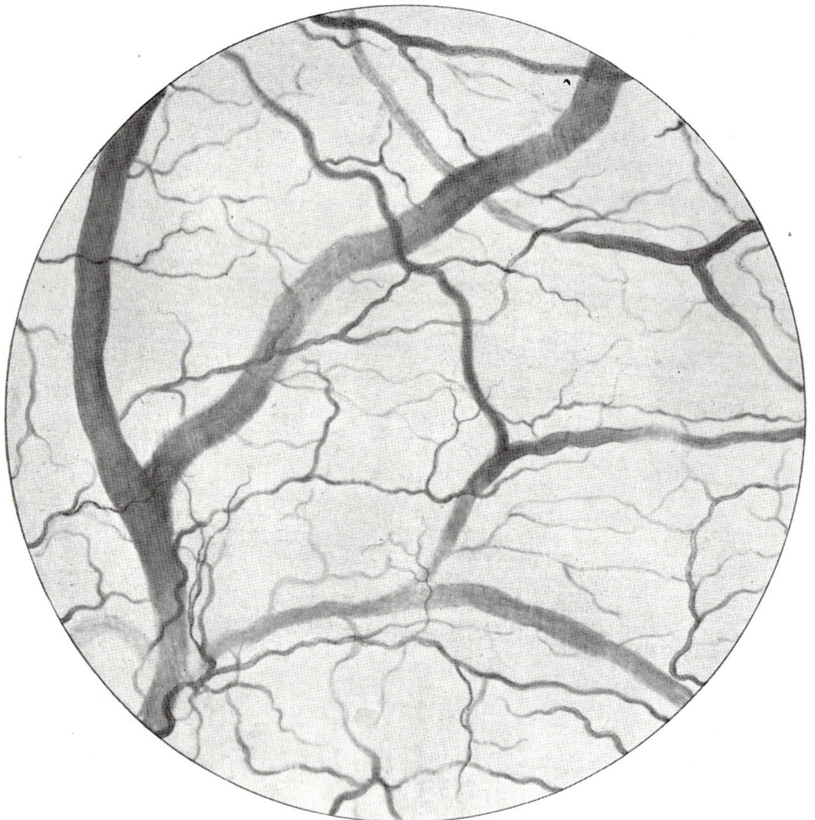

Fig. 55B.—Portion of a normal diaphragm, showing in contrast relatively few visible blood-channels.

This lasts only a short time before the ear becomes swollen and the skin tense. If it be pinched, the impression of the finger remains for a time. It becomes so thick and heavy that it hangs down, and its function must thereby be interfered with. Besides it is very tender and even spontaneously painful. At the least touch the animal jerks back as if burnt. Two or three days later the artery may be found contracted again to something near its normal size. In the injured area the redness persists, though it may be a darker, more violet color—the ear is cooler—blood seems to be passing through the vessels very slowly, and the swelling is gradually passing away. It may require ten or twelve days for all to become normal again—the part which has actually been injured is the last to recover, and then usually with the loss of its surface epithelium, but even there the circulation finally returns to the normal, the epithelium is repaired, and the inflammation is over.

If a transparent tissue is selected, the whole process can be watched in its development. In the region where the tissue has been injured, and for

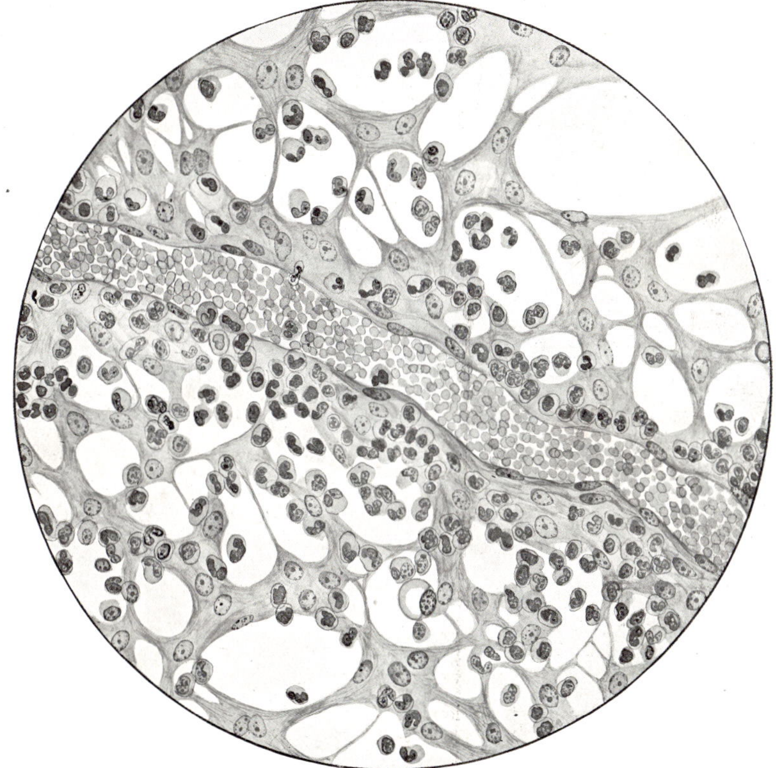

Fig. 56.—Inflamed omentum showing outwandered leucocytes about a small vessel.

some distance around it, the small blood-vessels are seen to widen. All the capillaries are stretched by the increased stream of blood, and contracted channels, which could not be seen before, reopen, and the blood courses through areas which were quite pale before. The stream, pulsating in the arterioles and steady in the venules, now rushes through with vertiginous rapidity. Though we cannot see it, there is probably even at this stage some filtering-out of clear fluid from the vessels into the crevices of the surrounding tissue. After a time, although the stream-bed remains wide, the current slows down until one loses the impression of a homogeneous, yellowish-red fluid hurrying along, and it becomes possible to catch glimpses of the corpuscles as they pass. Throughout all this one can see that in the venules, where there is no pulsation to disturb it, the arrangement of the corpuscles is peculiar in that they float in the centre of the stream, separated everywhere from the vein-wall by the clear plasma. With the slowing of the stream leucocytes begin to appear in this marginal stream and are rolled along the wall. They even seem to find the wall sticky, so that they adhere now and then, only to be turned over and dragged along by the rest. Still later some of them refuse to be dislodged, and one can see that they have fastened themselves to the wall by piercing

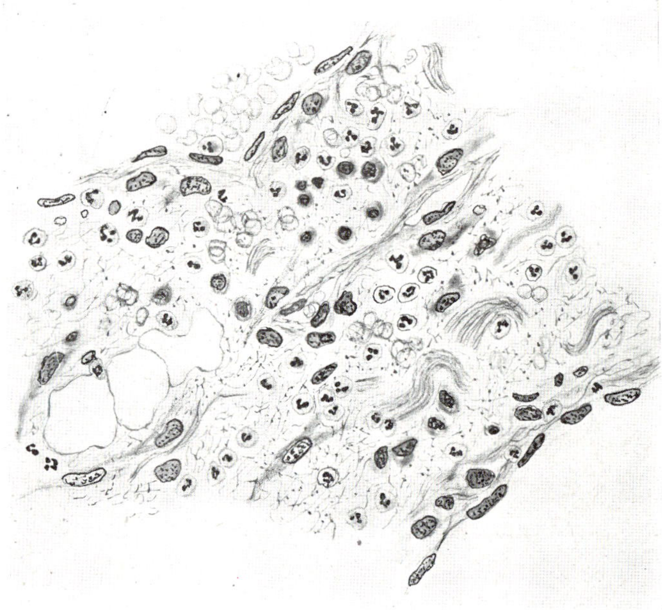

Fig. 57.—Acute diffuse inflammation. Tissue is œdematous and shows exudate of leucocytes and red corpuscles in a network of fibrin. Some mononuclear wandering cells are present.

it with a protoplasmic process which may even project a little way on the outside. Such a leucocyte soon becomes dumb-bell shaped, with half its body outside the endothelial wall, the nucleus squeezing its way through the small hole forced by the protoplasm. It is not long before the whole cell escapes through this gap and wanders away among the fibres of the surrounding tissue. These are chiefly polymorphonuclear neutrophile leucocytes, which are the most numerous in the blood, and this is the process of active emigration which formed the crucial feature in Cohnheim's classical observation, and which is one of the most significant occurrences in the whole process of inflammation (Fig. 56).

Along with the leucocytes, or behind them, red corpuscles escape passively to the outside, and during the whole time fluid has filtered through unobserved until now the cells and fibres of the tissue around the blood-vessel are spread apart widely by its great accumulation—the inflammatory œdema. Since this fluid is coagulable like the plasma of the blood, and since there are injured cells in the neighborhood to set free thrombokinase, there soon appears a delicate coagulum of fibrin stretching in fine filaments through the spaces forced open by the fluid (Figs. 57, 58, 59).

If the injury is extreme, the current of blood may come to a complete

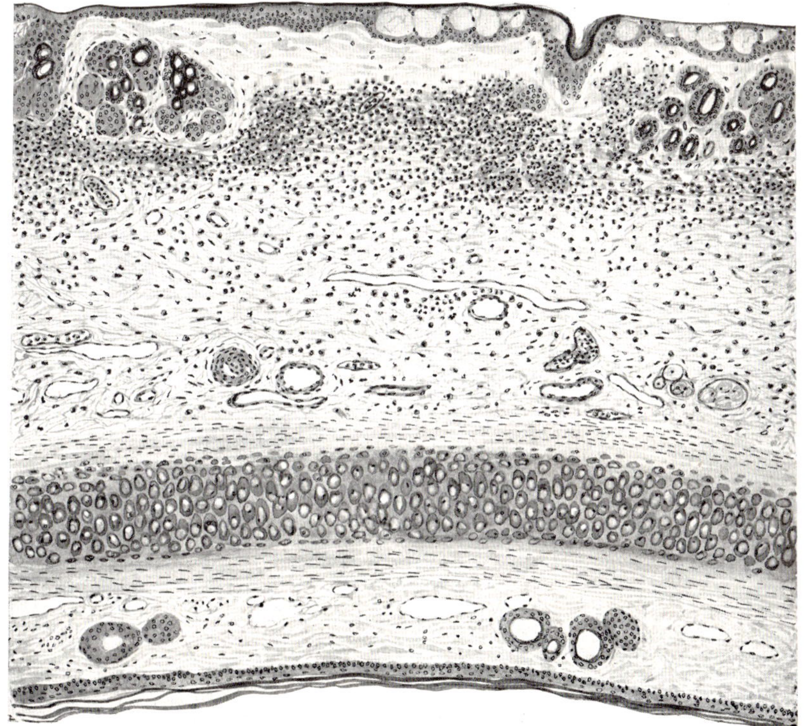

Fig. 58.—Inflamed rabbit's ear showing blisters in the skin and inflammatory infiltration of the subcutaneous tissue.

stop in some of the vessels, and there emigration of leucocytes ceases. But in the others, although the corpuscles pass along very slowly, enough fresh blood seems to be brought to nourish the tissues.

The leucocytes and the fluid press toward the point where the tissues are most injured and surround those cells. If bacteria are present, the leucocytes may swallow them unless they have diffused around themselves too strong a poison. Then it seems impossible for the leucocytes to approach without being killed, perhaps because in order to do this they have to pass through dead tissue around the bacteria where they receive no oxygen. It is almost like firemen who are checked by the smoke, but they keep on rushing in past the dead bodies of those which preceded them.

Finally, as a rule, if the injury is not enough to cause the death of the animal, the bacteria are overcome. This is effected by the continued action of the fluid and the leucocytes in ways which we shall discuss. Or if there have been no bacteria, the dead tissue is permeated by the exuded fluid and invaded by the leucocytes.

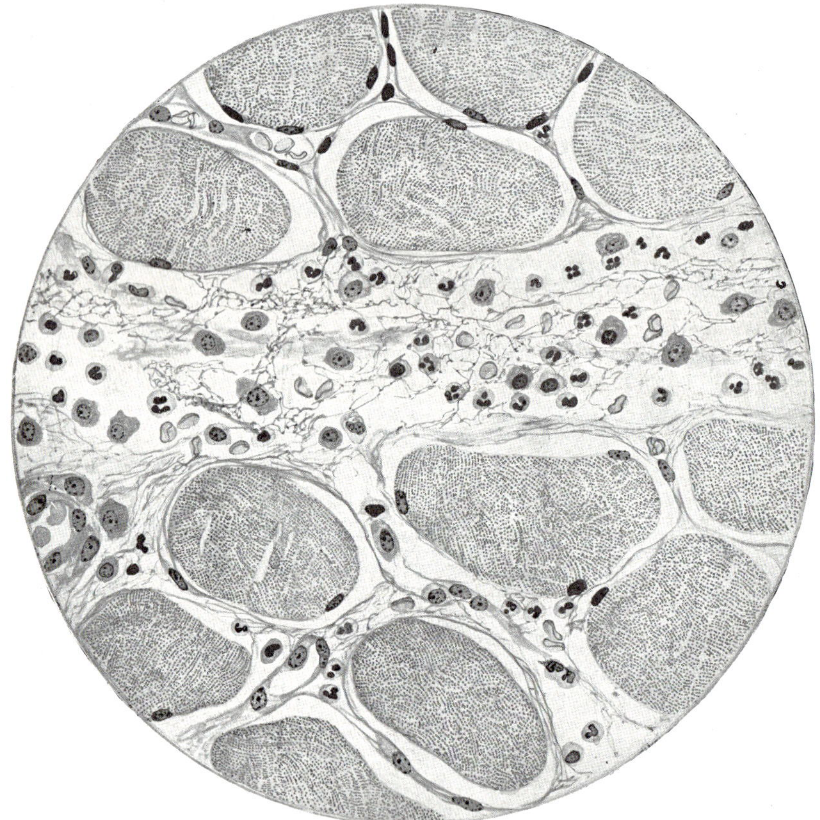

Fig. 59.—Acute myositis. Diffuse acute inflammation with mononuclear wandering cells as well as leucocytes, red corpuscles, and fibrin.

After this the process becomes an effort to clean up the débris. Partly by self-digestion, partly through digestion by the leucocytes, the dead cells and fibres are liquefied or reduced to a fine granular fluid and absorbed through the walls of the lymphatics. The dead bodies of leucocytes suffer the same fate, and those which remain alive aid by carrying particles through the walls of the lymphatics, where they are swept along into the next lymph-gland. There any such particles or dead cells are exposed to the digestive action of the cells of the lymph-gland.

Thus the area is cleared of débris; the blood-vessels gradually return to their normal calibre, their walls again become normal and contract, and the circulation resumes its normal rate. Naturally gaps are left in the tissue where cells have died and been removed, but the repair of these gaps will form another chapter.

It is seen from this that inflammation is really a complex but well-rounded mechanism, designed chiefly to pour over injurious substances and dead tissue a fluid and cells rich in neutralizing materials and digestive ferments, which tend to quench the action of the injuring agent and to liquefy the débris for removal. From this point of view it seems a purposeful and beneficial reaction.

Probably every inflammation is accompanied by some general disturbance, such as fever, of which we shall have more to say later. When the injury is intense enough, poison may be absorbed from the injurious agent or even from the dead tissue to affect the nervous system and other organs and to cause disturbance of their functions, and what we know as illness. Even the fever itself may bring along with it disturbances in function. In all cases, too, there is likely to be a change in the blood in general, consisting in a great increase in the number of leucocytes. This leucocytosis is a convenient index of the existence of an obscure inflammation, and results from the great over-production of the cells of the bone-marrow and their liberation into the blood.

While the inflammatory reaction may thus happily succeed in overcoming the injury and restoring the cleansed area to a condition in which it is ready for repair, it is not always so. The injurious agent may persist, as in the case of bacterial infections, or it may be frequently repeated, in the case of physical or chemical injuries, so that a smouldering fire is kept up for a long time. The persistent reaction, which is then often spoken of as chronic inflammation, comes to differ from that which is quickly finished, chiefly in that, among the wandering cells which appear in the tissue, there arrive swarms of mononuclear forms which are slow to move, being attracted chiefly by dead tissue or other substances unlike those which draw the neutrophile leucocytes. The congestion of the vessels and the œdema may subside, being kept up chiefly along the frontier. Most confusing, however, is the fact that, if so much time is occupied, reparatory processes appear and are closely interwoven with those of defensive character. The mononuclear cells emigrate in small numbers with the polymorphonuclears in the acuter forms, but now they come in such numbers that one cannot escape the idea that many of them wander in from the crevices of the adjacent tissue or are even formed *in situ* by multiplication of those which first appear. They assume many forms, and many of them grow to a great size as they move about, swallowing up particles of dead tissue or even whole cells which have been injured. When the area is finally and permanently rid of the injurious substance, and when all the débris of dead tissue is cleared up, these cells in their turn slip away into the spaces of the tissue or into the lymphatics and disappear into distant parts of the body.

With this bare outline of the inflammatory process we may pass to the discussion of some of the underlying principles.

The Widening of the Vessels.—The widening of the blood-vessels is probably due to complete paralysis of their walls, at any rate in the actually inflamed areas. Klemensiewicz, who holds this idea, showed that the vessels of the web of the frog's foot could be made to contract by electrical stimulation of the medulla or of the vessels themselves, but if the foot were inflamed, no such stimulation affected them in the least. Section of the sympathetic fibres to a part allows of a temporary great dilatation of the vessels. In the rabbit's ear section of the auricular nerves, on the contrary, causes their contraction. Sensory stimulation will reflexly cause vascular engorgement, but while all these conditions may be produced first, and will thereupon modify the course of an inflammation set up in that region, they are quite different from the changes in the vessels which inflammation entails, and which cannot be greatly altered by section or stimulation of nerves when it is once well developed. Inflammation in a rabbit's ear flushed by section of the sympathetic proceeds more rapidly and intensely than in a normal ear, and inflammation in a rabbit's ear rendered anæmic by section of the auricular nerves goes on imperfectly, so that in the end the injured ear becomes necrotic and drops off. But, after all, these are only superimposed influences, and, as we have shown, inflammation runs its course, complete in each detail, in a limb which has been amputated and then reunited by vascular suture, so that there can be no possibility of the existence of any nervous connection with the central nervous system. All this is in accord with Klemensiewicz's statement that the walls of the vessels, including the capillaries, are completely paralyzed and deprived of their contractility.

The Changes in the Rate of Flow.—The stream in any given stream-bed ordinarily runs more slowly when it reaches a widened stretch, but here, where there is a choice of channels, it is more influenced by the friction against the wall, and consequently runs through these widened vessels at a rate more nearly approaching that in the larger vessels than before. It is for this reason that the part feels hot—not that there is any appreciable amount of heat produced by increased metabolism in the inflamed area, but merely because, in a superficial tissue, the blood, when coursing normally, has time to cool, while now there is no such opportunity and the temperature of the part approaches that of the interior of the body. Probably we could determine no difference in temperature between an inflamed loop of intestine and a normal one in the same person.

The slowing of the stream and the passing out of the leucocytes into the marginal or plasma zone are much harder to explain. One is practically compelled to think that there is a change in the endothelial lining of the vessel of such a character that it becomes rough or sticky, and thus offers more friction to the passage of the blood-stream. Some have thought that the blood itself becomes thickened by the loss of fluid through the vessel-walls, and that this increased viscosity might explain the sluggish stream, but there is no convincing evidence that the venous blood from an inflamed area has any perceptibly greater viscosity than the arterial blood. Schlarewsky and others have shown that any suspended particles passing in a stream of fluid through a tube are governed by a centripetal force which keeps them in the axis of the stream, but that, with slowing of the stream, this force is relaxed, and first the lighter, then the heavier, particles are allowed to approach the periphery. Apparently this would explain the marginal position of the leucocytes as the stream slows, but it does not touch upon their adhering to the wall and finally penetrating it. Nor does it throw any light upon their increasing abundance in the whole circulating blood, for which two things quite different causes must be sought.

Chemiotaxis and Phagocytosis.—It has been observed, in watching free swimming amœbæ and other unicellular or even multinucleated organisms which are mobile and jelly-like (myxomycetes), that their movements are largely influenced by changes in their surroundings, or even more definitely by physical or chemical stimuli. Of special interest is their behavior toward soluble substances, some of which attract, while others repel, them. One of the myxomycetes, for example, which grows on tanbark, will move actively along a moist surface toward a drop of an extract of that bark, while it will move just as actively away from a solution of glucose or of some salt. Nevertheless, it can be accustomed to these latter things so as to be attracted rather than repelled by them. This is an example of chemiotaxis, or the stimulation to motion by a chemical substance, in the one case positive, in the other negative. Attempts have been made (A. B. Macallum and others) to explain this activity as due to alterations in the surface tension of the protoplasmic mass, and apparently this is the true basis, although it becomes complicated when we come to explain how the response changes as the amœboid organism accustoms itself to a repellent substance and is finally attracted by it. Probably a similar explanation will hold good for the tactile irritability which is evident in those amœbæ or other cells which come into contact with some insoluble particle. In such a case the protoplasm flows around the particle and encloses it completely unless it is too large, when it spreads itself over the mass as far as possible.

This is the process of phagocytosis in its beginning, and both it and chemiotaxis are things which can be closely simulated by non-living substances. Thus a drop of chloroform in water will stretch itself along a thread of shellac brought against it, and, dissolving it as it goes, keep moving along the thread until it is saturated.

All of this applies equally well to the mobile cells of the body, particularly to the leucocytes, and Metchnikoff especially has laid great stress upon the fundamental rôle which it plays in inflammation, for while in lower forms these mobile mesenchymal cells form the means of defence, arriving at the point of injury by their own motility, in vertebrates there is added a convenient blood-vascular system, with its rapid current, which brings the leucocytes to the injured area and then slows up so that they may emigrate through its walls and reach the spot. Were it not for this slowing and the roughening and stickiness of the endothelium in that region, the leucocytes would all be swept by without any chance of reaching the place where the injury occurred.

Many ideas have been expressed as to the reason for the passage of the leucocytes through the wall, but it seems that the weight of evidence is in favor of their active penetration between the cells in response to the attraction of some diffusible soluble substance which is either the injurious agent itself or produced by its destructive action on the cells of the tissue. It is so evident that dead tissue killed by any mechanical means or by being deprived of its blood supply, as in the case an an infarction, can act in this way to attract the leucocytes, that in every case it must play a part. Experimentally it has been shown that extracts of dead cells are positively chemiotactic. Nevertheless, the leucocytes appear in so much greater number when bacteria or some chemical irritant cause the inflammation that unquestionably these poisonous substances themselves have a powerful influence.

All forms of leucocytes are not equally attracted by each substance, and indeed some things actually repel one form while attracting another. Thus while in most inflammations the polymorphonuclear neutrophile cells are prompt to respond in great numbers, cells of the type of the lymphocyte are most abundant in the inflamed areas in typhoid fever and even in tuberculosis. So, too, in the lesions produced by many animal parasites, such as the trichina, the polymorphonuclear eosinophile cells appear in great numbers. It is not clear that any bacteria exercise a definitely repellent action on the neutrophile leucocyte, although it seems that this may be so in typhoid fever.

Leucocytosis.—How the impulse is sent to the bone-marrow, when there is a localized infection, to call forth the storm-like discharge of new leucocytes into the blood, is not very clear. Certainly far more are formed and liberated than could possibly be accounted for by any dearth in the circulating blood caused by their departure from the blood-vessels, and it seems necessary to believe that some chemical substance circulating in the blood causes this great hyperplasia. If one reflects that a leucocytosis of 30,000 to 40,000 per cubic millimetre is not unusual, the colossal number of new leucocytes quickly formed and thrown into circulation becomes a matter of wonder.

The Wandering Cells.—It is clear that in the adult animal the greater number of the cells are intimately and permanently attached to their neighbors, and in virtue of this coherence tissues are formed which are stable. The rest of the cells are not so fixed, but wander about loosely or are driven about with great speed, as in the case of the red corpuscles and leucocytes of the circulating blood. Even in the circulating blood the leucocytes have the power of moving at their own volition, but this power comes to its proper expression only in the crevices of the tissues, where they are at leisure and are not hurried along by the force of the heart. There it is easy to recognize such free cells by their clear-cut outline, their independence of attachment to other cells, and by their bulging or lobose pseudopods. If the tissue is allowed to grow cold before fixation, most of these cells will be found to have retracted into a round form, but if it is dropped in small pieces, perfectly fresh and warm from the living animal, into some solution which will fix it instantaneously, the wandering cells are seen caught in all sorts of attitudes, and often stretching out long arms or twisting their way among the fixed cells.

It is very generally agreed now that these wandering cells take no part in the formation of any fixed or stable tissue, but are probably always nomadic until they perish. It is not so certain that the fixed tissues do not give origin to wandering cells. This forms the subject of a discussion which has lasted for years, and is even now far from a conclusion. It seems proved that if we go far enough back in the development of the embryo, it may be shown that the wandering cells, all of which are of mesoblastic origin, arise from exactly the same cells as give rise to the various types of connective tissue. In other words, in this early stage the formation of blood, including red corpuscles as well as leucocytes, takes place nearly everywhere in the mesenchyme or original connective tissue. Maximow and also Dantschakow, have described this very clearly in a number of recent papers, and have shown that among the branched connective-tissue cells which make up this soft tissue there appear spaces (Fig. 60). The connective-tissue cells or fibroblasts bounding these constitute a lining, and soon become modified and divide to form round cells, some of which fall into the space while others maintain themselves as lining cells. These are the first endothelial cells and the forerunners of the blood-cells. From such round cells which fall into the new blood-channel there arise red corpuscles, lymphocytes, and even the granulated leucocytes, and these may wander out among the other cells and back again. Many of those which remain nucleated and devoid of hæmoglobin leave the blood-channels and pursue a wandering existence in the tissues.

Later in the development of the animal such processes of blood formation become localized in certain specialized blood-forming organs, such as the bone-marrow, the lymphoid tissues, and possibly some other places. For a time the liver is active as a blood-forming tissue, but it loses this power later. The spleen appears to retain the hæmatopoietic power through life, although it acts also as a scavenger of débris of blood-cells.

Under pathological conditions it seems that very many other situations in the body may become endowed with the capacity for blood formation—a change sometimes called a myeloid transformation; thus actual bone-marrow may be formed in the lung or the kidney or in the artery wall, or the spleen may come to contain the elements which are recognized in the bone-marrow as the producers of leucocytes and red corpuscles. But these things are abnormal and transitory, and ordinarily blood formation is rather restricted to the definite blood-forming organs. In this way the relation of the wandering cells to the fixed tissues becomes fairly clear. That they are of common original stock with the connective tissues is shown by the early development, but that these connective tissues draw away and become specific producers of similar connective tissues only, in

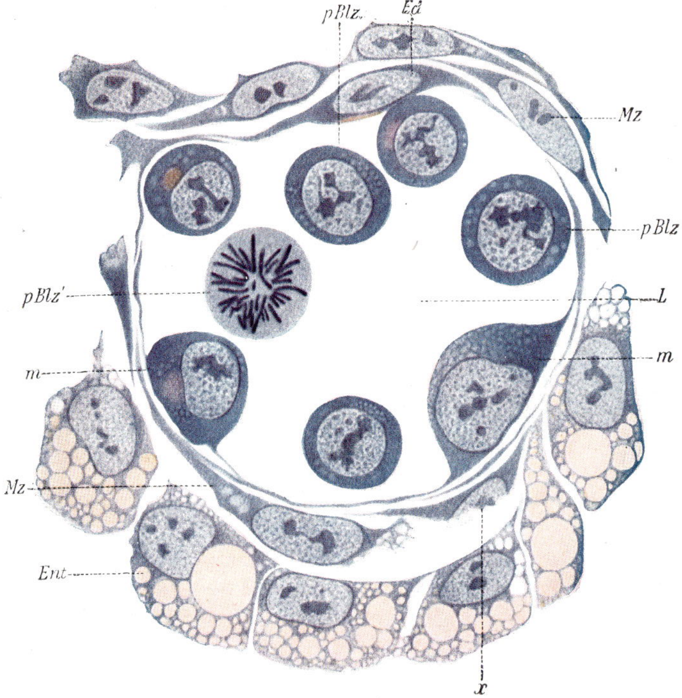

Fig. 60.—Early development of wandering cells in embryonic tissue (Maximow). Cross-section of a vessel of the area vasculosa with primitive blood-cells (*p. blz*) in the lumen. Rounding off of endothelial cells (*m*) and their conversion into blood-cells; *mz*, mesenchyme cells; *ed*, endothelium.

later life, leaving the wandering cells to be formed by specialized cells grouped in organs for that purpose, is equally clear.

Description of the cells concerned may be found in every text-book of histology, although it is true that some of the types become conspicuous or are produced only under pathological conditions.

In the circulating blood there are found normally, beside the red corpuscles and platelets (which are derivatives of the megalokaryocytes of the bone-marrow), several types of mobile leucocytes. Of these, the *polymorphonuclear leucocytes* with neutrophile granules are most prominent, and form about 70 per cent. of all the white cells. Similar to them in many respects are the *eosinophile cells,* which differ in possessing shining granules staining brightly with eosin, but these form only 1 or 2 per cent. The remainder consist of cells with rounded nucleus and protoplasm containing few granules or none at all. The smaller of these, with relatively little protoplasm, are the lymphocytes. Larger paler cells with palely stained round or indented nucleus are variously known as *large mononuclear cells,* large lymphocytes, etc. Occasionally there are found single examples of the forerunners of the polymorphonuclear leucocytes in the form of large mononuclear rounded cells with neutrophile or even eosinophile granules (*myelocytes*), and about as rarely leucocyte-like cells which contain distinctly basophilic granules in their protoplasm (*mast leucocytes*).

In the bone-marrow, where the manufacture of the cell contents of the blood is very active, there are found all the precursors of these cells. There there are many indifferent non-granulated cells, much like the primitive cells in the embryonic tissue, from which so many varieties arose. These can be supposed to give rise, along different lines of specialization, to the cells as they are found in the blood. One process of differentiation doubtless leads to the formation of larger and smaller lymphocytes. This certainly occurs in the bone-marrow, although these cells are known to be produced in especially great numbers by the lymphoid tissue distributed throughout the body. Another line of development from an early undifferentiated type of cell which is originally the same as that just described leads, through the appearance of hæmoglobin in the protoplasm, to the successive formation of *megaloblasts* (large nucleated red corpuscles), *normoblasts* (smaller nucleated red corpuscles), and finally through the loss of nucleus to the non-nucleated ordinary red corpuscles or *erythrocytes.* Sometimes in the stress of rapid delivery of these red corpuscles to the blood in cases of anæmia some of the nucleated megaloblasts and normoblasts are swept out into the circulation. The third important line of development, beginning with an indifferent nucleated cell, leads to the production of large round cells with large, pale nucleus and non-granular protoplasm (*myeloblast*), which may acquire either neutrophile or eosinophile granulations. These in time give rise respectively to the neutrophile and eosinophile polymorphonuclear leucocytes (Fig. 61).

Osteoblasts and osteoclasts in the bone-marrow take no part in blood formation, but the large giant-cells with budding nucleus and granular protoplasm (megalokaryocytes) constantly give off fragments of their protoplasm to the blood-stream and thus produce the platelets (Wright).

In the lymph-glands, as well as in the Malpighian bodies of the spleen, the tonsils, and all the lymphoid nodules scattered along the alimentary tract, there are found many lymphocytes lodged in a reticulum and associated closely with networks of lymph-sinuses and lymphatic channels. In the reticulum there are many large pale cells which may be concentrated in the middle of each lymph-cord or island in the gland to form the so-called

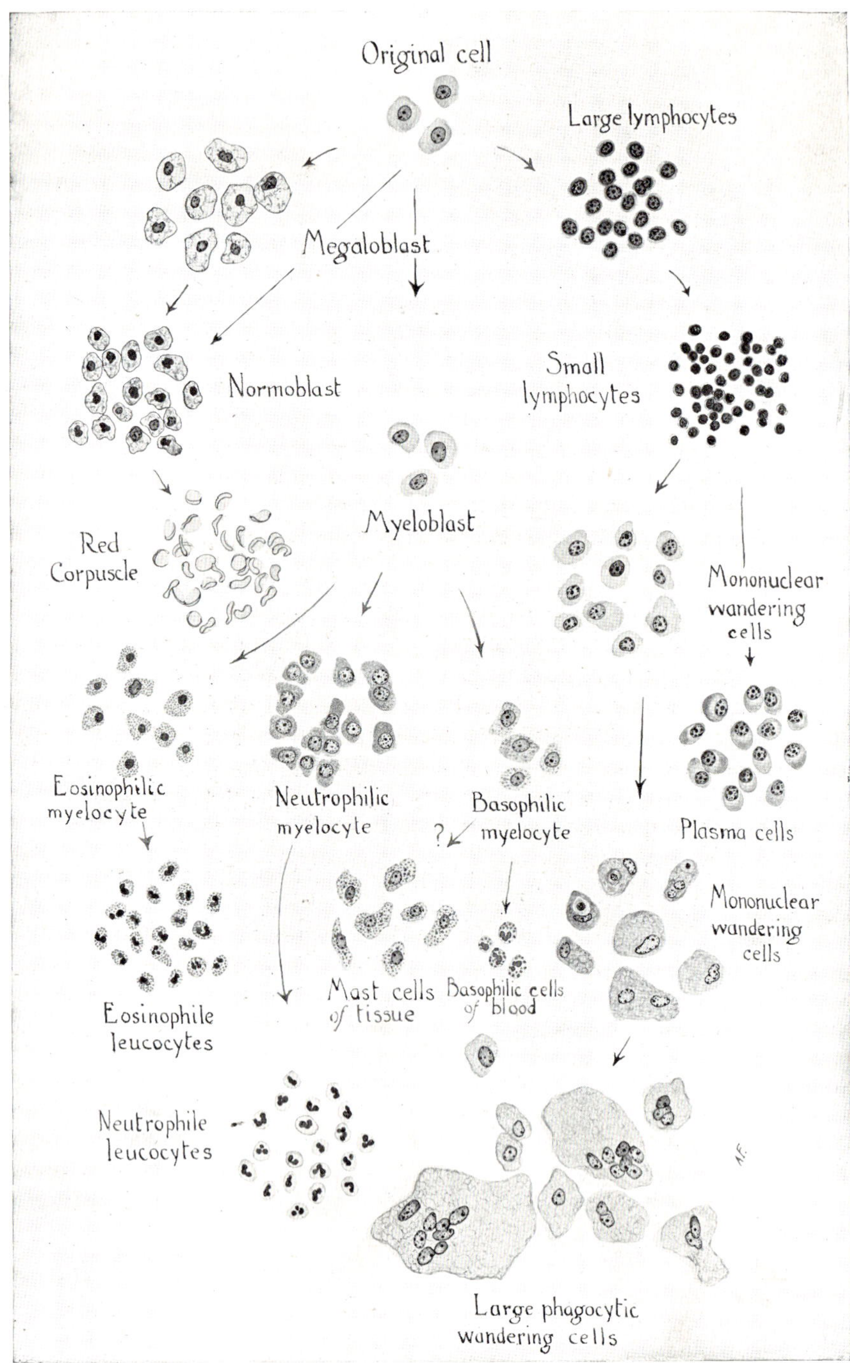

Fig. 61.—Genealogical tree of the wandering cells of human tissues as they appear in ordinary sections. The cells are drawn to scale, and the arrows indicate their relationship.

germinal centre (Fig. 62). Although it was stated by Flemming that these large cells gave rise by mitosis to the lymphocytes, there is still much dispute about the actual origin of the smaller cells. Marchand, in reviewing the work with its divergent results, concludes that large macrophages are certainly formed from the reticulum cells and endothelium of the sinuses, but that it is difficult to prove the origin of the lymphocytes from the large cells of the germinal centre.

These cells have different morphological characters and phagocytic powers, and although we know that lymphocytes are produced in this tissue

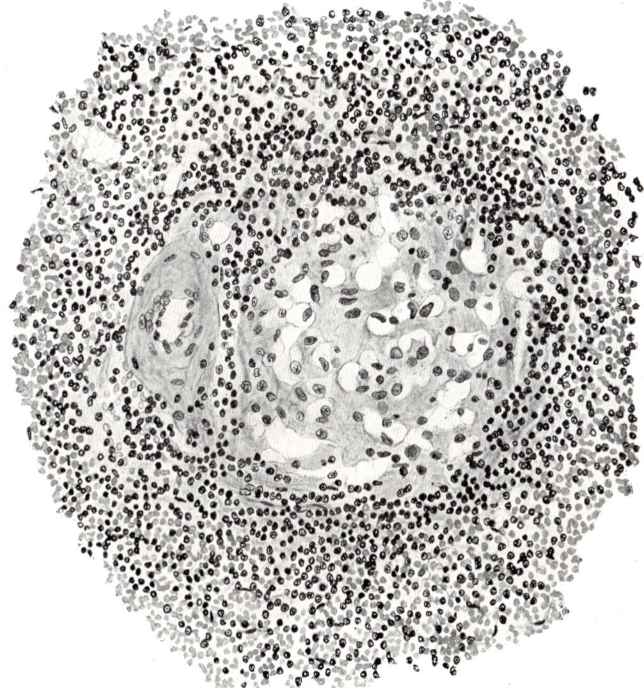

Fig. 62.—Germinal centre in Malpighian body of the spleen.

and although the general tendency is to derive them from the reticulum cells, this origin has not actually been proved.

In the course of many infections the sinuses of the gland, and even the neighboring tissues, become packed with large mobile mononuclear cells which are most voraciously phagocytic and engorge themselves with every sort of cellular débris (Fig. 63). Marchand and others regard these as the macrophages derived from the reticulum cells and from the endothelium of the lymph-sinuses. Mallory, in his study of typhoid fever, has laid special stress on their endothelial origin, and even speaks of them as endothelial leucocytes. It seems to me difficult, however, to distinguish between these and the large mononuclear wandering cells in general, and difficult to assign to them with certainty an origin different from that accepted for those which infiltrate tissues at a distance from lymph-glands.

Conditions in the lymphoid nodules of the intestinal wall and other organs, in the Malpighian bodies of the spleen and the tonsils, correspond exactly with those in the follicles of the lymph-glands. In the splenic pulp there are also cells of the type of lymphoid cells, and larger ones which act as macrophages. That they may be contributed in great numbers to the circulating blood is shown clearly by Morris' recent studies of the blood of the splenic vein. Other tissues, including the connective tissues in general, especially where they lie in relation to the walls of the blood-vessels, the omentum, the stroma of the mucosæ of the intestine, etc.,

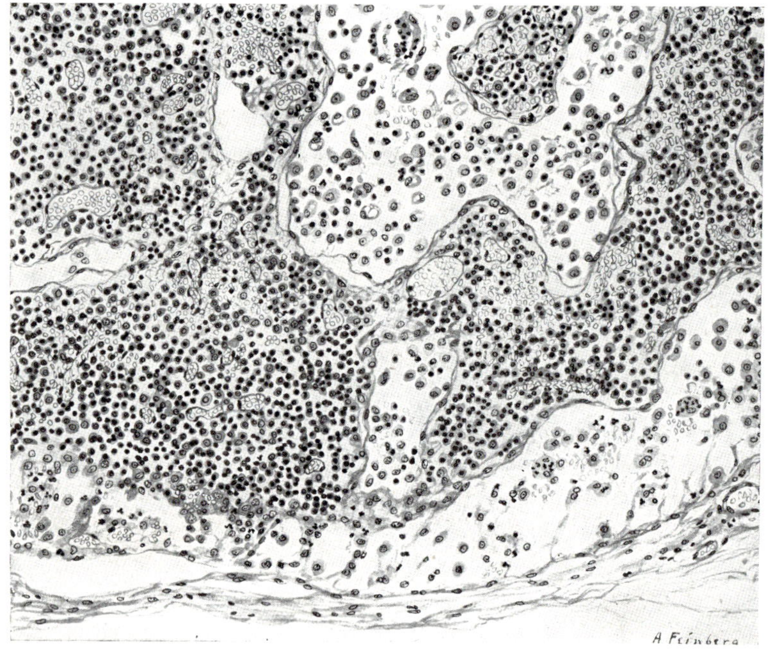

Fig. 63.—Lymph-gland showing phagocytic wandering cells in the lymph-sinuses.

harbor wandering cells in considerable numbers and many forms. It is true that, except in the mucosa of the intestine, these cells are normally very inconspicuous, but they appear in great numbers when there is any stimulus to attract them.

Ranvier described the so-called *clasmatocytes*, or cells which could break off and discharge parts of their protoplasm, as occurring in the tissues, but it is to Marchand especially that we owe the recognition of the normal existence in the crevices of the tissues of mononuclear cells which have wandered out of the vessels and become sessile in their outer walls or in the neighborhood. To these he has given the name *adventitial cells*. They are quite amœboid, and respond to chemiotactic influences, showing great phagocytic activity. They hurry through the tissues in great numbers to the seat of injury when certain sorts of inflammatory processes are set up, and it is through their multiplication that a part at least of the accumulation of cells often spoken of loosely as round-cell infiltration arises.

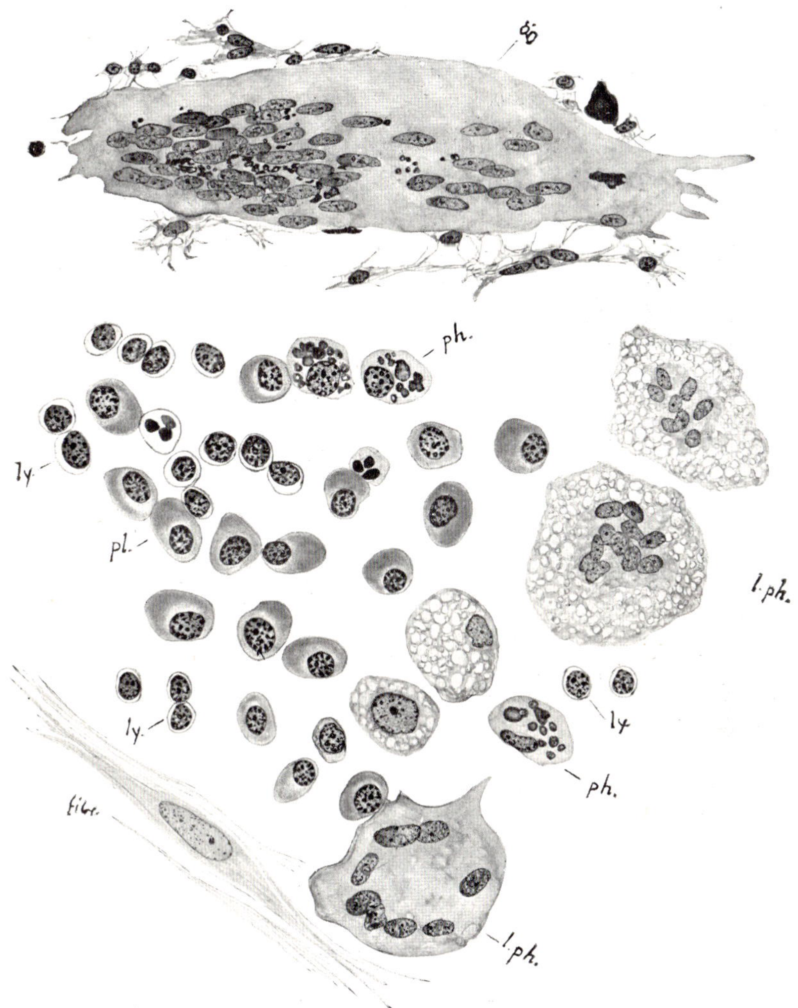

Fig. 64.—Group of polyblastic or wandering cells of various types: *ly.*, Lymphocytes; *pl.*, plasma cells; *ph.*, phagocytic cells of large size, some containing blood-pigment, others, *l.ph.*, containing much fat; *g.*, foreign-body giant-cell formed about granules and crystals of bismuth; *fibr.*, connective-tissue cell.

Such gatherings of cells have for years occasioned discussion, and this is one of the sources of origin which Marchand emphasizes and defends. The others will be referred to.

Besides the adventitial cells, there are others in the tissues which are similar in their general form, but distinguished by their staining properties and by their behavior. These are the *mast cells*, which are found most abundantly in the walls of the bronchi and intestine and about the blood-vessels. Whereas the adventitial cells show a few metachromatic granules staining red with azur dyes, the mast cells are full of large basophilic granules, which stain purple with dahlia and also red with azur or polychrome methylene-blue.

The recent papers of Maximow dealing with inflammation, abscess formation, the participation of mononuclear cells, and the formation of scar tissue throw much light upon the subject. By the use of porous foreign bodies embedded in the tissues he showed that lymphocytes which had wandered out from the blood-vessels appeared, as it were, in pure culture in the spaces of the foreign body, and subsequently grew and developed until, in their various stages, they became identical with all the forms of large mononuclear wandering cells with abundant protoplasm and phagocytic activity (Fig. 64). Fusion of several such cells produces giant, syncytium-like cells with many nuclei which are particularly able to engulf foreign bodies and are known as foreign-body giant-cells. (This was confirmed by Lambert, who cultivated lymphoid cells *in vitro* with lycopodium grains as foreign bodies (Fig. 65).) This whole group of wandering cells, derived by gradual metamorphosis in the new environment from lymphocytes which had emigrated from the blood-vessels, he designates as polyblasts, suggesting thereby the variety of forms which they may assume. He thinks it conceivable, though not probable and not proven, that they may become fixed tissue-cells. At most he will say that they become imprisoned between the fibres of connective tissue, and are then hardly distinguishable from those cells. Although he tends to regard them as the product of emigrated cells, he derives them equally readily from the wandering cells of the tissue which may have emigrated a long time before and lain latent in the tissues for that time. Nor is it doubtful that they reënter the blood-vessels at times. There is thus no real inconsistency between this view and that of Marchand.

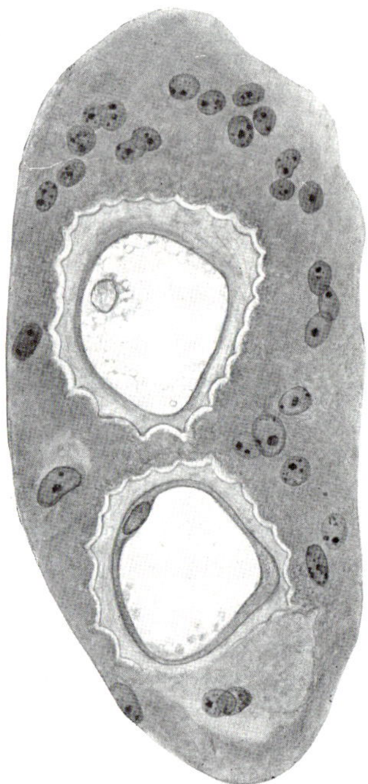

Fig. 65.—Foreign-body giant-cell in tissue culture, enclosing two lycopodium spores.

We find thus three sources mentioned for the variegated crowd of mononuclear wandering cells that swarm about areas where inflammation has existed for a time. (1) The reticulum cells and the endothelial cells of the sinuses in lymph-glands, the lymph-nodes of the intestine, and in the spleen. (2) Cells which are normally found in the adventitial tissues of vessels and scattered elsewhere in the crevices of the tissue, and (3) lymphocytes which emigrate from the blood-vessels and in the tissues develop into amœboid forms, quite like those already there. Other possibilities doubtless exist, as, for example, in the case of the very similar fat-granule cells found in softened areas of the brain which Fr. Marchand describes as originating from the neuroglia cells. In all cases, however, they have finally the same general characters, and although these different origins are quite possible, it seems unfortunate that so much stress should be laid upon this point—for Mallory almost every phagocytic cell is an endothelial cell—for Maximow they are all overgrown lymphocytes. To me it seems that while the endothelial cells in spleen, liver, and lymph-glands have undoubtedly phagocytic activity, the origin of wandering cells from them is least well proved. Further, it is perfectly obvious that myriads of mobile wandering cells do exist normally in the tissue, and that the lymphocytes do actually emigrate from the vessels, and, according to Maximow's careful observations, change their form in the new environment. These two sources, which are in the end identical, seem, therefore, perfectly sufficient to explain every accumulation of mononuclear wandering cells, and on this basis we shall speak of them by that name only.

Among them there occurs one peculiar form which is obviously derived from the lymphocyte through a modification of its nucleus and protoplasm. This is the so-called *plasma cell* described by Unna, which occurs normally in the intestinal mucosa and elsewhere and appears in great numbers in many forms of long-standing subacute inflammatory reactions (Fig. 64). Tuberculous granulation tissue and gonorrheal salpingitis afford examples of such conditions. The cells are rather larger than lymphocytes—somewhat amœboid, but in fixed preparations they usually assume a rounded or oval form, with the nucleus excentrically placed, generally at one end of the cell. The nucleus, whose chromatin is in coarse masses, is surrounded by a pale halo, while the remaining protoplasm takes a bluish stain with ordinary nuclear dyes. Such cells, which may be regarded as a type slightly differentiated from the rest of the tribe of mononuclear wandering cells, are conspicuous because they are so constant in their form. They are not commonly phagocytic, but probably active in producing a digestive ferment.

Goldmann has studied all the wandering cells of the tissue with reference to their behavior toward certain dyes, such as pyrrhol-blue, isamin-blue, etc., which can be injected into the living animal and are taken up with sharp selectiveness by certain cells only. Kupffer's stellate cells of the endothelium of the liver capillaries stain brilliantly in this way, and so do the interstitial cells of the testes. Some of the epithelial cells of the renal tubule store up the stain in granular form in just the same way, while allowing the passage into the urine of other portions of it. In the connective tissues by no means all the wandering cells are stained, but only certain mononuclear cells, which are thus distinguished by him as pyrrhol-cells from lymphocytes, mast cells, etc. What special functional activity of these cells confers this peculiar power upon them is not clear.

The mere fact that these cells take up in their nuclei or protoplasm or in their granules certain stains in a specific way does not, after all, afford us much information as to their true character. It would be more important to determine something as to their function. Metchnikoff, in his studies of inflammation and immunity, has been at great pains to show the analogy between the activities of the wandering cells of the body and those of amœbæ or other amœboid simple protoplasmic organisms. These latter swallow up bacteria and other substances, and by the aid of ferments or cytases digest them. These ferments, he says, are also present in the wandering cells of the body, and differ according to the type of cell, the small neutrophile leucocyte possessing a so-called microcytase, while the mononuclear cells or macrophages, which eschew bacteria, except such as the tubercle and leprosy bacilli, and digest with avidity cell débris, carry out their digestive processes by the aid of another ferment which he calls macrocytase. Therefore the plasma of the blood is scarcely bactericidal as compared with blood-serum, in which digestive ferments are found, owing to the disintegration of leucocytes in the process of clotting. He does not distinguish sharply between such ferments and the complement or alexine of the serum, but does sharply separate the "fixateurs" or "amboceptors" which are produced, he thinks, by the phagocytes, but set free into the plasma as specifically adapted substances capable of preparing the bacteria, etc., which stirred up their production, for solution by the complement. In any case he regards the phagocytes as the great source of these ferments.

Many writers have recognized the power of certain tissues to digest themselves *in vitro* (autolysis), and have observed that the neutrophile leucocytes produce a strong proteolytic ferment capable of digesting fibrin, gelatin, etc. Most of them, however, according to Wiens, have denied the production of a ferment by lymphoid cells. Opie has cleared the matter up very well by finding that the ferments of different cells require for their activity different reactions. He states that the polymorphonuclear neutrophile leucocytes and their ancestral granulated cells produce a trypsin-like ferment which acts best in an alkaline or neutral medium to digest proteins. Its action is often combated by an anti-enzyme, which is present in the plasma of the blood and in other body fluids. It is resistant to heat up to 70° or 75° C., and is therefore quite different from the complement of the serum, which is destroyed at 55° C. When formed in great concentration in a focal area of inflammation, the enzyme far outstrips the neutralizing anti-enzyme, and brings about the liquefaction of dead tissue, as in the case of an abscess. When in the presence of a great exudation of fluid, as in the pleural cavity, its action may be held in check. This proteolytic ferment Opie calls leucoprotease. Contrary to the results of other workers, he finds that, if the correctly feeble acid reaction be offered, the mononuclear cells also show the formation of a proteolytic ferment which is more like pepsin in its character, although it is unable to act in so strong an acid as is favorable to pepsin. This ferment, which he calls lymphoprotease, is produced in the lymph-glands and in all accumulations of lymphoid cells, and of the various types of larger wandering mononuclear phagocytic cells which go to form Metchnikoff's group of macrophages.

While these ferments are evidently used inside the cell in the case of the particles which have been ingested, it seems certain that, in the formation of pus, as in the abscess, they are diffused from the bodies of the disintegrating leucocytes, and in the free fluid effect the solution of the adjacent injured and dead tissue. This function of the wandering cells is, of course, of immediate importance in connection with their task of cleaning up the injured area to prepare it for repair. While the proteases thus produced are active in the solution of undesirable material, their unbridled action might be detrimental. As a matter of fact, it is shown by Jobling and Petersen that the anti-ferment known to be present in the serum and to restrict the action of the ferment is a recognizable chemical substance, usually a soap or other combination of an unsaturated fatty acid. It is possible to remove or decompose this substance or to saturate the fatty acid with iodine and thus release the ferment to its full activity. The presence of excess of such soaps in the tubercle bacilli seems to be the cause of the delay of liquefaction of tissue brought to necrosis by those bacilli. It is seen from this that we are at the beginning of our knowledge of the activities of the wandering cells. What other ferments they produce has been as yet only imperfectly studied, although we have evidence that others, such as oxydases, are produced by some of them, and there are surely more.

Pain in Inflammation.—Doubtless the cause of pain in inflamed tissues is different in various parts of the body, for in certain confined places it is not hard to imagine that the accumulation of exudate stretching sensitive tissues would cause suffering, which might be relieved, as is so often the case, by an incision which allows the exudate to escape. Still it has been objected that pressure and tension on the nerve-endings are not sufficient to cause pain, since local anæsthesia can generally be produced by injecting some indifferent solution into the tissues until they are distended. Therefore it has been thought that the poisons which caused the inflammation also irritate the nerve-endings. Possibly this is so, but an inflamed area following a burn is as painful as one resulting from bacterial infection, and in sunburn no pain is felt during the injury, but only when the inflammation is at its height. Possibly the hyperæmia itself renders the sensory nerves hyperexcitable, as seems to be true in the case of non-inflammatory hyperæmias.

LITERATURE

The student should particularly consult the papers of Maximow with regard to the cells concerned in inflammation and the repair of tissue, as follows:

Maximow: Ziegler's Beiträge, Suppl. 5, 1902; 1905, xxxviii; 1907, xli. Arch. f. mikr. Anat., 1906, lxvii; 1909, lxxiii; 1910, lxxvi.
Adami: Inflammation, Macmillan, 1909.
Jobling and Petersen: Jour. Exp. Med., 1914, xix, 239, etc.
Klemensiewicz: Die Entzündung, Jena, 1908; Festschr. Univ. Graz.
Lambert: Jour. Exp. Med., 1912, xv, 510.
Marchand: Verh. Deutsch. path. Gesellsch., 1914, xvi, 5. (Lymphocytes.)
Metchnikoff: Lectures on the Comparative Pathology of Inflammation, 1893.
Opie: Harvey Lectures, 1910, 192.
Samuel: Ergeb. d. allg. Path., 1895, i_2, 64.
Schridde: Entzündungslehre, Jena, 1910.
Weidenreich: Arch. f. mikr. Anat., 1909, lxxiii, 793. (Literature.)
Wiens: Ergeb. d. allg. Path., 1911, xv_1, 1.
Ziegler: Ziegler's Beitr., xii, 152. (Historical and critical.)

CHAPTER X

DEFENCES OF THE BODY (Continued)

Fever. *General nature of the reaction. Its chemical characters and relation to immunity.* **Immunity.** *Nature of injurious agents. Types of resistance. Artificial immunity. Phagocytosis. Lysins, agglutinins, antitoxins, etc.*

FEVER

General Nature of the Reaction.—It is common knowledge that fever is likely to accompany inflammation, and, as in the case of inflammation, the efforts of physicians and healers of all sorts have been directed toward cutting it short on the idea that it in itself is the harmful process. Only in the last decade has it become vaguely appreciated that there is real evidence that fever, on the contrary, is a reaction elaborated to a considerable degree of perfection, which aids in the defence of the body against the advance of an injurious agent by facilitating the production of the substances which are formed in the body to neutralize poisons or kill bacteria.

From this point of view it would seem, to say the least, short sighted to give a patient in fever an antipyretic drug which will cut short the febrile reaction.

Fever is a reaction which seems to be carried out under the control of the nervous system, and especially of the vasomotor mechanisms which have to do with heat regulation, the most striking feature of which is the elevation of the temperature of the body above the normal. This is not the result of an excessive heat-production, although there is a moderate increase in the production of heat, but rather of the retention of an undue proportion of the heat produced. In the course of fever the body gives off more heat than it normally would at rest, but not nearly so much as it would during active exercise. Indeed, the heat-production during exercise may be increased 200 or 300 per cent., but such is the accuracy of adjustment of heat loss to this increase that the temperature of the body remains normal. During fever, on the other hand, the production of heat is increased only 20 or 40 per cent., but the dissipation of heat is not proportional, and therefore the temperature rises. Heat is given off, but, as Liebermeister has said, the regulating mechanism is altered to react for a different standard of body temperature. It is tuned up to a higher pitch, so that it begins to allow of the escape of heat only at a higher level, just as we might screw up the thermoregulator of a thermostat so that its temperature would stand at 40° instead of 35°.

The regulating mechanism is found in the vasomotor apparatus of the vessels of the skin, in the secretory activities of the sweat-glands, in the respiration (especially in the dog, which cools itself by panting), in shivering, and partly, in human beings, in conscious changes in the clothing. A striking instance of the coördinated working of all these arrangements is seen in a chill, which is so frequent an accompaniment of toxic or bacterial injuries with inflammation. The superficial vessels of the skin are contracted so that little blood is carried to that radiating surface. The skin is pale or livid. The sweat-glands stop secreting, so that the cooling effect of evaporation of the sweat is held in abeyance; the smooth muscles in the skin contract and pull it into gooseflesh; the person feels cold, cowers together, covers himself heavily with blankets, and shivers violently, thus turning stored-up energy into heat. Every available mechanism is brought into play to stop the dissipation of heat and to warm up the body, and in spite of the sensation of cold, the temperature of the interior is at its highest during the chill!

Later, when chemical processes are under way to produce the moderate excess of heat which is observed in fever, these contractions of the cutaneous vessels, etc., are no longer kept up, and the skin may be flushed and even moist, but still the balance is so adjusted that a little less heat is dissipated than is produced—enough, at least, to keep the temperature above the normal.

Chemical Characters of Fever.—Naturally, since fever is a process concerned with heat-production, the most painstaking efforts have been made to ascertain its nature by the study of the changes in metabolism during febrile diseases, but so varied and complex are the conditions that it can hardly be said that the results have brought out any very definite and characteristic changes peculiar to fever as such, and independent of the direct effect of the underlying cause. It is generally agreed that oxidation is increased over that found in the normal individual at rest, but it is not so certain that it is qualitatively altered. From a study of the excretion of nitrogen, together with a comparison of the amounts of carbon dioxide and oxygen in the expired air, it has been thought that the increased oxidation affects especially the nitrogenous or protein constituents of the body, and indeed not so much the labile or circulating proteins as those which actually form part of the living tissue. It is known that the store of carbohydrate is rapidly depleted, but it was thought until recently that the other ordinary fuel used in the production of heat energy—the fat—was relatively little encroached upon. Now May, Grafe, Coleman and Shaffer, and others state that in fever, too, the fats form a particularly important source of heat, and that if sufficient carbohydrate and fat be supplied to the febrile patient the waste of body proteins may be prevented. Indeed, Grafe thinks that this attack on the living tissues which was traditionally emphasized as the most typical feature of febrile metabolism, is due altogether to inanition, and that qualitatively the febrile metabolism need not differ greatly from the normal.

In many fevers, especially in pneumonia, there is a curious retention of sodium chloride, which is then excreted in great amounts after the fever is over. Water may be retained in the same way. The metabolism of other inorganic substances may suffer alteration in this way or that as well, but, on the whole, it is difficult, if not impossible, to put one's finger on any of these changes and say that this is characteristic of the metabolism of fever.

In all these studies little attention has been devoted to the anatomical changes in the disease, so that it is not surprising that there are discordant results. If there is extensive destruction of tissue produced by the poisons of bacteria, or if great quantities of leucocytes appear in the tissues and are broken down, digested, and absorbed, as in pneumonia, there must be changes in the nitrogen output. It is difficult, too, to estimate what part of the increased oxidation is due to the heightened temperature itself, quite aside from any other cause, for it has been shown that artificial overheating produces an increased oxidation.

But aside from the mere existence of dead tissue which can be used as fuel and appear in the excreta, and the later result that heightened temperature facilitates further burning, there must be some original cause for the intensification of the oxidation process, even if it prove that it is not qualitatively but only quantitatively altered.

Relation to Immunity.—So closely has attention been concentrated on the questions of disturbances in metabolism that the biological significance of fever has been somewhat neglected, but recently Rolly and Meltzer, Loewy and Richter, Fukuhara, and others have published results which show it in a clearer light. They found that if animals were artificially kept at a high temperature in a thermostat room, they were able to develop a much more effective defence against intoxication and infection than those left outside at ordinary temperatures. Briefly, Rolly and Meltzer showed that the high temperature itself had probably no injurious influence on the growth of bacteria in the body. Further, that if a fatal dose of bacteria or of a toxin be given, no special difference could be observed between heated and unheated animals. But this sort of infection, by the sudden introduction of enormous quantities of bacteria or of a toxin hardly occurs in nature. Instead, a few bacteria get into the tissues and then gradually increase in number, or in their growth produce an increasing amount of toxin, so that time is given for the appearance of a defensive reaction. If, now, the experiment be arranged in the same way, small doses of bacteria or toxin being injected at intervals, the heated animals showed a great advantage over the controls. They lived longer, and many of them survived doses which inevitably killed the control animals.

When they studied the details of these experiments more carefully, they found that it was not that the high temperature merely prevented the growth of bacteria—it might do so in test-tubes, but in the body the bacteria grow well enough at febrile temperatures. Phagocytosis proved difficult to compare in the two sets of animals, but *in vitro* they found that it was increased by temperatures ranging even up to 41° C., so that probably the conditions for its development are improved by high temperatures in animals. When they studied the formation of specific antibodies, however, they found a great difference. Antitoxins they did not investigate, but agglutinins and bacteriolytic substances were produced far more quickly and in much greater amounts than in the control animals.

New as these results are, they seem to open the way to a more fruitful study of fever and to confirm the somewhat vaguely expressed idea that it is in a way analogous to the vascular reaction in inflammation in that it is the process which facilitates the more essential activities of the phagocytes and the production of defensive chemical substances in the body.

LITERATURE

Loewy and Richter: Virch. Arch., 1896, cxlv, 49.
MacCallum: Archives of Internal Medicine, 1908–9, ii, 569.
Richter: Oppenheimer's Handb. d. Biochemie, 1910, iv_2, 104.
Rolly and Meltzer: Dtsch. Arch. f. klin. Med., 1908, xciv, 335.
Vaughan: Proc. Assoc. Amer. Phys., 1911, xxvi, 191.

IMMUNITY

Nature of Injurious Agents.—The body may be regarded as a kind of tube with thick walls, into which there extend cavities open to the exterior. These cavities, as well as the lumen of the digestive tract, with all its diverticula, are outside the body, and poisonous fluids or bacteria can exert their influence only when they pass through the lining membranes into the real interior. An injury to the lining membrane, often produced by the bacteria themselves, exposes the interior of the body, just as in the case of an abrasion of the skin, to invasion, but many poisons can be absorbed without such cell destruction.

These surfaces then constitute the *portals of entry* of all the injurious agencies from the outer world, whether in the form of inanimate poisons or live creatures which can live and multiply in the interior of the body, to its detriment. Sometimes entry is immediate, but it is well known that the outer and lining surfaces of the body may and do swarm with living creatures, many of which are permanently innocent, while others are only waiting an opportunity when the guard is weakened to force their way through the walls and attack the vital organs inside.

Externally the impermeability of the skin acts as a defence, while in the case of the lining membranes, fluid secretions tend to wash away noxious materials or annul their effects, in which they are often aided by phagocytic cells. So in the conjunctiva bacteria are quickly washed down into the tear-duct; in the upper respiratory tract ciliated cells wave back every kind of particle, and from all the adenoid apparatus leucocytes are ready to emerge on alarm. In the biliary ducts, as in the genito-urinary organs, bacteria are kept in check by the stream of fluids, often aided by valvular arrangements to close the channels, which wash away the bacteria and disinfect the lining surfaces. Nevertheless, all these defences are often overcome. Through the skin the attack may be successful not only by way of ordinary wounds, but by the aid of biting insects and other animals, or even in the case of some worm larvæ by their own penetrating force. Through the mucosæ entrance is forced by the destructive action of the organisms themselves, though this is often aided by mechanical factors which protract their contact with these tissues or by the failure of the phagocyte guard from the interior. Thus the upper intestine or the bladder, which normally keep themselves practically free of bacteria, quickly become perfect hotbeds for their growth if an obstruction prevents the escape of the intestinal contents or the urine.

Aside from mechanical or physical injury, then, the body suffers from the effects of destructive chemical substances which may be wholly derived from the inorganic or inanimate world, or may be produced in some way by living beings. Indeed, the greatest danger comes from the latter when, as is so often the case, these living beings establish themselves in the body or on its surface and manufacture their poisons on the spot.

A word should be said here about the rather obscure question of their interfering with the well-being of their host by the mere abstraction of the materials necessary for its nutrition and metabolism. Possibly this may occur in the case of some of the larger parasites: they may drain away the blood or, as in the case of malaria, eat out the blood-cells, but probably even in the most obvious of such cases the greatest harm is done by the poisons which these creatures produce. On the other hand, Dibbelt has lately maintained that in the fulminant bacterial infections which kill in a few hours death is not due to the formation of poisons, but rather to the wholesale withdrawal of oxygen from the tissues. Such a result might be comparable to that in cyanide poisoning, in which metabolism is brought to a standstill by the stoppage of oxidation processes.

Of all the living parasites which thus insinuate themselves into the body, only a few, such as the diphtheria and tetanus bacilli, produce a soluble, diffusible poison or toxin which, by itself circulating through the organs, can cause the symptoms of the disease. Such bacteria can, therefore, live and grow, even in a very small spot in the tissues, and yet diffuse enough poison to kill the animal. Practically all the rest, whether animal or vegetable, fail to do this, although they cause the most intense and frequently fatal diseases. The fluids of animals dying of these diseases will not cause the disease in other animals if the parasites are filtered out, and the fluids in which they have grown are found not to contain any appreciable amount of poison. Still, if their bodies are ground up, a poisonous material or *endotoxin* may often be found mixed with their body proteins in the extract made from the débris. How they produce the disease is, therefore, very difficult to learn, and generally we are content with the idea that they become harmful only when they die and are broken up in the tissues, liberating their endotoxin. That their body proteins under the influence of the ferments of the host may act as poisons, too, begins to seem probable, and will be referred to again.

It should be observed that the harmful effects of one invader are often greatly intensified when it is accompanied by another, and, indeed, some bacteria and even protozoan parasites seem hardly able to cause an infection without the help of others. Such *mixed infections* are very common, and may be simultaneous, or one may thrive in the soil prepared by the other.

Types of Resistance.—Poisons very similar to those produced by bacterial and animal parasites are secreted by venomous animals and plants, or may be extracted from them. Indeed, it is quite difficult to draw any sharp line of demarcation in the long series of poisons beginning with the simple inorganic substances, and passing by way of the complex synthetic compounds to the highly intricate combinations, of whose nature we are generally ignorant, which we find in the toxins and toxalbumins and other protein substances which play such an important rôle in disease. In general, however, it is found, through the biological test, that it is only toward the complex, protein-like poisons that the body can elaborate special defensive substances. Even though the others may finally be tolerated, it is through some other mechanism. Thus it is well known that through long habit animals or human beings may become able to swallow doses of such poisons as arsenic, morphine, etc., which would be far more than enough to kill an ordinary being, but our ideas as to how this tolerance is produced are very vague. Certainly no substance is produced in the body which will neutralize the poison, and it seems that it must be due to some change in the metabolism of the cells themselves.

There is, even without any such gradual case hardening, a natural insusceptibility on the part of some animals to injury from certain poisons; thus an almost unlimited quantity of the most intensely active tetanus toxin, a milligram of which would kill thousands of mice, can be injected into a scorpion or an alligator without producing the slightest malaise, and a long time later it may be found still lodged in the tissues. Certain animals are equally resistant to invasion by bacteria which can produce the most deadly disease in others, apparently because their defensive phagocytes are so active that long before the bacteria can gain a proper foothold they are all seized upon and devoured. Whether this is an inherited character, resulting from the survival of those thus fitted to resist infection, it is difficult to say. The immunity is not absolute, however, for influences, like exposure to cold or heat, great fatigue, or other illnesses. may so break down the resistance that, after all, the animal succumbs to infection. Race immunity is doubtless an example of this kind, and race susceptibility illustrates its opposite—the South Sea islanders succumbed in thousands to measles because their ancestors had never had to contend with it. On the other hand, children in our countries sicken with such so-called children's diseases because they alone have not acquired immunity by having had the disease themselves.

In all the ills produced by living invaders there exists a struggle for supremacy—even for existence—between the host and the parasite, in which the stronger prevails and in which defences are developed not only by the host, but by the invader as well. It is doubtless through this that the bacteria accustom themselves in passing from the body of one animal to another to the action of the defensive reactions of the host, and become thereby more virulent. This is made evident in some cases by the formation, under these circumstances, of capsules which are formed in the bacillus of anthrax, the pneumococcus, etc., as they grow in the animal body but not in cultures. The capsulated forms become less susceptible to phagocytosis and it is even stated that infection can occur only when capsules are formed. In addition to this protective covering such bacteria are thought to become more formidable through the production of more active poisons which injure the phagocytes ("leucocidins," "aggressins"). Danysz found that bacteria in culture may be accustomed gradually to the presence of arsenic, so that they finally grow in relatively strong solutions and in the course of this adaptation acquire a capsule. Indeed, it is clearly shown that certain protozoa, the trypanosomes, may, like the Styrian arsenic-eaters, become so used to arsenic that they live on unhurt in the body through a continued bombardment with the new synthetic arsenic compounds, if only they have managed to survive the first doses.

We know so little about the defences of the parasite, however, that at present we must exemplify the principles by reference to those of the host. We realize that, normally, animals have well-developed powers of defence, although these are efficient in such different degrees in different animals that we must surmise that they are not conferred in their full perfection on all at their creation, but have been gradually acquired through the survival of those best provided, who in turn bequeathed them to their offspring. These defences may guard against simple poisoning or against the inroads of living parasites, and we shall see that they do not lack in variety to correspond with these different forms of injury. Already we have found that certain general mechanisms, inflammation, and fever have been developed alike in all animals, but we have been forced in both instances to recognize the fact that these reactions are mere auxiliary mechanisms designed to bring into play to the greatest advantage, and in the most opportune concentration during sudden emergencies, other more profound and more subtle processes, phagocytosis, and the chemical neutralization of poisons which we admit as the essential agents of defence.

For a time there were those who maintained that the activity of the phagocytes constituted practically the whole defensive armament, while others, enthusiastic over their new discoveries, were just as sure that the neutralizing substances in the body fluids were all-important. But now a reconciliation of these cellular and humoral doctrines has been effected, because it has been shown that they are very largely interdependent, phagocytosis depending upon the presence of auxiliary substances in the plasma, while in turn the leucocytes are important in producing other defensive fluid substances.

Artificial Immunity.—From time immemorial it has been known that a person who has had smallpox, or typhoid fever, or yellow fever, or any one of a host of diseases can hardly have another attack of the same disease: he is immune. On the other hand, there are certain diseases, such as pneumonia, diphtheria, erysipelas, furunculosis, etc., which seem to predispose to a repetition. While we are yet far from clear as to the reasons for this latter fact, we have learned a great deal about the security conferred by the immunizing sort of diseases. It is not necessary that the illness should be severe to give this lasting protection, and, recognizing this, it was the habit, many years ago, to court mild attacks of such a deadly disease as smallpox in order to be safe in the midst of an epidemic where the disease was severe. This was the beginning of man's intentional use of artificial methods of providing immunity, a plan which, under the influence of the phenomenally intelligent studies of such men as Pasteur, Ehrlich, and von Behring, has extended until it promises now to become the very most important practical achievement of medicine. It has proved possible to devise methods by which security from parasitic disease can be attained without risking any serious preparatory illness, and to intensify the strength of this defence until it is almost absolutely unassailable. Further, instead of thus producing an active immunity by making the person go through an imitation of the disease himself, it is sometimes possible to cause an animal to go through the disease and then transfer the fluids of its blood to the body of the person, and with it the immunity, so that a *passive* immunity is conferred which may even stop the disease already in progress.

Several methods are thus in common use: (1) The parasites in full virulence, but in very minute doses, are administered so that the person finally overcomes and recovers from a mild attack of the real disease; (2) the same thing is accomplished by a larger dose of weakened, attenuated, or non-virulent parasites; (3) dead bacteria are used in place of the living, and produce a feebler but similar immunity; (4) the isolated poisons of the parasites are injected in gradually increasing doses so that the power is developed to neutralize the poisons or (5) from such an animal this neutralizing power is transferred to another which thus, without effort, becomes immune.

Space will not allow more than the merest outline of these processes. Details may be read with the help of the general references given to the literature, which is colossal.

Phagocytosis.—As has been stated above, bacteria and other parasites are in normal animals taken up and digested by the phagocytes, but the help of the serum of the animal is most important—without it the leucocytes engulf very few bacteria. Denys, Wright, and others have shown that the serum contains *opsonins*, which act on the bacteria and prepare them to be attacked by the leucocytes. Neufeld found that in the serum of animals immunized by repeated introduction of those bacteria, somewhat more resistant bodies (*bacteriotropins*) appear, which exercise the same function in making the bacteria more approachable for the leucocytes. It appears that cytotropins, or substances which prepare foreign cells for phagocytosis, may be produced in the same way by injecting such cells. Aided by these substances, which bind themselves to the bacteria or foreign cells, but do not affect the phagocyte itself, the wandering cells exhibit a great phagocytic activity. Although the swallowing-up of a bacterium does not necessarily kill it, it commonly does so, and at any rate removes it for the time from the field of action.

Cytolytic and Bacteriolytic Reactions.—The introduction of foreign cells has other results than those just described. The serum of an animal which has received repeated doses of a certain foreign cell acquires the property of disintegrating and dissolving those cells. This reaction is highly specific, so that if red corpuscles of a dog be introduced into a rabbit there appears a *hœmolytic* serum which will destroy only red corpuscles and only those of the dog. Similarly, with inoculations of liver-cells, kidney cells, endothelial cells, etc., more or less specific *hepatolytic*, nephrolytic, or endotheliolytic sera have been produced. Other cells, such as those of animal parasites or bacteria, are responded to in the same way, and an intense trypanolytic or trypanocidal serum can be produced by injecting the bodies of trypanosomes, just as *bacteriolytic* (consequently bactericidal) sera result from the introduction of the dead bodies of bacteria. The fresh serum alone, quite free from phagocytic cells, has then the power to break up and destroy living bacteria brought into contact with it, whether in the body or in a test-tube. Such bactericidal immunity is not developed in the case of the Gram-positive micrococci. In any case it must be sharply distinguished from the antitoxic immunity which is referred to later.

Agglutination.—Another sort of reaction is often produced at the same time, the effect of which is to cause the special bacteria or cells which caused its production to stick together in clumps if they are brought into contact with the serum in a test-tube—not to so great an extent within the animal body. This is the so-called agglutination, which is so specific in its relations that it can be used for diagnostic purposes. Thus the serum of a person suffering from typhoid fever or one who has had the disease, and of such persons alone, will cause the clumping and immobility of known typhoid bacilli suspended in a culture.

Precipitins.—It is not even necessary to inject cells for the production of these antibodies, for the repeated injection of any foreign protein is responded to in the same way by the formation of a new substance which will specifically and exclusively act upon that protein at the first opportunity. It may, when a new quantity of the protein and the serum are brought together, form a cloudy precipitate, or, and sometimes coincidentally with this effect, it may break down the protein into simpler but still complex substances, some of which are poisonous.

The first of these phenomena is practically useful as a biological test in the recognition of proteins. Thus it may be necessary, for legal purposes, to say whether a blood-stain is composed of human or ox blood. The clear serum of a rabbit which has been treated with human blood-serum will become clouded if a trace of the dissolved blood-stain be added to it in case it really is human blood, but no precipitate will appear if the blood came from an ox. Conversely, the serum of a rabbit treated with ox blood would serve to recognize that blood.

The second phenomenon which is probably intimately related with the precipitin reaction has only recently come into prominence, because of the observation that the sudden introduction of a second dose of a certain protein into an animal already immunized to that protein may kill it. This effect, which is accompanied by certain characteristic symptoms,—vasomotor paralysis, fall in temperature, inefficient heart action, dyspnœa, urticaria, etc.,—is known as an *anaphylactic shock*, and the condition of the animal as *anaphylaxis*. Much ingenious experimentation has been carried out in the attempt to analyze and explain this phenomenon. In general it was thought to be the effect of poisoning by peptone-like bodies or proteoses produced by the partial digestion of the protein of the second dose by the combined action of the specific antibody developed in response to the first dose and the normal alexin or complement of the blood plasma. It seemed that all of this might occur in the circulating blood, since it was sometimes found possible to mix the antibodies and protein or antigen *in vitro* and to produce the characteristic symptoms by the injection of the mixture, and since passive sensitization of a normal animal might be produced by injection of the blood of a sensitized animal, after which injection of the protein would give anaphylactic shock. But partly because it was found to require time after the transfer of the sensitized blood before the injection of the antigen or protein could produce a distinct shock, partly because sensitized animals completely perfused with normal blood were still sensitized, and partly because strips of smooth muscle from sensitized animals were observed to contract on exposure to solutions of the antigen so dilute as to leave unaffected strips of muscle from a normal animal, it has been decided that anaphylactic sensitization is largely an affair of the tissue cells. It seems that the antibody upon which the reaction depends is not altogether free and floating in the circulating blood, but that much of it remains sessile, attached to the cells. It is for this reason that the effect is so intense, since the poison is produced in or on the cells. It is even suggested that possibly the presence of abundant antibody in the blood might protect the cells by combining with the antigen before it reaches them. Such explanations assume that the poison is produced from the antigen or injected protein. As a matter of fact, more nitrogen is excreted as a sequence of the anaphylactic shock than could be accounted for by that much protein, and this with other things has given rise to another explanation. Substances such as kaolin, agar, bacterial bodies, etc., mixed with normal serum produce poisons like those which cause symptoms of anaphylactic shock. In the animal body the increase in nitrogen excretion shows that a proteolytic ferment must attack the proteins of the serum. While Friedberger thought that the poison produced from bacteria injected into sensitized animals was due to cleavage of the bacterial proteins, Jobling points out that bacteria as well as kaolin or other inert substances can absorb anti-enzymes (unsaturated lipoids, etc.) of the serum and thus release proteolytic ferments which affect cleavage of the proteins of the serum into poisonous proteoses. Whatever the nature of the mechanism by which they are produced, it seems clear that the poisons are the cleavage products of protein. Even if it be true that after the injection of cells, bacteria, or such materials as kaolin, the poisons may be evolved by the action of proteolytic ferments on the proteins of the serum, the evidence in other cases of sensitization in animals, as by foreign serum, seems to support the idea of the participation of a specific antibody and the complement both in the tissue cells and in the blood.

The reaction depending upon this production of poison, when a special protein to which the animal has been spontaneously (through disease) or artificially immunized, is directly or parenterally introduced, is made use of for diagnostic purposes, as, for example, in the tuberculin and luetin tests, in which the proteins of the tubercle bacillus or of the Spirochæta pallida are injected into the skin. Such a small dose, instead of overwhelming the nervous system and producing a fall in temperature, affects it only to the extent of stirring up a febrile reaction.

Antitoxins.—In those cases in which bacteria produce a soluble toxin, as well as in the case of soluble toxins of animal or vegetable origin, the body will respond to the repeated injections of the toxin by the production of a soluble *antitoxin* which circulates freely in the blood and combines with and neutralizes quantitatively a fresh injection of the same toxin. This will happen quite as well in a test-tube or in the body of another animal if the serum of the immunized animal be removed and mixed with the toxin in the test-tube or injected into the body of the other animal. In the latter case the neutralization of toxin already introduced will take place in so far as it is still uncombined. The first animal has acquired an active antitoxic immunity, while a passive antitoxic immunity is conferred on the second one by the injection. This is the basis of the use of the well-known diphtheria antitoxin of von Behring. The commercial preparation is nothing more than the serum of a horse, which, by repeated increasing doses of diphtheria toxin, has been brought into a state of active antitoxic immunity. It is quite specific, and the diphtheria antitoxin is therefore useless against tetanus, or vice versa.

The participation of these various phenomena in natural and acquired immunity is not always perfectly clear. The simplest is perhaps the antitoxic immunity in which the poison is neutralized, as an acid might be neutralized by an alkali, while the bacteria causing the disease are left unharmed. The immunity conferred by one attack of the disease is probably a combination of bacteriotropic and phagocytic activity with bacteriolytic immunity. So, too, the immunity produced by vaccines of dead and attenuated bacteria. Bacteriolytic sera have not been very successfully produced except in the case of a few bacteria, such as cholera, typhoid, etc., but even when they are active they seem unable to cut short the progress of the infection in the animal, possibly because they lack the presence of sufficiently active bacteriotropins. An animal may be able to destroy a quantity of bacteria injected into the peritoneum, but still be unable to withstand infection by way of the intestinal tract. Local application of these sera is, therefore, often desirable and effective in conditions such as meningitis, where the infection itself is essentially a localized one. In all cases the intense specificity of the reaction makes itself felt, so that a bactericidal serum or bacteriotropic substances which might aid in the destruction of one strain of streptococci may fail of all activity in the case of another hardly distinguishable except by such a biological test.

The Side-chain Theory.—To explain all these phenomena, and to further the discovery of others, Ehrlich has constructed a hypothesis known as the side-chain theory, which, although even yet not proved in all its details, is marvelously perfect in its agreement with new facts as they are brought out and in its serviceability in showing the direction in which new facts may be sought. He conceives of the cells of the body as provided with certain molecular arrangements or receptors, by means of which they normally anchor and bind to themselves substances which they require for their metabolism. Such substances are ordinarily useful, but they may be injurious. In that case the cell may be destroyed. If not, those receptors are at least thrown out of function and the cell is to that extent injured by having anchored to itself the toxin. With its natural powers of repair it produces new receptor groups, and since, as Weigert has expressed it, the process of regeneration leads to the production of an excess, the loss is more than made up. These new receptors have the same facility in uniting with toxin groups, and being in excess, they are discharged by the cell into the circulating fluids. There they by themselves anchor toxin molecules and thus prevent them from reaching the susceptible cells. Without such receptors the cell is, of course, insusceptible of being affected by the toxin, and hence perhaps the natural immunity of some animals.

In the case of the opsonins, bacteriolytic substances, and all the cytolytic and antiprotein reactions, the specific antibody is produced in a similar way by the susceptible cells as a result of the influence of the foreign protein or cells (antigens), but in these instances it is found that the specific group, or antibody, thus produced cannot act alone to destroy the foreign cell or protein, but must call to its aid a ferment-like substance normally present in the serum—the so-called *alexin* or *complement.* There are many of these complements, and they do not all unite equally easily with the specific immune bodies. They are easily destroyed by relatively low temperatures or by any other injury, such as drying, the action of chemicals, etc. The fact that the specific immune body requires the aid of the complement has shown that it itself is merely a link specifically able to connect or introduce the non-specific complement into combination with the special cell or protein against which it has been developed. It is for this reason that Ehrlich has named it the amboceptor or linking body, although Bordet and others thought of it as a mere mordant-like material, which sensitized the cell to the attack of the alexin. Amboceptors or immune bodies are resistant to heat, drying, etc., and may be kept in good condition for years. Their characters have been particularly well shown in the experiments of Ehrlich and his school on hæmolysis, and those of Pfeiffer on bacteriolysis. Left in contact with heated immune serum, in which all complement has been destroyed, the foreign cells bind to themselves the amboceptor, but no destruction of the cells occurs. The addition of fresh unheated normal serum which contains the non-specific complement allows hæmolysis or bacteriolysis to take place at once. Bacteriotropins, agglutinins, and precipitins appear to be simpler substances not composed of a specific resistant and a non-specific labile portion. Their action is not altogether clear, although there are many ingenious theories for which the student is referred to the literature.

LITERATURE

Only general reviews which give further literature references are cited.

Aschoff: Ehrlich's Seitenketten-Theorie, Jena, 1902. (Zeits. f. allg. Physiol., 1902, i.)
Besredka: Kraus and Levaditi, Handbuch d. Immunitätsforschung: Anaphylaxie.
Biedl and Kraus: *Ibid.*, 255.
Dold: Bakterien Anaphylatoxin, Jena, 1912.
Ehrlich: Gesammelte Arbeiten, Berlin, 1904.
Friedberger and many others: Kolle u. Wassermann, Handbuch der Bakteriologie.
Metchnikoff, E.: Immunité dans les maladies Infectieuses, Paris, 1901. Lubarsch-Ostertag Ergeb., 1896, i_1, 298.
Moro: Lubarsch-Ostertag Ergeb., 1910, xiv_1, 429.
Sauerbeck: *Ibid.*, 1907, xi_1, 690. (Opsonine, Aggressine.)
Sobernheim: Krehl u. Marchand, Handb. d. allg. Pathol., 1908, i, 417.
Vaughan: Proc. Assoc. Amer. Phys., 1907, xxii, 268. (Split Products of Proteins.)
Wassermann, A.: Volkmann's klin. Vortr., 1902, No. 331 (Chir. No. 94).
Consult especially,
Zinsser: Infection and Immunity, New York, 1914; Arch. Int. Med., 1915, xvi, 223. (Anaphylaxis.)

CHAPTER XI

DEFENCES OF THE BODY (Continued)

New-growth of tissue. General characters. Influence of various agencies on growth. Growth stimuli.

NEW-GROWTH OF TISSUE AND REPAIR

We are very ill informed with regard to the principles which underlie the growth of tissues, and any discussion of them soon leads us to a point beyond which we cannot go without invoking the deceptive aid of such expressions as vital force, inherent vitality, etc. There have been many efforts to explain the manifestations of life on a chemical or physical basis, but while they explain very well what happens, they leave us with little notion of what the real spark is which starts the setting free of energy, whether its result be a functioning of the cell as we see in a muscular contraction or the division of one cell into two.

We do know well enough that new-growth of tissue occurs when tissue is destroyed. Much of this compensatory new formation may take place somewhere quite far away from the point of injury, but at any rate there is a local patching which, when the tissue destroyed is a highly specialized one, is usually carried out by the ubiquitous connective tissue. The patch is, therefore, not likely to be of the same dignity as the original tissue, and serves mainly to reëstablish continuity.

Since injury often excites the inflammatory reaction also, the two may become inextricably entangled, so that there has long been confusion with regard to "inflammatory new-growth." This is especially true when, on account of the persistent repetition of the injury, the inflammatory reaction continues for a long time, and attempts at healing are repeatedly partly frustrated. But the most intense inflammatory reaction may occur with hardly any new-growth of tissue, as in pneumonia, and, on the other hand, regeneration and repair sometimes take place with no visible signs of inflammation. The two processes seem distinct in their causes, in their aims, and in the cells which participate, so that though they occur together they should not be confused. If we reflect upon this, even though we meet with difficult and questionable cases, we must realize that that process which we call inflammation consists essentially in the flooding of the injured tissues, by special mechanisms, with an excess of wandering cells and the fluids of the blood which tend to neutralize the injurious agent and clear away the débris and then to fade away and disappear, having taken part in no new formation of tissue. Repair, on the other hand, is the new formation, from neighboring cells, of a more or less complex, permanent, and coherent tissue which takes the place of that which was lost.

It seems not unreasonable to suppose that the warmth and good blood supply which are so characteristic of inflammation might favor this process of repair, or even that the irritant itself, when it becomes diluted in its extension into the tissue, may act as a stimulant to cell growth. The conception of "inflammatory new-growth" or "productive inflammation" must depend upon this last possibility, and there will arise occasion to discuss it further. For a long time there was doubt as to the rôle of the many kinds of wandering cells which appear in old areas of inflammation, and as long as they were thought to be able to give rise to connective tissue, the influence of inflammation on new growth seemed very great. Now, however, since Maximow and others have shown their rather specialized wandering character, and it is admitted only grudgingly that they have any part in tissue formation, the matter becomes clearer and we have to deal with wandering cells as concerned with inflammation and fixed tissue cells with repair.

Nowhere, however, could there be a more convincing instance of the effect of a chemical stimulant acting to excite a rapid new-growth of tissue than in the case of the sudden phenomenal proliferation of leucocytes in the bone-marrow, and the flooding of the blood with these cells when some bacterial poison is absorbed from an area of inflammation.

We must ask ourselves what are the causes which lead to the growth of tissue in general, and the new-growth of tissue in particular, and we find that, while we have some information concerning those things which influence growth, we are reduced to theories when we attempt to explain the actual causes. Underlying it all we must recognize one essential thing which distinguishes a live cell from a dead one, namely, the ability to absorb and assimilate nutritive substances, building them up into its own protoplasm, and then, by the exercise of a certain amount of energy, to divide its nucleus and protoplasm in such a way as to form two new cells in place of the old one. Given this power, which we cannot explain, we may as well go on to discuss the conditions and influences which guide this growth, and which are directly chemical or physical in their nature.

The materials for growth must be supplied, and are precisely selected by the cell in quantities to suit its metabolic processes. Water, protein, carbohydrate, and fatty substances, inorganic materials, and oxygen are absorbed, and carbon dioxide with various other substances, elaborated or excreted by the cell, are given off. We realize that growth is inhibited by faulty nutrition or by an inadequate blood supply, and that the healing of a wound is slow and imperfect in those whose metabolism is impaired by old age or illness. The idea that increased activity in growth is brought about by an excessively rapid and abundant blood supply has long been held, and there is some evidence in its favor. A rabbit's ear kept flushed with blood by the section of the sympathetic nerves is said to grow more rapidly than the other, and to outstrip it, while conversely it is well known that rapidly growing tissue makes its appearance with an excessive provision for blood supply in the form of numerous wide capillaries which disappear when the tissue becomes mature. Still, the situations in which we may study the effect of an excessive blood supply in comparison with an adequate one are generally complicated, and give us little light on the subject.

When tissue is grown artificially in a hanging drop of blood plasma, all these influences come most clearly to view, and it is quickly apparent that growth stops at once when the supply of nutriment contained in the drop of plasma becomes insufficient. The effect of warmth is most apparent there also, and it can be shown that, whereas at very low temperatures growth does not occur at all, it begins and increases slowly in rate as the temperature is raised until, at a certain point, it finds the optimum conditions. Higher temperatures than this are unfavorable, and growth becomes slower and slower until a point is reached at which it is completely inhibited. In living animals this can be demonstrated to some extent, inasmuch as the ear of a rabbit kept warmer than normal for a long time is said to grow so that it becomes larger than the other ear, which has not been so treated.

In this last instance, as in the case of the influence of the nervous system, it is difficult to decide which of several things may be the real cause of the growth, for in such a rabbit's ear the warmth tends to widen the blood-vessels and thus bring increased supplies of nutrition to the part. Indeed, it is somewhat doubtful whether the nervous system has any direct influence over growth, even though we speak so confidently of trophic nerves. For while an extremity which has been paralyzed fails to grow as the normal one does, this may well be due to its inactivity and the consequent diminution of the blood supply.

Mechanical influences play a considerable part in determining growth, although it is well known that in plants at least a force can be exerted by growing tissues far greater than that which might ordinarily be used to interfere with their growth. Here again there enter the complicating factors of interference with nutrition and light, which are most powerful to disturb growth, for while a tree growing in a crevice can split a rock and roots can lift up pavements, one may apply a relatively slight pressure so as to cut off nutrition and light, and growth will be blocked.

Continuous pressure applied to organs or extremities in the animal body interferes with their growth or causes the cells to atrophy and disappear, as we see in the deformed livers of those who lace tightly and in the misshapen skulls of those Indians who bind the heads of their children. But intermittent pressure, as that of a shoe which pinches, tends rather to cause an excessive callous growth of epidermis. We might multiply examples of the growth of tissue in response to various sorts of mechanical tensions and strains, a growth which forms the basis of the wonderful adaptation to function so generally observed when tissues or organs are subjected to changed conditions. Thus the arching lamellæ of bone which are precisely calculated to meet the strain at the upper end of the femur are, after a time, rearranged to suit the new conditions with equal mechanical perfection when the bone has healed after a fracture.

Probably few persons who survive an extensive injury, and in whom this process of readjustment to new conditions is going on, live long enough to allow it to be quite perfected, but there are frequently found in such persons the most extraordinary adaptations.

It is only in those tissues which have to do with movement and support, however, that the inciting cause of the new-growth of tissue is chiefly mechanical, and it must be remembered that in other organs whose function is not of a mechanical nature other influences are at work to bring about the readjusting new-growth. A good example of the mechanical type is seen in the establishment of a collateral circulation when an important vein or artery has been obstructed. Numbers of channels which were previously insignificant become large, thick-walled vessels and give passage to the pressing stream of blood in a roundabout way, so that it may rejoin the original channel beyond the obstruction. A remarkable instance of this which showed a complete obstruction of the superior vena cava is described by Osler.* A bulky mass of new vascular channels was so formed as to convey the blood from the upper part of the body over a long detour to the heart (Fig. 8).

Obstructions placed before tissues which act mechanically in such a way as to make it difficult for them to carry on their function nearly always cause a growth of the tissue, so that it becomes stronger and forces the barrier. This is seen in the heart and in all those muscular structures, such as the intestine and the bladder, whose duty it is to move their contents by contraction. Above a tumor which obstructs the colon the wall becomes enormously thick and powerful, and so does the wall of the bladder when, through the enlargement of the prostate, urine is evacuated with difficulty.

In the repair that follows a loss of substance these mechanical influences are not quite so plain, but they undoubtedly play a part. New tissue is formed hurriedly and in great quantities to replace that which was lost, and although at first it seems to grow in a somewhat disorderly way, it quickly shows an adaptation to its purpose. All this is probably guided, at least in part, by the influence of the solid materials with which the cells come in contact, for while the young connective-tissue cells and blood-vessels can grow by themselves and form an even swelling tissue, the more usual and natural way for them is to grow upward into a network of fibrin filaments along which they creep and which, in turn, they dissolve and destroy (Fig. 66). Epithelium grows and spreads out on a surface when

* Johns Hopkins Hospital Bulletin, 1903, xiv, 169.

that is offered, but scarcely penetrates into a feltwork of fibrin. These are differences in the "inherent vital characters" of these cells, for when isolated from all connection with the body and growing in the hanging drop of plasma, they show the same peculiarities in their growth; connective-tissue cells sprout out in every direction so long as they may follow the course of a filament of fibrin. Epithelium grows in a sheet, just as it tends to do on the surface of a healing wound (Figs. 67, 68, 69).

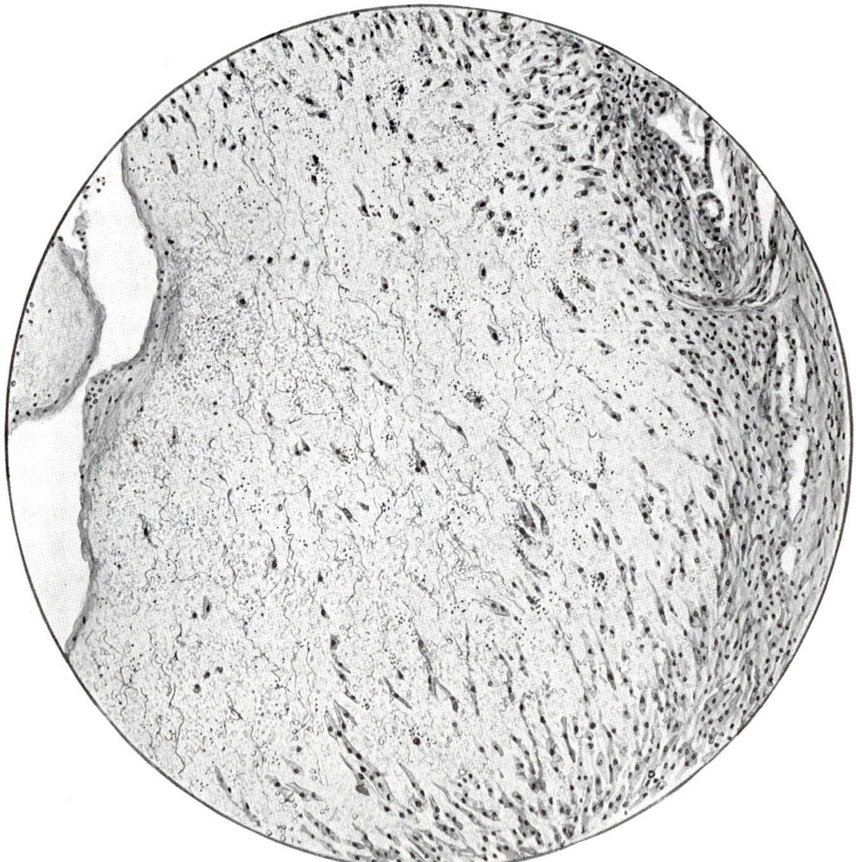

Fig. 66.—Fibroblasts growing into a thrombus.

Even the simplest of these forms of tissue proliferation can hardly be ascribed directly to any mechanical influence, but it is clear that the cells in their growth are guided and directed to some extent in this way. There must be remembered always the underlying tendency of the living cell to assimilate food materials, increase its substance, and divide.

Functional Equilibrium.—Is there then some stimulus from without which accentuates this tendency, or is the tendency merely allowed full play by the withdrawal of some restraining influence? This has been the subject of debate for many years, for while Virchow held that there exist actual growth stimuli which might indeed act through the injury or destruction of certain cells, Weigert declared that cells grew because the mutual resistance of the tissues was set aside, the equilibrium disturbed, and, as John Hunter before him had thought, the cells grew impelled by the loss of the physiological limitations which one tissue element opposes to another. John Hunter had spoken of the stimulus of incompleteness; Weigert regarded the tissue growth which occurs with inflammation not as

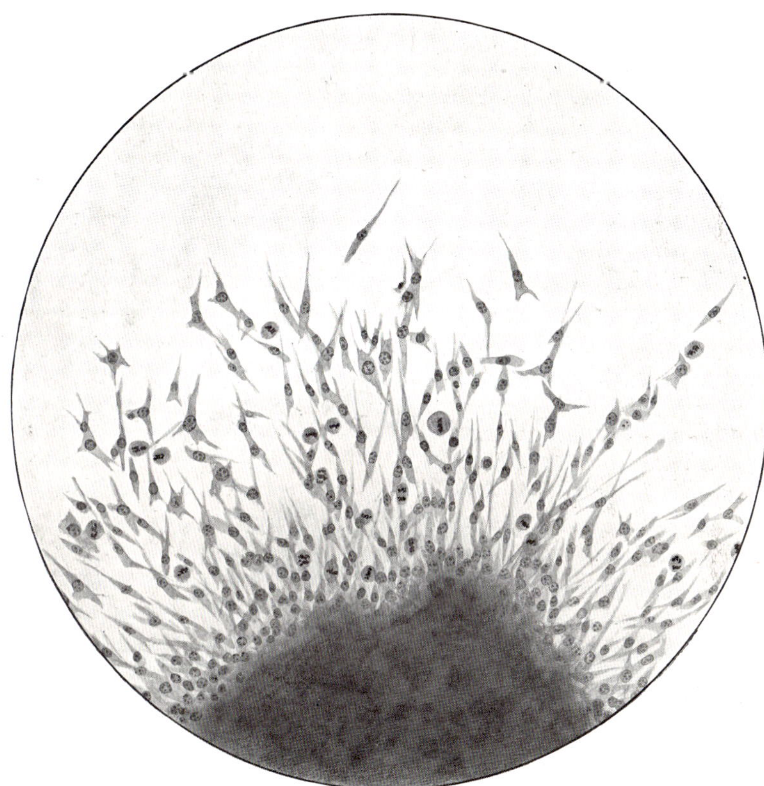

Fig. 67.—Characteristic growth of connective tissue cultivated *in vitro*. There are many mitotic figures.

the result of a stimulus, but only as the consequence of the tissue defect. According to him, it was quite unproved that there is any direct idioplastic stimulus.

The existence of a certain equilibrium among tissues, and the remarkable effects of its disturbance, have long been recognized, but this equilibrium cannot be looked upon as a merely mechanical one. Nor is it to be explained on any simple chemical basis. We are perhaps nearest to the truth if we say that it rests chiefly upon a balance between the functional activities of different tissues. If, in the functioning of a cell, certain material is consumed, the cell makes this up by its assimilative processes. If functional activity is maintained at an extreme, so is the assimilation, and the cell even increases its size and functional power, or, after accumulating an excess of cell material, divides into two cells, so that the function is better maintained (hypertrophy; hyperplasia). But no mechanical or chemical disturbance in the body will give more than a motive for this.

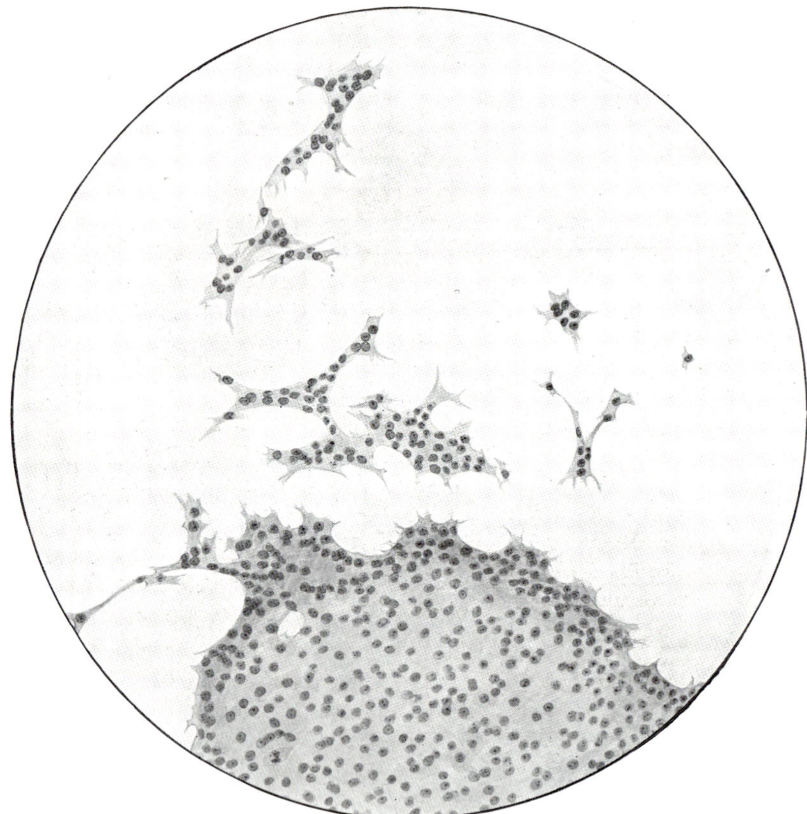

Fig. 68.—Characteristic growth of epithelium in culture.

The process itself depends on that inherited power of growth by which the cell adjusts itself to the new conditions.

When they reach maturity, the bodies of any one kind of animal have, as we know, a characteristic form and a recognized average size, but a good deal of variation from the standard is still compatible with life. Within the body the interrelation of organs seems to be much more precisely calculated, just as the works of a watch must be calculated throughout, although the case may have any form. It seems probable that there may even be an actual numerical relationship between the cells of different organs, so that a disturbance of this balance is felt if cells are destroyed in one. It is known, of course, that each organ is able to put forth in an emergency a vastly greater functional activity, since it has a reserve power which constitutes its margin of safety, but this effort is felt at once and shortly leads to the multiplication of the cells and the increase of the functional power. This is true whether the emergency results from the destruction of some of the cells or the increase in the demand upon the organ.

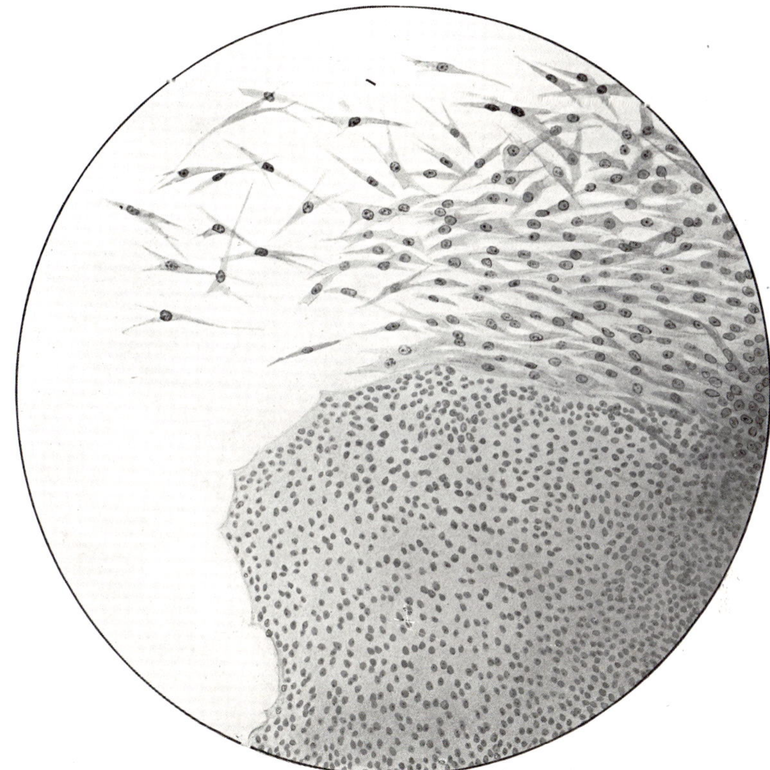

Fig. 69.—Epithelium and connective tissue growing side by side in a culture made from the intestine of an embryo.

This is the functional equilibrium of the tissues which is maintained very precisely by the increase and reduction of the various functional units. But there is also a mechanical equilibrium. The tissues grow in certain arrangements, and the organs assume certain normal forms which are the result of the action of various tensions and strains not always easy to recognize or calculate, and the end-result is the recognized normal body form. It requires a very extensive disarrangement of the tissues to obliterate the trend of these tensions and strains and allow the body to heal into any unusual or inappropriate form. Usually, if time is given, the healing of any moderate injury goes far toward restoring the normal body form and thus the mechanical equilibrium.

When an injury is such as to unbalance for a time this mechanical equilibrium, there occurs a new formation of tissue to replace that which was lost, and in time the original mechanical conditions may be well restored and the body form reinstated, but it would be rash to state that this was carried out solely because the mechanical equilibrium was disturbed or that the cells grew because pressure relations were altered on one side or the other. There is always the other factor to be considered, namely, that the loss of tissue, even when it is merely supporting tissue, involves an unbalancing of the functional equilibrium, so that the growth occurs also to reinstate that. However, even with these two reasons it is difficult to explain the purposeful methodical growth of tissue which so precisely accomplishes the healing of a wound, but in its detail, in which fibrin plays a part, guiding the direction of growth of the new cells so that they stretch across from one side of the wound to the other, a plan is doubtless being carried out which has become a routine after a long process of evolution, and is now merely the common means, regardless of the reason for growth.

That the unbalancing of the mechanical equilibrium can hardly be considered the main reason for the new-growth of tissue becomes clear when we consider cases in which it can be practically eliminated. When, for example, some poison kills a part of the liver-cells in each lobule of that organ, multiplication of the remaining cells occurs while the bodies of the dead cells are still in position and little change in the pressure relations can have arisen. So,' too, on the removal of one kidney, or even when its function is annulled by obstruction of the ureter so that it becomes atrophied or enlarged into a sac of fluid, growth occurs in the other kidney until it is able to do easily the work of both (Fig. 70). These are examples of the results of an unbalancing of the functional equilibrium which seems, upon due consideration, to be the most important factor in this question of new-growth.

Active Stimuli to Growth.—Still the question remains whether there exist means by which growth can be directly and actively stimulated. The great difficulty in answering this question lies in our being unable to eliminate the factors of the unbalancing of the mechanical and the functional equilibrium by the injury which these stimuli cause in the cells, and for this reason we may await with interest the results of systematic experiments with the application of such supposed stimuli to tissue growing *in vitro* where mechanical conditions can be controlled and functional demands reduced to a minimum. Further, in those frequent cases in the animal body in which the very excess of the new tissue produced seems to argue the existence of some special stimulus to growth, we must eliminate the possibility that this new tissue may represent the accumulated product of repeated attempts at repair, each of which has been partly frustrated

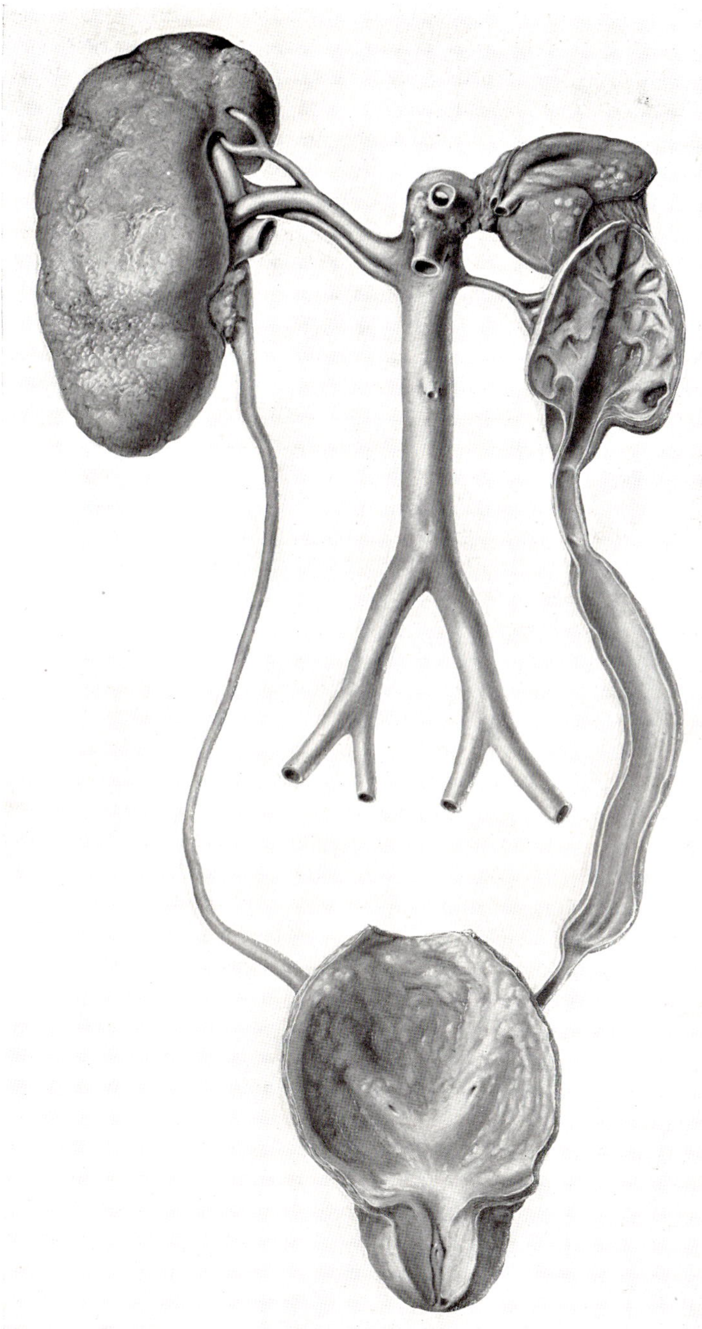

Fig. 70.—Atrophy of left kidney following obstruction of the ureter. Corresponding enlargement of the opposite kidney.

by a new injury, so that even the repairing tissue is injured and responds in an attempt to repair itself. It is readily seen that this process, kept up for a long time, would end in the formation of a great quantity of scar tissue, or, at the margin of a chronic ulcer, of a greatly thickened and irregular epithelial growth.

But in the present state of our knowledge it is impossible to deny the existence of direct stimuli to tissue growth, although it seems that this facile explanation ought to be used perhaps a little less freely than is done in most text-books. There are certain substances, such as the stains Sudan III and scarlet red, which, when injected into the tissues, provoke an extraordinary growth of epithelium, cartilage, etc., which in some cases finally looks almost like a tumor. Similar results have been obtained with skatol, indol, etc., and even with ether water. It is not quite clear how these substances act nor what part is played by the injury they produce in the tissues, but the new-growth is far in excess of what would be needed for repair. They are all soluble in lipoid substances, and it is possible that their effect is due to their attacking the lipoid membrane, which is supposed to envelope each cell, thus exposing the cell to outward influences from which it has been protected. This is somewhat allied to Loeb's methods of stirring up artificial or parthenogenetic development in unfertilized egg-cells, for in that process he emphasizes the importance of lipolytic substances in their action upon the envelope of the cell. In that case, however, the segmentation which is started is rather a process of the development of a cell endowed with great energy of growth, while in the mature cell the latent potential energy must be converted into an active form and greatly intensified.

Very vague, too, are our notions about the substances which cause the sudden new-growth of tissue at the onset of puberty, and especially those which produce the remarkable changes in the breasts and other organs in pregnancy. Doubtless these are chemical substances which circulate in the blood, as has been shown in the case of those malformed twins which, being fused together, have a common circulation, and in whom pregnancy in one affects the organs of the other (Blazicek sisters, one of whom became pregnant, after which the breasts of both secreted milk).

Other instances in which the increased or perverted activities of the organs of internal secretion are followed by a great overgrowth of all or a part of the tissues are well known (gigantism, acromegaly), and, on the other hand, the extreme stunting of growth from the failure of these secretions is equally well known (myxœdema, cretinism, etc.). There are conditions, too, such as the pulmonary osteoarthropathy of Marie, in which the absorption of poisonous material from the widened and infected bronchi produces a great overgrowth of the extremities—actually a sort of gigantism (Fig. 71).

Infections and Foreign Bodies.—Of daily interest in regard to the new-growth of tissue is the influence of infections and of foreign bodies, among which may be classed dead tissue and fibrin.

Many infections lead to inflammatory reaction without necessarily resulting in any great destruction of tissue or any very evident reparatory process. But this is doubtless partly dependent upon the situation of the infection, for while the pneumococcus may produce a pneumonia which will disappear, leaving only a few gaps in the respiratory epithelium to be filled up by the neighboring cells, the same organisms in the pleura or pericardium are likely to produce an exudate the replacement of which by new tissue leads to the permanent binding together of those surfaces. Nevertheless, even there the adhesions may be slight or absent, and the extent of new formation of tissue appears to depend upon the extent of the injury.

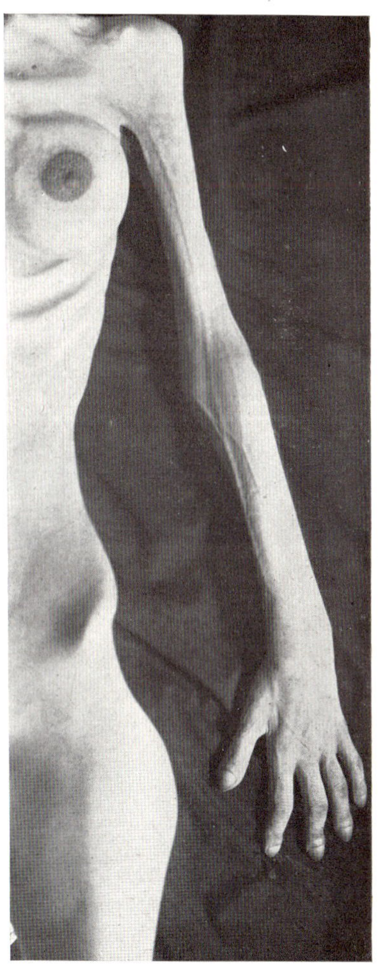

Fig. 71.—Secondary hypertrophic osteoarthropathy showing enlargement of the forearm and hand.

The result of the destruction of tissue by bacteria seems to differ from that produced mechanically chiefly in that the bacteria persist after the repair has begun and repeat the injury. This is notoriously true of those resistant bacteria and animal parasites which remain lodged in the tissue for a very long time. It is true of the tubercle bacillus and of the Spirochæta pallida, which linger after completing their first injury to the tissue until they are encased in a nodule of new tissue, and then still longer, until, by their poisons, they cause the necrosis of the cells of that nodule, which is then replaced by a wall of cells a little further out. The first nodule seems far in excess of what was needed to repair the injury caused by the bacilli, and the question arises at once whether its abundant cells have not grown in direct response to a stimulus furnished by the bacillus. Probably so, but the matter is so complex in the animal body that it seems possible to decide it, if at all, only by recourse to experiments with isolated tissues growing *in vitro*.

All the factors which decide the inception of growth are at work when a portion of tissue is left dead and surrounded by living tissues in the organ, as in the case of an infarct. Scavenging leucocytes attempt to remove the coagulated material, but before they can make much impression on it the gap in the organ is patched by a new-growth of tissue and the dead material, which blocked and choked this gap, is replaced by the new tissue. The functional replacement occurs elsewhere, and at this point there is only a growth of fibrous tissue and blood-vessels to restore continuity and remove the irritating foreign substance. Perhaps unbalancing of the mechanical equilibrium is important, but it seems that the presence of the fibrin-containing necrotic tissue offers a chemiotactic attraction which guides the growth of the invading blood-vessels, and it may be that it is really a chemical stimulus to growth. An exudate of fibrin on the surface of the peritoneum or pleura, where no unbalancing of mechanical or functional equilibrium can be caused by its presence, exerts the same influence on the underlying tissue and is quickly replaced by a new tissue. So, too, a clot in the course of the blood-stream, whether it obstructs the circulation or only lies on the wall of the heart.

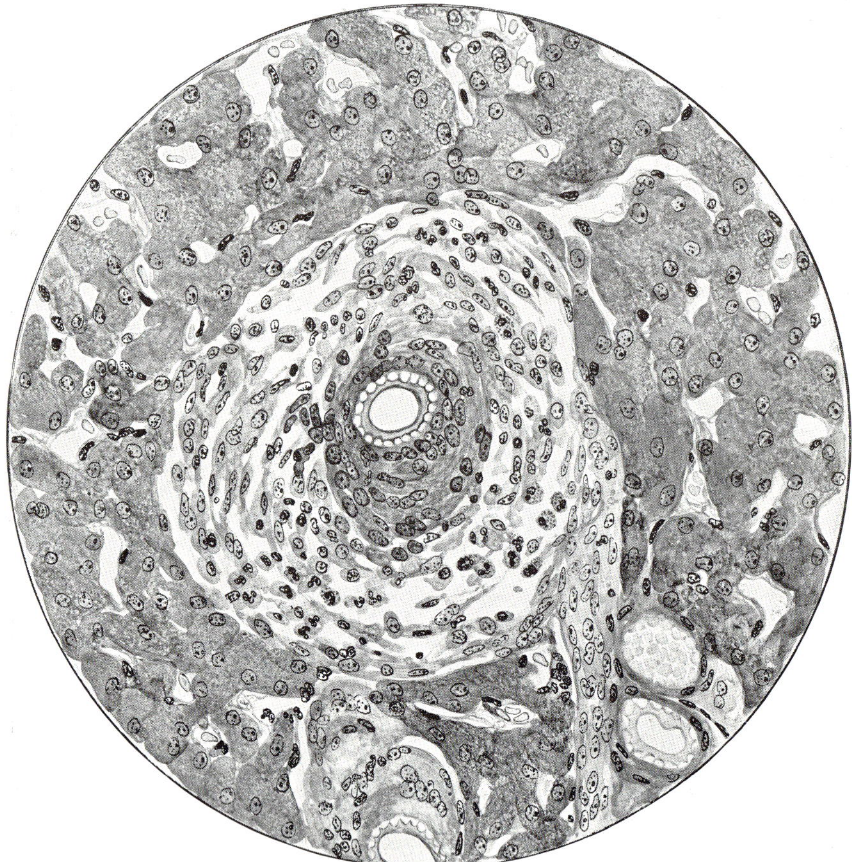

Fig. 72.—Tubercle-like capsule formed around a lycopodium spore introduced into the liver through the portal vein.

Inert foreign bodies are attacked in the tissues by wandering cells of all sorts, just as the fibrin and dead cells are attacked and dissolved or surrounded; but they too, soon find connective tissue and blood-vessels flowing in about them, so that they are quickly encapsulated or permeated by these cells. Indeed, there is hardly anything which sets up such an extraordinary new formation of cellular fibrous tissue as a suspension of foreign particles, such as the diatom shells which form the fine dust of silicious earth or kieselguhr (Podwyssotzky). Perfectly insoluble, these particles can hardly act through any chemical stimulus, nor do they appear to cause any great injury to the neighboring cells or disturb the mechanical equilibrium to any great degree. Perhaps it may be regarded as a tactile stimulus which causes cells to grow around them, much as they follow threads of fibrin or the surface of the cover-slip in cultures. Indeed, as Lambert has shown by the aid of lycopodium spores, the cells in a culture which surround foreign bodies are not those of the connective tissue, but the wandering cells. Nevertheless, in the body the actual fibroblasts appear in time and form an outer capsule (Fig. 72).

The growth of tumors exemplifies in a singular way the stimulation of another tissue to growth. No matter what may eventually prove to be the reason for the unbridled growth of the tumor-cells themselves, we know that, standing as they do in close relation with connective tissue and blood-vessels, they stir up a growth in those structures which leads to the production of a most complicated and extensive organized stroma, which sometimes assumes forms totally unknown in the body and reaches a bulk far greater than that of any new-growth formed in the process of repair.

Analogies Between Embryonic Growth and Pathological New Formation of Tissue.—The dividing cells, and more especially the products of division which appear in the course of the new formation of tissue, are often spoken of loosely as embryonic cells; the tissue has returned to the embryonic state, and the ontogenetic phases are being reproduced. This seems hardly justified, since these new cells do not really resume the character of embryonic cells, which have such a great potential energy pushing them to unfold and develop. On the contrary, they are merely young cells of the type which has reached maturity, and whose growth energy has been finally reduced to a point which leaves them able to maintain the integrity of the organ, but not to develop further into a still more highly specialized and mature tissue. Even in those situations in which normally there is a constant active production of cells, as in the Malpighian layer of the skin or in the bone-marrow, the cells are mature in the sense that they do not tend to develop further, but merely produce new ones of the same kind. Even the fact that these new cells become much modified does not affect this idea.

LITERATURE

Various papers of Harrison, Lambert, Hanes, Burrows, and others. Summarized, Trans. Cong. Amer. Phys. and Surg., 1913, ix, 63.

CHAPTER XII

DEFENCES OF THE BODY (Continued)

Repair. Established character of tissues. Their early differentiation. Metaplasia. Regeneration as exemplified in the new formation of various tissue.

REPAIR

General Phenomena of Repair.—When the body has reached its mature form, cells are newly formed only in sufficient quantity to make up for those lost each day in the ordinary wear and tear. Since cells are being constantly rubbed off the surface of the skin, the lower layers are just as constantly occupied in producing new ones. Since the red corpuscles of the blood are short-lived cells, they are constantly manufactured anew in the bone-marrow. These processes are so gradual and inconspicuous that it is hard to be sure that they are going on. But if a piece of skin be scraped off, or a few ounces of blood allowed to escape, there suddenly occurs a far more vigorous new formation of cells in the skin or in the bone-marrow.

Every obvious new formation of tissue in the grown person seems to occur as a result, which we might predict, of some disturbance which impairs or renders inadequate the function of that tissue. It is a response so appropriate to the situation and carried out with such moderation and in a manner so eminently suitable to the supposed purpose of restoring the functional equilibrium of the body that it is hardly possible to doubt that it, like inflammation, must be a plan evolved and elaborated through ages of natural selection for the preservation of the species. It is complicated and makes use of subsidiary mechanical aids, as we shall see (such as the filling of the gap across which tissue is to grow with fibrin); but whatever the details may be, the process is nicely adjusted to the purpose, and is so constant that we can predict with absolute certainty what will happen in a given case.

This, as every one will recognize, constitutes a striking difference between the regenerative and reparatory growth of normal tissue and the growth of tumors, in which one cannot foretell with certainty what will happen or where the growth will end.

The embryo grows according to an inherited plan, almost entirely protected from outward influences until the body form is reached. Yet then, too, so profound is the impression of this plan, if part of an organ or tissue be destroyed, regeneration and repair take place in such a way as to further the original plan as much as possible. Indeed, the degree to which this repair may proceed is greater in the embryo than it is in mature life.

Specificity of Tissues.—An important factor governing the repair or regeneration of tissues lies in the established character of the tissues themselves. According to the plan of development of the animal, the cells of each tissue assume at an early stage a specialized character which they retain tenaciously. When these cells divide and multiply after that, they breed true, as it were, and produce new cells which have the same form and function as themselves. This is the well-known specificity of tissues, which is pretty rigidly maintained in mature life. In the embryo we may, of course, pass back to stages where we can no longer recognize the character of the cell, and where we are unable, in the present state of our knowledge, to say that this cell is predestined to become a liver-cell and that a smooth muscle-fibre, for in reality the cells at that stage have not divided to the degree at which one of the daughter-cells takes one path while another follows a different one. They have not yet adopted their careers. But it is further clear that this is not only because we are unable to recognize their tendencies, but because, at a very early stage, these tendencies are not absolutely fixed. The original fertilized ovum forms by its segmentation the whole body, but after it has undergone its first division, each of those two segmentation spheres, if separated from the other, is capable of producing a perfect individual, as we so frequently see in those so-called single ovum twins which are of the same sex and remarkably alike in appearance. At later stages, when the segmentation has progressed much farther, the destruction of one or more of the segmentation spheres can be compensated by the adjacent cells, which assume their function, but there must come a stage, and that quite early, when such compensation can no longer be carried out; if, for example, all the formative material destined to produce the heart be destroyed, a monstrous fœtus would be formed without a heart. We cannot say, however, when this specificity is established, nor whether it is at very different epochs in the development, for different tissues. In any case it is only when all the cells are destroyed that the production of that tissue is made impossible. If any of this formative material be left, the processes of cell multiplication in the embryo are so efficient that even that remnant may be able to reconstruct as much of the tissue as is necessary.

The most important point is, however, the absence of differentiation at a sufficiently early stage, so that from an indifferent type of cell quite a variety of mature cells may arise. An example of this is seen in the primitive amœboid mesenchymal cells, which may develop into any one of the various sorts of connective tissue, or form the endothelium of blood- or lymph-vessels; or, on the other hand, remain amœboid and become specialized in the form of the lymphoid or myeloid cells of the blood, or even the red corpuscles. Such a variety of fates is not reached by these cells directly, but through a series of subdivisions and metamorphoses, and where once entered upon, the destiny of each developing cell is fixed. A connective-tissue cell can no longer give rise to a red corpuscle, nor the red corpuscle to a connective-tissue element. Nevertheless the whole scheme of the elaboration of such specialized cells as those of the blood, from simple amœboid mesenchymal cells, does not cease to exist when the embryo has grown into a mature individual, and amœboid mesenchymal cells are no longer scattered everywhere through the body. Instead, as we know for that particular tribe of cells, certain places, such as the bone-marrow and lymphoid tissue, are set aside as sites for the continued production of the elements of the blood by exactly the same process, and throughout life we can find in those places this progressive differentiation of the most elaborately specialized cells from undifferentiated forerunners. We are not informed as to any particular site in which such a differentiation of the other tissues occurs. Rather it seems that they merely repair their daily losses through a local multiplication of the differentiated cells.

While we know that most tissues are so specialized that they can assume only one form and one function, and in dividing give rise to no other type of cell, we recognize somewhat different degrees in this specialization. We cannot imagine the case, for example, in which, through division and multiplication of liver-cells, there might be produced pancreas tissue, although these organs arise in the beginning in much the same way, but we are quite accustomed to observe the alteration of one type of connective tissue into another. Here the specificity appears to be less rigid, for while we know that ordinarily white fibrous connective tissue produces only that type in its growth, it may be greatly altered in character by metabolic changes or by such mechanical influences as œdema or the prolonged action of a tension in one direction. Mucoid or mucin-holding tissue apparently arises in one way, while loose connective tissue may become tendon-like in the other.

Adipose tissue is specific in its appearance, and especially in infants or emaciated persons, in which the tissue is not entirely distended with oil-droplets, it can be seen in the form of lobules sharply marked out from the surrounding areolar tissue and supplied with a peculiar and abundant capillary circulation. Whether all fat, even in the most obese persons, is lodged in this special tissue only it is difficult to say with certainty.

It is in the complicated changes which go to the formation of bone that we see the most varied interrelations and modifications of connective-tissue structures. Both from cartilage and fibrous tissue, bone may be formed by the activities of certain specialized connective-tissue cells, the osteoblasts. In so far as bones are formed in the normal positions, we might believe that, at an early stage, this specialization of certain connective-tissue cells to the character of osteoblast formed the essential basis upon which bone formation is possible, but we are frequently confronted with the formation of perfectly typical bone in places, such as the wall of the aorta, where no osteoblasts could normally occur, but where areas of necrotic tissue had become encrusted with lime salts. It is for this reason that we must think that the specialization among connective-tissue cells is not so rigid as in more highly developed tissues, because it is obvious that in those cases some neighboring mesoblastic cells assume the function and form of osteoblasts, and then produce bone in the regular way.

Endothelial cells, both of the blood-vessels and of the lymphatic vessels, have a rather high degree of specificity, marking them off from other types of mesoblastic cells, and yet it is precisely with regard to these cells that the most extraordinary powers of assuming other forms and functions have been described. They are known to act as phagocytes, in some organs, and Mallory regards them as especially important in giving rise to the wandering phagocytic cells found in many infectious processes. In most places they act as a mere lining of the channel, but in some organs, as in the spleen, they are greatly modified in form, and appear to have more complicated functions. There, as in the liver, they are actively phagocytic, and it is said that they do separate themselves from the wall and pass in the blood-stream into the liver. (This I have never been able to observe.) In the bone-marrow, too, they are concerned closely with the formation of the new cells of the blood, just as they were in the early stages of embryonic life, when an endothelial cell arose from the amœboid mesenchymal cell merely because it came to be the border of a space which contained blood, or in which blood was formed from changes in some of the endothelial cells themselves. But while all this was true in that early embryonic state and may remain true in the bone-marrow and other sites of blood formation, there comes a period in the development of the embryo at which, at any rate, most of the endothelial cells are specialized to their function of lining blood- and lymph-channels. They grow* as distinct sprouting strands which later become hollow, among the other less differentiated cells. In later life this specificity prevails, at least for most of the endothelial cells which line the vessels outside of those special blood-forming sites, and for them function remains the successful lining of the vessels. Even when a thrombus fills the vessel and becomes replaced by fibrous tissue, the endothelial cells take no part in the formation of that tissue, but confine their growth to the production of a new lining membrane which will cover all the surface of the clot and extend into every crevice, so that the blood is kept from contact with the fibrin or the new fibrous tissue.

These examples have been cited to show, in a general way, the importance of the specificity of tissues and the different degree to which this holds good in different tissues. More will be said about it in connection with those more highly specialized structures in which it is held to far more strictly.

Metaplasia.—Metaplasia is a term used rather loosely to express the conversion of one tissue into another, but more accurately defined by Orth as the transformation of a well-characterized tissue into another equally well characterized, but morphologically and functionally different. For-

* MacCallum: "Relation of Lymphatics to Connective Tissue," Johns Hopkins Hosp. Bull., 1903, xiv, 142.

merly such processes were thought to be very wide-spread, and even Virchow did not hesitate to derive cancerous or epithelial tumors from a matrix of connective tissue, but now different explanations are available for most of the puzzling conditions in which a tissue is found in a position totally abnormal for it, and replacing the type which should occupy that place.

Metaplasia is not meant to include the morphological changes produced by mechanical means, such as the keratinization of the mucosa of a prolapsed vagina. Nor does it include such displaced embryonal tissues as develop normally in a wrong situation, islands of gastric mucosa in the œsophagus or of squamous epithelium in the stomach, bronchi, or gall-bladder, nor those which are mechanically displaced in later life, such as traumatic epidermal cysts, bone formation from displaced periosteum, etc. Another thing which lies outside the boundaries of this term is the growth of one tissue in such a way as to push back the normal and replace it. This happens, for example, when the skin about a healing tracheotomy wound grows through the opening and extends so as to line the trachea for a short way.

Metaplasia does not include the ordinary processes of differentiation which take place in the development of the embryo, nor those quite similar processes which continue in certain sites in adult life, such as the continuous differentiation of the tissue of the bone-marrow and the continuous destruction and new formation of bone by the action of the osteoblastic cells. It is difficult, therefore, to say just where the term will apply, for it is difficult to show that any well-characterized tissue is produced from another well-characterized tissue which is already differentiated. The tendency is rather to assume that when such a transformation does occur, it is through the mediation of cells which, like the bone-marrow in other cells, are not completely differentiated.

Such examples as we have to illustrate true metaplasia lead one to this opinion, and they are very limited in number and practically confined to epithelial and connective tissues.

Epithelial Metaplasia.—Under pathological conditions, such as the formation of an ulcer with subsequent healing, one may find that typical squamous epithelium appears to cover the gap, although the ulcer may be formed in a dilated bronchus or a gall-bladder, or even in the intestine. So, too, in eversion of the mucosa of the bladder in the so-called ectopia vesicæ, the mucosa is altered, sometimes to epidermal tissue, sometimes to a high cylindrical form.

Connective-tissue Metaplasia.—Among mesoblastic tissues there are so many examples of the persistence of groups of cells undergoing continuous differentiation that the appearance of the results of such differentiation in unusual places need cause little surprise. If we ligate the arteries of the kidney in a rabbit, the organ becomes necrotic and quickly calcified, after which true bone may develop about the edges of the mass. In precisely the same way the presence of necrotic material which becomes calcified may be observed in the sclerotic walls of the blood-vessels, in degenerated tumors, especially such as occur in the thyroid and in the uterus, in old caseous tubercles in the lung, in old adhesions in the pericardium or pleura, and in many other places. Apparently we must assume that undifferentiated connective-tissue cells exist near by which become specialized in their differentiation as osteoblasts, for these calcified necrotic areas become the basis upon which true bone is formed. In exactly the same way new sites of progressive differentiation are established in cavities left in such bone, in the form of a definite bone-marrow producing myelocytes, erythroblasts, and all the other characteristic cells. Is this to be defined as metaplasia? Certainly one tissue has been replaced by another, but hardly by a direct transformation. At most, connective-tissue cells serving some function unknown are transformed into osteoblasts. Doubtless the same thing occurs in the larynx or bronchi or in the costal cartilages, when in time they become ossified. Whether the bony metaplasia is of this sort in the case of tendons and muscles in the so-called myositis ossificans is uncertain.

REGENERATION

Regeneration of lost parts occurs with great readiness in the lower and simpler animals, and it is well known that their life can continue after the most profound mutilations by the simple expedient of forming anew whatever is found to be lacking. Details of the extraordinary experimental studies of these phenomena may be read in the books of T. H. Morgan, J. Loeb, and many others. As has been stated, something of this power of regeneration prevails in the embryo of higher animals and man up to a certain stage of its development. It may be expressed once more by saying that the fertilized ovum and the first segmentation spheres are totipotent. The cells produced in the course of later segmentations are multipotent, but the cells of the differentiated tissue are highly specialized, as a rule, and potent to produce others of the same type only. Quantitatively also the power of regeneration diminishes with the advance of development and cell specificity, but even in the mature human individual the latent power of these specialized cells for regeneration is often astonishing. While we recognize this decrease in the versatility of the cell in so far as its offspring are concerned, we must also recognize a very great difference among the mature tissues in their power to regenerate themselves, for although such slightly specialized tissue elements as those of the ordinary connective tissue, the periosteum, the epidermis, etc., regenerate very rapidly and extensively, those which are more highly specialized, such as the central nervous system, heart muscle, and striated muscle in general, regenerate themselves hardly at all, and any gap made in their substance must be filled by some inferior tissue which can grow fast and restore the continuity quickly. It need hardly be said that the tissue most commonly employed is the ordinary fibrous tissue. Over and over again we find this principle exemplified. In the heart there may be energy enough to form new muscle tissue in time, but when an area is destroyed, it is healed by fibrous tissue and not by muscle. In the liver, although the liver-cells can divide fast enough, the same thing prevails, and each gap left by their destruction is stopped up with fibrous tissue.

Thus, owing to the different powers of regeneration shown by various tissues, local repair is carried out sometimes by the injured organ substance itself, but more often by an inferior material, such as connective tissue. But even though such patching may occur there is, with few exceptions, some attempt made there or elsewhere to restore the original specialized tissue unless it has been destroyed to the last cell. Before discussing this process of local repair we may pass in review the phenomena which appear in the case of each type of tissue.

Epithelium.—All sorts of epithelium possess a quite remarkable ability to grow again and make up for that which was lost. As is so well known to

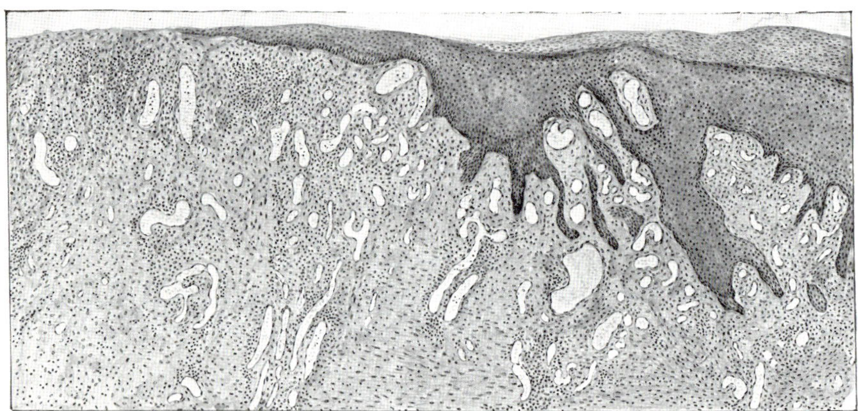

Fig. 73.—Growth of epithelium over a granulating surface. Irregular downgrowths of epithelium are an index of the delay in the healing.

every one, the surface epidermis will quickly grow out to cover again any abrasion or to heal over the granulating surface of an open wound (Fig. 73). This is so clearly visible in the case of a healing ulcer where the thin, pearly blue edges of the epidermis advance slowly from the margin toward the centre until the whole area is covered, that it seems strange that there could ever have been doubt as to the source of the epithelium. Yet for a long time it was questioned whether the epithelium might not be produced by the granulation tissue. More careful studies have shown, though, that the regeneration is strictly specific, and that all new epidermal cells are produced through division of those still alive about the margin of the wound. Apparently many of them move and stretch out to spread themselves over the uncovered area before any division occurs, because the karyokinetic figures are found a short distance back from the edge, and especially in the lower layers of cells. These less specialized cells seem to take a greater part in the new formation than those which have progressed some way toward the keratinization, and have, therefore, lost to some extent or completely their power of division. Groups or masses of new cells are thus formed and furnish the material for the further spreading of the whole layer, but if, as is so often the case, that spreading is constantly prevented, they accumulate and extend downward in rapidly thickening and very irregular interpapillary growths (Fig. 73). It is generally stated that direct or amitotic division plays a great part in this new formation of epithelium, but this statement receives very little support from the direct observation of growing epithelium *in vitro*.

Since such a conclusion is dependent upon finding distorted or constricted nuclei, or upon the failure to find mitotic figures, it seems hardly convincing. No one can fail to accept the evidence concerning the growth by mitosis, but there seem to be very few instances in which the appearance of a cell with its nucleus constricted in the middle, and a corresponding constriction of the protoplasm, must be accepted as showing that two new cells of normal capacities are thus being formed. The appearance may so readily be due to pathological conditions, and the chance of abnormalities in the amount and arrangement of chromatin in the new cells is so great, that I hesitate to accept the process of amitotic division as a normal method of reproduction and growth in the organs of the higher animals. Of course, we have abundant observations of this sort of division in simpler forms, and one may not deny its existence or its importance, but at least it seems clear that such a process should be more closely investigated rather than so unquestioningly accepted. If there is any truth in the theory of Hansemann that tumor growth may be imitated by the unequal or irregular separation of chromosomes in dividing cells, then amitotic division, where the separation of chromatin material into two nuclei is guided by no such precise mechanical process as in mitosis, may well be the source of such inequality.

The regeneration of surface epidermis produces a smooth layer of cells without any reformation of such specialized epidermal structures as sweat- and sebaceous glands and hairs. Yet, as Minervini points out, the interpapillary downgrowths and the fine markings of the palm are formed again after years. Of course, if the abrasion be so superficial that these glands and hair-follicles are not completely destroyed, they may regenerate themselves from the remnants, and may also produce the less specialized surface epithelium.

The epithelium of the mucous surfaces behaves in exactly the same way, growing out from the edges to cover, with a smooth layer, the denuded area. Glands are regenerated from the epithelium which remains in their depths if they have not been completely destroyed. This is the common result in superficial ulcerations of the intestinal tract, and indeed one receives the impression that, even though the whole mucosa be destroyed over a small area of the intestine, as in the deep typhoid ulcers, it may be restored to a semblance of the original much more rapidly than in the case of the skin. After all, the production of crypts or villi is a rather simpler matter than the new formation of sweat- and sebaceous glands and hair-follicles from the epidermis.

In the epithelial organs new specialized and perfect gland tissue is produced essentially by subdivision and multiplication of the remaining specialized cells. It is true that an elaborate effort toward their regeneration is made by the less highly specialized cells which constitute the lining of the ducts. From the very fact that they are less highly specialized, and therefore more resistant, these cells survive in places where all the gland epithelium is destroyed, and remain alone in that area as a possible source for new gland tissue. They multiply, and the ducts bud out and ramify in all

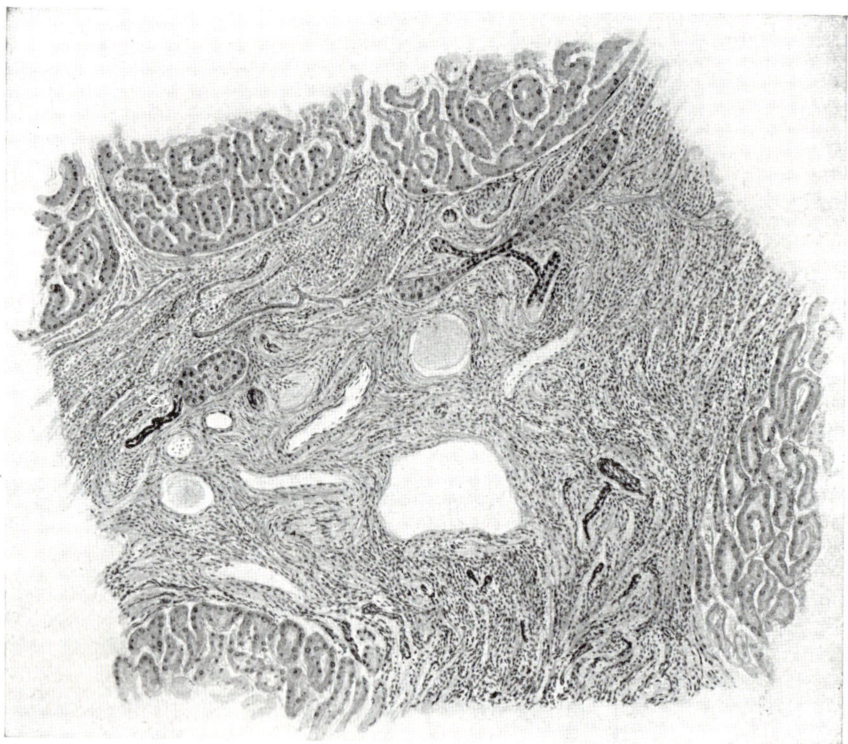

Fig. 74.—Formation of new liver-cells at the ends of sprouting bile-ducts in cirrhosis of the liver.

directions, but generally end in forming new connections with the gland tissue which remained alive after the injury, and whose duct connections may have been disarranged. Occasionally one may find, in a cirrhotic liver, a definite formation of new specialized liver-cells at the end of a growing bile-duct (Fig. 74). The cells are seen to be fresh young liver-cells from their characteristic staining and their lack of pigment, but such things are rare and can play no very important part in the restitution of the functional liver tissue as compared with the profuse multiplication of the already differentiated liver-cells which remain in the fragments of the liver lobules which have not been destroyed.

In the kidney, in the same way, the increase in the specialized secreting cells comes from the multiplication of survivors which have reached that stage of differentiation, and not from the cells lining the conducting tubules. If all the cells of a convoluted tubule are destroyed, that tubule collapses and compensation occurs through the enlargement of another tubule. It is by no means denied that differentiation of less specialized tissue occurs in the course of regeneration in adult life, but it seems that the repair of highly specialized tissue is more readily and more commonly assumed by the remnants of tissue which has already reached that stage of differentiation.

Connective Tissues.—These tissues are preëminently capable of regenerating themselves rapidly and in profusion, so that they form the bulk of the new material used for local repair. In nearly all their modifications they are resistant to injuries, and will survive and grow readily after treatment which would kill more delicate tissues in a short time.

The character of their specificity has been discussed already, and it has been shown that, although in places undifferentiated cells persist and furnish the specific differentiated cells of the blood throughout life, most of the connective tissues of the body are differentiated, and in their multiplication reproduce the same type of cell. Nevertheless, the assumption of osteoblastic functions by connective-tissue cells quite away from the original osteoblasts is sometimes seen, and certain other lapses from strict specificity may be observed.

Ordinarily, white fibrous or areolar tissue produces, by the division of its cells, other cells of exactly the same character. The elongated cell, poor in protoplasm but with prolongations in all directions among the dense fibres in which it lies embedded, swells before division and retracts some of its processes. It becomes somewhat rounded and denser than the adjacent cells, and by division gives rise to two young cells which are temporarily rounded, but quickly put forth pseudopods and acquire an elongated form. A great variety of forms may be found, but the vesicular nucleus and the elongated form generally suffice to distinguish these cells from the more rounded mononuclear wandering cells.

Occasionally, when newly formed connective tissue arises to constitute the lining of a cavity in the body or to form a bursa, the superficial cells which form the actual lining become flattened and assume the characters of endothelium. This is exemplified in Fig. 75, which is from the granulation tissue lining an infected space left after an operation, among the muscles of a dog's neck. The cavity was filled with turbid fluid full of leucocytes. The new tissue is of the ordinary type, with distinct projecting granulations, but everywhere covering this nodular surface, and extending down into the crevices between them, there is a layer of cells resembling endothelium, although much stouter. These cells are often in two layers for a small space, and pass over by insensible gradations into the fibroblasts underneath. Evidently this is a mild kind of metaplasia, analogous to that which occurs in the first formation of endothelium.

While at first these new cells lie loosely about so that the spaces between them accommodate fluid and wandering cells, they later produce in the marginal parts of their cytoplasm the fibrils which stain differently from the general protoplasm, and which, increasing in number and in thickness, become arranged in roughly parallel form, so as to produce a dense fabric in which the cells themselves finally become rather inconspicuous. This process, so carefully studied by Minervini, Maximow, and many others, constitutes the formation of scar tissue. The early stages are seen, how-

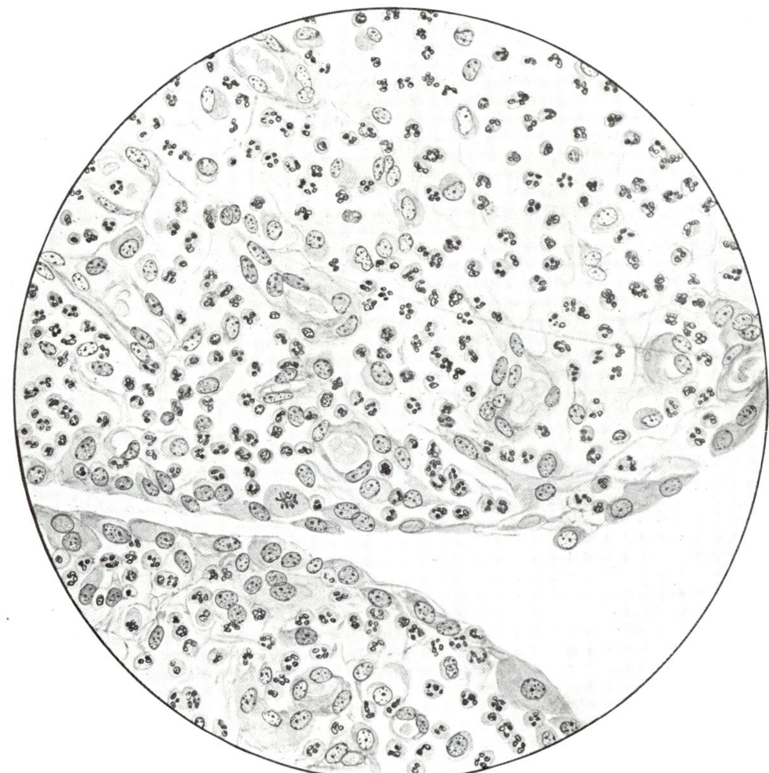

Fig. 75.—Granulation tissue lining a cavity showing endothelium-like flattening of the innermost cells.

ever, to especial advantage in cultures of connective tissue in which the fibroblasts are seen to grow out separately from the margin, showing in the most beautiful way their long, sheet-like processes, and dividing actively by mitosis beneath the observing eye (Fig. 67).

Elastic Tissue.—The regeneration of elastic fibres is to be observed after the lapse of time in newly formed connective tissue, but perhaps especially in those places, as in the lung or in the vessel-wall, where those fibres play a particularly important part. There has been much discussion of the possibility that they may arise in the intercellular substance, but the work of Jores, Nakai, and others seems to show clearly that they are formed by differentiation of the protoplasmic processes of the cells. Though chemically and physically different, they are produced in much the same way as the collagenous fibres, and there is no way of distinguishing the mother-cells from each other. Nevertheless, although Jores thinks the collagenous and elastic-forming cells the same, it seems probable that, with finer methods, we may be able to show that they are differentiated from each other before they proceed to form their different fibres. Apparently the new fibres do not grow in connection with the old ones, but increase in size by accretion. Sometimes, however, as in the walls of blood-vessels, we may see very plainly that a new distribution of the lamellæ or fibres is brought about by the splitting and separation of the old ones.

Fat Tissue.—There is much evidence that the adipose tissue of the body is specialized at an early stage, and remains distinct from other forms of connective tissue. In the infant it is segregated in lobular masses in which, in the beginning, the large, round, isolated cells which are to become fat-cells have a deeply stained granular protoplasm, which later becomes filled with globules of fat until it is stretched out into a thin film and its nucleus pressed to one side. In wasting disease the fat may disappear from the cell and be replaced by fluid. In a sense regeneration occurs through the refilling of these cells with fat, but if the tissue is destroyed, it must probably be regenerated by the methods used in its first formation. In the neighborhood of old inflamed areas one may often distinguish, within the outline of an empty fat-cell, many polygonal or rounded cells with finely vacuolated protoplasm. These Marchand regards as evidences of regeneration or new formation of several fat-cells in place of one. Others (Maximow) have, however, thought of these cells as invading phagocytes which have taken up some remaining globules of fat.

Cartilage and Bone.—Defects in cartilage are in part healed by the formation of fibrous tissue scars, but regeneration of actual cartilage also takes place. According to Marchand, this is brought about chiefly by the activity of the perichondrium, which produces a callus-like growth of new tissue which gradually assumes the characters of cartilage. Borst and certain Italian writers maintain, however, that the cartilage itself takes part in this new formation, a method which certainly prevails in such animals as the salamander; and that the defect is filled largely by the active division of its cells.

Bone is regenerated by methods identical with those concerned in its first formation. On account of its easily recognizable arrangement, it can be seen more readily in bone than elsewhere that a constant resorption and building-up is in progress throughout life. By means of osteoblasts the well-preserved Haversian systems are irregularly eroded, and new Haversian systems fitted into the gaps thus left through the activity of the osteoblasts. The cells concerned in the regeneration and new formation of bone are always the osteoblasts, or at least cells which have assumed the function of osteoblasts. Therefore bone can be formed by the osteogenetic layer of the periosteum and by the endosteum, but probably not by the bone-corpuscles, which are buried in the rigid bone. If all the cortex of a bone be removed and the periosteum left intact, a new bone may be formed by the activities of that membrane—it can even be transplanted into some distant region of the body, where it will begin once more to produce bone, provided always that the nutrition be maintained and that the actual osteogenetic layer be not destroyed. Membranous bone is formed anew in the same way by the production of a mass or sheet of spindle-cells, some of which assume the characters of bone-corpuscles and give up part of their cell-body to the fibrillar substance, which first becomes hyaline and then calcified.

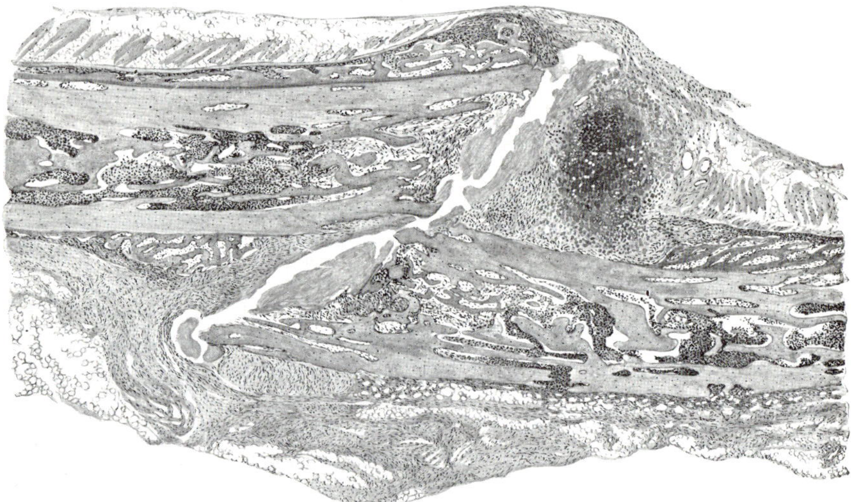

Fig. 76.—Early stage in the healing of fractured bone, showing periosteal new-bone formation, together with fibrous and cartilaginous growth.

In fractures the broken ends of the bone are at first surrounded by a hæmorrhage, but after the escape of blood from the bone-marrow is stopped by clotting, regeneration and healing begin through the proliferation of new tissue from the periosteum and endosteum. These produce a callus which flows in between the separated ends of the bone as the intermediary callus. It consists at first of cartilage and osteoid tissue, that is, tissue with homogeneous ground substance inclosing the newly formed cells, and having the form of bone without being calcified. The osteoid tissue may be laid down as a solid layer on the surface of the old bone, or, through the guiding action of blood-vessels, assume a spongy form. Solid new formed tissue of this kind may be transformed later into spongy bone by the invasion of blood-vessels, and that in turn become compact by later growth. The cartilage which is formed by the activity of the periosteum is similarly invaded by osteoblast-carrying blood-vessels and converted into osteoid tissue, and finally into bone, exactly as in the intracartilaginous bone formation of the embryo. Great defects in the bone produced artificially or by disease may thus be made good, although for a time the new bone thus formed is very abnormal in its arrangement. Later modifications tend to reduce it with wonderful accuracy to the form best adapted to meet the strain put upon it.

Smooth Muscle.—Experimental and other study of the healing of defects in smooth muscle seems to show little activity in this regard—sometimes mitotic division has been described, sometimes a new formation by amitotic division, but more recent studies tend to the idea that there is in higher vertebrates very little regeneration of the muscle itself, but that healing brought about by scar tissue brings together the muscle edges at the site of the defect.

Striated Muscle.—Two distinct methods of regeneration occur, as pointed out by Volkmann, Schminke, and others. In one, new separate cells are formed from the remains of the fibre by collection of the protoplasm about its nuclei within the sarcolemma (sarcoblasts). These develop, just as the embryonic muscle-fibres do, by the gradual appearance of striated fibrils in the elongating cell. In the second method a bulbous end is formed in continuity with the remains of the muscle-fibre with a great number of nuclei, and the elongation and differentiation of this protoplasmic mass give rise not to new fibres, but to increase in the mass of the muscle substance. Many authors have ascribed all of this to amitotic division of the nuclei, but many mitoses have been observed, and doubtless play the usual important part in the reproduction of this as in other tissues.

Heart muscle has been thought to regenerate itself little, if at all, any loss of substance being made good by a patch of scar tissue. Indeed, this seems to be generally the case, although Heller has recently described clear evidences of regenerative activity in the heart-muscle fibres, and we have seen one case in which a condition resembling closely the formation of the bulbous ends in the skeletal muscles appeared. The fibres could be traced in the scarred areas into deeply stained swollen masses of protoplasm, with numerous nuclei which seem to represent growing ends.

Blood- and Lymph-vessels.—In the early stages of embryonic growth blood-channels seem to be formed anywhere in the mesenchyme by the mere separation of the cells, with later alteration of the innermost cells adjoining the cavity thus formed into definite flattened lining or endothelial cells, which in turn may produce any of the elements of the blood. Channels formed in this way are capable of obliteration by collapse and the adhesion of their walls, while other new channels are being formed. Thus it happens that in a network of such spaces there is finally emphasized one passage which, after the collapse of the rest, survives because it is best adapted to carry the blood according to the existing needs and pressure relations. Thus in early life the whole process is very labile, and the relation to the connective tissue extremely intimate. It is maintained by some that lymphatic channels are formed in the same way, becoming secondarily connected with the blood-vessels, but Sabin has shown that their genesis may be traced to an actual sprouting from certain points in the well-formed vessel-wall, of blind-ending canals which finally ramify in all directions in the tissue and constitute the lymphatic system. At any rate, there comes a period, somewhat later in embryonic life, at which the promiscuous formation of blood-vessels or lymphatics from spaces in the mesenchyme seems to be restricted, and thenceforth the endothelial cells become permanently specialized to carry out that function only and to give rise, by their division, to all subsequent endothelial cells. After this epoch new vessels are formed only by the formation of an endothelial bud from the wall of a vessel, which may grow out as a mobile strand of endothelial cells moving through the tissue until it meets another such strand. Exactly the same process is carried through in the case of the lymphatic channels, which are quite as completely walled off from the connective tissue by endothelial cells as are the blood-vessels.* When such strands of endothelial cells, which at first may be no more than whiplash-like protoplasmic filaments, become united with others so as to form a bridge and become thickened into a double row of cells by mitotic division, there gradually appears a cleft in the middle through which blood-corpuscles are forced. There has been much discussion as to the part played by connective-tissue cells in this process, but the evidence seems to be overwhelming in favor of the idea that when connective-tissue cells take any part they act merely as supporting cells, applying themselves to the outside of the new tube, of which the essential lining layer is composed of endothelial cells alone (Marchand). Coffin has traced carefully the formation of lymphatic vessels in newly forming granulation tissue, and has found that they appear in precisely the same way as the new blood-vessels.

Bone-marrow, Lymph-glands, and Blood.—Bone-marrow regenerates itself rapidly after destruction through injury, disease, or poisoning, by the formation of a new connective tissue rich in vessels, in which there appear later fat-cells and the specific blood-forming cells. As to the source of these, some authors (Haasler, Enderlen, Marchand) have held to the idea that they are derived from the division of those which remained behind or are brought to the marrow cavity by the blood-stream or by wandering through the tissues. Others (Maximow, Weidenreich) regard them as derivatives of the young, undifferentiated connective tissue formed upon the invasion of blood-vessels with their periosteal cells into the cartilage. This seems well enough established in the case of embryonic marrow formation, but is more difficult to accept in the regeneration of marrow in the adult, although it is perhaps supported by the observation of the new formation of marrow in bone produced in such organs as the lung or aorta.

* MacCallum: "Relations Between Lymphatics and Connective Tissue," Johns Hopkins Hosp. Bull., 1903, xiv, 142.

Lymph-glands and nodules of lymphoid tissue reappear, without doubt, in areas where they have been destroyed, but the mode of their regeneration is not very clearly understood. In the case of an autopsy assistant who had suffered repeated infections of the hands, after which infected lymph-nodes had been dissected from the axilla, new nodes appeared under the skin about the shoulder as well as in the axilla. Similarly, in the intestine, after destruction of Peyer's patches and solitary nodules, through ulceration in the course of typhoid fever, repair and new formation of these structures are in time very complete. Undoubtedly, as Ribbert points out, there are many scattered lymph-follicles in the tissues which become evident only when they are caused to swell by some inflammatory reaction, and it is possible that these, through their enlargement, compensate for the loss of the original lymph-nodes in places where the latter have been destroyed or removed. In the spleen, when the amyloid has occupied the whole of each Malpighian body, one may sometimes see, as in Fig. 42, the counterpart of this in the new formation of lymphoid nodules all through the splenic pulp. Bayer and others state that complete lymph-nodes may be newly developed in fat tissue, but it seems probable that this occurs rather in connection with preëxistent lymph-channels than with relation to the fat tissue itself.

The Blood.—Constant new formation of these cells occurs on account of their brief tenure of life in the circulating blood. *Lymphocytes* are undoubtedly produced in great quantities in the lymph-nodes, wherever they may be, and are turned into the blood either by way of the lymphatic channels or more directly into the veins. Bone-marrow, spleen, and possibly thymus also play a part in their production. When traced to their ultimate source in the undifferentiated rounded mesenchymal cell, they are seen to have the same origin as the granulated cells and the red corpuscles, although for the granulated cells Naegele and Schridde claim a separate ancestor in the non-granular myeloblast. The granular myelocyte, which is formed from a preceding non-granular cell (whether it be the specific myeloblast or the common ungranulated ancestor of all), and which gives rise to the granular polymorphonuclear leucocyte, is ordinarily found in greatest numbers in the bone-marrow, but it may be formed in the spleen, in the lymph-glands, in the liver, in the thymus, and in various other places, so that the regeneration of the *granular polymorphonuclear leucocytes, eosinophile* as well as *neutrophile,* may take place almost everywhere. Nevertheless, the chief site of this formation, and in normal conditions the only site, is the bone-marrow. The forerunner of the *red corpuscle,* a non-granular, non-hæmoglobin-holding cell, may shrink as it acquires hæmoglobin, and thus become the normoblast, which, on losing its nucleus, becomes the ordinary red corpuscle. Large hæmoglobin-holding nucleated cells which are possibly forerunners of the normoblasts are the megaloblasts. They are sometimes swept into the blood when regeneration is active in an extreme anæmia.

Leucocytosis.—Infections of all sorts cause regeneration of the greatest intensity in the blood-forming tissues, so as to furnish to the blood the necessary phagocytes. Polymorphonuclear leucocytes may be produced there with rapidity in a quantity far exceeding that ever called for in ordinary regeneration to make good a loss. It is not uncommon, then, to find the leucocytes chiefly of this type, numbering 50,000 or 60,000 per cubic millimetre, and cases are described in which this outrush, bringing with it the myelocytes, has so flooded the blood as to produce the picture of an acute myeloid leucæmia. Other infections, such as typhoid fever, through exerting another kind of chemiotactic action, attract to the blood chiefly the mononuclear cells. It is even difficult to produce a polymorphonuclear leucocytosis in those cases. Similarly in tuberculosis, syphilis, and many other infectious processes, most of which progress slowly, and in malaria and other protozoan infections, the stimulus produced by the infective agent calls forth the production not of polymorphonuclear leucocytes, but of mononuclear forms.

Thus there is a certain independence among the cell types in their regeneration. Red corpuscles are produced in great numbers when those normally present have been destroyed, and generally there is a considerable coincident outpouring of leucocytes, but this too is dependent upon the nature of the destructive agent and not merely upon the fact that regenerative activity is going on in the bone-marrow.

When blood is suddenly removed, as by an extensive hæmorrhage, regeneration begins in the bone-marrow (often very slowly after an extreme hæmorrhage), and the red-corpuscle content of the circulating blood is gradually restored to normal. Naturally, immediately after the hæmorrhage the number of red corpuscles in the circulating blood per cubic millimetre is unchanged; then there comes quickly an absorption of fluid from the tissues and from the digestive tract to make up the necessary volume of blood, and with this dilution the red corpuscle content per cubic millimetre rapidly sinks. It is not until after the third or fourth day that the regenerative process begins to overtake this diluting process, so that from that time on the red-corpuscle content steadily rises. It may be observed that this new formation proceeds rather spasmodically, as indicated by the periodic "crises" of normoblasts which are swept out into the circulation. In the bone-marrow during this process evidences of most active growth of these cells can be found, and although they are present in such great numbers, it can often be seen that they are arranged roughly in groups or islands among the granular and other cells.

Chronic anæmias which follow long-continued infection or intoxication, or repeated small losses of blood, as from bleeding hæmorrhoids, cause the same regenerative processes. The marrow of the long bones, normally yellow and composed chiefly of fat, becomes dark red, solid, and granular, and is found to be made up of compactly crowded formative cells and their products. In many cases, of course, the benefit from this regeneration is as promptly frustrated by the continued destruction or loss of the cells as they appear in the circulation. There are a few cases in which, in spite of extreme anæmia, no sign of regenerative processes begins in the bone-marrow ("aplastic anæmia"), and others in which it is prevented by the extensive destruction of that tissue by tumor growths or otherwise. The extreme anæmia produced by benzol poisoning seems to depend largely upon its coincident destructive effect upon the bone-marrow and blood.

Nervous Tissue.—If a peripheral nerve be cut, the proximal portion remains alive, except for the last two or three Ranvier's segments, but the whole peripheral portion degenerates. The myeline sheath loses its homogeneous character and breaks up into globules which now stain with fat stains. The axis-cylinder becomes granular and disintegrated. The cells of the sheath of Schwann or neurilemma increase greatly in size and number, and become actively phagocytic, engulfing and removing the débris of the myeline sheath and axis-cylinder.

Up to this time the degenerating fibres show the presence of black-stained globules in the position of the myeline sheath by the method of Marchi, but after the phagocytic activity of the cells of the neurilemma is completed, nothing is left of the medullary sheath, and such degenerated and emptied fibres can now be made out best by their lack of staining, in contrast to the neighboring well-preserved medullary sheaths, which become blue black with Weigert's medullary sheath stain. The proliferated cells of the sheath of Schwann now become arranged closely together in long, tubular strands—the so-called "band fibres." At this point arises the difference of opinion upon which there has been strife for many years. v. Büngner, Bethe, and others maintain that, inside these band fibres, there are formed new axis-cylinder fibres without any connection with the ganglion-cell, and quite independent of the proximal portion of the fibre from which they were originally separated. The weight of evidence, however, is overwhelmingly on the side of those (Waller, Ranvier, Howell, His, Ramón y Cajal, Perroncito, Stroebe, Harrison, and others) who have shown that new fibres appear growing along in these tubular band fibres, but only as sprouts from the axis-cylinders, which are still in the proximal part of the healing nerve and still in connection with the ganglion-cell. It is shown that the ends of these axones in the tip of the proximal stump become bulbous or branched, or peculiarly altered into a basket-like arrangement, and that when the peripheral portion is brought into apposition with this stump, filaments penetrate into the guiding canals furnished by the Schwann's sheath tube, and grow down them until they reach the end-organs and reëstablish connections there. If there is a large gap between the two ends of the nerve, the accomplishing of this process is delayed. It is hastened, on the other hand, by the accurate suture of the cut ends to one another. The band fibres thus form merely a guide for the newly sprouting axone, and in no case give rise to new axone material themselves. All this is particularly well shown by Harrison's experiments, in which he showed that axones could grow out to a great length if offered merely a suitable moist medium upon which to grow, and were not entirely dependent upon the facilitating and guiding influence of the band fibre. Functional capacity of such nerves is restored in a remarkably short time, and seems to depend largely upon the character of the nerve-endings and not upon the precise rediscovery by the axones of their proper band fibres. Indeed, a nerve accustomed to convey one set of impulses may be artificially united to a peripheral stump which had been used to act as the mechanism for a quite different sort of activities, but the old impulses will now produce the new function characteristic of the new nerve terminations. Such a person has to learn to interpret and control his impulses—in other words, learn again to do the right thing at will.

In the central nervous system a similar type of regenerative process is attempted, but seldom carried far, because no proper paths seem to be prepared for the guidance of new fibres. At the scarred edges of wounds or defects, either in the brain or in the spinal cord, the same bulbous or branching ends of fibres are to be found, but there is little evidence of their crossing the scar and reëstablishing the original connections. There is also little positive evidence of regeneration on the part of ganglion-cells—mitoses are sometimes seen, but at best it is only an attempt at new formation. Healing of a defect in the brain takes place partly by scar-tissue formation and partly later by the production of a rather broad zone of sclerotic neuroglia. The cleansing of the area is carried out by the so-called granule cells, large, rounded, mobile cells filled with globules of fat which accumulate in great numbers in areas where destruction of nervous tissue has occurred (Fig. 15). These cells, which are especially abundant in areas of softening, infarcts, etc., in the brain, resemble the mononuclear phagocytic wandering cells very closely, and are regarded as such by Borst and others. Although this view seems perfectly plausible, it is contended by others, including Fr. Marchand, Morzbacher, and Tanaka, that they are really wandering cells of neuroglial origin.

LITERATURE

Coffin: Johns Hopkins Hosp. Bull., 1906, xvii, 277.

Goldzieher and Makai: Ergeb. d. allg. Path., 1912, xvi_2, 344.

Jores: Ziegler's Beitr., 1900, xxvii, 381; 1907, xli, 167. (Elastic Tissue.)

Marchand: Process der Wundheilung, 1901.

Maximow: Ziegler's Beitr., xxxv; Suppl. v; xxxiv; xxxviii. (Suppuration.)

Minervini: Virchow's Arch., 1904, clxxv, 238. (Scars.)

Nakai: Virchow's Arch., 1905, clxxxii, 158. (Elastic Tissue.)

CHAPTER XIII

DEFENCES OF THE BODY (Continued)

Transplantation of tissues and organs, its limitations. Healing of wounds—by direct union, under a crust, by granulation tissue, etc. The healing of an open ulcer, of inflamed wounds and abscesses. The healing of special tissues.

TRANSPLANTATION OF TISSUES AND ORGANS

The result of attempts to transplant tissues or whole organs from one animal to another, or from one portion to another in the same animal, is a matter of great surgical interest, and also of importance in contributing to our knowledge of the growth of tissue and the function of the organs themselves thus transplanted. It is treated in detail by Marchand, Borst, Stich, Makai, and many others, to whose papers the reader is referred.

To graft tissue or a whole organ into a new situation is a matter of technical difficulty, but success depends not only upon the skill with which the operation is carried out, but also upon the nature and age of the animal, nature of the tissue, the intimacy of relationship of the new host, the efficiency of the blood supply (often the restitution of the nerve supply), and, finally, in many cases, the functional need for such tissue.

It seems possible to carry out successfully far more extensive transplantations in the lower animals, such as worms and cœlenterates, than in higher forms. Probably this is because of their greater adaptability, and is quite like their great power of regenerating tissue and organs. At any rate, one may easily transplant half the body of one of these creatures by a sort of grafting on to half the body of another. But this can be done in embryos of much higher animals also, with the production of remarkable monsters. Complex organs, like the eye, may be implanted in unusual situations with a certain success which could not be attained in adults.

The success with which tissues can be transplanted is, to some extent, parallel with their degree of specialization and their need of constant and abundant blood supply. Little difficulty is experienced in transplanting epidermis from one situation to another, or even from one individual to another. The so-called Thiersch grafts, which are thin films of epidermis, sometimes including the upper layer of the corium, are used daily in surgical operating-rooms to cover large denuded areas, and there is seldom any question about their success. So, too, bone with its periosteum may be made to fill a gap in another bone. With more highly specialized tissues transplantation is more difficult, probably because their cells will not survive long enough to allow capillary blood-vessels to grow in from the new site.

Nevertheless, pieces of thyroid, parathyroid, adrenal, etc., have been implanted in a cavity made in one tissue or other, and have grown and functionated generally only after necrosis of the central part, with survival and increase of the marginal layers. It is important to observe that in some cases, as in the transplantation of bone or nerves, the graft may survive only as a sort of splint which supports and guides the new-growth of tissue from the host, which finally absorbs and replaces it entirely. This is always true with nerves whose specialized structures invariably degenerate, but not always with bone, which may remain active and itself permanently occupy the new site.

Transplantation of whole organs by anastomosis of the blood-vessels has been carried out in a number of cases, notably by Carrel, and often with successful functioning of the transplanted organ. Thus in one animal the transplanted kidney was able, after the removal of the other, to maintain the life of the animal for a long time.

The reimplantation of an organ or tissue into the same animal is an *autoplastic* operation—its transfer to another animal of the same species is a *homoplastic* operation, while a *heteroplastic* transplantation involves its growth in an animal of another species. Transplantation of whole organs has succeeded so far, only in autoplastic operations, although homoplastic transplantations of extremities or peripheral tissues have been successful. Heteroplastic transplantations have been uniformly failures. It is, therefore, necessary to have the most favorable possible conditions for the renewed growth of the more sensitive tissues, although those less dependent upon an uninterrupted blood supply may sometimes be transferred to other animals of the same species with success. Evidently the foreign biological character of the blood of another species makes life impossible for the graft. Mechanical conditions, too, are important in the success of a transplant, and a piece of skin transplanted into the peritoneum or between the muscles is sure to act merely as a foreign body and be encapsulated.

Another influence which is undoubtedly of great importance is that of the nerve supply. As though one were to cut the electrical connections in moving an electromotor, and expect it to work in its new position, we look for proper renal activity or thyroid activity in a tissue deprived of all connections with the nervous system. If such function ever does recur, it seems that it must be accompanied by new formation of nerve connections. This is a problem for future study, and is complicated a little by the fact that some autonomic nervous activity can go on for a short time in plexuses, etc., severed from central connection. Thus in a freshly amputated and reanastomosed leg inflammation proceeds normally, probably aided by axone reflexes in the autonomic fibres. Later, when these have degenerated, the phenomena of inflammation fail to appear on application of irritants.

Finally, it has seemed, especially from some experiments of Dr. Halsted, that successful implantation and growth of such organs as the parathyroid depend upon a need for their functional activity. In animals with a normal amount of parathyroid substance he found it impossible to make an extra gland grow, while he succeeded in one already deprived of most of its parathyroid tissue. This seems a plausible suggestion, and has been supported by others, but as yet it is hardly possible to set it down as a general law.

LITERATURE

Borst: Proceedings XVII. Internat. Congress, London, 1913, Sec. 3, pt. 1, 171.
Halsted: Jour. Exp. Med., 1912, xv, 205.
Makai: Ergeb. d. allg. Path., 1912, xvi_2, 344.
Marchand: Process der Wundheilung, 1901.
Stich: Ergeb. Chir. u. Orthopädie, 1910, 1.

HEALING OF WOUNDS

While the principles remain exactly the same, the details in the healing or making good of any destructive injury to the tissues vary with circumstances, and it forms a great part of the skill of the surgeon to be able to leave the tissues upon which he has operated in the most favorable possible condition for repair. Neglect of these precautions, which concern chiefly the mechanical adjustment of the tissues which should grow together, their proper nutrition, and the exclusion of infection, will readily defeat his object, no matter how ingeniously he has planned to cure his patient. As in the early days of surgery, the wound will in a short time break open and discharge a flow of pus and fragments of dead tissue, blood-vessels may burst their ligatures, and the secondary hæmorrhage, dreaded of old, will follow. All this depends upon the malnutrition of tissue from crushing or cutting off the blood supply, and the infection which can thrive in such dying or dead tissue or in the material accumulating about it. But if the tissues be carefully brought together by light pressure, or by sutures so arranged as to leave them all very richly supplied with blood in rapid circulation, the few bacteria which are always to be found in every wound, no matter how carefully made, are easily overcome by the living tissues, and healing proceeds apace.

Healing by Direct Union.—It is in wounds treated with this careful attention to the condition of the tissues, or in wounds so superficial and limited that apposition and good nutrition of the tissues are secure of themselves, that healing occurs with the slightest reaction and with the least requirement for new formation of cells.

If a clean incision be made through the abdominal wall and the tissues approximated edge to edge by sutures throughout, they become glued together almost at once, and in a short time heal together, with an almost imperceptible linear scar, with never any very evident inflammatory reaction and no sign of actual suppuration. In such an incision only the cells along the line of incision are killed,—some bleeding occurs, and between the approximated edges a little blood remains,—or if the escape from the blood-vessels has been stopped, at least a little coagulable fluid oozes out between these edges. This clots about the severed cells and cements the surfaces together (Fig. 77). A few leucocytes appear from the slightly widened adjacent vessels. Mitoses arise in nearby epithelial cells of the epidermis, and in the connective-tissue cells close to the wound. Blood-vessels sprout from those on either side, and accompanied by fibroblasts grow across, absorbing and removing the fibrin and the dead cells which the

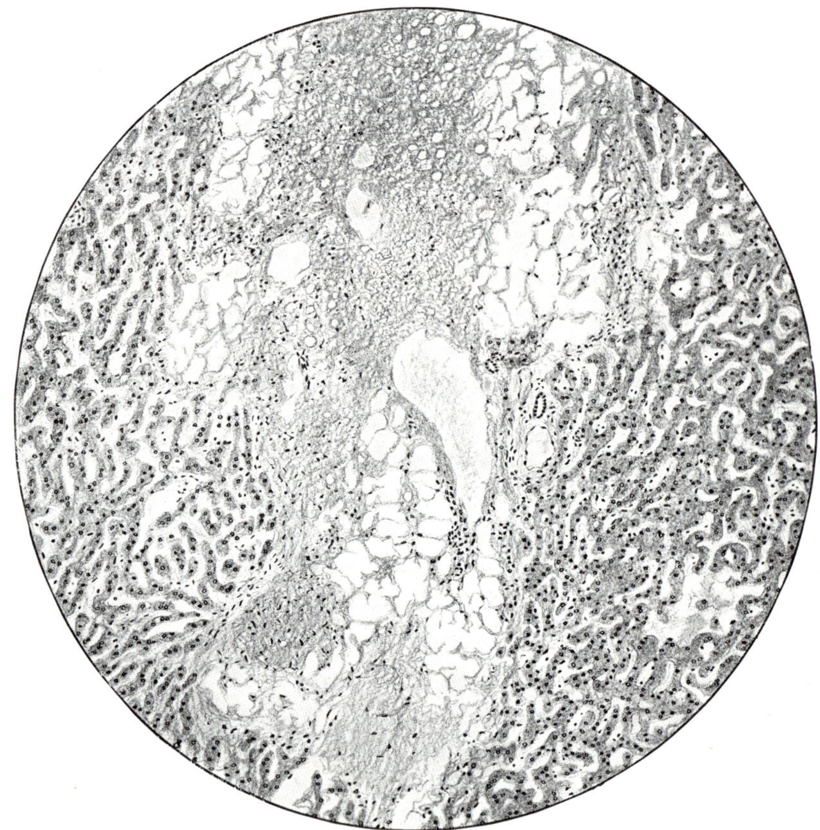

Fig. 77.—Fresh stab wound of the liver. A few cells have been killed and the edges glued together by the clot.

leucocytes help to liquefy, and replacing this material by a more permanent bond. Later this new connective tissue matures into a scar. Epithelium has by this time been pushed across to cover the outer surface and the peritoneal lining cells to close the interior, and the wound is healed. This is healing by first intention (Fig. 78).

Healing Under a Blood-clot or Crust.—In many cases, when apposition has not been so exact or when more tissue has been destroyed, a good deal of blood and serous fluid oozes out on the surface, clots, and dries, or the cavity of a wound whose edges are not brought together may fill up with blood which clots and remains. So good is such a clot as protection against infection that, at times, surgeons have intentionally allowed large spaces to fill up in this way (Schede, Halsted), and have carefully preserved the clot as a covering. Not only is it a protective substance, which, on account of

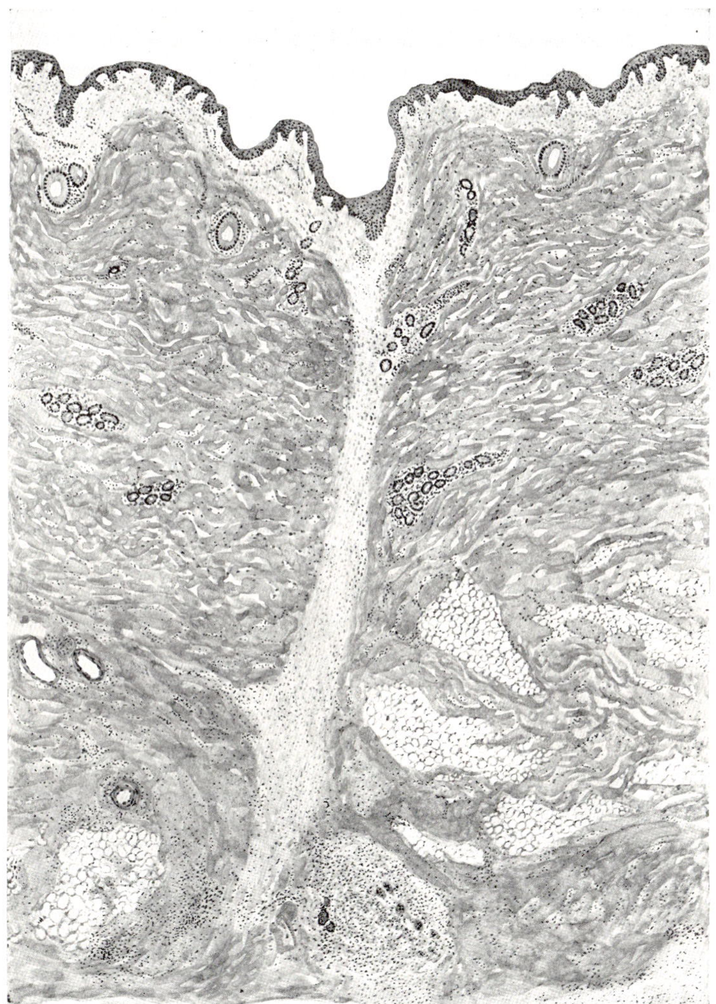

Fig. 78.—Scar of healed surgical incision through the abdominal wall.

its bactericidal power, does not decompose or become further infected, but it forms a nutritive material, and at the same time a scaffolding for the up-growth of blood-vessels and fibrous tissue.

When there is only a little blood or inflammatory or serous exudate which dries on the surface of the wound, healing proceeds under the protective crust thus formed, and is found complete when it drops off. Quite the same process goes on if the crust is formed by the necrosis and drying up of the superficial tissue. The epithelium works its way beneath this dried mass and quickly grows over the surface of the underlying living tissue, even if it has not been covered by any thick, new-formed granulations. This is the peculiarly favorable feature of healing under a crust that, with such perfect protection, the new epidermal covering is completed without the previous slow and tedious formation of granulation tissue. It is true that later much new tissue of that sort is produced beneath, but at least it is closed in from the air and goes on unnoticed, the process being essentially finished and secured when the epidermal covering is complete.

Granulation Tissue—Secondary Healing.—When a wound is infected with bacteria, it is not apt to heal throughout any great part of its extent. Instead, it breaks open and discharges a purulent exudate, and heals finally by "second intention," in a way rather different from those just described. It builds up from the bottom a new connective-tissue layer which, beginning by covering and masking all the exposed structures with a thin gray film, heaps itself up in an ever thicker nodular, translucent, grayish-red substance, until the whole space may be filled or even until the granulation tissue projects in soft, fungus-like masses above the level of the skin. This sort of reparatory growth is by no means limited to infected wounds—it is the regular method of filling up and repairing any and every gap in the tissue. It is inconspicuous and limited in the two sorts of healing already described, because in the one case very little of it is needed before healing is complete, and in the other because the epidermal covering is so soon finished that connective-tissue growth is held in check and covered from view.

If an open wound or ulcer be kept clean and moist and therefore unable to cover itself by a crust, it must heal slowly from the bottom. In the same way a space among the tissues kept open by the presence of bacteria and an accumulation of fluid will close itself gradually by the formation of a complete wall of new young connective tissue, which is gradually drawn together by the absorption of the fluid (Fig. 79). Any foreign body embedded in the tissues stirs up the same response. About it on every side, as though it were a space to be filled, there develops a wall of new tissue (Fig. 80). A portion of tissue itself, killed by any means, becomes a foreign body, and is treated in the same way—hence an abscess with its mass of bacteria and surrounding dead tissue is in time encapsulated. Any group of cells in an organ, such as the liver or kidney, on being killed and absorbed, leaves a gap which is filled up by a new-formed connective tissue not limited exactly to their site, but extending a little into the neighborhood.

Other examples of this same tendency are seen when it is not dead tissue, but fibrin, that acts as the foreign body, and the replacement of a fibrinous exudate on a serous surface (Fig. 81), or of a thrombus in a blood-vessel by the growth of granulation tissue (Fig. 82), is perfectly well known.

In all cases the mechanism is the same. It is the standard method of

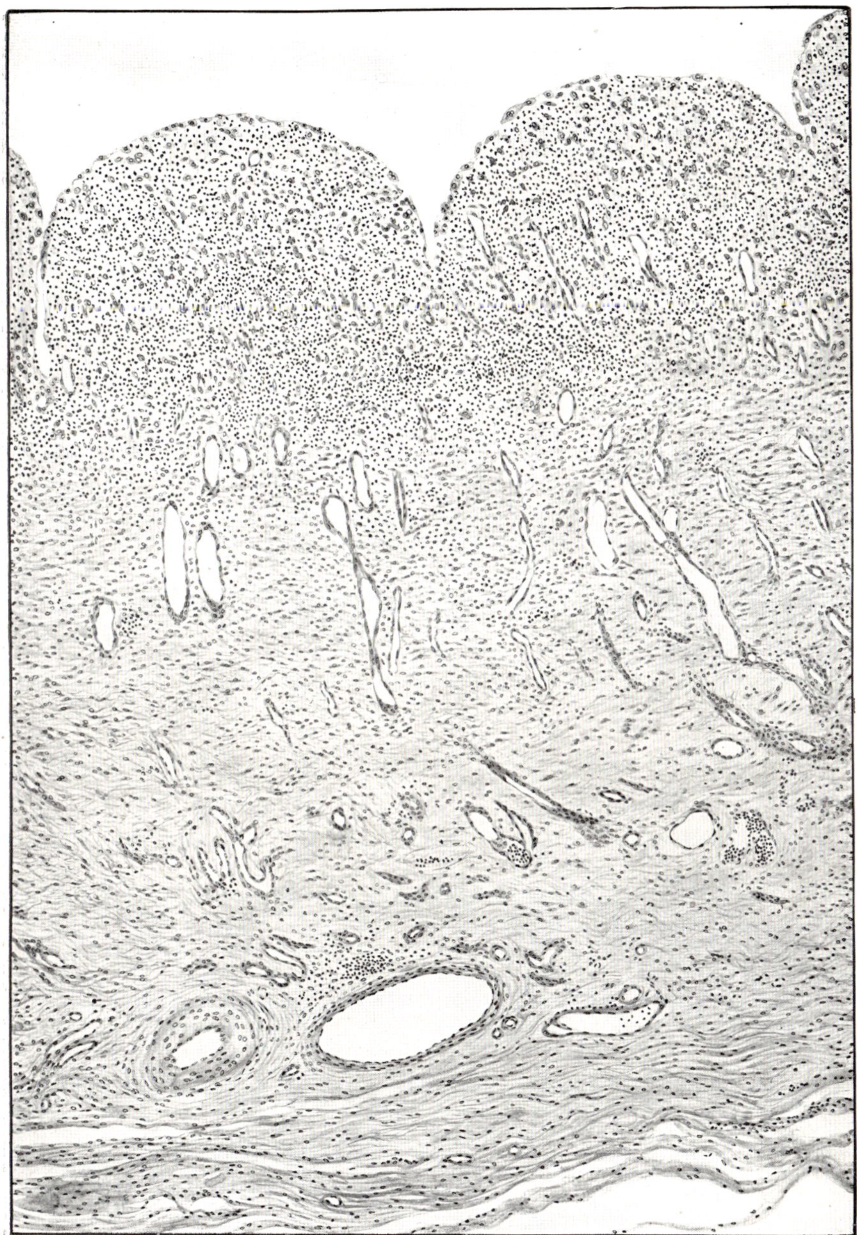

Fig. 79.—Granulation tissue lining a space left between the muscles in a dog's neck.

healing adapted to deal with the most varied types of injury, but always proceeding on the same principles toward the patching of the injured area.

The degree to which inflammation is mixed with it depends upon the sort of injury, and the nature of the wandering cells found in the new tissue depends upon the sort of injurious material and débris that must be treated and removed. The healing of an open ulcer may serve as one example.

Even if such a loss of substance is produced by actually cutting out a piece of tissue, bleeding soon stops, and the cut surface is found moistened by a thin layer of fibrinous exudate. Within an hour, although the surface

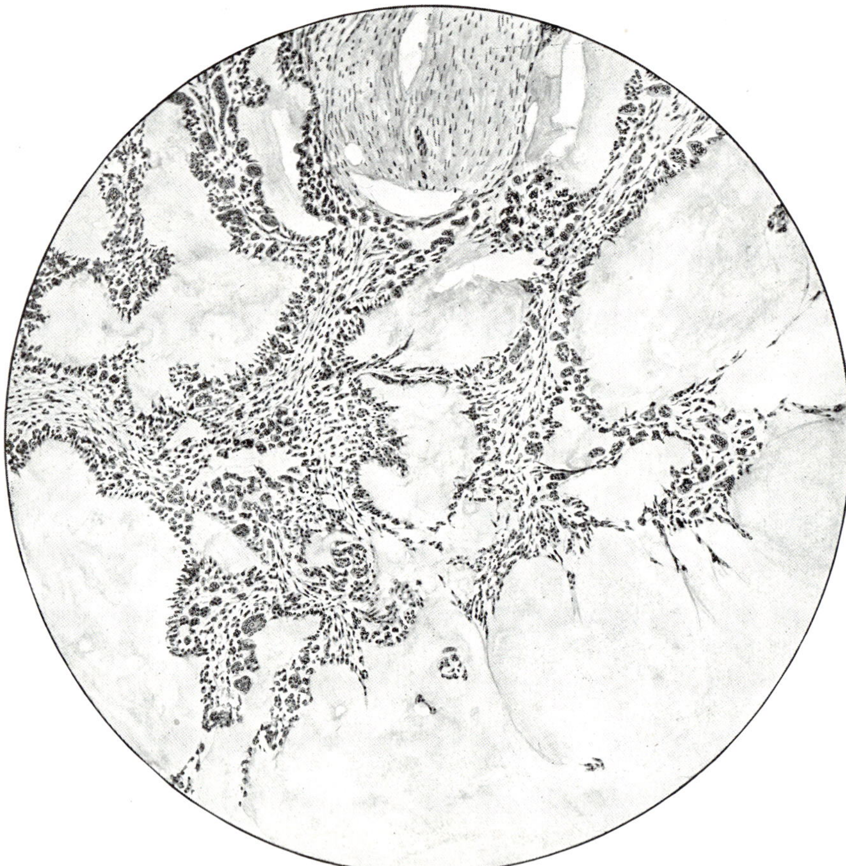

Fig. 80.—Granulation tissue with giant-cells developed around a foreign material (paraffin) injected into the tissues.

becomes reddened by the widening of the capillaries, it is found, on injecting the blood-vessels, that none of the colored mass oozes out on the cut surface. The cut ends of the vessels are closed by the fibrinous exudate, and by contraction, many are definitely thrombosed. The exposed surface contracts somewhat, the skin edges tend to turn inward, and, as healing progresses, this contraction plays a considerable part in forwarding the closure of the wound.

The reparatory process begins first, in all probability, by the amœboid stretching out of the adjacent connective-tissue cells, and even of the epithelial cells at the skin edge. This is readily observed in tissues grown

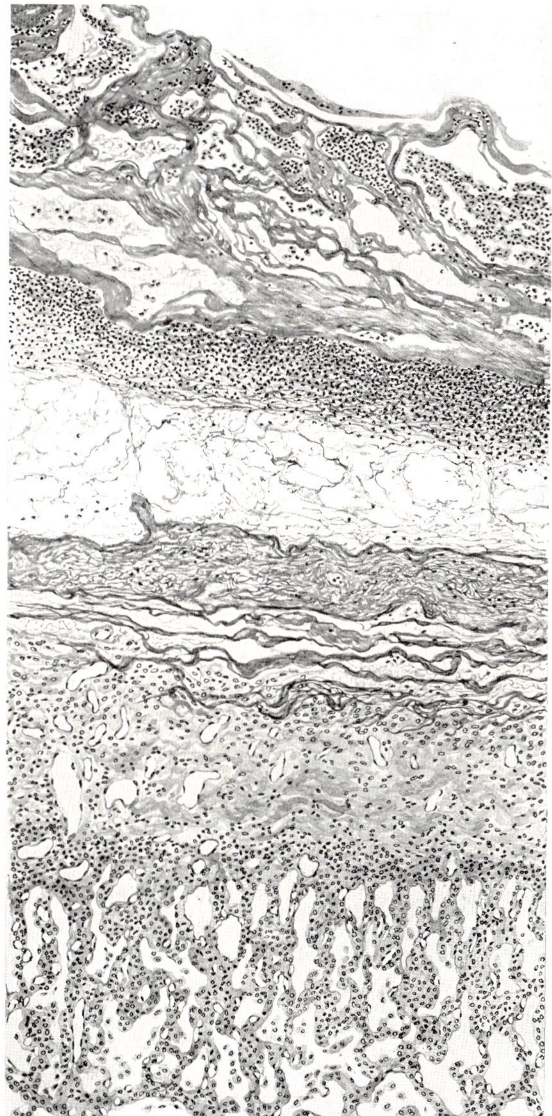

Fig. 81.—Organization of a fibrinopurulent exudate on the pleural surface by new blood-vessels and connective tissue from the pleura.

in vitro, and it seems probable that it occurs here too, since the mitotic figures which indicate the new formation of cells are found some distance back from the actual margin of the wound. Connective-tissue cells reaching out their pseudopods from among the intercellular fibres find guidance in the filaments of fibrin. Through their multiplication and that of the endothelial cells of the blood-vessels a recognizable amount of new tissue is formed in the course of a day or two. At the same time an acute inflammatory process arises, with all the features described above: The vessels widen and pour out their fluid and cellular contents; the tissue becomes œdematous and infiltrated with leucocytes and scattered red

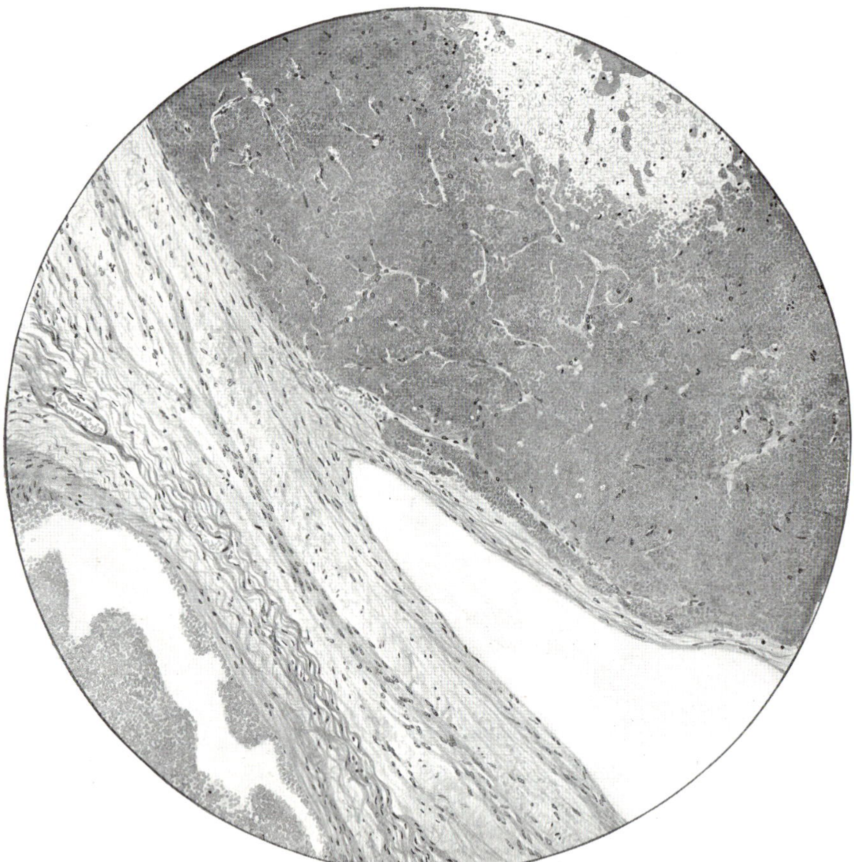

Fig. 82.—Thrombus formed behind a valve in a vein, being invaded by blood-vessels and fibroblasts.

corpuscles—on the surface, more exudate of leucocytes and fluid is poured out, and the network of fibrin becomes thicker; mononuclear wandering cells appear in numbers from the blood-vessels and from their resting places in adjacent tissues; sprouts of endothelial ce ls spring up from the intact capillaries and stretch forward into the fibrin, making way for themselves by their mobility and digestive power. Spread open into tubes by the pressure of the blood, they become complete capillaries, carrying a current of blood. With them there grow upward the fibroblasts, with their long branched protoplasmic processes, supporting and surrounding the vessels. Growing upward in this way, the capillaries anastomose and form arches, and it seems probable that it is this arching forward of the vessels which brings about the granular appearance of the surface of the new tissue (Fig. 83). Thus an actual new tissue is formed, and continues to be formed with the greatest rapidity. It consists, as is evident, of abundant blood-vessels and young fresh connective-tissue cells, all spread apart by fluid,

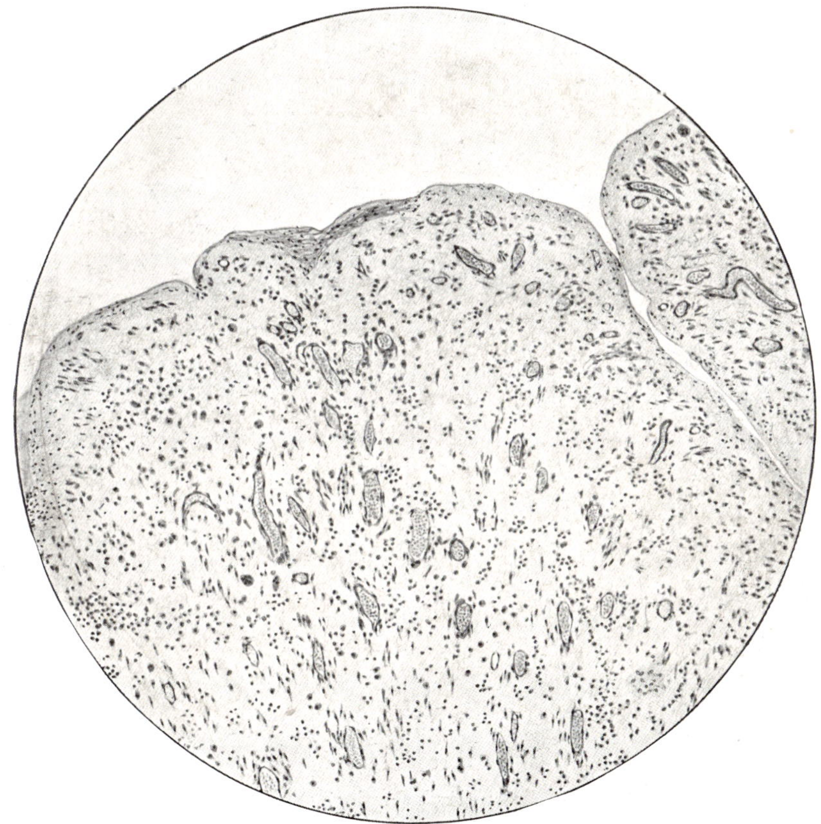

Fig. 83.—Granulation tissue formed in the healing of an ulcer.

a large portion of which is an inflammatory exudate. Therefore it is easy to understand that this tissue should appear as it does. It is a soft gray or grayish-red, gelatinous, translucent layer of irregular nodular surface, bleeding at a touch, but quite insensitive to pain. When it is found, as it often is, in surroundings abundantly infected with bacteria, the inflammatory reaction becomes more intense, and the purulent secretion oozes out on the surface (Fig. 84).

Granulation tissue is subject to the same circulatory and other disturbances that affect other tissue—it may be congested with venous blood or become very œdematous in patients whose circulation is embarrassed. Checked in its growth by some injury, that which remains becomes compact and forms the basis for the growth of a new layer. It may, therefore, present very different appearances in different cases, although in its essentials it is the same in all.

Having grown to such an extent that it fills or nearly fills the gap, one becomes aware of the fact that a thin, grayish-blue film of epithelium is

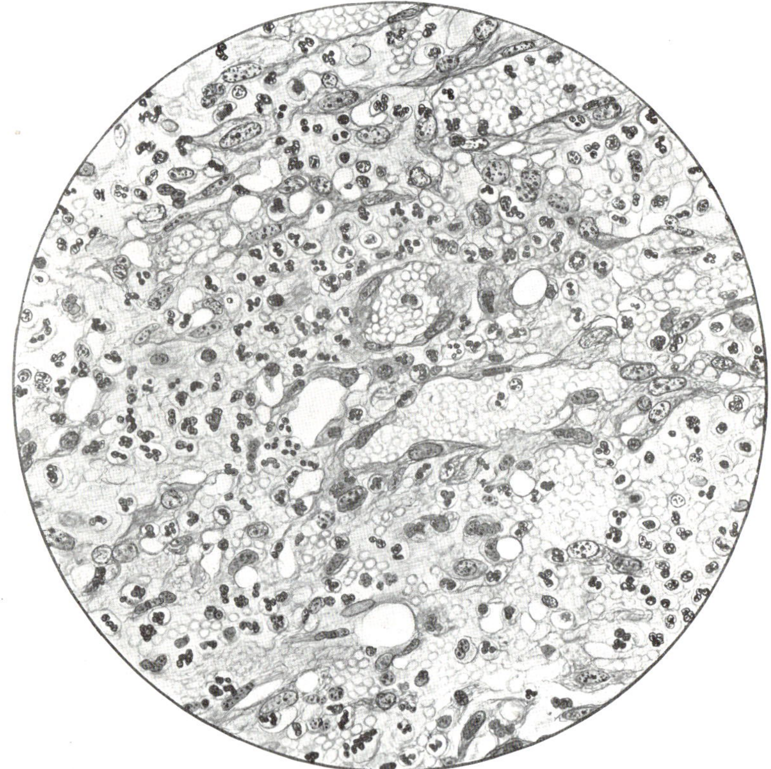

Fig. 84.—Granulation tissue showing acute inflammation.

spreading out from the edges toward the centre of the wound, to cover the granulations, much as ice in its first formation spreads out from the edges of a pond. One can also plant a fragment of epithelium in the form of an island in the middle of the surface of the granulation tissue, and if successful, the spread of new epidermis will take place from there in just the same way, meeting that from the margin and completing the covering of the granulations (Fig. 73). Bluish at first, the new epidermis gradually becomes thicker, more opaque, and white. Naturally this process occurs most readily when the granulations are clean and oozing only a little serous fluid—it is often frustrated by infection and the consequent inflammatory process.

Finished in this way, the site of the original wound is occupied by a highly vascular, purplish looking tissue, hidden under a smooth, pearly layer of epithelium, which has none of the lines and markings of the normal skin—no hairs, no sweat- or sebaceous glands, and no nerves. From this time on a process of maturing of this tissue begins, which, as has been said, tends to mould it into the form of that which was lost. Much new connective tissue is formed. The new cells produce abundant new intercellular fibrillar substance. Many of the too abundant blood-vessels are pressed shut and disappear. Since the venous side is first compressed, the new scar retains for a time its congested appearance. The purplish healed area grows paler and firmer until, in the end, it becomes very white, hard,

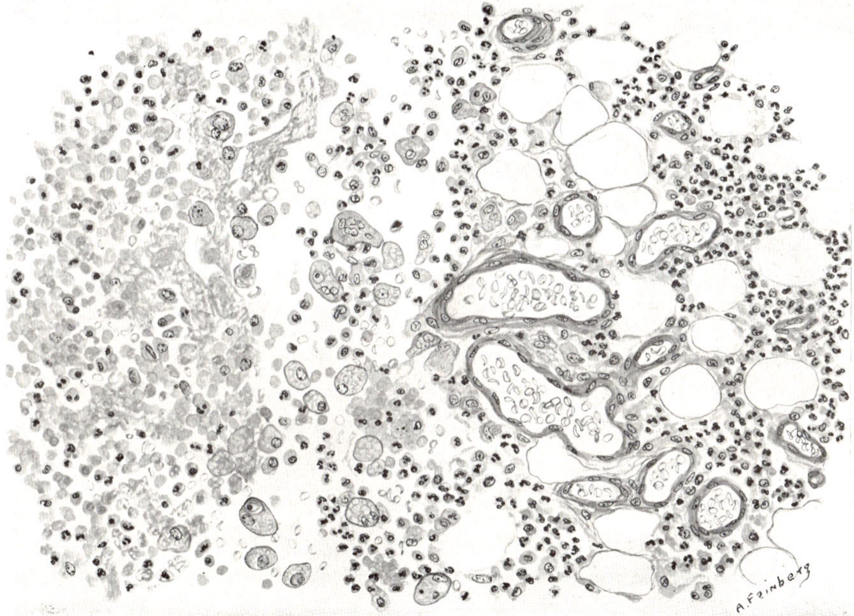

Fig. 85.—Margin of abscess in fat tissue with large phagocytic cells containing cell débris.

and tendon-like, and that dense connective tissue which is the final product of the growth of the granulation tissue we know as a scar. In the first healing of the wound and in the course of formation of the granulation tissue a good deal of contraction occurs, and if it is an extensive superficial wound, such as might be caused by a burn of the skin, this contraction is apt to deform the person. After the scar is definitely formed, it tends rather to stretch out again (Minervini) or relax, and this extension is accompanied by a development in which nerves grow in, so that the place again becomes sensitive, and new cutaneous papillæ arise. The fine lines or wrinkles reappear when the scar becomes flexible, and on the palms or soles the characteristic fine corrugations develop in time and again cross the scar by which they were interrupted. Almost every one may test the truth of this in his own hands.

Abscesses.—In an abscess which has existed for some time we are accustomed to find the dead tissue separated from the living by a wall of this same granulation tissue. It forms all around in just the same way, but it is peculiar in the extraordinary number of wandering cells that haunt the meshes of its connective-tissue network. Inflammation still proceeding actively insures this, and such a wall, from this character, has often been called a pyogenic or pus-producing membrane. There is nothing peculiar about it though, and the point of greatest interest is the extraordinary array of very large, highly phagocytic, mononuclear wandering cells which crowd into this marginal tissue and aid in the cleaning-up process. They are probably free wandering cells, members of Maximow's group of polyblasts, although some writers think them derivatives of the fibroblasts, and others of the endothelium. As shown in Fig. 85, they are often loaded with fat and the débris of other cells. (See Chapter XIV concerning the formation of abscesses.)

Sinuses.—Sometimes such an abscess may break through the skin and discharge its contents, or if deep seated, it may burrow a long way and finally burst through the skin. A long channel or sinus results, and all along its course a lining or wall of granulation tissue is formed. As long as the infection persists in the original site this sinus may stay open and will discharge the products of inflammation. This is especially likely to be true if dead tissue, such as a fragment of necrotic bone or a foreign body, remains in the depths. Such a process is common with deep tuberculous lesions, with actinomycosis, and with various other chronic and tenacious infections, and sometimes the granulation tissue itself gives us a clue as to the nature of the infection.

Psoas Abscess.—A good example is seen in the tuberculous destruction of the centrum of one or more vertebræ, which reduces the bony substance to a soft, creamy, or mortar-like fluid. Inclosed as it is, this fluid seeks a way of escape and burrows under the psoas muscle and down along its course, to appear as a bulging sac at the femoral ring. Bursting out there, a sinus is established which leads from the inner side of the thigh far up to the mid-dorsal region. It is only its great extent which makes this example peculiar though, for with tuberculous disease of the hip-joint or tuberculous osteomyelitis at any point, the same thing may occur. The granulation tissue lining the sinus is quite like any other, except in that it is particularly rich in mononuclear wandering cells and contains tubercles and tubercle bacilli. It is, therefore, a precarious material for healing, since it itself is very prone to become completely necrotic, leaving only a basal part alive. On this remnant new granulation tissue forms. It is for this reason that there is built up about tuberculous lesions such a great amount of scar tissue, and this is true for actinomycosis and other infections of like character and for syphilis.

Fistulæ or channels leading into openings in hollow organs are lined in the same way by granulation tissue, which is often partly covered by epithelium, which grows inward from the skin or outward from the mucosa.

Closure of these channels takes place partly by their gradual contraction, partly by their being choked with the ever-thickening lining of granulation tissue which finally fuses together to obliterate the lumen.

HEALING OF SPECIAL TISSUES

The healing of special tissues need not detain us beyond the description of one or two illustrative cases, since they are merely examples of the regenerative processes already described.

Serosæ.—The flat lining cells of the serous cavities are peculiarly active in their growth, and cover with amazing rapidity any defect in their continuity. When, for example, a loop of intestine is brought through the abdominal wall and sutured there, its surface, where it passes, is glued to the parïetal peritoneum by fibrin after the briefest interval, and in a very short time the serosa cells become continuous from the abdominal wall back over the intestine.

In peritoneal infections and inflammations these cells are much injured. When a fibrinous exudate is poured out upon their surfaces, burying them in its depths, they finally disappear, unless, as sometimes happens, the exudate arches up over a group of them—then they grow round to line this latter space and form a sort of cyst in which they preserve their characters. Many such little cysts may arise in this way, and are common enough in the pericardium; between them granulation tissue springs up into the exudate and, uniting with that from the opposite layer, finally composes itself into a fibrous adhesion or synechia (Fig. 86).

Exactly the same sort of thing is seen in *blood-vessels* in which thrombi have formed—if there is a point in the wall upon which the thrombus has not been laid down, the endothelium persists, and through multiplication of its cells, relines the little cavity thus left, while granulation tissue grows in and replaces the thrombus from the exposed tissues between these cavities (*cf.* Fig. 87). *Mucosæ* heal in exactly the way described for the skin, although the healing seems to take place more rapidly. Regeneration of the special features of the mucosa, including lymph-nodules, villi, etc., occurs in time, so that the scar may hardly be found.

Wounds and Injuries of Parenchymatous Organs.—Wounds in such organs as the liver heal with the formation of a scar, exactly like wounds in any other tissue. More interesting is the healing of the minute, but widely diffused foci of destruction of cells which are so common in the course of intoxications and infections. Different cells are picked out for destruction by different injurious agents, and it is very hard to tell why. Chromic salts kill one set of renal epithelial cells, uranium salts another; the poison of eclampsia destroys the cells of the liver lobule nearest the portal veins; that from the streptococcus peritonitis produces a midzonal necrosis (Opie), while the circulatory disturbance in chronic passive congestion destroys the cells about the efferent vein. The healing processes which follow each of these lesions are practically identical, but are modified by the differences of their situation.

They proceed by the gathering of phagocytic cells which dissolve or carry away the dead bodies of the specific cells of the organ, whereupon

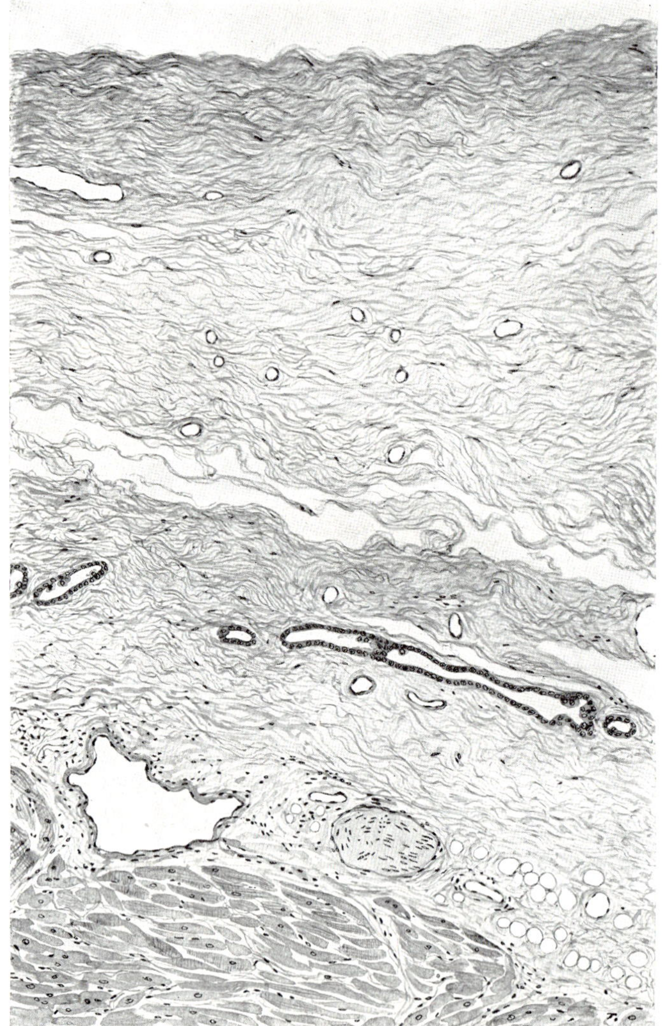

Fig. 86.—Chronic adhesive pericarditis showing small spaces in the connective tissue which represent the remains of the pericardial cavity.

the connective-tissue framework in which they had been supported collapses. As in other places where tissue has been destroyed, a healing or patching process ensues which consists in a new formation of connective tissue and blood-vessels—a granulation tissue bounded on all sides by the uninjured organ substance, so that it cannot show any free nodular surface, but otherwise quite like that which fills up a healing ulcer. In the course of time such tissue settles into a scar. When organ cells are destroyed in small groups or singly, there may be a very fine diffusion of

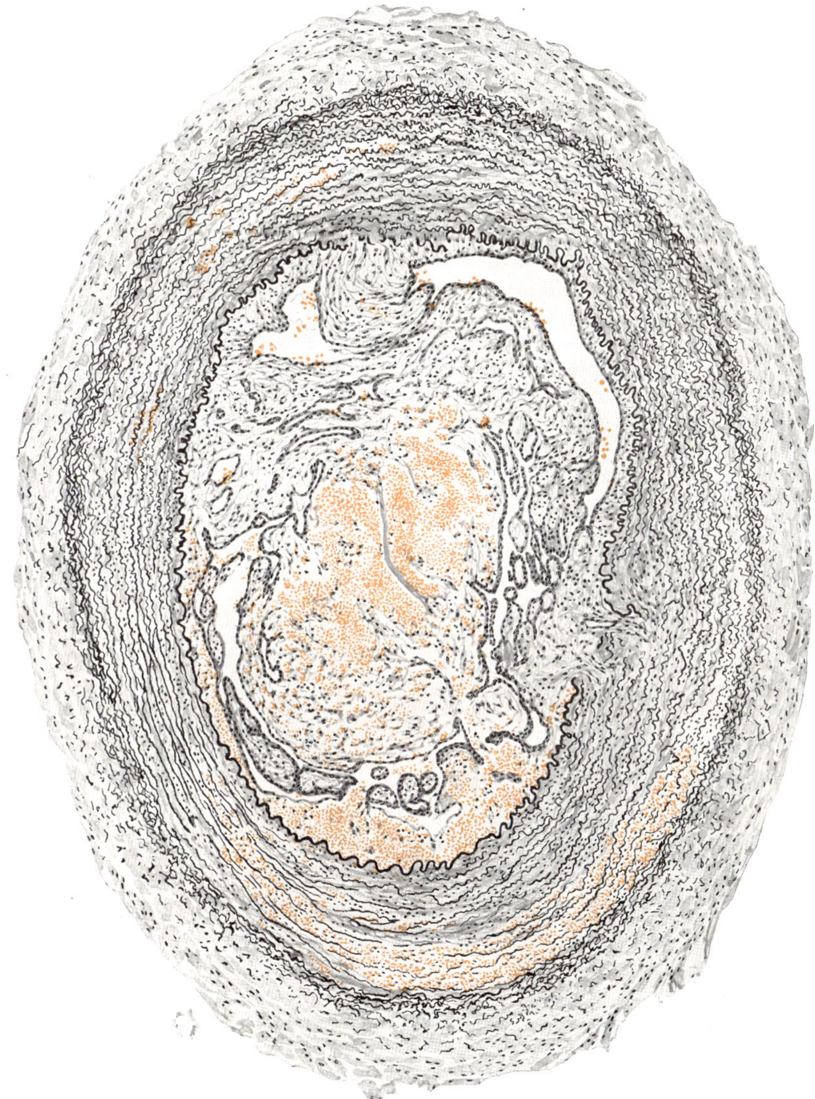

Fig. 87.—Organized thrombus in a blood-vessel canalized by clefts which are relined with endothelium.

this scar tissue, and we have the condition known as cirrhosis in the case of the liver, and often loosely spoken of as chronic interstitial nephritis, pancreatitis, or hepatitis, as the case may be. That this latter term is practically always misleading may be shown, however, by a study of the development of the lesion. The diffuse scarring and shrinkage of the organ is not due to an inflammation of the interstitial connective tissue, with the development of scars which contract and constrict the epithelial cells between them. On the contrary, the highly specialized epithelial cells are the first to suffer destruction by the poisonous substance which is the primary cause of the disease, and the scar formation is essentially a reparatory response to their disappearance. There is practically no evidence that the scar tissue causes any further injury to the epithelial cells. Of course, it is true that the scar tissue may seem to be in great excess of what was necessary to repair or patch the gap produced by the loss of epithelial cells, but it must be remembered that in such cases the process of epithelial destruction and patching with connective tissue has been repeated frequently through years, each new scar heaping itself upon the old one near by. The constant regeneration of epithelium from remnants makes this possible, but there is also the possibility that the new connective tissue itself may be injured and later repaired in voluminous fashion.

CHAPTER XIV

ILLUSTRATIVE EXAMPLES OF INFLAMMATORY PROCESSES

Catarrhal inflammation. Serofibrinous and fibrinopurulent pericarditis, pleuritis, peritonitis, appendicitis, endocarditis, lobular pneumonia, puerperal infection, pyæmia, abscess formation, diphtheritic inflammation.

THE form assumed by the inflammatory reaction varies somewhat with the intensity and concentration of the irritant, and with the kind of tissue involved, but in principle it is the same throughout. Names are rather loosely applied to these different forms which indicate in some degree their anatomical characters. Thus a catarrhal inflammation is an affection of a mucous surface in which the irritant is not intense enough in its action to kill the epithelial cells. The same irritant applied to the peritoneal or pleural surfaces might produce an exudation of fluid with few leucocytes only. A somewhat more intense injury in these serous cavities or in the alveoli of the lungs may occasion the exudation of a layer of fibrin on the surface—a *croupous* inflammation. If the irritant is such as to cause the necrosis of the epithelium and the underlying tissue, with an extremely intense, often hæmorrhagic, inflammatory reaction, in which the fibrinous exudate infiltrating into the dead tissue binds it together into a membrane-like layer, we speak of it as *diphtheritic* or pseudomembranous inflammation. Although the diphtheria bacillus gives rise to a good example of this type, it must be remembered that the term merely indicates the anatomical condition, so that not every diphtheritic inflammation is caused by the diphtheria bacillus. According to the distribution of the inflammatory irritant in the tissues the inflammatory reaction may be diffuse or concentrated. In the first instance, if it be very intense and accompanied by a fibrinopurulent exudate, it is often called *phlegmonous;* in the second, in which, on account of the concentration of irritant and exudate, necrosis of the tissue and intense digestive liquefaction ensue, an *abscess* is formed. Putrefaction may be associated with the more extreme necrotizing injuries if the tissue is exposed to invasion by putrefactive organisms, and this character, often spoken of as *gangrenous*, is added to the inflammatory reaction.

CATARRHAL INFLAMMATION

Catarrhal inflammation is well represented by the familiar coryza, which is an acute inflammatory reaction following the invasion of a variety of bacteria into the upper air-passages. It is probable that the infection is favored by exposure to cold, by drafts, and all the other widely credited causes of colds, but undoubtedly the main factor is the transmission of the bacteria from some infected person. Recurrences may well be due to the infection of pockets in which handkerchiefs are carried. The Micrococcus catarrhalis, influenza bacillus, pneumococcus, or one of many other organisms may be concerned. The infection is quickly followed by dryness and reddening of the mucosæ, which then swell up and secrete a profuse flow of clear, mucoid fluid with some desquamated epithelial cells. Later, from the advent of leucocytes, the mucus-containing fluid becomes thick

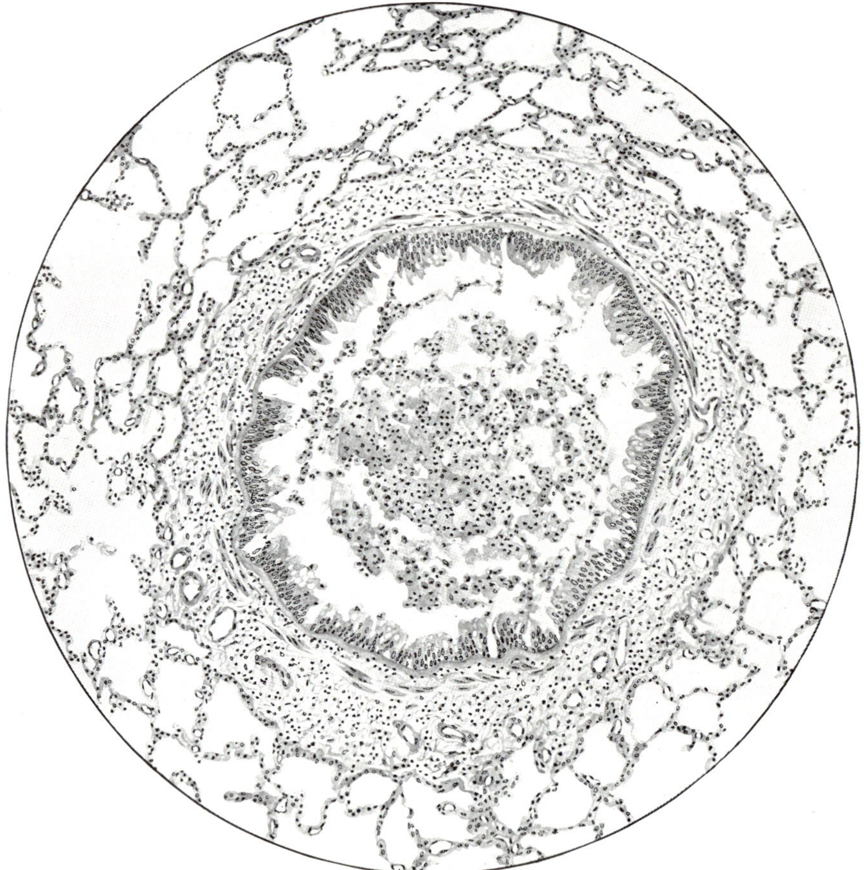

Fig. 88.—Catarrhal inflammation of a bronchus.

and yellow. After a time it decreases in amount and dries on the mucous surfaces, producing crusts. The mucosa in section shows great hyperæmia and œdema, with an excessive production of mucus by the goblet-cells of the epithelium. Between these cells there wander leucocytes, but no fibrin is formed on the surface (Fig. 88). Catarrhal inflammations appear in every mucous surface, with characters similar to those just described. When it is the affair of a narrow tube, such as the gall-duct or the Eustachian tube, the swelling of the tissue may produce obstruction.

The more intense *serofibrinous* and *fibrinopurulent* inflammations are well illustrated by the various effects produced by bacteria in the serous cavities.

PERICARDITIS, PLEURITIS, PERITONITIS

The general characters of these processes are similar, and they differ chiefly in their mode of origin, or rather in the portals of entry of the organisms which cause them.

The walls of all these cavities are richly supplied with blood-vessels, and in the peritoneal cavity there hangs the peculiar omentum, which is largely composed of such vessels, although it may be also laden with fat. In each of the spaces there is normally a little clear fluid. Each is lined with flattened cells of mesoblastic origin, which are not identical with the endothelium of the blood and lymphatic vessels. These form a complete lining without any orifices or stomata, such as have been declared by so many authors to exist. The relation of the lymphatic channels to pleura and pericardium is very inadequately studied, but in the case of the peritoneum it is better known. In the abdominal surface of the diaphragm and in the floor of the pelvis are the two most conspicuous areas, where an absorbent mechanism is presented. There, there project between the connective-tissue fibres, which are spread apart in lozenge-shaped spaces, thin-walled, sac-like endothelium-lined structures which connect abundantly in the depths of the tissue with lymphatic trunks. These are completely lined by the endothelium, and separated from the peritoneal cavity practically only by this cell layer and the overlying layer of serosa cells. Occasional fibres stretch across them when they are distended like a rope across a full sail. There is no direct communication with the peritoneal cavity, but fluids enter by diffusion, and solid particles are carried through by leucocytes between the cells, or are pressed through free along the same lines. Bacteria injected into the peritoneum reach the retrosternal lymph-glands or the thoracic duct by this route very quickly indeed.*

Many leucocytes and mononuclear wandering cells lie in the omentum and elsewhere in subserous tissues, and the serosa cells themselves are somewhat phagocytic.

Absorption from the pleura seems to occur, in part at least, through the lung, since, when carcinoma cells are scattered in that cavity, they lodge and grow on the surface and later invade and actually inject the lymphatic channels running toward the hilum.

Pericarditis may be caused by a great many organisms, among which the most common are the pyogenic micrococci, the unknown cause of rheumatism, and the tubercle bacillus. They are thought to be brought directly to the pericardium by the blood-stream, since it is difficult to trace a direct extension from a pleural infection, and such pleurisies occur so often without pericarditis. It seems, however, that they must sometimes enter in this way or from adjacent lymph-glands. Endocardial and myocardial infection may also extend to the pericardium. That bacteria may be introduced in stab wounds or other forms of traumatism is obvious. Rather curious is the frequent occurrence of pericarditis in the terminal stages of chronic nephritis, and in those cases it is generally difficult to find any bacteria.

---

* MacCallum: "Absorption of Granular Materials from Peritoneum," Johns Hopkins Hosp. Bull., 1903, xiv, 105.

Sometimes only a thin film of fibrin is exuded on the pericardial surfaces without effusion of fluid (dry pericarditis). In that case a loud creaking or rubbing sound is made by each movement of the heart. If, then, fluid appears in excess, the surfaces are held apart, and the sound is lost or cut short. So, too, when a thick soft layer of fibrin is formed on the surface the sounds may be greatly muffled. In this condition (serofibrinous pericarditis), or even when the fluid is pus-like (fibrinopurulent pericarditis), one may observe that, through the motion of the heart, the fibrin is beaten

Fig. 89.—Acute fibrinous pericarditis. There is also a similar exudate on the pleural surface.

into compact ridges which run, roughly speaking, in certain transverse and oblique lines which are fairly constant. The heart is given a very shaggy appearance by this process (Fig. 89).

If a very great deal of fluid be exuded into the pericardial cavity, the sac is gradually dilated and will accommodate a large amount—far more than could be forced into it suddenly. There comes a time, however, when the heart is greatly embarrassed by this fluid because it can no longer expand properly to receive the blood.

This condition is especially well seen when a sudden hæmorrhage occurs into the pericardial sac, and may be imitated experimentally by distending the sac with oil or salt solution under pressure. The arterial pressure falls, the venous pressure rises, and the heart collapses and stops beating. If the pressure is removed quickly enough, it will recover, with restoration of normal pressure relations.

In other cases, as so often happens, when little or no fluid is exuded, or if, later, the fluid is absorbed, the pericardial layers covered with exudate come together and adhere; granulation tissue springs up from each surface and, replacing the fibrin, binds the pericardial sac to the surface of the heart. Blood capillaries arising from opposite layers anastomose with one another and complete the organic union of the two surfaces, by forming a vascular fibrous tissue. The motion of the heart stretches and keeps loose these adhesions, so that practically always the heart can move about a little within the sac. Nevertheless, if dense adhesions exist also between the outer surface of the pericardium and the lung, the heart in contracting will be forced to pull directly upon the lungs and upon the diaphragm. This shows itself in each contraction by a drawing in of the diaphragmatic insertion, which visibly retracts the chest-wall along that line in children, and is followed by a very great hypertrophy of the whole heart. In other cases in which the external adhesions are absent there is no such hypertrophy.

The fresh exudate is composed, of course, of outwandered leucocytes, red corpuscles, and fibrin, beside the fluid. Most of the serosa cells persist for a time in an indistinct row in their old site (Fig. 90), while, as stated above, they remain able to proliferate actively in any place where they are not covered by exudate, and quickly reline any part of the pericardial cavity which has not been obliterated. In the midst of the fibrous adhesions one may find spaces lined with such cells which have proliferated in this way. The adhesions may be localized in certain areas, where they are usually drawn out into bands. If these break through, the stumps flatten themselves into opposed plaques which remain for a long time on the surface of the heart and the opposite area of the sac-wall as the so-called tendinous flecks or milky patches. Other explanations are offered for these thickenings of the epicardium, and will be referred to later.

If very thick, dense layers of fibrous tissue are formed—if the adhesions are firm or tunneled with channels filled with yellowish, opaque fluid, or if, with the thickening of the sac and epicardium, a hæmorrhagic, fibrinous, and fluid exudate accumulates, the tuberculous nature of the affection may be suspected, and close inspection will usually show little nodular tubercles in the granulation tissue (*cf.* under Tuberculosis).

Pleuritis or **pleurisy** arises in a similar way, although there are more opportunities for the advent of infection into the pleural cavity. Every pneumonic process which approaches the surface of the lung causes at least a localized pleurisy. The occurrence of a sterile, hæmorrhagic infarction in the lung is equally productive of a localized pleural exudation or coagulation of fibrin. The types of exudate and the method and results of its organization, with the formation of adhesions, are exactly as in the case of the pericardium (Fig. 91). Great accumulation of fluid in the pleural cavity relieves at once the pain caused by the rubbing together of inflamed surfaces, but tends to cause dyspnœa through the compression of the lung. There are also direct anatomical changes produced in the lung by this

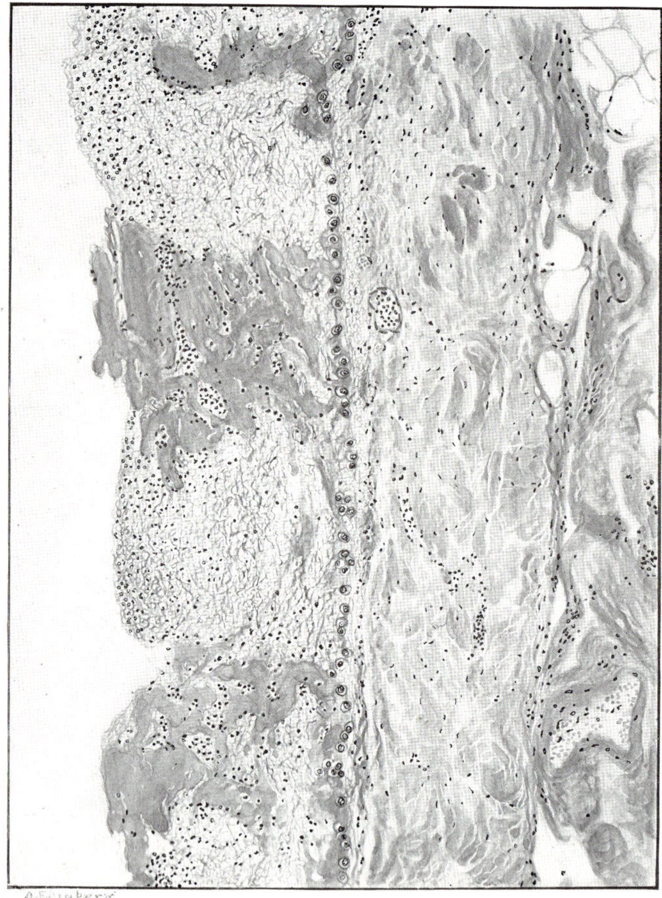

Fig. 90.—Acute pericarditis, parietal pericardium. Cross-sections of compact ridges of older fibrin are separated by a network of fresher fibrin. The serosa cells are still visible.

pressure, consisting essentially in the collapse of the alveoli, with the expulsion of the contained air.

Slight inflammatory processes in the pleura may heal completely, leaving no trace behind. More severe alterations with fibrinous exudate usually cause the formation of granulation tissue to replace the exudate, which finally binds together the pleural surfaces with adhesions. Repetition of the infection may call out a new exudate in the meshes and crevices of these fibrous adhesions. In other cases an abundant purulent exudate persists for a time and becomes walled off (empyema) and surrounded by a dense fibrous capsule which must be cut into and evacuated if recovery

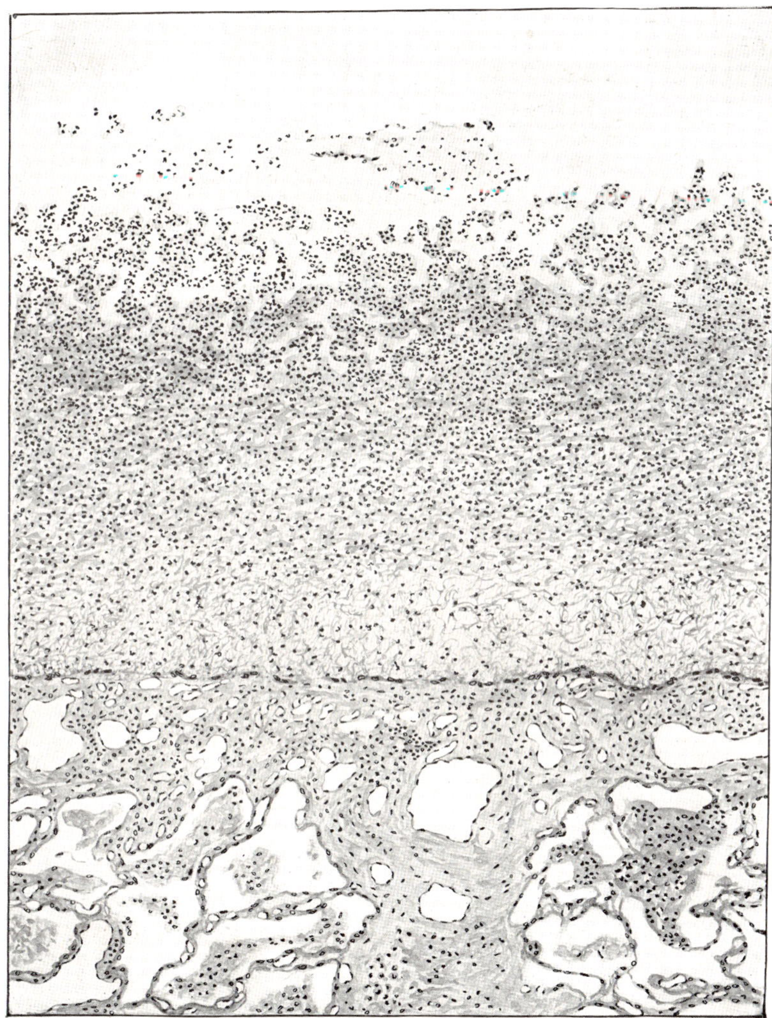

Fig. 91.—Acute fibrinopurulent pleurisy. The serosa cells are still to be seen covering the lung.

is to be expected in a reasonable time (Fig. 92). Otherwise a long time is required for the thickening and gradual removal of the exudate, and in the meanwhile the pleural tissues about it become enormously thickened and form a dense, tendon-like wall as hard as cartilage and sometimes nearly an inch thick. Great deformity of the chest follows such protracted empyemas, for if the accumulation of exudate is large, the lung is generally found compressed into a small mass retracted against the vertebral column, and fixed in this compressed state by the growth of fibrous tissue throughout it.

Peritonitis.—Little is known of peritoneal inflammation produced without the agency of bacteria, although in some instances in which bacteria

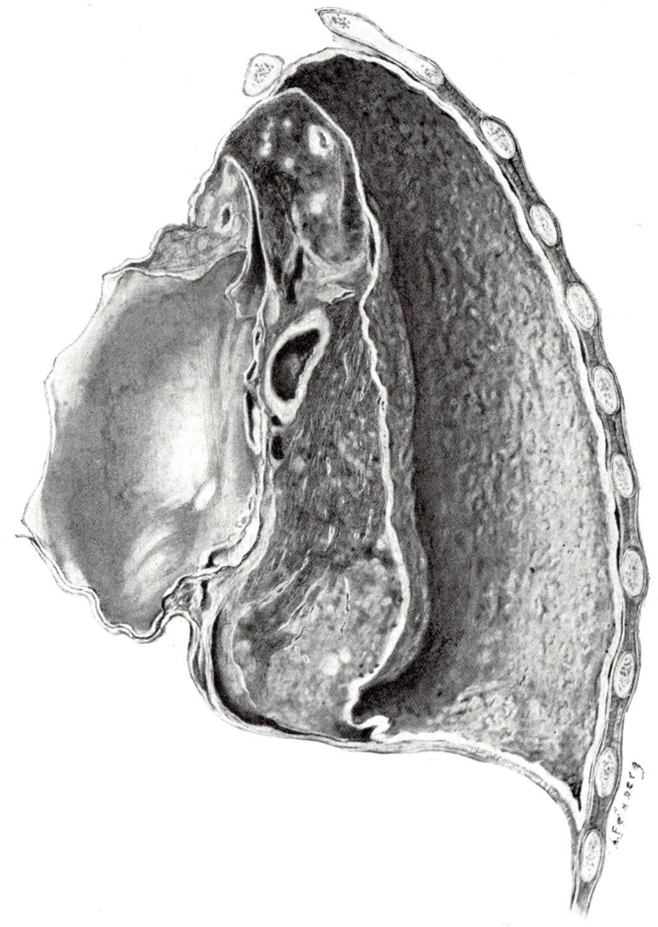

Fig. 92.—Empyema with thick fibrinopurulent exudate lining the pleural cavity. Compression and atelectasis of the lung caused by the large amount of fluid which was in the pleural cavity.

have not been actually demonstrated the exudate has been ascribed to chemical irritants. Bacteria may enter by way of the blood-stream, by growth and spreading from an adjacent or contained tissue which is diseased, or by being directly introduced through a wound in the abdominal wall or a perforation of one of the bacteria-laden organs which lie in the peritoneal cavity. Naturally, the variety of organisms which may be concerned is almost unlimited, but in the ordinary course of events the pyogenic micrococci and bacilli of the colon group are most commonly found. The tubercle bacillus occupies a special place as a common excitant of peritoneal inflammation, and the gonococcus is occasionally responsible. Of other organisms, something will be said elsewhere.

From an anatomical point of view peritoneal inflammation resembles closely that of the pleura and pericardium, except that it is more frequently seropurulent in character. Nevertheless, there are many instances, especially when the inflammation is not diffuse but confined to a limited region, in which it appears as fibrinous or fibrinopurulent exudate, which glues together opposing surfaces and is soon replaced by a growth of blood-vessels and connective-tissue cells which form fibrous adhesions. This is, of course, the most favorable type, for the adhesions prevent the further spread of infection and may themselves be mechanically harmless, or later, when healing is complete, even become attenuated and finally disappear. On the other hand, a general diffusion of bacteria, especially if there be injured tissue, foreign material, or a considerable accumulation of fluid to favor their growth, leads to hyperæmia of the whole enormous surface of the peritoneum, with the pouring-out of quantities of fluid, leucocytes, and fibrin, and the absorption of much poisonous material and many bacteria into the blood-stream. Naturally, the outcome of such an infection depends upon the balance between the power of resistance of the individual and the virulence of the bacteria, and this balance is greatly affected by the presence of injured tissue in the peritoneum. The normal peritoneum can annihilate many more bacteria without the appearance of any peritonitis.

Primary or hæmatogenous peritonitis is often produced by the pneumococcus, which gains entrance to the body by way of the tonsils or some similar portal of entry. In a case recently observed at autopsy no distinct lesion which could have played this part was discoverable on most careful search, and yet the whole peritoneal surface was covered with a thick, greenish-yellow, fibrinopurulent exudate which slipped off easily into the turbid fluid which filled the cavity. The Pneumococcus mucosus was there in pure culture. Secondary forms of peritonitis include those which follow gunshot or other wounds of the abdomen, among which surgical operation wounds unfortunately hold a high place, because they are so frequently concerned with infected tissues and organs in the cavity. The seriousness of such injuries as gunshot or stab wounds lies chiefly in their opening into the stomach or intestine and allowing the escape of food or fæcal material loaded with bacteria. The peritonitis which follows surgical intervention is usually the result of unskilful attempts to anastomose intestinal loops or other infected organs in which tissues are left stretched and badly supplied with blood, or sutures passed through an infected area with constriction of too much tissue.

Secondary peritonitis resulting directly from disease of the organs lying in the cavity may begin in several ways. Ulceration of stomach or duodenum proceeds often to perforation and discharge of their contents. Were it not for the food, the juices of these parts of the digestive tract are almost sterile, and prompt surgical operation with closure of the perforation usually cures the patient. Typhoid ulcerations in the lower ileum, tuberculous ulcers, amœbic and other dysenteric ulcers and the phlegmonous and gangrenous forms of appendicitis rupture and perforate in the same way, with discharge of bacteria of the intestinal contents, as well as those which have directly caused the lesion. Of these, the typhoid ulcers are perhaps least likely to be guarded by adhesions. Even without actual perforation, peritonitis arises when the wall of the intestine becomes necrotic, so that bacteria can wander through, as happens in strangulated hernia, intussusception, volvulus, infarction of the intestine through embolism or thrombosis of the mesenteric vessels, etc. In intestinal obstruction from whatever cause the part of the intestine above the obstruction becomes greatly dilated and stretched, and its mucosa ulcerated, so that the passage of bacteria through the wall is easy, even if not precipitated by actual rupture of one of these ulcers.

Extension of the infective process from inflammatory lesions of the gall-bladder and ducts, from renal and perirenal abscesses, from the Fallopian tubes, or even through the walls of the uterus in puerperal infections, occurs but requires no special explanation here.

Gonococcal infection by way of the Fallopian tubes may produce diffuse peritonitis, with rather dry, tenacious exudate of fibrin. It is not common.

APPENDICITIS

The extraordinary frequence of appendicitis, and its extreme seriousness in many cases, make its study important. It will serve well as an example of bacterial infection, followed by inflammation and generally by healing.

The wall of the appendix is composed of various tissues which correspond with those making up the rest of the intestine. The lumen may be stretched into cylindrical form, but in general collapses into a narrow space, which is Y shaped on cross-section, one limb of the Y reaching toward the mesenteric attachment. The mucosa sinks into crypts, as in the colon, but has no villi. It is peculiarly rich in agminated nodules of lymphoid tissue. The appendix most commonly extends inward to the brim of the pelvis from the cæcum, but great variations are found in its position, as well as in its size, its mesenteric attachment, and in its relation to the folds of the peritoneum. These matters of surgical interest may be read of in Kelly's monograph.

Appendicitis is an acute infectious disease produced by the invasion of bacteria from the lumen into the mucosa and other walls. The hæmatogenous infection of the appendix wall by bacteria transported from infected tonsils, which Kretz regards as a common origin of appendicitis, has not been clearly shown to take place. If it does so, it must be considered an exceptional occurrence, and does not explain the majority of cases in which infection from the lumen can be conclusively demonstrated. Appendicitis may heal, leaving characteristic scars which predispose to a renewed attack, and it is usually in this way, that is, in the occurrence of repeated attacks, that one is justified in speaking of a chronic appendicitis.

Strangely enough, there is still much question as to the bacteria which cause it, and probably several sorts are concerned. Aschoff and his students find a Gram-positive diplococcus and Gram-positive bacilli as the most characteristic organisms. Apparently, streptococci, perhaps accom-

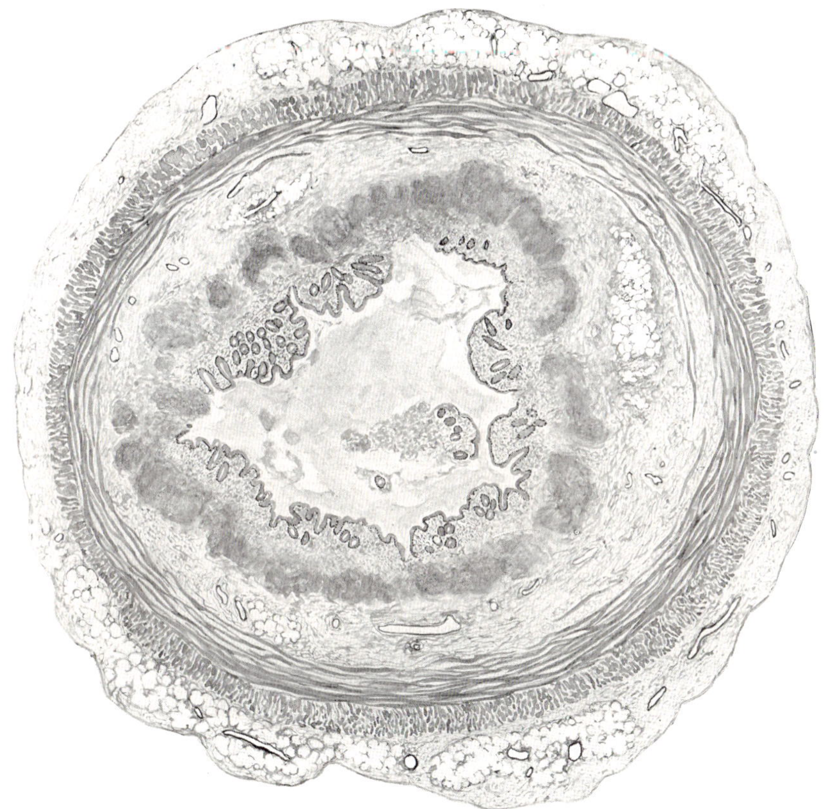

Fig. 93.—Acute appendicitis with beginning necrosis of the mucosa.

panied by the colon bacillus, have been found most often, but a great many other forms are also described, even including certain anaërobic bacilli. Mechanical factors favor the lodgment of the organisms in the mucosa, especially the kinking or sharp bending of the terminal portion or the presence of obstruction caused by previous inflammation and scarring. Infected foreign bodies of a sharp angular form may have the same effect, but the prevalent idea that foreign bodies are commonly present and the ordinary cause of the disease is quite erroneous. Nearly all the "cherry-stones" and "date-seeds" or "grape-seeds" which are found in the appendix are really not seeds at all, but concentrically laminated masses of fæcal material. They are injurious inasmuch as they may cause obstruction and allow bacteria to accumulate behind them, but Aschoff insists that they do not themselves injure and infect the mucosa, but that they rather protect it.

As may be determined from the study of the very early stages, infection

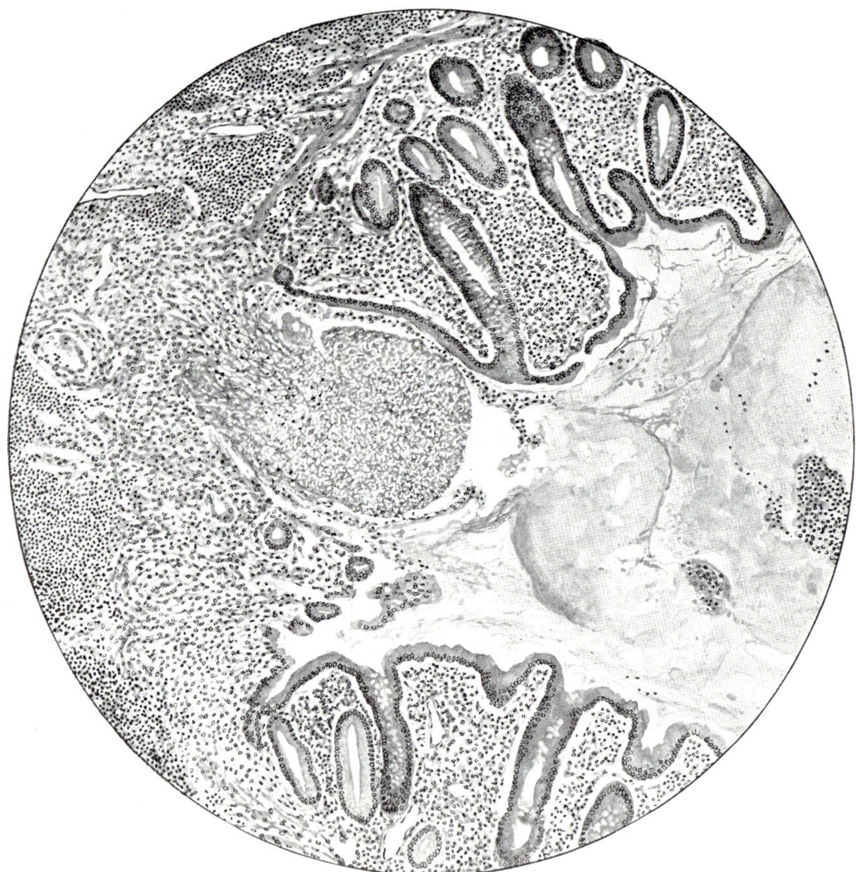

Fig. 94.—Acute appendicitis. A portion of Fig. 93 enlarged to show the earliest changes.

begins in the mucosa in the bottom of one of the grooves which form the Y- or X-shaped lumen in cross-section. Starting as a tiny break in the epithelium, with an underlying accumulation of polymorphonuclear leucocytes, the inflammatory reaction spreads outward in a widening area toward the outer surface. This diffuse inflammation may be practically bacteria free in its outer part, but nevertheless reaches the serosa and extends along the walls of the appendix. It is the phlegmonous type of

Aschoff, and may sooner or later show the formation of small abscesses anywhere in the affected region. Such abscesses, causing liquefaction of the wall, bring about perforation either into the lumen of the organ or into the peritoneum. Such rupture to the outside is, of course, the origin of an acute spreading peritonitis, unless it is limited by adhesions from a previous attack. Even without actual perforation, however, the extension of the phlegmonous inflammation sets up an acute fibrinous exudative peritonitis over the wall of the appendix itself. The organ is swollen and reddened, and roughened by the presence of the fibrin. When an abscess approaches the surface, it is recognizable as an opaque yellow spot in the congested wall (Fig. 95).

It is even more common to find that, instead of remaining as a minute lesion of the mucosa, the infection spreads so as to cause rather extensive patches of necrosis, in which the outlines of the crypts can still be made out, although a dense fibrinous exudate welds the dead tissue of the mucosa into a sort of false membrane. Numerous hæmorrhages accompany this, and with the loosening and discharge of the false membrane deep ulcers are left (Fig. 96). Extension into the depth is rapid, and may proceed to destruction of the whole thickness of the wall and perforation, especially since the cavity is often distended to bursting with the exudate. Such extreme lesions are not likely to heal, and unless saved by operation, the patient succumbs to a general peritonitis. If, however, there have been previous attacks of milder character, the appendix may have become adherent to the surrounding tissues by the organization of fibrinous exudate between its surface and that of adjacent coils of intestine. In that case the material discharged through the perforation may not pass into the general peritoneal cavity, but only into contact with these adhesions, where an abscess is then formed. Such periappendiceal abscesses are sometimes quite large, and may contain the necrotic débris of the appendix, floating in pus. They are perhaps not so common now as formerly, nor so common as they would be in an age of less prompt and aggressive surgeons.

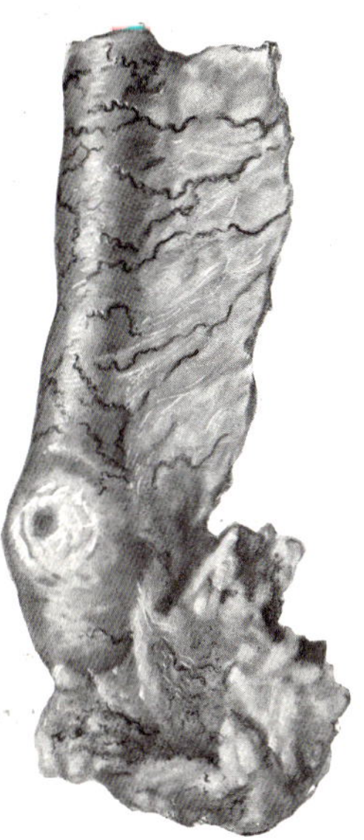

Fig. 95.—Acute appendicitis with perforating ulcer.

Slighter lesions which stop short of destruction of the whole wall may heal without intervention, and such a person is then liable to a renewed acute attack unless his appendix is removed by operation in the interval. The mucosa may not have been very widely destroyed, especially in the suppurative form, but even when it is ulcerated away over one side of the lumen, it is regenerated from that which remains and the lumen is kept open. If it be destroyed all the way round, the cavity usually collapses and becomes obliterated by a continuous growth of granulation tissue (Fig. 97). Even when the destruction has been very slight and the inflam-

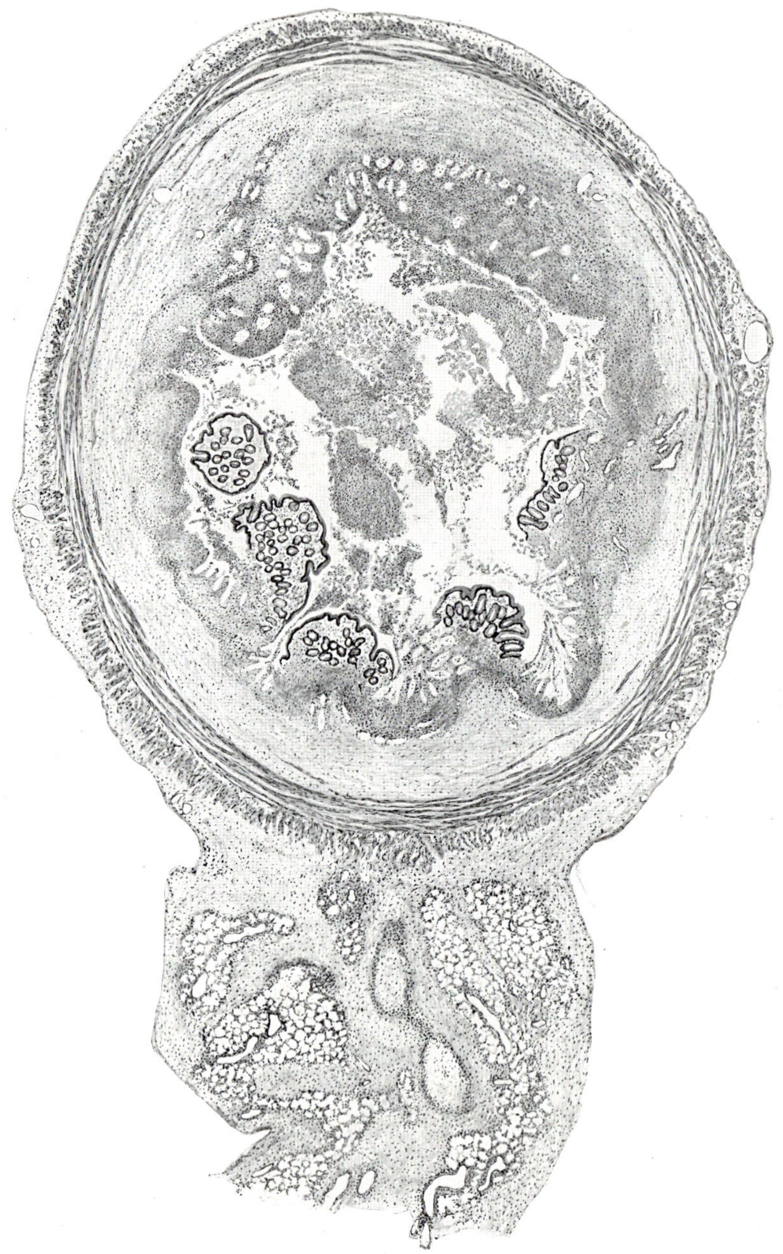

Fig. 96.—Acute phlegmonous appendicitis.

matory reaction in the walls moderate, scars are left which indurate the submucosa and which persist in the interstices of the musculature. The elastic tissue, which has a characteristic arrangement for each layer, is partly destroyed, and though regenerated, is left greatly distorted.

Various complications and sequelæ occur, among which is the general or localized peritonitis already mentioned. This, if survived, often leaves adhesions, which may later cause mechanical obstruction to the intestine, either by kinking and constricting loops, or by facilitating the occurrence

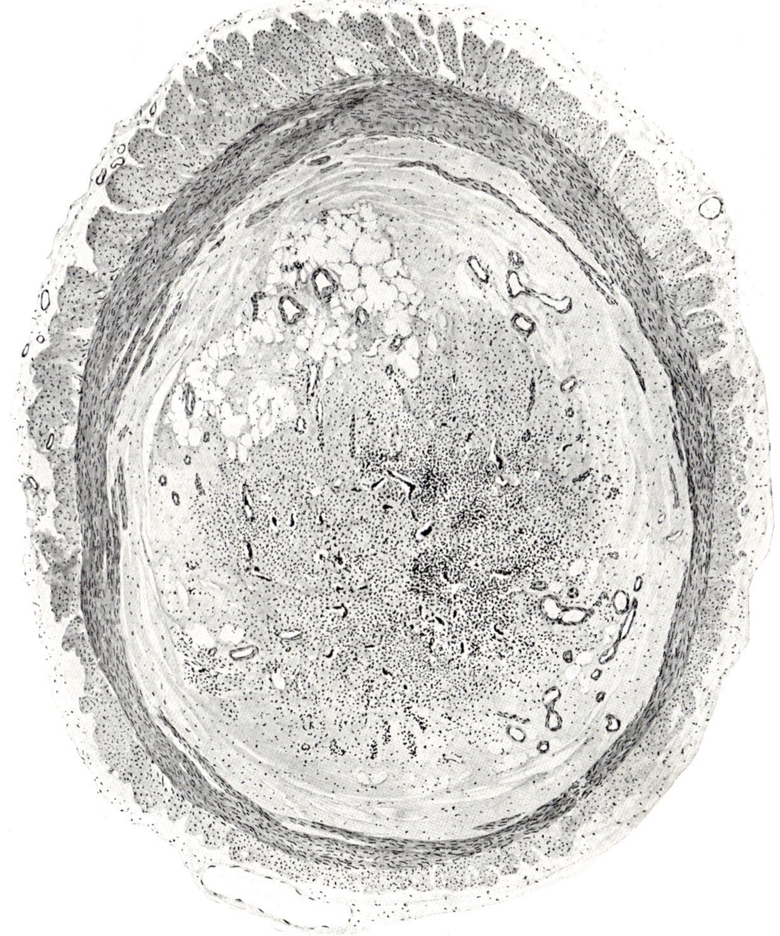

Fig. 97.—Sequel of old healed appendicitis. Obliteration of lumen.

of internal hernial entanglements. Extension or burrowing of the peri-appendiceal abscess may lead to the accumulation of pus in extraordinary places, among which the subdiaphragmatic region about the liver, in front or behind, and on either side, is conspicuous. These are the so-called subphrenic abscesses, which may, of course, have other points of origin.

Thrombosis of the nearby iliac and femoral veins may follow appendicitis, but more serious, and even more characteristic, is the formation of an

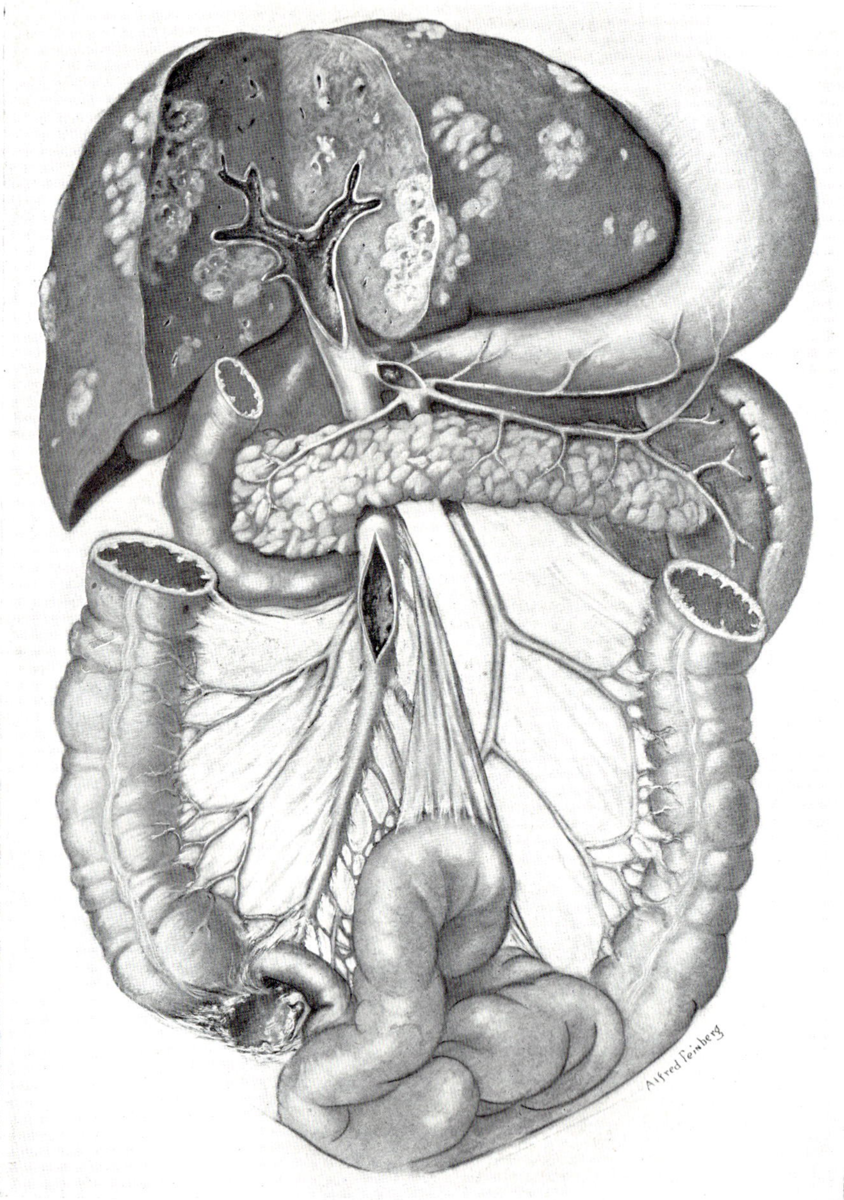

Fig. 98.—Suppurative pylephlebitis arising from appendix abscess. Numerous abscesses in the liver.

infected thrombus in the branches of the portal vein which lead away from the appendix itself. On this day of writing a case has been observed in which the branches of the vein leading from an abscess around the appendix were found filled, not with blood, but with a purulent, greenish-white material. The main trunk of the vein, greatly dilated and thickened, was full of the same material. The splenic vein was plugged at its entrance by a firm thrombus, so that the inferior mesenteric vein which joins it before that point was reached evidently discharged its blood by way of the splenic vein and anastomosing channels to the stomach and œsophagus. In the liver every branch of the portal was full of soft, purulent thrombus material, and there were numerous large abscesses and groups of smaller ones. This is the so-called *suppurative pylephlebitis*. In this case the infection extended even further, and there were abscesses in lungs and spleen (Fig. 98).

LITERATURE

Aschoff: Wurmfortsatzentzündung, Jena, 1908.
Aschoff: Ergeb. d. inn. Med. u. Kinderh., 1912, ix, 1.
Kelly and Hurdon: Diseases of Vermiform Appendix, 1905.
Kretz: Mitth. a. d. Grenz. d. Med. u. Chir., 1907, xvii, 1.
Kretz: Verh. Dtsch. Path. Gesellsch., 1907, x, 229; 1910, xiv, 157.
Noll: Mitth. a. d. Grenz. d. Med. u. Chir., 1907, xvii, 249.
Oberndorfer: Ergeb. d. allg. Path., 1909, $xiii_1$, 527.
Wätzold: Ziegler's Beitr., 1907, xlii, 260.

ENDOCARDITIS

Bacterial or other injury to the heart valves or to any other part of the endocardium is like injury to the endothelium of the blood-vessels, and is peculiar in its results inasmuch as any reaction must occur in the streaming blood. The common effect, just as in the case of a vein, is the formation of a thrombus upon the injured place. This generally occludes the vein, but in the wider space of the heart, and especially on the valves, where the stream is rapid, it forms an irregular cap of platelets with a little fibrin and a few leucocytes and red corpuscles. It is rather important to realize that this is not exactly the same as an exudate poured out from the capillaries of a serous surface, for in the case of the valves it appears on a tissue which has no capillaries, and has itself a structure corresponding with that of a thrombus. Later, if the thrombus contains active bacteria, leucocytes wander to it through the valve, and capillary blood-vessels stretch out from the base of the valve through its substance until they reach it. Then one may see a true inflammatory reaction in progress. Of course, when bacteria settle on the endocardium, covering the musculature of the heart, the primary thrombus formed by the passing blood is far more quickly joined by an acute inflammatory reaction from the heart-wall (Fig. 99).

It seems that all cases of thrombo-endocarditis are really dependent upon the invasion of bacteria into the endocardium, although it is not always possible to demonstrate their presence. The mild and beginning forms that produce very small warty or verrucose vegetations are the ones in which it is most difficult to find organisms. They occur very often with rheumatism, of which, in spite of the persistently repeated claims that it is the effect of diplococcus or streptococcus infection, we do not yet know the cause.

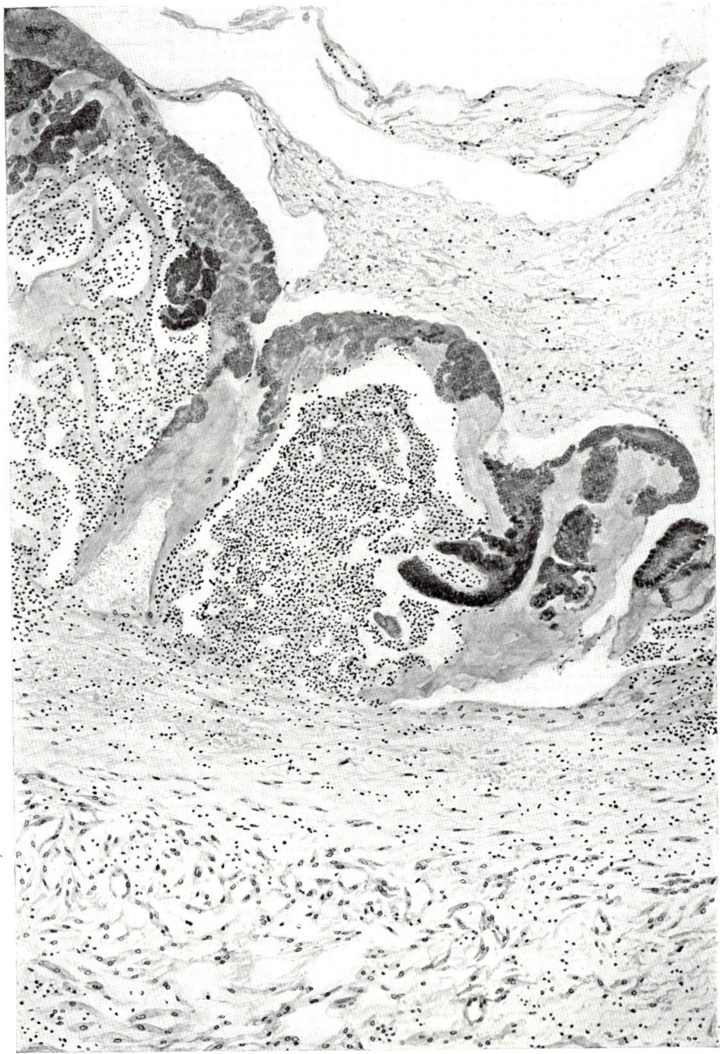

Fig. 99.—Acute endocarditis. Vegetations upon the wall of the auricle showing great numbers of bacteria and an intense inflammatory reaction.

It is thought possible that toxins alone might produce destructive lesions of the endothelium of the valves, and numerous experiments have been made, with some success, in producing such endothelial injuries because it seemed possible that they might in turn afford a foothold for bacteria. There are thickenings of the valves which occur in old people, and which are thought to be gradually produced by mechanical strain, and there are thickenings and distortions brought about by a process apparently identical with arteriosclerosis (Beitzke, Martino). But the lesions which we may call endocarditis seem to be essentially bacterial in origin.

Many organisms are concerned in the production of endocardial vegetations, but the different forms of streptococci, the Staphylococcus aureus, the pneumococcus, and the gonococcus are by far the most important. The influenza bacillus has been found several times, and various other bacteria in single cases, but such organisms as the typhoid bacillus, the diphtheria bacillus, the colon bacillus, etc., are probably not the actual cause of the lesion, although they may be found as secondary invaders.

Clearly, the bacteria reach the valves by way of the circulating blood, and from the situation of the vegetations one cannot escape the impression that they lodge directly upon the surface of the valve. It is not at any indifferent point, but, as is clear from the inspection of any large series of affected hearts, upon the so-called line of closure, that they produce their first effects. It is easily seen that the valves do not come together only at their very edges, but rather along a somewhat thickened or fortified line a short way back from the edge, this line being supported in the case of the semilunar valves by the corpora Arantii. In these valves the delicate film which forms the actual edge accurately completes the closure, even though it is often perforated by many fenestrations. So, too, in the tricuspid and mitral valves, upon the backs of which the insertions of the chordæ tendineæ are spread out in several rows, the filmy edge which is also held tense by delicate cords accurately completes the closure. Thus, it is not on this complementary film that vegetations first appear, but definitely along the main line of closure, from which they extend so as to involve any other part of the valve, the heart-wall, or the chordæ tendineæ. How they happen to lodge there has long been discussed, and it has generally been thought that the mechanical beating together of the valves at this point catches them up from the blood and drives them into close contact with the tissue, so that they cannot slip by as they do over the smooth walls of the arteries. Nevertheless, one sometimes sees independent lesions of the same kind on the endocardium of the auricle or ventricle. Rosenow has recently revived the old view of Koester that bacteria reach the valve as emboli by way of the capillary blood-vessels. This idea was disproved by the work of Coen and v. Langer,* who found that the semilunar valves contained no capillaries, and the atrioventricular valves were supplied only at their base, so that such embolism seemed impossible. Whether this is quite true or not, Rosenow has shown that, with large injections of the Streptococcus viridans, he can produce bacterial colonies in the substance of the valves beneath intact endothelium, and surrounded by a gross hæmorrhage. Such hæmorrhages are best seen two or three days after the injection, and before any obvious vegetation has appeared on the valve. Whether they offer the explanation of the mechanism of the first appearance of endocar-

* Arch. f. mikr. Anat., xxvii; Virch. Arch., 109.

dial vegetations is by no means settled, and Rosenow himself states that they can be most easily understood in those cases in which previous injury of the valves has led to their vascularization.

Very complete injections of the dog's heart can be made by clamping the aorta and injecting India ink into the carotid before the heart has quite stopped beating. The whole heart instantly becomes black, and on opening it and washing it in a stream of water the valves stand out perfectly white against the black background. Under the stereoscopic microscope it is clearly seen that the capillaries end like the top of a hedge along the base of the semilunar valves, not one of them penetrating its substance. In the mitral and tricuspid valves they are spread apart more loosely, and do not end so

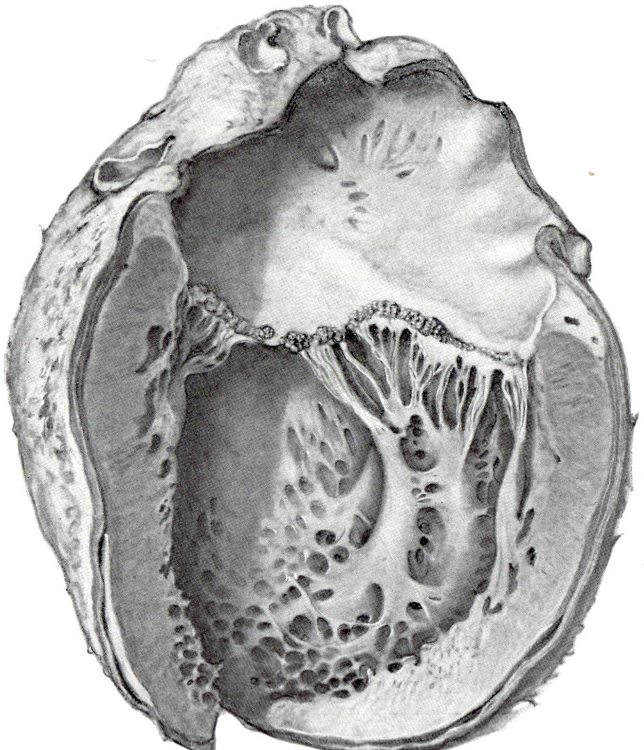

Fig. 100.—Verrucose endocarditis of the mitral valve with chronic adhesive pericarditis. (From a case of rheumatism.)

regularly along a line. Occasional long, thread-like capillaries extend into the valve for about a third of its length, but not one approaches the marginal portion. The papillary muscles are black with the injection, but only the smallest pencil of capillaries spreads into the root of each chorda tendinea, and the actual cord contains none. In the normal dog's heart the line of closure is not perfectly smooth, but slightly corrugated or nodular, and even after the India ink has been washed away in a stream of water, so that the endocardium is perfectly clear, one may see under the microscope minute granules of the ink adhering in these irregularities. Is it not possible that this unique area of roughness mechanically affords a foothold for circulating bacteria, just as it retains particles of the ink?

While cases of endocarditis differ among themselves in detail according to the bacteria concerned and their localization, they are alike in principle. Those following rheumatism show the smallest thrombi or vegetations along the line of closure, although with time these may be added to until a considerable size is attained. This is the so-called verrucose endocarditis, and the vegetations in which it is often impossible to find any bacteria become organized quickly, so that they are firm and gray and no longer easily pulled off. Even with fairly complete healing they may be recognizable by their form, but in other cases the scar leads to thickening and shortening of the valve, which, with the nodular irregularities along the edges, make the closure inefficient (Fig. 100).

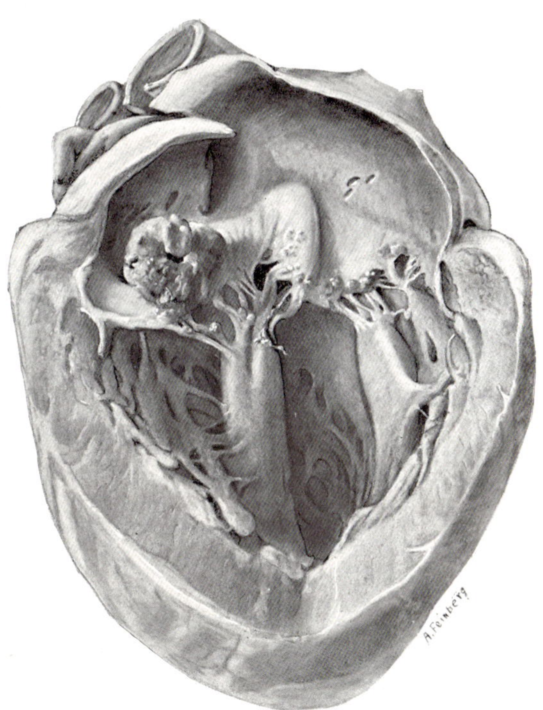

Fig. 101.—Large vegetation upon the mitral valve obstructing its orifice. There are smaller vegetations at other points.

The streptococcus is likely to give rise to larger vegetations, which grow rapidly and are found in a crumbly, soft state. Occasionally they are so massive as practically to occlude the whole valvular orifice (Fig. 101). This is true, too, of those produced by the gonococcus, although there a hint as to the nature of the infection may be gained from its frequent occurrence in the valves of the right side of the heart, and from the rapid destruction of the valves themselves, so that one frequently sees great thrombus masses flapping back and forth on the end of a thread of tissue, which is all that remains of the valve. Naturally, either obstruction or an extreme insufficiency follows such events. Naturally, too, emboli of infected thrombus particles are scattered into the circulation. Such *ulcerative endocarditis* may be produced by the Staphylococcus aureus, which is rapidly destructive, and also by the pneumococcus. Every position may be ultimately assumed by the vegetations; they grow away from the line of closure to the edge of the valve, and down into the sinus of Valsalva or along the chordæ tendineæ (S. viridans). These may rupture, since it is the advance of bacteria which determines the extension of the vegetations, and the necrotic ends of the broken chordæ flap loosely in the blood-stream and are capped with thrombus material (Fig. 102). Vegetations extend along the auricular wall, covering whole patches of it with a flattened, rough mat of thrombus, or, where the broken chordæ flap against the endocardium there are sown bacteria which rapidly cover themselves with new thrombi. Loss of substance through necrosis of the valve itself underneath the vegetation often leads to perforation, so that blood regurgitates through the

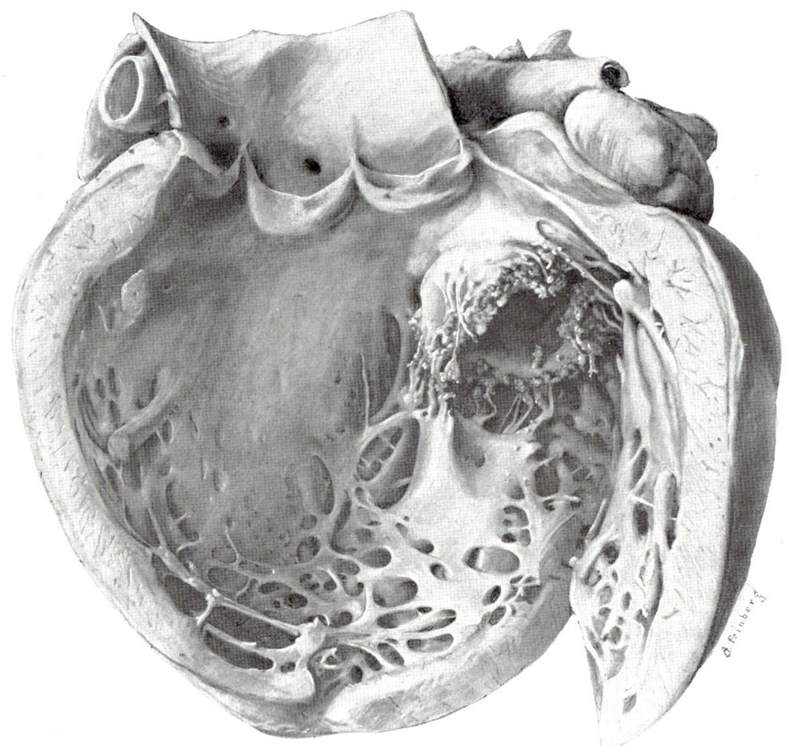

Fig. 102.—Endocarditis involving the mitral valve and causing rupture of the chordæ tendineæ, which are covered with vegetations.

hole thus formed. The edge of such a perforated valve may swing loose in time as a thread bearing a thrombus, and we have seen such a thrombus still attached driven into the orifice of the coronary artery, blocking it completely and causing death. Or if the valve is not at once perforated, it may bulge at the weakened part into a sort of aneurysmal sac which projects into the ventricle, or in the case of the mitral valve, into the auricle.

In some cases when the vegetation extends to the base of the valve the myocardium may become involved, and a burrowing abscess extend far into its substance.

Libman has studied the subacute form of endocarditis produced by the Streptococcus viridans, and finds that it affects the aortic, and much more commonly the mitral, valve, producing large yellow, pink, or greenish vegetations, rarely with actual ulceration of the valve. Auricular vegetations (Fig. 103) and others involving the chordæ are common, and bacterial emboli are scattered in numbers, producing characteristic embolic glomerular lesions in the kidney and gross infarcts in other organs. Although, as in the other forms, the blood is infected with these bacteria, there may come a bacteria-free stage in which the vegetations heal. This is accomplished by the calcification of the thrombus, together with its organization and the great distortion of the valve. But just as the vegetations in this infection are found to have developed upon the scars of older lesions, so upon these healing vegetations new bacteria may be developed and begin the process anew.

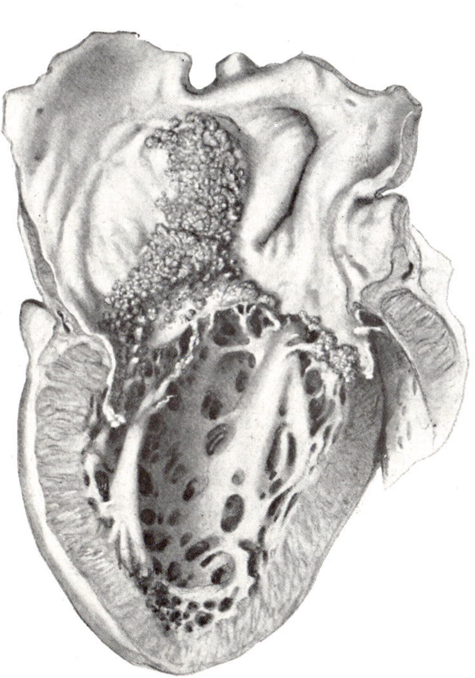

Fig. 103.—Mural vegetations on the left auricle accompanying vegetations of the mitral valve and chordæ.

Probably in all forms of bacterial endocarditis some such healing may occur if the patient can live long enough, but such roughened valves are very susceptible to new localization of the bacteria. At best such healing is advantageous only in that with it the danger of succumbing to the bacteria is at an end, but the disease cannot be said to be healed when a large, calcified mass still hangs on a valve, or when the valves are shortened, thickened, and distorted by the scars that replace the thrombi.

The anatomical results are then, as may be gathered from what has been said, as follows: Fresh vegetations are produced along the line of closure on the face of the valve, more commonly in the case of the mitral and aortic than in that of the tricuspid and pulmonary, although these are also frequently affected. The bacteria may be destroyed before they produce any greater injury to the valve than is sufficient to cause the thrombus formation, upon which organization of the thrombus occurs exactly as it might anywhere else, except that blood-vessels must grow a long way to reach it. With the completion of this process the valves are left beaded with nodules of fibrous tissue, which later shrink and flatten themselves, and although with the most favorable result the delicacy of the valve is impaired and the smoothness of its closing surface lost, still no great degree of insufficiency may result. When the bacteria are not so easily destroyed, they grow in the substance of the valve and cause more or less necrosis, followed by loss of substance not only from the overlying thrombus, but from the valve itself. This ulceration and crumbling of the larger vegetations afford a source of emboli, and by eating away the valve give rise to a more and more extensive insufficiency with regurgitation of the blood. Even without ulceration, large heaped-up thrombi prevent the accurate closure of the valves, with the same result. They in their turn may become organized, and the eroded remnants of valves may heal, naturally with the production of extraordinary deformities and distortions.

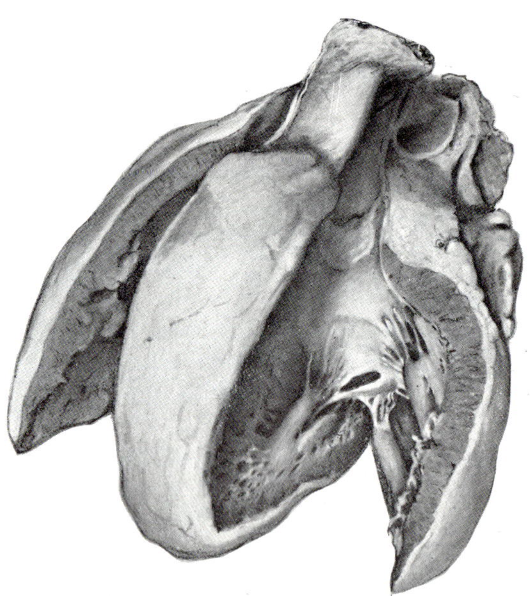

Fig. 104.—Mitral stenosis. Great narrowing and scarring of the mitral orifice, which stands open. Hypertrophy of the right ventricle and left auricle. The heart is viewed from the apex.

Large vegetations may in themselves block the passage of blood through the valvular orifice, producing a kind of acute stenosis. But beside this there is the effect of healing, which commonly thickens the whole of the valves, welding them together with dense plaques of fibrous tissue, which form in the place of the vegetations and extend up on the valves toward their base and toward the angles, where they adjoin one another. The contraction of this tissue brings together into a narrow slit the boundaries of the valvular orifice, producing the well-known stenosis of the valves (Fig. 104). In the case of the mitral there is commonly a great thickening of the left auricle and of its endocardium, and from the mitral ring down to the mitral orifice there is formed a dense, rigid funnel at the bottom of which is the small crescentic slit with rough, nodular edges, often discolored by yellowish pigment and made rigid by extensive deposits of calcium. The edges of this orifice, if brought together, fit pretty well, and appear as an irregular line in the bottom of the otherwise smooth and rounded funnel. From that line down to the actual edge of the valve is a precipitous surface representing the thickness of the valve and fitting the opposite one. Often, however, the valve is so rigid that this orifice stands permanently open, causing insufficiency as well as stenosis. The chordæ tendineæ are very much shortened and thickened into dense white cords. Sometimes, as in a case studied recently, the stenosis is produced by scars occupying only the edges of the valves, so that their basal parts remain delicate and soft, and sometimes, though rarely, there remains a delicate edge on each valve

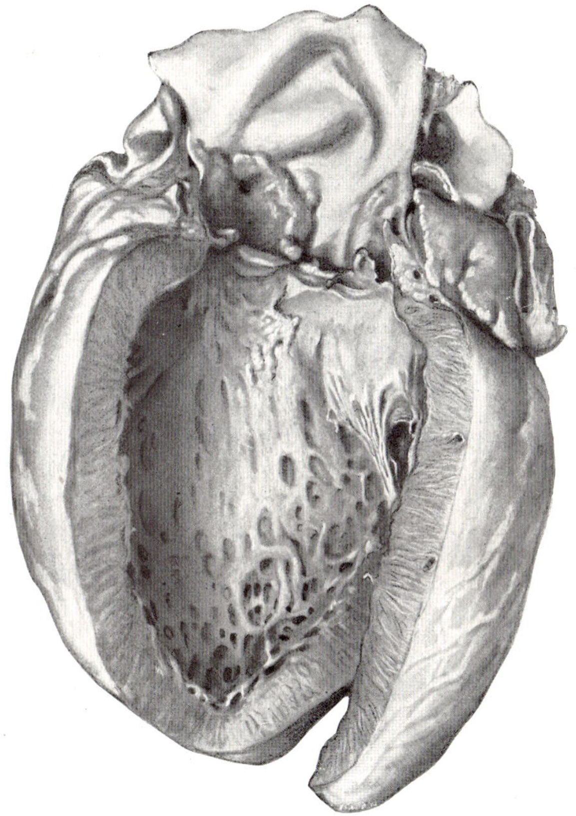

Fig. 105.—Insufficiency of aortic valve. Hypertrophy and dilatation of left ventricle. Thickening of endocardium below the incompetent valve.

capable of completing the closure, so that there is stenosis without insufficiency. On the edges of the stenosed valves it is common to find fresh vegetations. In the case of the aortic valves exactly the same things may arise—the valves are sometimes thickened and stiffened by old scars in which lime salts are deposited, or their edges alone may be thickened into round cords which interfere with accurate closure (Fig. 105). When the valves are greatly thickened, they adhere by their angles and fuse into a sort of triangular orifice, bounded on all sides by rigid, jagged, calcified walls which offer great obstruction to the passage of the blood-stream and are useless to prevent its eddying back when systole is over.

That combinations of these things may arise is often exemplified, as in a case just observed, in which there was found tricuspid stenosis with exquisite minute fresh vegetations, similar fresh vegetations along the line of closure of the pulmonary valves, extreme mitral stenosis, again with a fringe of minute thrombi, and thickened, insufficient aortic valves with thrombotic deposits on their ventricular surfaces. The effects of all these changes we shall discuss elsewhere. Here it suffices to show them as examples of the processes of inflammation and repair.

Although it has been said that endocarditis is essentially a bacterial disease, distortions of the valves may arise (especially in the case of the aortic) through syphilitic infection of the aorta involving the valves, and apparently also through the ordinary arteriosclerosis. Syphilitic aortitis, involving, as it does, the lodgement of the spirochæta in the adventitia and media of the vessel, may apparently be reproduced in the aortic valves themselves. Its early stages have not been studied, but the healing processes, like those in the aorta, result in scars and retractions, and it is shown that this course of events, never at any time accompanied by thrombotic vegetations, may shorten, thicken, and distort the valves in such a way as to produce a marked regurgitation. Indeed, a very large proportion of the cases of aortic insufficiency develops on the basis of a syphilitic infection, and the Wassermann reaction is an indispensable clinical procedure in every case.

Whether the ordinary arteriosclerosis is of as much importance as was once thought in encroaching upon these valves and disturbing their function is questionable. There are many cases in which, with an old arteriosclerosis, the aortic valves are found united at their angles and thickened, but it is impossible to say with certainty that this is the uncomplicated effect of the sclerosis. It is true that such fatty and sclerotic plaques are found on the back of the mitral valve, but the part they play in actual disease of the heart-valves is relatively slight.

LOBULAR PNEUMONIA OR BRONCHOPNEUMONIA

Focal or patchy inflammation in the lung due to infection beginning in the terminal bronchioles is an exceedingly common condition, of serious import in both children and adults. It is not strictly lobular in its distribution, since only a part of each lobule may be affected or several lobules at once; nor is it in all cases caused by a primary infection of the bronchi, since a practically indistinguishable condition may arise through distribution of bacteria into the lung by way of the blood-stream. In most of those cases, however, the bacteria are carried in emboli of thrombus material, and the lesions are apt to assume the form of abscesses in the lung substance.

In spite of these objections the names bronchopneumonia and lobular pneumonia will remain in common use.

Bacteria exist quite commonly in the respiratory tract in small numbers, causing no disturbance, but if the carrier of such bacteria be weakened by another disease, by injury, exposure to cold, or any of a great variety of things that seem to lower resistance to infection, invasion and destruction of the tissue of the bronchioles may occur. It is doubtless partly for this reason that lobular pneumonia forms such an extremely common terminal event in protracted illness from chronic nephritis, rickets, typhoid fever, chronic anæmias, long-standing tumor-growths, etc. It is partly on this account, too, that this form of pneumonia is so very common in the course of certain acute diseases, such as measles, scarlet fever, and diphtheria, but there the additional reason exists that the whole upper air-passages are usually intensely infected. The coryza of measles, the sore throat of scarlet fever, and the membranous exudate of diphtheria which may extend into the small bronchi are well known.

Another well-defined group of cases exists in which foreign material infected with bacteria is aspirated into the bronchi because, for some reason, the ordinary protective reflexes fail This is seen in extremely ill, delirious, or unconscious patients, in intoxicated people, in the insane, and in patients anæsthetized for surgical operations. Vomiting gives an opportunity for the aspiration of gastric contents, but saliva drawn into the bronchioles is also laden with bacteria.

It is evident that almost every sort of bacteria may be concerned in one or other of these forms. Especially when foreign particles reach the bronchi, it is likely that many different organisms will accompany them. In the cases which seem to begin spontaneously the pneumococcus is very common. In those associated with exanthematic diseases and diphtheria the streptococcus is prominent, but other pyogenic microörganisms, as well as the influenza bacillus, Friedländer's bacillus, and many others may play important parts.

The lung is commonly quite glossy on its pleural surface, but if any foci of consolidation lie very near, the pleura is found covered with a thin, fibrinous exudate at least over that region. On section the consolidated parts can be felt, and can usually be seen as slightly elevated patches, varying in color from a dark red or blackish red through the precise color of the remainder of the tissue to paler and paler grayish rose or yellowish gray (Fig. 106). It is hard to see them when their color is quite the same as that of the surroundings, but they can generally be made evident by gently pulling the lung tissue this way and that. The alveoli stretch out into long rhombs as though one stretched diagonally a fine silk gauze, but those which contain exudate resist this slightly and stand out by contrast.

They vary in size from the minutest foci, which occupy only a few alveoli about the termination of a bronchiole, to large, confluent areas which stretch over a considerable portion of a lobe of the lung. The variety in their appearance and color is largely due to the fact that the exudate changes in color as time passes. Red corpuscles, which give it a dark or hæmorrhagic hue at first, fade through being broken up, and the grayish color of the increasingly abundant leucocytes comes into view. The exudate is often very loosely arranged—with only a few cells in each alveolus and, in many cases, probably most of those in children, it does not form such rough projecting plugs as in lobar pneumonia. From the bronchi there may usually be expressed a drop of purulent fluid. But in other cases the consolidated patches are firm, and the alveoli filled with projecting masses that are in every way like those seen in lobar pneumonia.

When they are very small and arranged in clusters around the ends of the bronchial branches, their relation to the bronchi can be easily made out, both microscopically and on inspection of the gross organ, but when they become confluent, this relation is no longer so clear.

Microscopically, the condition is equally variegated in appearance. At times, when a sudden aspiration of infected foreign material has occurred

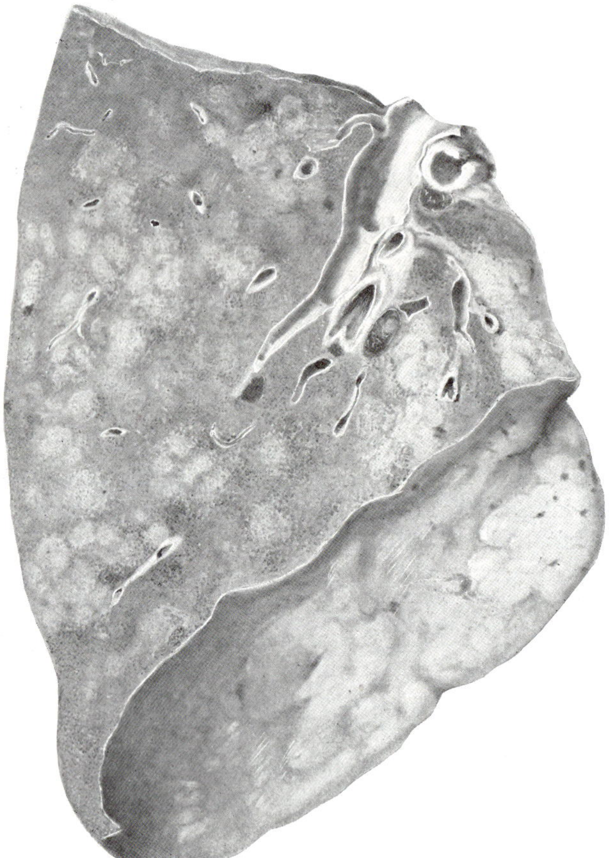

Fig. 106.—Lobular pneumonia in adult lung, showing patchy areas of consolidation.

shortly before death, these particles can be seen in the bronchioles or alveoli loaded with bacteria, and surrounded almost solely by red corpuscles. Such foci are soft, impalpable, and deep red. In other cases time is given for the growth of enormous numbers of bacteria, which fill the bronchus and every alveolus, but which, although they destroy the tissue, seem to kill the patient without rousing any inflammatory reaction. Such patches are soft and gray, and often surrounded by a zone of hæmorrhage. When much gastric juice has been drawn into the lung, one may smell it and distinguish yellowish, green, opaque discolorations about the bronchi and in patches in the lung. The tissue is softened and disintegrated, generally without much inflammatory reaction. It is probable that death always follows rapidly, and that partial digestion of the injured tissue proceeds after death.

Ordinarily, however, fewer bacteria reach the terminal bronchiole, and

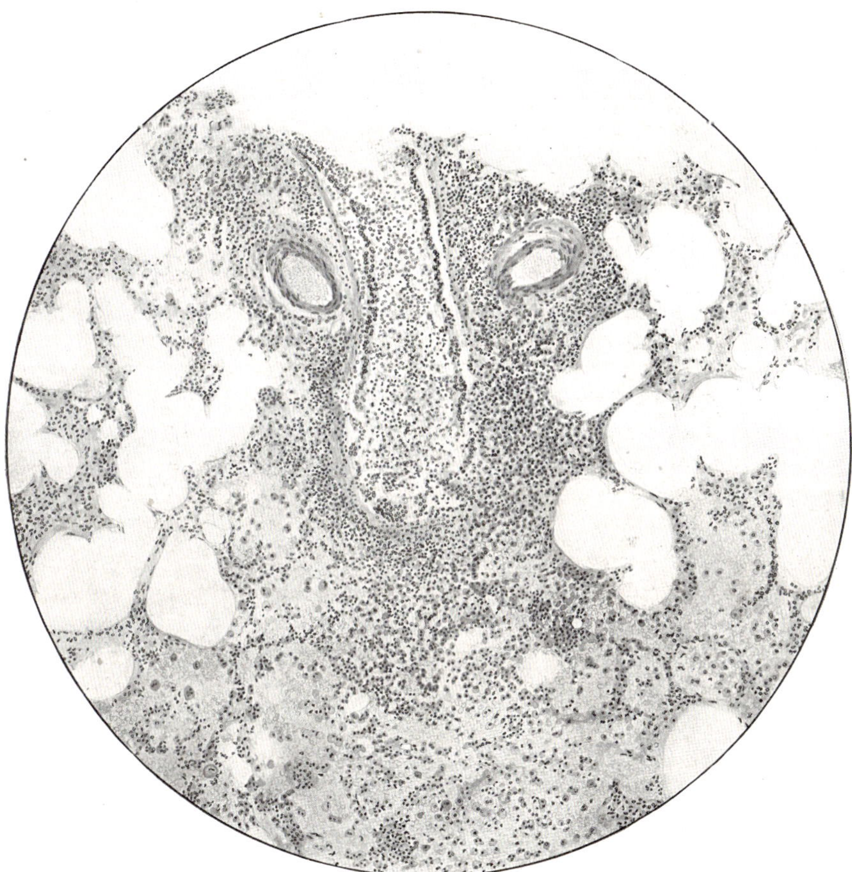

Fig. 107.—Bronchopneumonic patch showing infiltration of bronchial and alveolar walls with the inflammatory exudate.

have time to produce a distinct inflammatory reaction. When they lodge in a respiratory bronchiole, that is, one which has one wall of bronchial type lined with cylindrical epithelium, while open air-cells form the other side, an abundant exudate of red corpuscles and leucocytes appears about them in the lumen, and immediately pours itself into the air-cells. If they lodge in a complete tubular bronchiole a little further from the air-cells, the bronchiole becomes filled with exudate, its wall infiltrated with the same cells, and the process extends rather through the bronchial wall to the air-cells outside it (Fig. 108). Somewhat later the air-cells which form the termination of the bronchiole become filled also by direct extension. If the exudate is fluid or very soft, the respiratory movements may force it into the air-cells, emptying the bronchiole. There are thus two ways in which the infection may reach the actual lung substance from the lumen of the end bronchioles—by penetrating the inflamed wall or by ex-

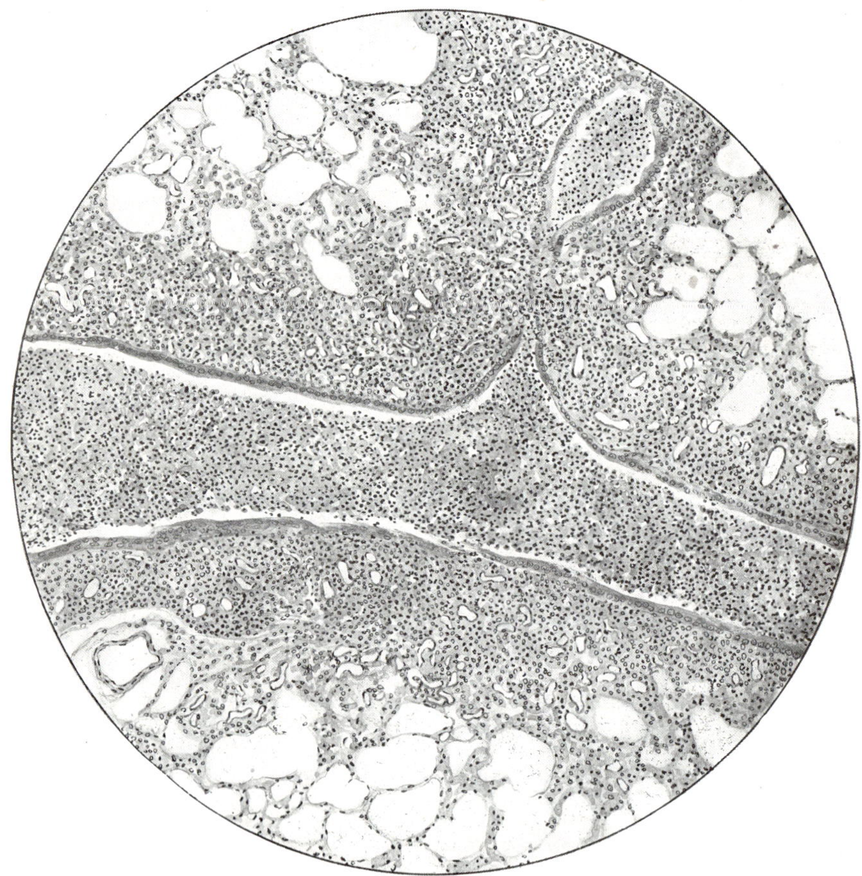

Fig. 108.—Terminal bronchiolitis with involvement of adjacent air-cells.

tending into its own air-cells. The exudate consists of polymorphonuclear leucocytes and red corpuscles, with many desquamated epithelial cells and some mononuclear wandering cells. In many cases a network of fibrin is formed, particularly in those alveoli which lie near the margin of the patch, but there are, as has been so generally stated in the text-books, others in which it is difficult, if not impossible, to demonstrate any fibrin, the exudate remaining as a loose collection of cells. This has given rise to the term catarrhal pneumonia, which is, however, not a particularly accurate designation.

The walls of the air-cells, like those of the bronchi, are also infiltrated with fluid and leucocytes, and in the more chronic forms of bronchopneumonia this affection of the interstitial tissue, which may result later in the formation of much œdematous, soft connective tissue, in those situations, becomes a striking and distinctive feature, in which it differs from lobar pneumonia.

The complete occlusion of the bronchioles by the exudate leads quickly to the collapse of its air-cells, since the imprisoned air is absorbed or dissolved by the passing blood. This atelectasis is often evident on the surface of the lung in the form of patches of purplish, pasty tissue sunken below the surroundings. On the other hand, if the occlusion is incomplete, the alveoli may become overdistended with air, in the manner described in another chapter.

The healing of this type of pneumonia, brought about by the annihilation of the bacteria and the complete or partial liquefaction of the exudate and its absorption, occurs rather more slowly than in lobar pneumonia, and its retardation by the organization of the exudate into fibrous strands is more common. Occasionally in children in whom bronchopneumonia has lasted for some time and is rather mild one finds that the exudate is largely composed of desquamated epithelial cells, with leucocytes and fibrin, and that these epithelial cells have fused to form syncytial masses of protoplasm, with many nuclei. These "giant-cells" often extend from one alveolus to another, or line a whole air-space while inclosing masses of fibrin or leucocytes. In severe bronchopneumonia the walls of the bronchi and of the air-cells are, as has been said, much infiltrated by the inflammatory exudate, and their destruction and the formation of a definite abscess in place of the focus of pneumonia may take place. On the other hand, the introduction of putrefactive bacteria, together with those which injure and destroy the tissue, may set up a condition far different from that ordinarily seen. This is the so-called *gangrene of the lung*, which leads not only to the death of the lung tissue, but to its softening into a violently foul-smelling, greenish, shreddy mass, semifluid in character, which is usually fairly well marked off from the surrounding tissue by a zone of coagulated lung substance. Cavities of considerable size lined with ragged, floating shreds of dead tissue discharge part of their contents into the bronchus, so that a foul odor is given off with the breath. Buday and others find in this, as in other examples of progressive infectious gangrene, many organisms, but especially frequently a combination of fusiform bacilli and spirilla, which they regard as the specific cause of the condition, and as being sufficient to cause the necrosis of the tissue as well as the putrefaction.

Around such an area the alveoli are found to be filled with a dense exudate composed largely of fibrin, with many leucocytes and red corpuscles.

LITERATURE

Buday: Ziegler's Beiträge, 1910, xlviii, 70.
Hecht: Ziegler's Beiträge, 1910, xlviii, 263.
Karsner and Meyers: Arch. Inter. Med., 1913, xi, 534.
Ribbert: Bruening u. Schwalbe, Handb. d. Krankh. d. Kindesalters, ii, 465.
Steinhaus: Ziegler's Beiträge, 1901, xxix, 524.

PUERPERAL INFECTION

Particularly favorable opportunity for the development of a serious infectious process is offered in the puerperal uterus, not, as is so often stated, because in the detachment of the placenta many blood-channels are torn open, but because tissue which is no longer permeated by the circulating blood is often left adhering to the uterine wall, and because fluid stagnates in the cavity. It is the same danger which threatens the patient after an unskilful operation upon some internal organ in which a portion of tissue is left constricted so as to be deprived of its blood supply. It is practically the same danger of infection that exists in a strangulated hernia.

An example will make this clear: A man whose leg was crushed and torn below the knee was treated by a surgeon who washed out the dirt from among the exposed muscles, stopped the bleeding, and sewed up all the tears in the skin. Within a few hours the sutured skin became tense almost to bursting, and when the stitches were removed, a bloody, turbid fluid poured out. Next day the muscles and shreds of tissue were bathed in thin pus, the man's temperature was high, and there were evidences of a rather profound poisoning. In spite of every proper surgical intervention he finally died, and many abscesses were found in lungs and elsewhere. Undoubtedly the accumulation of fluid within the sutured skin gave a medium for the growth of bacteria from the dirt left behind, and at the same time rendered the tissues anæmic through pressure.

Differences of opinion still exist as to the source and nature of the bacteria which are responsible for puerperal infection, and doubt prevails still as to whether they may be the bacteria already present in the genital tract, or only those introduced by the hand or instrument of the operator. Krönig adheres strongly to the latter view. The Streptococcus pyogenes in one or other of its modifications (*q. v.*) is almost always found, although the pneumococcus or staphylococcus may be the organism concerned, and various bacilli, including the Bacillus aërogenes capsulatus, may play a part.

In cases of criminal abortion at any stage in the course of pregnancy infection is likely to take place on account of the haste and secrecy with which instruments are forced into the uterus at the hands of persons ignorant of the conditions of bacterial growth. Fortunately, with the advance in the knowledge of bacteriology puerperal infection is no longer the dreaded scourge of obstetrical practice that it once was before the time of Semmelweiss. Even yet, however, the cases in which, after a complicated delivery, infection occurs are not all too rare. It may result only in a temporary fever, or, on the other hand, it may advance to general septicæmia and death. The uterus is found to be large, relaxed, and soft, with the enormously enlarged blood-vessels characteristic of the later stages of pregnancy. The external os projects into the vagina as a swollen, greenish-black, rough, friable mass. The whole cavity of the uterus is lined with the same greenish-black, ragged, necrotic tissue, the walls on section grayish red and œdematous, the veins open and full of blood. The Fallopian tubes contain a turbid fluid. No changes are found in the organs except the acute splenic tumor and the cloudy swelling of the liver and kidneys which are so regularly seen in acute infections. But everywhere the tissues

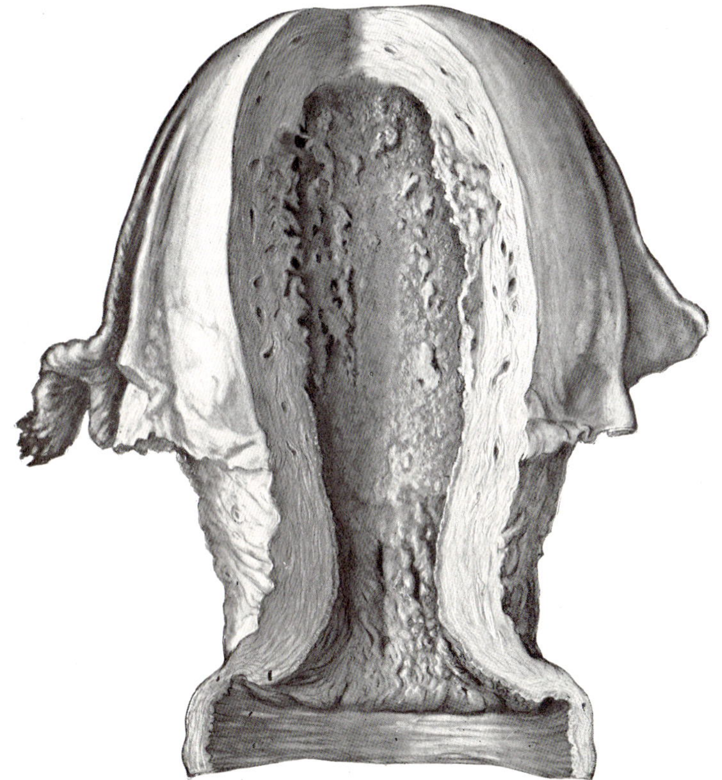

Fig. 109.—Puerperal endometritis. In this case there was no thrombophlebitis.

are blood stained, the lining of the heart and aorta are quite red, and over thorax, arms, and legs there is a network of broad, brownish purple lines which show where the laked blood in the cutaneous veins has stained through into the skin. Such is the result of the rapid spread of the hæmolyzing streptococci into the blood.

In other cases, when the resistance is not so readily overcome, the process is more localized. The dead tissue lining the uterus may remain odorless, or, when there is a mixed infection with putrefactive organisms, it softens into an extremely foul, putrid mass. In other cases a fibrinous exudate rich in leucocytes forms over the superficial necrotic tissue, and blends with it so as to form a sort of false membrane (diphtheritic or pseudomembranous endometritis) (Fig. 109). Beneath this the wall is densely infiltrated with leucocytes, red corpuscles, and fluid, and abscesses with local liquefaction of the muscular tissue develop and may extend even to the outer surface. Extension in this way or along the Fallopian tubes to their fimbriated ends is likely to produce a peritoneal infection which hastens the fatal outcome. Otherwise the broad ligament and adjacent pelvic tissues become infected and enormously thickened and infiltrated with the spreading inflammatory exudate. Great abscesses may develop in these tissues, and at an even later date extend and rupture into the peritoneum.

The infection may be communicated to the rest of the body in two other ways—one by the lymphatics, the other by the formation of infected thrombi in the veins. In the first case the lymph-channels become swollen and distended with pus, adjacent lymph-nodes are enlarged and softened, and bacteria finally pass into the thoracic duct and blood. The second process is far more striking in its appearance. Section through the wall of such a uterus shows numerous great canals, which were the veins, now filled with greenish-yellow pus, their walls converted into opaque yellow material or destroyed entirely so that the uterine musculature itself, edged with yellow, necrotic tissue, forms the wall of the canal. For a long distance nothing remains of the more solid thrombus, and one may trace such channels far out into the broad ligament and to the walls of the pelvis. Aschoff raises the question as to whether this thrombosis is the direct result of the infection, but I cannot doubt it. The fluid may partake of the foul character of the uterine lining in the putrefactive cases. Fragments of such infected thrombi, or even the liquefied material, may be swept into the blood-stream, and emboli are lodged in different organs, while the blood is flooded with bacteria. Hence the development of abscesses in lungs, kidney, brain, etc., or even in the joints (pyæmia). These may be foul and gangrenous when the uterine inflammation has that character. Hence, too, the production of endocardial vegetations, which assume an ulcerative and destructive character and form the source of more infected emboli.

ABSCESS FORMATION, PYÆMIA, ETC.

Certain bacteria, notably the staphylococci, show a marked tendency to grow in the tissues in closely packed colonies about which the cells are rendered necrotic for varying distances. A violent inflammatory reaction ensues, and the immediate neighborhood becomes tumefied, red, and painful. Coagulable fluid exuded from the vessels into the necrotic tissue clots there, and converts it into a firm mass, rather larger than it originally was. Leucocytes in great numbers accumulate outside these neighboring vessels, and wander into the necrotic mass, dying and becoming disintegrated as they pass beyond the zone of safety into the poisoned area. Such quantities of them appear, however, that the proteolytic ferments which they produce become sufficiently concentrated to digest the outer portions of the coagulum, so that it comes to lie loose in a cavity surrounded by a thick yellowish fluid filled with intact and partly disintegrated leucocytes (pus). At this stage the remainder of the coagulum, loaded as it is with bacteria, constitutes the core or central plug (Fig. 110), often recognizable when an abscess is incised or when it bursts through the skin. Later the ferment

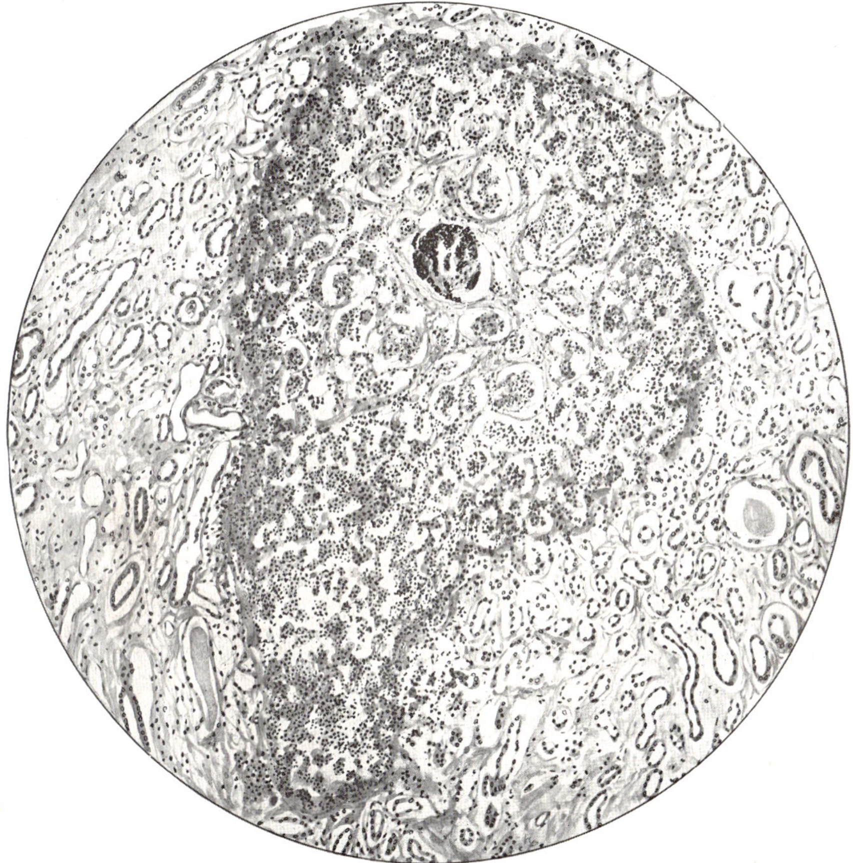

Fig. 110.—Abscess of the kidney, showing central core or necrotic tissue with bacteria.

process may succeed in dissolving the whole of it, and the abscess is then merely a cavity filled with pus and surrounded by an intensely inflamed wall. Further necrosis of this wall may occur, and the abscess increases in size, often in the direction of least resistance, so that the pus seems to burrow its way along natural lines of division of the tissues. It is reabsorbed only with difficulty, and unless it is evacuated by the surgeon or bursts its way to a free surface or into the lumen of some hollow organ, it remains *in situ* for a long time and is gradually inspissated and thickened.

In this case, and indeed in all abscesses which persist for a long time, even when they have been opened, a thick layer of granulation tissue springs up to line the cavity and to encapsulate the remainder of the pus, or more frequently to obliterate the cavity. This granulation tissue is exceptionally thickly infiltrated with leucocytes, and shows the presence of many large, mononuclear wandering cells, which become larger as they approach the surface of the granulations. Here they exhibit their voracious phagocytic characters, loading themselves with the débris of injured and dead cells, and usually containing many large fat-droplets (Fig. 85).

When bacteria and dead tissue are quite removed, as when an abscess is opened and thoroughly cleansed, healing proceeds rapidly and the granulation tissue later forms a dense scar.

Abscesses arise at the point where direct introduction of the bacteria from without takes place, or else they appear, often in numbers, through the transportation of infected emboli from some focus of infection in another part of the body. These emboli may consist practically of masses of bacteria, and while the flooding of the circulating blood with organisms of this sort is known as septicæmia, the condition which we are discussing is often called pyæmia.

Abscesses from direct introduction of bacteria are often seen in the skin, where they are called boils or furuncles, or, when very large, with several communicating centres of infection, carbuncles. Most often the organisms are rubbed into a hair-follicle by a chafing collar, or in some similar way, hence their great frequency on the back of the neck or on the buttocks. Frequently, too, they are seen about the nose or lips. The course of such abscesses is modified by the thickness of the skin and the obstruction to their breaking through. Thus an abscess within the red line of the lip readily ruptures and is cured, while one which arises a few millimetres away, in the thick skin, may be much more extensive and last much longer.

In some persons whose resistance is lowered by any one of the many things which seem to have that effect, such as overwork, unsanitary surroundings, or wasting diseases (among which are other infections, such as typhoid fever), a whole series of boils may make their appearance—one is no sooner healed than another appears. In these cases it seems that the skin becomes smeared with the bacteria, which readily find the opportunity to lodge in hair-follicles or sebaceous glands and to form abscesses. From the fact that bacteria of a pyogenic character are normally present in the superficial layers of the skin it appears that the matter of resistance is of the greatest importance. When a number of hair-follicles become infected side by side with the staphylococcus, a most extensive necrosis of the skin and underlying tissue may occur (carbuncle), and with the liquefaction of each focus of dead material a perfect honeycomb of communicating passages filled with pus may be formed.

Such, in brief, are the circumscribed abscesses. As the result of pyæmic distribution of emboli or cocci they appear in the lungs, heart, kidneys, or any other organ (Fig. 111). In the lung such a focus, at first very hæmorrhagic, is soon found to have a gray, solid, or rapidly liquefying centre, surrounded on all sides by a barrier zone of hæmorrhagic pneumonic consolidation, outside of which the lung is œdematous. Such abscesses seem to reach a considerable size before coming into communication with a bronchus. Frequently confluent with one another, their origin may

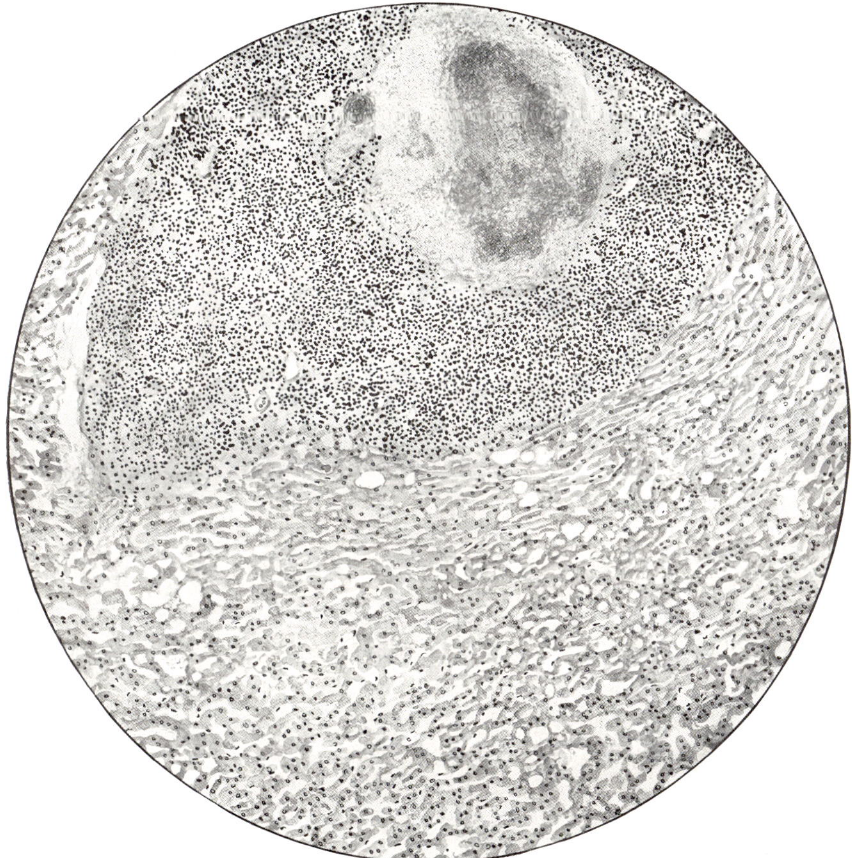

Fig. 111.—Abscess in the liver. The drawing shows the compression and destruction of the liver-cells and a broad layer of leucocytes surrounding the central mass of bacteria.

generally be traced by finding a whole colony of cocci lodged like an injection mass in the lumen of a central blood-vessel. So, too, the embolus may be found in the blood-vessel in the centre of those deeply hæmorrhagic abscesses sometimes found in the submucosa of the small intestine. Rupture of such abscesses through the mucosa leaves a ragged ulcer which heals by granulation.

While there is thus a great similarity in the mode of formation of abscesses wherever they occur, it must be recognized that the feature which they have in common is the concentration of the whole effect, which not only allows the bacteria to kill tissue which might resist a less concerted attack, but also allows the inflammatory exudate (perhaps aided slightly by the ferments of the bacteria themselves) to digest and liquefy that necrotic tissue.

Phlegmons.—When the bacteria are spread quickly throughout a considerable area of tissue, as often happens in the loose tissues of the neck after invasion from suppurative processes in teeth, salivary glands, or mouth cavity, there is nowhere sufficient concentration to produce the effects seen in an abscess. The tissue is not all dead, and the exudate is so spread out that no liquefaction takes place. Such an intense diffuse inflammation may be called a phlegmon, and so dense and hard may the affected tissue become that the phlegmons of the neck are often called ligneous or woody inflammations.

DIPHTHERITIC INFLAMMATION

On any mucosa the invasion of bacteria or the destruction produced by a chemical irritant may cause a peculiarly intense inflammatory reaction, usually hæmorrhagic, and different from the milder forms in that the ne-

Fig. 112.—Diphtheritic enteritis. The inflamed and partly necrotic mucosa is covered with a tenacious layer of exudate.

crotic surface layer is welded together with the fibrinous exudate into a membrane-like film. This is well seen in the mucosa of the intestine when bacteria of the dysentery group invade it, or when, at the end of a long illness, streptococci or other organisms from the intestinal lumen attack it. Perhaps the most striking changes of this sort are produced in cases of poisoning with bichloride of mercury, possibly because the corrosive salt is excreted again into the colon.

In the early stage of any of these cases it is found, on stretching out the wall of the intestine, that certain parts of the mucosa are covered with a grayish or bile-stained, opaque, rough substance which may be scraped off, showing beneath it a raw surface (Fig. 112). Such patches are bordered or separated by mucosa, which is soft and velvety, but swollen and deeply hæmorrhagic. The distribution of the chaff-like exudate in the small intestine is primarily along the crests of the transverse folds or valvulæ—

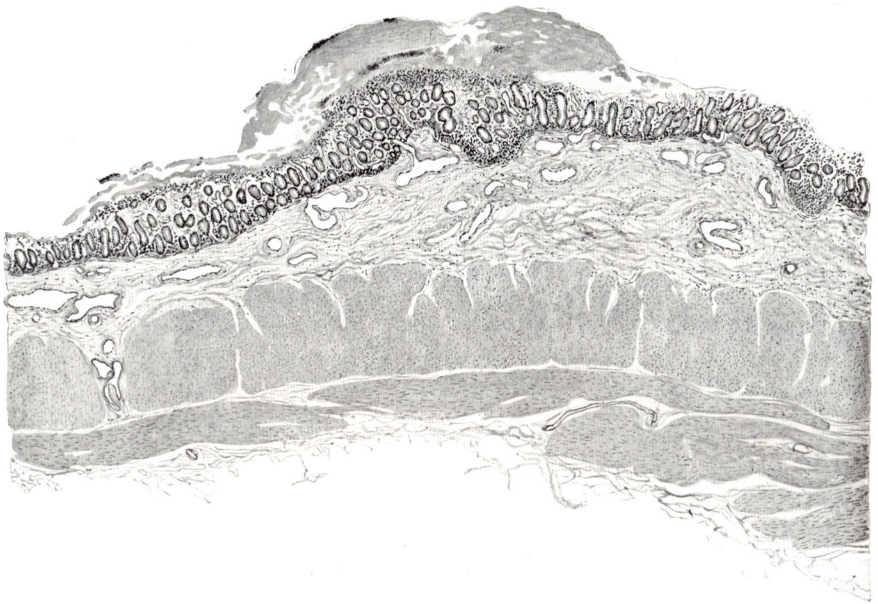

Fig. 113.—Diphtheritic enteritis. The inflamed and partly necrotic mucosa is covered with a tenacious layer of exudate.

in the colon, where it is far more commonly found, it is in patches, inasmuch as the intestine, in its contracted state, exposes only a part of its mucosa to the lumen. The rest is hidden in the depths of the folds, and less constantly exposed to the intestinal contents. Perhaps this is inconsistent with accepted ideas of the normal relation between the intestinal mucosa and intestinal contents, but the appearance of the inflamed intestine imposes such an explanation upon one, and it is easily conceivable that the presence of a sharply irritating substance might keep the walls at their maximum contraction. Thus, in addition to transverse or circular bands of exudate, there are three longitudinal streaks which correspond with the part of the mucosa thrown into relief by the longitudinal muscle-bands.

Microscopically, it is found that the superficial part of the affected mucosa is completely necrotic and sharply marked off from the underlying tissue, which is intensely inflamed (Fig. 113). Continuous with it, and overlying it, is a layer of matted fibrin filaments which can be traced continuously through the dead tissue. Through both parts of this dead layer of tissue, which constitutes the false membrane, remnants of leucocytes are to be found, with many signs of hæmorrhage, and in the tissue beneath and about the site of the pseudomembrane there is an exudate extremely rich in red corpuscles, leucocytes, and fibrin. All this is often particularly well seen in the stomach after intense corrosive poisons have been swallowed.

Later the œdematous and hyperæmic parts of the mucosa between the lines and patches of intensest injury become involved in the same process if the condition progresses and does not heal. The older sites of injury may then discharge the dead tissue into the intestine, and present themselves as ulcerations which may go deep into the intestinal wall. Such ulcers are found especially in the colon, and are characteristic of the more chronic forms of dysentery. They may arise, too, when there is an obstruction of the intestine, so that its contents accumulate above and remain a long time in the dilated upper part of the loop. Probably this dilation, with its stretching of the wall and narrowing of the blood supply, may be a contributory cause of the ulceration.

LITERATURE

Bumm: "Puerperal Infection," Arch. f. Gynäk., 1891, xl, 398.

Körte: Handb. d. prakt. Chir. (Bruns, Garre, Küttner), 1913, iii, 37.

Lenhartz: Septische Infecktionen, Nothnagel's Handb., 1903, iii_4, Abth. 1.

Nothnagel: "Erkrankungen des Darms und des Peritoneum," Handb. d. spec. Path. u. Therap., 1898, xvii.

Thorel: Endocarditis; extensive literature in Lubarsch and Ostertag, 1907, xi_2, 319; 1910, xiv_2, 331; 1915, $xvii_2$, 499.

CHAPTER XV

INJURY WITH INFLAMMATORY REACTION AND ATTEMPTED REPAIR.—NEPHRITIS

Nephritis: General nature of the process. Its diffuse character; acute and chronic glomerulo-nephritis, tubular nephritis, and interstitial nephritis. Arteriosclerotic disease of the kidney. Combined inflammatory and arteriosclerotic disease. Amyloid deposit. Summary. Functional alterations. Renal insufficiency.

NEPHRITIS

Disease of the kidneys which affects diffusely both organs, and which leads to structural alterations and disturbances in the function, recognizable by abnormalities in the urine and by various other symptoms, such as œdema, high blood-pressure, etc., has long been known as Bright's disease, or nephritis. Weigert, in his classical paper, pointed out the diffuse character of these diseases, which distinguishes them from other more localized affections, such as might be caused by an abscess or an infarct in one kidney or by a stone in its pelvis or an obstruction in its ureter. Still it must be kept in mind that although both kidneys are affected in the same way, one element of the kidney structure may suffer more than others. Thus the glomeruli may be especially injured, while the tubular epithelium escapes almost entirely, or the reverse may happen. So dependent are these elements upon one another, however, that in the long run the tubules are injured by the destruction of the glomeruli and vice versa.

Except in a few forms, we are ignorant of the causes of the different types of diffuse renal disease, so that it becomes difficult to repeat their production experimentally, or to classify them satisfactorily. It is hard to trace the progress of their anatomical development, since in human beings we can study in each case only one stage, and it is even yet uncertain what may be the final outcome of some of the alterations which are familiar enough in their acute stage. It is true that experimental nephritis will probably throw a great deal of light upon this problem, even though up to the present the most improbable substances have been used to produce nephritis in animals. Such substances as uranium nitrate, cantharidin, and rattlesnake venom are not likely to be the cause of nephritis in many human cases. Yet they produce changes which are, in principle at least, identical with those in human kidneys, and therefore give useful information.

As in the case of cirrhosis of the liver, we must believe that in the kidney the extreme distortions which are so frequently met with are probably the result of oft-repeated or constantly acting injuries rather than of a single one. It is the destruction and disappearance of some portion of the kidney substance, with the scar which forms in its place, that cause this distortion. The great variety in the appearance of the kidneys found at autopsy in persons who have shown the symptoms of diffuse renal disease becomes more intelligible when we consider that these appearances must vary not only according to the character and severity of the injury, but also according to the duration of the disease, since in the course of time the injured tissue which is still conspicuous in the acute stage, is removed, and its place taken by a scar. This decreases the size of the organ and allows the blood-vessels to show through more plainly, but the result is still further modified by the fact that whatever secretory tissue remains intact becomes hypertrophied, in order to compensate for that which was lost. It is easy to see then that, whereas in the acute stages of severe renal disease the kidneys may appear swollen, smooth, and translucent, with flecks of opaque yellow and of bright red in the cortex, they would look quite different if the person survived this attack for months or years. Then there would appear, in all probability, a very small, rough, granular organ, in which grayish, opaque nodules of the remaining secretory tissue project above sunken areas of reddish gray, translucent, scarred tissue, in which the red color is due to the visible capillaries. Further, the injury which, like a conflagration, suddenly destroys a great part of the secretory substance of the kidney, may finally, if the person survives, end in the production of a kidney which looks almost exactly like another which has gradually reached that stage through long years in which its nutrition has suffered through narrowing of its blood-vessels, and which never, at any time, had shown the picture produced by extensive acute injury. In other words, it is dangerous to conclude anything as to the real nature of the disease of the kidney from the mere outward appearance of the organs at autopsy. Even microscopical study often leaves us uncertain, although there are generally traces left which show the path by which the highly elaborate structures have reached this stage of commonplace wreck.

To have a clear idea of the nature of such disease we must follow the symptoms throughout its course, and, above all things, make clear-sighted tests of the functional capacity of glomeruli, tubules, etc., under standardized burdens. Up to the present we have not learned to correlate these things precisely with changes which we can see in sections of the kidneys, since sometimes blood-capillaries or tubules which seem anatomically intact are quite unable to carry out their normal function. Beside this, each of these structures has a variety of special functions which may separately become defective, without our being able to suspect this from any change in their appearance.

Only the very grossest correspondence then is possible at present between the anatomical changes and the functional disturbances. This, however, we can say—that when several glomeruli with their tubules are quite obliterated and converted into scar tissue, they no longer play any part in the symptoms of the disease, except in so far as the kidney substance is reduced by their loss. It is aside from this, in the better preserved tubules and glomeruli, that we must look for changes to correspond to the altered secretion. It is perfectly easy to understand, therefore, that since the remaining tissue may retain its normal state and hypertrophy to compensate for the areas which have been lost, such a kidney, sprinkled with obsolete scars, might carry on its functions perfectly normally. Doubtless that is exactly what happens in many cases in which a single injury—say from the ingestion of a poison or from a single attack of some acute infectious disease—is entirely healed, by the scarring of the destroyed areas and the compensatory enlargement of the tissue that is left. Perhaps the majority of the cases in which the pathologist at autopsy writes down "slight chronic nephritis" are only instances of such obsolete scars in the kidney whose cause it is now impossible to tell.

From the point of view reached by anatomical study, it seems hardly justifiable to classify these cases sharply into groups. If we knew the ætiological factors, it would be different. Then we might say with assurance, this is the acute stage of the renal change produced by a protein intoxication, that the terminal result of a long-past infection with streptococcus. But it is only in a few cases that we can do this, and even when we can definitely assign an acute infection as a cause of the renal change, we are generally ignorant of the nature of that infection. So it is in the common scarlatinal nephritis. But we do know that streptococcus infections cause nephritis and are possibly responsible for the scarlatinal form, and that corrosive sublimate and a few other substances which have a chance of being introduced into the body can do so too. Other unusual poisons will in the same way injure the kidney, but they practically do not come into consideration except in experimental studies. Indeed, in the vast majority of cases we do not know what the injurious factor is, so that we cannot yet make our classification on this ætiological basis.

A division founded upon structural alterations is the one in common use, and yet it is very unsatisfactory, since, with the lapse of time, the responses to injury become so combined that we can never outline perfectly sharply which is cause and which is effect. Even a division according to disturbances in function leaves much to be desired, since totally different conditions, both renal and extrarenal in nature, may cause the same changes in the excretory power of the kidney.

With this in mind we may consider first the anatomical changes and then the defects in function.

Some of the things which are noxious to the kidney stir up an acute or inflammatory reaction, while others seem to destroy tissue and leave the gap to be filled up by regenerating cells or by scar tissue without any very striking inflammatory response. Especially is this thought to be true in those cases in which arteriosclerotic thickening and narrowing of the renal arterioles diminish the nutrition of small patches of kidney substance, so that their place is taken by fibrous tissue in which the remains of obliterated tubules and glomeruli persist. On this account many authors set this group apart as quite separate from the other diffuse renal affections, but they seem to me so closely related in principle and marked by such similar derangements of function that I prefer to class them with the rest, especially since we are not in all cases perfectly sure that the arteriosclerosis is not caused by the renal disease rather than the reverse.

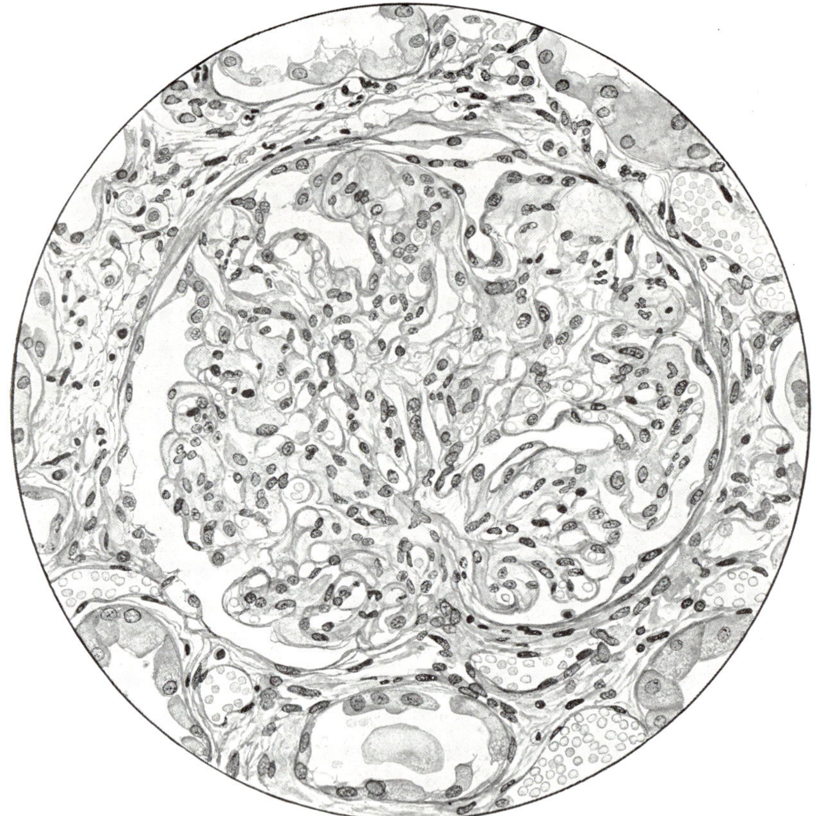

Fig. 114.—Glomerulus with capillaries occluded by hyaline thrombi and adherent to capsule.

In studying any large series of cases one meets with instances (*a*) in which the injury primarily affects the glomeruli; others (*b*) in which the glomeruli are apparently intact, while the tubular epithelium has suffered, and still others (*c*) in which neither of those structures seems much changed, although there is an intense inflammatory reaction in the interstitial tissues. The results of these things are found in many cases in which extensive scars remain to show where the injury was done, and in which there are generally traces of some sort which indicate what was the character of the action. Besides these there are (*d*) kidneys in all stages advancing toward the condition of maximal scarring, in which there are not to be found the distinctive traces of initial destruction of the glomeruli or tubules proceeding with inflammation. In these the arteries are almost closed by sclerotic changes, and this offers the easiest explanation of their state; and then there is a group (*e*) in which, in addition to other injuries, the presence of amyloid causes extensive changes.

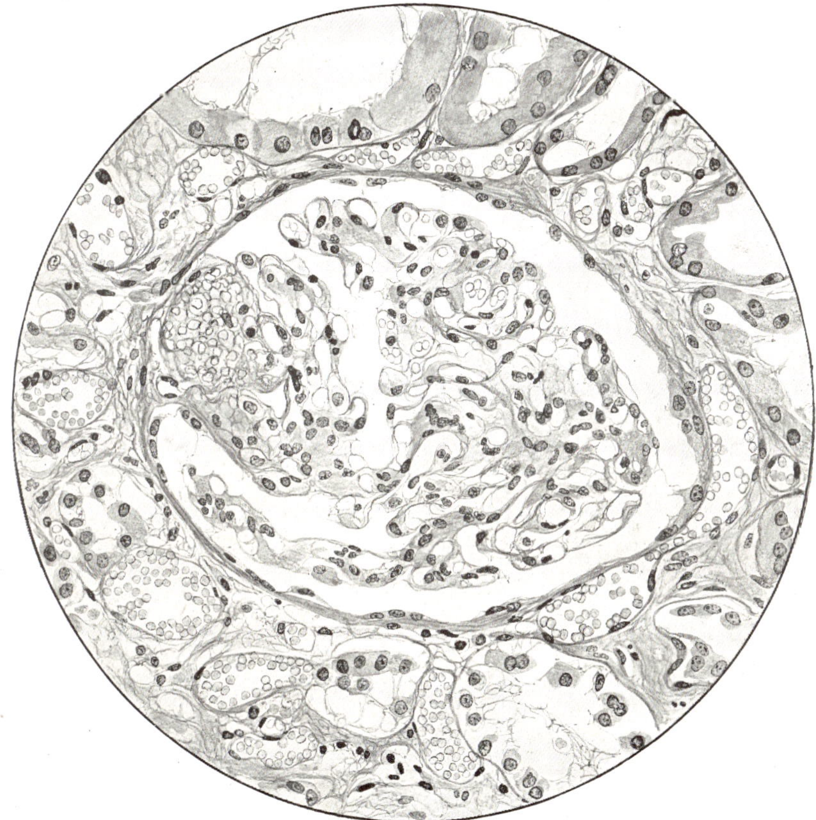

Fig. 115.—Glomerulus showing formation of capillary thrombus.

Of course, the healing of isolated local lesions of all sorts may produce local conditions closely resembling these, but their explanation follows simply from what may be said about the diffuse changes.

It is obviously unfortunate that such terms as chronic interstitial nephritis, chronic parenchymatous nephritis, etc., should be in such common use, since they do not express exact ideas. It is possible that there may be a chronic as well as an acute interstitial nephritis, but this is by no means what is meant by the term chronic interstitial nephritis, which is used of the late or contracted condition of a kidney in which the injury actually affected chiefly the parenchyma. Upon the complete destruction of this, of course, the scar tissue which remains in its place becomes the most obvious thing, and it is hard to escape the idea, at first sight, that it was the tissue primarily affected. So, too, the wide-spread use of the terms large white kidney, small red kidney, etc., is deplorable, since, though graphic, they express only the crudest and most misleading opinion of the nature of the lesion. As Ponfick complains, we might as well speak of a small blue lung or a large red liver.

(a) Acute and Chronic Glomerulonephritis

Scarlatina, streptococcus infections, especially the protracted subacute infections with the Streptococcus viridans, certain poisons used experi-

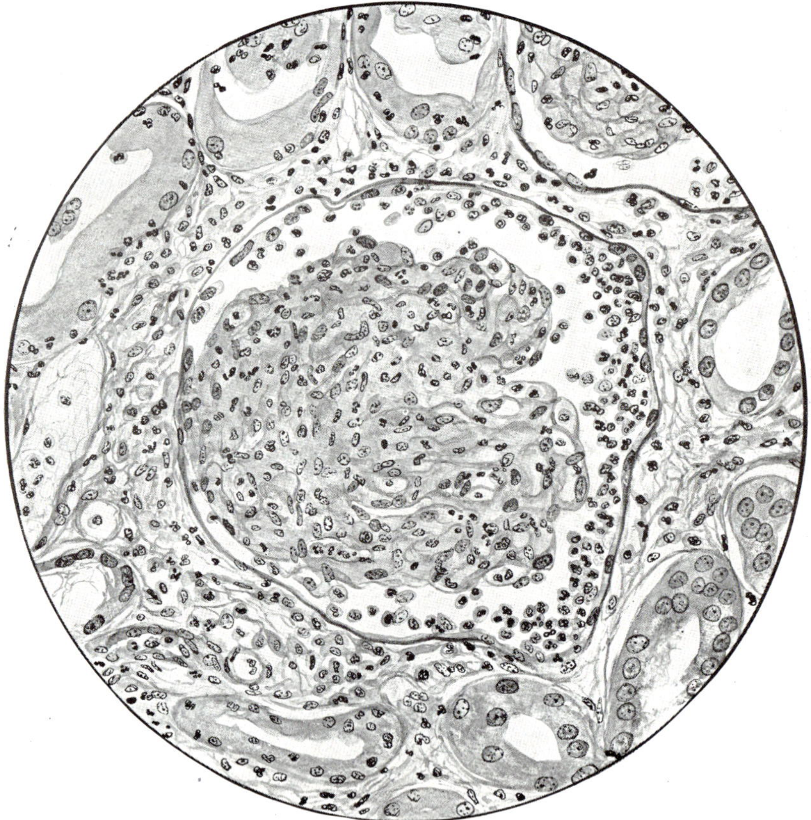

Fig. 116.—Acute glomerulonephritis. Glomerular capsule filled with leucocytes.

mentally, such as cantharidin, uranium nitrate, etc., and probably many other violent toxic agencies attack especially the capillaries of the glomerular tufts, finally producing extraordinary complex alterations in the whole glomerular structure, which heal with distortion or obliteration. Perhaps the simplest are those in which bacteria actually lodge in the capillaries, sometimes in clumps large enough to occlude the lumen or when bacteria or toxic substances injure the wall of the capillary and cause the formation of an occluding thrombus. Generally this happens in only a part of the glomerular tuft, while blood circulates still through the rest (Fig. 114). Such occluded loops become greatly swollen or distended by a mass of hyaline, pink-staining material, which seems to be formed chiefly by the agglutination and fusion of red corpuscles (Fig. 115). Ordinarily, it seems, we must believe that the pulsation of the arterial stream may be felt in the glomerular capillaries, which move a little backward and forward in the elastic capsule almost as the lung does in the pleura. But now, while the rest of the loops still slide on the parietal wall with their expansion and

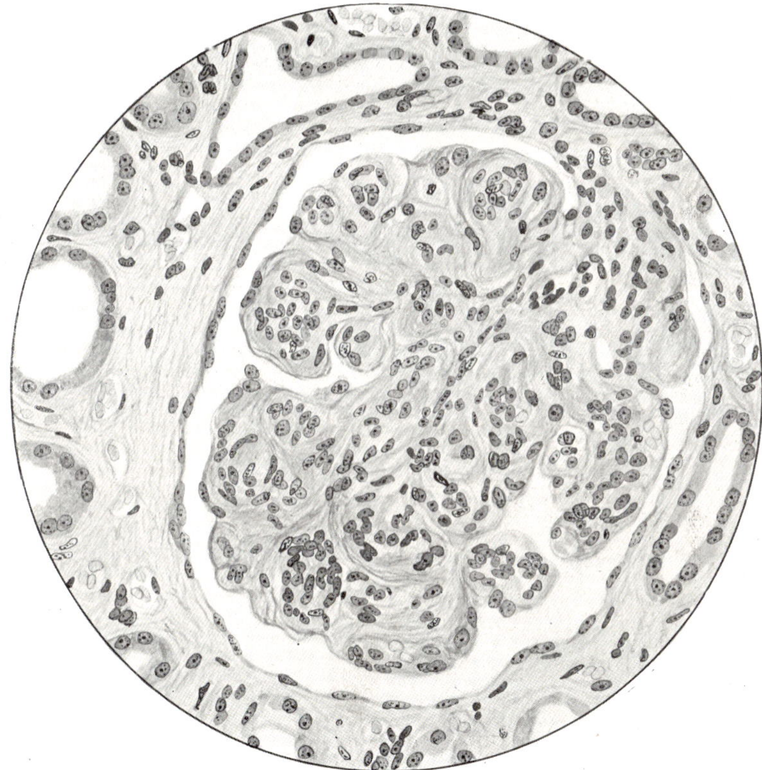

Fig. 117.—Intracapillary glomerulonephritis.

relaxation, the occluded ones become rigid, and because of their distension press continuously against one place in the wall of the capsule. This place quickly becomes adherent to the loop, and alterations appear in it like those which affect the loop itself. Later, just as in any other place where injured or dead tissue is left surrounded by the living, connective tissue grows through and replaces it, making the adhesion permanent.

In other cases, when the capillaries are not quite blocked, leucocytes may come in in numbers to approach the injured walls, so that all the loops seem stuffed with them, and even the capsule and the tubule are found to contain those which have penetrated the capillary walls (Fig. 116). Even more common than this is the slightly less tempestuous form in which the glomerular tufts become greatly enlarged through the appearance of quantities of cells in the lumina of the capillaries, which are not polymorphonuclear leucocytes, but look more like endothelial cells. At least they are mononuclear cells with indistinct outline, so fused together that their origin can hardly be made out. With them there is always an indefinite foamy or spongy mass of protoplasm which completes the occlusion of the

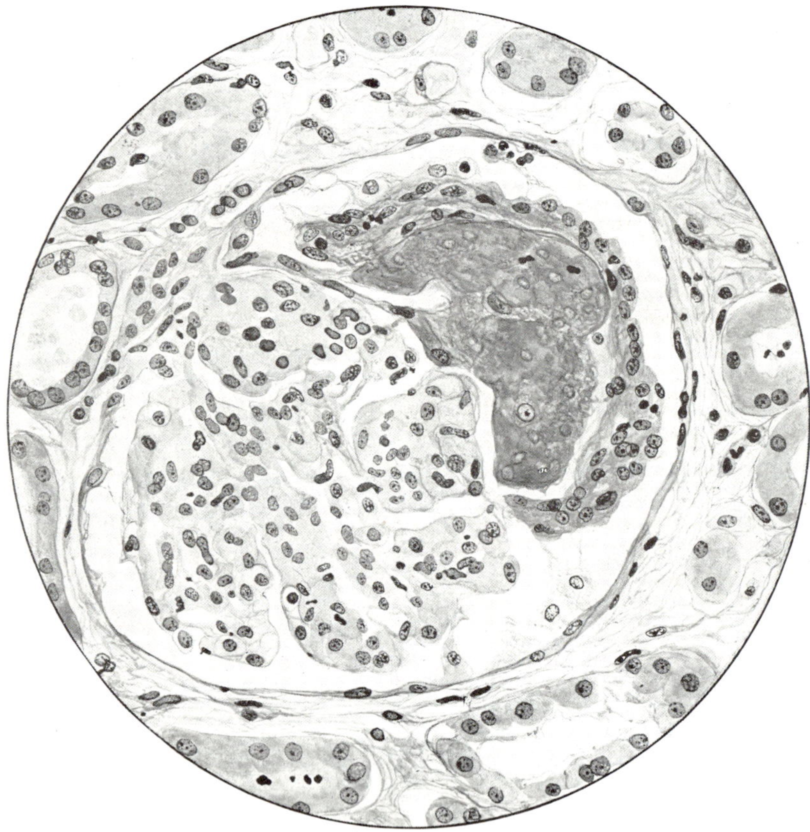

Fig. 118.—Hyaline clot in the glomerular capsule overgrown by epithelium.

capillary. Such glomeruli must be entirely impermeable, for practically all the capillaries seem to be thus obstructed by the mass of endothelial cells (Fig. 117).

The lumen of the capsule generally contains albuminous material or blood, with leucocytes and fibrin. That the lining epithelial cells become desquamated into this cavity at times is undoubtedly true, but I at least have never seen an instance in which they were abundant nor sufficient to produce the appearance known as the epithelial crescent. That is rather the outcome of a well-ordered proliferation which brings with it a supporting framework of connective tissue. When blood exudes into the capsule the corpuscles often fuse into a hyaline mass, which lies in contact with the epithelium (Fig. 118). This may be one of the stimuli for the proliferation of the epithelium, because just as in the case of the endothelium of a vessel which grows up to cover a mural thrombus, this hyaline clot soon becomes completely encapsulated by epithelial cells. So, too, whenever adhesions form between glomerulus and capsule, the epithelium becomes

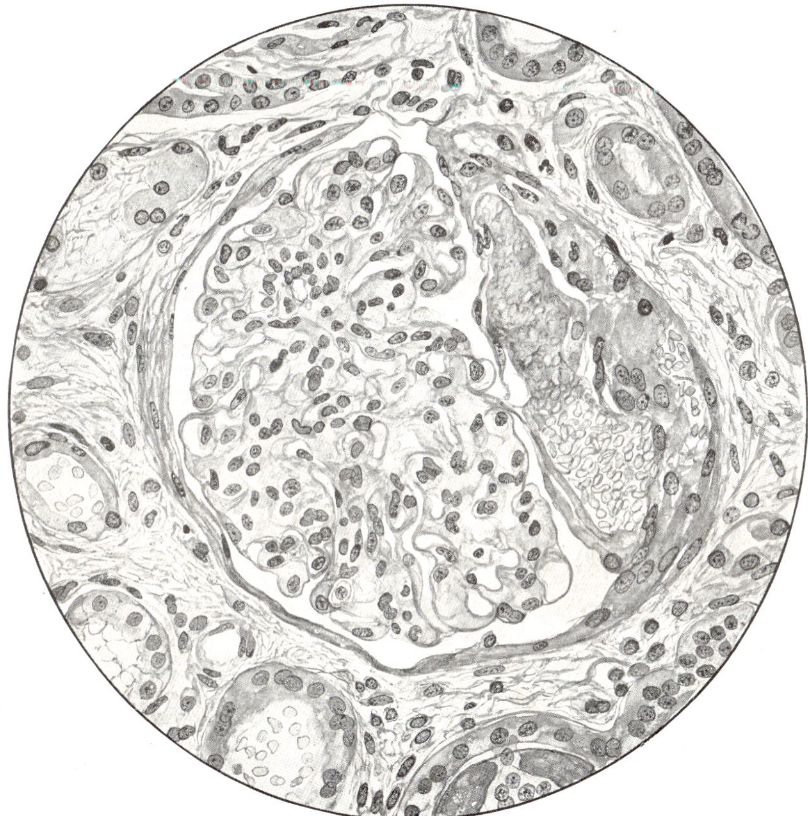

Fig. 119.—Glomerulus with blood-clot adherent to capsular wall.

continuous from wall to tuft (Fig. 119). In this way the cavity of the capsule may be divided into several chambers which communicate with one another. In more advanced cases, through the aid of still other mechanisms, the most extraordinary growths of the epithelium take place, always or nearly always in a simple layer, but in folds which unite with one another and thus form a sponge-like tissue all the cavities of which communicate with one another, with the main cavity of the capsule, and thus with that of the tubule (Fig. 120).

Flattened down in the narrow space of the capsule, this tissue at first sight gives the impression of a crescentic mass of desquamated cells, whence the term, "epithelial crescent" (Fig. 121).

All these changes cause the glomerulus to become greatly enlarged, so that it is conspicuous on the cut surface of the fresh kidney—all interfere greatly with the permeability of the glomerulus, and all are usually associated with changes of an inflammatory character in the membrana propria and surrounding connective tissue of the capsule. With adhesions and the replacement of the hyaline and necrotic capillary loops by connective tissue

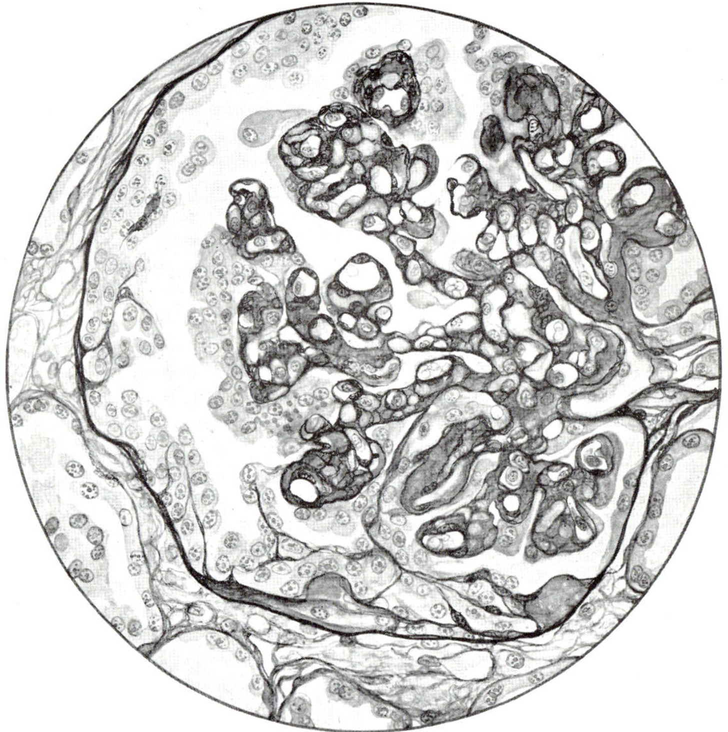

Fig. 120.—Proliferation of capsular epithelium in contiguous folds.

grown in from outside, the glomerulus may be in large part obliterated by being converted into dense fibrous tissue. Nearly always, however, even in the latest stages, there remain traces of the less affected capillary loops, and abundant indications of the method by which obliteration occurred.

The epithelium of the tubules is undoubtedly injured also, although for a time it shows relatively little change. Later the cells show every sort of degeneration, and globules, both of neutral fat and cholesterine esters, accumulate in them. With their desquamation and disappearance, or even with their shrinkage and atrophy, the tubule belonging to that glomerulus tends to collapse and becomes lost to view. Often for a time the epithelial cells are greatly swollen through the presence of small and large globules of refractive hyaline material, which stains like fibrin (Fig. 122). Often, too, the lumen is filled with blood, leucocytes, epithelial cells, and granules, or with hyaline moulds or casts to which these various things adhere, being swept down into the urine, to appear there as different sorts of urinary casts.

About the glomeruli and about the injured tubules there is generally

Fig. 121.—Glomerulus with epithelial crescent. The cavities among the epithelial cells communicate with one another.

some inflammatory reaction, shown by the presence of wandering cells (Fig. 123), and in the course of time in these somewhat œdematous areas new connective tissue forms in ever-increasing amounts until finally the obliterated glomeruli and atrophic tubules come to lie in a very dense framework of fibrous tissue. Aside from these areas, or intercalated somewhere among them, there are intact glomeruli with their tubules, which now carry on the work of the kidney. Such glomeruli actually enlarge, and the tubules increase in size and length through the multiplication, by mitosis, of their epithelial cells. It is a compensatory hypertrophy on the part of the remaining functional tissue. Such groups of tubules, until they themselves meet with destruction, form the prominent projecting granules which stand up on the rough surface of the contracted kidney in relief above the shrunken, scarred areas where the tubules are lost.

No attempt is made to subdivide types of glomerular lesions, because in every instance the whole of the glomerulus is somewhat altered—where the change seems to be intracapillary, search will reveal changes in the epithelium of the capsule, and, when the striking alteration seems to be in

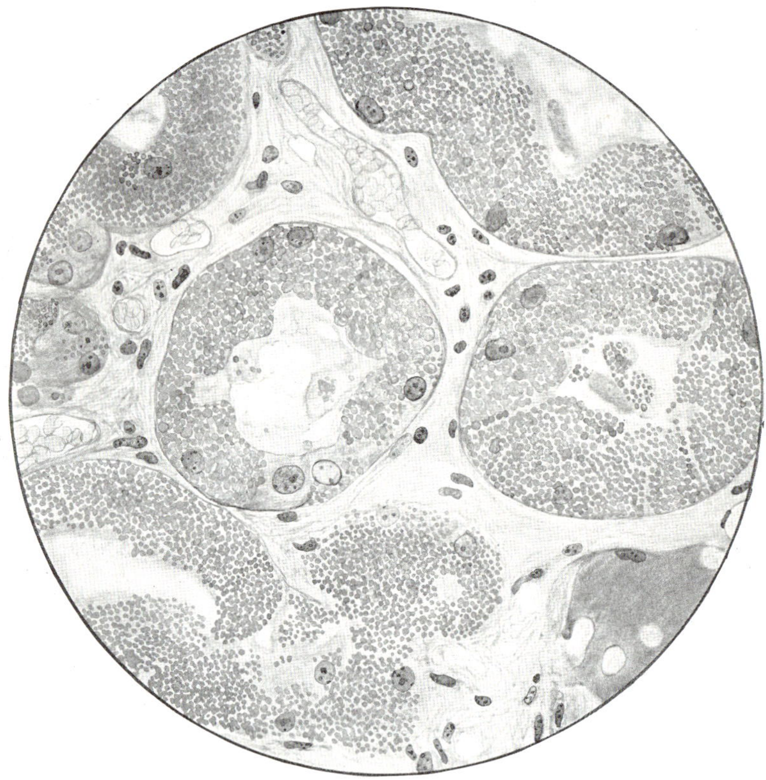

Fig. 122.—Colloid or hyaline droplets in the epithelium of renal tubules.

the epithelium, traces, at least, of occluding thrombi will be found in the capillaries.

Such lesions of the kidney are recognizable in the gross organ in the early stages by the swelling of the glomeruli, which project as pale, translucent grains, and by the opacity of the cortex, with its sprinkling of ecchymoses. Even much later the swollen kidney is still quite smooth when the capsule is pulled off and generally pale, grayish, and translucent, though mottled thickly with flecks of yellow opacity and to a less extent with hæmorrhages (Fig. 124). Occasionally the hæmorrhages are very abundant,—almost confluent, so that the organ is deep red or almost black,—but that is rare. With the gradual removal of the fat-containing, opaque, degenerated epithelium, the kidney decreases in size, the translucent, gray, fibrous stroma sinks together, the hypertrophied intact tubules stand out as gray nodules from the intervening tissue, where, now that the epithelium is gone, the capillaries begin to show through red—and in the end we have a small,

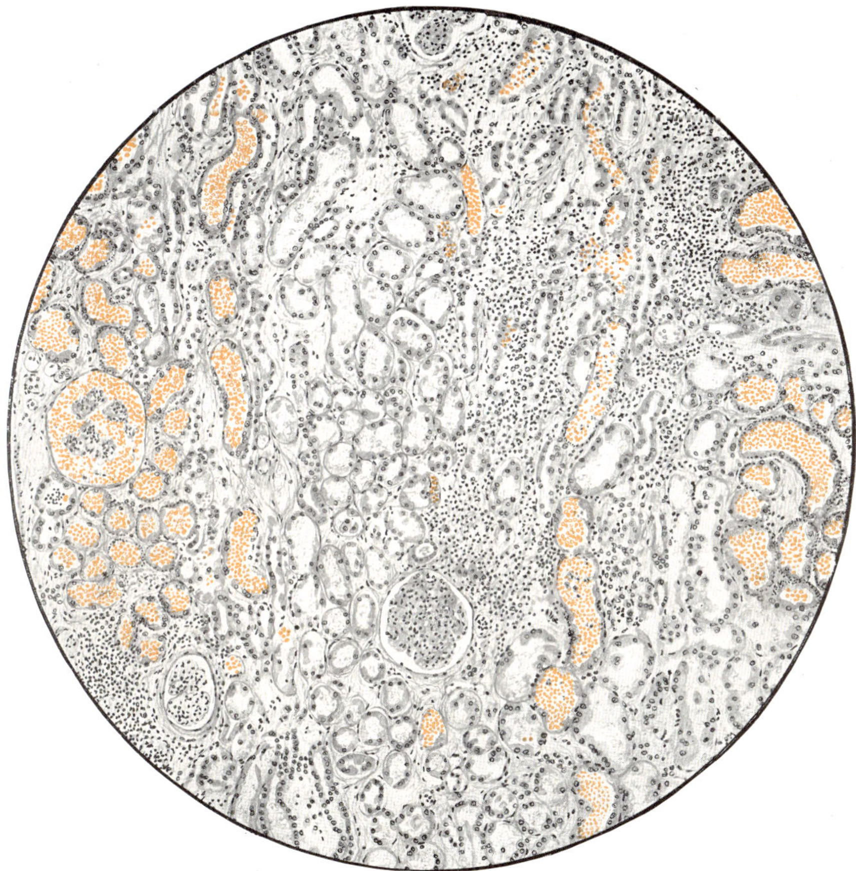

Fig. 123.—Acute diffuse nephritis with epithelial degeneration, œdema, and infiltration with leucocytes and hæmorrhage.

hard, reddish-gray organ, roughened by granules of gray over which the capsule is quite adherent—the so-called secondary contracted kidney (Figs. 125 and 126).

Naturally, the disturbance of function must change as the kidney progresses through all these stages of the disease. Very striking, however, in the beginning is the diminution of the amount of urine, its high concentration and admixture with blood, albumin, and casts, and the coincident œdema. Later the whole clinical picture may change, as shall be described later.

(b) Acute and Chronic Tubular Nephritis

Destructive lesions, affecting especially the epithelium of the tubules, and followed by more or less inflammatory reaction, result from various poisons, among which bichloride of mercury, uranium nitrate, and chromates are more familiar. Baehr has recently described an exquisite tubular lesion produced by iodine. But there are many others of less definite nature, since general peritonitis and septicæmias are sometimes accompanied by quite analogous changes, and the acute nephritis of pregnancy is commonly of this type. In eclampsia, too, one sometimes finds the tubular epithelium necrotic. In any series of cases anatomically studied one must be careful to rule out possible postmortem autolytic changes, but with this in mind, there are still found many instances in which a great proportion of highly

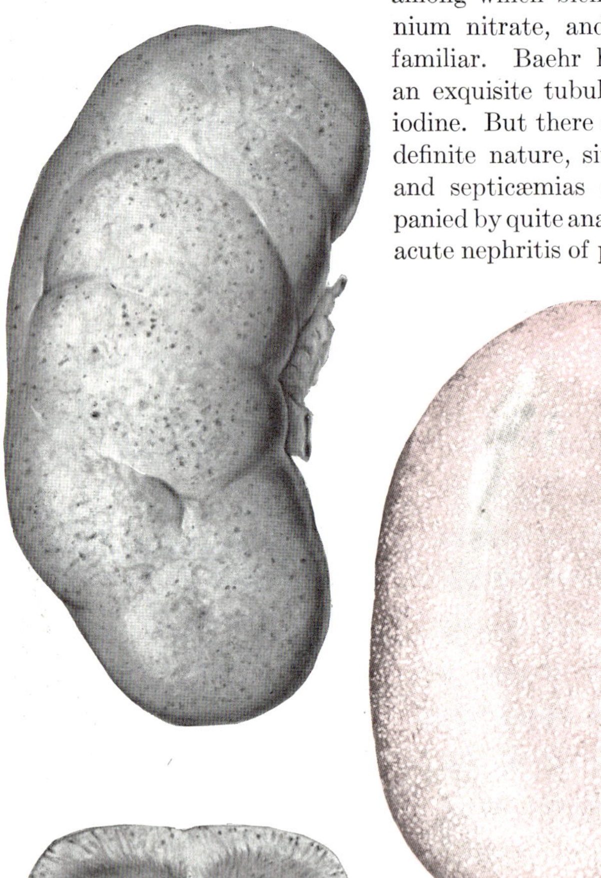

Fig. 124.—Acute and subacute nephritis, showing punctiform hæmorrhages and opaque yellow flecks which are produced by the degenerated epithelium.

Fig. 125.—Secondary contracted kidney, representing later stage in the development of the diffuse glomerulonephritis.

sensitive epithelial cells of the convoluted tubules are necrotic, as shown by their disintegration and the loss of their nuclei. Nevertheless, severe alterations of these cells may occur without proceeding to actual death, and in most infectious processes, including typhoid fever and pneumonia, and in such nutritional disturbances as result from chronic passive congestion,

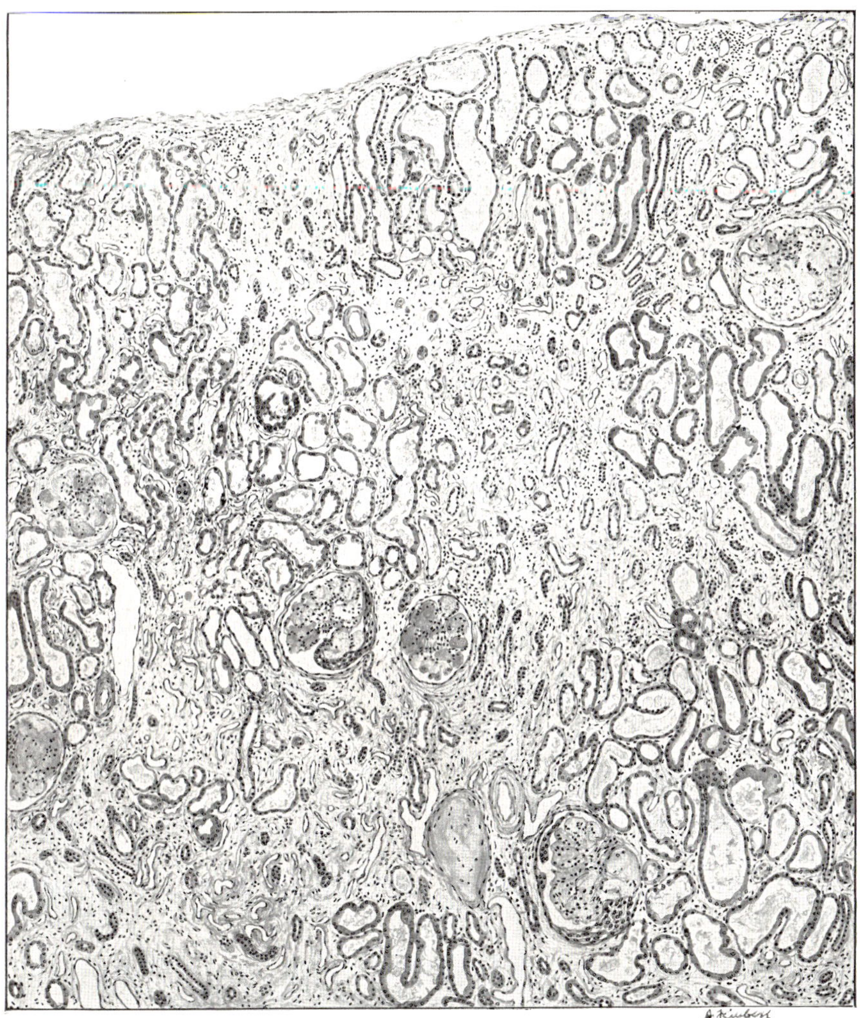

Fig. 126.—Chronic diffuse nephritis following repeated glomerular injuries (secondary contracted kidney).

striking functional derangements, referable at least in part to the tubular epithelium, appear, while nothing more than the so-called cloudy swelling can be demonstrated anatomically. In glomerulonephritis, in which the tubules often seem to be spared, the occurrence of mitoses in their lining epithelial cells, which is an indication of their extraordinary power of regeneration, may give a clue to their participation in the injury, even when actual destruction of the cells is not evident. So, too, the ultimate fate of the tubules in an area of atrophy, whether brought about by glomerular obstruction, by intoxication, or by malnutrition, gives us convincing evidence of the fact that their cells suffer very regularly, even though the glomerular lesions may be far more conspicuous.

Pure tubular nephritis is probably not quite so uncommon as is generally thought, since recovery with complete compensatory new formation of the

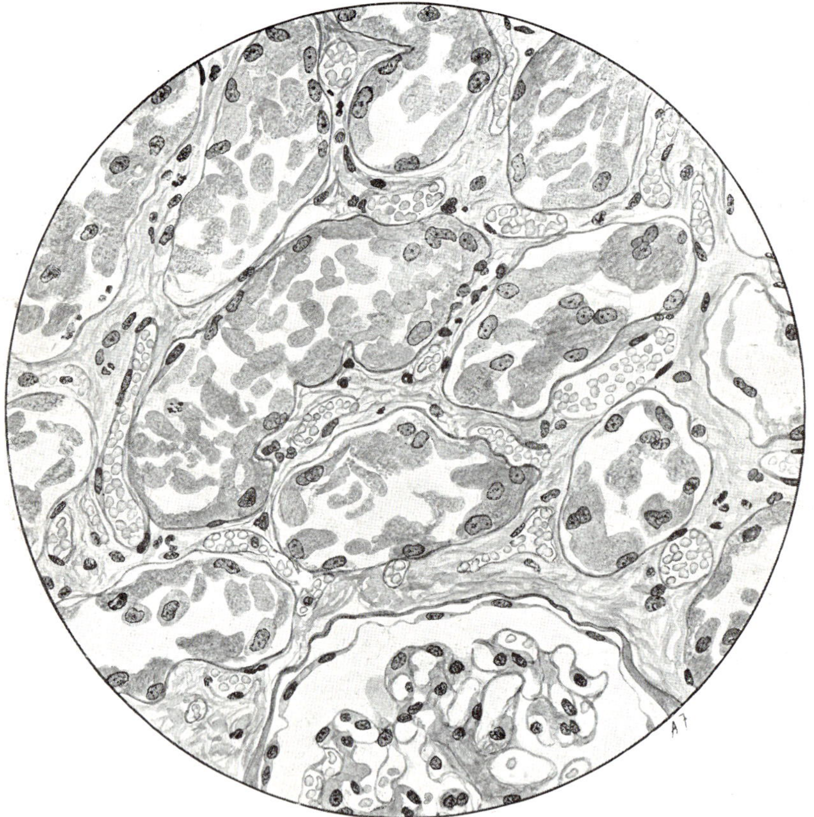

Fig. 127.—Destruction of tubular epithelium caused by poisoning with mercury bichloride.

cells seems so easily possible, and even when the affected tubules lose all their epithelium and collapse, the signs of their downfall, when some time later the person dies, are inconspicuous. Apparently when a tubule becomes permanently obliterated its glomerulus soon falls together in a bloodless state, and is, some time later, surrounded by a progressively thickening hyaline and connective-tissue capsule, which accompanies its complete obliteration. The best example of tubular lesions is that produced by mercuric bichloride, a condition which has become peculiarly frequent of late, and there one finds, side by side in the tubules, living and necrotic cells (Fig. 127). Those which have succumbed soon become formless masses, often calcified, which may be surrounded and encapsulated by the new epithelial cells which quickly grow from the division of those remaining intact (Fig. 128).

The ultimate result of destruction of the epithelium of the tubules must

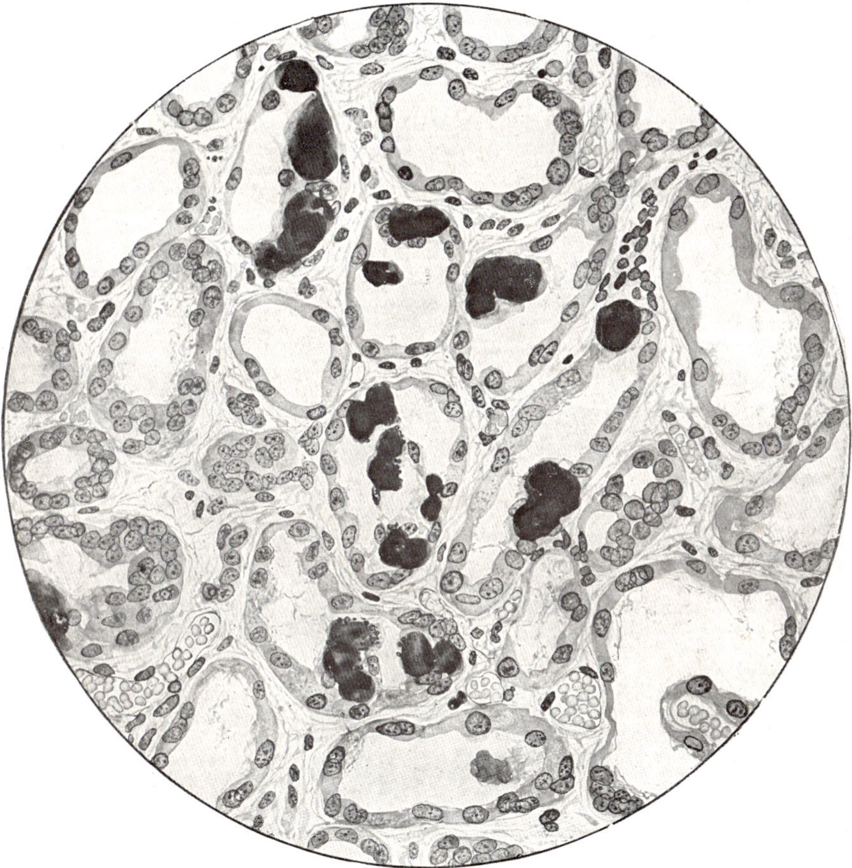

Fig. 128.—Later stage of nephritis following bichloride poisoning. The necrotic cells are calcified and surrounded by new-formed epithelium.

depend upon its extent, since if it be partial, the tubule may be perfectly relined from the cells which remain, while if it be complete, the collapse of the tubule will lead shortly to destruction of the glomerulus and the formation of a scar in the place once occupied by the whole structure. Doubtless this is the origin of some of the scattered scars which are so frequently seen in the kidney, but in its completed form it is almost impossible to say whether such a scar was brought about in this or in some other way.

Rarely one encounters renal changes resembling closely those produced by Baehr through the injection of iodine, and found in animals which have survived a long time.* In a case studied recently the kidneys were found to be smooth, pale, and hard, and on section the tubules were uniformly atrophic and shrunken, while the glomeruli remained large and conspicuous (Fig. 129). It is true that in this case the capillaries of the

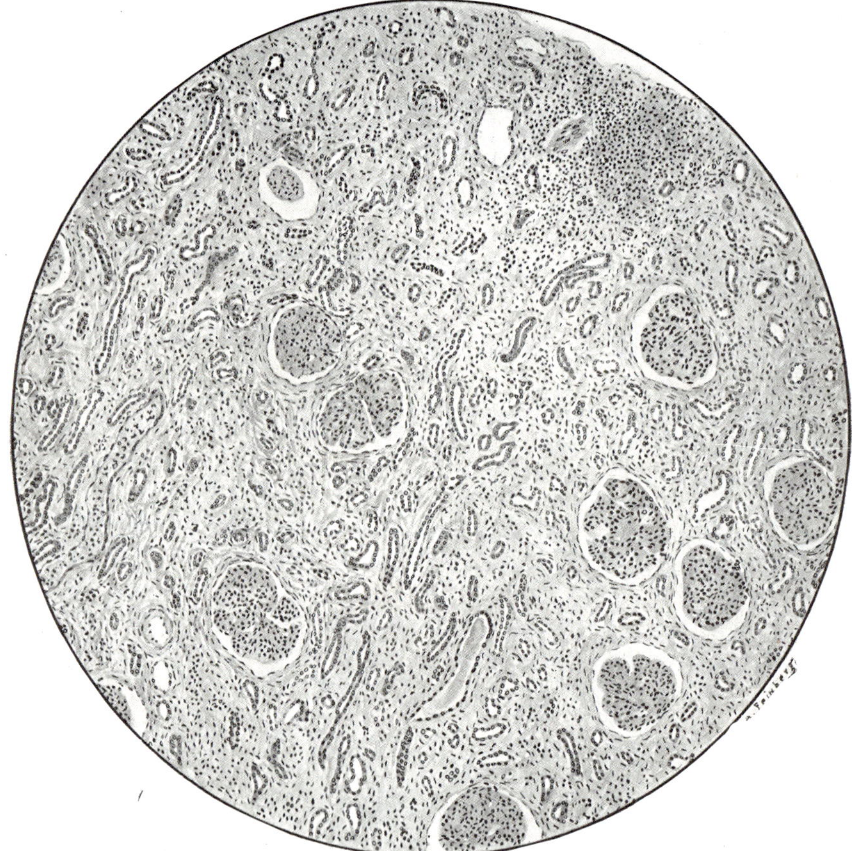

Fig. 129.—Subacute and chronic nephritis. Glomeruli fairly well preserved in spite of universal atrophy and shrinkage of the tubules which are embedded in scar tissue.

glomeruli appear to be blocked by masses of large cells, so that other interpretations of the whole condition are possible, but the general aspect of the cortex points to a primary lesion of the tubular epithelium.

(c) Acute, Subacute, and Chronic Interstitial Nephritis

By this is meant strictly the injury which seems to affect particularly the framework of the kidney, causing an inflammatory reaction there,

* Ziegler's Beit., 1913, lv, 572, Fig. 12.

while glomeruli and tubules are left more or less intact, with the resulting formation of scars throughout the organ. It does not apply to the several varieties of scarred, contracted kidneys, which are clearly the outcome of injuries to the specialized secretory mechanism, that is, to the great majority of the contracted kidneys, which are so commonly and loosely spoken of as chronic interstitial nephritis. It is perfectly recognized that, as Weigert pointed out, all forms of nephritis are diffuse in that every element of the tissue is somewhat affected, so that, in an instance in which the

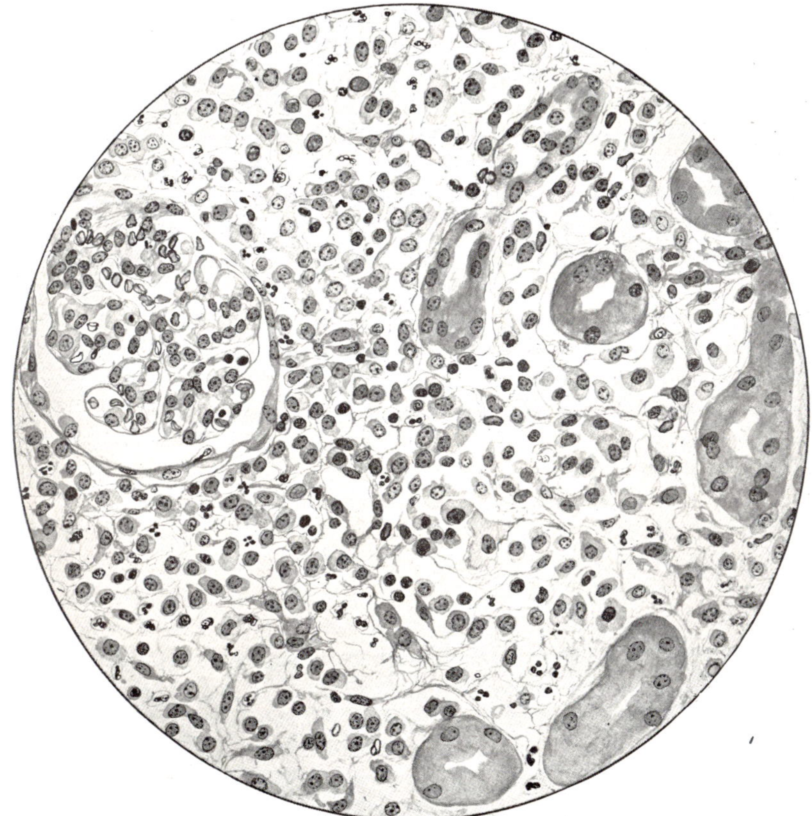

Fig. 130.—Acute interstitial nephritis from a child dying of diphtheria.

glomeruli show the most striking changes, the connective-tissue framework, as well as the epithelium of the tubules, also feels the shock and reacts. But it is entirely wrong to conclude, from the fact that in the late stages of such a condition, when much of the kidney substance has disappeared and is replaced by scar tissue, the connective tissue was the first thing to be affected, and that it, in its growth, has constricted and destroyed the secreting structures. It is not in this sense that we use the term interstitial nephritis, but rather to describe a quite uncommon condition, seen only once or twice among the last 500 autopsies at the Presbyterian Hospital, where the patients are chiefly adults, but much more frequent in hospitals for the infectious diseases of children. Councilman found 42 cases in such material in the course of two years.

In its rather focal distribution, the acute interstitial nephritis resembles somewhat the forms of acute suppurative nephritis, caused directly by the lodging of bacteria in the kidney substance, but the whole course, the type of wandering cells involved, and the absence of bacteria serve to distinguish it from them. It appears usually in the course of scarlatina or diphtheria, or other similar intense infections, perhaps more commonly in mixed infections than in pure scarlatina or diphtheria.

The swollen kidney shows on section clouding with grayish areas, which are found microscopically to depend upon the accumulation, between the tubules, of great numbers of wandering cells of several sorts (Fig. 130). Most of these are mononuclear, and vary in form from those resembling the lymphocyte to plasma cells and even much larger types. Usually there are also some polymorphonuclear leucocytes. There is a spreading apart of the interstitial connective tissue, and commonly a new formation of fibroblasts. The glomeruli seem to suffer very little or secondarily, as shown by the penetration of wandering cells through the capsule into the intracapsular space. The epithelium of the tubules may also be relatively intact, although wandering cells are sometimes found in the lumen. But the same changes are, as found in adults, by no means independent of alterations of glomeruli and tubules, and most often accompany them.

The healing, or rather the passing into a stationary, obsolete condition of this process, is difficult to follow certainly, but it seems probable that a rather diffuse thickening of the interstitial tissue in many areas may represent its last stages. No definite symptoms need accompany the acute stages, and the urine may be normal. If this be so, there seems no reason to suppose that the later stages should be productive of symptoms. This will naturally depend upon the extent of the injury to glomeruli and tubules.

(d) Arteriosclerotic Disease of the Kidney

It seems incorrect to discuss a disease of the kidney brought about by the gradual diminution of its blood supply under the heading nephritis, but the main principle is that here, too, an injury leads to the distortion of the kidney anatomically and functionally in a way like that produced by other injuries, which bring in their train inflammatory reaction. After all, the existence of an inflammatory reaction is by no means the most important feature, and this arrangement is for convenience, it having been said that if there must be a classification, it can be satisfactory and logical only when on an ætiological basis.

Long ago it was pointed out by Gull and Sutton that thickening of the walls of the renal vessels, causing their narrowing and hence depriving the kidney of blood, is found in kidneys which have lost much of their substance, and have become scarred and contracted. After long dispute it seems probable that the sclerosis of the vessels is actually the cause of these changes in the kidney, and not the incidental result of other injuries which also affect that organ. The arteriosclerotic thickening of the intima associated with an excessive reduplication of the internal elastic membrane extends into the smallest vessels, and may completely occlude them and narrow them to the minutest channel (Fig. 131). Usually the effect of this, inasmuch as most of the branches of the renal artery are thus nar-

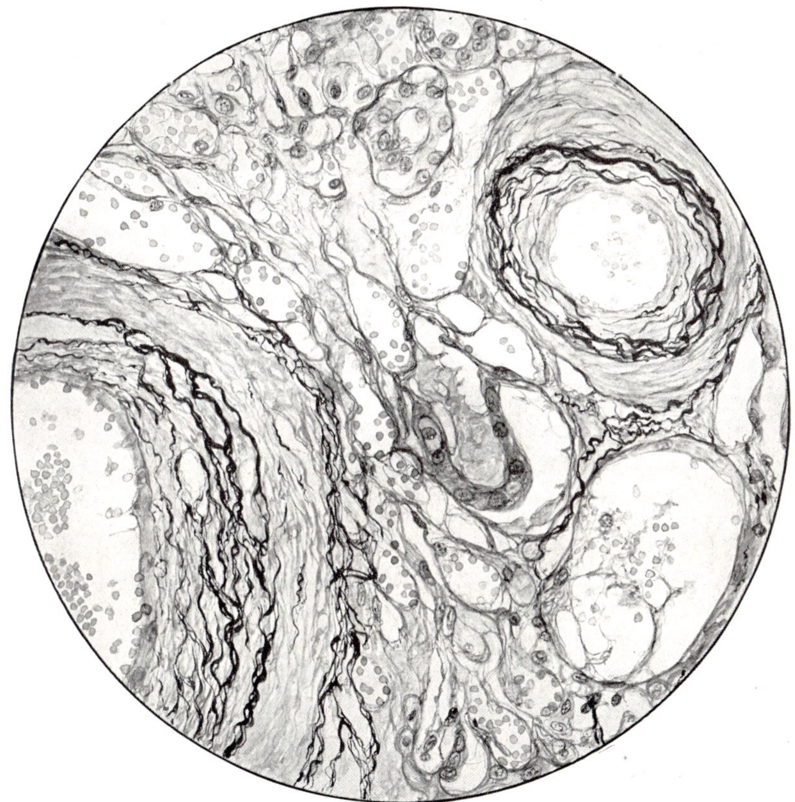

Fig. 131.—Arteriosclerotic narrowing of the renal vessels, with thickening of the arterial coat and reduplication of the elastic lamellæ.

rowed, is to produce many minute areas of malnutrition, in which the sensitive tissue suffers and finally atrophies away, to be replaced by a scar. This is the type of arteriosclerotic contracted kidney or primary contracted kidney which is most important and which we wish to describe.

There are some cases, however, in which, while most of the cortex is quite normal and shows itself to be smooth and normally lobulated on the removal of the capsule, there are numerous quite large depressions into which the capsule dips and becomes adherent (Fig. 132). These correspond with gross scarred areas sunken below the general surface, in which obliterated glomeruli and remains of shrunken tubules persist. Since the intervening tubules have collapsed or been reduced to narrow cords of cells, the persistent glomeruli concentrate themselves into a small space, and are embedded in scar tissue infiltrated with mononuclear wandering cells. The explanation usually given is that the sclerotic narrowing of the vessels is not uniform in all the branches of the artery, and that these are areas which have suffered especially. This explanation does not rest on an absolutely firm foundation, and since it is obvious that the scarred areas are entirely like slowly produced infarcts which are organized as fast as the cells disappear, it seems possible that, after all, they may have had an embolic origin. The functional disturbances in such cases are not especially marked, since there is much normal tissue to carry on the work.

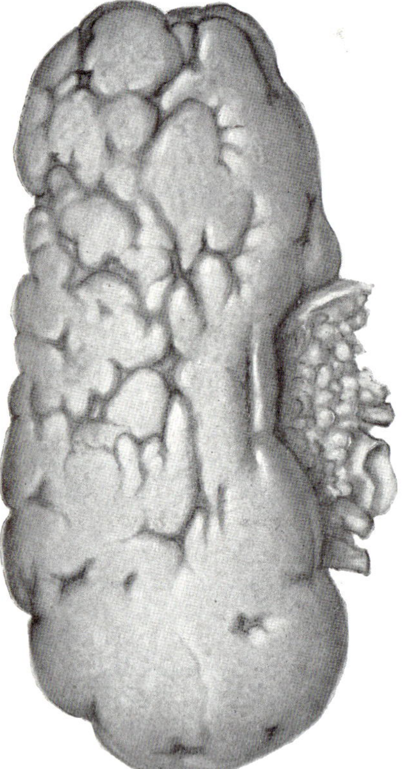

Fig. 132.—Atrophic scarred areas in renal cortex produced by arteriosclerotic narrowing of the vessels.

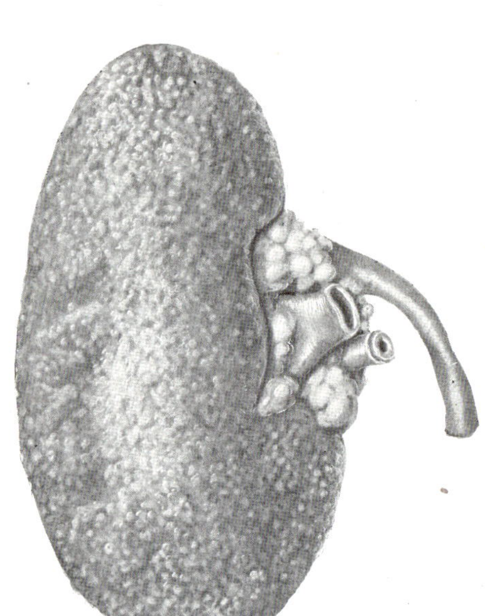

Fig. 133.—Arteriosclerotic contracted kidney (compare Fig. 136, which represents a section of this kidney).

The changes caused by diffuse sclerosis of the small branches is quite a different matter. Such kidneys are usually small and hard, and are often surrounded by a thick mass of fat. The capsule, which is thickened, is adherent to the surface, tearing it somewhat as it strips off, or in other instances it peels off easily enough. In any case it leaves a pale, mottled surface which is roughened by fine projecting nodules of a pale yellowish gray or pinkish gray color (Fig. 133). The scar-like tissue between these is translucent, grayish red, often allowing small vessels to be seen shining through beneath its surface. On section it is usually found that, with the decrease in size of the kidney in all directions, the space in which the pelvis lies is enlarged and filled with fat (Fig. 134). The blood-vessels are stiff and thick-walled, and even the minute ones on the cut surface stand open like rigid tubes. The pale cortex is greatly thinned, measuring sometimes not more than 2 to 3 mm., and in it one can no longer make out the ordinary striations in their usual parallel lines. Where they can be seen, they are greatly twisted and distorted and interrupted by the presence of opaque nodules of tissue which, beside projecting on the surface, are found deeper

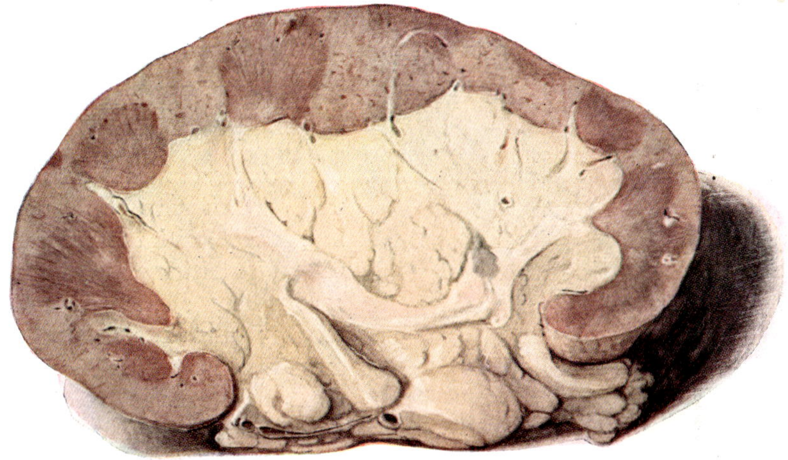

Fig. 134.—Old arteriosclerotic contracted kidney showing the filling of the widened space about the pelvis with fat.

in the cortex. Flecks of opaque yellow or deep red hæmorrhage are sometimes seen.

The gross appearance of such a kidney differs in no way, therefore, from the end result in a protracted glomerulonephritis (the so-called secondary contracted kidney), and in all probability something similar may result if the destruction be severe enough and time be given in the case of the tubular and interstitial forms. As a matter of fact, except perhaps through the presence of the strikingly thickened blood-vessels, it is difficult, if not impossible, to distinguish macroscopically the types of ultimate contracted kidney. The arteriosclerotic (so-called primary contracted kidney) may be very pale or quite dark red in color, but this depends in great part first on the exposure of the blood-capillaries in the translucent tissue, and then upon the degree of congestion of these vessels. The same difference in color may be seen in other contracted kidneys.

Small cysts filled with clear or dark-brown fluid are often seen projecting from the cortex (Fig. 135), but these seem not to depend entirely upon the scarring of the kidney, for they are quite frequently found in kidneys which have undergone no such change.

The microscopic alterations in the diffuse arteriosclerotic kidney are about as follows (Fig. 136): The arcuate vessels, the vasa recta, and the afferent vessels of the glomeruli show throughout or in patches such a thickening of the intima as greatly to encroach upon the lumen, but this cannot affect all the branches uniformly, for there are the projecting granules in which one finds the glomeruli enlarged and actively functional, and the tubules not only well preserved, but greatly hypertrophied, being both wider and, as shown by reconstruction, actually longer than the normal, and lined with cells of normal appearance. In every respect these seem to be magnified normal glomeruli and tubules which have undergone a work hypertrophy to compensate for many which have been lost. It is true that, with the progress of the malnutrition, these epithelial cells often show degenerative changes and become granular and disintegrated, or enormously swollen from the presence of large and small hyaline droplets. In most instances, as in almost all destructive renal changes, fat accumulates in drops in the epithelial cells, and, as in the inflammatory forms, these fats may be both glycerin and cholesterine esters, showing well all the chemical and staining peculiarities of those two types, as well as their different effect upon polarized light. It is the presence of the fats, hyaline droplets, etc., which confers the opacity upon the degenerating projecting granules of the kidney surface. In the kidneys, in which the process is less active, these granules have practically the color of the normal organ.

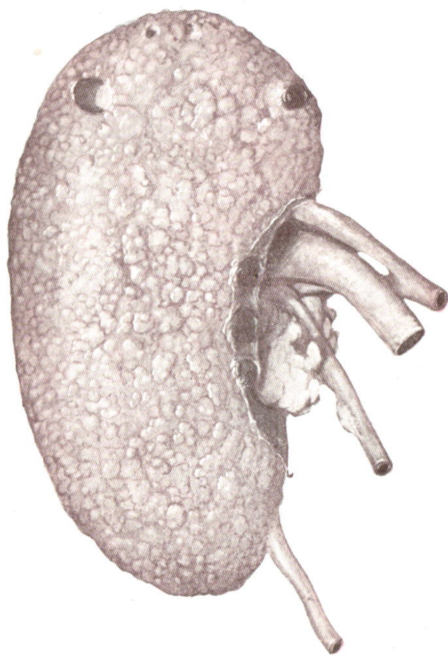

Fig. 135.—Arteriosclerotic contracted kidney with cortical cysts.

The more severe changes in the tubules produce a variety of appearance. Many of those which have already become enlarged through the compensatory hypertrophy become greatly dilated, probably through obstruction at some point lower down. These are found to be filled with a homogeneous, pink-staining fluid, which is retracted from the wall during fixation, and

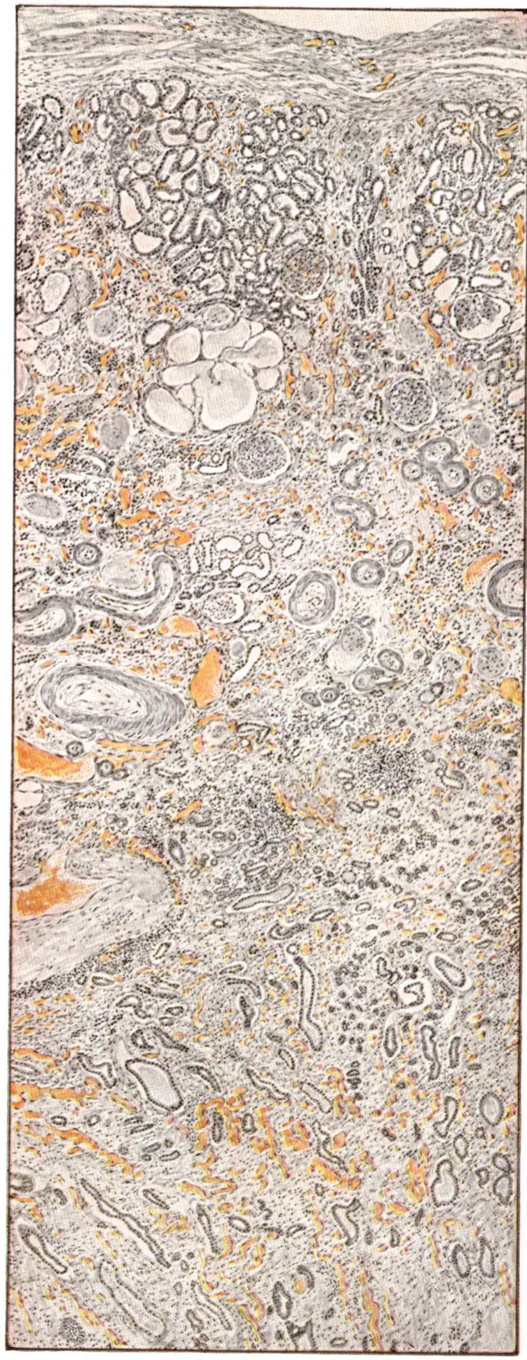

Fig. 136.—Cortex from arteriosclerotic contracted kidney (Fig. 133). Narrowed blood-vessels and obliterated glomeruli and tubules are conspicuous. Hypertrophied and dilated tubules are present in groups.

lined with extremely low, flat epithelium (Fig. 137). The other tubules in the more frankly scarred areas show no epithelium like that which normally lines the convoluted tubules. The cells which remain are cubical, slightly granular, or with clear protoplasm, and often desquamated or distorted and shrunken. There is scarcely a lumen left, and the epithelial cord is generally inclosed in a membrana propria, which has become greatly thick-

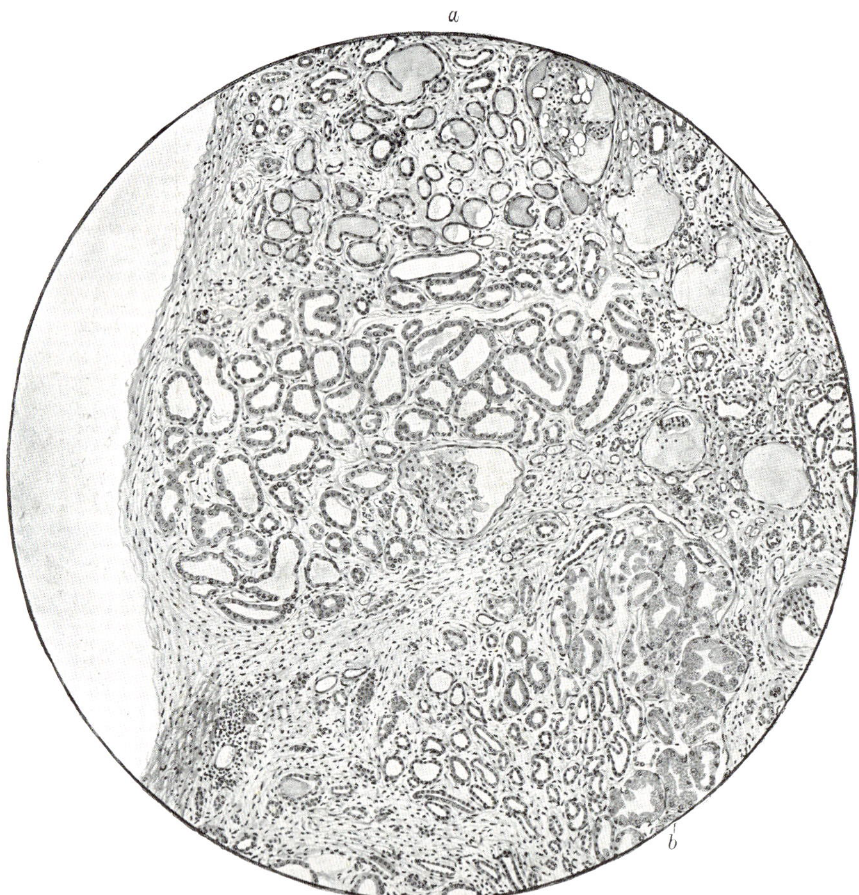

Fig. 137.—Projecting nodule of active cortical tissue in arteriosclerotic kidney: *a*, Dilated tubules; *b*, degenerated tubular epithelium.

ened by the apposition of a vague, irregular, wrinkled hyaline substance which stains blue with Mallory's connective-tissue stain (Fig. 139).

The glomeruli may be quite intact and enlarged, or they show some stage in the complex process leading to their complete obliteration. It seems that in this type of renal disease the obliteration of the glomeruli is brought about by quite different changes from those seen in acute and chronic glomerulonephritis, and it is generally possible, even at a late stage, to recognize which sort we are dealing with. But it would be hazardous to state that the changes about to be described are peculiar to the effects of arteriosclerosis. They probably depend on a great variety of injuries to blood-vessels and tubules, and doubtless play a part in the end results of tubular and of acute and chronic interstitial nephritis as well. Certainly they are common in all those very abundant cases in which atrophic and scarred areas occur in the kidney, without marked vascular change and in which we are left with no definite clue as to the real nature of the injury.

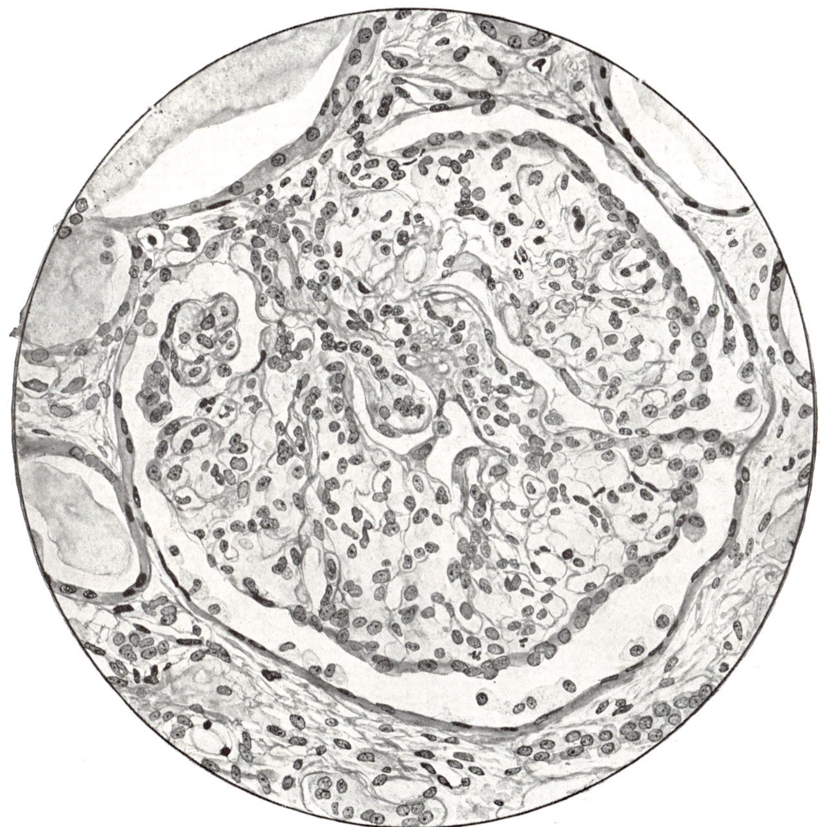

Fig. 138.—Glomerulus from arteriosclerotic kidney. The capillary tuft is converted into a compact mass, smoothly covered with epithelium.

In all cases the capillary loops become, sooner or later, impermeable to blood. This may happen through narrowing of the afferent vessel, or through collapse of the capillaries themselves, possibly the result of obstruction of the tubules and a short-lived distension of the capsule with urine, or through changes in the glomerular capsule. Here the impermeability is not the result of thrombotic occlusion of the capillaries, as in the glomerulonephritis. Nevertheless, unless they collapse completely, these capillaries are left filled with a formless material which may be derived partly from the remaining blood-corpuscles or from proliferation of the endothelium. In the end it stains yellow with van Gieson's stain and has no recognizable cellular character. Evidently the epithelial cells between the loops fuse and disappear, and finally the rather solid tuft is smoothly covered with epithelium in a continuous layer (Fig. 138). At any rate, the collapsed glomerulus remains visible a long time and is recognizable as such. It may finally adhere to the capsule, but such adhesions are not characteristic, as in glomerulonephritis.

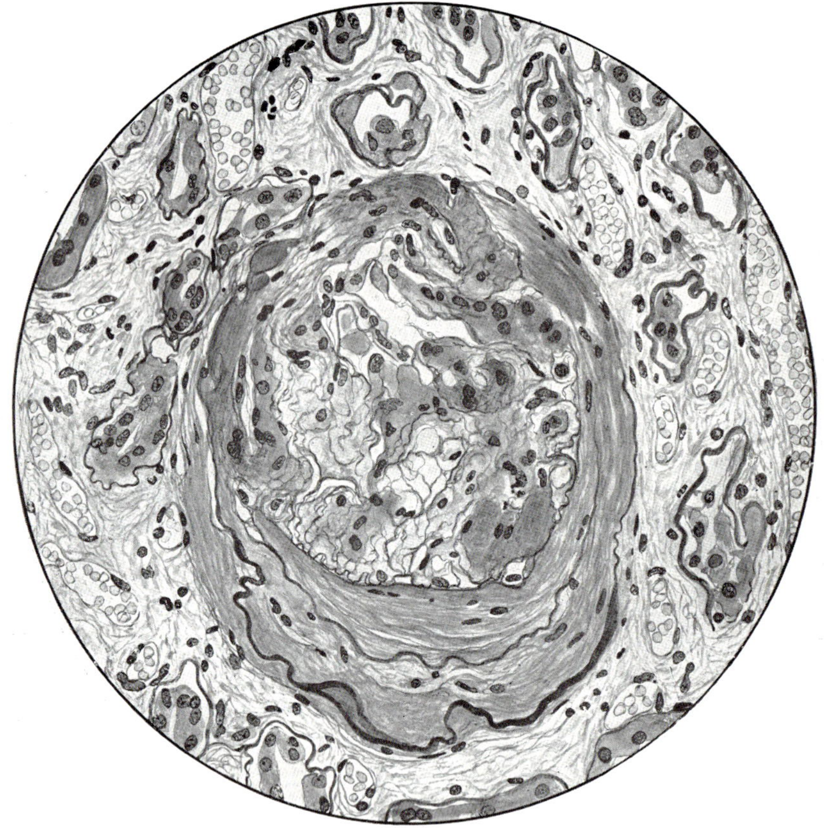

Fig. 139.—Late changes in the glomerulus in an arteriosclerotic kidney. Collapse of tuft with great thickening of Bowman's capsule. Atrophy of adjacent tubules.

Changes in the capsule are practically constant, and by many thought to be the cause of the collapse of the glomerulus either through constriction of the vessels at the hilum or through direct compression of the whole glomerulus. They consist in hyaline swelling of the membrana propria, with masses of hyaline bulging into the capsular lumen, or in new connective-tissue formation around the outside, or in a combination of the two.

These things lead to an extraordinary thickening of the capsule surrounding the collapsed glomerulus, so that this comes finally to look like a small, wrinkled structure in the centre of a great hyaline and fibrillar mass. By this time the capsular epithelium has disappeared, and the space of the capsule being lost, the hyaline and fibrous material incloses the glomerulus tightly (Fig. 139). In later stages the whole becomes fused and reduced to a homogeneous, hyaline, scar-like nodule. In other cases hyaline material appears in the outer wall of the capsule, in the walls of the efferent vessels,

Fig. 140.—Hyaline changes in a glomerulus.

and even in the walls of the capillaries of the tuft outside the endothelium, and it is easy to see that its increase may lead to the collapse of these capillaries and the final obliteration of the glomerulus (Fig. 140).

The connective tissue outside the glomeruli, as well as that between the tubules, becomes, in the course of time, remarkably increased in amount and very tough and firm. In its meshes the blood-vessels, obliterated glomeruli, and traces of tubules become very closely ranged, because of the disappearance of so many structures which were there before. This is in a sense a condensation of the kidney substance, and if the connective tissue were stretched out to the original size of the kidney, it would seem less abundant. Infiltration with wandering cells of the mononuclear type is almost the rule. Doubtless they appear as scavengers in an organ where tissue downfall is so constant (Figs. 136, 137).

(e) Combined Inflammatory and Arteriosclerotic Disease

Although the effects of toxic and bacterial injury to the kidneys with the striking alterations of glomeruli have been described separately from the effects of arteriosclerotic changes in the blood-vessels of the kidney, leading finally to the destruction of glomeruli and tubules, still by far the commonest condition is that in which these types are combined in the same kidney. It is unnecessary to enter into detail with regard to the structural changes in such altered kidneys, and it will perhaps suffice to say that in any series of cases in which renal changes appear, as those of a chronic diffuse nephritis, it is extremely common to find marked intimal thickenings in the blood-vessels, as well as evidence of thrombosis and inflammatory changes in the glomeruli and destructive alterations in the tubules.

It is, of course, conceivable that the inflammatory reactions to toxic or other injuries may supervene in kidneys already somewhat injured by the narrowing of their blood supply. On the other hand, it is just as easy to understand that the kidneys of persons who have survived for a long time repeated toxic inflammatory processes may, in the natural course of events, show some defects from arteriosclerotic changes of the blood-vessels which are so common in persons of mature age. It must, therefore, be understood that, while it cannot be stated directly that toxic lesions in the kidney bring about arteriosclerotic changes, or vice versa, the combination of the effects of these things must be recognized in a very great number of cases.

AMYLOID DEPOSIT

Amyloid deposit in the kidney has been very generally regarded as constituting a special type of nephritis, but it seems that this material may appear just as it does elsewhere, in an organ which is otherwise, for a time at least, practically normal, so far as one can see, while in other instances its appearance is associated with any or all of the changes described in progressive nephritis. It is clear, then, that in the most extreme degrees of scarring (Fig. 141), distortion, and contraction of the kidney, we may find amyloid, as well as in those acute and subacute stages in which the secretory elements of the kidney are still present, though often much injured.

Most commonly amyloid is found in kidneys which are greatly swollen and pale, with mottlings of opaque yellowish-white, and sometimes hæmorrhages. The capsule is not adherent in this stage, and the surface of the kidney is quite smooth or slightly granular. The tissue is often gray and translucent, except in the yellow, opaque areas, where fat-globules and dead cells are accumulated and the glomeruli are visible and prominent as translucent points. On the application of iodine they flash out into a bright brown color, showing very distinctly their arrangement along the straight vessels of the cortex. Often, too, there are brown lines in cortex and pyramid which indicate the presence of amyloid in tubule or vessel-walls. Microscopically, the minuter blood-vessels are surrounded by the pink-staining amyloid which lies directly under the endothelium. In the glomeruli (Fig. 142) one finds it especially abundant, occupying the same

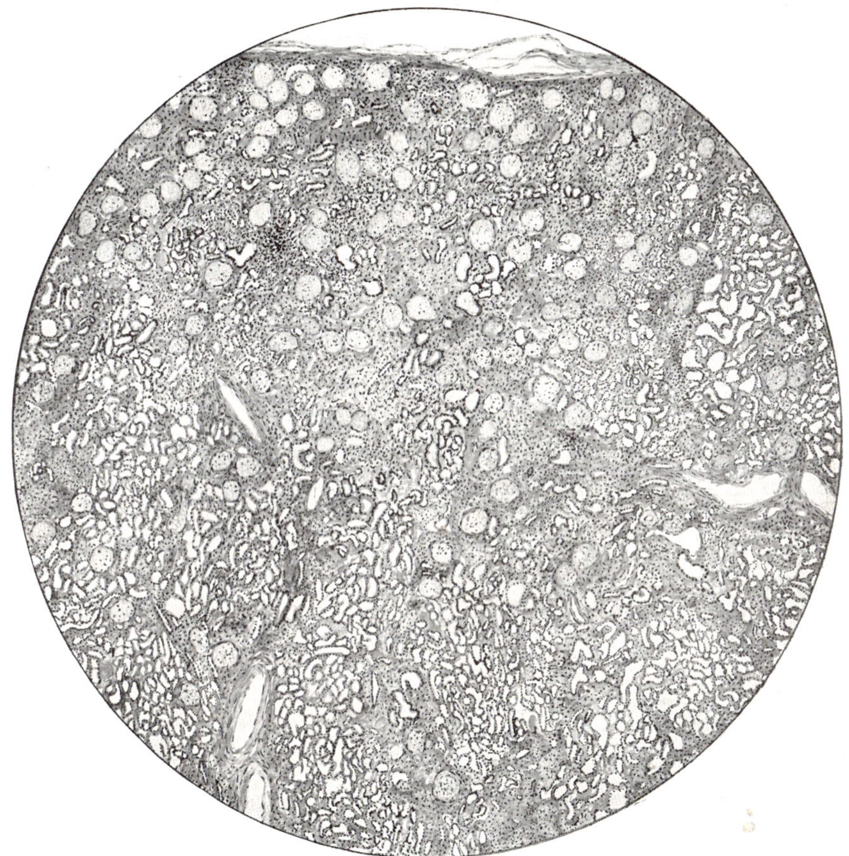

Fig. 141.—Extreme scarring of the kidney, with amyloid. The glomeruli approach each other, since the tubules have been destroyed.

position, and thus separating, in the capillaries, the endothelium from the epithelial covering. Sometimes it thus forms a tube lined with endothelium, through which blood may still pass, but if it becomes more abundant, the lumen of such a tube is narrowed, and although one or two endothelial cells may still persist there, it becomes obstructed, as far as the passage of blood goes. In late stages the glomeruli become almost solid masses of amyloid. Thickening of the capsule may occur, but there are not usually adhesions with the glomerular tuft. The membrana propria of the tubules may, in the same way, become the point of deposit of the amyloid, especially in the pyramids.

The epithelial cells of the tubules show the most advanced degenerative changes, being loaded with fat-globules or becoming desquamated. Hyaline droplets with great swelling of the cell are common, too (Fig. 143). It is characteristic of such amyloid kidneys that in patches the tubules become greatly dilated and lined by very flat, low epithelium. In other

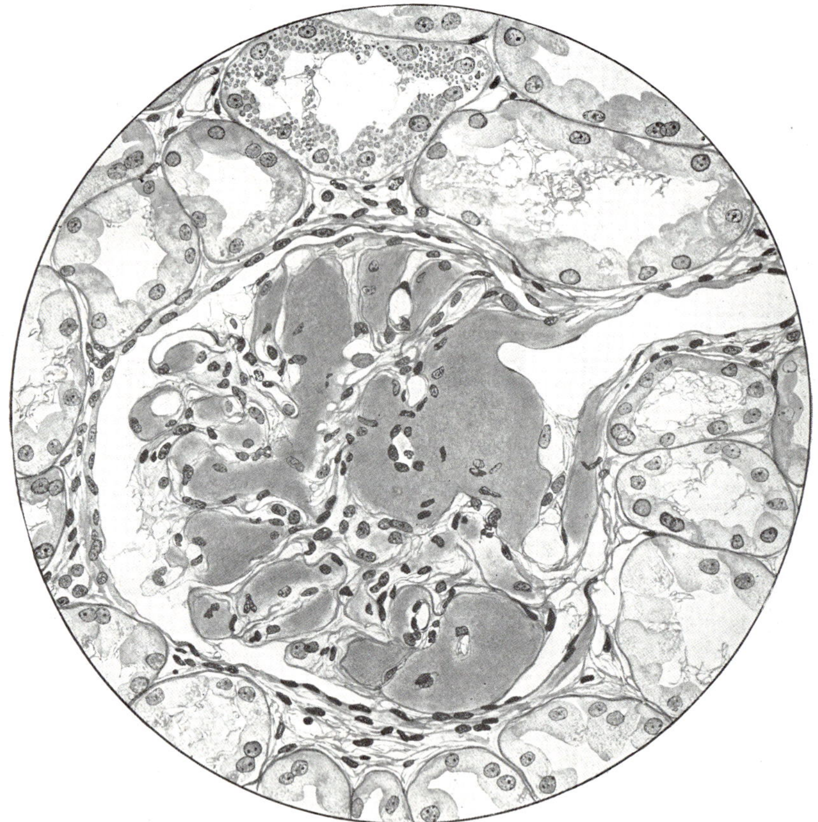

Fig. 142.—Amyloid in glomerulus. The amyloid lies between the endothelium and the capsular epithelium in each capillary.

areas, with the obstruction of the glomeruli, the tubules atrophy and collapse, and the region is involved in scar tissue. The blood-vessels may or may not be sclerotic. The further changes in more advanced cases differ in no essential from those seen in other contracted kidneys, and it is difficult to say whether the presence of the amyloid caused the degeneration of the cells. Possibly the destruction of the cells and the presence of amyloid were the parallel results of the same long-standing intoxication, for, as has been stated before, the source of the amyloid is connected with the existence of some protracted intoxication or infection.

It is, perhaps, because of the usual existence of some such disease as syphilis, tuberculosis, or malignant growth, with their secondary anæmia, that the heart and blood-vessels fail to hypertrophy. Indeed, during the life of these patients blood-pressure seldom runs high, though exactly why arterial hypertension should fail to appear in amyloid disease is not clear.

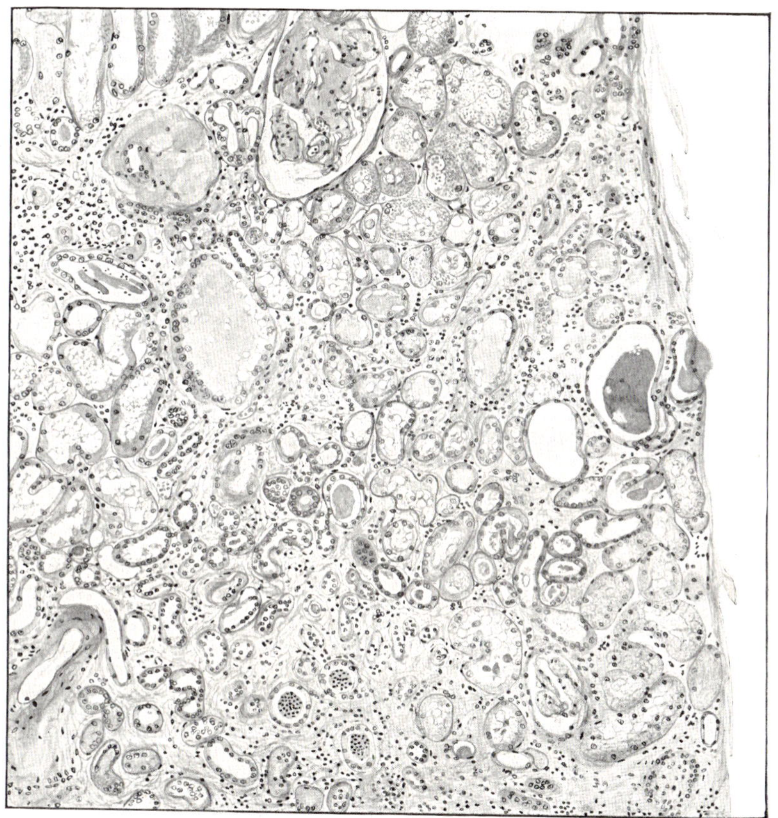

Fig. 143.—Subacute and chronic nephritis with amyloid. Tubules show epithelial degeneration and dilatation.

Probably the amyloid has little to do with this, for in the later stages, when renal tissue is largely destroyed, a rise in blood-pressure may occur. It has been suggested that the amyloid involvement of the adrenals may prevent the rise of pressure.

The urine is abundant, with low specific gravity, and pale, but rich in albumen; hyaline casts and epithelial and other cells appear there. It has never been shown, though, that the specifically staining amyloid plays any part in forming these casts.

In general, then, while some of the symptoms of nephritis are changed by the amyloid in the kidney, we may regard its presence there as incidental, rather than as the cause of the nephritis or as constituting a new form of the disease.

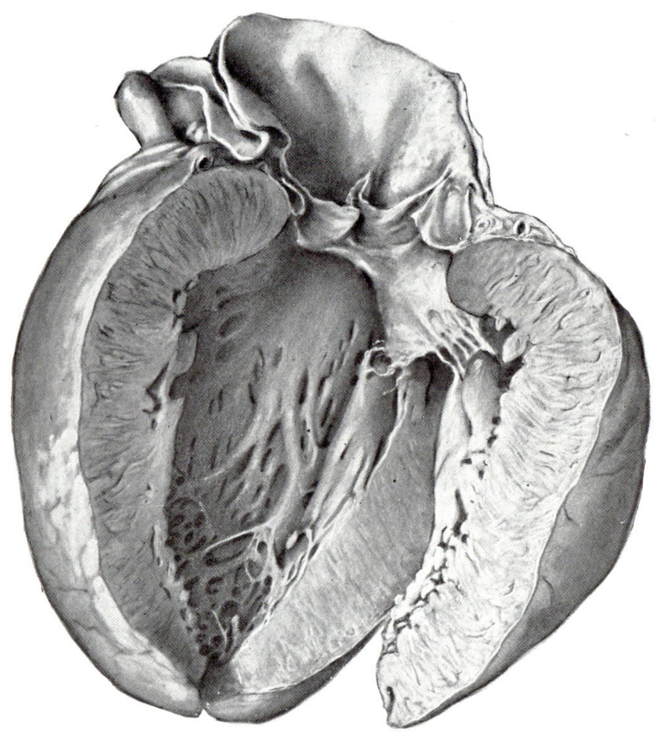

Fig. 144.—Great hypertrophy of the heart affecting especially the left ventricle, in chronic nephritis without valvular lesion.

SUMMARY

If, now, we consider together all the anatomical changes found to occur in the kidneys, we find that they are the effects of various injuries, with responses arising according to clearly defined principles, and ending, if time be allowed, in the production of altered organs in which one may recognize great destructive effects side by side with strenuous attempts at healing and at compensatory hypertrophy. The injuries are of many different kinds: they affect one or other part of the kidney predominantly; they frequently occur in combination, and they often act repeatedly and persistently over a long time. No sooner, then, is one injury complete, the dead tissue removed, and the place healed, with perhaps some compensatory growth of functional tissue elsewhere, than a new injury ensues, and in another place, or even in the compensatory new tissue, the whole process begins again. Nor is this all—the destruction or distortion of one element entails the downfall of another—the tubule is dependent on the glomerulus, and the glomerulus on the tubule, both on the blood supply, so that an injury anywhere has far-reaching results in this complex organ.

It is difficult to unravel, then, the anatomical effects of such injuries acting singly, but far more so when they are combined. A still greater difficulty arises, however, when we attempt to estimate the importance of these anatomical changes, since we know that the function of the kidney is affected so profoundly by alterations of the cell which do not show themselves at all to our eyes, even with the best of microscopes, aided only by our present technical methods.

We recognize certain types of change in each element of the kidneys. The tubular epithelium may be swollen and granular in various infections and intoxications: the cells in all severer injuries usually become clogged with droplets of fat, glycerin, and cholesterine esters, or with peculiar hyaline droplets, or they finally pass through even more profound changes and lose their structure, becoming necrotic. These things in one form or another are common to all sorts of nephritis. In the lumen of the tubules we find fluid holding albumen, and therefore coagulable, granular débris, epithelial cells, leucocytes, red blood-corpuscles, and finally curious moulds or casts which are hyaline, compressed products of the fusion of all these things, characterized often by the adhesion of better preserved leucocytes or epithelial cells or granules. Slipping down the tubule, they appear in the urine. The glomeruli may have their capillaries obstructed, when bacteria or poisons injure them, by thrombi formed from the blood, or by masses of leucocytes or proliferated cells. Rigid loops adhere to the capsule, the capsular epithelium proliferates to cover these adhesions, or to encapsulate exudate which appears in its lumen. Or, on the other hand, the blood may be shut off from these capillaries from a point in the afferent vessel at some distance, or by the obstruction of the tubule and the consequent accumulation of secretion in the capsule, or even by the thickening of the capsule with hyaline changes. The end result in every case is the impermeability and final obliteration of this complex mechanism.

The blood-vessels may be sclerotic and thickened, so that their stream-bed is narrowed, or, as we have just said, they may be occluded or compressed, but all these changes lead alike to an obstruction of the blood-flow. The framework of the kidney responds to the loss of the structures which it supports by an attempt to replace and heal the loss, or it itself is injured and heals, often with excess of tissue. It probably plays little part in embarrassing and trammeling the tissue of more important function, although this idea has so long been held to be true.

Injuries may occur, and renal tissue be destroyed and removed and replaced by a scar, and yet the remaining tissue will grow to compensate for this loss until the kidney resumes perfectly the normal function. If too much tissue is destroyed, signs of renal insufficiency will arise, but a relatively small amount of normal renal tissue will suffice to carry on the normal function. Diseased renal tissue, however, is at once inefficient in some respects, and symptoms arise to show it. So it is that we may have normal function in a kidney in which there are many obsolete scars of an old injury, because the remaining tissue is normal and equal to its task, while in other cases, what seems a relatively slight change, may cause great disturbances in function.

FUNCTIONAL ALTERATIONS—RENAL INSUFFICIENCY

From the changes observed anatomically in human kidneys, it is clear that the injury may affect the blood-vessels, including the capillaries of the glomeruli, the epithelial cells of the glomeruli and tubules, or even the connective-tissue framework, and it has already been seen that the functional disturbances vary with these different lesions. But what we find in the injured kidney is usually a combination of these changes, because one entails another in course of time, and it is only rarely that we are able to study the very beginning of the disease. Besides, what we see is, for the greater part, not the direct effect of the injury, but evidence of a reaction or response on the part of the tissue. It is true that we can see destructive changes in the epithelium after necrobiotic or fermentative processes have combined with the accumulation of the materials of metabolism to make them evident, but it is important to bear in mind that extreme functional disturbances may result from injuries which produce in the cells no changes that we can see. The functional activities of the cells go on in a mysterious, invisible way that we may appreciate only by the results, and to certain cells there seem to be assigned special duties, even in the course of a single renal tubule. Thus Aschoff states that uric acid is secreted in the first and second division of the convoluted tubule, while sugar passes out through its fourth division or is stored in those cells in the form of glycogen. Carmine is secreted in solution, but may be stored in the epithelial cells in granules. Similarly water and salt are specifically secreted by certain cells, which may cease their function long before any morphological change is visible in them or resume it without having ever shown such a change.

Of course, when cells are obviously injured or killed and disintegrated, their function falls away with them, and glomeruli whose capillaries are plugged with clots no longer filter out water, but these are very gross changes which we may not find at all in a kidney whose disability is, nevertheless, extreme. And yet we continue to insist on finding them and attempting to correlate them with the functional changes in order to establish a classification of renal disease. We must know far more about the exact site of functions, and we must be able to disentangle extrarenal influences from the actual renal changes before we succeed in this. For at most such scars represent areas where kidney substance has been completely lost, and they give an indication, therefore, of a possible quantitative insufficiency of that part which remains. But if, as so often happens, the remaining tissue is functioning, but in a perverted way, symptoms arise.

Of these symptoms, perhaps the most common is the excretion of albumen in the urine, sometimes merely a recognizable trace, sometimes such a large quantity that a thick coagulum is formed when the acidulated urine is boiled. This evidently depends upon some injury to the endothelium of the glomerular capillaries, or the renal epithelium, and the wonder is not so much that the albumen should appear, but that it should be so completely retained by the normal kidney. It is most abundantly excreted in the acute stages, and in chronic forms of nephritis in which the injury to the structures of the kidney is actively progressing or passing through an exacerbation. In the more completed conditions, such as are found in the old contracted kidneys, where, although there are great distortion and loss of substance, the active injury has ceased, there is little or no albuminuria, although evidences of renal deficiency may persist, and at any moment with a new poisoning the albumen may reappear in the urine.

Red blood-corpuscles and leucocytes, as well as epithelial cells, come down the tubules when there is acute inflammation, and hyaline casts or moulds of the tubules are an almost constant accompaniment of all the more active processes. Exactly what goes to form the casts is not certain, but it seems that they must arise from the fusion of many things, including the débris of cells, hyaline droplets which are found in the epithelium, albuminous materials, and sometimes fibrin. Adhering cells which are better preserved are easily recognized.

Variations in the amount of water excreted are extreme, and do not always accord perfectly with what we should expect from the anatomical state of the kidney. Schlayer has attempted to establish the idea that this depends upon variations in the sensitiveness of the capillary walls—that with increasing severity of the injury there may be at first an increase in the sensitiveness, and consequent secretory activity or permeability of the capillaries, which results in the excretion of an excess of water, while later the more injured wall becomes less sensitive, and oliguria or finally complete cessation of urine flow (anuria) results. Aschoff objects to this that extrarenal conditions of blood-pressure and blood supply are more than sufficient to account for these variations; but it may be that these extrarenal conditions themselves affect the sensitiveness of the renal capillaries. A disturbance of water and salt excretion, or a deficiency in the whole renal activity, as shown by injections of phenolsulphonephthalein, may be greatly accentuated by chronic passive congestion. When the renal substance is greatly reduced, as in the old contracted kidneys, a great amount of water is excreted, with relatively little solids, while actual cessation of urine or the excretion of only a little, with high specific gravity, accompanies the acute destructive stages. The reasons for these differences are not known, but it is suggested that the high blood-pressure and rapid stream through the kidneys so characteristic of the contracted stage may account for the polyuria, while the specific inability of the glomeruli to excrete water, or more probably its specific inability to excrete sodium chloride and other inorganic substances, may explain the oliguria or anuria of the acuter stages.

Sodium chloride passes into the urine through the quite specific activity of some of the epithelial cells, and when these fail, it is retained in the tissues. Since the tissue fluids must remain isotonic for the cells, water is reserved to dilute this concentrated salt solution, and the consequence is œdema, hydrothorax, and ascites. Little doubt can exist as to the nature of this nephritic œdema, for if such waterlogged patients are deprived of salt in their food and given water in restricted amounts, the œdema quickly disappears, to reappear at once if a considerable ration of salt be allowed. Thus in the case of a man who entered the hospital with enormous swelling of arms and legs and great accumulation of fluid in pleura and peritoneum, a salt-free diet restored the normal appearance very quickly. In two weeks this man lost 35 pounds in weight, and this experience is practically of daily occurrence.

But with this it must not be forgotten that there are often mechanical reasons also for the lessened excretion of water. Thrombosis of the glomerular capillaries, or their plugging with leucocytes and endothelial cells, as well as their compression by exudate in the capsule, or by proliferation of the capsular epithelium, makes them impermeable for the blood and directly interferes with their function. Similarly it is conceivable that the tubules may be obstructed by desquamated cells and casts, but although these things have their part, they are probably not so important as the disturbances of the specific function of the secreting cells themselves.

Nitrogenous substances, such as urea, are often retained in the blood in the same way, and although urea itself seems to be a relatively harmless material, it has always been thought that the retention of some such substances, as yet unrecognized, is responsible for certain general conditions which are frequently associated with nephritis. Of these, the most important are uræmia and vascular hypertension.

Uræmia is an intoxication of unknown cause which may arise in connection with any sort of nephritis, but is commonest in those in which very extensive destruction is quickly produced, and in those contracted kidneys in which an extreme diminution of the kidney substance is finally reached. It may result in all sorts of nervous and mental disturbances, delirium of the most violent sort, delusions, etc., ending in coma or convulsions. The name, indicating a retention of urea, does not give a true explanation of its cause, and we are still in the dark concerning it.

Arterial hypertension, in which the systolic blood-pressure may reach 250 mm. of mercury or more, is a characteristic accompaniment of some forms of nephritis. It is found beginning in the acute or subacute stages, but reaches its maximum in the more advanced conditions of longer standing. Jores thinks that it is particularly associated with the so-called primary contracted kidney, with arteriosclerosis, but this does not seem to be strictly true, for we have found the highest pressures in cases in which there had evidently been inflammatory disease of the glomeruli, and in combinations of the inflammatory and arteriosclerotic processes. The cause of this high blood-pressure is again a mystery. It has been thought to be due to the narrowing and obliteration of the blood-channels in the kidney, but it is clear that ligation of the renal arteries does not elevate the general blood-pressure. Nevertheless, compression of the kidneys seems to have some effect in this direction, and the gradual reduction of the kidneys by their piecemeal removal does produce a permanent rise in blood-pressure after a certain proportion of the kidney substance has been destroyed. These experiments leave us still with the problem, however, as to whether obstruction of the circulation or inefficiency of the kidney is the important factor. Schur and Wiesel have thought that chronic nephritis is accompanied by hypertrophy and excessive activity of the adrenals, and that constriction of the arterioles by the epinephrine thus produced should account for the high tension, but evidence for this is very weak. No one has found a sufficient quantity of epinephrine in the blood to support this idea. Still, the general opinion is that some sort of vasoconstrictor material must be retained in the blood to keep up such a high pressure. The heart, especially its left ventricle, becomes greatly hypertrophied, and in time even the walls of the vessels thicken their muscular coats. Arteriosclerotic changes in the vessels are common, and may play some part in producing the high pressure if it can be shown that it causes the narrowing of arterioles in general. This, however, is so variable that it does not afford a satisfactory explanation. Albuminuric retinitis, which is a change often accompanied by arteriosclerotic modifications of the retinal vessels, and marked by the presence of hæmorrhages and shining deposits of cholesterine in the retina, is very frequent in the course of nephritis. Actual blindness may be caused in this way. Acute pericarditis and acute diphtheritic enteritis are also frequent terminal affections.

LITERATURE

Aschoff: Archives of Internal Medicine, 1913, xii, 723.
Baehr: Jour. Exp. Med., 1912, xv, 330; Ziegler's Beitr., 1913, lv, 545.
Fahr: Frankf. Zeits. f. Path., 1912, ix, 15.
Frey: Dtsch. Arch. f. klin. Med., 1912, cvi. 347.
Gull and Sutton: Medico-Chir. Trans., 1872, lv, 273.
Harvey: Proc. N. Y. Path. Soc., 1912, xii, 154.
Herxheimer: Ziegler's Beiträge, 1909, xlv, 253.
Janeway: Amer. Jour. Med. Sci., 1913, cxlv, 625; Trans. Cong. Amer. Phys. & Surg., 1913, ix, 14.
Jores: Deut. Arch. f. klin. Med., 1908, xciv.
Löhlein: Ergebn. d. inn. Med. u. Kinderh., 1910, v, 411; Arb. a. d. Path. Inst., Leipzig, 1906, Heft 4.
Muller, Fr.: Verh. Dtsch. Path. Ges., 1906, ix, 64.
Ponfick: Verh. Dtsch. Path. Ges., 1906, ix, 49.
Schlayer: Beihefte zur Med. Klinik, 1912, viii, 211; also several papers in Dtsch. Arch. f. klin. Med., xcviii, ci, cii, civ, etc.
Volhard and Fahr: Die Brightsche Nierenkrankheit, 1913.
Weigert: Volkmann's Samml. klin. Vortr., 162, 163.

CHAPTER XVI

INJURY WITH INFLAMMATORY REACTION AND ATTEMPTED REPAIR (Continued).—INJURY AND REPAIR OF THE LIVER

Cirrhosis of the liver. Structure of the liver in relation to disease. Direct injury to liver-cells. Acute yellow atrophy, eclampsia, and infections. Repair and compensatory hyperplasia. Cirrhosis: its various types. The alterations in architecture involved. Obstruction of portal circulation. Collateral circulation. Biliary and hypertrophic cirrhosis.

INJURY AND REPAIR OF THE LIVER

As in other organs, injury is possible in the liver in all sorts of ways, but we shall discuss here more especially those changes which are caused by the introduction of the destructive agent by way of the blood-stream or bile-ducts. Poisons or infections may enter in these ways, and produce all degrees of injury to the liver tissue with many types of reaction. On the other hand, the lack of some nutritive substance in the blood, or even the mere extreme sluggishness of its course, may be sufficient to disable or even to kill some of the liver-cells. As in other organs, the elements which make up the liver tissue are not all equally resistant, and it is constantly evident that the highly specialized liver-cells are injured or killed by poison, which leaves the less delicate gall-duct epithelium perfectly intact and capable of growth. The connective-tissue framework and blood-vessels are even more hardy, and show little effect from injuries that ravage the liver-cells.

Since in many of the cases which we are about to consider, the noxa reaches the tissue by way of the blood, it is clear that if there are any peculiarities in the way the blood-stream is distributed there may be corresponding variations in the concentration with which the poison reaches the liver-cells.

Structure of Liver.—The surface of the living organ is uniformly red, but on the death of the animal, and especially if the blood be allowed to escape from the large veins, a distinct fine lobulation becomes visible because the blood is pushed on in every arterio-venous communication to the venous end. On this account the portion about the efferent vein normally looks red, while the rest is paler, showing the brownish color of the liver-cells. If all the blood be washed out, the liver is uniformly light brown.

These lobules are not sharply marked off from one another, but anastomose in such a way that, from the arrangement of the cells alone, it is not easy to say where one begins and another ends. Naturally, the lobule should be, as suggested by Sabourin, the unit mass of tissue which pours its secretion into a terminal branch of the bile-duct, but even there it is difficult to determine how much of the bile-duct shall be adopted as belonging to one lobule, and the lobule tends to be a branched mass, forming a mantle around the end ramifications of the duct. It has exactly the same relation to the portal vein and hepatic artery. This relation is made very distinct in chronic passive congestion when the parts of the liver tissue most distant from the portal vein, that is, nearest to the efferent vein, are destroyed (*cf.* Fig. 147). Unfortunately, the efferent veins which receive capillaries from adjacent lobules become so conspicuous from the radial way in which these capillaries enter into them that they are almost irresistibly attractive in a single section, as the centre of each mass which they drain. A purely artificial lobule, set up around the central (efferent) vein, has become the time-honored lobule of the liver, and the more so because in the pig that mass is sharply outlined by fibrous tissue. Doubtless we should break away from this conception and speak always in terms of the true lobule, but it would cause great confusion and add little of great value. Wherever greater clearness can be reached by considering the liver on the basis of Sabourin's lobule it will be done.

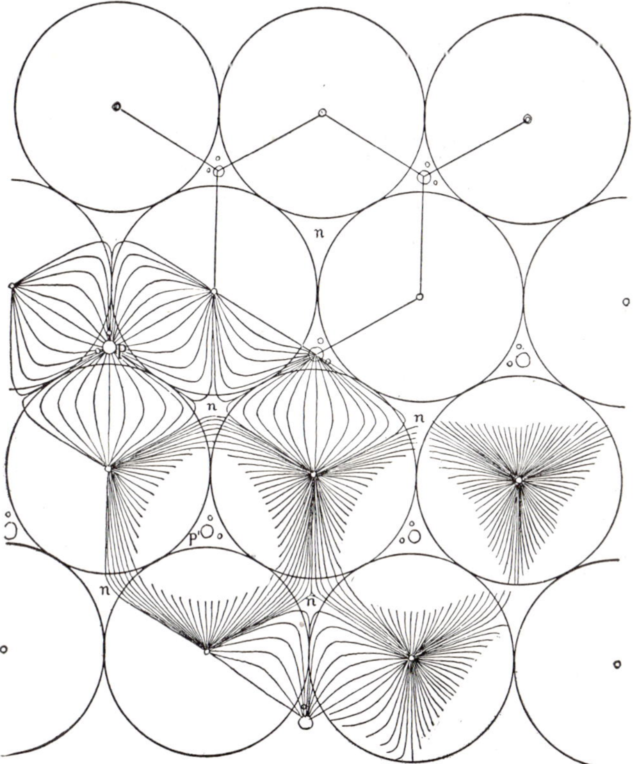

Fig. 145.—Diagram of the liver lobule (Mall).

The great supply of blood is brought in by the portal vein, but from the capillaries of the hepatic artery which unite with those of the portal where they enter among the liver-cells, blood under higher pressure gives impetus to the venous stream, driving it forward toward the efferent vein. The portal vein may be ligated and its blood diverted into the vena cava without causing the death of the liver tissue, and so, too, the hepatic artery may be obstructed without effect, but if the smaller branches of the portal vein are occluded where the hepatic arterioles join them, the blood supply is cut off from the liver-cells and they die. Capillaries once formed, after the union of portal and hepatic terminals, run in part directly to the efferent veins, but some take a more roundabout course, so as to supply liver-cells not lying in that direct line (Fig. 145). The disadvantageous effect of this longer course becomes apparent in chronic passive congestion.

The bile-ducts branch minutely so as to connect with the end of each complex cord of liver-cells, the bile capillary, bounded on all sides by liver-cells, forming the continuation of their lumen. The bile-duct epithelium, although of the same origin as the liver-cells and presumably endowed with the same potentialities of specialization, has not become so differentiated and remains as less highly organized, but more hardy cells, with the simpler function of lining the ducts.

Direct Injury to the Liver-cells.—With such a distribution of the circulation it is not surprising that injuries to the cells are often zonal in their

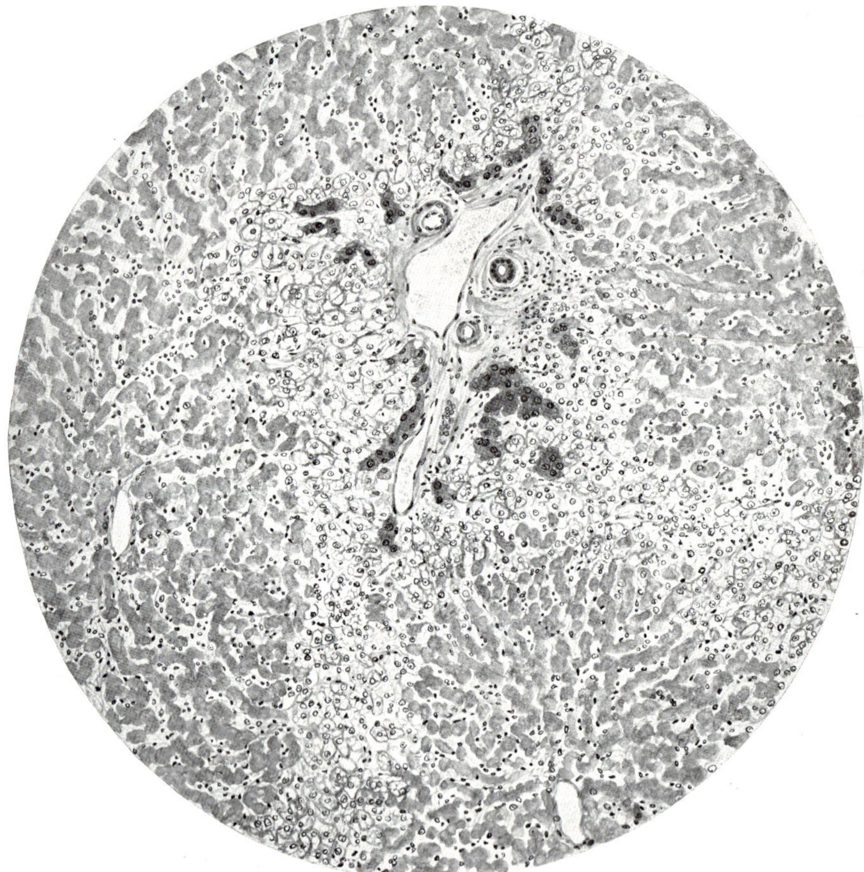

Fig. 146.—Necrosis of liver-cells about the efferent vein in each lobule: case of streptococcus peritonitis.

arrangement. It is true that in many infections practically all the cells may appear turbid and cloudy, and in extreme accumulations of fat in the liver all the cells may contain globules, but usually such alterations are not so uniform. The fat may be lodged especially in the cells nearer the portal vein, or, on the contrary, especially in those about the efferent vein. When there is actual injury sufficient to kill the cell, it may affect the cells of the zone nearest the portal vein, as in eclampsia gravidarum, or the zone farthest from the portal vein, and therefore encircling the efferent vein, as in chronic passive congestion, chloroform poisoning, many acute infections, especially those in which generalized peritonitis (Fig. 146) or other extensive and intense inflammations occur, and in all that ill-defined group of cases known as acute yellow atrophy of the liver. Sometimes, as Opie points out, in intense infections, and especially where a toxic injury is combined with bacterial infection, a zone midway between portal and

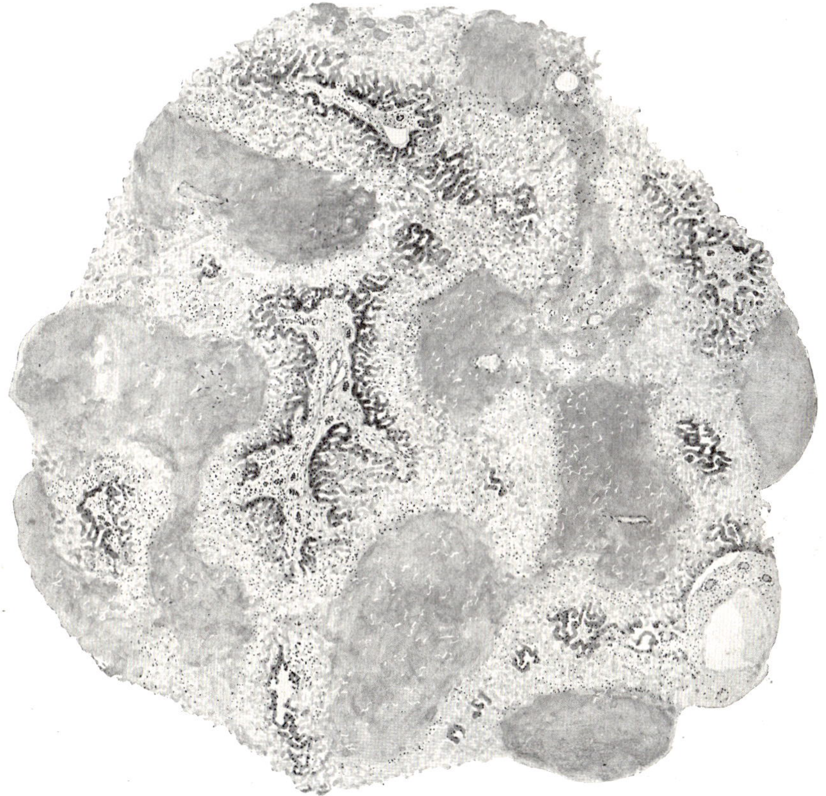

Fig. 147.—Chronic passive congestion, destruction of liver-cells extending from one efferent vein to another and isolating the periportal tissue.

efferent vein may be picked out for necrosis. One cannot doubt the determining influence of the blood-stream in producing these differences of distribution, although it is not always easy to understand it. Opie has shown that colored materials injected into the hepatic artery or portal vein during the normal circulation tend to lodge in the middle zone, and one might imagine that a peculiarly acrid poison could destroy the first cells it impinged upon, as happens in eclampsia, but how is one to explain the extensive and often sharply limited necrosis of the cells farthest from the entrance of the blood, which is so frequently seen in the conditions mentioned above? In the case of chronic passive congestion it is probable that those cells which receive the blood last are poorly nourished by the stagnating stream, which becomes less able to supply oxygen as it reaches the neighborhood of the efferent vein. It is interesting that, in this case, as in many infectious and toxic injuries, the cells along those capillaries which take a long course to empty into the efferent vein suffer throughout a region everywhere equidistant from the portal vein and artery, but not everywhere equidistant from the efferent vein. Therefore in these cases the necrotic tissue does not merely encircle the efferent veins, but extends from one to

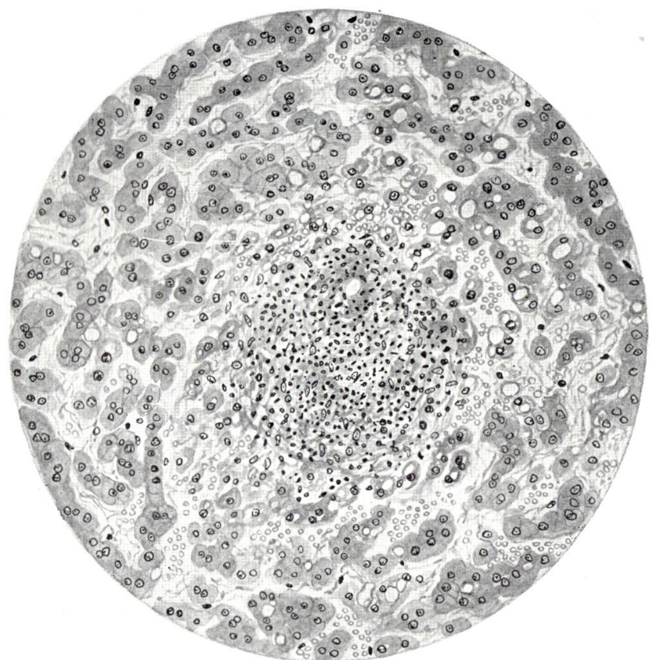

Fig. 148.—Focal necrosis with invasion and fragmentation of wandering cells: typhoid fever.

another. If we accept Sabourin's lobule, the whole periphery of the lobule is necrotic; if we regard the efferent vein as the centre of the lobule, the necrotic area occupies the centre of each lobule, and stretches across to join that about the centre of each adjacent lobule (*cf.* Fig. 147).

But although injury and destruction of liver-cells may often be distributed in a zone of each lobule, it is very frequently focal. In numbers of infectious diseases, such as typhoid fever, diphtheria, malaria, smallpox, and in poisoning with diphtheria toxin, ricin, abrin, and similar things, one discovers small groups of cells situated anywhere in the lobule which have been killed and coagulated (Fig. 148). Why those cells should have been picked out for destruction it is not easy to say. Some authors, including Mallory, believe that emboli of cells or agglutinated red corpuscles, often supplemented by fibrin thrombi, so occlude the capillaries about a tiny group of cells as to deprive them of their blood supply and thus produce an anæmic necrosis. In spite of the difficulty of finding another satisfactory explanation, there is much that seems hardly plausible about this. It is true that such cell emboli are often found, but it is hard to believe that they could so completely surround a group of cells in the liver as to render it anæmic. Even then it would seem that such a small mass of tissue might absorb enough nutriment by diffusion to keep it alive. On the other hand, if a mass of liver-cells did die, one might expect its capillaries to become thrombosed.

It would seem that injection of granular material into the mesenteric vein ought to decide this question at once. In my hands such injection (corn-starch) does rarely produce focal changes which will probably lead to necrosis of the liver-cells, but these are in the beginning areas of tearing of the tissue by hæmorrhage evidently as the result of plugging of the capillaries. In those areas stretched and dismembered cords of liver-cells are found; the remainder are pressed back and flattened, but none are necrotic. This is very different from the familiar appearance of most focal necroses, in which the tissue is not in the least disarranged, but each cell has died where it stood. In all the rest of the experiments the grains lodged singly or in groups in the capillaries, without producing the least change in the liver-cells. (See further discussion under Typhoid Fever.)

If chloroform be administered to an animal for an hour or two and its liver examined after a time, marked changes are to be found in the liver-cells nearest the efferent vein. In case the chloroform has acted mildly, these are chiefly evident in the great accumulation of fat, but in other animals where it has acted longer or more intensely, these cells are quite dead, their nuclei failing to stain, while the cell-body is coagulated and deeply stained with eosin. This may be ascertained by excision of a small piece of the liver tissue shortly after the poisoning, the animal being left alive. After three weeks the liver is found restored to practically its normal condition, so rapid is the removal of the dead cells and the regeneration of new ones from those which remain. By combining bacterial infection with chloroform poisoning Opie has produced much more profound injuries which are not so readily repaired. In the zonal necroses which accompany intense septic infections a similar anatomical condition is produced. All the liver-cells most distant from the portal vein, that is, encircling the efferent vein and stretching to the region of the next, are necrotic. Nevertheless, in these areas of cell death the endothelial cells and connective tissues remain alive. Nearer to the portal vein in each lobule is a zone of cells distended with fat-globules, and still nearer the liver-cells seem intact (Fig. 146).

Acute Yellow Atrophy.—This name is loosely given to those cases in which some unknown agent suddenly produces a destruction of liver-cells so wide-spread that signs of acute insufficiency of the hepatic functions appear. It occurs most commonly in young women or men, and often in pregnant women, but may also affect children. Sudden malaise, symptoms of indigestion, nausea, rapidly deepening jaundice, vomiting of blood, delirium, mental dulness, and coma lead to death. The urine is deeply jaundiced, but contains also amino-acids in crystal form, such as leucin and tyrosin. At autopsy the liver is found very much decreased in size, and very soft and mushy, of an opaque ochre yellow color, often with areas of red. In each lobule all the liver-cells, often with the exception of those nearest the portal veins, are reduced to a necrotic débris. If, as rarely happens, the person survives, regeneration takes place to some extent in a way that shall be described.

It is in such extreme injuries, and perhaps only there, that the liver actually shows itself insufficient. This is a point which is far too frequently overlooked by clinicians who search for tests of hepatic function to apply to cases in which there may be scattered focal necroses, or in which regeneration has restored the normal functional strength of the organ. As we shall see, in even the most extreme cirrhosis of the liver there need be no functional insufficiency. Icterus is present in the most intense form, doubtless

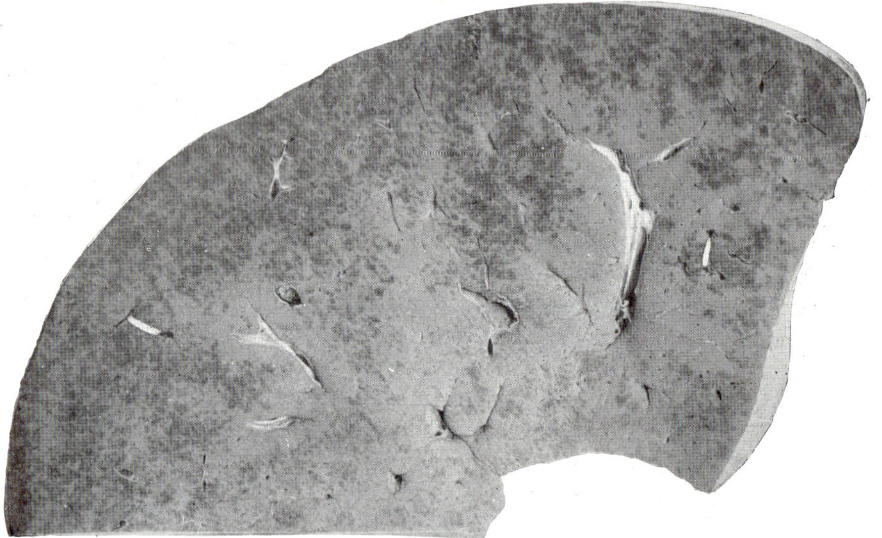

Fig. 149.—Hæmorrhagic necrosis in the liver in puerperal eclampsia.

because the columns of liver-cells which form the walls of each bile capillary are interrupted, so that the bile which is still formed escapes into the blood. Hæmorrhages into the mucosæ and elsewhere are abundant, partly on account of the jaundice, but partly, perhaps, because the liver, which is so important in the formation of fibrinogen, has ceased that function. The amino-acids in the urine and tissues probably appear in large part because they are ordinarily brought to the liver in that form from the intestinal wall, and finding the deamidizing power of the liver in abeyance, they pass on into the general circulation.

Eclampsia gravidarum is a condition appearing before, during, or after childbirth, and accompanied by the most violent convulsions and evidence of the most extreme disturbances of metabolism, somewhat similar to those found in acute yellow atrophy. Nothing certain is known of its cause, although Schmorl at one time thought that syncytial masses from the placenta swept into the liver produced the necroses found there, while others ascribe them to the action of poisons derived from the fœtus or from the placenta. At autopsy the liver is found sprinkled with hæmorrhages, which may become confluent into great patches (Fig. 149). These hæmorrhages correspond with areas of necrosis of the liver-cells beginning essentially in the periportal region of each lobule, but often becoming confluent (Fig. 150). In and about them, it is true, one may sometimes find syncytial masses in the capillaries, but it no longer seems probable that this explains the condition, since they occur as well in normal pregnancy.

In the other infectious and toxic processes mentioned, in which scattered focal necroses occur (typhoid fever, diphtheria, etc.), one finds anywhere

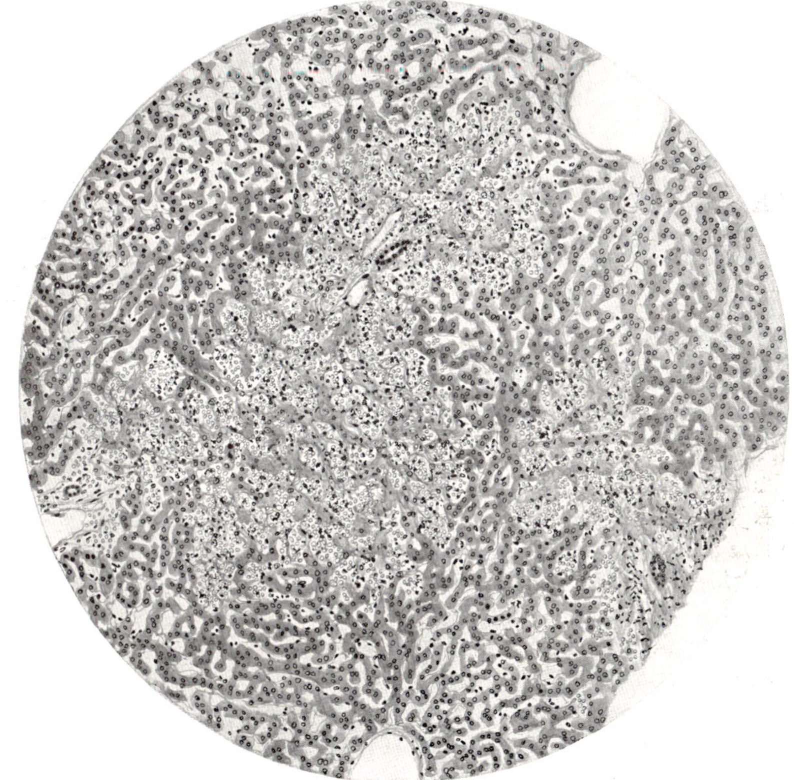

Fig. 150.—Eclampsia gravidarum. Peripheral focal necrosis with hæmorrhages.

in the lobule circumscribed areas in which the liver-cells are dead. Here, as in the zonal type, delicate hyaline thrombi are common in the capillaries, entangling the many wandering cells which hurry there and which are active in dissolving and removing the débris of dead cells.

Repair and Compensatory Hyperplasia in the Liver.—The liver possesses very great powers of repairing losses of its substance. Whipple has shown that destruction of the liver-cells throughout two-fifths of each lobule in the dog can be repaired in a few weeks by the removal of the dead cells, and their accurate replacement without any distortion of the lobule.

Thus the necroses so constant in typhoid fever are healed without an appreciable scar. This power belongs not only to the highly specialized liver-cells, but also to the epithelium of the bile-ducts, which, if they become disconnected from their liver-cell strands by the destruction of some of the cells, quickly bridge the gap and reëstablish the connection. All these cells multiply by mitotic division, and are guided in the direction of their growth by the persisting liver framework. Thus, when all the liver-cells

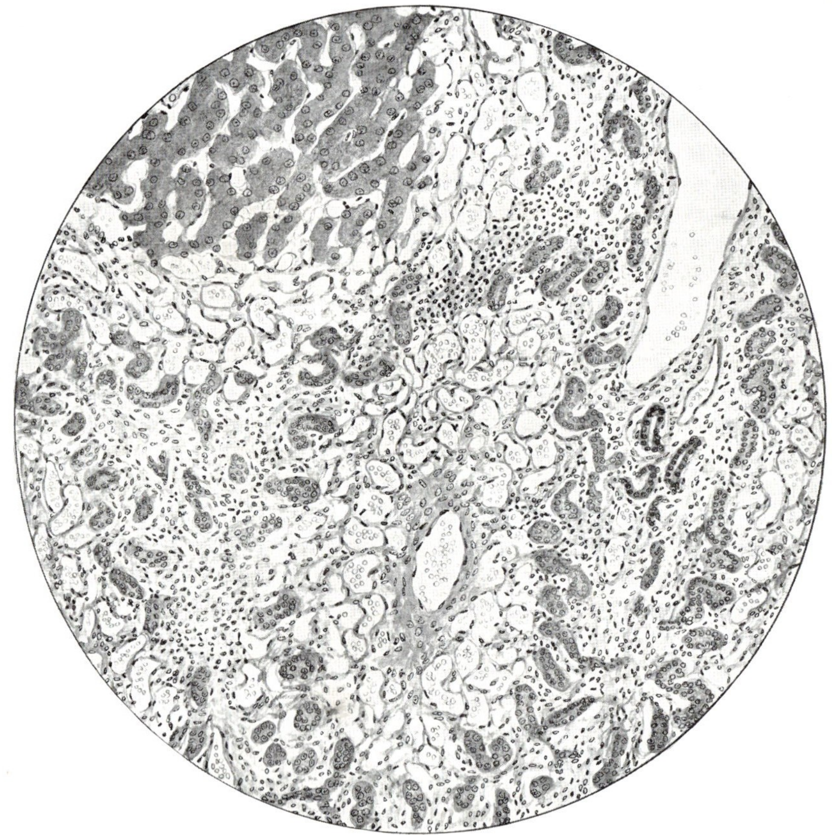

Fig. 151.—Beginning repair of the liver by sprouting bile-ducts after destruction of all the liver-cells in a lobule.

about the efferent vein of the lobule have been destroyed, numerous karyokinetic figures can be found in the cells of the adjoining zone, where they are so loaded with fat-globules, but are rather fewer in the better preserved cells immediately about the portal veins (Fig. 146).

Often recognizable as young cells by their pale, clear protoplasm and convex outline, these fresh liver-cells, together with some of the older ones, push their way along the spaces formerly occupied by those which were killed, unless those spaces are collapsed and obstructed. If all the cells of the lobule are annihilated, the framework remains, and is often held open by the rigidity of the tissue about it (Fig. 151). Then there is no source for new liver-cells. Broken ends of bile-ducts which formerly connected, one with each of these strands of liver-cells, remain uninjured in the portal spaces and now grow out with bulbous ends into the framework of the lobule toward the efferent vein, that is, in the Sabourin lobule they sprout out from the central bile-duct. In the lobule in which the efferent vein forms the centre these bulbous bile-ducts appear to grow centripetally. There has been much dispute as to whether they can actually produce new liver-cells. I believe they can to a limited extent, as shown in Fig. 152, where the club-shaped masses were unquestionably liver-cells and new, since they contained none of the pigment which was so abundant in all the

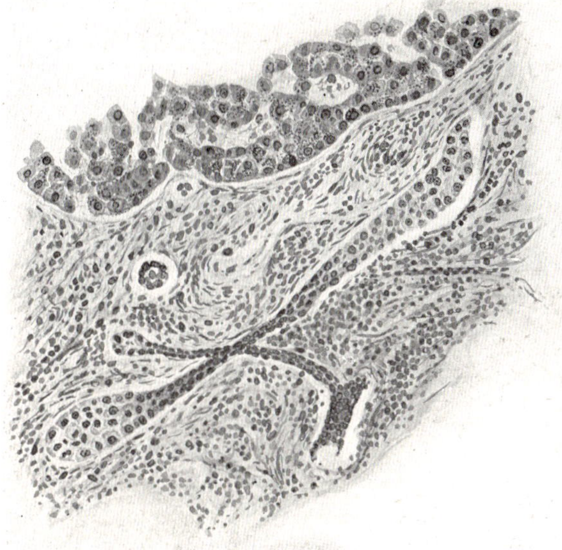

Fig. 152.—Formation of liver-cells by bile-ducts.

older liver-cells. That they can thus become differentiated seems certain, but probably they do so but seldom, and then produce very few liver-cells. Melchior thinks this process very important, but it seems that he assigns to it cells otherwise produced.

Thus healing or readjustment of breaks in continuity may be easily carried out by the liver-cells and the bile-duct epithelium. It must not be supposed, however, that the framework of the liver is always left undisturbed, so that repair can proceed so easily and accurately. It may collapse when the liver-cells are gone, and become consolidated into a scar-like band. Then bile-ducts may push their way into it and new liver-cells may be formed there, but their arrangement will not be that of the normal lobule.

Perhaps the simplest available example of repair in an extensively injured liver is furnished by a case studied some years ago, that of a boy who had gone through a severe illness, which may have been acute yellow atrophy of the liver, six months before his death. In the mean while, up to his death from an infection, he had been fairly well. The liver was greatly reduced in size, but contained a tumor-like mass in the right lobe, composed of dark-green lobules like swollen liver lobules. Throughout the general liver substance every liver-cell had been destroyed; the framework had remained intact with the bile-ducts and blood-vessels, and from every bile-duct branching sprouts were growing into the old framework, although nowhere producing definite liver-cells. In the right lobe a portion of liver tissue had evidently been left intact, and this had become the tumor-like mass by the symmetrical enlargement of each remaining lobule. This mass, which was finally about the size of a small orange, must have been very much smaller at first, and yet it sustained life and prevented any serious symptoms of hepatic insufficiency. This exactly corresponds with Ponfick's experimental results, in which he found that, after removal of a large part of the liver, the remainder enlarged by a symmetrical growth of each lobule, new liver-cells being formed everywhere by division of the old ones. No rearrangement of liver-cells, bile-ducts, nor blood-vessels was necessary in this case, and we have the effects of a single great injury before us. (Similar cases, in which many large nodules of liver tissue are found embedded in a scar-like organ, are probably also due to a single injury (Fig. 153).)

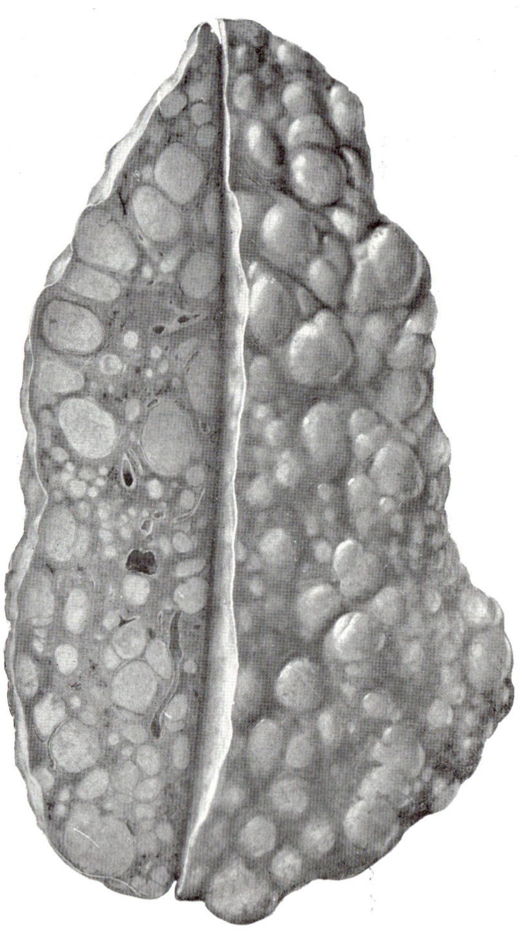

Fig. 153.—Coarse cirrhosis of the liver with large nodules of regenerating liver-cells.

CIRRHOSIS OF THE LIVER

This is a term applied to an extensive diffuse scarring of the liver which has followed the destruction of much of the liver substance. It is regularly accompanied by wide-spread regeneration of the functional liver tissue, usually sufficient to prevent the appearance of any signs of hepatic insufficiency.

There are great difficulties in classifying all the different types of cirrhosis, because, except in about three or four, we are ignorant of their causes. The rest we have to classify, then, on the basis of the anatomical and functional disturbances, which is not very satisfactory. We know that syphilitic and tuberculous infection can produce scars throughout the liver, with profound distortion of the organ, and that obstruction of the bile-duct will in the end set up a peculiar type of scarring about the bile-duct branches, with deep jaundice—but with regard to all the other cases of cirrhosis in which these things are readily excluded we are still rather at sea. Of course, in the lay mind the abuse of alcohol is held responsible for cirrhosis of the liver in a quite unprejudiced way, but although it may well play some part, its influence is undoubtedly greatly exaggerated.* Longcope's recent experiments, which show that lesions resembling those found in cirrhosis may be produced by repeated anaphylactic shocks caused by injections of egg-white or other protein, are most suggestive of an origin through protein sensitization and intoxication. But the most accurate approach to this anatomical condition has been made by those authors (Opie and others) who have combined bacterial infection with various poisons, such as chloroform, which destroy liver-cells. Probably it is in some such protracted and complex injuries that we shall find the actual cause of the disease, but undoubtedly, as in any scar, the same commonplace result may have a great variety of original causes. The anatomical condition of the liver, and the occurrence or absence of certain associated disturbances, such as jaundice, obstruction of the portal blood flow and ascites, enlargement of the spleen, etc., form the further basis for classification of the cases, and we find that the following types may be separated:

1. *The Ordinary Nodular Cirrhosis* (*Laënnec's Cirrhosis; Atrophic or Portal Cirrhosis; Hobnail Liver; Alcoholic Cirrhosis, etc.*).—Liver rough and nodular, tends to be smaller than normal, no jaundice, marked portal obstruction, with ascites and enlargement of the spleen. Ætiology obscure.

2. *Obstructive Biliary Cirrhosis.*—Liver enlarged, smooth, or granular. Jaundice. Clay-colored stools. Scars following bile-canals. Usually no portal obstruction nor ascites, but spleen may be enlarged. Ætiology: Obstruction of bile-ducts, usually accompanied by infection.

---

* It is misleading to try to determine this relation by estimating the percentage of the cases of cirrhosis of the liver in which there has been abuse of alcohol. If, instead, we study a great number of chronic alcoholics, we find (Simmonds) a relatively small percentage of cases of cirrhosis of the liver. On the other hand, great accumulation of fat in the liver is common in alcoholics. Experimental administration of alcohol to animals produces no cirrhosis, even when enormous doses are given over a very long time.

3. *Hanot's Cirrhosis, or Primary Hypertrophic Biliary Cirrhosis.*—Liver large, smooth, diffusely and finely scarred. Jaundice, with no gross obstruction of bile-ducts; bile-stained stools; no portal obstruction; splenic enlargement. Ætiology obscure, possibly an infectious process.

4. *Syphilitic Cirrhosis, Congenital or Acquired.*—In the congenital form the liver may be large, smooth, and diffusely scarred, or it may present gummata which later become scarred. In the acquired form gummata heal with large scars, producing deep grooves and lobulations in the liver. No jaundice; no marked portal obstruction.

5. *Tuberculous Cirrhosis.*—Especially with tuberculosis of peritoneum, producing thickening of Glisson's capsule, with constriction and distortion

Fig. 154.—Diffuse nodular cirrhosis of the liver.

of the organ. In another form with many tubercles in the liver the process is somewhat like the syphilitic.

There are unquestionably many other types, for any injury recovered from and healed may leave its trace in the form of a cirrhotic process.

1. **Diffuse Nodular Cirrhosis.**—In the ordinary cirrhosis one finds the liver hard and stiff—sometimes larger than normal, but generally shrunken and deformed and roughened all over by projecting nodules of a yellowish-brown or chestnut-brown color (Fig. 154). The capsule is generally thickened and sometimes finely granular, but through it one can see that the shrunken tissue between the nodules is gray and translucent, often showing little veins in the depths of the depressed areas. It is hard to cut, and in

extreme cases creaks or cries under the knife. The cut surface shows just the same appearance—rounded or irregular nodules of liver tissue of variable size projecting as little plateaus from the gray, translucent groundwork. Every kind of variation in the appearance of these nodules may occur (Fig. 155); sometimes they are all quite small and uniform, more often some of them are larger, and these tend to be pigmented or bile stained; occasionally they are all very large,—even as large as marbles,—and widely separated by a rather loose, vascular connective tissue. In

Fig. 155.—Irregular nodular cirrhosis with ascites. Half of liver.

some cases the liver substance forms the great bulk of the organ, so that scars can be traced through it with difficulty; in others the whole organ seems to be composed of solid elastic fibrous tissue, with only scattered pockets of greenish or brown granular liver substance embedded at intervals through it. The liver tissue itself may be made up of quite normal-looking cells, or the cells may be loaded with fat or pigment, or be actually on the way to necrosis and disintegration.

All these variations are of subordinate importance though, and further study shows that in principle these cases are all very similar. Large isolated masses of liver appear when only widely separated groups of cells have been spared and have been allowed ample time to regenerate as much liver tissue as possible. Small, closely packed nodules result when destruction has occurred in smaller foci, and some portion of nearly every lobule has survived. Even the most casual examination shows that these nodules have no longer anything like the normal arrangement of the lobules. They are not, as a rule, isolated nodules, for reconstruction of serial sections shows that they are almost all connected together into an irregular network, but they have lost their regular relation to the original portal veins, bile-ducts, and hepatic veins. They no longer even approach uniformity in size, nor can one find a central vein in each. Instead, they generally

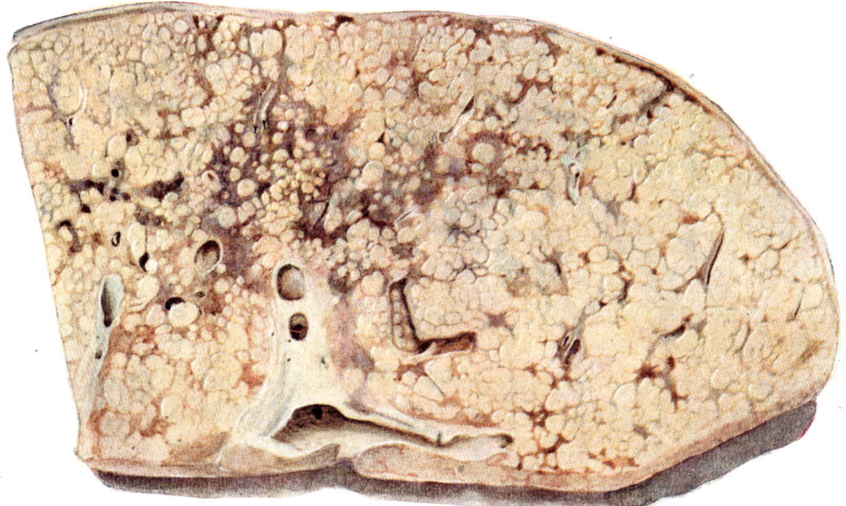

Fig. 156.—Cut surface of the liver; nodular or Laennec's cirrhosis.

appear in section as smooth, finely granular, almost velvety, solid masses of liver-cells and nothing more.

Microscopical study confirms all this (Figs. 157, 158). Everywhere in the section there are found patches of liver-cells arranged in a most disorderly fashion. All bear evidence of having been enlarged by the multiplication of their cells, so that the arrangement with reference to portal and efferent veins is all that will tell us whether we have the enlargement of a whole lobule or of an isolated group of cells. In the latter case the patch will have no portal and no efferent vein immediately connected with it, but is merely a conglomeration of liver-cells with intervening capillaries which have grown into a perfect labyrinth, and allow the passage of blood with some difficulty. The whole lies surrounded by vascular connective tissue, in which there are many wandering cells, and in which one can see numerous tortuous bile-ducts. Very often one can make out in this tissue what must have been the efferent vein which originally drained the lobule of which we have just considered the hypertrophied remnant, and, indeed, this vein doubtless still drains that overgrown remnant (Fig. 159). Portal veins are also visible, but they are commonly in no clearly recognizable relation to the liver-cells, but lie quite far away in the intervening tissue. So, too, the original bile-ducts can be seen, but there are many other sinu-

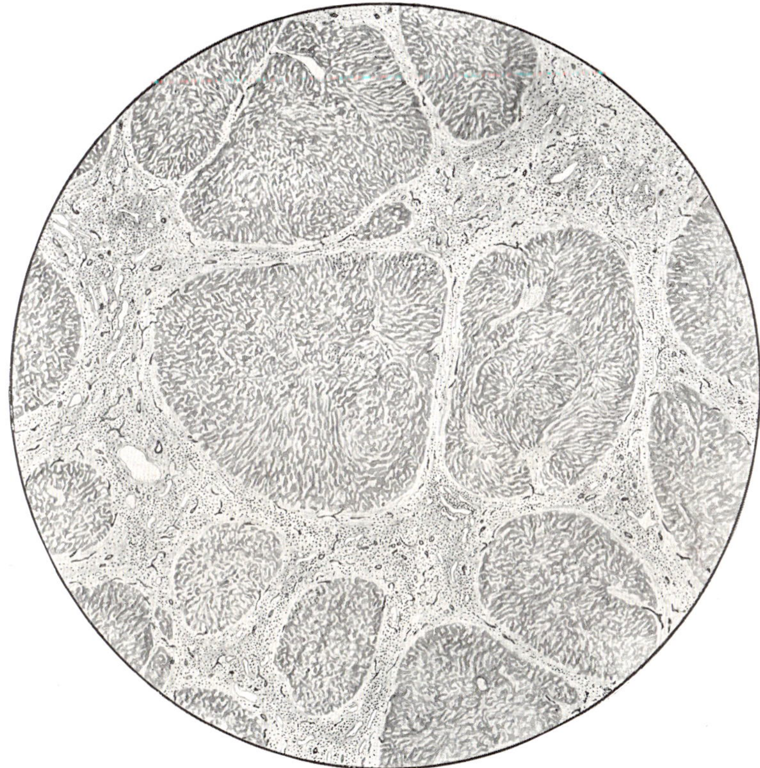

Fig. 157.—Nodular cirrhosis of the liver. The low-power drawing shows the irregular arrangement of the remaining liver tissue and the distribution of the newly formed bile-ducts.

ous channels lined with epithelium which branch abundantly and which one may trace into connection at one end with the bile-duct, at the other with a strand of liver-cells in one of the nodules (Fig. 160).

There has been much dispute as to their nature, and they have been thought by many to be compressed liver-cells, but everything goes to show that they are bile-ducts, for the greater part newly formed from the stumps of those which were left, and now growing to reëstablish connection with the liver-cells. The slight part they play in the new formation of liver-cells has been mentioned. Of course, in any such strand of tissue as we find between the nodules of liver-cells a great many bile-ducts, portal veins, etc., are concentrated together through the collapse of many lobules whose skeleton framework goes to form a large part of the strand, but the newly formed ducts can usually be recognized.

One might trace out the fate of any isolated portion of a lobule which remained after the devastation of the rest in this process, but the process of reëstablishment of relations is the same no matter how much or how little of the original lobule remains. It is as though groups of liver-cells were transplanted into a vascular tissue rich in bile-ducts. They acquire the

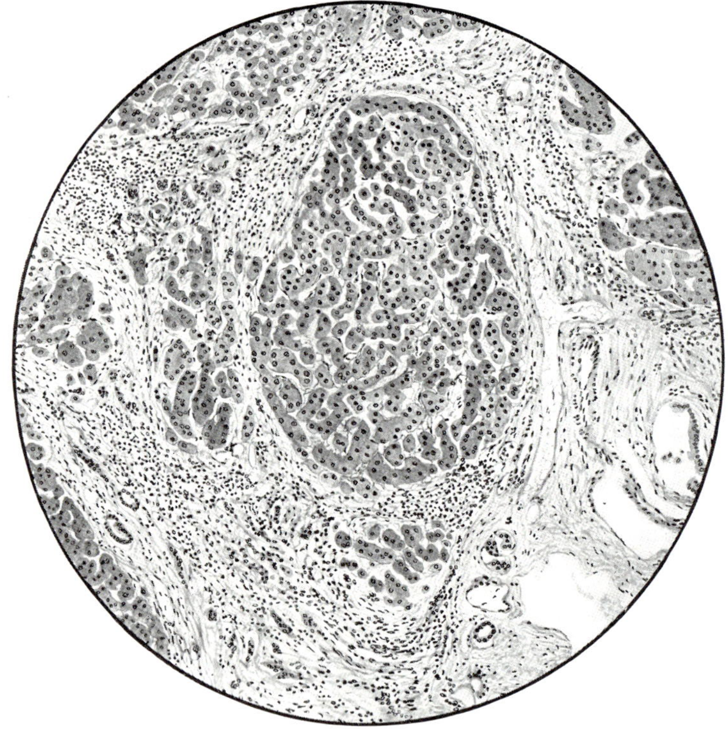

Fig. 158.—Nodular cirrhosis showing atypical arrangement of liver-cells in each nodule.

best vascular connections possible for their situation, and the ends of the strands unite with the sprouts of bile-ducts which approach them, after which the liver-cells multiply as fast as possible to produce a larger nodule, which will compensate in function for the cells which were destroyed. There is no evidence of the compression of the liver-cells by the fibrous tissue in which they are growing—rather one might say the fibrous tissue is pushed aside and compressed by them. Nor is there any justification for the term lobular cirrhosis, since, as we see, it is by no means a question of the enveloping of lobules in fibrous tissue. Although many conflicting views have been held, it seems clear enough that the injurious agent effects the destruction of the liver-cells in the first instance, and that the scarring and the hyperplasia of the epithelial remnants are reparatory processes.

Very commonly the liver-cells are quite normal in appearance and function, and doubtless they are so for weeks and months at a time. If the attacks of the injurious agent could be stopped, there is no reason why compensatory hyperplasia should not go on until the organ had once more its full complement of cells in an abnormal arrangement. But they are, of course, as always, susceptible to injury, and for that reason they are

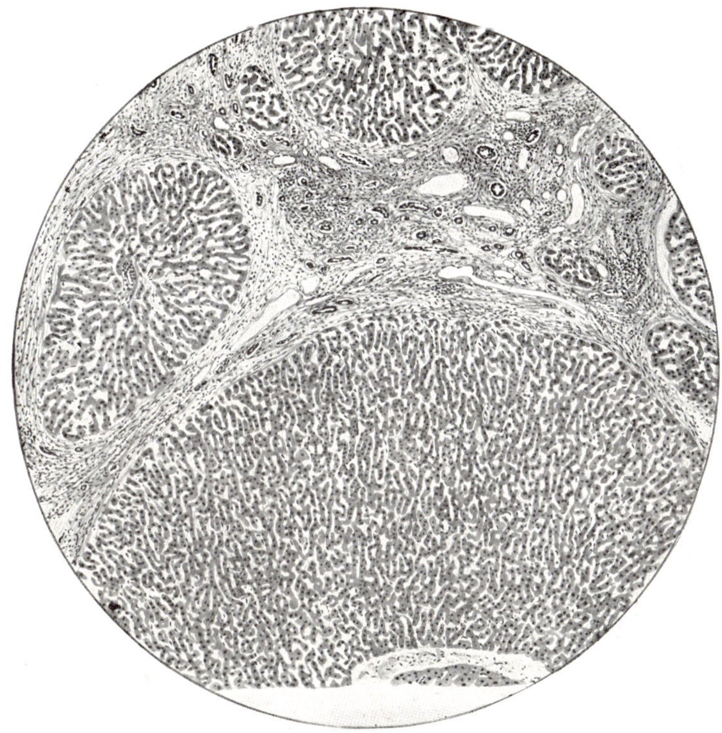

Fig. 159.—Nodular cirrhosis with very great hyperplasia of the liver-cell nodules. Observe the distorted relation of portal and efferent veins to the liver tissue.

often found at the death of the individual, loaded with fat or injured in some other way. Some of these injuries may be of the series which is still at work, adding to the changes which bring about the cirrhosis, but others may be independent, and we might expect to find focal necroses in the liver-cells of a man who has long had a cirrhotic liver and who dies of typhoid fever.

The whole condition is brought about in exactly the same way as the scarring of the kidney with compensatory hyperplasia. The liver-cells are killed in patches—whole lobules and groups of lobules at a time, or only parts of lobules. There remain irregular masses of liver tissue partly disconnected from their bile-ducts. The framework of the rest of the tissue collapses and shrinks, and is kept in that position by the growth of new fibrous tissues, but through that tissue blood still streams readily. The bile-ducts which were interrupted by the death of the liver-cells send out sprouts which attempt to connect again with liver-cell strands. The masses of liver-cells quickly increase in size by multiplication of their cells, new capillaries are formed in every direction, and this labyrinth of

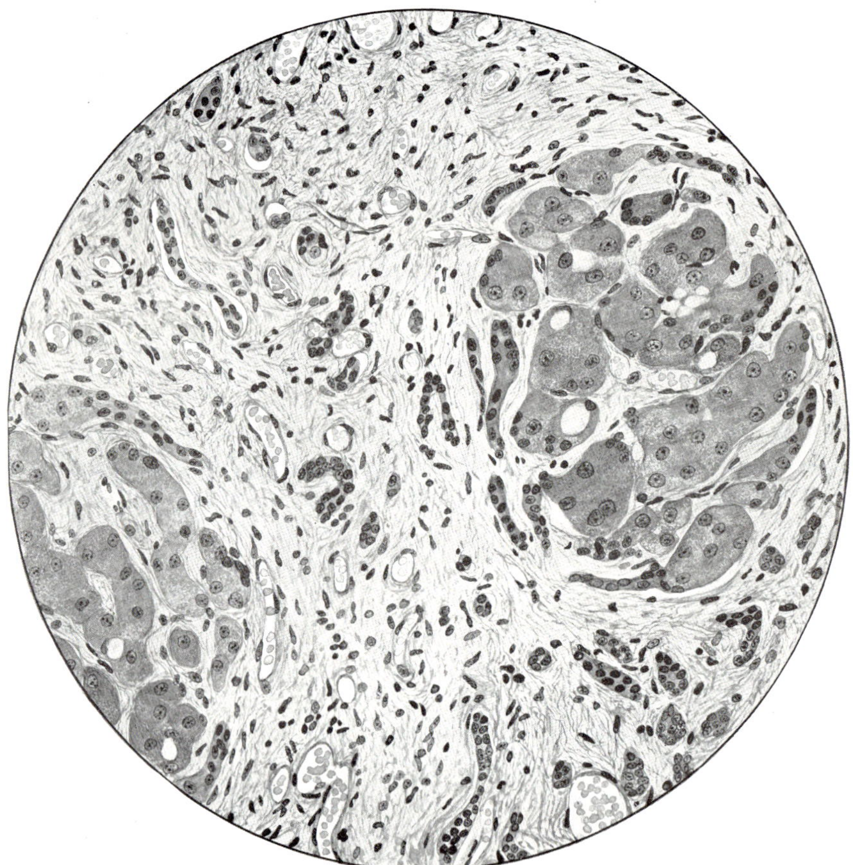

Fig. 160.—Cirrhosis of the liver showing the reunion of bile-ducts with the liver-cells.

cells expands, pressing the stroma away on all sides. For a time the liver-cells are normal, but then comes another injury, and many of the hyperplastic nodules are partly destroyed. The whole process is repeated, and not only once, but many times. It is clear that this must lead to an extraordinary distortion of the liver's structure. There are no longer lobules, but only nodules produced by the hyperplasia of smaller groups of cells which were left intact.

Obstruction of the Portal Flow.—With advancing cirrhosis of the liver it becomes difficult for the portal blood to pass through, and all the branches of that vein come to be distended, sometimes even to the point of bursting. The organs which are drained by them are swollen and blue from the stagnation of venous blood, and their function is disturbed. Digestion is impaired, and the spleen becomes greatly enlarged. Fluid filters through into the peritoneal cavity, and the ascites accompanying cirrhosis may be of the most persistent.

Why so much obstruction should occur is not as simply explained as might appear at first sight. With the great reduction in the size of the liver much of the stream-bed is doubtless obliterated. The rigidity of the scarred organ may prevent the normal distensibility of the blood-vessels, but the capillaries of the scarred bands are still more easily injected than those of the regenerated nodules of liver tissue. In the liver nodules, on the contrary, the tortuous course of the new capillaries offers an increased resistance to the flow of blood.

Herrick* has offered the explanation that the communications between the hepatic artery and the branches of the portal vein become far wider than normal in the cirrhotic liver, so that the high arterial pressure is communicated directly and obstructs the outflow from the veins, much as it does in an arteriovenous aneurysm. The long-continued overdistension of the portal branches is sometimes partly relieved by the widening of certain communications between the portal system and the branches of the vena cava, which always exist but are normally too small to be of any use. These are well described by Charcot† and are diagrammatically shown in Fig. 161. They are:

1. Anastomoses between the left coronary vein of the stomach and the œsophageal veins which open into the azygos or intercostals. These communicating channels often become enormously enlarged (œsophageal varices), and may burst into the œsophagus, with fatal results (Fig. 162). The coronary vein may also anastomose with superior or inferior diaphragmatic veins.

2. Anastomoses exist between branches of the inferior mesenteric vein, the superior hæmorrhoidals, and branches of the internal iliac veins, the inferior hæmorrhoidals. These are apparently not especially efficient, and hæmorrhoids are said not to be common in cirrhosis.

3. The veins of Retzius, which originate in the walls of the intestines and through a little trunk empty into the vena cava or one of its branches.

4. The veins of Sappey, or accessory portal veins, which originate in some organ other than the digestive tract, and, after forming a trunk, reach the liver and ramify in its substance. Some of them are quite useless in establishing a collateral circulation, as, for example, those which connect the omentum or the gall-bladder with the liver, or those which constitute the vasa vasorum of the portal vein, hepatic artery, and bile-ducts. But the veins of the suspensory ligament which unite with those of the diaphragm are useful. So, too, are the para-umbilical veins (*Umb C*, Fig. 161), whose roots communicate with the epigastric, the internal mammary, and the subcutaneous abdominal veins. They enter the liver along the obliterated umbilical vein, and are distributed to the lobules along the longitudinal groove, to the portal vein to the left of the umbilical ligament, or to the still permeable part of that ligament. They are important channels of communication, and sometimes appear in their swollen state under the skin of the abdomen radiating from the navel (caput medusæ).

Of course, other collateral channels arise through the formation of adhesions between the abdominal organs and the walls of the abdomen, and they are often intentionally produced for this purpose by an operative procedure (Talma's operation).

At times the collateral circulation reaches an efficiency which allows the patient to live on without ascites or symptoms of chronic passive congestion, but usually it is not

* F. C. Herrick: Jour. Exp. Med., 1907, ix, 93.
† Charcot: Maladies du Foie, Paris, 1882.

so complete. Jaundice in the type of cirrhosis described above is rare, and when it does occur, is probably due to some accessory cause.

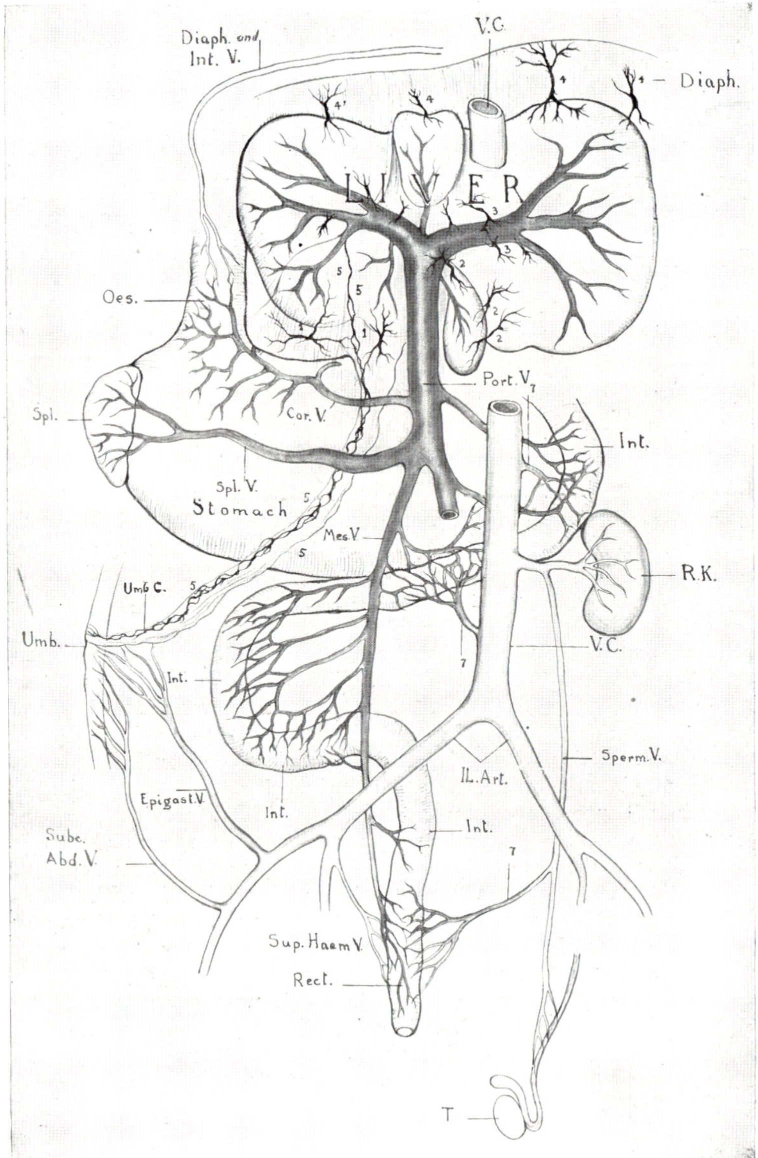

Fig. 161.—Diagrammatic representation of the collateral circulation established in cirrhosis of the liver (from Charcot): 1, 2, 3, 4, 5, Accessory portal veins of Sappey; 7, 7, 7, veins of Retzius. The organs are viewed from behind.

2. **Obstructive Biliary Cirrhosis.**—It has been shown experimentally (Vaughan Harley, Ogata, and others) that, in certain animals at least, the

occlusion of the bile-ducts results in the destruction of some of the liver-cells and in the formation of scar tissue in their place. This is especially striking in zones about the portal veins and bile-ducts, and in these zones numerous new bile-ducts sprout out. The addition of infection to the mechanical stasis of the bile intensifies the process. The same thing is

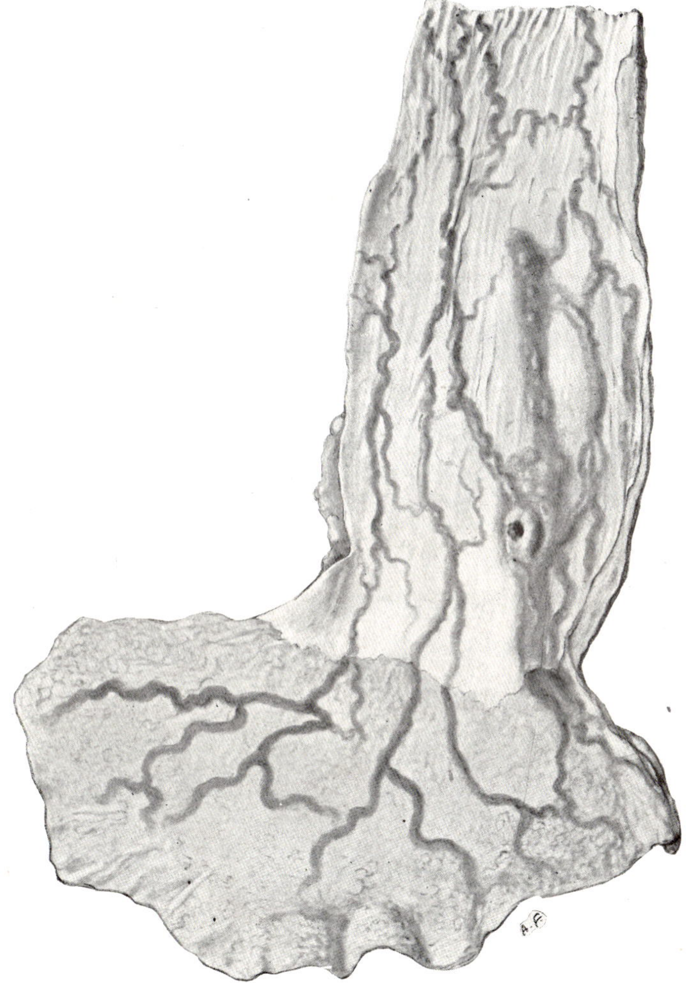

Fig. 162.—Collateral circulation in cirrhosis. Œsophageal varices with rupture and fatal hæmorrhage (liver of this case shown in Fig. 155).

true in human beings when the hepatic or common duct becomes obstructed by a gall-stone or by a tumor-growth. Jaundice results promptly, and the liver becomes swollen and deep green in color. After this obstruction has lasted some time slight irregularity of its surface arises, and on section delicate scars can be seen. There is rarely time for the development of any such extreme changes as have been described for the diffuse nodular cirrhosis. The spleen becomes enlarged, but there is, except in advanced cases of long standing, no obstruction to the flow of portal blood. In a man aged fifty-five jaundice appeared and quickly deepened to a dark, greenish bronze color. At the autopsy several jack-stone-shaped black gall-stones were found in the gall-bladder, at the fundus of which a small cancer had developed. A secondary growth from this lay embedded in

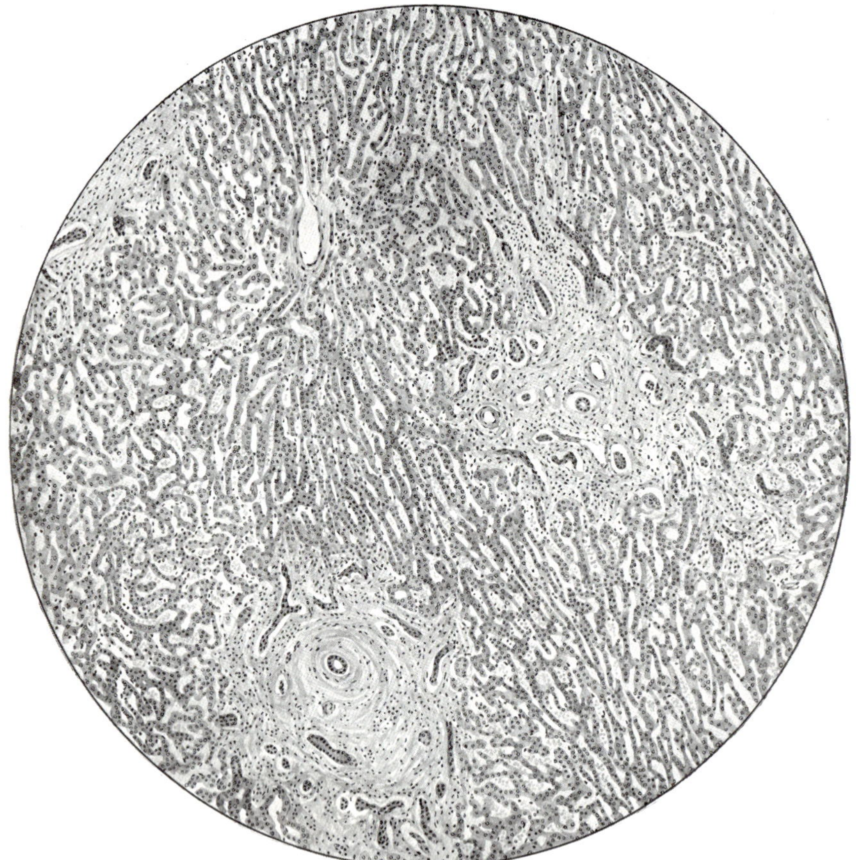

Fig. 163.—Biliary cirrhosis.

the liver in such a way as to surround and compress the hepatic ducts as they left the liver—below this the ducts were normal; within the liver they were distended to a phenomenal degree. The liver was deep green, flabby, and coarsely lobulated, although only slightly wrinkled on the surface. Even on section there was no great departure from the regular lobulation. Microscopical study showed each larger bile-duct twig and portal vein surrounded by a loose scar tissue infiltrated with leucocytes, and rich in young, sprouting bile-ducts, evidently growing out to join the remaining liver-cells after the destruction of many of those nearest the portal space (Fig. 163).

Apparently in the cases of longest duration a great deal more distortion of the liver may occur, but it does not approach that seen in the previous type.

3. **Primary Biliary Hypertrophic Cirrhosis (Hanot's Cirrhosis).**—There exists much confusion as to what Hanot actually meant to include in his type of hypertrophic cirrhosis with icterus and without ascites, but Heineke

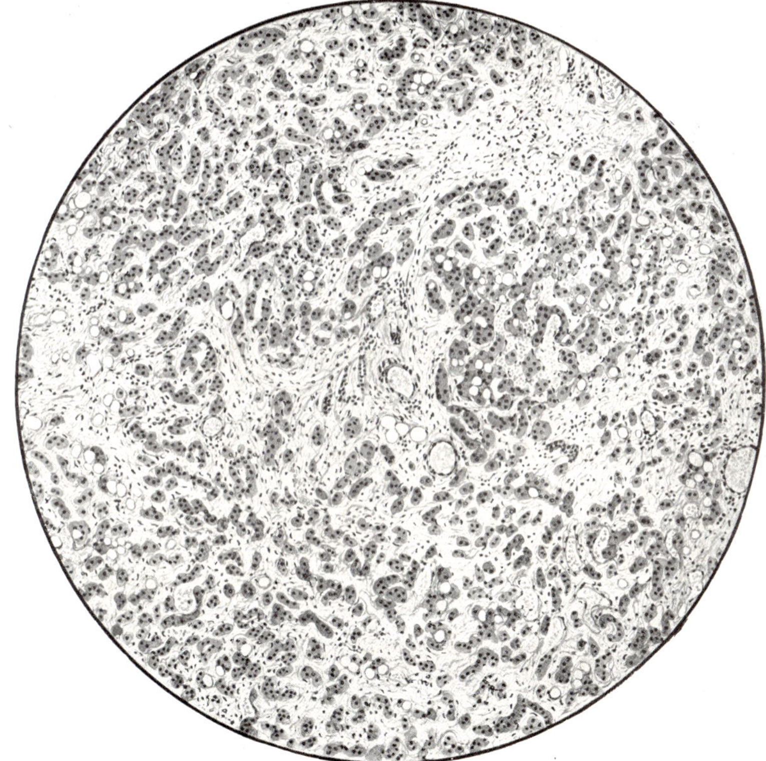

Fig. 164.—Hanot's cirrhosis.

describes it as a change resulting from the inflammation of the minuter bile-ducts, and producing a fine, almost intercellular, scarring throughout the liver, with its enlargement—enlargement of the spleen, fever, but no portal obstruction. There are other cases in which there is the same deep jaundice but no evident inflammation of the bile-ducts (Kretz), and still others in which there is no jaundice. Nevertheless, in these too the liver is found greatly enlarged, hard, and smooth, and on section no definite lobulation whatever can be made out. Microscopically there is found a finely diffused network of scar tissue all through the tissue, separating the lobules into little groups of cells (Fig. 164).

LITERATURE

Ackermann: Pathol. Bindegewebsneubild. in der Leber, Berlin, 1894.

Ford: Amer. Jour. Med. Sci., 1901, cxxi, 60.

Heineke: Ziegler's Beiträge, 1897, xxii, 259.

Kretz: Verh. Dtsch. Path. Gesellsch., 1904, viii, 54; 1905, ix, 260. International Clinics, 1905, iii, fifteenth series, 289.

MacCallum: Johns Hopkins Hosp. Reports, 1902, x, 375. Jour. Amer. Med. Assoc., 1904, xliii, 649.

Meder and Marchand: Ziegler's Beiträge, 1895, xvii, 143.

Ogata: Ziegler's Beiträge, 1913, lv, 236.

Opie: Jour. Exp. Med., 1910, xii, 367.

Ponfick: Virch. Arch., cxviii, cxix, cxxxviii.

Ribbert: Deutsche med. Woch., 1908, $xxiv_2$, 1678.

Vaughan Harley: Brit. Med. Jour., 1898, ii, 1743.

Whipple: Jour. Exp. Med., 1911, xiii, 136.

CHAPTER XVII

FURTHER ILLUSTRATIVE EXAMPLES OF DESTRUCTIVE AND REPARATIVE PROCESSES

Arteriosclerosis. Structure of arteries. Anatomical changes in arteriosclerosis in aorta and other vessels. Pathogenesis and ætiology. Syphilitic arteritis in aorta and smaller vessels. Obliterative endarteritis. Thromboangeitis obliterans. Aneurysms, various types; their effects and their relation to syphilis. Apoplexy; location of hæmorrhage in brain.

ARTERIOSCLEROSIS

Structure of Arteries.—The structure of the arteries changes as we pass from the aorta into the branches and finer ramifications. Everywhere, however, there is, as in the case of the veins and lymphatics, a lining membrane composed of a single layer of flattened endothelial cells which offers a smooth surface and acts as a protection for the blood against any contact with other tissues.

In the aorta the outer wall or adventitia is composed of a loose connective tissue carrying blood-vessels, nerves, etc., and containing a loose network of elastic fibrils. The middle coat or media is composed of elastic tissue, smooth muscle, and connective tissue. The elastic tissue which forms the most prominent feature is arranged in a complex of laminæ, with fibrils which run obliquely and connect the laminæ. In a cross-section one sees the main circular strands of elastic tissue about equidistant from one another, running with a somewhat wavy course around the vessel, and connected by numerous oblique, bridge-like fibres; but since in a longitudinal section one sees exactly the same thing, it seems evident that were the elastic tissue isolated, one might discern something roughly approaching the form of a series of imperfect concentric tubes. It seems to be about as though one should paste on a sheet of paper, one after another, pieces of gauze irregular in size and outline, gluing only their edges where they happen to fall, until a uniform thick layer is produced, and then make a tube of the whole, except that each piece of gauze, where it stands away from the underlying and overlying pieces, should be connected with them by many oblique threads. In a tangential section of the media the muscle-fibres, instead of being perfectly circular in their course, form a sort of herringbone pattern, and are surrounded everywhere in the same meshes by loose white fibrous tissue.

There is a vague outer condensation of the elastic fibres which might be called the external elastic lamella, but at the inner margin of the media there is a continuous membrane, uninterrupted except for certain fenestrations, which would correspond to the sheet of paper in the model—the internal elastic lamella. It is difficult to decide whether this should be taken as part of the media or part of the intima, but it is more convenient to consider it with the latter. Blood-vessels, the vasa vasorum, springing from the roots of the intercostal arteries, etc., penetrate the adventitia and extend part way through the media.

The intima of the aorta, which in very early life seems to show little but the endothelial layer resting upon the internal elastic lamella, develops in later life a much more complex structure. Just inside the internal elastic lamella there is a layer composed partly of smooth muscle running longitudinally, and partly of fibres and lamellæ of elastic tissue which are abundantly connected with the fenestrated membrane. This is the musculo-elastic layer inside which a second layer may generally be distinguished, composed of similar elastic structures intermingled with white fibrous connective tissue. Within this is a third layer immediately beneath the endothelium, which is made up of connective tissue alone, the cells of which show beautiful branching processes. Although with the advance of age the intima thus becomes progressively thicker (Jores), it is normally a very thin layer as compared with the media.

The branches of the aorta and smaller vessels differ from this in their structure, especially in that the elastic tissue of the media is far less abundant, so that the smooth muscle becomes the predominant element of that layer. The elastic tissue is for the most part concentrated in a layer between the muscular media and the adventitia, where it forms an exaggerated external elastic lamella. The radial fibres of Dürck, which run irregularly from the internal elastic lamella to this outer layer, are more clearly seen in the arteries of medium size than in the aorta. They can be stained by special methods, and probably differ somewhat from the elastic fibres proper. They act apparently as dilators of the vessel.

In the smaller arteries the intima becomes simplified until finally, in the very small vessels, the endothelium lies almost directly upon the internal elastic lamella. Nevertheless, in many small arteries, especially in such organs as the kidney, stomach, etc., the internal elastic lamella splits in the third decade into three or four concentric layers, between which are connective-tissue elements. It will be seen that much attention has been devoted to this reduplication of the elastic lamellæ in the discussion of arteriosclerosis. In accord with these differences in structure between the aorta and smaller vessels we may expect differences in their pathological alterations.

Arteriosclerosis is the term in most general use for that disease of the arteries which leads to their loss of elasticity, and changes in the appearance and structure of the intima and other coats which lead to dilatation and deformity of the artery. The condition is sometimes spoken of as atheroma of the arteries, and there is much in favor of the name atherosclerosis, suggested by Marchand, but the old term, endarteritis deformans, of Virchow, is now but little used.

We may consider in turn: Arteriosclerosis (properly so called), syphilitic arteritis, endarteritis obliterans, although doubtless this list is far from exhausting the list of related vascular changes.

ARTERIOSCLEROSIS PROPER

The earliest changes recognizable in the aorta as the beginning of arteriosclerosis are found in the form of very slightly elevated, flattened yellow streaks, which usually run on the posterior wall of the vessel, longitudinally, between and about the openings of the intercostal arteries, although they are not by any means confined to this position (Fig. 165). With further advance of the disease these yellow patches are to be found diffusely distributed among the older lesions. Sections passing through them show that, while the artery is normal elsewhere, the elevation is due to a distinct thickening of the intima produced by a new formation of connective tissue, with small and large wandering cells (Fig. 166). Both the original branched connective-tissue cells and the wandering cells are found to be loaded with fat. Such fat is by no means lodged only in the deeper layers of the intima, but extends up to the surface, where the fat-laden wandering cells

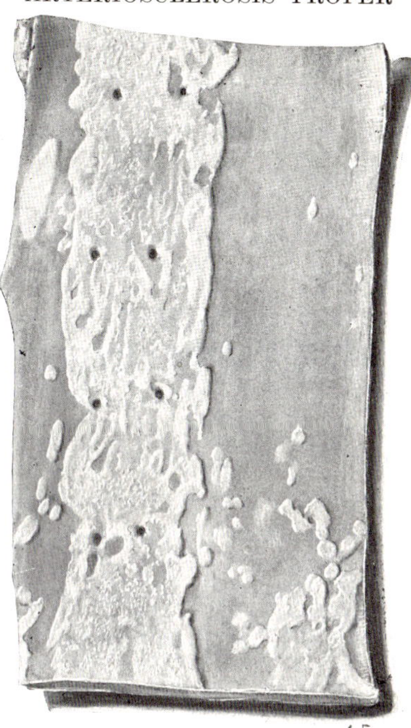

Fig. 165.—Fatty streaks and patches in the intima of the aorta.

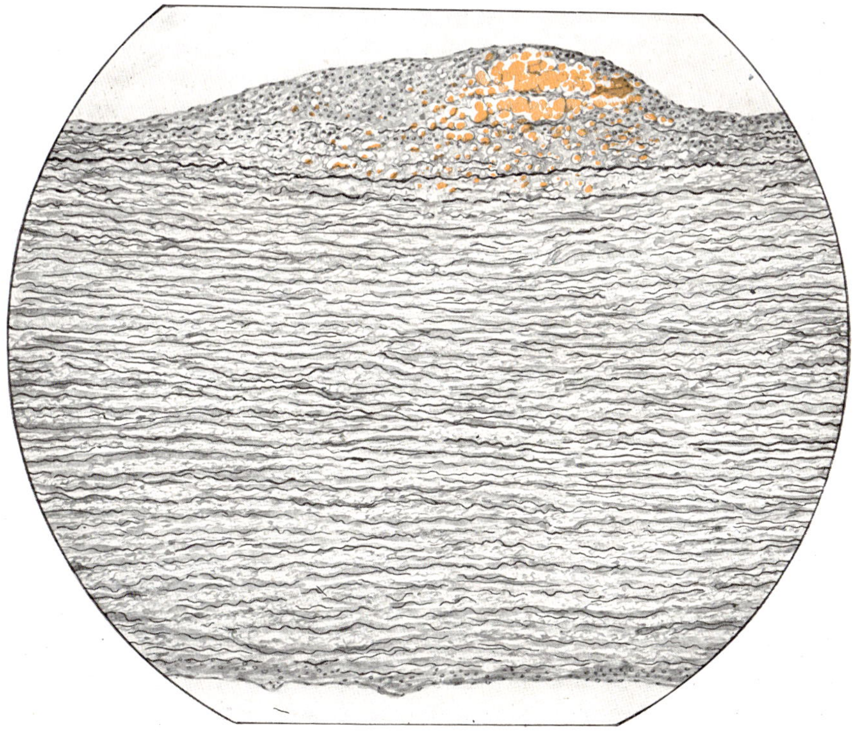

Fig. 166.—Section through a fatty streak in the aorta. (The fat is stained red with sudan.)

lie free in crevices. If the upper layer of the intima be stripped off and laid flat under the microscope, the branched connective-tissue cells with their fine fat-droplets can be well seen.

In a later stage the hillock of thickened intima becomes more extensive and thicker, and the tissue becomes hyaline or necrotic about the most abundant accumulation of fat. The superficial or innermost layers become very much thickened, and are now composed of a dense, homogeneous connective tissue (Fig. 167). Rarely do the vasa vasorum penetrate from

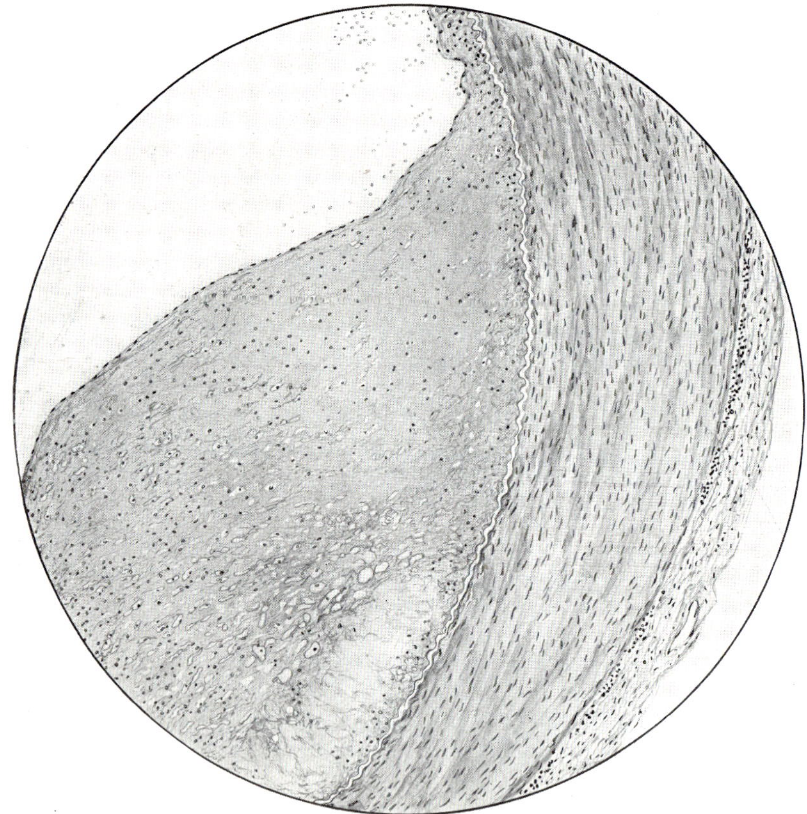

Fig. 167.—Margin of a relatively fresh arteriosclerotic plaque.

the media to take part in this new formation of tissue, and generally they can be found only in the later stages, although it is stated that injections reveal an increased richness in the vascular supply about the patches of disease. Nor is there any invasion of wandering cells at all commensurate with the new formation of tissue. The dense connective tissue formed over the mass of fat containing tissue is bluish white and translucent. It covers the yellow, opaque, fatty material, so that it now appears to lie in the depths of the intima, encroaching on the musculo-elastic layer and the internal elastic lamella. When such an aorta is opened, the most common and characteristic appearance of arteriosclerosis is revealed (Fig. 168). Elevated rounded or irregular plaques or patches stand up from the intimal surface like solidified drops of paraffin. They are often about the orifices of the intercostal arteries, but may occur anywhere. They seem hard and homogeneous, but on cutting through them there is always to be found the mass of opaque, yellow, fatty material hidden in their depths. From the cut edge this yellow mass can be expressed or dug out, and its soft, mushy character was the origin of the name atheroma. Often the fat extends so as to form a yellow halo about such a plaque, the opaque material shining through the relatively thin surrounding intima.

168.—Arteriosclerotic plaques in the aorta about the intercostal arteries.

At this stage the internal elastic lamella underlying the plaque generally shows fragmentation or interruptions, or it is frayed out into several thin laminæ which again unite at the other edge of the plaque. This is best seen in the smaller arteries (Fig. 169), but is visible also in the aorta, and is regarded by Jores as the most characteristic feature of true arteriosclerosis. Usually the longitudinal muscle-fibers of the musculo-elastic layer are involved in the necrosis in the depths of the plaque, and in great part destroyed. Delicate elastic fibrils appear in the new tissue which forms inside the musculo-elastic layer, and are thought by Jores to arise independently of the lamellæ of that layer. They are, he thinks, more characteristic of such changes as occur in the obliteration of vessels in inflammatory processes or in the organization of thrombi than of the true arteriosclerotic changes.

The media under the plaque, which, for the sake of the various theories which have been put forward, has been studied with especial care, generally shows surprisingly slight alterations. Very definite thick plaques may form in the intima, while the underlying media seems practically intact, although we realize, of course, that ordinary staining methods may well fail to reveal qualitative changes in the elasticity of the elastic tissue or the contractility of the muscle. Nevertheless, there are often slight accumulations of fat in that layer, and it is generally thinner under the plaques than in neighboring regions. Indeed, such thinning out may, especially in the smaller vessels, proceed almost to the complete disappearance of the coat, leaving us to determine whether this is the primary injury to the vessel-wall which is compensated for by the formation of the plaque, or the result of pressure from the plaque itself. Again, we have to determine whether the necrosis which occurs in the substance of the plaque is due to malnutrition of the central part of that mass of tissue or to primary injurious processes affecting the newly forming tissue. The time-honored explanation has been that nutrition from the vasa vasorum on the one side, and from the blood in the main vessel, on the other, kept alive the outermost and innermost layers of the plaque, while allowing the centre to

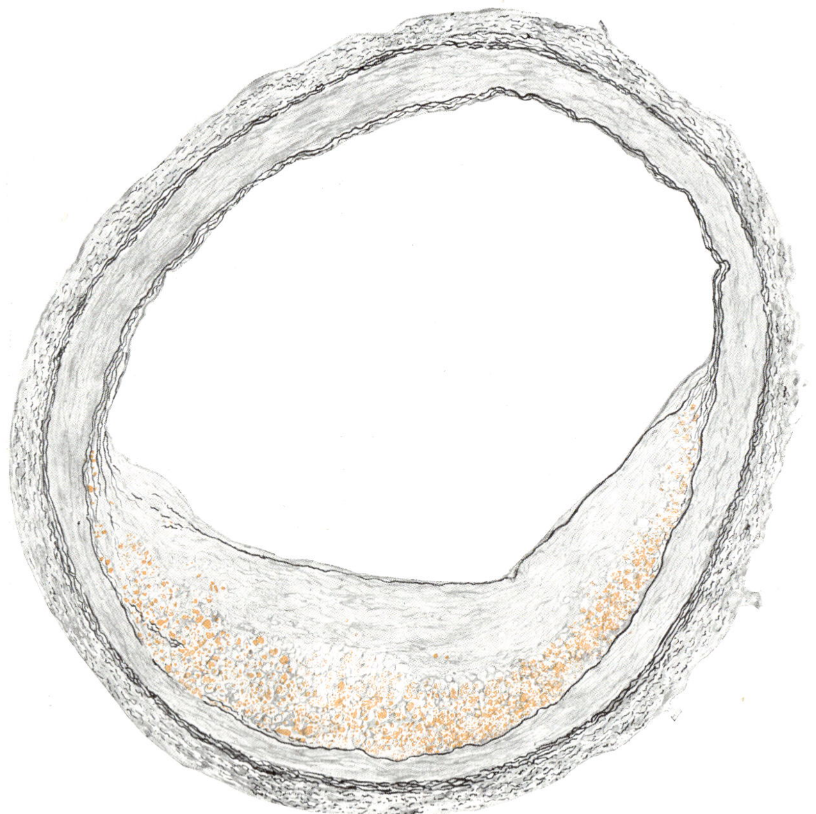

Fig. 169.—Sclerotic plaque in the mesenteric artery, showing reduplication of elastic lamellæ. Lipoid substances are stained red with sudan.

perish (Fig. 170). At any rate, the central mass often becomes very soft, so that if the inner wall or roof of this sac gives way, the contents are washed out into the blood-stream and the ragged edges and base of such an "atheromatous ulcer" are exposed to the circulating blood, often with the result that a thrombus forms in that situation.

The soft material is found to be rich in crystals of cholesterine as well as globules of fat, some of which are evidently cholesterine esters, since they

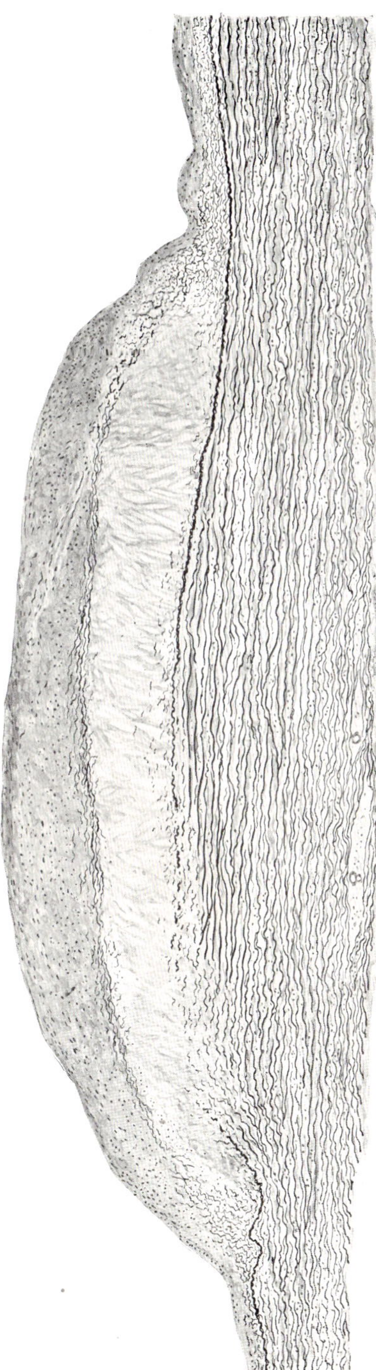

Fig. 170.—Section of an older sclerotic plaque in the aorta, showing cholesterine crystals in the necrotic atheromatous substance.

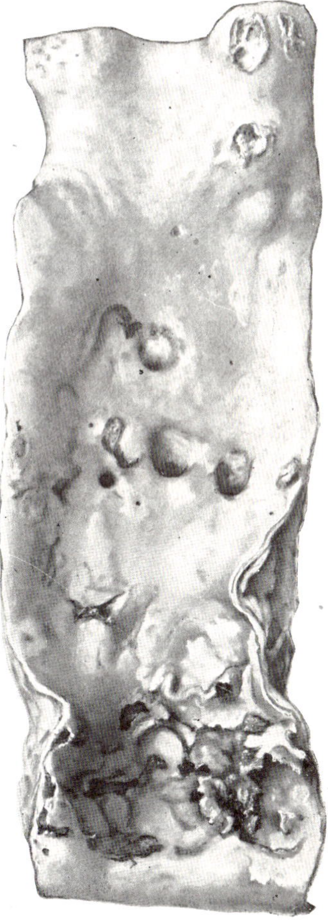

Fig. 171.—Late stage in arteriosclerosis of the aorta: ulceration and calcification.

are doubly refractive, while others are neutral fats. Granules or little spherules or larger, irregular masses of calcium and magnesium phosphates also appear, and, indeed, the deposit of calcium salts may be so great that the whole plaque becomes converted into a solid plate of stony material which will crack with a dry snap, like a scale of oyster-shell (Fig. 171). Such plates correspond, of course, fairly well with the contour of the artery, although they project awkwardly when the vessel is laid open. Usually they are smoothly covered with a delicate layer of intimal tissue and endothelium; otherwise they form a base for the deposit of thrombi. Actual

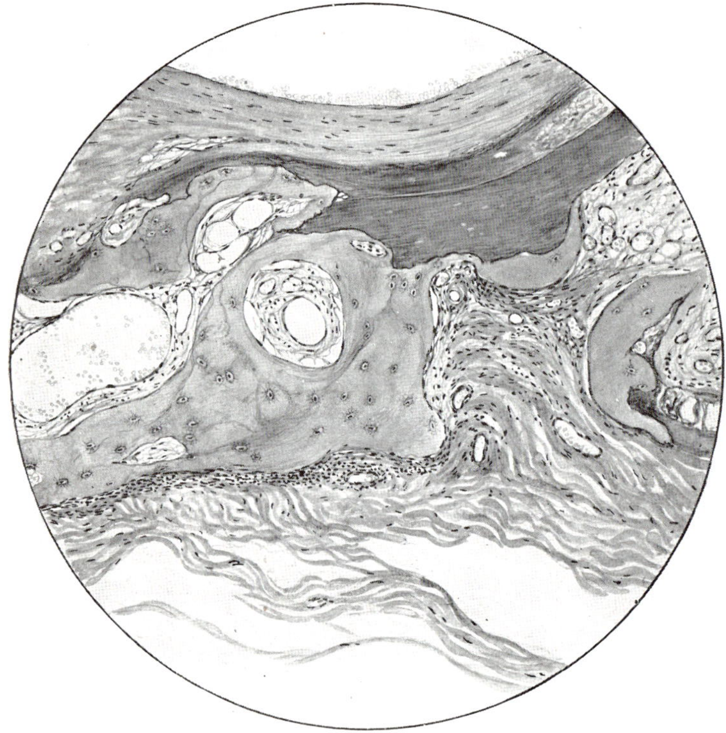

Fig. 172.—Calcified plaque in arterial wall with bone and bone-marrow formation.

bone formation may occur, with marrow cavity and marrow rich in cells, either in calcified plaques in the vessel-wall or in old calcified thrombi which adhere to it (Fig. 172).

The sequence of events which leads to the presence of crystals of cholesterine, granules and masses of calcium, etc., has been explained by Klotz and others as follows: Glycerin and cholesterine esters are deposited in the tissue of the plaque, but readily split up and become saponified, with liberation of the soluble glycerin and crystalline cholesterine. Of the soaps formed, with the resultant fatty acids, calcium soaps are insoluble, and remain where they are formed until the advent of phosphates in the circulating fluids, whereby another reaction occurs which leaves the calcium in the form of hard calcium phosphate.

It must be obvious, from this description, that since all these stages may and frequently do occur at one time in the same aorta, the most variegated appearance is produced. Smooth, rounded, gray eminences scattered along the aorta, and especially about the orifices of the intercostal and other arteries, are interspersed with irregular yellow patches of staining of the relatively unthickened intima, while atheromatous ulcers and

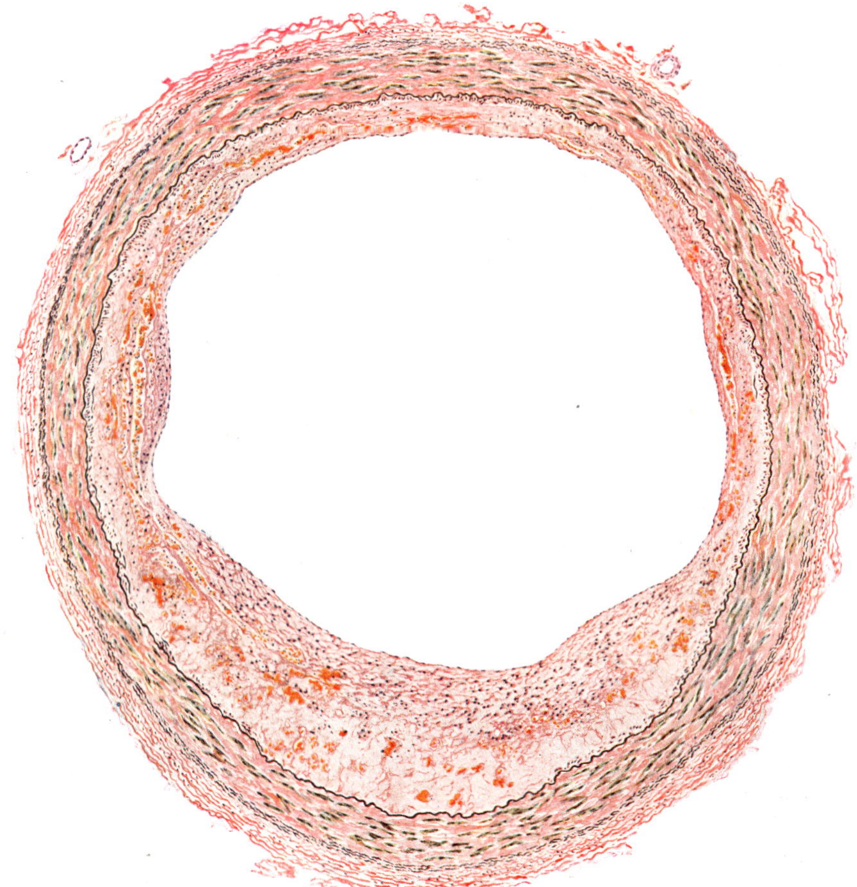

Fig. 173.—Arteriosclerosis of the renal artery showing fat-laden wandering cells in the thickened intima.

sunken, calcified remnants of former atheromatous plaques occur side by side with them. Sometimes the calcification is so extensive that the aorta is converted into a rigid tube.

In all cases there is very great diminution of the elasticity of the artery wall, although its rigidity may be increased. Usually the aorta in advanced sclerosis is dilated and lengthened so that it curves from one side of the vertebral column to the other, and bulges irregularly at different points. Distension of such an artery reveals the rigidity and inelasticity of the affected parts of the wall, while other places may still be quite elastic.

Exactly the same processes in the same sequence are found in the branches of the aorta (Figs. 173, 175). In these branches, in comparison with the calibre of the vessel, the intimal plaques may be far thicker, so that they go far toward obstructing the channel. It is by no means rare that the lumen of such an artery as the superior mesenteric or the splenic is reduced to a mere slit for a short way as it passes the projecting mass.

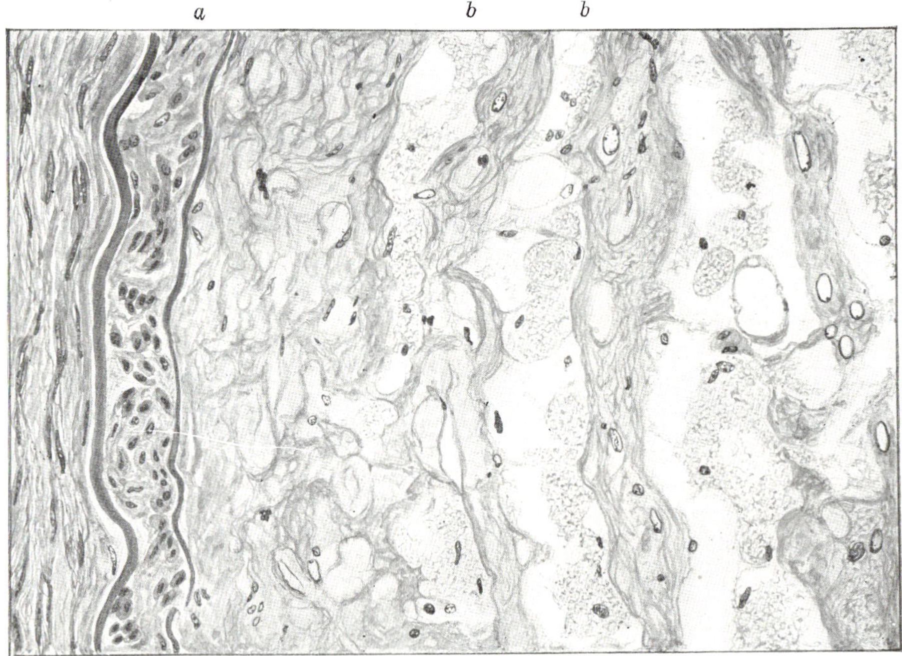

Fig. 174.—Lower layer of the intima from Fig. 173, showing the musculo-elastic layer (*a*) and the fat-holding wandering cells in crevices (*b*).

A cross-section at such a point reveals the misshapen lumen crowded over to one side of the artery, and bounded on one side by the normal wall of the vessel, with its wavy internal elastic lamella, on the other by a great mass of tissue over the outer side of which the media stretches as a thinned-out layer and the internal elastic lamella as a tense straight line. The blood-pressure in the distal part of such a vessel must be greatly reduced, and yet one may find a series of plaques of this kind ranged along its course. The smaller ramifications of the arteries in the organs often show particularly well such relatively huge masses of new tissue bulging out one wall, and encroaching greatly upon the lumen. The endothelium accommodates itself to the decreased surface it must cover, and is seen to be intact until, through its injury or otherwise, a thrombus completes the occlusion of the vessel. Calcification of the necrotic and fatty plaque occurs, exactly as in the aorta.

This process may occur in the arteries of the extremities, where it seems to be especially common in cases of diabetes, and may, by causing the narrowing of the vessels and their final occlusion by secondary thrombosis,

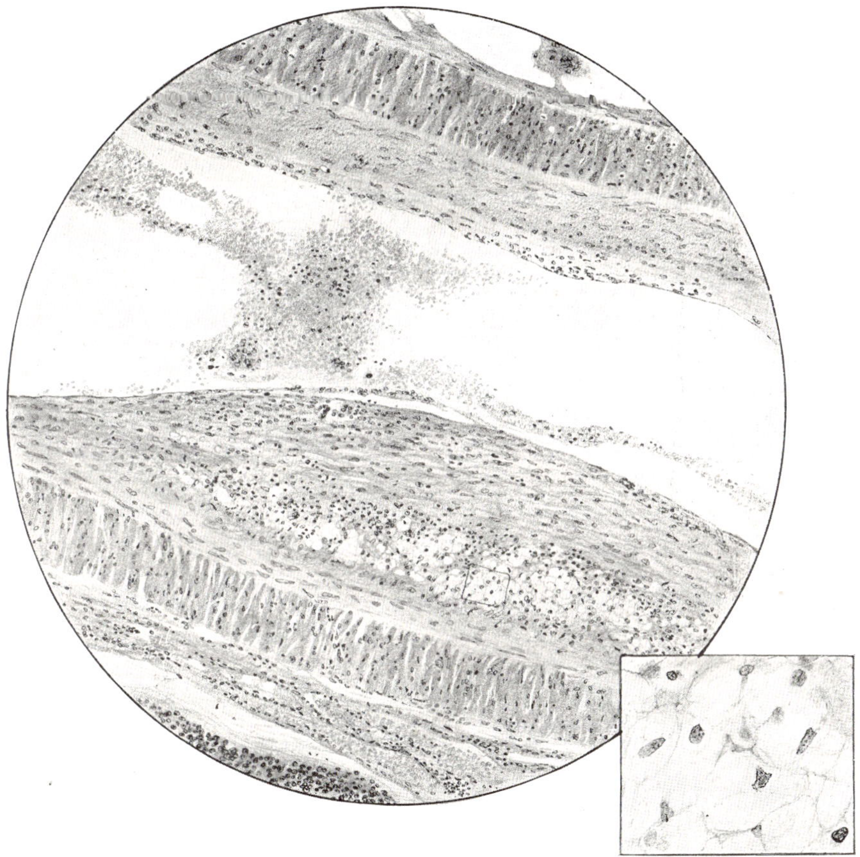

Fig. 175.—Coronary artery encroached upon by a thick arteriosclerotic plaque.

give rise to the senile and diabetic forms of gangrene. Other changes in the peripheral arteries are, however, often concerned in the production of gangrene, and we shall describe them later in discussing obliterating endarteritis.

A special form of sclerosis of the peripheral arteries which gives them the appearance of being ringed, like a trachea, with stony concretions, was distinguished by Mönckeberg, although known long before. In this condition, which is found chiefly in the arteries of the lower extremities, the lesion begins in the media, where degenerative and destructive changes in the muscle-cells, associated with the deposit of fat-droplets, are followed by calcification, which appears first in the form of granules of lime salts, which

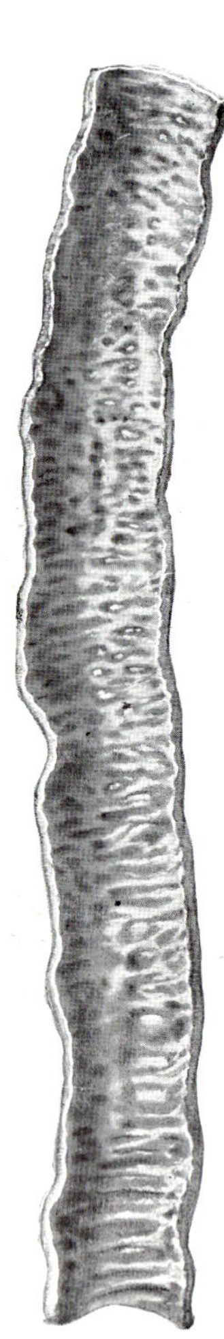

Fig. 176.—Femoral artery showing transverse rings of medial calcification (Mönckeberg's sclerosis).

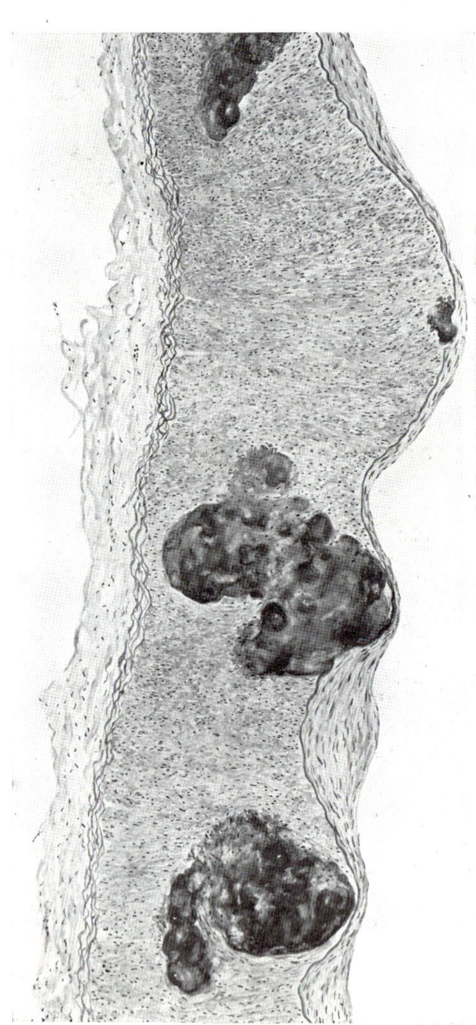

Fig. 177.—Medial sclerosis of Mönckeberg in a femoral artery in longitudinal section. The calcified rings are seen in cross-section.

later become welded together into irregular rings which may even occupy the whole thickness of the media. Such zones, which are often beaded by further concretions, sink below the level of the adjacent more normal intima when the vessel is opened (Fig. 176). The internal elastic lamella is stretched straight over them, as though they had solidified while the vessel was at its maximum dilatation. In many cases, however, they are by no means so regular, but press through and interrupt and distort the elastic lamella (Figs. 177, 178). Granulation tissue of a cellular sort arises to surround them, and extends through the breaches in the lamella into the region of the intima. Sometimes actual bone with marrow cavities and red marrow forms in these places by a metamorphosis of the calcified material through

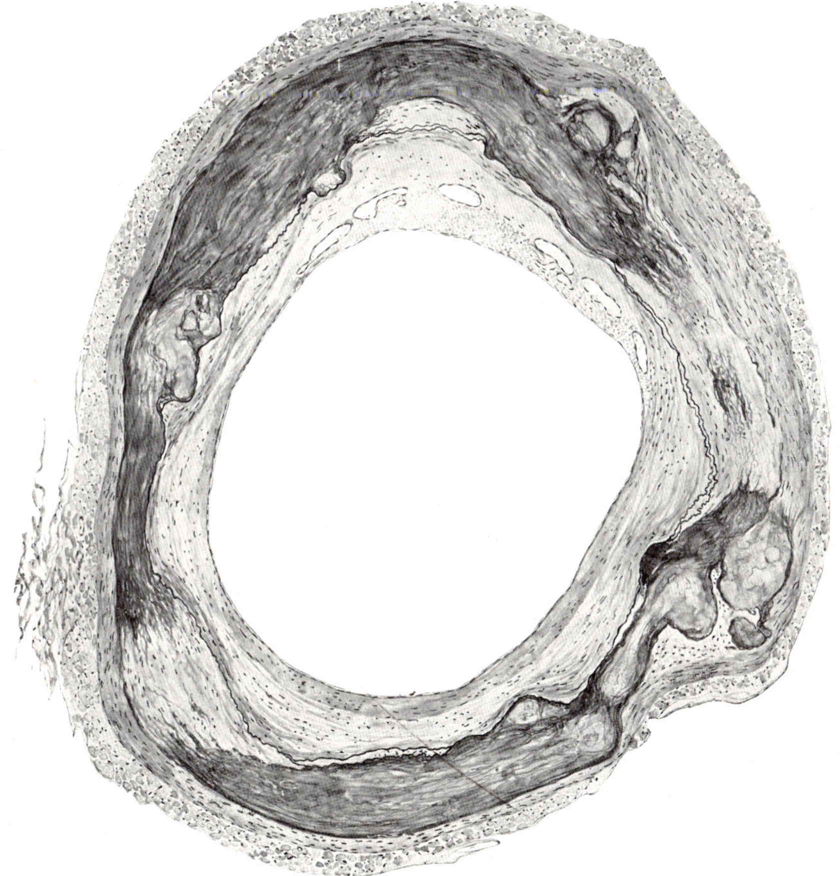

Fig. 178.—Mönckeberg's medial calcification in a peripheral artery.

the production of osteoblasts from the granulation tissue. The intima is often, but not always, thickened over the calcified rings, sometimes with great fraying out of the internal elastic lamella and loss of the recognized relations, but there is rather little evidence of necrosis or the accumulation of fat in such a thickened layer. It appears on section rather more like a granulation tissue, and often contains blood-vessels or spaces. This comparatively common condition does not tend specially toward the obliteration of the vessel, which is rather dilated and lengthened so as to fall into sinuous curves, readily seen in x-ray photographs even through the shadows of the bones.

Mönckeberg regards it as independent of true arteriosclerosis, since it differs from that condition in the slight changes in the intima and in the extreme alterations of the media. Its existence in the peripheral arteries does not signify that there are arteriosclerotic changes in the internal arteries and aorta. Nevertheless, it is frequently combined with arteriosclerosis in the form of extensive intimal thickening, and it is then difficult to separate the two processes if, indeed, they are really different. Occasionally extraordinary masses of new tissue may be formed inside the internal elastic lamella in such a way as almost completely to block the lumen. Such obstructing tissue, which converts the artery into an extremely thick-walled tube with pin-point lumen, generally extends only a short way, so that the vessel opens out again into a wide tube. Several such strictures may be found in a single artery, suggesting that they may have been due to the organization of thrombi with secondary canalization, although they can be equally well explained as arteriosclerotic thickenings of the intima. Such changes commonly lead to great reduction of the blood supply of the extremity and gangrene of the toes or foot, and it is probably this type of change which most frequently occurs in diabetic and senile gangrene.

Pathogenesis and Ætiology.—We are at present, in spite of numerous theories, practically ignorant of the cause of arteriosclerosis. Rokitansky thought the plaques deposited from the blood; Virchow regarded the whole process as inflammatory, whence his designation, endarteritis deformans; Köster also regarded it as inflammatory, but rather in Cohnheim's sense, as an exudative process, because he traced the formation of a cellular exudate in the vessel-walls from the vasa vasorum. Thoma elaborated a theory based on the idea that the cutting-off of the placental circulation at birth must necessitate an adaptation of the calibre of the blood-vessels to the changed amount of blood. This, he thought, was effected by a thickening of the intima of the vessels, especially those which lay in the course of the old umbilical blood-stream. To this process there might be compared the thickening of the intima in arteriosclerosis, which evidently occurs at those points, where, owing to some primary weakening of the musculature of the media, there arose a local bulging of the vessel-wall. In such a bulging area the passing blood-stream would eddy and be retarded, whence the intimal growth, which should be just sufficient to compensate for the bulging-out of the media and thereby reinstate the original level of the intimal lining of the vessel. Naturally, such a patch would be thrown into relief by the elasticity of the arterial wall after it is laid open. It is evident that many criticisms of this theory may be offered.

In general there has prevailed insistently the idea that the changes in the vessel-wall are due in some way to heightened arterial blood-pressure.

The favorite situation of the lesions in the arch and about the orifices of the branches has been explained on the ground that pressure relations at those points constitute a more severe test of the strength of the wall than at other points in the aorta. Marchand, Aschoff, and others look upon arteriosclerosis as a degenerative process, brought about largely by the overworking of the vessel-wall, due to heightened blood-pressure (sudden strains, Albrecht). They see in the connective tissue a substance more rigid and less distensible than the elastic tissue, which at least maintains the strength of the wall. Aschoff finds the weakening due to degenerative changes in the intima, with its elastic lamella, and not, as Thoma supposed, to primary changes in the media.

Jores described the progressive thickening of the intima with the normal advance of age, and declared that such a thick intimal coat is especially prone to degenerative changes which occur at the level of the musculo-elastic layer. The reformation of the elastic tissue by repeated splitting off of lamellæ from the internal elastic lamella is characteristic of true arteriosclerosis, as contrasted with the obliterative changes in the vessels where the elastica is formed in new, delicate, independent fibrils in the new tissue of the intima.

The present state of our knowledge is unsatisfying, but it seems that we are far from having proved that the heightening of blood-pressure as such has more than a guiding influence upon the development of the lesions, just as the structure of cancellous bone and other tissues is adapted in growth to the strain put upon it. It is true that Klotz claims to have produced arteriosclerosis in rabbits by hanging them head downward for a long period, but rabbits are notoriously subject to spontaneous arterial lesions, and Lubarsch and others have been unable to confirm his results. Arteriosclerosis sometimes occurs in the pulmonary artery in cases of mitral stenosis, or in the arch of the aorta in cases of stenosis of the aorta at the isthmus, but it is often absent in these cases, and there are other explanations than the high pressure to offer when it does occur. It is common in cases of nephritis when the pressure is high, but there again we are unable to say that it is the high pressure *per se* which is responsible for the disease of the arterial wall, and not some other factor which may have caused the nephritis. There are many cases of arteriosclerosis without high blood-pressure, even though the walls of the arteries may be very much altered. In these it is clear that the cause of the sclerosis must be sought in some other factor.

It seems more probable that, as the French have so long suggested, arteriosclerosis is the effect of some injurious or poisonous agent acting upon the intima of the arteries, as it might upon any other organ, with destruction, fat accumulation, and repair. What this agent may be is as yet uncertain. Every sort of poisonous substance has been experimentally administered to animals either by mouth or by injection into the blood-stream or tissues, but without any very constant results. The ætiological factors commonly held responsible, alcohol, lead, nicotine, etc., have occasionally given rise to changes comparable to those of arteriosclerosis, but not constantly—indeed, with alcohol and lead the experiments have generally proved negative. Adrenalin (Josue and others) will produce medial lesions and calcification, with corresponding intimal scars in rabbits, and various bacterial toxins, especially those extracted from staphylococci (Saltykow), give rise to changes even more closely resembling those of arteriosclerosis. But so far none of these substances can be set down as the proved cause of the condition. Recent Russian observers —Chalatow, Anitschkoff, etc.—have found that cholesterine and its esters, on being fed to rabbits, lodge in the intima of the aorta and produce tissue proliferation there, resembling those of arteriosclerosis. On the other hand, the idea asserts itself that since repeated anaphylactic shocks may produce lesions in liver and kidneys (Longcope), they may also cause injuries to the arterial walls. All these things are yet in the experimental stage, but it seems probable that long-continued and oft-repeated injuries, such as might arise during chronic infections, chronic intoxications, or in sensitive animals from repeated absorption of the sensitizing protein, may constitute the underlying cause of injury, which is responded to by reparatory processes and by an accumulation of fats and fatty acids which may be protective.

LITERATURE

Anitschkoff: Ziegler's Beiträge, 1913, lvi, 379.
Aschoff: Beihefte z. med. Klinik, 1908, 4, 1.
Faber: Arteriosklerose, Jena, 1912.
Hübschmann: Ziegler's Beiträge, 1906, xxxix, 119.
Jores: Wesen der Arteriosklerose, 1908.
Longcope: Jour. Exp. Med., 1913, xviii, 678.
Marchand: Verh. d. XXI. Cong. f. inn. Med., 1904.
Mönckeberg: Virchow's Arch., 1903, clxxi, 141; 1914, ccxix, 408.
Saltykow: Ziegler's Beiträge, 1908, xliii, 147.
Thoma: Virchow's Arch., xciii, xcv, civ, cv, cvi, cxii.
Thorel: Ergebnisse der allg. Path., ix_1, xi_2, xiv_2.

SYPHILITIC ARTERIAL DISEASE

For the sake of convenience, and because of the confusion which has existed for so long between syphilitic disease of the artery and true arteriosclerosis, that condition may be described here. Other infectious agents cause disease of the vessels of a more or less specific character, but none lead to such important alterations as syphilis. It affects the aorta as well as the smaller vessels, and is then apparently the commonest original cause of insufficiency of the aortic valves, as well as aneurysm formation. In itself, without these ultimate effects, it may often be recognized during life by certain clinical phenomena, such as the reflex respiratory disturbances described by Longcope.

Since its recognition by Doehle and Heller, and especially since the papers of Chiari and Benda, syphilitic disease of the aorta has come to be quite clearly understood, because the ætiological factor, the Spirochæta pallida, has been found in the lesions, and even made to produce similar lesions in animals. Then, too, the anatomical changes are quite comparable with those produced by syphilis elsewhere, and are sometimes distinctly gummatous in character. They are found in all three coats of the vessel, and affect the vasa vasorum as well. In the adventitia, and extending into the media or even into the intima, there are found around these vasa vasorum collections of wandering cells of the character of lymphoid and plasma cells, sometimes with multinucleated giant-cells. The vasa vasorum are often obliterated in this process. The cellular granulation tissue

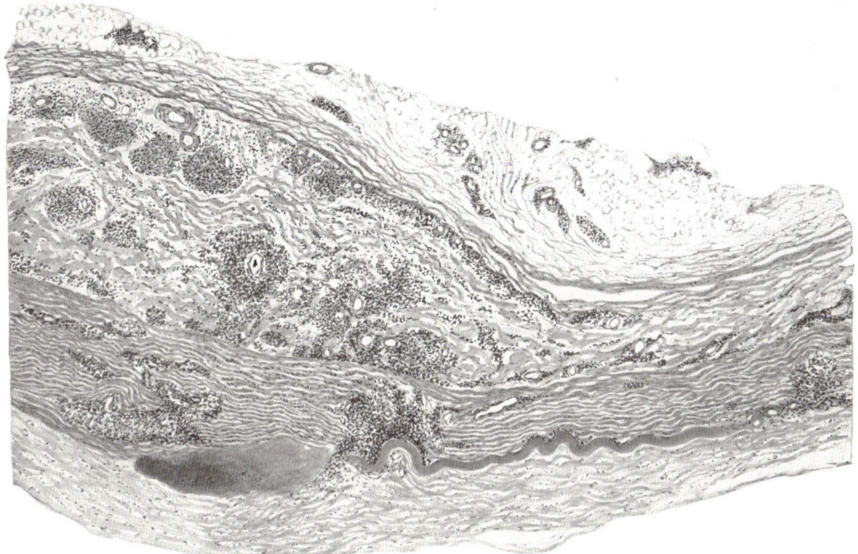

Fig. 179.—Syphilitic aortitis. Gummatous foci about vasa vasorum in the adventitia and media. Frequent breaks in the media.

may occupy considerable space, and may even be evident on the surface of the artery as a nodular mass. Such are, clearly enough, gummata, for they tend to become necrotic in their centres and present, in general, the architecture of gummatous nodules seen elsewhere. Nevertheless, it is more common to find mere collections of cells of less characteristic arrangement in the adventitia and media. They often surround necrotic foci, or are found side by side with quite extensive necrosis of the media. One sees sometimes patches of necrotic media in which the arrangement of the elastic lamellæ and muscle is still visible, as in an anæmic infarction, and about these there forms the cellular granulation tissue. Later such necrotic patches are absorbed and scarred, a process which adds to the distortion of the artery. If the artery be examined at this stage, which is the one most commonly seen at autopsy, the media will be found to be interrupted repeatedly by irregular strands of scar tissue rich in wandering cells, and when the elastic tissue alone is stained, one receives the impression that that layer is composed of mere fragments or clumps of elastic fibres strewn along at intervals. Such interruption of its continuity must greatly weaken the aortic wall, and goes far to explain the ready development of aneurysms on a syphilitic basis. Over such a tattered media the intima is found to have formed a thick, irregular layer of hyaline fibrous tissue, in which there is relatively little fat to be found (Fig. 179). Cholesterine crystals and calcium deposits are equally rare, unless, of course, as frequently happens, the syphilitic disease is developed in an aorta already the seat of a true arteriosclerosis. In the syphilitic intimal thickenings the internal elastic lamella shows no such regular fraying up into accessory lamellæ as is seen in arteriosclerosis. It suffers wholesale interruptions and destruction with the rest of the elastic coats.

Fig. 180.—Gross appearance of syphilitic aortitis.

The gross appearance of the aorta is most clearly to be understood on the basis of these microscopical changes. There is a great roughening of the lining, which is thrown up into irregular folds and nodular swellings, some translucent and pearly, others yellowish and opaque where there is fat accumulation. But nowhere is there any formation of calcified plates nor any ulceration. Beginning usually at the aortic orifice, and generally involving the aortic valves, this change is most commonly found in the arch and extending downward into the descending aorta, where it usually stops abruptly at a point somewhere above the orifices of the abdominal vessels. Rather rarely it extends below these, and the rest of the vessel is smooth and elastic, or there is a sharply outlined patch in only one part of the vessel. The aortic valves are thickened and shortened, so that they become insufficient, and the aortic ring is widened, intensifying the incompetence of the valves. A further characteristic of the appearance of the intima is its peculiar wrinkling. It is thrown into longitudinal rugæ, quite unlike anything seen in arteriosclerosis (Fig. 180). Thinned out and scarred areas are frequently seen in the walls, and dilatations of all sorts, from small saccules to aneurysms of the hugest size, may accompany the later stages of the disease. The orifices of the intercostal vessels may be partly occluded, and even the carotids may be narrowed at their mouths. This encroachment on the lumen of the branches of the aorta is most important in the case of the coronary vessels, which may be constricted at their origin to a very small calibre, since it seems probable that it is in some cases responsible for the symptoms of angina pectoris.

In the smaller arteries and veins, such as those of the meninges, syphilis causes changes which are much like those produced by tuberculosis, in that minute gummata are formed in the walls, growing in the adventitia and intima, and destroying the intervening media in such a way as to produce an excentrically placed nodule, which greatly narrows the lumen and appears as a little pearly lump in the course of the vessel (Heubner, Nonne, Versé, Goldsborough). Such lesions of the meningeal vessels are usually accompanied by a definite cellular meningitis, similar to that caused by tuberculosis, and in which the wandering cells are predominantly of the mononuclear types. The most varied clinical symptoms result, as one may read in the monograph of Nonne.

LITERATURE

Benda: Handb. d. Geschlechtskrankh., 1913, iii.
Chiari, Benda: Verh. Dtsch. path. Gesellsch., 1904, vi, 137, 164.
Döhle: Dtsch. Arch. f. klin. Med., 1895, lv, 190.
Fukushi: Virchow's Arch., 1913, ccxi, 331.
Goldsborough: Johns Hopkins Hosp. Bull., 1902, xiii, 105.
Longcope: Arch. Int. Med., 1913, xi, 14.
Nonne: Syphilis und Nervensystem, 1902; second edition, translated by Ball, 1913.
Versé: Ziegler's Beiträge, 1913, lvi, 580.

OBLITERATIVE ENDARTERITIS—THROMBOANGEITIS OBLITERANS

It has been pointed out that typical arteriosclerotic thickening of the intima may narrow or almost obliterate small arteries in some cases, and that calcification of the media, often associated with such internal changes, may also do this. There are still other physiological and pathological methods of occlusion which are especially important in the small vessels when the mechanics of the circulation or the protection of the body requires their obliteration. In the embryo one channel survives in a plexus of vessels because the others are closed by the mere adhesion of their walls when blood is no longer forced through. When the course of the circulation changes, as it does after birth with the enlargement of the pulmonary stream-bed, the old channel through the ductus arteriosus is gradually closed by a growth of the intimal tissue which narrows the lumen. This method is probably the one used in the slow obliteration of the blood-vessels in the atrophy of such organs as the breast, uterus, and ovaries in which, after sexual activity is over, the blood supply is diminished. Nevertheless in these vessels calcification of the media is frequently seen (Fig. 181). In other situations chronic inflammatory processes throughout the tissue are accompanied by a gradual occlusion of the small blood-vessels by a slow thickening of their intima by the new formation of connective-tissue cells beneath the endothelium. It is difficult to draw a sharp line between the narrowing of vessels because of the lack of an adequate blood-stream, and this effect of

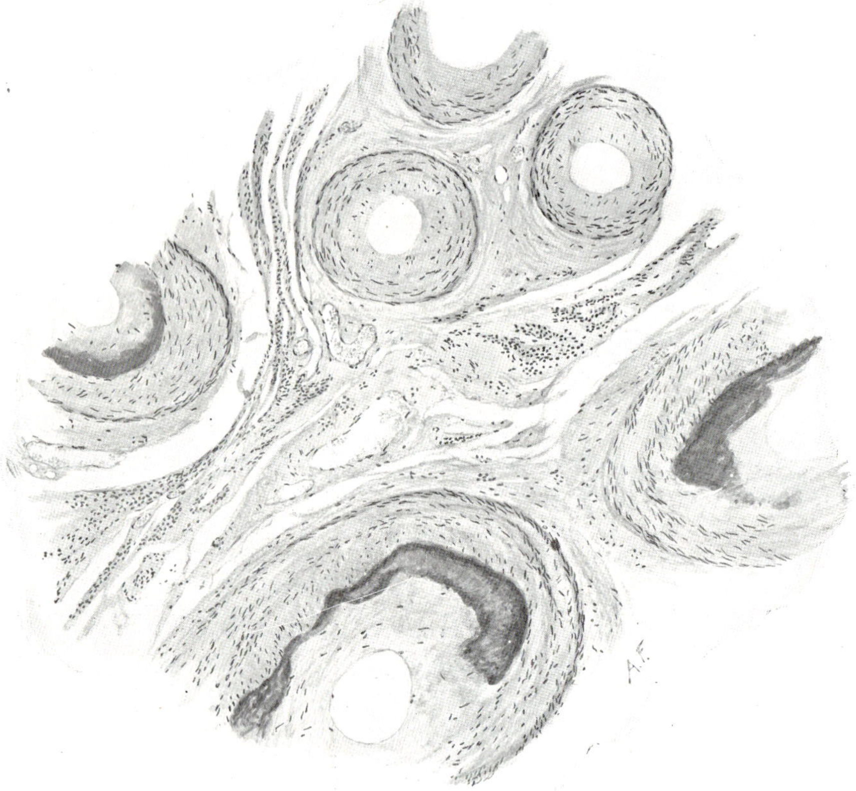

Fig. 181.—Wall of senile uterus: obliterative endarteritis with calcification.

surrounding injury and inflammation. Such "obliterating endarteritis" is common in the shrunken kidney of chronic nephritis, in indurative affections of the lungs and other organs caused by tuberculosis and syphilis, in some tumors, and in a host of other sites of protracted injury and irritation. Sometimes, as in the advance of a tuberculous cavity or in the wall of a gastric ulcer, the closure of an artery which is being encroached upon may be a life-saving event. It is only when the excavation proceeds too rapidly and surprises the vessel that great hæmorrhages occur in chronic phthisis.

The plugging of a vessel by a clot or thrombus often has a protective significance in that it abruptly obstructs the flow of blood. It is the natural method of stanching hæmorrhage, and although it may be ineffectual when a large vessel is cut, it successfully closes the torn ends of the small ones. When a vessel is ligated, a clot forms at the point of the ligation and extends to the next branch, where the blood-stream is still active. If the wall of the vessel is injured, the stream may continue until the lumen is filled by the clot which forms on the walls. Since this is formed in the moving blood it will have the character of a thrombus. When a vessel is obstructed at a point by a thrombus so that the lumen is open on each side, efforts are made to reëstablish the circulation. The thrombus is "organized" by the springing up of capillaries and connective tissue from the vessel-wall which replace it with a vascular granulation tissue. Crevices in its substance are lined with endothelium and constitute new blood spaces. The dilatation and anastomosis of these new vessels and blood spaces may produce new channels which will again carry blood through the obstructed area. They are in time supplied with muscular and elastic coats like those of any other vessel (Fig. 182). A vessel thus reinstated seems like an elastic cord, but from its cut end many fine streams of blood spurt.

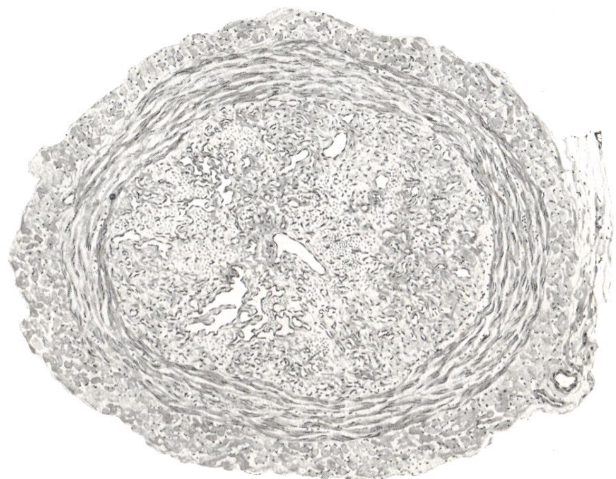

Fig. 182.—Vein with old thrombotic occlusion recanalized by new blood-channels.

Thrombotic occlusion with organization appears to play a prominent part in another form of obliterating endarteritis which occurs in the arteries of the extremities. Von Winiwarter described the obliteration as due to proliferation of soft tissue from the intimal coat, while Zoege von Manteuffel and Weiss thought it essentially the result of thrombosis with organization.

Apparently both processes can occur, and in the end-result it is difficult to determine exactly how the obliteration occurred, although it is easy to distinguish these obliterated vessels from those which have been obstructed by arteriosclerotic thickenings of their walls. This can be made clear by describing the process as it affects the peripheral arteries.

In some cases in relatively young people, and principally in Russian Hebrews, serious symptoms arise without any warning, beginning with coldness and pallor of the extremities, pain and peculiar tickling or burning sensations, inability to walk more than a short way without rest, and finally gangrene of the toes or of the whole foot or leg. The inability to walk, which is called intermittent claudication, is explained by the fact that the arteries of the extremities are practically pulseless, and converted into a firm cord, so that not enough blood reaches the muscles to allow them to contract properly.

In these cases x-ray pictures show no shadow of the vessels whatever, and, indeed, they are usually found not to be calcified. On section, too

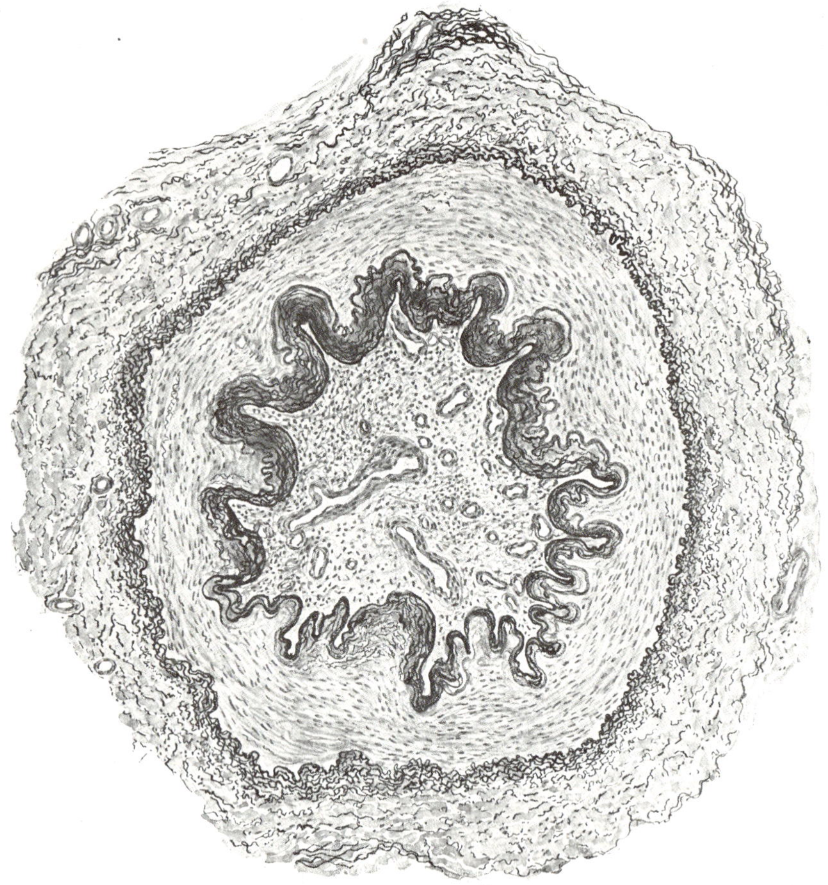

Fig. 183.—Obliterating endarteritis (thrombo-arteritis obliterans) with shrinkage of the walls and partial recanalization.

(Fig. 183), they present an extraordinary contrast to those found in senile and diabetic gangrene, inasmuch as there is little or no change in the media, although it and the adventitia and surrounding tissue may be infiltrated with wandering cells and indurated by the new-growth of fibrous tissue. Nor is the internal elastic lamella stretched, distorted, and frayed out, as in that more truly arteriosclerotic process. Instead, it maintains its normal wavy contour around the lumen of the vessel. But the lumen is filled with vascular granulation tissue, sometimes with endothelium-lined spaces, through which a little blood may flow.

In this case, too, there is a question as to whether the obliteration is due to a growth of tissue from the intima or to the organization of a thrombus, but thrombi are so generally present in all stages that Bürger concludes definitely that it must be named thromboangeitis obliterans. The obstruction is generally accompanied by the formation of adhesions between the vessel and the surrounding tissue, and although no definite ideas as to its causation are to be found in the literature, it seems probable that it is of infectious or toxic nature.

LITERATURE

Bürger: Amer. Jour. Med. Sci., 1908, cxxxvi, 567.
Von Winiwarter: Arch. f. klin. Chir., 1878, xxiii, 202.
Weiss: Dtsch. Zeitschr. f. Chir., 1894, xl, 1.
Zoege von Manteuffel: Arch. f. klin. Chir., 1898, xlvii, 461.

ANEURYSMS

A difficulty has always existed in deciding exactly what constitutes an aneurysm, since there are so many different forms of enlargement of the artery and cavities in connection with arteries which might fall under this name. There has long been a distinction between true aneurysms, in which the cavity was supposed to be formed by the stretching of the wall of the artery itself, and spurious aneurysms, in which rupture of the artery wall opened its lumen into a blood-filled cavity formed in the tissue outside. But since it has been shown that in all cases the wall of the sac is formed of tissue of a character very different from that of the normal arterial wall, this distinction is anatomically no longer so valid, although naturally the conditions set up in these ways are in principle very different. Benda has tried to cut this knot by saying that an aneurysm is any pathological widening of the arterial lumen caused by change in its walls, which for a time, at least, stands in open communication with its blood-stream.

The most common aneurysms are saccular widenings of the artery, opening out from its regular channel by a wide or narrow orifice, but the opening may be so wide, and the distension so shallow, that the saccular form is lost, and if, as sometimes happens, the widening occupies the whole circumference of the artery, we have a fusiform aneurysm or aneurysmal dilatation. Aneurysms of these types occur in diseased arteries in many situations. They are most common in the aorta, especially in the region of the arch, but may arise in any part of its course or in any of the smaller arteries—even in those which lie embedded in the substance of an organ.

Generally classed with aneurysms are certain peculiar widenings and enlargements of the blood-vessels, which also increase their length so that in a given area a whole mass of wide, tortuous, and tangled, pulsating vessels is found (*cirsoid* or *racemose aneurysm*). One is inclined to suspect that this rare form may be of a nature more allied to that of angiomatous tumors, and distinct from ordinary aneurysms.

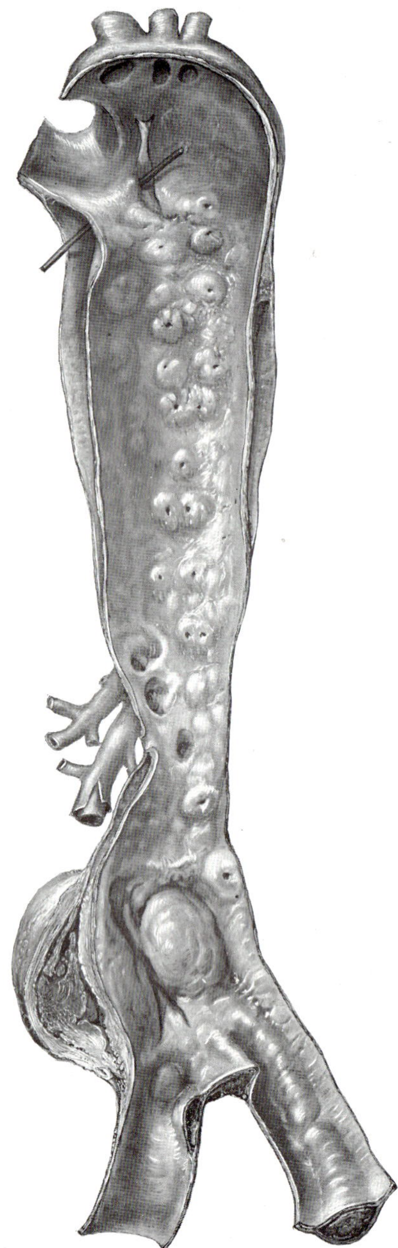

Fig. 184.—Dissecting aneurysm of aorta splitting the arterial wall far into the branches. A hæmatoma near the bifurcation of the aorta.

Dissecting aneurysms are produced by the rupture or tearing of the inner coats of the artery—usually the intima and half of the media, and the extravasation of the blood into a cavity which it makes for itself by burrowing into the wall of the artery. In sclerotic arteries it is easy to split the wall in this way, and the blood may work its way down the whole length of the aorta and along many branches, converting each partly or completely into two tubes, one within the other, and separated by the extravasated blood (Fig. 184). After this the blood may break through the outer tube and accumulate somewhere in the tissues, or again through the inner tube, thus reëntering the regular circulation. Except in the last case the whole process is really merely the formation of a hæmorrhage or hæmatoma in the artery wall, but it sometimes happens—and I have seen one case*—that when the rupture back into the lumen of the vessel takes place, the extravasated blood actually circulates, and the space in the wall becomes lined by endothelium, so that something like a double aorta is produced (Fig. 185).

Arteriovenous Aneurysm.—Occasionally when a stab wound or the wound produced in venesection opens an artery and a vein side by

* MacCallum: Johns Hopkins Hosp. Bull., 1909, xx, 9.

side, a hæmatoma or massive extravasation of blood into the tissue appears, and later retains its communication with both vessels, so that the blood

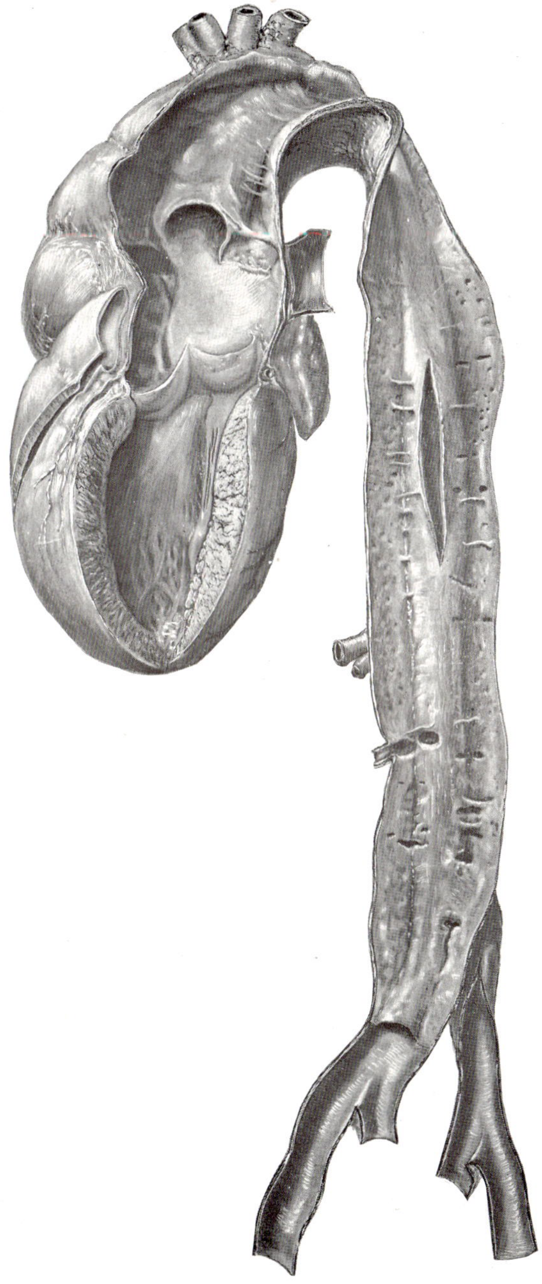

Fig. 185.—Old dissecting aneurysm which has ruptured again into the aorta and established a double aortic channel.

circulates through it from the artery into the vein. Such a cavity forms a dense, fibrous wall for itself, and the communication is permanent. In a

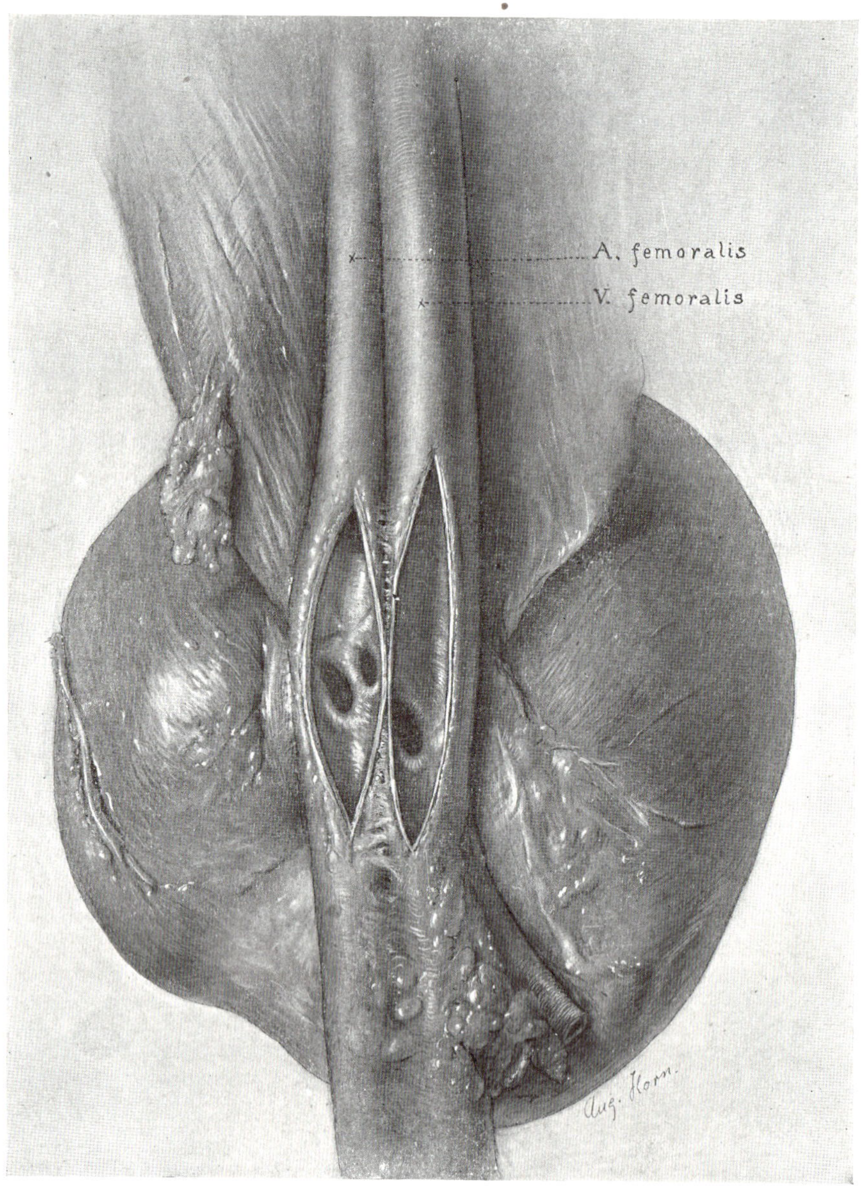

Fig. 186.—Arteriovenous aneurysm caused by a stab wound of the femoral artery and vein.

case seen in Baltimore the femoral artery and vein communicated in this way through a great sac. There was a loud, humming murmur, and a thrill over this sac, and the pressure of the arterial blood into the vein prevented the return of the venous blood from the leg. On the shin of that leg there were great varicose veins, and a persistent varicose ulcer, quite like those seen in old people, although the other leg of this boy was perfectly normal.

In other cases, the so-called *false aneurysms*, the artery alone is ruptured, and the hæmatoma becoming encapsulated, remains in open communication with the blood-stream, being constantly washed out by an eddy of blood.

Of all these, it is evident that the most important and interesting form is that which develops through disease of the arterial wall by a gradual bulging out of some portion into a sac, or widening of other form. As to the ætiology, we are even yet insufficiently informed, although the work of Doehle, Heller, Benda, Chiari, and others on syphilitic aortitis has thrown much light on it. There is great diversity of opinion as to the part played by syphilis, for although Heller found 85 per cent. of aneurysms to be due to syphilis, Braun, in a very large collection, found only 17 per cent. Marchand, too, finds the percentage of proved syphilis rather low. Nevertheless, the character of the syphilitic disease of the arterial wall, which is so preëminently calculated to weaken it in the presence of a strong blood-pressure, makes it seem probable that more accurate methods of investigation will show the participation of that disease in a very large proportion of the cases, if not in all. But at present many of them seem to be associated only with the ordinary type of arteriosclerosis.

Of course, it must be remembered, however, that encroachment of destructive tuberculous processes may weaken the outer wall of an artery and allow the production of a small aneurysm, just as the advance of a gastric ulcer toward such an artery as the splenic may allow it to bulge and finally rupture in the base of the ulcer. So, too, emboli of bacteria may weaken the arterial walls, and multiple "mycotic" aneurysms appear, while certain parasitic nematodes living inside the arteries in the same way produce aneurysmal dilatations (strongyle infection in the horse).

The general character of an aneurysm may be made clear by the description of one of the commoner forms—the saccular aneurysm of the aorta. In such a case (Fig. 187) it is found that the sac most commonly springs from the convexity of the arch, and that intense arteriosclerotic alterations of the aorta surround its mouth. The orifice is round or irregular in outline, and the edge is rolled over into it somewhat, so as to almost overhang its cavity. The cavity itself may reach a very great size, the sac thus formed pushing aside the surrounding organs or embedding itself in them in the most remarkable way (Fig. 188). Mechanical effects produced in this way are of great variety, depending largely upon the point of origin and size of the sac. Pressure on the recurrent laryngeal nerve produces an alteration of the voice from spasm or paralysis of the vocal cord, coughing, dyspnœa, etc. Pressure on the trachea flattens it and causes dyspnœa—later, the aneurysm may rupture into it, after eroding its wall. The lungs yield and collapse before the aneurysm. Pressure on a bronchus narrows it, and behind the obstruction bronchiectasis arises. When the sac reaches the bony structures of the thorax, which do not yield, it hammers its way through them, appearing under the skin through a hole in

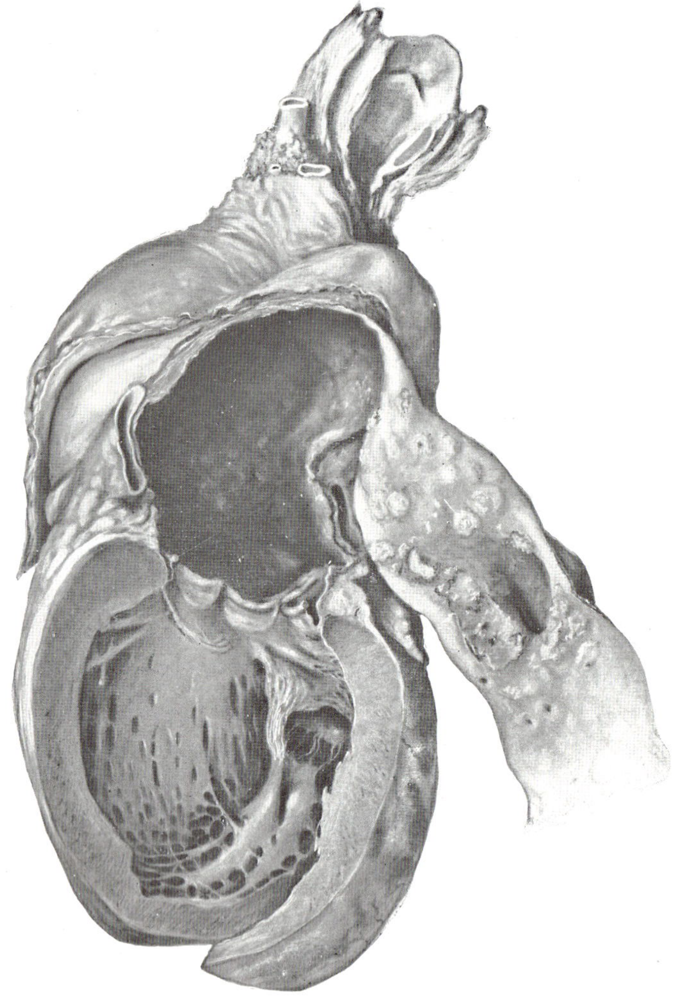

Fig. 187.—Aneurysm of aortic arch. Aortic valvular insufficiency, probably syphilitic. A second aneurysm in the dorsal aortic wall.

the ribs or sternum. If it extends backward to the spine, it destroys the centra of the vertebræ even down to the spinal canal (*cf.* Fig. 29), leaving the yielding intervertebral discs standing almost unaltered—in the same way it may break through the ribs in the back and appear under the skin there. Then it is not long before the skin becomes thinned out and bluish, and finally the sac ruptures, so that death follows at once. Often it ruptures long before reaching the skin—into the pleura or pericardium, trachea, or œsophagus, or even into the superior or inferior vena cava.

The character of such a sac which can produce a huge and destructive tumor, which destroys itself as soon as it completes its advance, must be interesting. It is not really composed of the stretched-out walls of the vessel, for microscopic examination with suitable stains shows that prac-

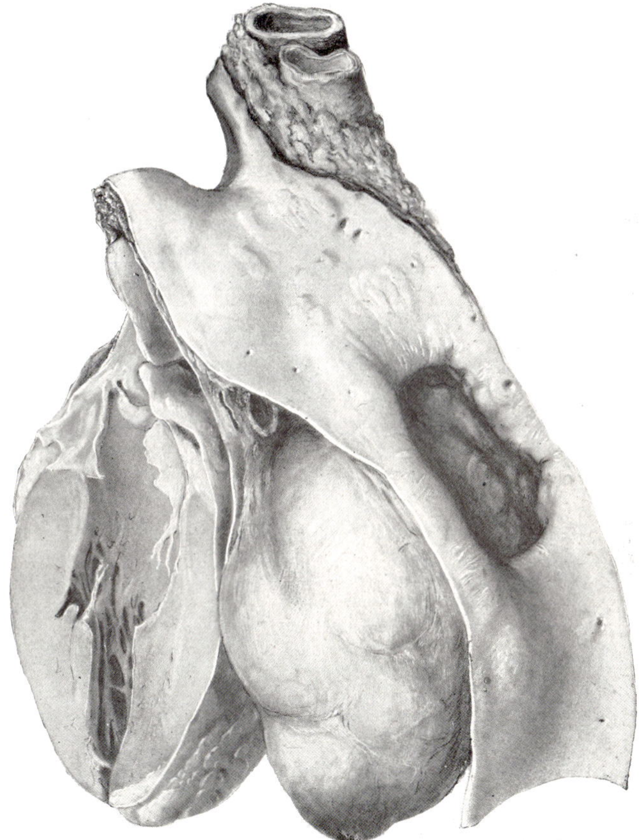

Fig. 188.—Saccular aneurysm projecting between the aorta and the heart. Its orifice shows in the aorta.

tically all those elements stop sharply at the edge of the orifice (Fig. 189). The elastic tissue and the muscle are suddenly interrupted. Endothelium may persist and attempt to line the sac, but it is evident that it soon fails in this and is lost. Indeed, nothing but connective tissue, and that essentially new formed, goes to make up the sac. It grows largely by new breaks in the wall which seem to be made good by further formation of fibrous tissue. The current of blood eddies about in the cavity, and its pulsation gives the sac its power of breaking down the resistance of the tissues. But the endothelial lining is imperfect, and thrombosis occurs, and if time be allowed, as it so often is, layer after layer of compact thrombus material may be hammered down on the wall of the sac until it is in large part filled up (Fig. 190). Occasionally the aneurysm may be completely obliterated in this way. The character of the fibrous wall is such that little

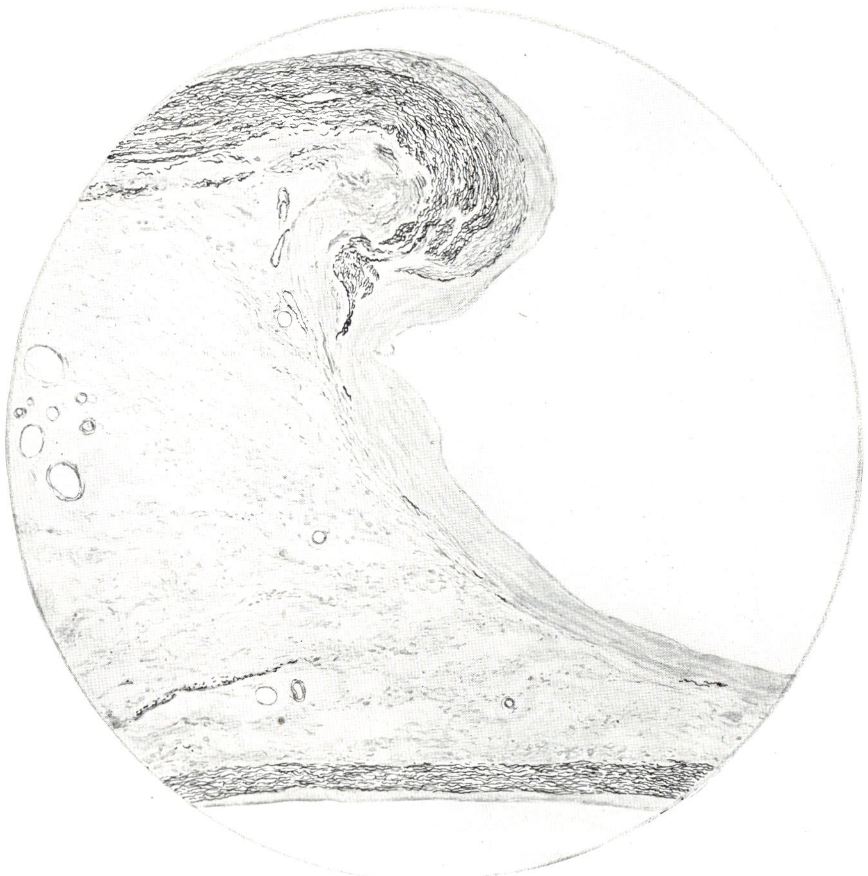

Fig. 189.—Edge of a small aneurysm, showing the abrupt cessation of the elastic tissue at the margin of the sac. One wall of an adjacent vein is seen at the bottom of the drawing.

upgrowth of organizing granulation tissue into the thrombus appears, and the lower layers become even more compact, until, on a smoothly cut section, they look like onyx. The wall itself becomes hyaline, and it is often impossible to say, in a microscopic section, where the wall ends and the thrombus begins. In the smaller and fresher aneurysmal sacs the wall, wrinkled and irregular, is generally shining, thick, and rather translucent, and quite uncovered with thrombi or covered with only the merest film.

Quite the same characters are found in aneurysms in the abdominal aorta or its branches, in the arteries of the extremity or the head. Sometimes several small ones occur side by side, even in the aorta; sometimes when one in a peripheral artery has been cured by operation, a new one will appear in another vessel. There was a syphilitic negro cook on a steamboat who returned to the hospital three times, each time with a new aneurysm. But usually one is enough if it affects the aorta, and all the vaunted

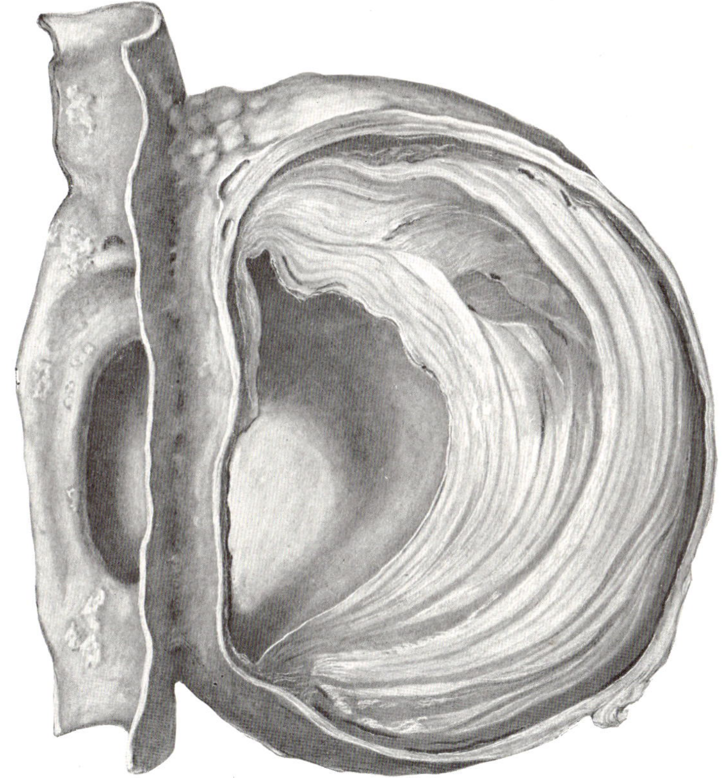

Fig. 190.—Aneurysm of the abdominal aorta, with laminated clot almost completely filling it.

methods of cure are rather unsatisfactory, except in rare cases. In the small arteries of the brain Charcot has described miliary aneurysmal sacs which are said to be the points at which hæmorrhage occurs in apoplexy.

LITERATURE

Benda: Ergebn. d. allg. Path., 1902–1904, viii, 196.
Marchand: Verh. Dtsch. path. Ges., 1904, vi, 197.
Osler: Practice of Medicine, 1905, sixth edition.
Osler and MacCallum: Johns Hopkins Hosp. Bull., 1905, xvi, 119.

CEREBRAL APOPLEXY

Hæmorrhage into the substance of the brain is one of the most direct consequences of arteriosclerotic changes in the arteries, and may be briefly discussed here. While hæmorrhages may, of course, occur in the meninges, and even in the brain, as a result of injury and in connection with infectious processes, the most characteristic and common forms are those which arise spontaneously or in the course of some violent exertion, from rupture of one of the arteries which penetrate into the brain substance. Many branches are liable to such rupture, but in fact it most frequently occurs in

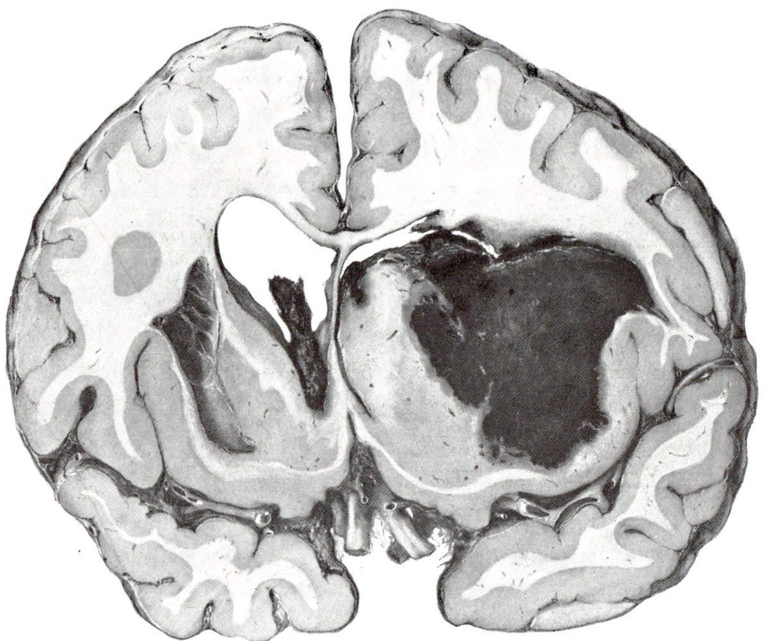

Fig. 191.—Apoplexy, both fresh and healed. The large, fresh hæmorrhage has burst into the ventricle. The old one is represented by a cavity with pigmented walls in the substance of the opposite hemisphere. There is a small clot in the ventricle of that side.

an artery which turns off at right angles from the middle cerebral artery to pass to the lenticular nucleus and internal capsule. This is the so-called lenticulostriate artery, named by Charcot, on account of its frequent involvement in apoplexy, the artery of cerebral hæmorrhage. It is not usual for hæmorrhage to occur from diffusely sclerotic arteries: rather it arises from definite local alterations which are described as miliary aneurysms. These are minute globular enlargements of the artery, two or three millimetres in diameter, which are not very conspicuous, but which may be found by carefully washing away the brain substance with a stream of water. Even the ruptured one may be demonstrated in this way.

The hæmorrhage may occur in the cortex, in the basal ganglia involving the central portion of the brain, in the crura or pons, or even in the medulla or spinal cord. In these latter cases other causes are usually at work. Hæmorrhage into the cerebellum is not very uncommon. In by far the greater number of cases the hæmorrhage is found to involve the corpus striatum and the internal capsule; sometimes, as shown in the drawing (Fig. 191), bursting into the cerebral ventricles. Such extravasation tears through the soft tissue, interrupting nerve-fibres and destroying nerve-cells. It is irregular in extent and in outline, and at the margins there are always little extensions into the adjacent tissue, where one usually finds the lymphatic sheath of each vessel distended with blood. The mere appearance of such a quantity of blood inside the rigid cranial enclosure is enough to raise the pressure there, and by compressing the brain generally, to cause unconsciousness and a general flaccid paralysis, and it is in this condition that the victim falls in the street. Later, when some of the blood has been absorbed and the pressure lowered, the direct effect of the tearing of the nerve-tracts becomes evident, and a clear-cut hemiplegia or one-sided paralysis stands out instead.

If the hæmorrhage is not confined to the brain tissue, but bursts through into the ventricles, much freer bleeding can occur, and the blood filling both ventricles and running down through the aqueduct of Sylvius intensifies the effects of increased general pressure.

The distribution of the paralysis depends, of course, on the situation of the destruction of the brain substance. The hemiplegia is complete when face, arm, and leg on one side are paralyzed, and this arises when the hæmorrhage involves the internal capsule and the beginnings of the pyramidal tract high enough to include the origin of the facial nerves. If, however, it is in the lower part of the pons, the nuclei of the cranial nerves may be injured, and then the facial paralysis will be on the side opposite that of the arm and leg. (*Cf.* Osler's Medicine, 1905, fourth edition, 972, Fig. 9.)

Healing of the area of hæmorrhage takes place by the disintegration of the blood and its gradual removal by phagocytes. Sometimes a cavity is left, lined by granulation tissue, which is deeply pigmented and contains a clear yellow fluid (Fig. 191). The neuroglia may play a large part in forming the wall of this cavity.

LITERATURE

Monakow: "Gehirnpathologie," Nothnagel's spec. Path. u. Ther., 1897, ix, pt. 1.
Ellis: Publications, Jefferson Medical College, Phila., 1915, v, 1.

CHAPTER XVIII

TYPES OF INJURY: PHYSICAL AND MECHANICAL INJURIES

Mechanical injuries: Pressure, direct violence affecting bones, central nervous system, etc. Gunshot and other wounds. Secondary effects: Complication with infection. Shock. Experimental study and various theories. Effects of heat: Burns, heat-stroke, insolation. Effects of cold: Freezing. Effects of light-rays and radiant energy on skin, blood-forming organs, etc. Electricity: Effects of strong currents.

MECHANICAL INJURIES

THE variety of mechanical injuries is almost infinite, and is constantly increasing and changing with the invention of new machinery. The old swashing blow with the broadsword has given place to the penetrating wound of the high-speed bullet; wounds of encounter with wild beasts are rarer now than those from the fall of an aëroplane. But the principles concerned are relatively few, and with a knowledge of the complexities of organ structure and function the effect of any type of injury can be pretty readily constructed.

In general, mechanical force may be applied to the body in the form either of pressure or of stretching, and according to the shape or character of the instrument, and the rate and violence with which it is applied, different results follow. Thus gradual exposure to a high air- or water-pressure will produce one sort of effect, while a sudden blow with a blunt weapon or crushing between two flat surfaces will have quite a different outcome. If the instrument be sharp or impinge upon the body with great velocity, it cuts or penetrates, separating tissues which might be only bruised or dislocated by a blunter or more slowly moving object.

Distension by gases or fluids, stretching and tearing of extremities caught in machinery, and the dismemberment of the body by the force of an explosion are examples of the application of a stretching force which often involves the exertion of pressure also on some other part of the tissue.

The effects of such violence are not only upon the tissues directly attacked, but since the whole structure of the body is in a state of elastic tension, the severing or destruction of any tissue allows those remaining to gape apart. Especially is this true of the elastic blood-vessels, in which the blood is under high presssure. Any break in the wall of one of these vessels opens more widely and allows the escape of blood. Nor is the effect of any such mechanical injury necessarily limited to its direct result. Here, as elsewhere, it is usually one link in a chain of events which in the end leads to quite unexpected terminations. Thus a man whose back is broken will die from the formation of abscesses in his kidneys, but there is a long series of causes and effects which finally bring this about. It is an example of the far-reaching effects of injuries to the nervous system.

A brief account of some of the common types of mechanical injury will suffice to direct the reader to the literature of the subject.

Pressure.—A diver seen deep in clear water through a glass-bottomed boat becomes perfectly white from the compression of the blood-vessels of the skin. Doubtless this may have some influence upon the general blood-pressure, but when air is supplied through a helmet, no great discomfort is felt if the changes of pressure are gradual enough. The same anæmia, lasting for a long time, if locally produced by the weight of the body on the bed, or by a tight bandage, may be more complete in the area affected, and if the circulation is sluggish, and especially if the nerve supply is interrupted, death of the anæmic areas will follow (decubitus, bed-sores). Thus a person paralyzed by an injury to the spinal cord will quickly develop deep ulcers over the sacrum, heels, etc., if left lying in one position, and the same is true of those bedridden by some disease or infection which greatly lowers their vitality. Violent mechanical pressure on the trunk, as in cases of people buried under an avalanche of coal or grain, or caught under an elevator, may cause death by actual crushing, but short of this it produces an extreme obstruction of the circulation by preventing the movement of the venous blood toward the heart. The head and neck become blue black, and hæmorrhages occur from the burst vessels. Slighter pressure applied continuously to any tissue over a long time interferes with the completeness of its blood supply, and prevents or stunts its growth. Well-known examples are found in the distorted feet of Chinese women, the flattened heads of certain Indians, etc. Tumors, pressing in their growth against other tissues, cause the cessation of growth and gradual absorption. This is true everywhere, but becomes especially striking in the case of the rigid bone, which can be hollowed out by an advancing tumor growth. Practically the same thing is seen in the liver as the result of constriction by tight clothing, but also in the form of deep grooves over the upper surface, which correspond with rigid, contracted bands of the diaphragm. Aneurysms which push aside yielding tissues and destroy in their advance bone and anything else which is resistant, afford another example in which the effect of pressure is probably aided by the actual beating of the pulsating sac against the bone, for such eroded bones show not only wasting or atrophy of the tissue, but fragmentation of the bony lamellæ.

On the other hand, intermittent pressure which allows the resumption of the circulation and of the proper metabolism of the cells in the intervals often causes an excessive growth of tissue, as one sees in the case of corns and other callosities, and probably also in the ingrowing toe-nail.

Heightened air-pressure, to which workers in caissons and submarine engineering operations are subjected, is injurious chiefly through sudden changes in the degree of pressure. The sudden application of a high pressure may cause hæmorrhages in the ears. Sudden decompression produces a whole series of phenomena, chiefly dependent upon the expansion of gases which cannot readily escape; the air in the middle ear and the gases in the intestine produce discomfort or injury by being suddenly released from pressure. Most important, however, is the appearance, in the form of bubbles, of the gases which under higher pressure were dissolved in the blood. These are chiefly nitrogen and carbon dioxide, and if a workman is too quickly "decompressed," that is, if he remains too short a time in the air-locks in which the air is at an intermediate pressure, these bubbles appear in the blood-stream and act as emboli, plugging the arterioles and obstructing the blood supply until they can be redissolved. In this way the sensitive tissue of the brain and cord undergoes anæmic necrosis in focal areas, and if death does not follow, extensive paralysis and other nervous disturbances appear (the so-called "bends" of caisson workers) Tearing of the tissues by such bubbles seems less important. Exposure to low atmospheric pressure, as in balloon ascensions, mountain climbing, etc., brings with it symptoms that are milder because the change of pressure must be more gradual. Rapid respiration, rapid pulse, and an increase in the number of red corpuscles of the blood are evidences of adaptation to the lowered oxygen tension of the atmosphere. Weariness, nausea, drowsiness, fainting, etc., make up the condition known as mountain-sickness.

Trauma.—Violence in the form of blows may, of course, have many different results. The commonest is perhaps the bruising of tissues, with the stretching and tearing of many minute blood-vessels, from which blood escapes and filters into the crevices round about. If the tissue is soft and loose, as it is below the eye, a blow may cause a very extensive infiltration of blood, while in a denser place a much harder knock will leave no such great black-and-blue spot. At first it is red or purplish red, but with the stagnation of the escaped blood a venous color supervenes which, in the course of the next days, gives place to a series of changing colors as the hæmoglobin of the laked blood passes through the stages of the formation of hæmosiderin and its gradual removal. Hues of green and brown and yellow finally fade away completely after all the pigmentary remains of the escaped blood have been carried away.

A stronger blow or a twist may dislocate a joint; that is, separate the two articular surfaces by stretching the articular ligaments or by forcing one bone through them. Hæmorrhage occurs, as a rule, and unless the bone is replaced properly, new tissue may be formed in such a way as to render the abnormal position permanent. Such a blow may, even though it does not break the skin, cause the rupture of internal organs or the fracture of a bone. In the first case, if the organ is a solid one, rich in blood-vessels, like the kidney or liver or spleen, a great or even fatal hæmorrhage may occur. This does not necessarily follow, however, for occasionally there are found evidences of recovery from rupture of the liver in the presence of masses of liver tissue surrounded by, and healed into the omentum.

Fracture of bones can occur in a thousand ways known to every one. It may be only partial, leaving the rest of the bone bent (greenstick fracture), or it may be complete, so that the fragments override and are held in the false position by the muscles. When the bone is shattered into many fragments (comminuted fracture), the dislocation may be even greater. Occasionally one fragment is driven into the substance of the other, so that it remains embedded there (impacted fracture). When the skin is broken and the fractured bone exposed to contamination from the outside (compound fracture), infection is very likely to occur. Fractures of the skull the bones of which are so intimately associated with infected cavities are also exposed to this danger which, in preantiseptic times, made a compound fracture almost inevitably fatal. Healing occurs by the formation of an abundant new tissue (callus) about and between the ends of the bone. Excessive at first, and composed of vascular fibrous tissue, cartilage, and spongy bone, it later becomes compact, diminished in amount, and consolidated into dense bone, which is gradually modified and adapted to give the greatest strength to the welded point of fracture (Fig. 192).

Blows on the head, besides causing fracture of the bones of the skull, which may be driven into the brain, are capable of injuring the brain either by concussion or by producing a hæmorrhage from either or both sides of the dura, or from the pial vessels before or after their entrance into the brain. A blow on the skull frequently produces its greatest injury at a point opposite that upon which it impinges (*contrecoup*).

The mechanism of contrecoup has been variously explained in a vague way as the effect of driving the soft brain substance against the unyielding opposite side of the skull, the concentration of forces passing round the arc, etc., but to me it seems more plausible to assume that the skull, like a hoop struck sharply at one point, takes an elliptical form, so that the side opposite the blow actually approaches that which is struck. At any rate it is common to find laceration of the brain and meninges with hæmorrhage, at a situation most distant from the blow.

Concussion is recognized as the effect of a shock to the brain substance, which, although it produces no obvious gross lesion of any sort, does cause unconsciousness of brief or longer duration and many temporary disturbances of the intellect, sensory, or even motor sphere. It is thought to be due to dissociation or disarrangement of the cells, possibly with tearing of many dendrites, axones, and association-fibers.

Meningeal hæmorrhage is important above other hæmorrhages, not only because it may tear into and destroy the soft brain substance, but because it can, even when it is outside the dura, occupy so great a space within the rigid cranial cavity as to compress the brain, and especially to prevent the access of blood (Fig. 194). A gradually deepening loss of consciousness with flaccid paralysis of the whole body may lead to death—the blood-pressure rises very high, while the pulse sinks. Operative removal of the clot may allow all the functions to return to normal almost instantly. Much greater violence is necessary to wound the spinal cord, but crushing

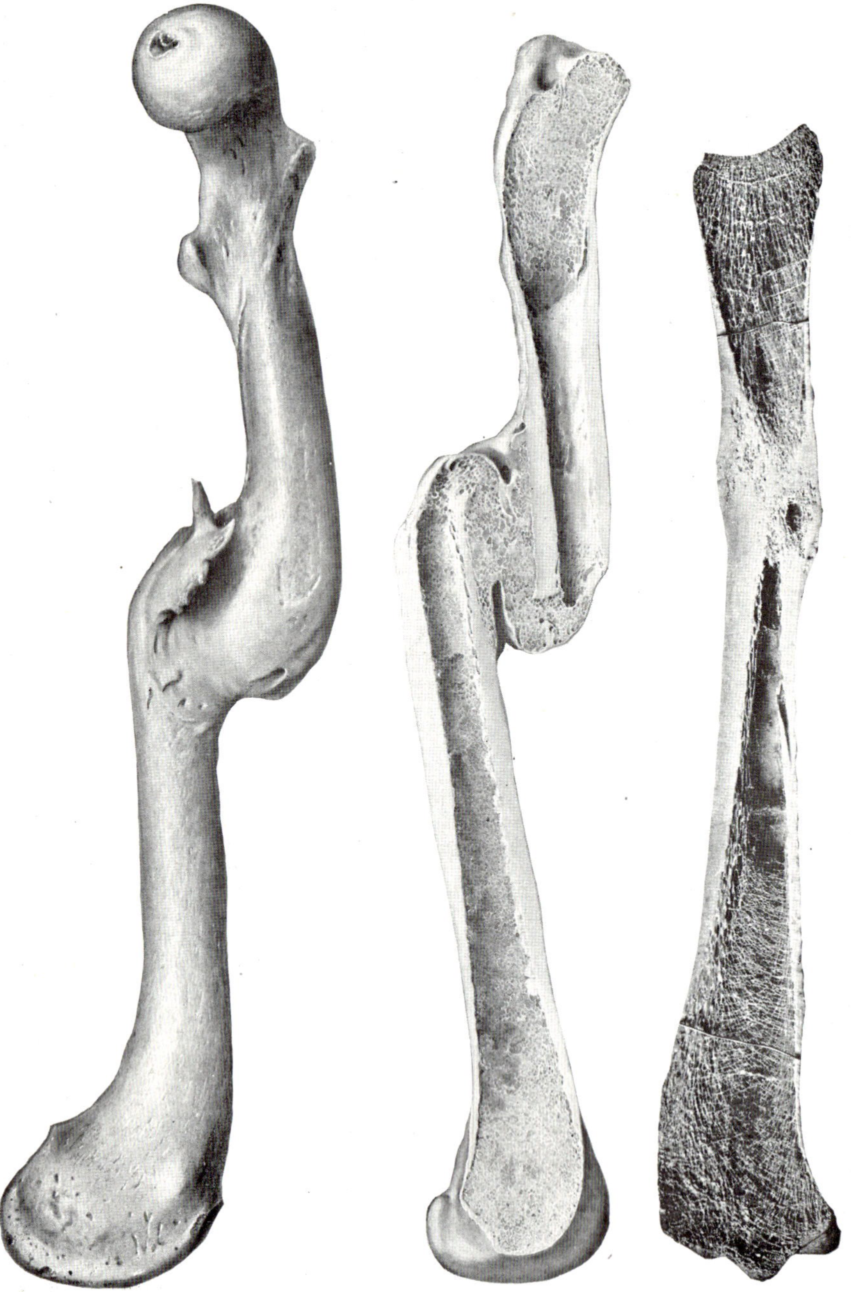

Fig. 192.—Healed fracture of middle of femur, shown also in section.

Fig. 193.—Well-healed fracture showing remaining overstrengthening of the shaft.

and twisting force may fracture the vertebræ or dislocate them so as to sever or compress the cord. Extravasation of blood in the substance of the cord (*hæmatomyelia*) extends up and down in the gray matter, destroying much of the tissue as it burrows, but, as a rule, not entering the white matter. The so-called *compression myelitis*, produced by crushing, occupies part or all of the diameter of the cord, and interrupts the course of the fibres. In such an area, débris of cells and fibres remains, together with quantities of phagocytic wandering cells loaded with globules of lipoid material from the disintegrating myeline sheaths.

The effects vary with the extent, and especially with the position, of the injury. Low down in the spinal cord the lower motor neurons are especially affected, and paralysis is flaccid, leading to atrophy of muscles and reaction of degeneration. Higher up a lesion gives rise to a mixture of upper and lower neuron types, while still higher the effect is to produce paralysis predominantly of the type following destruction of the upper motor neuron, such as comes from a lesion of the brain: the muscles retain their tone, do not atrophy, and stimulation of the nerves shows no change of electrical reaction. The paralyzed area may be entirely anæsthetic, or with a zone of hyperæsthesia at the upper limit. Other disturbances of sensation also occur. Reflexes are variable, and after a time may be exaggerated, especially with high lesions. The sphincter of the bladder is not paralyzed, although other muscles controlling urination are, so that the bladder becomes greatly distended.

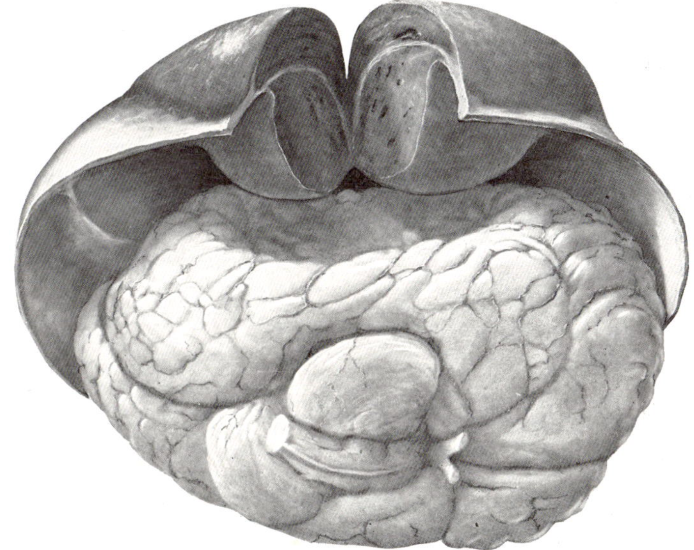

Fig. 194.—Subperiosteal and subdural hæmorrhage in new-born child with compression of the brain.

Wounds made with a cutting instrument sever tissues and allow them to gape apart, or in the case of stab wounds, penetrate various organs. They are especially important in that blood-vessels are laid open, nerves cut, and hollow organs punctured, so that their infected contents are allowed to escape. Aside from the direct destruction of the tissues traversed, such wounds are also dangerous because dirt and bacteria are carried in to the tissue. In all these respects they are similar to gunshot wounds, which have, however, a special character, depending on the type of missile and the force and velocity with which it passes through the tissues.

Gunshot Wounds.—A hard bullet of very high velocity passes cleanly through the body. A soft bullet spreads and tears the tissue, inflicting much greater damage: either will shatter bones in its course. A bullet almost spent or of low velocity may be deflected by a bone and pursue a most devious course, so that its track is difficult to follow, even at autopsy. The path of a bullet widens as it proceeds, especially in the case of the soft ones, so that the wound of exit is larger than that of entrance. Ordinarily such a bullet brings practically no infection to the tissues unless it carries in with it bits of clothing. It was for this reason that the Japanese in recent actions bathed and put on sterilized clothes.

Immediate Effects.—In all cutting and penetrating wounds the most important immediate effect, unless the brain or spinal cord is injured, is likely to consist in the laying open of blood-vessels. A wound of the heart is fatal not especially because the heart is injured, but because blood escapes into the pericardium (hæmopericardium), and by occupying the limited space, prevents the entrance of the venous blood into the heart and stops the circulation. In the case of the aorta or other large vessel, death results rather from direct escape of blood into the pleura or pericardium or to the outside. A vessel, in virtue of its elasticity and muscular contractility, gapes open and allows a maximum escape of blood if it is only partly cut through, while if completely cut across, an artery of moderate size may retract among the muscles, and partly by their compressing effect, partly by its own contraction, the flow of blood may be stopped before a fatal loss has been suffered.

Peripheral nerves may be cut through, or crushed and later surrounded by dense scar tissue formed during the healing process, and in either case the injury may be sufficient to prevent the transmission of impulses. Degeneration of the peripheral portion of the nerve quickly follows, and in a few days lipoid globules are found in place of the myeline sheaths, the axis-cylinders are disintegrated, and electrical stimuli produce no effect (Fig. 31). There may be recovery of the power to transmit impulses if the injury is not too severe, and in the meanwhile the muscle loses its power to contract to galvanic stimuli, but soon recovers it and becomes more excitable than normal. During this period of high excitability, which later passes away, the contraction is, however, not instantaneous, but slow and lazy, and almost without effect (reaction of degeneration of Erb). There are many variations in these relations, depending upon the extent of injury of the nerve and the degree to which the muscle suffers, which must be read of elsewhere. Trophic disturbances, thought by many to be due to the destruction of special trophic nerves, consist in the gradual wasting of the muscle. It is shown that constant fine stimuli are being sent to muscles in health maintaining their tone, and that when the nerve is cut and the muscle becomes flaccid, its metabolic gaseous exchange is far less than that of the properly innervated muscle, even when completely at rest. It seems possible that this might be the basis upon which atrophy after section of the nerve could be most readily explained.

Secondary Effects.—Many secondary results follow such injuries as have been mentioned, some of which can be avoided by proper surgical care. Hæmorrhage, as already stated, may cost the person's life through sheer loss of blood or through the compression of the brain or the heart; the perforation of an aneurysm into the trachea may fill the lungs and practically drown the individual. But in another way, especially in the brain and spinal cord, the burrowing of blood in the soft tissues is most destructive. In the walls of the aorta, particularly when the seat of arteriosclerotic changes, a blow or strain may break the inner layers, usually the intima and half of the media, and allow blood to escape into a space which it tears open in the middle of the media, the so-called *dissecting aneurysm*. In one case of this kind the formation of a huge hæmatoma about the roots of the splanchnic nerves was apparently the cause of paralysis of the intestine, with such extreme distension as to tear the muscular coat in many places.

The occurrence of *bacterial infection in wounds* adds, of course, greatly to their seriousness, and many mere pin-pricks terminate fatally because bacteria have been introduced. This is common in the case of streptococcus and tetanus infections, but it is equally true of syphilis, glanders, anthrax, and a host of other infections. Indeed, it is the very insignificance of the wound, leading to its being neglected, which affords opportunity to the bacteria to gain a foothold. The presence of any foreign body in conjunction with the bacteria helps them greatly in gaining this foothold, and it has been shown repeatedly, in the case of experimental infection, that bacteria which fail to grow when inoculated into an animal alone, will often do so if implanted together with some inert foreign material. Sometimes this acts by merely protecting the bacteria, but at other times it forms a medium upon which they can grow and multiply. This is true of extravasation of urine when the bladder is ruptured, or of accumulations of tissue fluid in the cavity of a wound. Most important in this respect, however, is the presence of dead tissue in a wound exposed to infection. This has been mentioned before, but from a surgical point of view cannot be mentioned too often. No matter how rigid the aseptic technique, the leaving behind in the wound of any considerable quantity of tissue constricted so as to be incapable of surviving, is almost sure to be followed by infection. In other cases the foreign body itself may be irritating and destructive of tissue, so as to furnish a place in which bacteria can thrive. Perforation of the stomach or duodenum, which are in themselves nearly sterile, nevertheless sets up peritoneal infection because of the escape of food and of the irritating digestive juices. Perforations of lower portions of the intestine are even more quickly productive of infection because of the colossal numbers of bacteria which pour out with the intestinal contents into the peritoneum. This is one of the chief sources of danger in gunshot wounds of the abdomen in which several loops of intestine may be pierced.

The crushing or shattering of tissues, involving rupture of blood-vessels, often allows the entrance of groups of cells or single cells of various organs into the blood-stream in such a way that they are swept along and lodge as emboli in the lungs or elsewhere. This is most commonly true of the bone-marrow, where, instead of cells, droplets of fat may enter the blood-current. Practically every fracture of a bone and even severe blows upon bones may produce such *fat embolism* of the lungs. Usually it does no harm, and even at autopsy can be discerned only by the aid of the microscope, but occasionally the amount of oil is so great as to cause death by obstructing too many of the capillaries of the lungs.

Traumatism is, of course, a more serious matter for persons already weakened by disease than for those in full health, and it may be the occasion for the flaring up of an infection hitherto latent. On the other hand, the injury of tissues may produce a point of lessened resistance, where a subsequent infection can be established in a way scarcely possible in an uninjured person. This is doubtless the explanation of the common history of a fall or blow which antedated, by some time, the appearance of a focus of tuberculous infection in a bone or joint. This, too, is doubtless the immediate predisposing cause of the so-called contusion pneumonia of Litten, which follows crushing blows on the chest.

It must be remembered that certain persons suffer directly from slight injuries far more than others, for example, a scratch which would scarcely be noticed by a normal individual may allow a fatal hæmorrhage in a member of a hæmophilic or bleeder family, while a blow which at most might cause a bruise in one of us, will break the femur of one afflicted with osteopsathyrosis or fragilitas ossium. And in the same way the sequelæ of injury, such as wound infections, resisted easily by a normal person, will bring about the death of one whose resistance is low, with fulminant symptoms of general septicæmia. This was exemplified recently in the case of a man, apparently in good health, who had his tonsils removed preparatory to a vacation—a streptococcus infection ensued, of which he died in two days, with evidences of acute endocarditis and multiple embolism.

LITERATURE

Bailey: Diseases of the Nervous System from Accident and Injury, New York, 1909.
Henke: Krehl and Marchand, Handb. d. allg. Pathologie, 1908, i, 21.
Hill, L.: "Influence of Atmospheric Pressure," Lancet, 1905; ii, 1865, Proc. Roy. Soc., 1905–6, lxxvii, 442.
Lagarde: Gunshot Wounds, New York, 1914.
Möbius: Diagnostik der Nervenkrankheiten, Leipzig, 1894.
Stimson: Fractures, Phila., 1912.

SHOCK

This is a peculiar disturbance of almost all the functions of the body, especially characterized by apathy or torpor, dulling of sensibility, failure of the circulation with great lowering of the blood-pressure, irregular gasping respirations, which may be the first thing to fail completely, and subnormal temperature. Fischer's description of such a case may be quoted from Dr. Meltzer's paper:

"A strong and perfectly healthy young man was struck in the abdomen by the pole of a carriage drawn by runaway horses. No recognizable injury was done to any of the internal organs. Nevertheless, grave symptoms made their appearance immediately after the accident. The injured man was lying perfectly quiet, and paid no attention to anything going on around him. His face was drawn and peculiarly elongated, the forehead wrinkled, and the nostrils dilated. His weary, lustreless eyes were deeply sunken in their sockets, half covered by the drooping eyelids and surrounded by broad rings. The eyes had a glassy and vacant expression. The skin and the visible mucous membranes had a marble-like pallor. Large drops of sweat hung on forehead and eyebrows. The rectal temperature was subnormal. The sensibility of the entire body was greatly reduced; the patient reacted slightly, and only to very painful impressions. No spontaneous movements of any sort were made by the patient. On repeated and urgent requests he showed that he could execute limited, brief movements with his extremities. When the limbs were lifted passively and then let go, they fell down like lead. The sphincters were intact. The urine obtained by catheter was scanty and concentrated, but otherwise normal. The almost imperceptible pulse was rapid, irregular, and unequal. The arteries were narrow and of very low tension. The patient answered slowly, reluctantly, and only after repeated urgent questioning. His voice was hoarse and weak, but well articulated. On being repeatedly questioned, the patient complained of cold, faintness, and deadness of all parts of the body. When he shut his eyes he felt nauseated and dizzy. The respirations appeared irregular; long, abnormally deep, sighing inspirations interchanged with rapid and superficial ones, which were scarcely visible or audible."

This is a typical example of shock following traumatism, a condition well known to surgeons to come on immediately or a short time after some extremely painful injury, such as the crushing of a testicle or mangling or laceration of the body in machinery. It is especially common in injuries which involve the exposure and mishandling of the abdominal organs, but practically the same complex appears after extensive burns, and in the case of intense peritoneal and other infections and some intoxications. Possibly the infections and intoxications may be distinct in their mode of action, but in the present confusion of our knowledge the results seem to be practically identical.

An immense amount of experimental study has as yet failed to explain this phenomenon, or even to determine exactly what happens. Keen, Mitchell, and Morehouse, and later Crile, thought the fall in blood-pressure to be the essential feature, and this they explained as due to exhaustion of the vasomotor centre, which allowed relaxation of the peripheral arterioles and the accumulation of the blood in the large splanchnic veins. Crile advised massage or compression to drive the blood again to the heart. He observed, however, that death in most cases resulted from stoppage of respiration while the heart continued to beat.

Recently he has made this theory the basis of a method of anæsthesia in which blocking of the sensory nerves plays an important part. Inasmuch as this might prevent reflex disturbances of the circulation, it may be efficient, as he claims, in diminishing the shock at operations, but, as H. H. Janeway shows, it is not through protecting the vasomotor centres from exhaustion. This method is widely known on account of the new name, anoci-association.

Porter, Seely, Mann, and others have shown, however, that the vasomotor centre is by no means exhausted, but still active, and that the peripheral vessels are distinctly contracted and quite susceptible to vasoconstrictor impulses, which can be elicited by sensory stimulation. Nor is it a fact, as Boise claimed, that the heart is exhausted, for if blood be supplied to it and pressure maintained, it works perfectly well. The nervous control of the heart is intact; so, too, the nervous mechanism which controls respiration is able to respond to various stimuli, although (Mann) it is probably the most easily injured and most seriously damaged of the medullary centres. Henderson ascribes the whole phenomenon to an affection of the respiratory centre following the violent forced respiration which is set up by painful traumatism. This, he states, sets free so much carbon dioxide from the tissues that the condition of "acapnia" arises, namely, a poverty of the carbon dioxide which is necessary for the stimulation of the respiratory centre. Mere lack of oxygen, he says, has no influence in stimulating respiration, and in the absence of carbon dioxide the centre remains inactive, so that in this period of apnœa the individual dies from lack of oxygen. It seems hard to believe that the excessive respiration, which is often so slight, could produce so extreme a change, or that the carbon dioxide produced while the animal was dying for lack of oxygen should not be able to stimulate the respiratory centre, since throughout this time the heart continues to beat. Meltzer regards the whole process as the expression of a preponderance of inhibitory action of the nervous system, which after such extreme stimulation affects even the organs of fundamental importance, the regulation of which is usually so well protected.

Mann emphasizes the predominant part which injuries to the peritoneal contents play in the production of shock, and, finding great increase in the specific gravity of the splanchnic blood and changes in the relation of the blood-cells, thinks the symptoms due to the great loss of cells and fluid from the blood of the splanchnic vessels—a sort of acute inflammatory exudate. The production of shock in cases where such things are easily excluded seems to militate against this idea. Hæmorrhage does aid in the production of shock, and the effects of very severe hæmorrhage are hardly to be distinguished from it. So, too, the effects of such infections and intoxications as are found in general streptococcal peritonitis or in fatal diphtherial intoxication are, as has been pointed out by Pässler and Romberg, in every respect similar. They lay stress on the vascular relaxation and stagnation of blood in the great veins which involves decreased flow in the coronary arteries and cardiac failure, and I could confirm this by showing that if the blood-pressure be maintained by a mechanical device, and the blood driven, regardless of the vasomotors, through the arteries and veins into the heart, the imminent collapse is warded off. After all, the demonstration that in advanced shock the peripheral vessels are narrow proves nothing except that very little blood is driven into them at the time, since the carotid pressure is low, and is consistent with the stagnation of blood in the great veins. Much has been written by Crile and his assistants about disintegrative changes in the ganglion-cells of the brain in shock, but it seems that these may be rather the effect than the cause.

H. H. Janeway and E. M. Ewing conclude, from their experiments, that acapnia is not important in producing shock, but that artificial respiration can do so, when forcible enough, by preventing the flow of blood from the veins into the heart. Shock may be produced while the carbon dioxide content of the blood is high. Further, although the early stages of shock produced by the handling of the intestine are due to inhibitory efferent impulses, the nerve centres are not exhausted, but there is a complete local peripheral splanchnic paralysis, so that blood accumulates there, producing in the end a fatal fall in blood-pressure. This permanent loss of vasomotor control is the all-important factor in the development of shock. Stimulation of peripheral sensory nerves does not produce shock if the vasomotor mechanism is intact and blood-pressure is kept up, but extensive loss of blood and section of the splanchnic nerves, so that compensatory vasoconstriction is impossible, allows shock to develop in proportion to the lowering of the blood-pressure. Transfusion of a quantity of fresh blood from another animal will almost immediately relieve the symptoms, whence it appears that malnutrition of the heart may well account for the progressive intensification of the symptoms of shock.

LITERATURE

Crile: Exp. Inquiry into Surgical Shock, Philadelphia, 1899.
Janeway, H. H., and Ewing, E. M.: Annals of Surgery, 1914, lix, 158.

Keen, Mitchell, and Morehouse: Circular No. 6, Surgeon General's Office, 1864.
Malcolm: Lancet, 1905, ii, 573; Med. Chir. Trans., 1907, xc, 563; Clin. Jour., 1909, xxxiv, 328.
Mann: Johns Hopkins Hosp. Bull., 1914, xxv, 205.
Meltzer: Archives Internal Med., July, 1908, i, 571.
Seelig and Lyon: Jour. Amer. Med. Assoc., 1909, lii, p. 45, Surg., Gyn. and Obst., 1910, xi, 146.
Yandell Henderson: Amer. Jour. Physiol., 1908–1910, xxi–xxvi; Johns Hopkins Hosp. Bull., 1910, xxi, 235.

INJURIES FROM HEAT

Animals can live only within certain temperature limits, which are different for different forms. Lambert has shown, by culture of tissue *in vitro*, that there is a definite temperature at which cells grow, while growth decreases toward certain extremes at which it ceases. Nevertheless, these extremes may be passed without the actual death of the cell. Marchand and others have found that a temperature of 50° to 51° C. (about 122° F.) is sufficient to cause heat coagulation of leucocytes. So, too, distortion and fragmentation of red corpuscles occur at that temperature, and even the necrosis of epidermis and deeper layers of the skin. Actual hæmolysis is produced by a higher temperature—59° to 60° C.—or by longer exposure at the lower point.

Burns.—Actual burning or scalding through exposure to much higher temperatures causes various degrees of alteration in the skin, according to the intensity and duration of the action of the heat; the skin may be reddened, or blistered, or finally it may be actually roasted or charred. Burning of extensive skin surfaces usually causes death within twenty-four hours, but more limited burns and those of slighter intensity may be survived for a longer time or even permanently. The patient suffers the most excruciating pain, becomes delirious or stuporous, but extremely restless, and finally passes into coma which ends in death. The pulse is small, respiration rapid and shallow, and the blood-pressure sinks, producing the whole symptom-complex of shock, such as follows great trauma.

At autopsy nothing is found except congestion of the brain and meninges, and occasional small hæmorrhages in the mucosa of the digestive tract. The duodenal ulcers so often mentioned are really rare. Bardeen emphasized swelling and focal necroses in the lymphoid structures, but these seem to be not especially characteristic. There is a good deal of fragmentation of the red corpuscles and some laking of the blood. Hæmoglobin is excreted through the glomeruli and precipitated in irregular, globular masses in the tubules of the kidney; but although the hæmoglobinuria is marked, it does not indicate blood destruction enough to account for death. The blood is concentrated by the loss of plasma, evidently through great evaporation from the skin. Thrombosis of the minuter vessels has been described by several, but others have failed to demonstrate any such occlusion, and it can hardly play an important part. The suggestion has been made very frequently that some toxic material may be absorbed from the burnt skin which could account for the collapse and death, but there is no direct evidence of this. Extracts of such burnt skin have had little or no poisonous effect. In this uncertain state of knowledge it is generally believed that death is actually due to shock produced by the extreme insult to the nervous system.

Injurious Effects of High Temperatures.—The temperature of the so-called cold-blooded animals varies, as does that of any other object, with the temperature of the surrounding air, but in man and warm-blooded animals in general, the heat-regulating mechanism is effective to maintain the body-temperature at a fairly constant level. Clothes and other artificial protections are important in aiding this in the case of man, but even without them the mechanism will suffice for brief periods of exposure to extremes of heat and cold. There are numerous experiments (Blagden and others) to show that a man may remain for many minutes without any serious discomfort in a room the air of which is heated to many degrees above the boiling-point of water (120° C. or 248° F.). Saturation of the air with moisture, so that the cooling evaporation from the skin cannot take place, or a longer stay will finally break down this protection, with serious or fatal results.

Heat-stroke; Heat Prostration.—In very hot weather, especially in places where the air is heavily saturated with moisture, it is not uncommon for persons here and there, to fall unconscious in convulsions, and sometimes to die, as a direct effect of overheating. These are usually debilitated people, or those who make great muscular exertion in clothing which prevents the rapid evaporation of moisture from the skin surface. Occasionally in periods of extreme heat and humidity great numbers of people may be prostrated, as though the affection were epidemic (Alex. Lambert). The mildest effect (heat prostration) consists in headache, moderate rise in temperature, pains in back and limbs, and extreme exhaustion. More severe is the asphyctic form, in which great dyspnœa and cyanosis, with delirium or unconsciousness, are added to these symptoms. Still more severe, and very frequently fatal, is the hyperpyretic type, in which unconsciousness and collapse come on suddenly, or after several days of vague premonitory symptoms. There are convulsions, delirium, or profound coma, with shallow and gasping or very deep respiration, and finally failure and stoppage of the heart. The skin, at first covered with sweat, becomes hot and dry, and the temperature rises to phenomenal levels. Lambert describes one case in which the rectal temperature reached 117.6° F. Another which we observed reached 108° F. before death, but after death continued to rise to nearly 120° F. In that case the most advanced putrefaction with great distension of the body appeared within twenty-four hours after death, and this is a phenomenon regularly observed and worthy of study.

Nothing definite is found at autopsy to explain such a death. There is intense rigor mortis, which sets in at once; the blood is fluid, but thick and dark from the asphyctic phenomena of the last hours. No infection nor intoxication has been demonstrated. It is thought that the centres of the medulla are directly impaired, and that the extreme hyperpyrexia which follows the disordering of the regulating mechanism, as well as the disturbances of respiration and circulation, are of central origin. Hedinger found that those who died from heat-stroke revealed an imperfect development of the chromaffin system, which may have had a predisposing influence.

Sunstroke or **insolation** must be distinguished from this, since it is the effect of exposure, especially of the head and neck, to the direct rays of the sun. Violent headache, with excitement reaching to maniacal outbursts, convulsions, and loss of consciousness characterize the attack, and if it does not end fatally in this acute stage or some days later, there may remain permanent mental and nervous disturbances.

Nothing is found at autopsy except congestion and swelling of the face and scalp, and a similar hyperæmia and œdema of the brain and meninges. It is thought (Schmidt) that it is rather the bright rays of the sun than the ultraviolet rays which penetrate the skull and cause these injuries to the brain—an opinion which seems open to question.

LITERATURE

Bardeen: Jour. Exp. Med., 1897, ii, 501; Johns Hopkins Hosp. Rep., 1898, vii, 135.
Hedinger: Verh. d. path. Gesellsch., 1912, xv, 193.
Lambert, Alex.: Medical News, 1897, lxxi, 97.
Marchand: Handb. d. allg. Path., 1908, i, 49.
McCrae, J.: Trans. Assoc. Amer. Phys., 1901, xvi, 153.
Schmidt, P.: Arch. f. Hygiene, 1903, xlvii, 262.

INJURIES PRODUCED BY COLD

The heat-regulating mechanism in the case of man is rather less effective in exposure to cold than to high temperatures, and since it works only through retention of the body-heat, it fails when lowering of the oxidative processes reduces the production of heat. Our artificial means of protection have become absolutely necessary to us, since we are not hardened to the exposure of the whole body to cold, and are no longer thickly covered with hair.

With prolonged exposure to extreme cold there are at first excitement and unrest, but later the skin becomes livid or pale, blood is driven back into the interior of the body, the temperature sinks, metabolism is slowed in all the organs, and their activity consequently reduced, the limbs become stiff and weak, the person is overcome by an irresistible desire to sleep, the respiration grows shallow, and the pulse small and weak—the temperature still sinks, and when it reaches 20° to 18° C. the heart stops beating and death follows. Nothing distinctive is found at autopsy, and it seems probable that death is due to just these changes which have been mentioned, just as a perfused heart, beating well upon Ringer's fluid at body-temperature, slows down and stops if the fluid is cooled to 18° C. As to the possibility of recovery, it is easy enough to start the perfused heart beating again by warming the fluid, but the resuscitation of a person is a different matter.

There has been much discussion and experiment as to the resuscitation of lower animals which have been frozen, and the most divergent results have been obtained. It seems pretty clear, from many apparently trustworthy reports, that all sorts of animals and plants may be exposed to extremely low temperatures for a limited time, and then resume their vital activities when they are warmed again. But it is generally objected that they are not actually frozen—that is, their fluids do not actually crystallize, for when this occurs, the injury is too great to allow of recovery. Even when freezing does not take place, prolonged exposure to great cold kills. Lambert has shown this accurately with tissue grown *in vitro;* whereas by placing it in relatively concentrated plasma or salt solution it may be kept alive and ready to grow at −4° to −6° C. for five days, it is quickly killed in a less concentrated plasma, in which it actually freezes at this temperature. Even if it does not freeze, it is killed by ten days' exposure and by lower temperatures in a far shorter time, so that it cannot survive exposure to −20° C. for twenty minutes.

The noxious effect of the freezing is explained either as due to mechanical tearing of the cell as the ice crystals are formed, or to the concentration of salt around the crystals, or to the withdrawal of water from the cell to form the ice. It appears that the injury to the cell is the direct effect of the cold, and independent of the rate at which the tissue is thawed out. Rischpler describes in detail the anatomical changes, which consist in vacuole formation in the protoplasm and disintegration of the nucleus, and finally of the whole cell-body. It is easy to see that this must be followed by serious inflammatory reaction or by gangrene. This is indeed the case, but it must be stated at once that the gangrene of extremities which follows such chilling is by no means always directly due to the cold. On the contrary, it is the result of protracted ischæmia from extreme contraction of the blood-vessels or their obstruction by thrombi. Frozen feet or toes become livid or cyanotic, somewhat swollen, and pulseless, and turn purple and finally greenish black. The process is quite like the gangrene described in other connections, and the necrotic areas become sharply demarcated and dry up, or disintegrate or putrefy if they are not removed by the surgeon. Repeated freezing for very short periods at intervals is not so harmful as such long-continued freezing. Instead of necrosis, it tends to produce a remarkable hyperplasia of the tissue, with giant-cell formation in the epidermis.

Exposure to less extreme cold with moisture produces, especially in certain susceptible persons, slighter injuries, evidently largely dependent on the contraction of the vessels and the resulting anæmia. The fingers or toes are livid or cyanotic, and when brought back into the warmth, remain purplish, but swell and become painful and disabled (*chilblains*). After some days the epidermis may peel off in patches, while the normal color comes back gradually. Another exposure to cold will bring on another attack.

It is a matter of common experience with many people that if they sit in a draft or get wet and are chilled they "catch cold." This means that an infection of the respiratory tract occurs by bacteria which are present there during perfect health, but which gain a foothold and multiply because of favorable conditions produced by the chilling of the skin. Exactly what those conditions are is not clear, although it is generally vaguely stated that chilling of the skin causes congestion of the internal organs. This seems an inexact explanation, since congestion is usually rather inimical, than otherwise, to bacterial invasion (Bier). That some definite change is brought about is plain, however, from the fact that the same sort of exposure will cause painful stiffness in the muscles of the neck or back, which must be of inflammatory character (muscular rheumatism), while in other persons it brings on an attack of diarrhœa. Probably in all instances the chilling acts as a predisposing factor, favoring the invasion of bacteria, but it must be remembered that, although it is common in pneumonia, coryza, etc., it is by no means an indispensable factor, and every one realizes that it is perfectly possible to catch a cold from some one who is already suffering, without having been chilled.

LITERATURE

Lambert: Jour. Exp. Med., 1913, xviii, 406.

Marchand: "Die Kalte als Krankheitsursache," Krehl and Marchand, Handb. d. allg. Path., 1908, i, 108.

Rischpler: Ziegler's Beiträge, 1900, xxviii, 541.

LIGHT AND OTHER RADIANT ENERGY: ELECTRICITY

No attempt can be made here to discuss in detail this subject, which becomes daily more complex with the astounding discoveries in the realm of physics. References to recent works which present the subject from its physical aspect are given, so that the student may consult the literature.

Nature of Different Rays.—Radiant energy takes the form of rays moving with the same velocity, but with different wave lengths, according to which its peculiar character varies. Analyzed into a complete spectrum, it appears that the rays of greatest wave length are electric; then follow thermic, optically visible, and finally chemically active, rays, which have the minimal wave length. The atoms of each substance contain electrons which are positively and negatively charged. The vibrations of these electrons communicate electromagnetic vibrations to the ether. These waves, impinging upon other bodies, are absorbed by their electrons, which vibrate at the same rate, and since the electromagnetic vibrations of the negative electrons have the wave length of the ultraviolet rays, the latter are readily absorbed.

Some substances have the power, when thus influenced by certain radiations, of giving forth light-rays of another quality. This so-called fluorescence is of great biological significance.

Other forms of radiant energy, different from the electromagnetic transverse vibrations of the ether, are the so-called corpuscular rays, which consist in an actual bombardment of negative electrons at a velocity somewhat less than that of light. Where they impinge upon metals, they produce the Röntgen-rays. The positively charged electrons pass in the other direction, and correspond to the α-rays of radium. The shower of negative electrons, the kathode rays, correspond with the β-rays of radium. Where kathode rays strike upon metal or glass, there are produced the γ-rays, which are emanated from radium and are related to the Röntgen-rays. Like the electromagnetic rays, these corpuscular rays may produce electric, thermic, optic, and chemical changes (Aschoff).

Effect of Light Upon the Tissues.—*General.*—Ordinarily we meet with conditions in which the tissues are acted upon by a whole series of different forms of radiant energy at once, and until recently no attempt has been made to analyze accurately these effects, and to experiment with them by separating the waves of different length and allowing them to act alone. Of the visible or optically active rays, it has been said that those toward the red end have the longer waves and are associated with effects of heat—beyond the red rays are invisible rays with long waves, which are merely heat-waves. On the other hand, toward the blue-violet end the waves are shorter, and their photochemical action is intense; far beyond the violet are invisible rays spread out in the spectrum which have the greatest power of influencing chemical action. These very short-waved rays correspond most closely with the vibration of the negative electrons of the tissues, and are quickly absorbed by the most superficial layers, especially when they are colored by pigment deposits. The red and infra-red rays penetrate much deeper.

Little effect is produced by the red rays as compared with the violet and ultraviolet. They are capable of producing an influence upon cells only in the presence of oxygen. The ultraviolet rays have a really intense effect on the tissues, in which they seem to act as catalytic agents. It is not quite clear how they produce their peculiar influence, but it is apparently through inducing intense chemical decomposition and oxidation. Their relation to the lipoid substances is peculiar in that the rays sensitize them and prepare them for oxidation or fermentative decomposition. An intracellular oxidation is brought about without the advent of extra oxygen, through the facilitation of decomposition of the lipoid substances by the action of the light. For this the red-yellow rays require an actual excess of oxygen. Ferments are affected also, but perhaps only secondarily, by way of the altered lipoids, which themselves, under the influence of light, acquire a photoactivity.

Such effects may appear in extraordinarily contrasting forms, according to their intensity, so that at times a new impulse to growth is conferred, at other times the tissues are disintegrated and destroyed. A peculiar influence is exerted by fluorescent bodies, which may depend upon the new rays set free by them when exposed to light or to their acting in some way as sensitizers. In the dark their presence has no significance, but if bacteria in a fluid containing eosin are exposed to sunlight, they are killed very rapidly. Enzymes, hæmolytic substances, venoms and toxins, etc., are weakened or destroyed in the same way. The tissues of higher animals seem to be exposed to a new intensity of action of light-rays if they are impregnated with eosin or some similar fluorescent material (*cf.* Flexner, Noguchi).

Effects of Ultraviolet Rays.—The sun's light contains the ultraviolet rays, together with all the others, but they are produced much more abundantly by the electric arc and other artificial light. We may consider their pathological effects and their therapeutic use in pathological conditions.

Exposure to the sun or its reflected rays (from the surface of water or snow) produces the familiar sunburn. This is far more intense upon the tops of high mountains than at the sea-level, where the ultraviolet rays are to a great extent absorbed by the thick layer of the atmosphere.

The effect is not noticed at once, but after some hours there comes on an intense inflammatory reaction which is painful and often accompanied by blisters. The conjunctivæ also become inflamed. Evidently there is definite injury to the skin, for layers of it peel off after the inflammation has subsided. The blisters may leave white, scarred patches with pigmented border. Pigment is increased in the skin, and is recognized as distinctively protective in its function. Every one is familiar with the people who burn, others who acquire freckles, and still others who tan gradually to a dark brown without much suffering. The dark pigmentation of southern races and of negroes is evidently a protective adaptation for those living in hot countries.

Histologically, the epidermis in the sunburned place is found loosened and vacuolated, exudate permeates the corium, blood-vessels are widened, and in every respect the inflammatory reaction is like that produced by some mild chemical irritant. Occasionally the repetition of such sunburn in certain persons produces a chronic condition of pigmentation and excessive keratinization which may lead to cancer formation (the so-called *xeroderma pigmentosum*). In other persons the subject of certain diseases, such as smallpox, pellagra, etc., the sensitiveness to the effects of light is much intensified, and the example of buckwheat rash in cattle seems to make it probable that this susceptibility is due to the existence of a sensitizing or fluorescent substance in the tissues in those diseases.

Therapeutic use of ultraviolet and other rays is made in virtue of their more or less specific destructive influence upon pathological tissue elements. The epithelioid cells of cutaneous tuberculosis (*lupus vulgaris*) are especially susceptible to this effect. On the other hand, smallpox patients are kept in rooms from which the ultraviolet rays are excluded by red glass in order to protect their sensitized skin.

The Effects of x-rays and Radium on the Tissues.—In an x-ray tube the rays which start from the kathode and play on the anode (kathode rays) are really streams of negative electrons which impinge upon the metallic anode, and there cause the production of electromagnetic vibrations of the ether which are very short, very irregular, and discontinuous. These are the Röntgen-rays. There is a stream of positively charged electrons passing in the opposite direction, which, if the kathode is perforated, pass through the holes and are, therefore, called channel rays. From radium there are given off analogous rays, the α-rays, which, like the channel rays, are really a corpuscular stream of positively charged electrons swung off from the decomposing atom, while the similarly discharged stream of negatively charged electrons constitutes the β-rays, which correspond with the kathode rays. These, through striking on metal or glass, produce γ-rays, in just the same way as the kathode rays produce the Röntgen-rays. They are like the Röntgen-rays, but have a much greater power of penetration.

By the use of adequate filters the effect of the different rays can be analyzed.

Röntgen-rays have little injurious effect upon bacteria, but the α- and β-rays from radium kill them directly, although they do not render the medium in which they grow poisonous to them, as light-rays do. Toxins are variously affected, but the toxalbumins, such as snake venoms, are weakened by radium-rays.

In the case of animals and man, the action of Röntgen-rays and radium-rays is very similar, the β-rays behaving like the kathode rays. Their effects have been studied especially in certain susceptible persons, in whom the so-called x-ray burns have appeared after a relatively short exposure for diagnostic, or therapeutic purposes, and also in radiologists who have been careless in exposing their hands in operating the apparatus. Now that protection is afforded the radiologist by leaden screens, and the patient screened by a thick aluminum plate, the corpuscular rays which seem responsible for the injurious effects are eliminated, and burns are becoming a matter of history.

The Skin.—Although in some cases a reddening of the skin appears at once, this is usually due to heat, and the real effects of the burn become evident only after a long latent period of about two weeks. Then the skin becomes swollen and reddened, the hairs fall out, and a pigmentation appears. Blisters and excoriations with fibrinous exudate may persist for a time, or the skin becomes a necrotic slough over the affected area. Such ulcers as result from the discharge of this dead tissue show only slow attempts at healing, and repair is never complete, as is pointed out by Wolbach in some of his cases examined many years after the last exposure.

The hands of radiologists show best the chronic effects of long-repeated brief exposure, the lesions dating usually from the early days of radiology, when they neglected or were ignorant of screens. Really dreadful distortion and disfigurement have resulted in many of these men. The skin is dry, reddened, and scaly, with painful fissures and cracks here and there which refuse to heal, or after healing give place to others. The hairs are lost, and with the later atrophy of the skin sweat-glands also disappear. More extensive ulcerations, which are likewise very persistent, occur. The nails are thin and brittle, and are usually badly split and broken.

Wolbach has described the histological changes in many cases, and finds that the epidermis in places produces excessive dense keratinized layers; in other places the cells maintain their plump, deeply staining nucleus, and show no tendency to keratinization. At times vacuolated and evidently in process of downfall, the epidermal cells are often found in active mitosis growing downward into the corium. The corium is indurated in its depths, rarefied in the more superficial layers, where it becomes poor in cells and blood-vessels, and may show areas of necrosis. The capillaries which are there often become greatly distended, and are even so much widened as to give the appearance of telangiectases, through the skin. Such wide capillaries often become thrombosed, and Wolbach describes the invasion of these by the growing epithelial cells. Obliteration of arteries and veins and of capillaries in these layers of the skin by changes in the endothelium and by thrombosis and later organization, seems to him responsible for much of the necrosis in the corium and the inability to heal. With the destruction of the corium in foci, the epidermis is stimulated to grow down, invading unusual positions. It is not surprising, therefore, to find that this brings about actual epithelial tumor growth. There are many cases in which a proliferation of the epithelium, at first indefinite, later becomes recognizable as an actively growing skin cancer, which destroys the tissues in its line of progress and metastasizes into other organs. More will be said of this later, as it offers a point at which the study of cancer development seems promising.

The Blood-forming Organs.—Prolonged exposure to *x*-rays quickly diminishes the number of lymphocytes in circulation; the other leucocytes are affected slightly, but the red corpuscles seem, if anything, to increase in number. Brief exposure, on the contrary, causes an increase in the lymphocytes. Cases of leukæmia treated with *x*-rays sometimes show an extraordinary reduction of the white cells in the blood, while the red corpuscles are unaffected. Doubtless the influence is upon the blood-forming organs, which are especially sensitive to these rays. The spleen is quickly reduced in size and becomes much pigmented. In the thymus the lymphocytes disappear rapidly, and even the framework of epithelial cells is injured. Lymph-glands lose their lymphocytes and become mere skeleton frameworks. In the bone-marrow the red corpuscles do not suffer, but the lymphocytes and myelocytes are destroyed.

An animal thus deprived of its lymphocytes has been shown by Murphy to be far more than normally susceptible to tumor implantations and also to tuberculosis. On the other hand, Sittenfield and Kessel have thought they observed a retardation of the invasion of tubercle bacilli after exposure to *x*-rays.

Genital Glands.—Testes and ovaries are also highly susceptible to the injurious influence of the radiation, the cells of the testicular tubules which produce the spermatozoa being especially affected there, while interstitial cells of Leydig and Sertoli cells are apparently resistant. After sufficiently long exposure the spermatic fluid is found to be devoid of spermatozoa.

In the same way the Graafian follicles in the ovary suffer, although it is less easy to determine whether complete sterility is produced in that way.

Other Organs.—In all the other organs similar, if less definite, changes are produced, destructive when the exposure is intense enough, but rather stimulating to proliferation and cell division when less intense. Experimental radiation of developing eggs and embryos usually produces either death or the development of malformations of all sorts.

Pathological tissues seem especially susceptible to these rays, whether derived from radium or the *x*-ray tube, and an enormous amount of work has been done in the attempt to destroy cancer growths by their application, as well as in the treatment of various infectious diseases in the skin and other accessible situations. In general it may be said that while much destruction of tumor cells can be effected, the complete annihilation of a tumor is always questionable, since the rays are so readily absorbed by the overlying tissue. Hence the frequent recurrences from deep-lying cells which have escaped. On this account the method offers hope of cure only in tumors which are quite superficial. Even with the most careful filtration of the injurious corpuscular rays it seems impossible to have the others penetrate in sufficient intensity to kill tumor cells without doing other injury.

EFFECTS OF ELECTRICITY

Electric waves, such as the Hertzian waves, are not known to have any effect upon living beings. Most important are the effects of the passage, through the body, of powerful currents of electricity from artificial sources or from lightning.

Judicial electrocution or the accidental contact of the body with the conductors of some light or power current furnishes examples of the former. In electrocution the contact is carefully arranged, so that the current will pass through the nervous system. In accidents it usually happens that the person touches an overhanging conductor and allows the escape of the current through his body to the ground, or forms with his body a short circuit between two conductors. In the case of lightning he becomes in the same way a conductor through which the discharge from the cloud passes to the earth.

Except for the so-called lightning figures, which Jellinek ascribes to paralysis of blood-vessels, and which are branching red lines radiating over the skin, the effects of lightning and the passage of the electric current are the same.

Fatal shocks may be produced by a direct current with electromotive force of 500 volts. With alternating currents the effect depends partly upon the rapidity of alternation, and when this is extremely rapid, as in the Tesla currents, its passage may become quite harmless. The effect of such electric shocks depends largely upon the resistance of the skin and of the whole body, and differs in different animals. Horses whose resistance to conduction is very slight are especially sensitive.

The pathological effects are most evident in the skin and underlying tissues, where at the point of contact deep burns are produced, often destroying the tissue down to the bone. At the point where the current leaves the body a similar charred wound may be found, with an appearance almost like that of a gunshot wound, a resemblance which is often intensified by the singeing of the neighboring skin and by the radiating tears in the tissue. These wounds in non-fatal cases are, like x-ray burns, extraordinarily persistent and hard to heal. The exact cause of death is not clear, since little is to be observed in the internal organs aside from small hæmorrhages and the curious, irregular streaks of contraction and hyaline change in the muscles described by Schmidt. There are great changes in blood-pressure and evidences of shock, but whether these are due to changes in the medulla oblongata or to direct action upon the heart it is impossible to say.

LITERATURE

Aschoff: Krehl and Marchand, Handb. d. allg. Path., 1908, i, 144.
Councilman and Magrath: "Xeroderma pigmentosum," Jour. Med. Research, 1909, xxi, 331.
Flexner and Noguchi; Noguchi: Jour. Exp. Med., 1906, viii, 1, 252, 268; 1907, ix, 281, 291; 1908, x, 30.
Heineke: Mitth. a. d. Grenz. d. Med. u. Chir., 1905, xiv, 21.
Jellinek: Elektropathologie, Stuttgart, 1903.
Murphy: Jour. Exp. Med., 1914, xx, 397.
Porter: Jour. Med. Research, 1909, xxi, 357.
v. Schläpfer: Pflüger's Arch., 1905, cviii, 537; 1906, cxiv, 301.
Schmidt: Verh. d. Deutsch. path. Gesellsch., 1910, xiv, 218.
Wolbach: Jour. Med. Research, 1909, xxi, 415.

CHAPTER XIX

TYPES OF INJURY (Continued).—CHEMICAL INJURIES

Nature of poisons: their varying effects. Reaction of organism; elimination, detoxication, resistance. Auto-intoxication. Poisoning by illuminating gas, corrosive substances, cyanides. Chloroform, alcohol, metallic poisons, etc.

CHEMICAL INJURIES

Nature of Poisons.—Injurious chemical substances or poisons are those which enter into chemical reaction with the tissues in such a way as to injure them. All the activities of the body are based on chemical reactions, and many substances which we regard as foods are necessary and helpful to these chemical processes. Others which prevent them or actually destroy the structure of the cells are poisons.

Many of the substances which derange the activities of the cells do so only temporarily, and are changed into some harmless form or excreted completely before long. It is difficult to say, therefore, in many cases, whether or not we should call them poisons, but in some instances the repetition, through years, of the slight effects of single doses leaves the organs much altered, and we realize, in recognizing this chronic poisoning, that each dose had its own injurious effect.

It is essential to the complete understanding of the action of a poison that we should know its chemical composition, and that of the protoplasm with which it comes into relation, as well as the nature of the interaction. Perhaps even more important is a knowledge of the chemical process through which the cell carries on its function, and in which the poison interferes at some point, but at present it is only in the rarest instances that we possess all this information in accurate detail.

The study of all types of poisons is the province of toxicology, but it is equally interesting to the student of pathology for whom the structural changes and alterations of function form the subject of investigation. These are so manifold that no attempt can be made to describe them here, and we must be content with an outline of the principles involved.

Varying Effects of Poisons.—Without knowing why, we realize that the effects of many poisons vary greatly with their quantity and concentration, so that while small doses stimulate the tissues to intensified biological activity, larger or more concentrated doses have the opposite effect, probably because they render impossible some part of this activity. Often this is effected through making the tissue at first more sensitive, and then less sensitive, to the normal stimuli.

When a poison produces definite structural changes in the cells, its effect, so far as those cells are concerned, is permanent, although the animal may recover in virtue of the great reserve power of every organ, which can, with the remnant of its tissue, carry on the whole function long enough to tide over the crisis and allow new cells to form and repair the loss. But if, as is so common, the poisoning is repeated frequently, the efforts at compensation and repair finally become inadequate, and the man with advanced chronic nephritis dies from the effects of renal insufficiency.

The extraordinary resources in the face of such attacks, and the long life that may be dragged out with such injured organs, are very striking, in contrast with the sudden violent symptoms and death which follow a rapid and extensive destruction of their tissues. Of course, in the latter case the margin of safety is overstepped, and there is not enough tissue left alive to carry on the organ's function, but in the former, where the destruction is gradual, there is a chance for accommodation to the reduced efficiency of the organ.

Unlike these poisons, there are others whose action is a temporary or invisible one; the functions of the tissue elements are disturbed only while the poison is dissolved in their fluids, and quickly return to the normal when it is washed away. A familiar example is found in the awakening from narcosis, during which the ether or chloroform is thought to be dissolved in the lipoids of the brain-cells.

The body has numerous fairly effective methods of removing poisonous substances, or even of protecting itself against their action. Irritating corrosive substances are vomited from the stomach, which throws out a thick, tough layer of tenacious mucus to protect its mucosa against what remains. Elimination of poisons is hurried by the development of diarrhœa, but also occurs, in the case of volatile substances, through the breath, and in the case of many others through the kidneys or the intestinal mucosa.

In the case of some poisons, such as arsenic, opium, cocaine, alcohol, etc., it is a matter of common knowledge that habitués become able to take far larger doses than other people without any poisonous effect. The explanations attempted for this are very unsatisfactory, especially, perhaps, with regard to the hunger for morphine and alcohol which these people develop when the drugs are denied them, and which often produces such stormy symptoms. No such theory as Ehrlich has devised for the immunity or resistance which comes after poisoning with bacterial or animal poisons will apply here, for the mechanism seems to be quite different and is still to be discovered. In the case of arsenic it is said that the larger and larger doses of the drug fail to poison because the intestinal mucosa acquires the power of refusing to absorb it, so that even in a person able to swallow an enormous dose without any ill effects the subcutaneous injection of the same material is just as poisonous in small doses as it would be to the most unaccustomed person.

The mechanism of resistance to bacterial toxins, snake venoms, and some related plant poisons, such as ricin and abrin, has been detailed elsewhere. (*Cf.* Zinsser.) Its far-reaching importance cannot be overestimated, but even this mechanism may be turned to unfortunate use at times, as it seems to be in producing the anaphylactic poisoning and injury to the tissues (Longcope, Jobling).

On the other hand, there are some poisons, such as strychnine and digitalis, which have a so-called cumulative effect, in that successive doses seem to build up their effect upon those which have gone before, and act with increasing intensity.

While rapid elimination and variously acquired resistance thus work toward the warding-off of the effects of many poisons, there are many which are neutralized in other ways by losing their chemical characters under the influence of the body. Inorganic poisons, when they are simple combinations in the form of a salt, are dissociated as electrolytes in the body fluids, and the action is an action of separate ions. Arsenic, mercury, and lead act in this way, as kations, in virtue of their metallic peculiarities, while the anion in sodium bromide or fluoride or iodide is the one which appears as a poison. When the combination is very stable and complex, these metals may be introduced in forms in which they are not easily dissociated, and then fail to unfold their characteristic poisonous effects. It is further true that combinations of atoms, in themselves innocuous, may acquire, in virtue of their peculiar arrangement, toxic characters of the greatest intensity. Therefore it is not surprising that mere processes of oxidation may sometimes be capable of disarranging this fatal combination and rendering the poison inert. Similarly, synthetic combinations may occur with the same result—carbolic acid, in itself a violent poison, becomes harmless in the form of a double ethereal sulphate, while other substances are decomposed, sometimes to render them innocent, at other times only to liberate a more poisonous combination.

Interesting and complex antagonisms between various inorganic substances occur in their action upon cells, and in so far as they are not mere precipitations of the poison, are very hard to explain. Meltzer has shown that the injection of a calcium salt will awake instantly, from the deepest coma, a rabbit poisoned with magnesium, and the papers of J. Loeb throw much light upon similar antagonistic action between calcium and sodium or potassium salts, and many others, as tested on developing eggs, muscular activity, etc. He at least proves that it is not merely the neutralization of differently charged ions.

No effort shall be made here to give a classification of poisons; the student is referred to text-books on toxicology and pharmacology. In general poisons are derived from inorganic or mineral sources, from plants, including bacteria and fungi, and from animals. Of the inorganic substances, the most familiar poisons are the salts of heavy metals, such as lead, arsenic, antimony, mercury, chromium, manganese, etc., and the halogen group, fluorine, bromine, iodine. From plants come great numbers of highly poisonous alkaloids and glucosides, oils, terpenes, alcohols, and coal-tar products, as well as all the enormously complex toxins produced by bacteria and moulds, which have the special peculiarity of stirring up resistance and immunity in the poisoned animals. Quite similar in this respect are those other plant poisons of which ricin and abrin have already been mentioned. From animals there originate many vehement poisons, of which those specially secreted in glands for offensive purposes (snake venoms, etc.) are the most interesting. Other animal products, especially the partly digested or disintegrated proteins, such as albumoses, seem to be poisonous when introduced subcutaneously or intravenously; although they, like snake venoms, are innocuous if swallowed. These protein materials, including the venoms, also have the power of inciting a reaction of immunity, and, indeed, one can, by injecting frequently the proteins or the cells of one animal into another of a different species, produce in the blood of that second animal a substance which would be distinctly poisonous if now injected into the body of the first. Such cytotoxins, which include hæmolytic sera, have already been referred to.

Different in principle is the development of poisonous substances in putrefying fish or flesh. Although part of these familiar sudden and violent poisonings, which may end fatally in whole groups of people who have partaken of stale shellfish, fish, meats, or milk products, have long been ascribed to ptomaine-poisoning, it is possible that in most cases such epidemics are really due to infection with certain bacteria (*B. botulinus* of Van Ermengen, *B. enteritidis* of Gärtner, and allied forms).

Much is written of *autointoxication*, or the absorption of poison from some place where it is formed in the body itself. In so far as the proper evacuation of the excreta is interfered with by obstruction or disease of the excretory organs, this is easily comprehended. Obstruction of the intestine may be rapidly fatal, and so, too, may such disease of the kidneys, or obstruction to the outflow from ureters and bladder as can stop or greatly decrease the excretion of urine. Uræmic poisoning falls into this latter class. The absorption of bacterial poisoning from the unobstructed and otherwise not diseased intestine has long been widely accepted, but must be taken with caution, while it seems more confusing than helpful to class the alterations of metabolism which follow disease of the organs of internal secretion as autointoxication. Most of these are in reality the effect of the lack of some secretion proper to the injured gland, although, of course, in the imperfect metabolism, toxic substances may arise, as in the case of β-oxybutyric acid in diabetes (*q. v.*).

ABSORPTION AND GENERAL EFFECTS OF POISONS

Most poisons are taken into the digestive tract, although volatile or gaseous poisons may be absorbed in the lungs, and other substances, such as mercury, may penetrate the skin, or, as in the case of snake-venoms or the drugs administered in a hypodermic syringe, be introduced directly into the tissue or the blood-stream.

They act locally, as when strong acids or alkalies or caustic metallic salts corrode and kill the tissues, or else they are absorbed into the blood and then exercise a more general effect. When poisons are introduced into the streaming blood, they disappear very rapidly and are not to be quantitatively recovered from the blood, nor equally from all organs, but often concentrate themselves in certain tissues with a markedly selective action. Under such circumstances the poison often reaches the nervous system or other vital organs in greater concentration than after the slower absorption from the alimentary tract. Naturally, in the case of bacterial toxins and the less defined products of protozoan and other animal parasites, the distribution of the parasites determines to a great degree the spread of the poison, although there are, at least, two bacterial infections (diphtheria and tetanus) in which the bacteria grow locally on a mucous surface or in a wound, and diffuse their poison throughout the body.

It has been said that most poisons seem to show a certain selective action in the way they affect especially one organ or another. It would be better to say that those organs exhibit a special affinity for certain poisons, but it is usual to classify poisons as cardiac poisons, renal poisons, blood-poisons, etc. Since there is little in common among the members of such groups, the classification seems hardly rational, and we must believe that the organ absorbs them and is affected by them for different reasons. For example, of the poisons which affect the central nervous system, narcotics, strychnine, and magnesium salts must behave very differently.

Here, if anywhere, it should be easy to carry out the general aim of this book and set in order the pathological results on the basis of ætiology, but the number of poisons is so limitless, and their effects are so variegated, that any classification, to be at all accurate, must include an immense number of headings. For this space at least is lacking, and once more the student must be referred to works on toxicology and pharmacology. It is desirable, however, to discuss briefly the very common forms of poisoning which are found at autopsy, and which occur nowadays usually in cases of suicide or in persons who have worked with poisonous materials in one of the dangerous industries. Doubtless in the old days, when poisoning was a fine art, the subject was vastly more interesting.

Persons committing suicide by poison are generally ignorant of the painful effects of the poison which they choose to take, but are impelled, by the lurid descriptions in the newspapers, to swallow what some other suicide is said to have taken. Hence whole epidemics of poisoning with bichloride of mercury have occurred recently. Many other substances are used because they can be obtained easily, and this is true of carbolic acid and cyanide of potassium, and of the ever-accessible illuminating gas.

Illuminating-gas Poisoning.—The essential factor in this is the carbon monoxide, which is present in greater concentration in the so-called water-gas than in the other types of illuminating gas. Breathed into the lungs, it quickly replaces oxygen in the red corpuscles, by virtue of its very much greater affinity for hæmoglobin and the tenacity with which it holds to this combination. It can be gradually washed away by prolonged breathing of pure air or oxygen, so that carbon monoxide hæmoglobin is not a permanent and stable combination. The blood, and consequently all the organs, assume a bright, cherry-red color, which is little affected by the condition of asphyxia of the tissues, for it is as difficult for carbon dioxide to dislodge

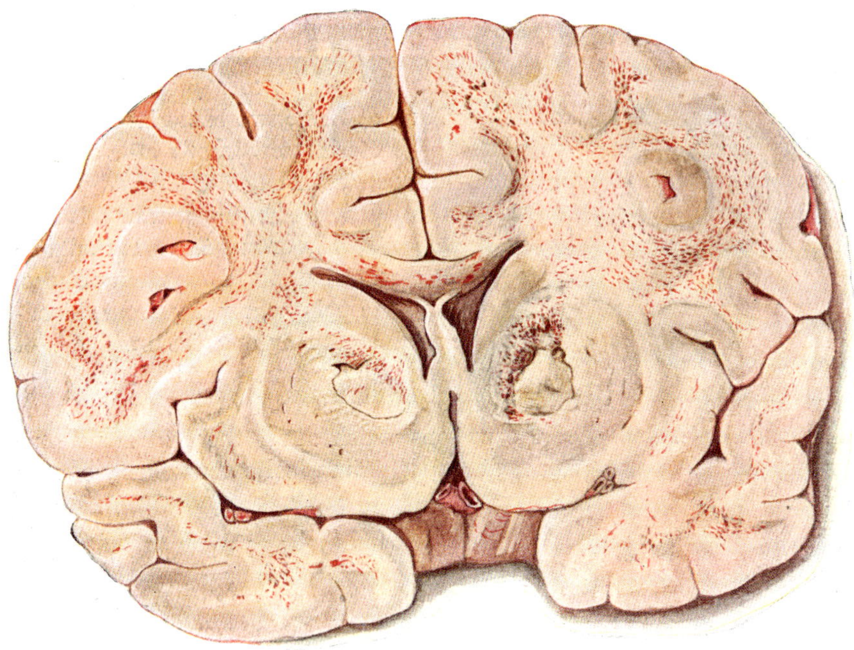

Fig. 195.—Carbon monoxide poisoning; symmetrical necroses in lenticular nuclei.

the carbon monoxide as it is for the oxygen. There are usually fever and leucocytosis, but no direct injury to the lungs, nor, as a rule, pneumonia. It is common to find at autopsy symmetrical areas of softening with minute hæmorrhages in the corpora striata and lenticular nuclei of the brain (Fig. 195).

Corrosive Poisons.—Strong acids and alkalies and some metallic salts, swallowed usually with suicidal intent, produce deep lesions in the stomach wall, which, while very characteristic when fresh, are more difficult to recognize as the typical effect of a particular poison when the persons survive long enough to allow the digestive action of the gastric juice to reduce them all to a similar appearance.

Nitric acid produces deep necroses in the stomach-wall which are discolored and mottled with white and black débris, but characteristically colored in places, at least, by the bright orange yellow of the xanthoproteic reaction. *Hydrochloric acid* fails to produce this color, while strong *sulphuric acid* chars the mucosa into a crumbly black mass.

In all these cases the immediate effect is to make the stomach contract sharply, so that the crests of the folds of mucosa are pressed together and form a smooth surface, while the depths between are protected and secrete much thick mucus for their further protection. Distension of the stomach tends to make the effect more diffuse, but food, when present, aids in the protection of the mucosa.

Carbolic acid is much favored by suicides, and is usually swallowed in concentrated form. White eschars about the mouth and in the œsophagus prepare one for the appearance of the stomach, in which again the crests of the folds suffer most intensely (Fig. 196). They are covered with a white, opaque layer of necrotic tissue. Carbolic acid is an excellent fixing fluid, and in microscopical preparation these areas of the mucosa seem perfectly normal. The fixation or coagulation may extend through the wall of the stomach and involve adjacent organs, which look as though they had been cooked. Lysol poisoning produces a peculiar effect in the stomach, and here, as in the case of carbolic acid, the deeper cells of the mucosa, killed but not fixed by the poison, are digested by the ferments of the stomach (Fig. 197). Uyeno has described extensive changes in the kidney from long-continued carbolic-acid poisoning. These are hardly to be found in the acutely fatal cases.

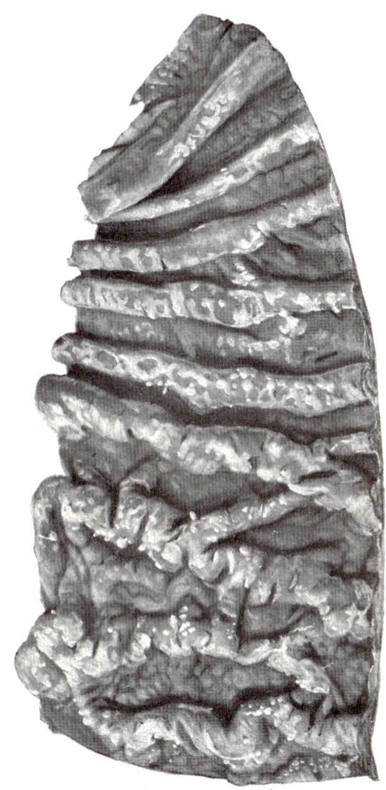

Fig. 196.—Carbolic-acid poisoning. Coagulation of crests of the folds of mucosa in the stomach.

Caustic alkalies are generally swallowed by mistake, and this accident is especially common among children in the south, where concentrated lye is sometimes used for household purposes. If they die, the gastric mucosa is found greatly swollen and hæmorrhagic, and often rather gelatinous, from the direct effect of the alkali. If they survive, the destructive changes which are commonly produced in the wall of the œsophagus lead to narrowing of its lumen by scar tissue. Such strictures must be dilated to prevent starvation.

Prussic acid and cyanides have no corrosive effect in the stomach, but the mucosa assumes a bright, chestnut-brown color which is characteristic. Here, as in carbolic-acid poisoning, the odor of the stomach-contents and tissue is a very great help in recognizing the nature of the poison. The cyanides cause death by their action on the nervous sytem and heart, and by their wide-spread interference with oxidation and ferment processes throughout the body.

Fumes from nitric acid, which, according to Wood, are essentially nitrogen tetroxide, although mixed with other oxides, may be inhaled in acci-

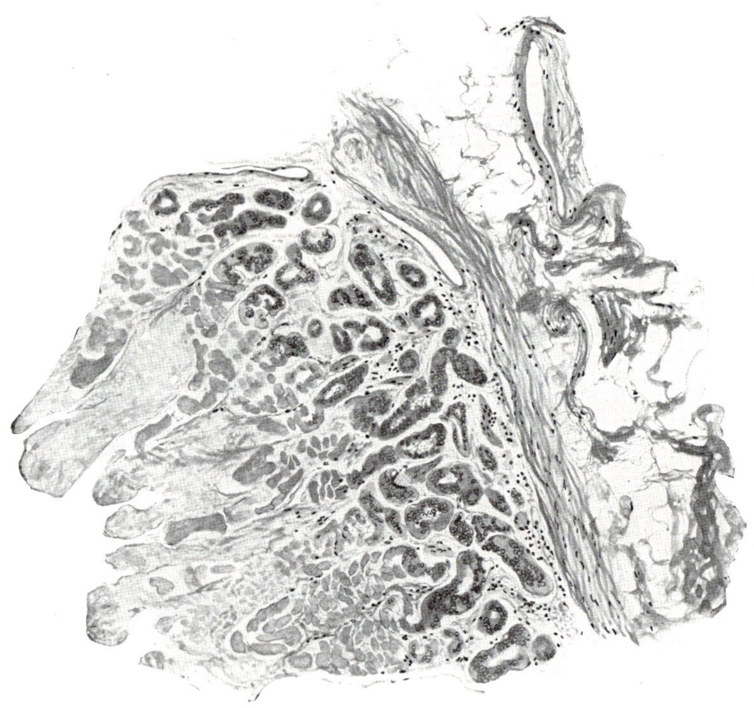

Fig. 197.—Lysol poisoning. Superficial necrosis and partial digestion of the gastric mucosa.

dents, explosions, etc., and may cause death, as in one case which we studied, with extensive desquamation of the lining epithelium of the lungs, with lobular pneumonia and œdema of the lungs. Strong *ammonia* and *chlorine* vapors have a somewhat similar corrosive effect, associated with other more general evidences of intoxication.

Other volatile substances can be absorbed through the enormous capillary surface exposed in the lungs, and take effect with a rapidity almost as great, as though they had been injected into the veins. Among these chloroform, ether, and the other narcotics are most prominent.

Chloroform has a distinctly poisonous effect, as is shown by the necrosis and fat accumulation which it produces in the liver. Its more rapidly fatal effects seem to be due to the paralysis of the heart which it brings about when administered in too great concentration.

Alcohol is, of course, the commonest of poisons that affect human beings. Methyl-alcohol in relatively small doses produces coma and death, or recovery with blindness. Its action is in part due to the fact that it is changed to formic acid in the tissues. Ethyl-alcohol has the well-known effect of producing drunkenness, and after protracted habitual use seems to give rise to many anatomical changes in the organs. The proof of this connection is not so clear as it should be, and is questioned by many, especially since such changes cannot be produced experimentally with any degree of constancy. This is true of cirrhosis of the liver, which can be caused by so many other kinds of injury and which is absent in such a large percentage of those who have abused alcohol to the last degree for many years. Nevertheless, it is unreasonable to deny its part in this process, since it undoubtedly has poisonous qualities and seems capable of such a banal effect. Probably it acts in this respect in combination with some other poisons. The destructive effects upon the brain are more evident in the functional disturbances which are clearly traceable (delirium tremens; alcoholic insanity, etc.). With regard to the relation of alcohol to chronic nephritis, arteriosclerosis, etc., the same may be said as for cirrhosis of the liver.

Mention may be made of a few poisons absorbed by workers in various dangerous industries. This subject is so broad that the reader is referred to the special literature upon occupational diseases.

Lead.—Chronic lead poisoning (saturnism) among painters occurs in pottery workers, white-lead workers, and many others who constantly deal with dusty operations with lead in various combinations, and is so common as to assume great importance among industrial poisonings. Acute lead-poisoning is rare.

Anæmia, intestinal colic, a bluish line along the gums of those who neglect the cleanliness of their teeth, paresis of the extensor muscles, resulting in the so-called wrist-drop and toe-drop, and occasionally outspoken mental disturbances are characteristic of this affection. Lead may be found in the brain, bones, kidneys, and liver in proportion varying according to different investigators. It is excreted in urine, fæces, saliva, bile, etc.

In the blood there is decrease of red corpuscles, which show a basophilic granulation, and there may be jaundice (icterus saturninus). The colic, which is very painful, is thought by Kobert to be due to an irritation of the motor nerve elements of the intestinal muscles and blood-vessels. A form of gout associated with chronic saturnism may be partly due to deposits of a lead combination with uric acid. Local anæsthesia and blindness occur. Cerebral disease, the so-called "lead encephalopathy," with depression, delirium, convulsions, and even general paralysis, is found to be due to chronic degenerative changes in the cortical cells, vascular changes, scarring, and meningeal thickening, together with pigmentation and small hæmorrhages. The condition resembles in some respects that found in dementia paralytica.

The motor paralysis affects some cranial nerves, but more especially the spinal motor nerves, musculo-spiral, peroneal, etc. It is a peripheral neuritis, not primarily an affection of the anterior horn cells, and the muscles show a secondary degeneration, although retaining for a time their excitability. Chronic diffuse nephritis of the arteriosclerotic type, with extensive scarring, obliteration of blood-vessels and glomeruli, is characteristic of lead poisoning, and evidently depends largely upon the effect of the poison upon the smaller blood-vessels.

Arsenic.—Once most extensively used for purposes of murderous poisoning and for suicide, arsenic poisoning is now accidental or connected with its absorption from adulterated foods or from various paints, and dyes used in coloring wall-papers, cloths, etc. There may be expected, therefore, acute and slow chronic poisoning. *Acute Form.*—When taken into the stomach in poisonous doses, the effect may be rapid death from direct influence upon the brain and heart, but more often the symptoms are referable to the digestive tract, where the lesions are accentuated by the reëxcretion of absorbed arsenic through the mucosa. Swelling, hæmorrhage, diphtheritic inflammation with ulceration, are characteristic, and in the mucosa of the stomach crystals or particles of the swallowed arsenic persist. When Paris green or some other brightly colored combination is swallowed, this is a conspicuous feature. Fat accumulation in liver, kidneys, and other intestinal organs is common. *Chronic Poisoning.*—In the chronic forms which may appear late, after even one severe poisoning, the nervous system suffers especially, but conspicuous changes are found in the skin. The cutaneous lesions are manifold, the most extreme being forms of excessive keratinization and deep pigmentation. The nervous changes have the character of a neuritis, with paralyses, followed by muscular atrophy and contractures. There may be also cerebral disturbances of varying degree. Most important is the danger of blindness from arsenical destruction of the optic nerves, after the careless use of salvarsan and others of the newer synthetic arsenical remedies. Arsenic is finally lodged in the bones, and may long be recognized there.

Phosphorus.—As an industrial poisoning in those who work in match factories, and as a poison accessible to all for suicidal purposes in the heads of old-fashioned matches, phosphorus is more important in Europe than in this country. *Acute poisoning,* with vomiting, depression, jaundice, hæmorrhages, swelling of the liver, etc., may lead to death. Aside from the hæmorrhages, which may be widely scattered, one finds intense icterus and great enlargement of the liver, with wide-spread necrosis and autolytic disintegration of the cells. Whatever cells are left are distended with fat and lipoid globules. With recovery, the liver decreases in size and may become greatly scarred. Kidneys, heart muscle, and even skeletal muscles are loaded with fat. *Chronic poisoning* occurs especially in those exposed to vapors of phosphorus, and is particularly characterized by producing necrosis of the jaws. This begins with suppuration at the root of a tooth, which sets free a quantity of pus, when it finally loosens and drops out. The destruction with suppuration does not cease there, but progresses, to destroy the whole jaw or even to extend into the neck. Evidently the aid of bacterial infection is necessary to the process.

Mercury. — Suicidal poisoning with mercuric bichloride is at present in favor, since the public imagination is stirred by the detailed reports of several cases. A few years ago there were cases of the same sort of poisoning due to the inordinate irrigation of wounds with this substance, which was used as an antiseptic. The poisoning from careless use of mercurial drugs or from the inunction of syphilitics with mercurial ointments is usually milder and more chronic in its course, and since it shows itself in salivation, the loosening of teeth, and fœtor from the mouth, is likely to be checked before producing a fatal result. Industrial poisoning with mercury is not uncommon in such trades as mirror making, gilding, thermometer making, etc.

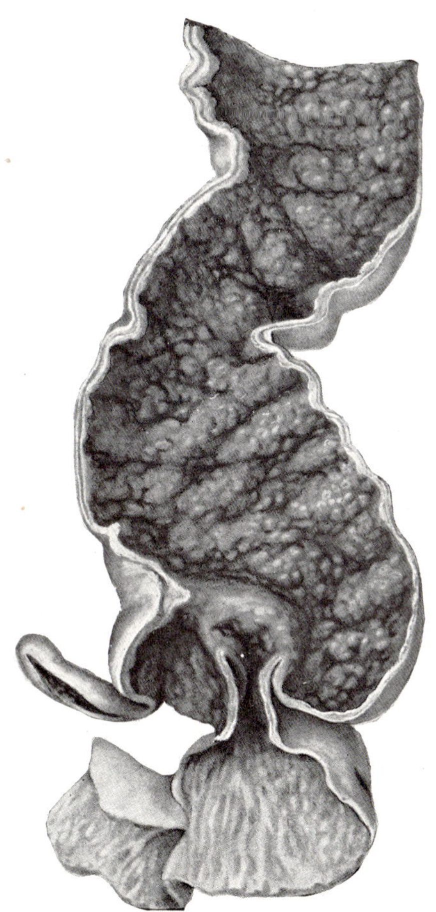

Fig. 198.—Mercuric chloride poisoning. Diphtheritic and hæmorrhagic colitis.

The acute poisoning provokes intense gastro-intestinal symptoms, with pain, metallic taste, vomiting, diarrhœa, etc. The stomach shows various lesions, according to the nature of the poison and the dose. A large quantity of a solution of mercuric bichloride may fix the mucosa so that it appears normal microscopically, although white and opaque to the naked eye. A solid tablet may, it seems, act intensely on one spot and cause the death of the tissue, with subsequent ulceration. If this be survived, the symptoms may practically disappear, but later others ensue—anuria and evidences of inflammation in the colon. Death follows days or even weeks later from renal insufficiency. Since mercury once absorbed is reëxcreted through the mucosa of the intestine, it is not surprising to find at autopsy the most intense diphtheritic and hæmorrhagic enteritis (Fig. 198). Mercury can be recognized by appropriate tests in the necrotic mass lying upon the mucosa, and in the mucosa itself. The kidneys present most extensive necrosis of the epithelium of the tubules, with deposition of calcium in and about the dead cells. Later, with the liquefaction of these cells or their disintegration by phagocytes, the calcium becomes coalescent in irregular masses within the tubules (Fig. 127). The remaining epithelial cells proliferate rapidly, to replace those which were lost, and often become large protoplasmic masses with many nuclei, which act as phagocytes and engulf those which are in process of disintegration (Fig. 128). (*Cf.* Heineke.)

It does not fall within the scope of this book to treat of the multifarious effects of poisons of plant and animal origin. They might be classified according to their point of action, as in other text-books of pathology, and mentioned by name, but except for their discussion in other connections, it seems better to refer the student to works on toxicology where they are satisfactorily treated.

LITERATURE

Boehm: Krehl and Marchand, Handb. d. allg. Path., 1908, i, 198.
Ford: "Plant Poisons and Antibodies," Centralbl. f. Bakt. u. Paras., 1913, lviii, 129.
Heineke: "Sublimate Poisoning," Ziegler's Beiträge, 1909, xlv, 197.
Jobling: Jour. Exp. Med., 1914, xx, 37.
Kobert: Lehrb. der Intoxikationen, 1902–1906, Stuttgart.
Loeb: "Antagonistic Salt Action," Biochem. Zeitschr., 1911, xxxvi, 275. Jour. Biol. Chem., 1914, xix, 431.
Longcope: Jour. Exp. Med., 1913, xviii, 678.
Meyer and Gottlieb: Lehrb. d. exp. Pharmakologie, Berlin, 1914.
Schall: "Aetzgifte," Ziegler's Beiträge, 1908, xliv, 458.
Thompson: "Illuminating Gas Poisoning," Med. Record, 1904, lxvi, 41; Occupation Diseases, New York, 1914.
Uyeno: "Exp. Carbolic Acid Poisoning," Ziegler's Beiträge, 1910, xlvii, 126.
Wood: Trans. Assoc. Amer. Phys., 1912, xxvii, 407.

CHAPTER XX

TYPES OF INJURY (Continued).—EFFECTS OF OBSTRUCTION OF THE FLOW OF CONTENTS OF HOLLOW ORGANS. OBSTRUCTION IN THE ALIMENTARY TRACT

Salivary ducts: bile-ducts (gall-stones, cholecystitis, jaundice). Pancreatic ducts (pancreatic cirrhosis, acute pancreatitis). Obstruction of digestive tract. Œsophagus, stomach (gastric ulcer). Intestine; varying mechanism of obstruction (hernias, intussusception, volvulus, compression or kinking by adhesions, paralysis, stenosis).

The possession of a duct or canal for the discharge of secretions, or for the reception and transmission of fluid, gaseous, or even solid materials, is an arrangement common to a great many organs. Wherever this plan is made use of, there may arise obstruction of the canal, and the effects which follow are so much alike that it seems desirable to consider them together, and to regard this as one of the types of injury which underlie pathological processes. The mechanical principles are very nearly the same in all, although it may at first glance seem absurd to bring together in any way such processes as bronchiectasis and hydronephrosis. As a rule, an accumulation of material occurs on one side of the obstruction, which causes the gradual widening of that part of the canal, while the part on the other side remains normal or even shrinks together. This and the general behavior of the organ depend, however, very largely upon whether the obstruction is complete or only partial. Some organs can go on secreting for a while, attempting to force their secretion into the duct against a complete obstruction, but in many cases they quickly stop all activity under those conditions and the duct never becomes distended. On the contrary, when the obstruction is only partial or intermittent, secretion or the entrance of material into the canal goes on until it becomes greatly dilated. Examples from various parts of the body will make these principles clear, and show further many modifying influences. These conditions, varying as they do, afford a large proportion of the operable disturbances which may be treated by the surgeon.

RESULTS OF OBSTRUCTION IN THE ALIMENTARY TRACT

Naturally, since the glands of the stomach and intestine open by individual canals, it is rare to find any obvious effect of their obstruction, although it is quite true that in some old inflammatory changes in the mucosa they may be constricted at their orifice or obliterated by healing processes so that their continued secretion distends them into tiny cysts. This is more frequent in the colon than elsewhere. But the accessory glands, which empty into the alimentary tract, are often victims of some form of occlusion of their ducts.

In the **salivary glands** this is not especially common, but there do occur calculous concretions in the salivary ducts which partly or completely occlude them and cause inflammation and dilatation of the duct, with gradual atrophy of the gland. Such calculi are rough and irregular and white, and are composed chiefly of calcium phosphate and carbonate.

Bile-ducts.—In the case of the liver, the canal giving exit to the biliary secretion is somewhat complicated by the presence of a reservoir, the gall-bladder, joined on laterally. Obstruction of the canal may, therefore, take place at such a point as to affect the whole system, only the lateral reservoir, or only the liver or portions of the liver. The obstruction may be caused by compression of these ducts from the outside at any point; by changes in their own walls, which, becoming thickened, encroach upon the lumen, or by some solid plug which may lodge at any point in their lumen. Not uncommonly these factors are found combined, as when there arises about an obstructing gall-stone an inflammatory thickening of the wall of the duct or even a tumor.

Much has been said in discussing the rather broader topic, jaundice, about the important part played by various forms of obstruction in its development, and this need not be repeated. The principles underlying such obstruction are, however, well exemplified in the variegated phenomena which are associated with the formation of gall-stones (cholelithiasis).

Gall-stones.—In the first place, it is becoming clearer in later years that the primary formation of gall-stones is itself largely dependent upon stagnation of bile, such as may arise in the gall-bladder if an intermittent or incomplete closure of the cystic duct be brought about by such things as tight lacing, pregnancy, or even the unequal sagging of the abdominal viscera. Then, although some bile moves in and out of the gall-bladder, there is stagnation, and even in the clear, uninfected fluid, cholesterine crystals may separate out and cluster about a central point until there is formed a solitary round or oval, slightly roughened, stone-like mass, which usually lies loose in the neck of the gall-bladder.* This is the first type named by Aschoff and Bacmeister, the *radiate cholesterine stone* (Fig. 199), because it is found on cross-section to be composed of coarse, radiately arranged crystals of nearly pure cholesterine, which project to produce the roughened surface of the stone. There is so little admixture of other materials that such calculi are quite clear or only pale yellow. Pure crystalline masses of this sort are not very common, for usually they become covered with yellow, brown, or greenish material by a secondary deposit. This happens when, after the stone has lain in the gall-bladder for some time, infection with bacteria arises around it and causes inflammation of the gall-bladder wall (cholecystitis). With the appearance of the inflammatory exudate, which is rich in calcium, there are deposited on the surface layer after layer of a combination of calcium and bilirubin. It may be emphasized that, whereas the cholesterine is a constituent of the bile and crystallizes out from it calcium appears in appreciable quantities only in the course of inflammation. Such a mixed stone with a nucleus

* Recent investigations of Stewart, Hermann and Neumann, and others show that, during pregnancy, the blood and bile are rich in cholesterine. Doubtless this is important in the production of gall-stones, which are so common in women who have borne several children.

Fig. 199.—Two large radiate cholesterine gall-stones, one of which is broken, together with several small, mixed pigment and cholesterine stones with outer covering of cholesterine.

Fig. 200.—Subacute and chronic cholecystitis with gall-stones. There is one rounded stone of pure cholesterine, together with nine faceted mixed pigment calculi. The small irregular mass was found in the duct.

formed of cholesterine and a mantle of calcium bilirubin may be regarded as the second type. The mode of its formation by apposition is shown in sections by the fact that each projecting crystal of the cholesterine nucleus is separately covered by a layer or two of the brown mantle before the depressions are sufficiently filled up to allow the next layer to be laid on smoothly.

There are other types, such as the laminated calcium cholesterine stones, and the soft, blackish green, calcium bilirubin concretions, which are usually formed in the hepatic ducts, and more rarely get into the gall-bladder; but all these are rarer and of less importance than the last form, which is the common mixed calcium bilirubin-cholesterine stone (Fig. 200). These form the great majority of all gall-stones, and occur sometimes in hundreds or thousands in a single case, although there may be only two or three large ones filling up the gall-bladder. These large ones are rounded or barrel-shaped and

Fig. 201.—Cross-section of a mixed cholesterine pigment stone which was cut and polished (enlarged).

faceted where they abut on one another. The smaller ones vary in color from pure, silky white through yellow, brown, and green to black. They may be so small as to be almost like sand, or a centimetre or two in diameter. Often a great number of stones of almost exactly the same size may be found together. Usually they are faceted against one another, and fit together by their polished surfaces like dice. Sometimes, indeed, they seem to show the effects of rubbing, for several laminæ may be exposed. On cutting through and polishing one of these there is found to be a soft, greenish-brown or yellow central mass which is composed of conglomerate crystals with much organic material and pigment, and then, surrounding this, there are laminæ, often alternating in color, of a much denser consistence, and composed, as stated above, of a mixture of cholesterine with calcium bilirubin (Fig. 201).

All the types of gall-stones described contain a great deal of organic material derived from desquamated epithelial cells and coagulated albuminous matter, as well as pigment.

Many of them contain bacteria, and are formed in infected bile and within a gall-bladder which is inflamed, because in this vicious circle the presence of the stone aids in giving a foothold to bacteria, while they in turn, through the inflammation they set up, aid in the growth of the stone.

The bacteria are of many sorts, but the typhoid and colon bacilli are common invaders, and doubtless the pyogenic cocci are important in causing the acuter forms of inflammation. How they enter has been much discussed. Probably the typhoid bacilli, since they are distributed everywhere by the blood-stream, might reach the gall-bladder in that way, but they may also be excreted from the liver in the bile, and may be found there for months after convalescence from typhoid fever. There is some evidence that they may, by being agglutinated in clumps, produce nuclei upon which gall-stones may form, but this evidence is not conclusive, since it has been shown that bacteria may quickly wander into such stones. The lower end of the common duct is always infected, so that, especially when calculi lodge in the duct and obstruct the stream, bacteria may wander up in that way. The occurrence of cholecystitis following appendicitis seems to suggest the possibility that bacteria may be carried from the appendix by way of the portal vein, and back into those branches which drain the gall-bladder.

Cholecystitis.—There is nothing peculiar about the inflammatory process in cholecystitis. The beginnings are seldom seen, but apparently infection takes place in the so-called Luschka's crypts, or under gall-stones which press on the wall. It commonly produces diffuse, abscess-like infiltration of the wall (*acute phlegmonous cholecystitis*), often with extensive ulceration of the mucosa. Gall-stones may come to lie in these deep ulcers, or even to pass through perforations in the wall if the ulcer goes deep enough, sometimes into a neighboring hollow organ, like the colon, if there have been adhesions, at other times into the open peritoneum. I have seen one case in which recovery took place after such a discharge of stones, and long afterward they were found hanging in fibrous capsules from the omentum like so many cherries.

Occasionally the acute forms of cholecystitis heal completely, but usually there are many recurrences, especially when stones persist and bile is stagnant, and the ulcerated mucosa, as well as the whole thickness of the wall, becomes much occupied by scar tissue (*chronic recurring cholecystitis*) (Figs. 202, 203, 204). The remnants of mucosa are thrown up into relief, and attempts at repair on the part of the epithelium result in the formation of distorted, gland-like structures, or even complicated, adenoma-like masses. Enormous thickening with rigidity of the connective-tissue walls may take place, and in these walls accumulations of wandering cells loaded with lipoid substances and bile-pigments give the whole a dull, ochre-yellow color.

The *mechanical effects of the gall-stones* are manifold, for by no means all of them are passed down through the cystic duct to escape into the intestine. Some do make this descent, causing great pain, and may lodge at various points. Occluding the cystic duct completely, they prevent ingress and egress of bile. That which remains in the gall-bladder is soon absorbed, but the sac does not collapse, for it is full of a clear, glairy mucoid secretion from its own walls. When there are other stones in the gall-

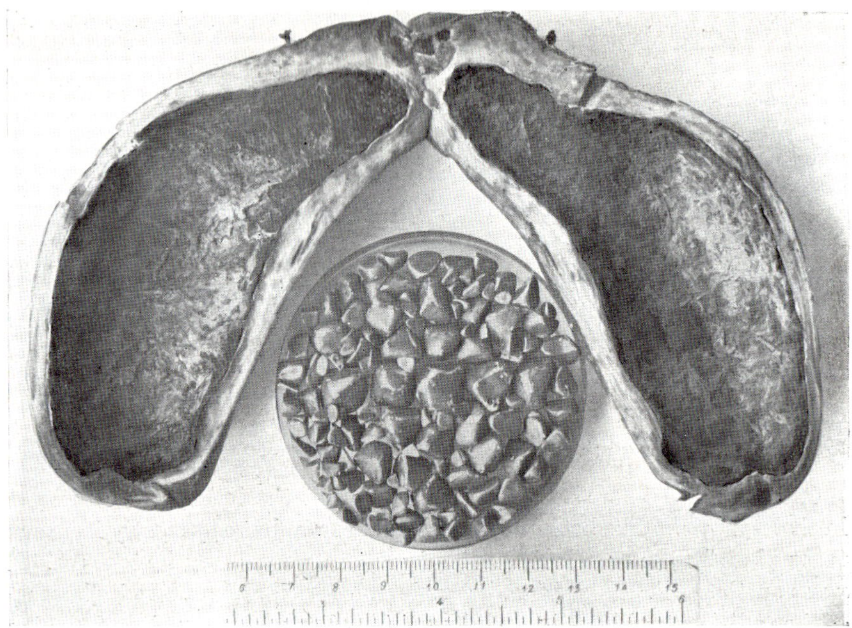

Fig. 202.—Acute and chronic cholecystitis with many faceted gall-stones.

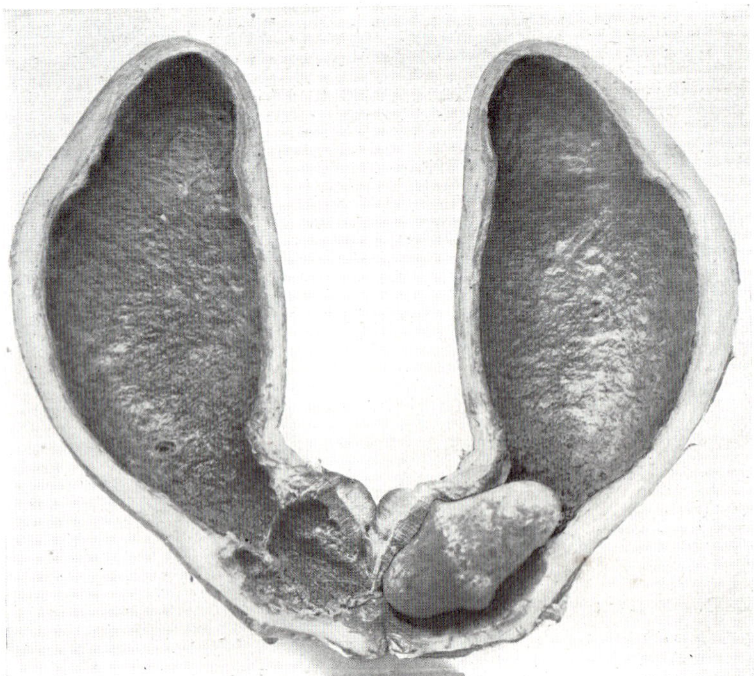

Fig. 203.—Large gall-stone impacted in neck of gall-bladder. Subacute and chronic cholecystitis.

bladder, it often happens that its thickened wall shrinks down about them until there is no lumen left, and the whole gall-bladder is reduced to a mass of stones tightly bound in a fibrous covering.

When the calculus passes into the common duct, *jaundice* results—a jaundice which may be lasting until the gall-stone is removed by operation, or by its escape into the intestine, or until the death of the patient. In those cases where the stone is not large enough to occlude the duct

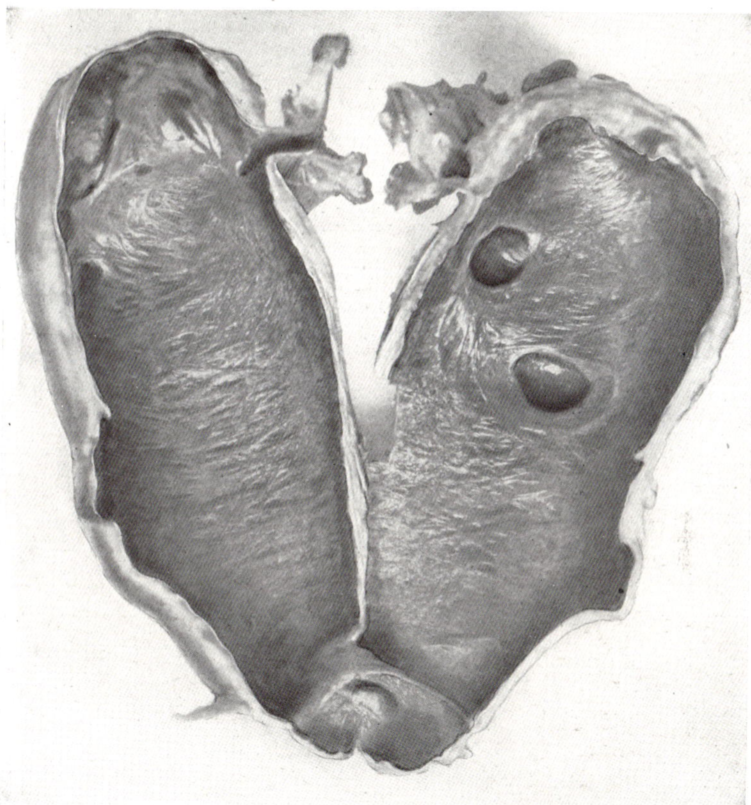

Fig. 204.—Chronic cholecystitis with scarring and diverticula.

completely, the jaundice may vary in intensity, but usually the accompanying inflammation is enough to complete the obstruction

When the ampulla of Vater is large and receives both bile-duct and pancreatic duct, and opens by a narrow orifice, the occlusion of this orifice by a small stone may cause the retrojection of bile into the pancreatic duct, an occurrence which is followed by acute hæmorrhagic necrosis of the pancreas, with all its sequelæ. Large gall-stones which escape into the intestine may become impacted, and even be sufficient to cause an obstruction of the intestine. Other mechanical effects may be produced by these large stones if they remain in an adherent gall-bladder through the pressure which they exert upon the adjacent organs; and there are a number of cases reported in which great dilatation of the stomach has followed the partial obstruction of the pylorus produced in this way.

Finally, the persistent presence of the gall-stones in one position in the gall-bladder may stir up a change in the character of the mucosa, so that

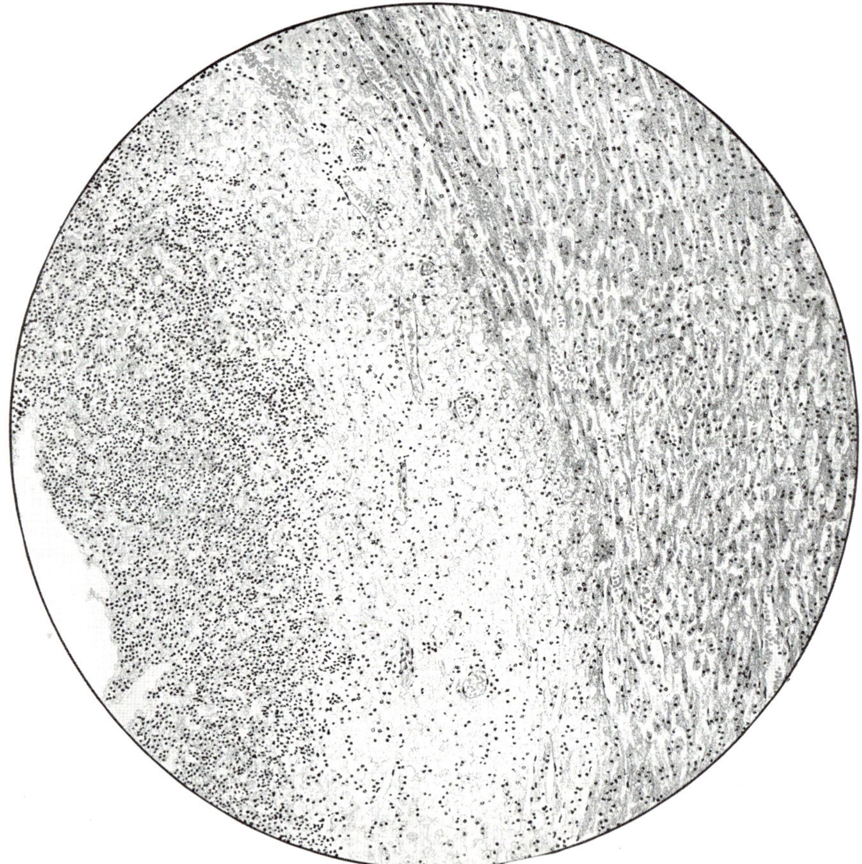

Fig. 205.—Margin of cholangitic abscess of liver, showing compression of liver-cells and layer of fat-laden phagocytes. There were multiple bile-stained abscesses resulting from obstruction by gall-stones and infection.

a cancerous growth appears there and tightly clasps the gall-stone. In one case I saw a round, radiate cholesterine stone held as in a cup in the fundus of the gall-bladder by the thickened cancerous wall, which passed over abruptly into the thin, unaffected wall of the rest of the sac. One could hardly escape the impression that the presence of the gall-stone had produced this change in the mucosa, although this idea is by no means accepted by every one.

In the liver itself obstruction to the escape of bile soon causes rupture of the walls of the bile-capillaries by destroying the liver-cells which form those walls. This is probably not merely a mechanical effect, but due to the poisonous action of the bile, as well as to the enforced inactivity of the cells. Indeed, Steinhaus, Beloussow, and others have described rather extensive necroses in the liver following in the wake of obstructive jaundice, and think that they may underlie the scarring seen in the so-called biliary cirrhosis. It is precisely in the liver, however, that obstruction of the ducts may be survived by the organ for a long time in spite of the most intense jaundice. Is it possible that this is because the cells are so actively engaged in carrying on functions which have nothing to do with bile production, so that, even when that is stopped, they are not entirely inactive? At any rate the effect of obstruction is far less obvious than in the case of other glands. In those cases in which obstruction of the bile-ducts is accompanied by infection of their stagnating contents it is common to find numerous abscesses (Fig. 205) scattered through the liver and evidently formed about the bacteria which have penetrated into the smallest ducts. These *cholangitic abscesses* may become quite large and contain pus which is deeply bile stained.

LITERATURE

Aschoff and Bacmeister: Die Cholelithiasis, Jena, 1909.

Bacmeister: "Aufbau und Entstehung d. Gallensteine," Ziegler's Beiträge, 1908, xliv, 528.

Naunyn: Klinik d. Cholelithiasis, Leipzig, 1892.

Riedel: Pathogenese, etc., d. Gallensteinleidens, Jena, 1903.

Ogata: Ziegler's Beiträge, 1913, lv, 236.

Obstruction of the Pancreatic Ducts.—Usually there are two ducts opening separately, and sometimes hardly anastomosing in the substance of the pancreas. One of these, the duct of Wirsung, which usually opens with the ductus communis choledochus, is much more exposed to influences which might block it than the other, the duct of Santorini, which opens separately. Tumors, especially adenocarcinomata of the head of the pancreas, gall-stones in the common bile-duct, aneurysms in neighboring vessels, and pancreatic calculi in the duct itself are the commonest causes of its occlusion, and exert their effect upon that part of the gland which it drains. The rest, which is drained by the duct of Santorini, may remain quite normal. Of all these causes, probably the tumor growths most commonly produce the completer forms of occlusion, while with the passage of gall-stones temporary and incomplete obstruction may arise. Occasionally, whether from infection of the duct or other causes, the mucosa lining the smaller ducts may proliferate into such voluminous folds as to plug the duct and set up the most intense changes in its drainage area (Winternitz). Pancreatic calculi are like irregular, rough bits of marble, and are, as their appearance suggests, composed chiefly of calcium carbonate. Their impaction in the duct may again give a foothold for bacteria, and when they are surrounded by an abscess-like area of inflammation, the obstruction is usually complete. When some pancreatic juice can escape, the duct is apt to become greatly dilated, and even when none can pass, one usually finds that the duct is widened behind the obstruction, perhaps from an earlier stage in which it was incomplete.

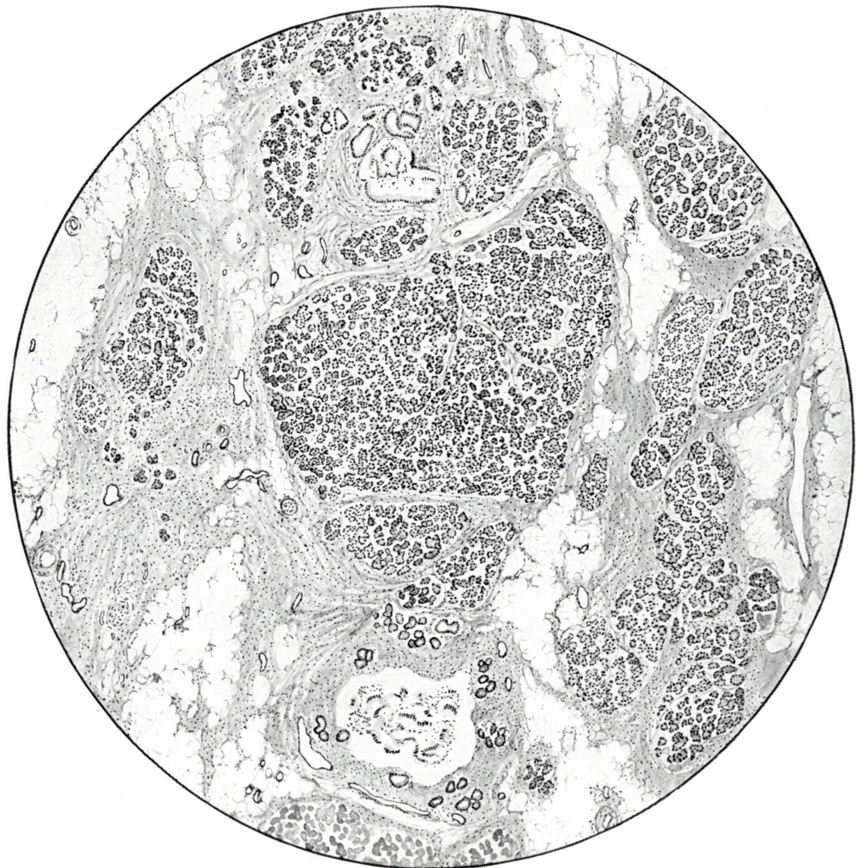

Fig. 206.—Chronic pancreatitis following obstruction of the ducts. Fat and fibrous tissue have replaced many lobules of the gland.

When the duct has been stopped up for a long time its drainage territory is usually found extremely shrunken, hard, and leathery, in sharp contrast to the well-preserved, lobulated part, which is still free to discharge its pancreatic juice by way of the other duct. Microscopically, one finds that the lobules have lost most of their acini and are hardly to be outlined. The remaining acini show a dilatation of their lumen and a thinning or flattening of the epithelial cells, and the whole of this persisting pancreatic tissue is embedded in abundant scar tissue, which has grown to replace those acini which are lost. It is evident that the damming-up of secretion under some tension and the enforced inactivity have led to the gradual disappearance of the secreting cells and their replacement by scar tissue (Fig. 206). Here and in many other instances it will be observed that there is no evidence that the scar tissue is the cause of the destruction of the pancreatic cells. On the contrary, there is every reason to regard its presence as an attempt to heal the gap left by the loss of those cells, because the islands of Langerhans, which occur in most of the lobules, and which are not connected with the pancreatic ducts, remain uninjured, and finally stand out conspicuously as about the only intact tissue left. Experimentally, we have ligated the duct of a large part of the pancreas in a dog, and found, after a year, that this portion was reduced to a thin film—a mere opalescence in the transparent mesentery in which pancreatic acini had disappeared and only islands of Langerhans were left.*

Acute Pancreatitis.—There are several forms of acute destructive changes in the pancreas in which obstruction in some sense plays a part, if only by allowing the introduction of the injurious agent into the gland. These are acute hæmorrhagic pancreatitis, with its less common sequel, gangrenous pancreatitis, and the more localized suppurative pancreatitis.

Fitz, in 1889, made clear the existence of these three affections, and described many cases. Since that time much anatomical and experimental work has shed light on their nature, but even yet there are many obscurities.

Acute Hæmorrhagic Pancreatitis.—This condition arises suddenly with violent symptoms of pain, collapse, cyanosis, and vomiting. In these respects it resembles rather closely obstruction of the intestines at a high level. Death follows quickly with general intoxication in most cases. If the abdomen is opened, there is a blood-stained fluid in the peritoneum, and in the fat of the omentum and mesentery there are found opaque white patches of pasty consistence. These are areas of necrosis in the fat, and are indicative of pancreatic disease. The pancreas is swollen and deep red or purplish-black in patches (Figs. 207, 208). On section, the brown or black patches are found to be rather dry and dull looking, and extend widely through the substance of the gland surrounded by hæmorrhage. In places they may be softened. Opaque, white, necrotic patches are found in the fat in the interstices of the pancreas. Microscopically, the dark areas are found to be patches of necrotic pancreas, infiltrated with changed blood, and showing about the margins, at least, an intense acute inflammatory reaction. Sometimes nearly the whole pancreas may have undergone this coagulative necrosis with hæmorrhage and inflammation. Occasionally the process is so fresh that there is but little inflammation, and Chiari suggests the name "acute hæmorrhagic necrosis" of the pancreas.

The cause of this was quite obscure, until Opie discovered a case in which a small gall-stone had become impacted in the orifice of the ampulla of Vater in such a way that neither bile nor pancreatic juice could escape, although bile could run back from the common bile-duct into the pancreatic duct. Naturally, if the ducts had opened side by side instead of into a common ampulla, or if the stone had been too large to obstruct the orifice of the ampulla only, no such access of bile to the pancreatic duct would have been possible. Opie readily showed that injection of bile into the pancreatic duct would produce acute hæmorrhagic pancreatitis in animals, and Flexner showed that gastric juice and many other irritating substances would do so too. He found that fresh bile was

---

* MacCallum: Johns Hopkins Hosp. Bull., 1909, xx, 265.
Kirkbride: Jour. Exp. Med., 1912, xv, p. 101.

most effective, that much mucus rendered its action far milder and produced rather chronic effects. Several other cases have been found in which exactly the same unfortunate combination of circumstances has led to the results found by Opie, but there are many cases in which no such good explanation is to be found.

Any injury to the pancreas which causes the death of cells and allows the escape of pancreatic juice into the tissues seems to be capable of causing a little of such hæmorrhagic necrosis, and it is probable that this is at the root of the formation of those

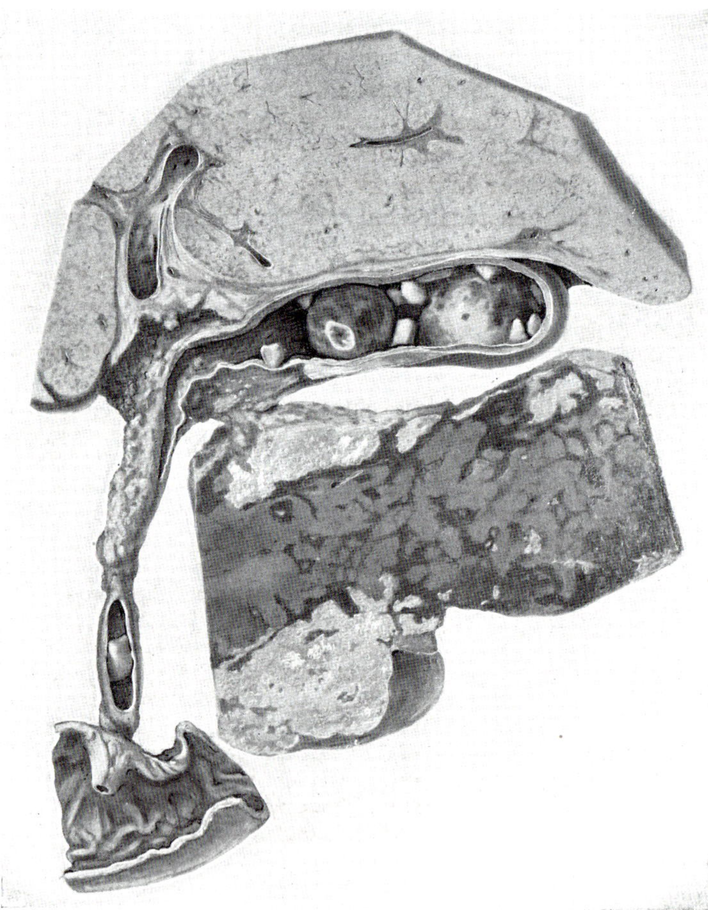

Fig. 207.—Acute hæmorrhagic necrosis of pancreas: cholelithiasis and impaction of a small gall-stone in the common duct and in the ampulla of Vater. Abundant fat necrosis.

areas of gangrene which are sometimes found in its substance. Doubtless if the person could live after an extensive hæmorrhagic necrosis, infection would follow by way of the ducts, and a putrefactive liquefaction of the dead tissue might occur. Whether such necrosis and self-digestion form the basis upon which localized infection and abscess formation occur in the gland is not so clear. The fact remains, however, that abscesses of considerable size are occasionally discovered there in cases in which intense symptoms point to their existence.

The fat necroses (Fig. 208) are due to the dissemination of the ferments of the pancreas, which are able, by their lipolytic action, to decompose the fat in the fat-cells which they have rendered necrotic. The neutral fats break up into free fatty acids and glycerin, and usually bunches of needle-shaped crystals of fatty acids are visible in these areas. Combinations with calcium salts often produce, in those situations, the insoluble white calcium soaps which add to the whiteness and opacity of the foci. Any injury to the pancreas which tears its tissue allows the dissemination of the ferments. In one case in which a small incision was made into a pancreas by accident in the course of an operation there appeared a crop of fat necroses in the neighborhood. Ligation of the duct usually produces them. In the cases of acute hæmorrhagic pancreatitis they are very

Fig. 208.—Pancreatic fat necrosis in the omentum.

wide-spread, and in animals in which this condition is produced experimentally they are found in the subcutaneous abdominal fat, and even in that of the pericardium and pleura. Lipases have been demonstrated in these areas, and also in the urine in such cases.

Of course, there is nothing in common between these forms of hæmorrhagic pancreatitis and the so-called *pancreatic apoplexy*, which is a rapidly fatal hæmorrhage into and about the pancreas from a large diseased artery. In one case at autopsy I found a retropancreatic hæmorrhage of almost two liters which came from the rupture of the sclerotic pancreatico-duodenal artery as it passed through the head of the pancreas.

LITERATURE

Balch and Smith: Boston Med. and Surg. Jour., 1910, clxiii, 384.
Fitz: "Acute Pancreatitis," Boston Med. and Surg. Jour., 1889, cxxi, 607.
Opie: Johns Hopkins Hosp. Bull., 1901, xii, 182.
Watts: Southern Med. Jour., 1913, vi, 174.

OBSTRUCTION OF THE LUMEN OF THE INTESTINAL TRACT

The most extraordinary variety of phenomena, based on slight modifications of a few underlying principles, occur here, and one might foretell easily enough the effect of obstruction at any given point. The same general types of occluding agent appear, but there are some modifications, owing to the strong muscular character of the wall of the canal. Foreign bodies in the lumen, tumors in the walls sometimes encircling the canal, constricting scars resulting from healing ulcers, twists and kinks and compression from outside by tumors or by constricting bands, the escape of a loop of intestine through a narrow hole in the abdominal wall, or the telescoping of a part of the intestine into itself—all these things and many others may impede the flow of the intestinal contents in the normal direction. Even the mere lack of propulsive muscular contractions over a length of intestine may be enough to allow the contents to stagnate and give the symptoms of obstruction (paralytic ileus).

Œsophagus.—Two common causes of œsophageal obstruction exist, namely, the narrowing of the lumen by the shrinkage of scar tissue formed in the healing of an ulcer caused by the swallowing of some corrosive poison, such as concentrated lye, and, secondly, the encroachment of a cancerous tumor growing from the mucosa. Other things, such as the pressure of a tumor or an aneurysm from the outside, may have a similar effect, and make it difficult or impossible for food to pass into the stomach. Extreme narrowing, usually at the cardiac end of the œsophagus, may be produced, in the stricture following ulceration, but since the food is easily regurgitated, there is usually no great dilatation of the canal above the closure, nor any very marked hypertrophy of its muscular walls.

On the contrary, in some rare cases, of which we have recently seen one, without any apparent obstruction the œsophagus may be found enormously lengthened and widened, so that it sags and kinks, and food is regurgitated unchanged without ever entering the stomach. There seems to be no explanation except that this may be a congenital anomaly. More localized dilatations are the traction and pulsion diverticula. The traction diverticula are common, and usually small and funnel shaped; they arise from the persistence of connections between the œsophagus and trachea, or from the adhesion and contraction of adjacent inflamed lymph-glands. The pulsion diverticula are the outcome of local weakening of the wall and the forcing out of a hernia-like sac. These may become quite large, and are annoying in that they receive the food until they are full, and may, by their bulk, offer obstruction to the main channel.

Obstruction in the Stomach.—The same types of obstruction are met with in the stomach, and the occlusion may be at the cardiac orifice or at the pylorus. In the first instance, in which the growth of a cancerous tumor is the common cause, the individual tends to starve, because food does not easily reach the stomach. In the second case, in which the cause is a cancerous growth or the contracting scar of a round ulcer at the pylorus, the orifice of the pylorus may be reduced to a very narrow channel (Fig. 209). Stagnation and accumulation of the stomach-contents follow, with great changes in the gastric juice, which often loses its antiseptic acidity. Putrefaction of all this material produces poisonous substances, which are absorbed, to the great detriment of the patient. Besides, the frequent vomiting causes the loss of much water and the normal constituents of the gastric juice, and one might surmise that this, as well as

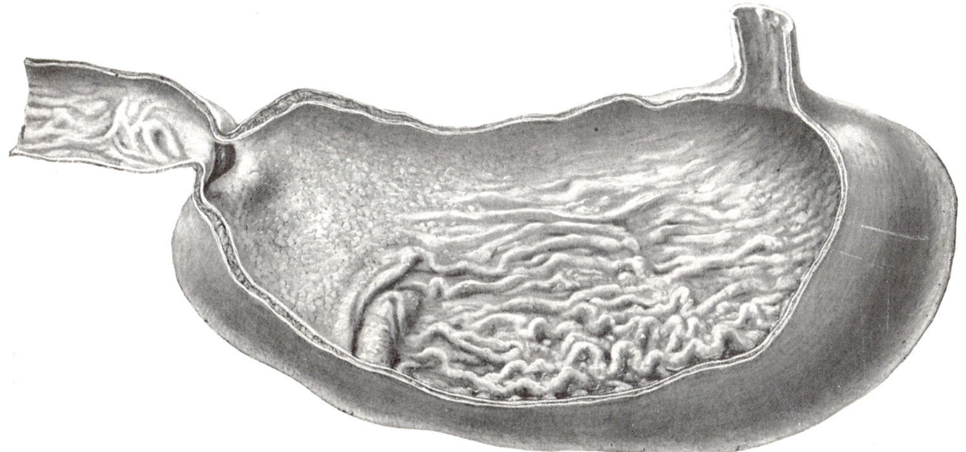

Fig. 209.—Scarred ulcer of the pylorus, dilatation and hypertrophy of the stomach.

the absorption of poison, could give rise to the symptoms which sometimes follow. Not uncommon among these symptoms is the development of tetany, with greatly heightened nerve excitability and violent convulsions. The stomach may become hugely dilated, so as to be capable of holding four or five litres, and the most incredible mass of material, dating from meals long past, may accumulate there. The wall becomes thick, the muscular coat hypertrophic, in the attempt to drive the contents through the pylorus, and the mucosa seems to hypertrophy by the production of new glands to comply with the necessity for covering all that increased space.

There are other ways in which such gastrectasis can be set up, as by the pressure of outside tumors or by the sagging of the stomach and the kinking of the pylorus, but the two causes mentioned are by far the more common. The symptoms are not acute in these cases, nor do they quickly end fatally, because vomiting is capable of relieving them to some extent.

Gastric Ulcer.—There are several types of ulceration of the gastric wall produced in as many ways, and distinguished by nothing specially characteristic. For while the intact living mucosa resists perfectly the digestive action of the gastric juice, anything like a strong corrosive poison which can kill the tissue, or even anything like a hæmorrhage, which may interrupt the circulation of a patch of mucosa for a time, exposes that area to the liquefying power of the juice, and in an incredibly short time there is produced an ulcer which extends to the depth reached by the anæmia or coagulation of the tissue. Even the little ecchymotic hæmorrhages which appear after violent vomiting present themselves very shortly as pits of pinhead size in the mucosa. Emboli in the larger vessels have no such consequences, since the intercommunication of the arteries is so extremely rich. If we try experimentally to produce an area of anæmia in the wall of the stomach of an animal, we fail, even though we tie several large vessels. Their current is instantly supplied backward, if necessary, from other arteries. It is only by injecting a suspension of coarse particles which plug all the small vessels, or by

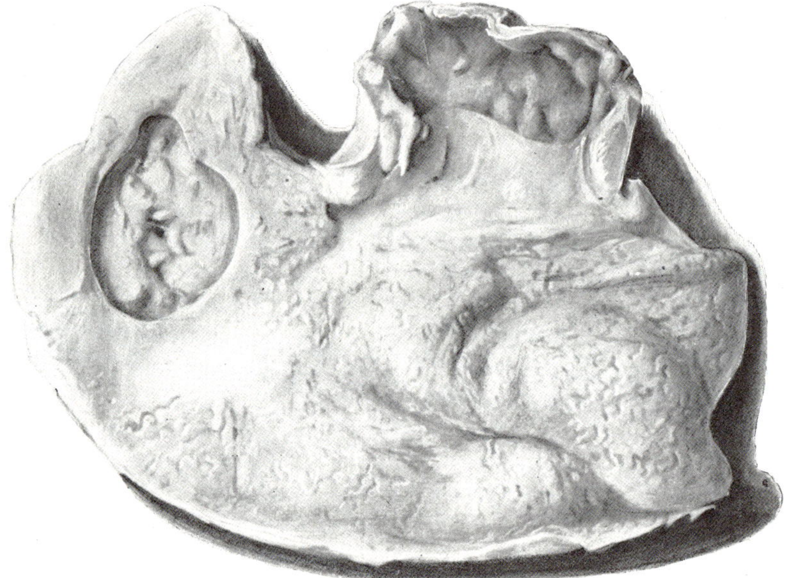

Fig. 210.—Gastric ulcer (round or peptic ulcer).

causing a spasmodic contraction of the muscular wall, which clamps down the collateral arteries, that we can produce an anæmia of the mucosa serious enough to allow the gastric juice to attack and digest it, and thus form an ulcer. But although many things will produce an ulcer, the mucosa is surprisingly capable of healing it over. I have removed large squares of the mucosa of the dog's stomach, only to find, a short time later, such complete healing that it was impossible to say where the ulcer had been.

It is perhaps a peculiarity, therefore, of the so-called peptic or round ulcers of the stomach that they persist as such. Most of them do heal, and we find only the scar, but others, although they are the seat of energetic efforts at healing, not only persist, but progress, boring deeper and deeper into the thickening stomach-wall. Very similar ulcers are found in the duodenum, where they follow a course much like that of the gastric ones. All the theories as to their origin seem inadequate, from that of Virchow, who thought them to be due to the embolic occlusion of the artery supplying that area, to the more recent ones, which attempt to incriminate bacteria and other parasites, or, as in the case of van Yzeren and Palma, ascribe them to changes in the innervation of the stomach, which maintains part of its wall in a bloodless state through cramp of the muscle.*

They occur in relatively young persons, usually in association with hyperacidity of the gastric juice, and cause a peculiar pain. There may be only one or several. Many of them are irregular in outline, and there are small ulcers, as well as wide-spread erosions, but the name arises from the fact that many of them are quite round and smooth (Fig. 210). Such ulcers look as though they had been cut out with a gunwad cutter, except that their base is terraced and funnel shaped, and may run slantingly into the stomach-wall, or else their edges are undermined. All around such an ulcer the wall becomes very thick and hard, so as to be easily recognized from the outside when the stomach is exposed. Often there are adhesions formed over it, so that in case the ulcer extends quite through the wall, it is likely to encounter first the adhesions and then the adherent organ. Since they often perforate the posterior and inner curvature of the stomach, the pancreas is likely to be the bulwark and to be rapidly excavated, until, sometimes, the splenic artery is cut into. The liver may sometimes form this buffer, but it is not very uncommon to have the gastric contents emptied through the perforated ulcer directly into the peritoneum. Microscopically, the edge of such an ulcer shows an abrupt cessation of the mucosa. The precipitous walls are lined with a thin layer of formless, hyaline material, and pass through the greatly thickened submucosa, the musculature, and even the thickened subserous tissue. There is often not much infiltration with wandering leucocytes to indicate any active inflammatory process. On the contrary, the ulcer may look as if bored through a dense, hard, fibrous tissue. In the floor of the depression one may sometimes see an artery laid bare, or even find its exposed wall so thinned that the blood-pressure has been sufficient to bulge it out into an aneurysmal sac. It is obvious, though, that one would be more likely, under such circumstances, to find the little sac burst into shreds after an alarming or fatal hæmorrhage had called attention to the ulcer.

Aside from these two dangers, the most serious effect of the ulcer may arise in the course of its healing, if it happens to encircle the pylorus. It is then that the contraction of the scar may produce the most extreme narrowing of that orifice, and a consequent enormous dilatation of the stomach.

Duodenal ulcers are similar in their course and even in their general effects, for they may perforate into the peritoneum or into blood-vessels or adjacent organs. They sometimes appear when gastro-enterostomy has been performed at the point where gastric juice pours into the intestine, and I have recently seen a case in which five ulcers burrowing and connected in the most tortuous way were formed in this manner.

Intestinal Obstruction.—Although there are many different ways in which the lumen of the intestine may be closed so that nothing can pass, the result is in one sense the same in all. Still, the effects of such obstruction vary according to the point in the intestinal tract at which it occurs, its completeness, and the condition of the intestinal wall.

In general, when the occlusion is produced by a foreign body which acts as a plug, the symptoms are rather less violent than when the canal is closed from outside, as it might be with a ligature. Far more important in this respect, however, is the fact that obstructions high up in the small intestine are usually accompanied by far more violent symptoms than those in the rectum or sigmoid flexure. Perhaps the fact that impaction of fæces in the rectum, with no discharge for days or even weeks, may cause

* Stromeyer: Ziegler's Beiträge, 1912, liv, 1.

nothing more serious than headache, will illustrate this, for sudden closure of the small intestine is very quickly followed by vomiting, pain, abdominal distension, and evidences of shock, with death in a few days if not relieved. These symptoms (grouped under the term ileus) are often especially fulminant, when something occurs to cut off the blood supply from the wall of the obstructed intestinal loop.

The actual cause of these extraordinarily intense symptoms has been searched for experimentally, and by other means, for years, but even yet it is far from being clearly understood. The intestine above the point of closure becomes distended with gas and a very foul-smelling fluid which swarms with bacteria. Even when there is no outward obstruction to the circulation, its wall is soon so stretched as to interrupt the free flow of blood in the capillaries, and necrosis and ulceration of the mucosa appear, often with actual tears in the muscular wall and serous covering of the gut. Kocher has called these ulcers distension ulcers. It is evident that poisonous materials are absorbed from this sac-like loop of intestine, which is practically like one huge bouillon culture of bacteria, and in many cases it is clear enough that the bacteria themselves have passed into and through the intestinal walls, and have caused not only an acute peritonitis, but a generalized infection.

In other cases, though, with just as intense symptoms, there may be no definite peritonitis nor general infection, and these make it necessary to find some other explanation. Hartwell and Hoguet think that in high duodenal obstructions the loss of water by vomiting is the important factor, while Whipple finds that, from the contents of the obstructed intestine, he can extract a material which, on being injected into the veins of other animals, produces all the symptoms which follow acute intestinal obstruction. This substance is derived from the mucosa of the obstructed intestine, its production being stimulated by the bacteria present in such numbers, and is purified by being precipitated with alcohol and washed. This is very recent work, and the problem of the nature of this process must still be regarded as an open one. Any one who has observed the colossal development of bacteria in the obstructed intestine will hesitate, however, to completely exculpate them, even though one would expect on that basis more intense symptoms from a low obstruction than from one high in the small intestine, which is the reverse of the fact.

MECHANISM OF INTESTINAL OBSTRUCTION

Ordinarily the contents of the small intestine are quite fluid, and the musculature of the colon, aided by that of the abdominal wall, is strong enough to expel the more solid contents of that part of the intestine. Still it occasionally happens that a foreign body which was swallowed and has passed through the stomach sticks somewhere in the intestine. This is true, too, of the so-called enteroliths, which may be very large, and partly composed of hair and of large gall-stones, as well as of the indurated masses of fæces which sometimes become impacted in the colon and obstruct it.

Tumors or aneurysms outside the intestine rarely compress it enough in the yielding abdominal cavity to produce obstruction, unless the tumors have surrounded it and involved it in their growth. After abdominal operation, however, in which the intestines have been roughly handled and displaced, and especially when there exists a focus of infection and inflammation of long standing, such as an abscess around the appendix, or a general infection of the peritoneum, adhesions are apt to bind the intestinal coils together. Then the symptoms of obstruction commonly appear, and the surgeon must separate and loosen and straighten out such loops. Usually in such a case the occlusion is produced by the angular kinking of the gut, but sometimes the most extraordinary long bands of fibrous tissue are found stretching from one point to another, entangling, as in a ligature, a loop of intestine. Doubtless this latter condition is brought about by the peristaltic and passive movements of the intestine, which entangle it in the adhesions.

Hernias.—Quite analogous to this method of obstruction is that found in the various sorts of hernias, where again the movements of the intestines (this time chiefly the passive movements, caused by the press of the abdominal muscles) forcibly intrude them into compromising situations. The omentum, and in some forms of hernias, even other abdominal organs, may be forced to accompany the intestinal loops. These structures pass through a weak point in the abdominal wall, pushing ahead of them a sac composed of the peritoneum, usually with accompanying layers of the tissues which lie outside it in that area. When the violent muscular effort is over and the heightened intra-abdominal pressure is relaxed, the intestine may slip back or be pushed back by the surgeon. But the sac remains, and the intestine is easily forced into it again—the more so as with each time it grows larger and receives more and larger loops of the gut, which may remain there without causing any trouble. Such a sac often contains serous fluid, and is subject to inflammations, just as is the peritoneum in general.

Inguinal hernias are those in which the sac is pushed through the abdominal wall just above Poupart's ligament. Those which pass through the internal abdominal ring, that is, outside the deep epigastric artery, pass along the track of the inguinal canal or through the unobliterated inguinal canal, when that has remained open, into the scrotum. They are the oblique inguinal hernias. Those which push through to the inner side of the epigastric artery and likewise project through the external abdominal ring into the scrotum are the direct inguinal hernias.

Femoral hernias are such as arise from the propulsion of a peritoneal sac through the space between the femoral vein and Gimbernat's ligament, beneath Poupart's ligament, to project through the saphenous opening.

Umbilical hernias are often of great extent when congenital, and may contain most of the abdominal viscera. They are acquired in later life through the protrusion of a sac through the weakened scar tissue about the navel, and are common in women who have borne many children. Hernias through the abdominal wall may occur anywhere where a large operation wound has resulted in delayed healing, and the scar has remained as a weak place.

Other hernias which are less conspicuous and far less common occur, and some of these are the so-called *internal hernias*. Thus the left side of the diaphragm may be thinned and stretched into a sac, and in a case which we recently observed nearly the whole of the stomach, the spleen, and the splenic flexure of the colon lay in this sac far up in the thoracic cavity. The most unexpected places may be pitched upon by the intestinal loops for invasion, and extraordinary results follow. For example, the fossæ about the junction of the duodenum and jejunum, which are ordinarily quite small recesses, may become distended into great sacs in which numerous loops of intestine are found ensconsed. The same is true of the fossæ about the cæcum and at the root of the sigmoid, and I have recently reported a case in which a notoriously weak place in the root of the mesentery of the jejunum was attacked, and just as a flock of sheep in a street, left for a moment to themselves, will hurry into any open door, the whole of the small intestine had become inclosed in a sac which hung to the right of the midline.

All this seems to have little to do with intestinal obstruction, but it is precisely in these hernias that a common form of obstruction takes place. For although ordinarily the neck of the sac is wide and the intestinal contents circulate through the loop in the sac without hindrance, more intestine than usual may sometimes be forced into the sac. All these hernias tend to grow in this way, and it may even happen that the abdomen is so emptied of its contents and contracted and the sac so large that it is impossible to reduce the hernia, that is, to replace its contents in the abdominal cavity. The formation of adhesions between the intestine and the wall of the sac may also make the hernia irreducible. Such a condition may exist for a long time.

If, through a sudden violent exertion, a loop of intestine be forced through a very narrow orifice, or if an excessive amount of intestine or too much of the intestinal contents be forced into the sac, the afferent and efferent portions as they pass through the neck of the sac become compressed. Then not only is it impossible to reduce the hernia, but the intestine is obstructed and all the symptoms of an acute ileus, distension of the loops above the constriction, fæcal vomiting, etc., make their appearance (incarcerated hernia). This is not all, however, for the compression of the veins of the mesentery of the incarcerated loops soon causes œdema of those loops, and increases still further the bulk of the contents of the sac until the flow of the circulation is quite stopped, and the whole included loop becomes the seat of a hæmorrhagic infarction (strangulated hernia). The wall becomes greatly thickened and infiltrated with blood, and dies, after which the bacteria in the lumen pervade the dead tissue and set up an inflammation in the sac. If some time elapses before the sac is cut open by the surgeon, the intestine is found to be purple or greenish black, but if relief is rapid, circulation may be reëstablished and the loop saved alive.

Somewhat similar in principle to this process is the prolapse of the rectum, in which the relaxation of the tissue in and about the rectal wall allows its mucous surface to be everted through the anus until a considerable length has been turned outside and protruded.

Intussusception.—Higher up in the intestine one portion of the wall may be telescoped into the next section below. This invagination or intussusception is frequently found to take place in the irregular peristalsis which arises just after death, perhaps more often in children than in adults. But it does occur also during life, and quickly leads to complete obstruction of the intestine and all the acute symptoms of ileus. For, as will be seen in the drawing (Fig. 16, p. 36), the portion which is invaginated drags with it its mesentery, while the portion which receives it is stretched until it constricts its contents closely. Especially at its beginning or upper end, where the mesenteric mass at least is most bulky, it forms a tight ring constricting the mesenteric veins. The result, as in the strangulated hernia, is the production of a hæmorrhagic infarction in the two internal folds, which thereby become even more swollen. It is said to have happened that the normal entering intestine, by healing to the upper end of the outer or receiving intestine, allowed the whole of the invaginated portion to be sloughed off and discharged per rectum, but this must be a rare occurrence. In the early stages, before circulation has been interrupted too long, the surgeon may pull out the intussuscepted part and relieve the whole condition. But after the infarction of the invaginated part is complete, a more radical operation is necessary. Irregular peristalsis is held responsible for this process, but sometimes there is a stalked polypoid tumor hanging from the mucosa which is forced along the intestinal canal and drags the wall with it. Once started, the invagination tends to increase rapidly.

Volvulus.—Volvulus is another type of constriction from without which depends upon the twisting of a loop of intestine through more than 180 degrees, so that the two ends of the loop compress each other as in a knot. For this there must be a long loose mesentery, and the condition is most common in the sigmoid flexure. Complete obstruction occurs, with the isolation of a loop. When the twist is tight enough to embarrass the circulation, the condition comes to resemble closely that in the strangulated hernia.

Instances of **post-operative obstruction** due to adhesions which compress or kink the intestine, or among which the intestine can entangle and strangle itself, are not very uncommon, but almost as common are those cases in which evidences of obstruction arise very soon after the operation, when there has been no time for dense adhesions to form, and in which, at a second exploration, the intestine is found bent on itself at a sharp angle above which it is greatly distended. These are rather hard to explain, but they seem to be due to a combination of a paralysis of the intestinal wall with any slight mechanical displacement, which, after the first handling of the intestines, is maintained even by weak fibrinous adhesions. The capability of mere paralysis of peristalsis in a length of the intestine to produce the symptoms of obstruction is well known (paralytic ileus), and the inert segment which does not help in the propulsion of the intestinal contents will, if it is long enough, prove to be as effective a barrier as a ligature. It is not always easy to explain how the paralysis is produced. Sometimes, as in a phlegmonous inflammation of the intestinal wall, when the infiltrated wall becomes rigid, the cause is clear, and so, too, are those in which thrombosis or embolism of the mesenteric vessels causes the death of a whole length of the intestine, with hæmorrhagic infarction, but at other times we are reduced to the idea that the nervous controlling mechanism is disturbed. I have already mentioned one instance in which a dissecting aneurysm had ruptured into the tissues about the aorta, so that there was a great clot of blood stretching from the upper thoracic to the lumbar region. The most striking symptoms were those of intestinal obstruction, for the relief of which an operation was performed. The man died, and at the autopsy the intestines were distended with fluid and gas to a colossal size, so that from the stretching the muscular wall showed numerous tears, but there was no obstruction except from the paralysis of the intestines.

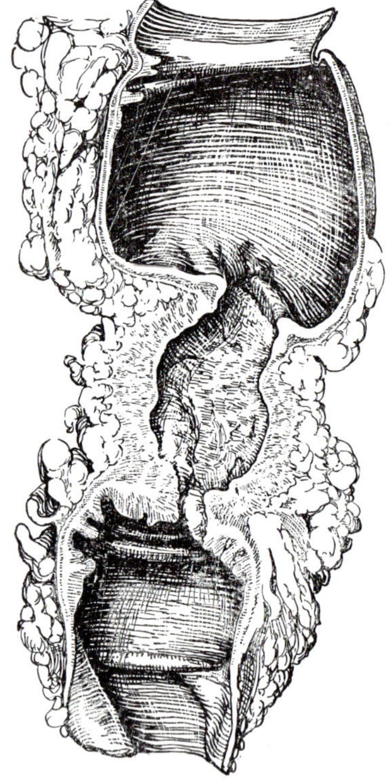

Fig. 211.—Carcinoma of the rectum encircling the gut and producing a stricture.

Stenosis and Stricture.—Finally, obstruction may be gradually produced by the development of a tumor encircling the lumen of the intestine, or by the contraction of a scar produced in the healing of a girdle ulcer. Cancerous tumors of this sort are most common in the large intestine, and they may produce obstruction by their increasing bulk or by the scar tissue formed after their partial degeneration. In the small intestine annular lymphosarcomata, and more rarely carcinomata, may cause the same thing. Ulcers of tuberculous origin rarely heal far enough to cause stricture, but syphilitic ulcers, especially in the rectum, frequently do so. All these things produce a gradual narrowing with slowly advancing incomplete obstruction, so that the symptoms are not the acute and violent symptoms of ileus. Instead, the intestine above the stenosis becomes greatly distended and also greatly thickened through the hypertrophy of the muscular wall, which attempts constantly to drive materials through the narrow opening (Fig. 211). Below the stricture the intestine is collapsed and thin walled. An almost continuous stream of fluid intestinal contents is driven through the stricture, and may cause the so-called paradoxical diarrhœa. Above the stricture the mucosa of the distended intestine often presents extensive ulcerations, which are thought to be due partly to its disturbed nutrition, partly to the stagnation of masses of infected fæcal material in contact with it (stercoraceous ulceration). Sometimes an acute diphtheritic inflammation of the mucosa of this area is produced in the same way.

Thus if we look back over this review of intestinal obstructions, we find that no matter what the mechanism by which occlusion of the intestine is produced, the effect is fairly constant, and varies only with the completeness and situation of the obstruction. It differs from the effects of the occlusion of the duct of a gland on account of the immediate vital importance of the intestine, its circulatory relations, and its abundant content of bacteria.

LITERATURE

Lichtwitz: Ergeb. d. innere Medizin u. Kinderh., 1914, xiii, 1.
Opie: Diseases of the Pancreas, Philadelphia, 1903.
Wilms: "Ileus," Handb. d. prakt. Chir. (Bruns, Garré, Kuttner), 1913, iii, 336.
Graser: "Hernias, etc.," *ibid.*, 421.
Hartwell and Hoguet: Jour. Amer. Med. Assoc., lix, 82.
Whipple, Stone, and Bernheim: Jour. Exp. Med., 1913, xvii, 286, 307.

CHAPTER XXI

TYPES OF INJURY—OBSTRUCTION (Continued).—OBSTRUCTION OF RESPIRATORY TRACT

Nose (coryza, adenoids, etc.). Larynx (œdema, diphtheria, foreign bodies, compression, stenosis); bronchi (foreign bodies, stenosis). Atelectasis: its causes. Mechanism of bronchial dilatation. Bronchiectasis. Emphysema.

NASAL OBSTRUCTION

In the upper air-passages, especially in the nose, there are several common forms of occlusion which impede respiration, with peculiar results. Swelling of the Schneiderian membrane in ordinary coryza may make it impossible to breathe through the nose, so that the throat becomes dried from the prolonged breathing through the mouth. More serious, because more prolonged, is the blocking of the nares by certain *polypoid œdematous fibromata*, which hang down from the septum, or by the growths of *adenoid tissue* which project from the roof of the pharynx. In young persons the latter, at least, give rise to great deformity of the face, with flattening of the features, which, since the mouth is constantly open, gives the person a most vacant expression.

The difficulty in breathing through the nose, with the consequent violent inspiratory efforts, brings about curious deformities of the chest. A lateral caving in of the soft ribs leaves the sternum prominent (*pigeon-breast*), while the tension of the diaphragm at its insertion may cause a furrow-like retraction of the ribs along that line (*Harrison's groove*).

OBSTRUCTION OF THE LARYNX

Spastic closure of the glottis in children, especially in such conditions as tetany, causes a peculiar difficulty in inspiration, with stridor (*laryngismus stridulus*), while paralysis of the vocal cords may produce a similar obstruction in another way. Actual asphyxia may occur. Asphyxia is much more commonly the result of œdema about the larynx or of other types of inflammatory exudate there.

Œdema of the Larynx.—This is, in many instances, only a part of a wide-spread œdema of the tissues such as is seen in cases of cardiac failure or renal disease, or due to some local disturbance of the circulation, which may be caused by posture, but at other times it is the effect of an inflammation in or about the larynx (Fig. 212). Masser and others have pointed out the existence of an erysipelas-like infection of the larynx and pharynx in the course of which extreme œdema may arise. So, too, abscesses in the neighborhood of the tonsils, and more especially the phlegmonous inflammations starting about the submaxillary glands (Ludwig's angina) or from the mucosa, or even the skin, may produce the most intense infiltration of the tissues of the neck, with inflammatory œdema of the especially loose structures of the larynx. The epiglottis swells into a balloon-like mass, and each aryepiglottic fold assumes huge dimensions, so that the opening of the larynx may easily be closed and suffocation ensue.

Diphtheria, by blocking the larynx and trachea with a tough, inflammatory pseudomembrane, may also asphyxiate a child, and it is to obviate this that tracheotomy is sometimes necessary. Exactly the same sort of asphyxia arises when a foreign body, such as a piece of meat, is drawn into the opening of the larynx (Fig. 213). Incredible as it may appear, it is not uncommon to find, in the autopsy upon drunken persons who have died with symptoms of choking, such masses so firmly wedged into the glottis as to be removed with difficulty.

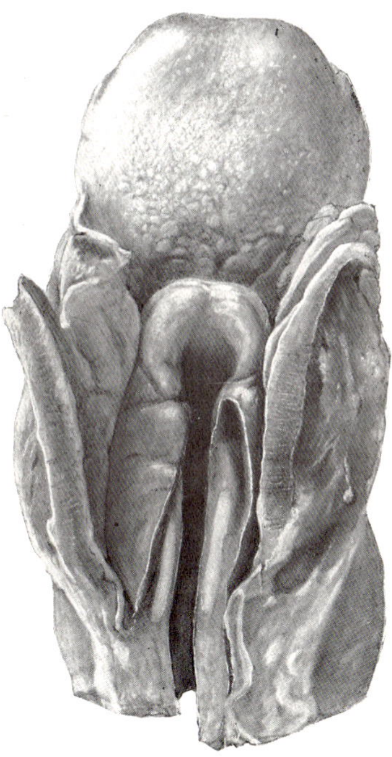

Fig. 212.—Œdema of the glottis.

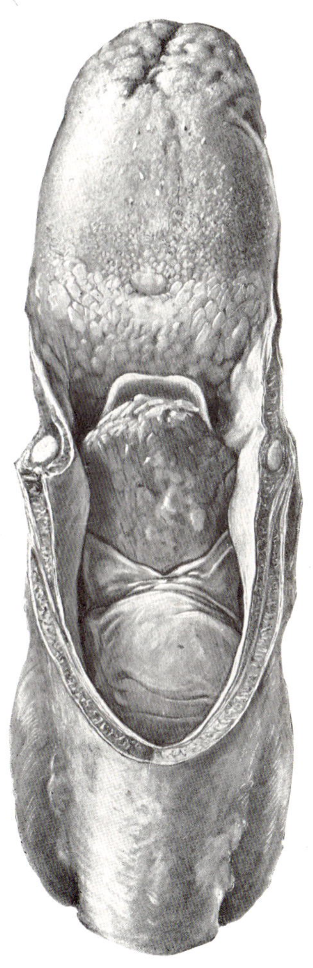

Fig. 213.—Meat impacted in the glottis. Sudden death from asphyxia.

From without, the *trachea may be compressed* by the growth of goitres, aneurysms, and tumors of the neck. In the case of goitres, it is not unusual to find the lumen of the tube flattened into a slit from the pressure exerted on each side. Dyspnœa increases in intensity with the narrowing of the passage. Syphilitic ulceration of the tracheal wall, with scarring, is no uncommon cause of stricture. The narrowing is generally ring-shaped, and may occur just above the bifurcation, or sometimes even in one of the main bronchi.

It will be seen that, while some of these conditions can last only a short time, others are of long standing and are gradually produced. The latter can in time produce anatomical changes in the lung which are perhaps less striking, though analogous with those produced by similar narrowing of the bronchi.

OBSTRUCTION OF THE BRONCHI

The bronchi, like the trachea, may be completely or only partly occluded in any part of their course by *foreign bodies* of all sorts accidentally drawn into the larynx. Seeds, fruit-stones, teeth, pieces of bone, nails, buttons, pieces of tracheotomy tubes, etc., are the common objects found there. In the case illustrated in Fig. 214 a fragment of bone, together with a tangle of string, partially occluded the large bronchus, supplying air to the middle and lower lobes, leaving the bronchus to the upper lobe quite open. Tumors, caseous lymph-nodes, and aneurysms may also gradually close the bronchus by pressure, or by actually growing into the lumen of the tube.

The result, when the occlusion is complete, is the collapse of the corresponding part of the lung (atelectasis), because the air which remains in the alveoli when the closure is completed is soon absorbed by the circulating blood.

Atelectasis.—The fœtal state of the lungs is comparable to the condition of collapse seen in later life, except in that, until the first breath is taken, the alveoli have never been expanded. Since, in the adult, the thorax has grown to a size greater than could be filled by the collapsed lungs, there is even in the position of forced expiration a disproportion which keeps the lungs partly distended with air. In the infant, for a time, so nearly does the lung tissue fill the thorax, that the air which is found in the lung is quite proportional to the respiratory movements. Atelectasis is, therefore, more easily produced or maintained in the infant than in the adult. Indeed, areas of lung tissue often remain undistended with air, and if the condition persists, become obliterated and reduced to scar tissue. In the adult, when the lung has been expanded, the condition of collapse may be produced by: (1) Complete occlusion of the bronchi, or (2) by pressure from without. Only exceptionally is collapse produced in another way, as in those cases in which, while the bronchus is widely open to the trachea, it communicates also through a hole in the lung with the pleural cavity. When air can thus enter the pleura without the necessity of expanding the lung, that tissue gradually collapses. This requires some time, so that if, instead, a hole is made in the chest-wall, complete collapse of the lung does not occur at once.

The first mode of production of atelectasis by complete occlusion of a bronchus depends upon the fact that the air in the corresponding alveoli after the obstruction is complete, is soon dissolved in the circulating blood, so that the alveolar walls fall together. The area appears sunken and of a translucent, bluish-purple color. On section it is pasty and often congested, the congestion being due to the kinking of the veins, which prevents the blood from escaping. Such airless patches are found about the regions of consolidation in lobular pneumonia, where they represent the parts of the lung supplied with air by branches of bronchi which, at a higher point, are obstructed by the inflammatory exudate. Precisely the same result is found if a foreign body completely closes the bronchus.

Pressure from without, the second cause referred to, is most effective when applied gradually and slowly, for the most forcible attempt to press air out of the lungs rapidly, fails unless the alveoli are ruptured, because the smaller bronchioles bend sharply on themselves and prevent the escape of the air. The growth of a tumor, however, or the gradual accumulation of fluid in the pleural cavity, may render airless the part of the lung pressed upon (*cf.* Fig. 92). A whole lobe or part of it, usually the lower and posterior part, may thus collapse into a soft, pasty, bluish, airless tissue, which sinks in water and gives no crepitation between the fingers. When cut into, it may be dry and inelastic, thus differing from an œdematous lung in which the air has been replaced by fluid. By stretching a little of the tissue, first in one direction and then in another, the movements of the alveolar walls, can be seen so plainly that the condition of collapse is easily distinguished from that of inflammatory consolidation. Adhesions between the alveolar walls and the growth of fibrous tissue through them sometimes indurate and solidify the lung permanently, so that it cannot expand again.

Bronchiectasis.—When the obstruction is incomplete, the bronchi distal to it become dilated (Fig. 214). This is because both inspiration and expiration become difficult in that portion of the lung on account of the partial blocking of the bronchus, although they go on easily enough in the rest of the lung. Quiet expiration is a more or less passive process, due to the elastic recoil of the distended lung, the sinking of the ribs from their actively elevated position, and the relaxation of the diaphragm and of the distended abdomen, although, of course, violent muscular contraction of the chest is available in forced expiration.

Thus the force available to carry air into the lung when the chest is expanded is the whole atmospheric pressure, part of which is used in stretching the elastic lung.* The force which drives the air out in quiet respiration is only the elastic contraction of the lung, aided by gravity and a relatively slight muscular action.

Consequently, if there arises a partial obstruction of a bronchus, offering

* Just what pressure relations will exist on each side of a complete obstruction of the main bronchus within the chest in inspiration will depend upon the amount of air already in the lung.

a constant resistance to the passage of air, inspiration will fairly readily overcome the resistance, drawing air into the distal part, while expiration will prove too feeble to drive it out. Air in such a case accumulates behind the obstruction until it is under a pressure equal to that which overcame

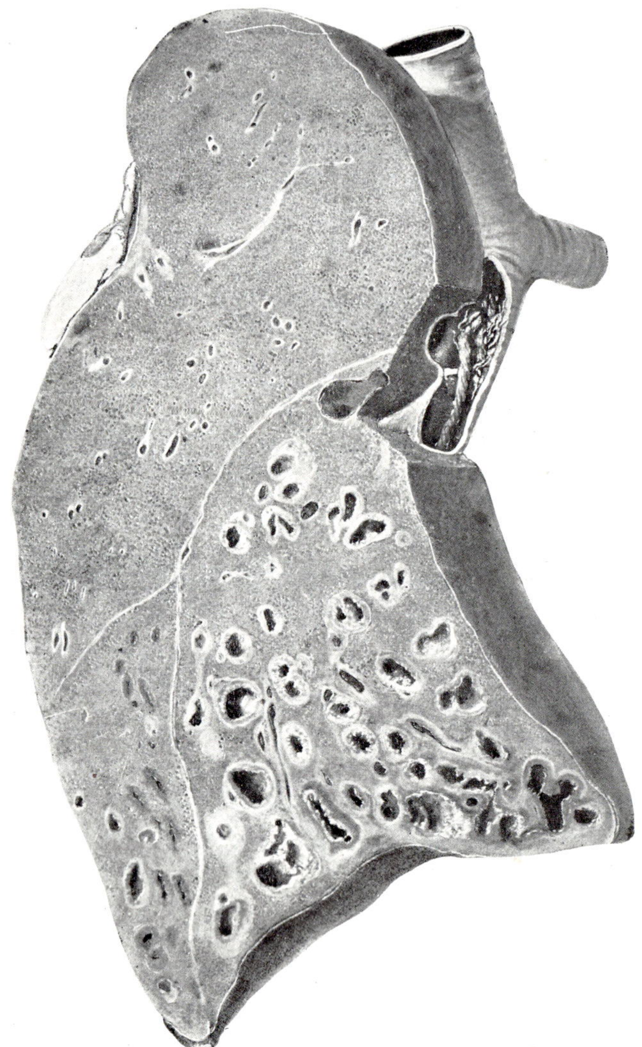

Fig. 214.—Partial obstruction of a bronchus by foreign bodies. Bronchiectasis involving the corresponding branches.

the resistance of the obstruction, and at this pressure it will remain as long as breathing continues, while other air passes in and out, just as tide-water passes in and out over a dyke, leaving a great depth imprisoned behind, up to the level of the top. It is this continuous distension of the obstructed bronchus which finally widens it and is a prominent cause of the condition known as bronchiectasis.

There are several different types of dilatation of the bronchi, which are best separated from one another according to their causes, rather than their anatomical form, although we are not well informed as to those causes.

Quite distinct is the group described by H. Meyer, Grawitz, Stoerk, and others as occurring in infants, and sometimes found persisting in adults. In this form the lung, or part of it, is found to be converted into a mass of cysts lined with high epithelium and full of fluid. Since they are generally not connected with bronchi, it seems hardly proper to speak of them as bronchiectasis. They represent rather a congenital malformation of the lung. Atelectatic bronchiectasis is that widening of the bronchi described by Heller, Buchmann, and others as occurring in portions of the lung which have become permanently collapsed in early life. Such a lobe or lobule of the lung remains unpigmented, and consists of a sponge of wide bronchi embedded in a firm tissue in which alveoli can no longer be easily distinguished. Such widening may well be the result of the tendency of a portion of the lung which is not taking its normal part in filling the thorax, to dilate during inspiration.

Other forms of bronchiectasis are acquired in later life, and are in all cases associated with infection and inflammation of the bronchi. This in itself is not sufficient cause for the widening of the bronchi until there is added to it a mechanical distension. By bronchiectasis is meant the formation of abnormally wide channels in the lung from the dilatation of bronchi. Since these cavities are surrounded by the stretched bronchial wall, the term does not include caverns excavated in the substance of the lung itself, although these may secondarily be formed in connection with true bronchiectasis by gangrene or tuberculosis. The bronchi may be widened during an acute inflammatory disease, but the larger dilatations are produced more slowly by chronic processes, and are often accompanied by the most profound changes in the surrounding lung tissue. When such cavities are formed, they may be recognized by auscultation and by the sudden discharge of great quantities of characteristic sputum, which have collected in them during the night when the patient does not cough.

Anatomically, they vary greatly in appearance. In those acutely produced, the bronchi are deeply congested, thin walled, and soft, and filled with a purulent secretion. They are usually associated with lobular pneumonic patches of consolidation. In the more chronic cases the same cylindrical dilatation may appear, but it is perhaps more common to find the widening excessive at the ends of the bronchi, so that they become club-shaped. Occasionally they are beaded with separate dilatations, or they may be blown out into wide sacs which can rupture into one another or into the pleura. In all these cases the bronchial wall is intensely inflamed and thickened by the accumulation of inflammatory exudate in its substance. The mucosa is thick and ragged, the musculature and elastic tissue spread apart, torn, and weakened, and the connective tissue as well, infiltrated with fluid and wandering cells. The cartilaginous plates tend to disappear, and a newly formed connective tissue occupies the bulk of the wall. All this tends to diminish greatly the strength and elasticity of the wall.

The lung tissue in these protracted cases is sometimes very emphysematous, but in others it is converted into a dense fibroid substance partly by the organization of inflammatory exudate within the alveoli, partly by the growth of fibrous scar tissue in the walls of the alveoli and the other tissues of the lung.

It is not well known what changes occur in the channels of communication between these widened bronchi and their alveolar tissue, but it is probable that, according as there is narrowing or complete obstruction of the tiny bronchioles at their entrance into the dilated bronchus, there will be emphysema or atelectasis in the corresponding alveoli.

Many theories have been formulated to explain the distension of the bronchi, but in these all are agreed upon one point only, that the infection and inflammation which weakens the bronchial wall and destroys its elasticity is a necessary factor. Not all cases of bronchitis are followed by bronchiectasis, and it may be that special bacteria, such as the influenza bacillus, which has often been found in bronchiectasis, are particularly able to cause the weakening of the wall.

Pleural adhesions generally accompany chronic bronchiectasis, and Corrigan and Biermer express the idea that in indurated and adherent lungs the contraction of the scar tissue between the bronchi pulls upon them from all sides and thus dilates them. Possibly this is true in some cases, but it cannot be a general explanation.

Others declare that the accumulation of secretion in the bronchi is sufficient to distend them to the degree found, but it seems that this can at best be only an accessory influence, because by itself the secretion can never exert any great pressure. Most writers, too, lay stress upon the effects of the violent expiratory effort with closure of the glottis in coughing, as capable of distending the bronchi. Reflection will show, however, that although under those circumstances the trachea might be distended, the pressure on the walls of the bronchi within the chest is from outside, so that it cannot distend them, as a rubber and glass model of the respiratory organs will demonstrate to perfection. Indeed, bronchiectasis may be experimentally produced in animals in the complete absence of cough. On the other hand, the violent inspiratory distension of the lung preparatory to coughing may be able to widen the bronchi if they are weak and it is constantly repeated.

This leaves the idea of the inspiratory dilatation, whether exerted directly or through the imprisonment of inspired air behind some obstruction, as the most plausible explanation. It was indeed the explanation given by

Laënnec in his first work on bronchiectasis in 1819, and it has been recalled by Aron, and by Thornton and Pratt in their experimental work. When we attempt to apply this explanation to the cases of bronchiectasis as they occur, we find that it is completely satisfactory in those in which there is an obvious partial obstruction. But there are many others where obstruction is not so obvious, and these offer difficulties. It is true that we may say that thick, sticky, mucoid secretion may exert a valvular action in the bronchi, preventing the easy exit of air; or we may assume, with Hoffmann, that the weakened bronchus may kink during expiration like an old rubber tube, while stretching open on inspiration, in this way fulfilling the theoretical conditions.

But these things are hardly definitely demonstrated as yet, and the question needs further study.

LITERATURE

Œdema of Larynx: Peltesohn: Berl. klin. Woch., 1889, xxvi, 931.

Congenital and Atelectatic Bronchiectasis: Grawitz: Virchow's Archiv, 1880, lxxxii, 217.

——— Stoerk: Wien. klin. Woch., 1897, x, 25.

——— Edens: Deut. Arch. f. klin. Med., 1904, lxxxi, 334.

——— Buchmann: Frankf. Ztsch. f. Path., 1911, viii, 263.

Bronchiectasis: v. Criegern: Akute Bronchiektasie, Leipzig, 1903.

——— Posselt: Med. Klinik, 1909, vi, 1845.

——— Thornton and Pratt: Johns Hopkins Hosp. Bull., 1908, xix, 230.

The effect of partial or intermittent obstruction of the air-passages upon the alveolar structure of the lungs may next be examined. It has been said that complete obstruction of a bronchus quickly results in atelectasis or collapse of the corresponding part of the lung, but it is also true that partial or intermittent obstruction causes an overdistension of the alveoli with air. There are many other causes assigned for the overdistension, but the importance of this one will become evident in studying the type condition, emphysema.

Emphysema.—Excessive distension of the alveoli may be produced rapidly in the lung, when the tissue of the alveolar walls is quite normal, so that if the air be allowed to escape, the alveoli at once return to their normal size, and their stretched walls to their normal thickness. If this overdistension be maintained at not too great a degree, the capillaries are, as Tendeloo has shown, widened so that nutrition of the alveolar wall may be well kept up. A still greater distension narrows and compresses the capillaries, so that the blood passes with difficulty or not at all. Nutritive changes possibly dependent on this great stretching and the impaired blood supply weaken the elastic alveolar wall after a time, so that it may remain permanently stretched, or, after the breaking of its elastic fibres, give way at one or more points. Then the margins about the hole retract, and two alveoli are thrown into one.* At times great sacs are formed on the surface and along the edges of the lung by this process, while the remainder of the organ is softened and assumes a very coarse texture, from the wide-spread loss of alveolar walls. Such a lung is very voluminous, but feels peculiarly soft and non-resilient. The characteristic crepitation or crackling felt on pinching the lung tissue is altered, and one has the sensation of bursting large bubbles under the finger instead of the fine crackling produced in the normal tissue. There is also a peculiar pallor, which is due to the obliteration of so much of the capillary bed and to the absence of coal-pigment.

Microscopically, the most striking feature is the large size of the alveolar spaces and the extreme thinness of the alveolar walls. With suitable stains one may observe the fracture of the strands of elastic tissue and the formation of holes in the walls, as well as the narrowing, obliteration, and rupture of the capillaries.

This is the chronic substantive emphysema in which one may sometimes discern evidences of attempts at repair in the new formation of elastic tissue and the growth of new blood-vessels and connective tissue. Atrophy of the lung tissue is perhaps the most characteristic feature of a subtype, the so-called senile emphysema. In old people the lungs are sometimes found to collapse into a very small bulk on opening the chest. They may contain much coal-pigment, but the tissue is extremely soft and wide meshed. In such cases it is customary to ascribe much of the thinning out and disappearance of the alveolar walls to senile atrophy, but it may be questioned whether it is not sometimes the end result of a very protracted process of the kind described above.

The causes of emphysema are somewhat different in the various forms, although only a few principles can be concerned. When, through lobar pneumonia, tuberculosis, tumor formation, etc., a large portion of the lung is rendered solid, so that it cannot expand with the enlargement of the thorax, the whole inspiratory effort is expended upon the remaining open lung tissue, which thus becomes overdistended (vicarious emphysema). So, too, in drowning, water is drawn in to fill part of the lung, while further violent inspiratory efforts above water overdilate the rest of the alveoli with air.

In many conditions in which the trachea or bronchi are partly obstructed, continued distension of the alveoli occurs by the imprisonment of air introduced in inspiration over the obstacle in the way described in connection with the formation of bronchiectasis. This is especially clear in the

* The alveolar walls contain a rich network of capillaries, abundant elastic tissue, and some wavy fibrils of connective tissue, and are covered on each side by the respiratory epithelium. The elastic tissue stretches across in coarse bands, frayed out here and there into fibres which join again in other directions to form new bands. Another set of fine fibrils arises from the elastica of the vessels and accompanies the capillaries (Orsos). Pores in the alveolar walls (pores of Kohn) are frequently seen, but there is much evidence that they are present only in diseased lungs.

case of valvular obstructions which allow inspiration only, as in the case of a stalked polyp in one of these air-passages, or a flapping film of diphtherial false membrane. It is true also of the thick, sticky, mucous exudate which may collect in the inflamed bronchioles in chronic bronchitis, and is particularly shown in the areas of emphysema which occur side by side with areas of atelectasis in the neighborhood of patches of broncho-pneumonic consolidation. Asthma, in which the bronchioles are narrowed partly by muscular contraction, partly by swelling of their mucosa and by exudate, presents the conditions mentioned. Inspiration is violent, and expiration prolonged and labored, and emphysema is the regular accompaniment. In all these cases it seems to be the inspiratory effort which is active in dilating the alveoli. Generally this is effective in producing a permanent anatomical change only when aided by a partial obstruction, and when kept up through a long time. Whether it itself can thus produce the nutritive disturbances which lead to rupture of the alveolar wall is not perfectly certain. Doubtless other injurious agencies may also play a part, because it is known that the lungs of certain people exposed to mechanical conditions of this sort develop emphysema, while others do not.

Nearly every writer on the subject ascribes the widening of the alveoli to the increased intrathoracic pressure produced by cough, which is a forced expiration during closure of the glottis, suddenly relieved by its opening. It must, however, be clear that, as in the case of bronchiectasis, the increased intra-alveolar pressure is produced only by their compression, with decrease in their size. Only in such an unprotected place as the suprathoracic apex of the lung could one imagine this pressure capable of blowing out the alveoli. In the sternal margins it is still more doubtful. But cough is preceded each time by an extreme inspiratory distension of the lung, which, incessantly repeated, might lead to changes in the size of the alveoli. Tendeloo presents some interesting arguments with regard to the predominantly marginal and apical distribution of emphysema, based on his ideas as to the unequal expansion of the alveoli in different parts of the thorax. His laws seem, however, to depend upon doubtful evidence, and must be read in the original. When there are no adhesions in the pleural cavity, nor consolidated areas in the lung, the expansion of all alveoli would appear to us to be uniform.

In wide-spread emphysema of long standing, such as often accompanies chronic bronchitis or asthma, the capillary bed in the lungs is so much narrowed by the obliteration of many channels that the blood passes with difficulty, and hypertrophy of the right side of the heart is a consequence.

Such persons usually present a peculiar thoracic deformity—the chest is enlarged, with the ribs constantly in the position of inspiration, so that further respiratory movements are shallow. The costal cartilages often become calcified and rigid, and Freund has suggested that this condition may be primary and constitute the real cause of the emphysematous enlargement of the lungs. The evidence is not clear, however, in favor of this idea.

LITERATURE

Eppinger: Ergeb. d. allg. Path., 1904, viii$_1$, 267.
Tendeloo: Ursachen d. Lungenkrankheiten, 1902. Ergebn. d. inn. Med., 1910, vi, 1.
Freund: Lungenkrankheiten u. Rippenknorpel-Anomalien, Erlangen, 1859.
Salis: Frankf. Ztsch. f. Pathologie, 1910, iv, 399.
Orth: Berl. klin. Woch., 1905, xlii, 1.
Orsós: Ziegler's Beiträge, 1907, xli, 95.

CHAPTER XXII

TYPES OF INJURY—OBSTRUCTION (Continued).—OBSTRUCTION OF THE URINARY TRACT

Urethral stricture; prostatic obstruction. Hypertrophy of prostate. Cystitis. Urinary calculi. Hydronephrosis. Renal calculi. Ascending renal infection; pyelonephritis.

THE course of the urinary tract in the male is beset with so many more difficulties in the form of narrow places than in the female that the greater proportion of obstructions may naturally be expected in that sex.

URETHRAL STRICTURE

In the female the bladder opens by a canal so short and wide that obstruction to the flow of urine is seldom observed below the ureters. In the male it may occur at the prepuce, at the meatus, in the urethra, and especially in its prostatic portion, and at the vesical orifice. *Phimosis*, which is a congenital or acquired narrowing of the prepuce, may sometimes be sufficient to offer a considerable obstacle, and even give rise to fatal complications. A similar effect is produced by those constrictions of the meatus by scar tissue which occasionally follow the healing of an ulcer of the glans or a syphilitic chancre. It is, however, much more common to find the narrowing of the urethral canal higher up, and there it is due sometimes to mechanical *trauma*, but far more often to *gonorrhœa*. When the urethra is torn across, as in those cases in which a man falls from a height astride a beam, it is difficult even for the surgeon to secure such perfect healing that there is not some narrowing at the place. Nevertheless, such cases are very amenable to treatment. Far different are those in which, in the course of a protracted gonorrhœal infection, the wall of the urethra becomes ulcerated and infiltrated with inflammatory exudate. This usually produces its most profound effects in the bulbous portion, although other places may be involved instead. The organisms penetrate deep into the mucosa, and lodge in the lacunæ and crypts, where they keep up the injury in the most persistent way. Healing with scarring of the ulcerated tissue results in the narrowing of the canal, and such *strictures* (Fig. 215) frequently make it impossible for the bladder to empty itself. To this are often added the injuries caused by forcible attempts to pass catheters which, in inexperienced hands, pierce the urethral wall and wound the surrounding tissue. The healing of these false passages, added to the mass of scar tissue around the urethra which constricts and deforms it, is the cause of ever-impending occlusion.

PROSTATIC OBSTRUCTION

Complex conditions exist about the region of the prostate, so that a variety of alterations take part in producing obstructions there. Among these abscess of the prostate and cancerous tumors springing from the gland are important, but by far the most common is the so-called hypertrophy of

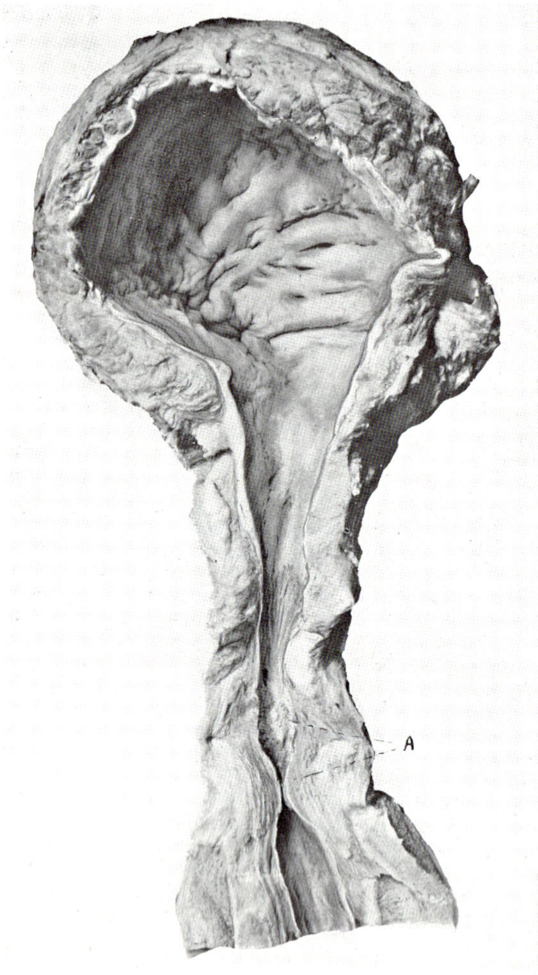

Fig. 215.—Gonorrhœal stricture of the urethra. At *A* the urethral canal is surrounded by scar tissue and greatly narrowed. There is hypertrophy of the bladder.

the prostate of old men. The obstruction caused by an abscess is transient, and depends upon the bulging of the prostate until the urethra is pressed flat, while that caused by the cancer is quite irregular, because the tumor may encroach on the urethra in any way. But the hypertrophy of the prostate follows roughly certain general rules, and the type of obstruction is for that reason fairly constant.

Hypertrophy of the Prostate.—Despite the most lengthy discussions, our ideas are still quite hazy as to the reasons for the enlargement of the prostate which is so frequent in men over sixty years of age, and even as to its anatomical characters the most diverse statements are made. It is evidently desirable that more accurate observations in this regard should be made and analyzed.

The prostate is a sexual gland derived from the Wolffian body, just as are the seminal vesicles, and its function is not to control the flow of urine, but to furnish its secretion in jets at the moment of ejaculation, in such a way as to mix it with the sperm in the urethra. In accord with this requirement we find that its abundant smooth muscle is arranged around the glands, so that it can suddenly exert pressure upon them. The internal sphincter of the bladder controls the discharge of urine, and is practically independent of the musculature of the prostate. So, too, the external sphincter of Henle, which consists largely of voluntary muscle, is independent, although its fibres extend in some cases into the prostate.

The bulk of the gland tissue in the prostate is collected in the lateral lobes, where it forms pyramidal radiating masses opening through 40 or 50 ducts into the urethra. The glands are acinar, lined with cubical or cylindrical epithelium, and often contain yellow, horn-like, concentrically laminated concretions (corpora amylacea). The posterior commissure is chiefly muscular, and contains few glands. There are a few, however, which extend upward toward the bladder inside the sphincter. There are also urethral glands there, such as are to be found throughout the course of the urethra. The anterior commissure is tightly connected with the symphysis pubis.

Enlargement of the prostate is due, in the great majority of cases, to the development of more or less distinct nodules of a granular, opaque, and rather spongy appearance, embedded in the substance of the original gland, which itself may be much compressed by their presence. They are surrounded by the dense stroma with some muscle, but, on the whole, the muscle seems to be rather atrophied than increased. Taken together, these nodules may often be shelled out in one large, irregular mass, leaving the remnants of the old prostate tissue.

Microscopically, they are composed of newly formed glands, which ramify abundantly and are lined with cylindrical epithelium. Often these are partly filled with papillary growths of epithelium. At other times they are more nearly tubular than acinar in form. From the cylindrical form of the epithelium and the extraordinary ramification and papillary ingrowth, it seems clear that these are newly formed glands, and that there is an enormous multiplication of these elements.

Without such hyperplasia of the glands the increase of the stroma and of the smooth muscle may sometimes cause enlargement of the prostate, but such cases are not common, and those in which there is a distinct myoma or muscular tumor growth are rare. In the glandular nodules one occasionally finds cystic dilatations which may contain epithelial débris and sometimes concretions, although the latter are not so frequent as in the original glands.

Inflammatory infiltrations of wandering cells are common, especially about the ducts. The enlargement may affect one or both of the lateral lobes, and is sometimes rather diffuse, sometimes irregular, inasmuch as it is produced by only a few nodules. In these cases the prostatic urethra, being fixed to the symphysis pubis, is stretched backward so as to assume the form of a narrow slit, which is bowed backward and may even be enlarged instead of being constricted (Fig. 218). This need not produce any obstruction, and urination is often normal. But such increase in the bulk of the lateral lobes tends to displace the posterior half of the ring of the sphincter upward, so as to form a transverse muscular fold (Mercier's barrier) behind the vesical orifice of the urethra, which may act as a valve. In another set of cases there appears, often in association with hypertrophy of the lateral lobes, a pear-shaped mass of glandular tissue which springs up inside the sphincter and lifts up the floor of the trigonum, projecting upward into

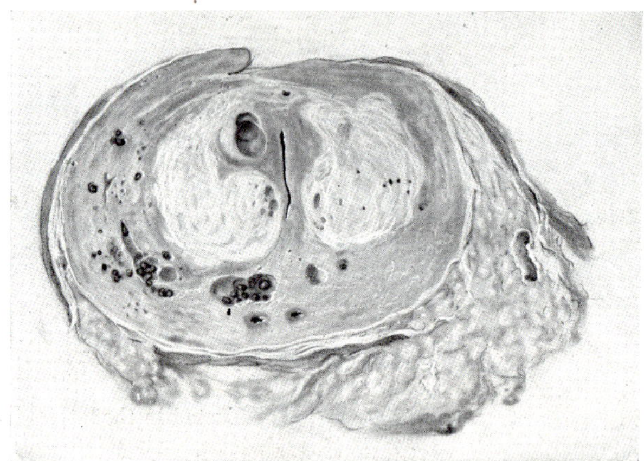

Fig. 216.—Hypertrophy of lateral lobes of prostate. Cross-section showing lateral compression of urethra. Prostatic concretions.

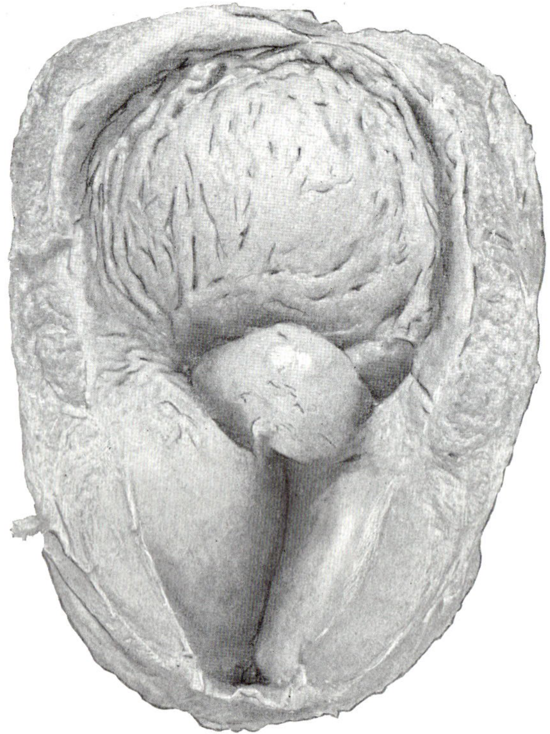

Fig. 217.—Hypertrophy of lateral and middle lobes of prostate. Great hypertrophy of the bladder.

the bladder. This is the hypertrophied midlobe, which seems to arise from hyperplasia of that insignificant group of glands which lies in the midline and extends in front of the posterior half of the sphincter.* It may attain a great size, and in one of our specimens must weight at least 50 grams. Obstruction to the outflow of urine is almost sure to result, because with the contraction of the bladder the midlobe, extending as it does through the sphincter, acts as a conical plug to close the urethral orifice. Besides, the stretching of the sphincter from its presence is often sufficient to produce incontinence of urine.

As to the nature and cause of this enlargement of the prostate, numerous ideas have been expressed, most lasting among which are—(1) that of Ciechanowski and many others that it is the result of a chronic inflammation, due probably to gonococcal infection of long standing, with the formation of scar tissue about the ducts, constricting them and producing dilatation of the glands, and (2) that maintained by Chiari and others,

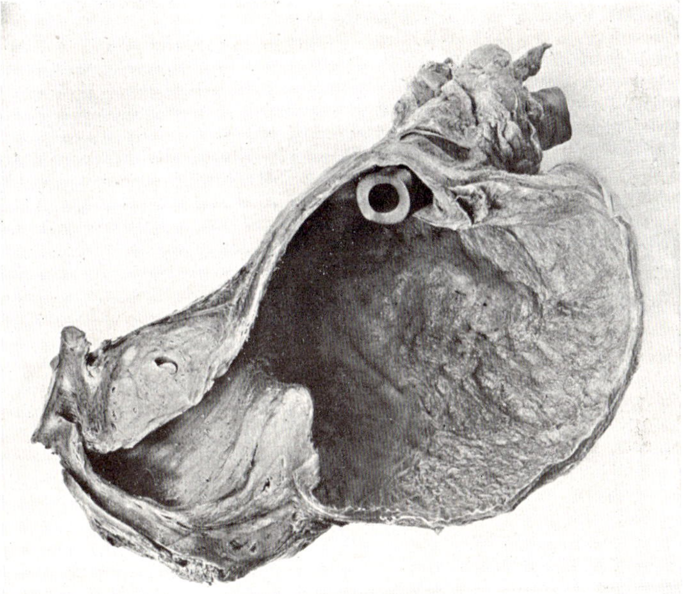

Fig. 218.—Hypertrophy of lateral and midlobes of prostate, showing anteroposterior widening of the urethra.

that it is a definite new-growth of adenomatous or tumor-like character, the direct cause of which is unknown. Chiari distinguishes the nodules as papillary intracanalicular adenomata, fibro-adenomata, and tubular adenomata.

With regard to these theories, it may be said that it seems impossible to explain the enormous solid growths, as Ciechanowski does, on the basis of mere obstruction of the ducts, especially in the case of the midlobe, which must arise from such a rudimentary group of glands. At any rate, many authors fail to find inflammatory processes in all cases, and regard them, when found, as secondary infections. Still we are familiar with

* It must be said here that Marion and Lendorf have recently declared that the enlarged midlobe, and, indeed, most, if not all, of the enlargements of the prostate, develop inside the sphincter from the urethral glands and not from the prostate at all. They support this view by the statement that the prostate is seen compressed and flattened outside of the stretched layer of muscle which represents the sphincter.

certain infections, such as the coccidiosis of the rabbit's liver, which produces colossal overgrowths of epithelium, so that it is not inconceivable that infection might be at the origin of the process, although not in so mechanical a way. The condition arises most commonly, if not exclusively, in married men, and has been ascribed to sexual excesses. It begins usually long years after gonococcal infection has subsided, even if it ever were present, and the nodules tend to recur when removed. Thus it is that some authors unhesitatingly refer them to the effects of inflammation, while others just as firmly relegate them to the category of tumors. Ribbert feels no doubt as to their tumor nature, and shows that as adenomatous nodules they are derived from a group of glands on each side of the urethra near the colliculus and belonging to the great lateral lobe, which he calls the *lower urethral prostatic glands*. The growth of such nodules is accompanied by some enlargement of the adjacent gland tissue. The adenomata of the sphincter region below the urethra (midlobe) usually develop only in association with those of the urethral prostatic glands.

LITERATURE

Ciechanowski: Mitth. a. d. Grenzg. d. Med. u. Chir., 1900, vii, 183.
v. Frisch: Nothnagel, Spez. Path. u. Therap., 1899, xix.
Wichmann: Virchow's Archiv, 1904, clxxviii, 279.
Chiari: Strassb. med. Zeitung, 1912, ix, 1.
Ribbert: Ziegler's Beiträge, 1915, lxi, 149.

OTHER FORMS OF OBSTRUCTION

It is not only in the urethra that obstructions to the emptying of the bladder appear, for plugs may be formed in the bladder itself. These are often loose in the cavity of the bladder, in the form of urinary stones or foreign bodies, which have been pushed into the bladder through the urethra. Then there are the stalked, papillary, tassel-like tumors, which very commonly reveal themselves later as carcinomata, and which can drift into the urethral orifice and cause a temporary obstruction. Tumors invading from the uterus or rectum through the bladder-wall may block the urethra, just as the tumors of the bladder-wall itself, but their usual fate is to break down into a canal into the rectum or vagina, which allows the escape of urine but renders infection of the bladder inevitable.

Very important in connection with the mechanical obstruction of the flow of urine is the presence of solid calculi composed of materials derived from the urine. These are found not only in the bladder, but in the pelvis of the kidney, and, indeed, it seems that the renal pelvis is the seat of original formation of many of them. It is not clear that obstruction has anything to do with their primary formation, although the growth of some of them at least seems to be greatly favored by such changes in the urine as follow obstruction. But they themselves are effective, just as in the case of gall-stones, in acting as plugs which retard the flow of urine either intermittently or continuously.

Urinary Calculi.—Concretions of crystalline material, mixed usually with some organic substance, and found at any point from the renal papillæ and renal pelvis to the urethra, constitute the group of urinary calculi. According to their position, they have the opportunity to assume one form or other, and an irregular mass from the pelvis of the kidney, if it be swept into the bladder, is likely to become round by the continuous application of new layers of crystals. These calculi vary in their chemical composition, and accordingly in their appearance, depending partly upon the position in which they are formed, but chiefly and almost entirely upon the chemical character of the urine in which they form. Since the urine may frequently change its character during the months or years which go by in the growth of the stone, the end result is apt to be made up of layers or laminæ of quite different color, consistence, and chemical composition (Fig. 219).

Ebstein thought that the organic or albuminous supporting framework which one can find in every calculus was the necessary skeleton upon which the deposit of crystals took place, and that without such a nucleus of organic material no crystallization in this form would occur. Aschoff, Moritz, Kleinschmidt, and others dispute this, and think this organic meshwork which is present in crystals, even when they are made to form in urine *in vitro,* is an accidental accompaniment of the crystals, probably formed through their own power of absorption. Still, they admit that it is of some help in hold-

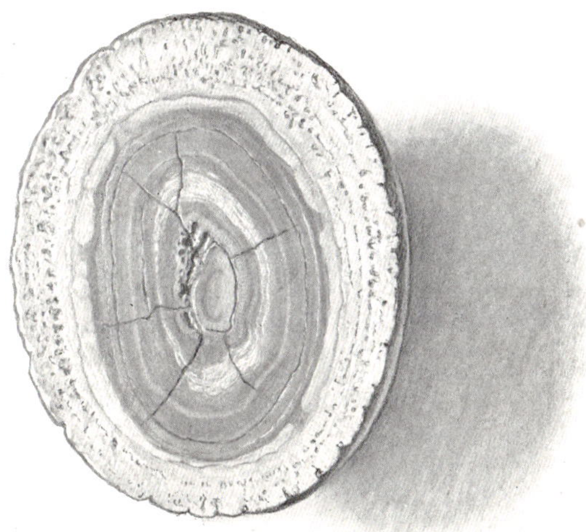

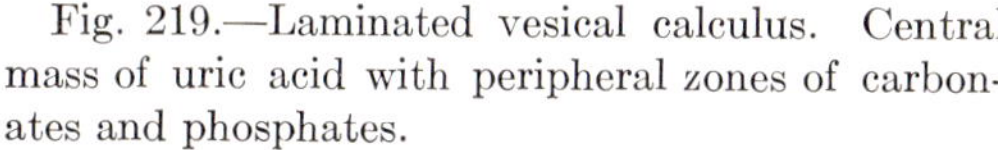

Fig. 219.—Laminated vesical calculus. Central mass of uric acid with peripheral zones of carbonates and phosphates.

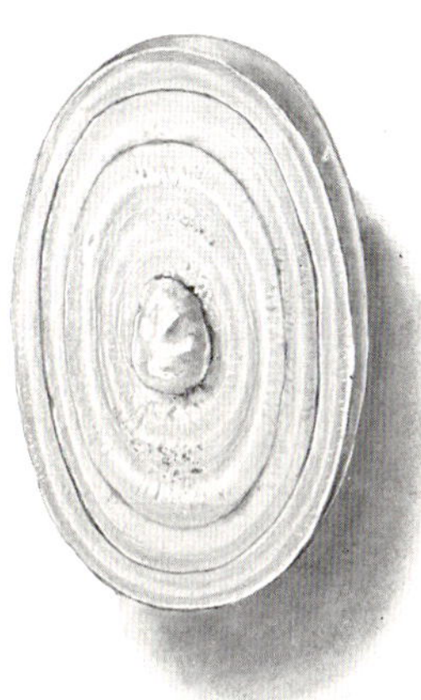

Fig. 220.—Urinary calculus of uric acid in laminæ about a central quartz pebble.

ing the forming stone together. The application of new layers of crystals to a concretion already formed is thought to occur, just as rock candy crystallizes on the string. But it involves the idea of an oversaturation of the urine with crystallizable substances, or else such changes in the urine that it becomes less able to hold those substances in solution. Thus if the urine is acid, uric acid may crystallize out, while if it is alkaline, phosphates, ammonio-magnesium phosphates, and ammonium urates may appear. Or something may cause the precipitation of those colloid materials in the urine which tend to hold the uric acid in solution, after which it quickly appears in crystalline form. Bacterial infection, especially when it produces ammoniacal decomposition of the urine, is favorable to the formation of phosphatic concretions.

Thus there is no insurmountable difficulty in explaining the growth of such stones once started, but it is more difficult to explain their origin. Of course, some are formed around foreign bodies—hair-pins, pieces of catheters, etc., which have been introduced into the bladder, but these incrustations are relatively rare (Fig. 220). Ebstein and others, including Kleinschmidt, are reduced to the explanation that most calculi, whether found in the renal pelvis or in the bladder, are formed originally in the tubules of the kidney. This idea has been elaborated especially for the uric-acid stones, because they are the commonest and because the conditions found in the so-called *uric-acid infarcts* of the kidney do explain their origin fairly well. These are frequent, especially in the kidneys of children and infants, and produce a curious yellow streaking of the papilla of the pyramid, sometimes with actual stony concretions embedded in ragged cavities near its tip. Microscopically, it is found that this is due to the abundant excretion of uric acid by the cells of the tubules. Sometimes (Aschoff) these are uninjured and secrete the uric acid in minute crystals on their surface. Other cells may be destroyed in the process. The uric acid appears in minute, round "sphæroliths," which become massed together with an albuminous material, secondarily gluing them together. This forms the primary concretion, which may pass quite out through the urethra, or may form the nucleus for a urinary calculus.

Calculi may form in normal non-albuminous urine, and may grow to a considerable size without causing any symptoms —usually from their angular form they wound the wall of the renal pelvis or of the bladder, and then cause bleeding and inflammation, which in turn are likely to change the reaction of the urine and initiate the deposition of layers of material of a different character from that which composed the stone. When the stone causes obstruction and bacteria are introduced, this change in reaction and the deposit of phosphates are inevitable.

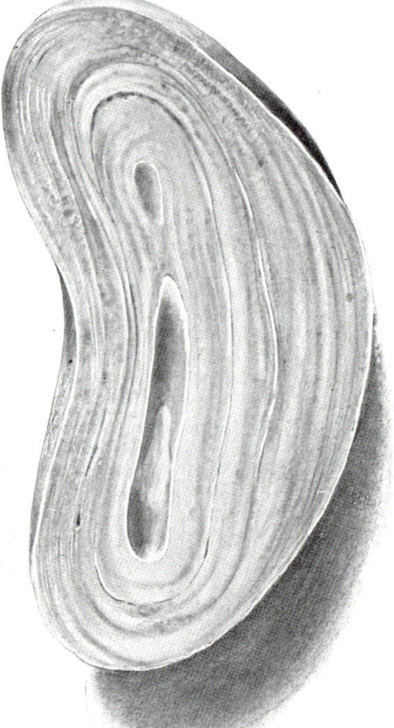

Fig. 221.—Uric-acid calculi with fine lamination.

Kleinschmidt classifies all these calculi as non-inflammatory and inflammatory, in each of which groups there are primary and secondary formations which represent stages in the history of the stone, just as do successive strata in a geological formation. Several of the crystalline substances in the urine may form concretions without any appreciable admixture of other things, so that in these calculi the chemical composition is the same from the centre to the surface. Such practically pure concretions are those composed of uric acid, calcium oxalate, xanthin, cystin, or calcium phosphate. Some of them grow in the same way as mixed stones to a large size. In other cases they form the nucleus upon which, with a change in the character of the urine, layer after layer of other substances are deposited. When there is no inflammatory process, such secondary stones may be formed upon a uric-acid concretion as nucleus with layers of uric acid and urates, or layers of oxalates and calcium phosphate. So, too, a calcium oxalate nucleus may be turned into a secondary calculus by being enveloped in layers of uric acid or calcium phosphate.

When bacterial infection and an inflammatory process supervene, phosphates, especially the ammonio-magnesium phosphate, sometimes with calcium carbonate, etc., make their appearance as strata of white, rather crumbly crystals, on the surface of one of these nuclei, just as they form an incrustation over any foreign body in the bladder. Indeed, they may form the whole calculus by themselves, without any obvious non-inflammatory stone or foreign body as a nucleus.

Uric-acid calculi (Fig. 221) are hard, smooth, oval or rounded stones when formed in the bladder, or moulded to the cavity when in the renal pelvis. There is often a central granule of ammonium urate about which fine, delicate yellow or yellow-brown laminæ of very compact appearance and great regularity are laid down. In other cases the consistence is more like that of pumice-stone, especially when there is much admixture of urates and the lamination is correspondingly indistinct.

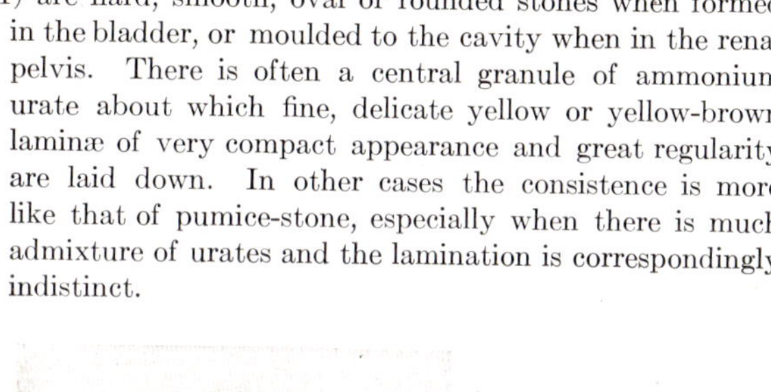

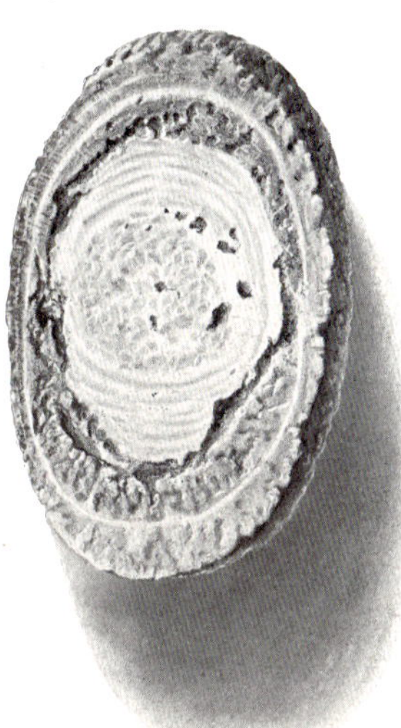

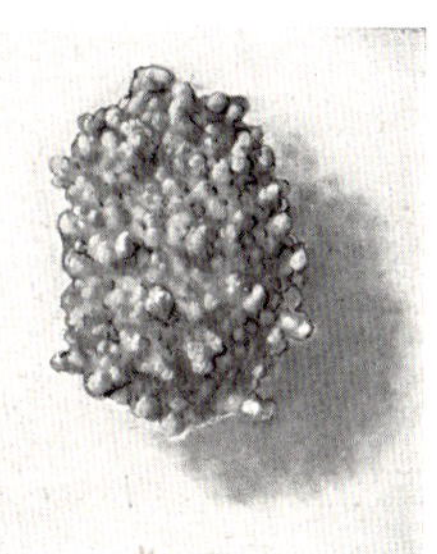

Fig. 222.—Vesical calculi formed of calcium oxalate. One in section shows laminæ of phosphates and carbonates.

Pure calcium oxalate stones are rare, but mixed stones in which it forms a considerable part, are common. They are often formed about a nucleus of uric acid or urates, and the oxalate covers this in layers of varying thickness, distinguished by their dark-brown color and by the extremely rough, jagged external surface which they present (Fig. 222). The irritation caused by this usually leads to the deposition of carbonates and phosphates, which fill up the depressions and smooth off the surface (Fig. 223). Urates may also alternate with layers of oxalates. Such stones are extremely hard, usually fairly round, and occur especially in the bladder.

Phosphatic Calculi.—In other cases, especially when the bladder is inflamed, ammonio-magnesium phosphate and calcium phosphates and carbonate predominate, usually on a nucleus of uric acid. These stones may or may not be laminated (Fig. 224). They are nearly pure white, with occasional yellow or brownish layers, and the surface is rough. Rarely, instead of being chalk-like, these phosphate stones are radially crystalline. The non-laminated type are usually round and rough, loosely built, pumice-like concretions of a yellowish-white color, but material of this sort is often deposited irregularly on

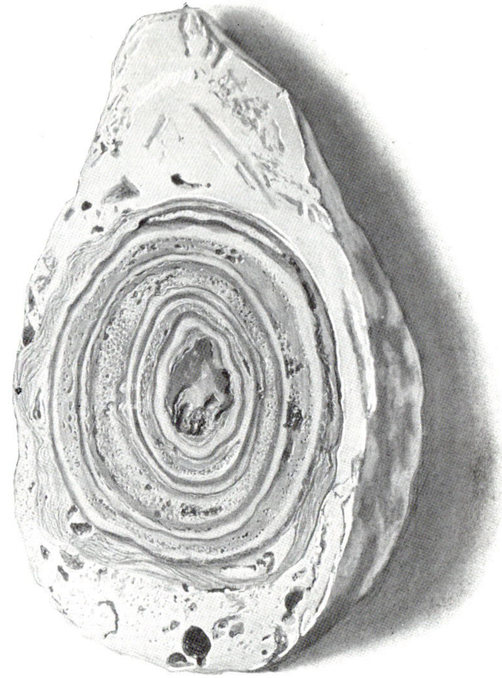

Fig. 223.—Mixed oxalate and urate calculus coated with phosphates.

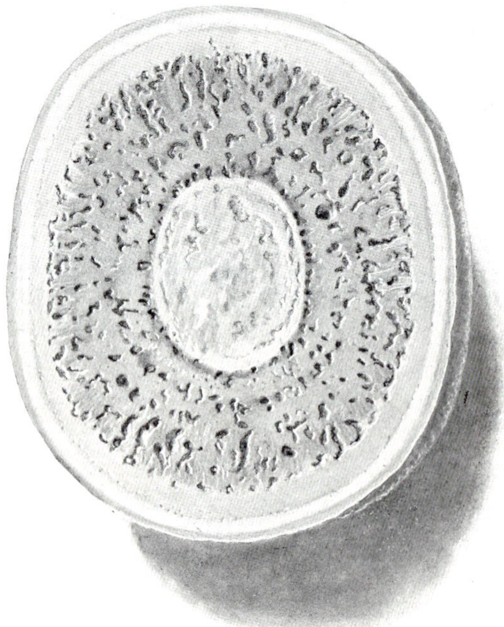

Fig. 224.—Phosphate calculus with a layer of oxalates.

other stones, especially when they are cracked or irregular and lodged in a bladder where there is ammoniacal decomposition of the urine.

The obstruction produced by calculi is dependent, as long as they are loose in the bladder, upon the posture of the patient and upon the size and shape of the stone, so that unless it is impacted in the urethra, the obstruction is intermittent.

LITERATURE

D. Kleinschmidt: Die Harnsteine, Berlin, 1911.
W. Ebstein: Natur u. Behandlung der Harnsteine, Wiesbaden, 1884.
H. A. Fowler: Johns Hopkins Hosp. Reports, 1908, xiii, 507.

Paralytic Dilatation of the Bladder.—Normally, when the bladder is filled to a certain degree it tends to contract and empty itself, the act of micturition being under the voluntary control of a sphincter, and being in itself the effect of nervous reflexes by way of nerves which run to and from the lumbar and sacral cord. When injury of the spinal cord results in complete paralysis of the lower extremities and of the lower part of the body, as is so frequently the case in fractures of the spine, etc., neither afferent nor efferent impulses are effective. There is no sense of overfilling of the bladder, no desire to micturate, and often no power, even by the aid of the abdominal muscles, to empty the bladder. Hence it gradually becomes distended to an enormous size, and must be emptied by the introduction of a catheter.

CYSTITIS

These various conditions offer a more or less insuperable obstacle to the discharge of urine from the bladder, and the immediate result is its incomplete instead of complete evacuation. Ordinarily the residual urine does no harm, except in that it occupies space in the bladder which thereupon fills more quickly, so that micturition becomes abnormally frequent. That is true so long as the urine remains sterile, but with increased difficulty in urination it may become necessary to pass a catheter into the bladder, and sometimes this operation falls to the hands of the patient himself. Naturally, in such conditions it is not long before bacteria are carried into the residual urine and find there an excellent culture-medium. As soon as this happens, the urine, which may have been clear before, becomes turbid and alkaline, full of bacteria, desquamated epithelial cells, and leucocytes, showing that the response to infection in the form of an acute cystitis has appeared.

Naturally, a great variety of bacteria may be concerned in this process, and in such cases there is commonly a mixture of several forms, sometimes even with yeasts and fungi in addition. The inflammation (cystitis) which they set up will vary in its intensity according to the type of infection, but more especially according to the degree of obstruction and the resistance of the individual.

Forms of Cystitis.—We may distinguish catarrhal, purulent, and diphtheritic forms, and there are others that almost merit the name gangrenous.

In the mildest infections the bladder-wall becomes swollen and reddened, and a few leucocytes pass through. The urine is acid when Bacillus coli is the infecting agent, but otherwise it is often alkaline, with a small amount of ammonia and a sediment of phosphates, desquamated cells, and mucus. The purulent form follows upon more intense infections, and is characterized by hæmorrhages in the mucosa and pus-containing urine. These hæmorrhages may be mere petechiæ.

In the diphtheritic form much more extensive hæmorrhages appear, surrounding the patches of most intense inflammation. In these areas the bacteria are found to have caused a superficial necrosis, with the coagulation of a layer of yellowish or greenish fibrin upon the surface and into the depth of the necrotic mucosa. The loosening of such a false membrane leaves an ulcer with hæmorrhagic base, and surrounded by a deep-red halo. Such ulcers are usually found at first upon the more prominent parts of the wall, where the muscular trabeculæ project, and upon the smoother trigonum. In advanced, long-standing cases, though, the ulcers become deeper and may cover much of the bladder-wall, some of them are scarred, while others are newly formed; discoloration occurs; there arises much blackish-green staining, probably largely from sulphides, which blacken the hæmosiderin formed in the hæmorrhagic areas, and the bladder-wall presents an extremely foul, ragged, and deeply stained surface. In a bladder of this type the urine contains all the materials which could be shed from such a wall.

Usually a great dilatation of the bladder follows upon such long-continued obstruction to the outflow of urine. Its walls become stretched, and particularly those portions which lie between the main muscular trabeculæ may be bulged out into diverticula. At the same time there is a distinct hypertrophy of the muscle bundles—a work hypertrophy which arises in the oft-repeated attempt of the bladder to discharge its contents (Figs. 215 217). Whether the dilatation or the hypertrophy will predominate depends upon the age and general condition of the patient. There are old men without much obstruction in whom atrophy of the muscle of the bladder allows it to become distended and to retain residual urine.

The entrance of the ureters into the bladder is oblique, through the muscular wall, so that the more tensely the bladder is distended, the greater is the pressure tending to flatten and close the end of the ureter as it slants through the bladder-wall. In addition to this the actual orifice is guarded internally by valve-like folds of mucosa which readily allow the urine to pass downward only. Therefore the entrance of fluid from the bladder into the ureter is normally excluded, and it is impossible, even with great force, to inject colored fluids into the ureter by distending the bladder with them. It requires some destructive change in the intravesical part of the ureter to make this influx possible—either the erosion of all these guarding tissues or something which will render the ureter so rigid that it will not collapse when the bladder is distended. Nevertheless, it is evident that if it becomes difficult for the urine to escape from the bladder, it becomes equally difficult for it to leave the ureter and enter the bladder, so that an obstruction which ends in distension of the bladder is equally an obstruction to the escape of urine from the kidneys and ureters.

EFFECTS OF OBSTRUCTION ON THE KIDNEYS

We have now to consider the effects upon the kidney with its pelvis and ureter of—(*a*) Obstruction without infection; (*b*) obstruction with infection; and (*c*) the rare infection by way of the urinary tract without obstruction.

Hydronephrosis, by which is meant a dilatation of the pelvis of the kidney, often accompanied by hydro-ureter and practically invariably by a distension and thinning of the renal substance itself through the accumulation of fluid in that cavity, may result from various causes. All those types

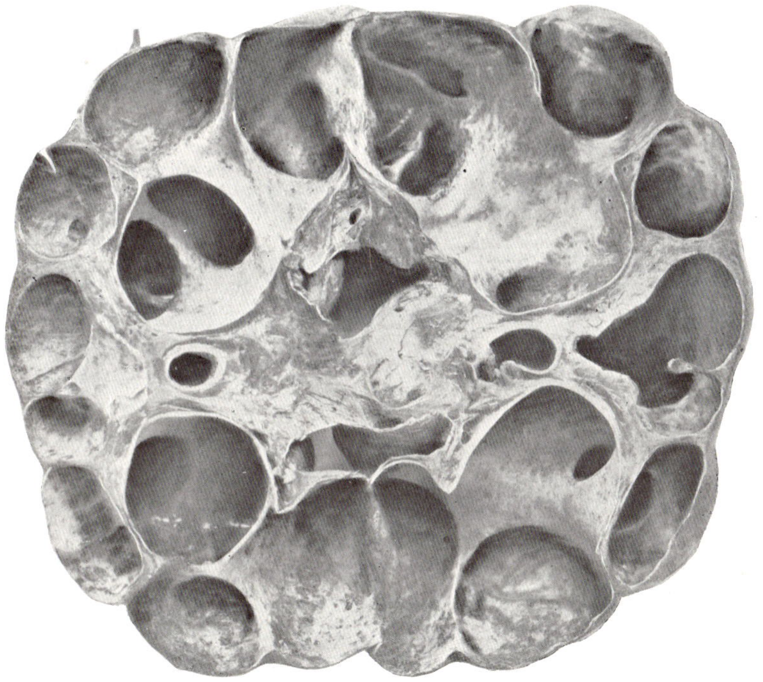

Fig. 225.—Hydronephrosis with extreme dilatation of calyces. The halves of the kidney are laid apart. The ureter is seen in section.

of obstruction which lead to distension of the bladder may be accompanied by hydro-ureter and by hydronephrosis, but in addition there are those in which the ureters are blocked in some way. Therefore in the latter group the hydronephrosis may be unilateral. The pressure of tumors from the outside, such as those which arise from the uterus and ovaries, even if they do not invade the substance of the ureters, often sets up such a blocking of their lumen. The same effect may be produced by an inflammatory process in the ureteral wall which leads to stricture formation, and Sampson has diagrammatically figured the effect in this direction of those operations for the removal of pelvic tumors in which the blood supply of a portion of the ureter has been disturbed. Necrosis with scarring, and even rupture of the ureteral wall after the distension has begun, may follow.

Renal calculi formed in the pelvis of the kidney, when small enough, pass through the ureter, causing intense pain, but, as is well known, there are normally several constrictions in the course of this tube, and the calculus may stick at one of these so as to cause complete or partial plugging. Higher in the neck of the ureter or in the pelvis itself the same thing may happen.

Renal calculi, formed as has been described above, present themselves in various forms and sizes, the larger ones being moulded into the calyces and about the papillæ so as to present a complete cast of the pelvis of the kidney, branching into each recess and extending in a pointed, curved projection down into the ureter (Fig. 226). Sometimes

Fig. 226.—Renal calculus in pelvis forming a complete mould of all the calyces, and extending into the ureter.

they are in several pieces, and the fragments may be fitted to one another as though articulated. At the other extreme we find small, loose, irregular calculi, sometimes no more bulky than coarse sand. It seems that unless they become impacted in the ureter these calculi cause no great distension of the pelvis. In children the common uric-acid infarcts already mentioned are often associated with concretions which may be partly embedded in the renal substance itself.

Finally there are some deformities of the pelvis, especially with relation to the insertion of the ureter, which can give rise to hydronephrosis, and which in turn are emphasized by it. These are especially the instances in which the ureter springs from a point high up in the pelvis and leaves it at an acute angle. There is then a valve-like arrangement, which is brought into play by any disarrangement of the kidney and completed by the distension of the pelvis. Sometimes the ureter divides before it reaches the hilum of the kidney, so that the pelvis is in several compartments with their corresponding calyces and papillæ. Then it is possible to have a partial hydronephrosis if only one of these branches is obstructed.

The fluid which accumulates is generally clear, and contains urea and other urinary constituents, although in unusual proportions. It has generally been looked upon as urine, but except perhaps in those cases in which the obstruction is intermittent, it will be seen, from the mode of development, that it must differ a good deal from normal urine. It often contains casts of the renal tubules and desquamated epithelium.

Cohnheim made the statement that only partial or intermittent obstruction is followed by great distension of the pelvis, while complete obstruction results in cessation of the flow of urine and atrophy of the kidney.

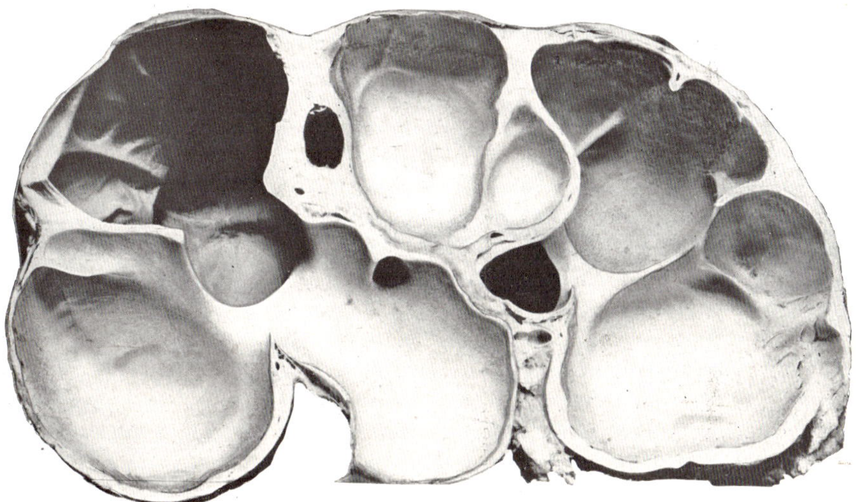

Fig. 227.—Extreme hydronephrosis. The calyces have been distended into spherical cavities, so that all trace of the papilla disappears.

In human beings this has the appearance of being true, for in cases of complete obstruction of the ureter one finds the kidney reduced to an insignificant, flattened, fibrous mass, in which hardly any well-ordered renal substance can be found (*cf.* Fig. 70). On the other hand, an intermittent or partial obstruction can cause the distension of the ureter and pelvis until a sac is formed which may occupy a great portion of the abdominal cavity. But it has been shown recently by Ponfick and others that the absolute closure of the ureter is followed by such distension of the pelvis and the kidney as to reduce the kidney to a thin layer of firm fibroid tissue. In the earlier stages the bulk and weight of the kidney substance, exclusive of the accumulated fluid, actually increase up to about thirty-six days after the ureteral ligation, after which they decrease steadily. In view of this we may easily conclude that the atrophic remnants which we find in human beings after the ureter has been plugged by a stone are the final results of a much longer period of obstruction than even the seven months through which Ponfick watched his experiments.

With the distension of the pelvis the calyces become widened and the papillæ flattened until in time they come to form only circular portions of the wall of the hemispherical calyces, the orifice being located only as a slight central elevation with radiating blood-vessels and tubular markings. Even more complete distortion occurs, and hardly any trace of the papilla is left—the whole kidney is reduced to a multilocular sac (*cf.* Fig. 227) in which the partitions, as Ponfick points out, are held in place by the blood-vessels, whose course they indicate. The section shows that the pyramids lose their radiate appearance because the tubules come to lie parallel with the surface of the kidney (Fig. 228). The cortex becomes very thin, and loses its striations, which are obscured in the gray, scar-like tissue which takes their place. It is strange that sometimes this effect is very

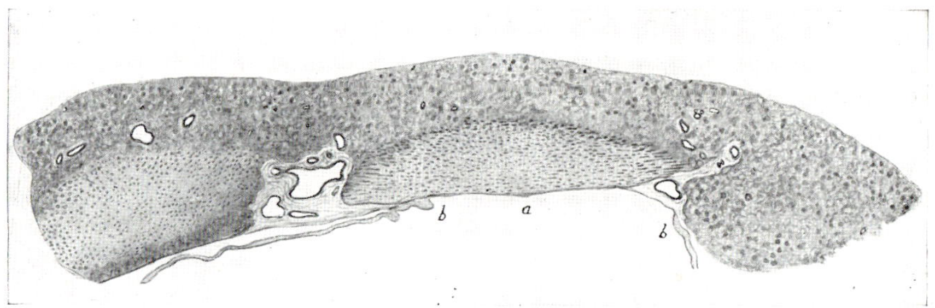

Fig. 228.—Hydronephrosis. Section shows the thinning and flattening of cortex and pyramid, with great distension of the pelvis and calyces. The flattened papilla is at *a;* the margins of the calyx, at *b*, *b*.

irregular, so that one finds patches of relatively thick renal cortex scattered in the otherwise thin wall of the sac. Possibly this is due to the unequal diminution in the blood supply of various areas of the cortex, which comes through vessels which run in the partitions of the sac and may be exposed to different degrees of pressure.

It is a remarkable secretory process which produces a fluid which may attain a pressure higher than that of blood. Ponfick describes the appearance of hyaline casts, of leucocytes, and especially of red blood-corpuscles, together with a coagulable fluid in the tubules and glomerular capsules. The epithelial cells, at first swollen, later become flattened, and even the glomerular tufts may disappear, leaving spaces that look like tubules. There is apparently the formation of an actual exudate of inflammatory character in response to the destructive effect upon the cells. Associated with it comes a diffuse formation of abundant new connective tissue everywhere between the tubules and about the glomeruli. The end-result is that we have in an advanced case an extraordinary thinning-out of the renal substance, which assumes a gray, uniform, translucent appearance, and an almost leathery consistence. In this the tubules are found lined by a uniform flattened epithelium, and often interrupted by the collapse of their walls, so that spindle-shaped or even rounded portions remain, filled with hyaline casts. The glomeruli are obliterated and converted into fibrous nodules, or else surrounded by a thickened fibrous capsule, and everywhere the interstitial connective tissue is prominent, not only through its actual increase, but because of the disappearance of many tubules. It will be seen that this process is, in nearly every respect, analogous to that which follows the ligation of the duct of such a gland as the pancreas.

Ascending Renal Infection.—In all forms of obstruction to the outflow of a secretion we have traced the liability of the tissues to infection, and the kidney is no exception to this rule. With the advent of virulent bacteria in an already formed hydronephrotic sac there arises an inflammation which is of a far more intense character than any which may have been associated with the mere mechanical obstruction, and when the sac is filled with a purulent fluid, we speak of the condition as *pyonephrosis*. A similar condition, naturally with somewhat different course and clinical symptoms, may arise when the distending fluid is from the first infected and the inflammatory process is intense throughout. Thus, when there appears an infection about impacted renal calculi which may not in themselves have caused an effective obstruction, or when an obstruction lower in the ureter or in the bladder or urethra causes the damming-up of urine which quickly becomes infected, we have a distension which is by no means so great, but in which the pelvic walls are injured by the bacteria and present a hæmorrhagic, ulcerated, and purulent surface.

It is hard to draw a line between the cases in which the distension is predominant and those in which the inflammatory processes are more imposing. These latter, which are known under the name *pyelitis*, or more usually *pyelonephritis*, constitute a form of ascending suppurative nephritis which is most commonly associated with obstruction and stagnation of urine. But it must be borne in mind that, with very slight differences, an inflammatory process in the kidney with suppuration and secondary inflammation of the pelvis may be caused by bacteria brought to the kidney through the blood-stream when there is no disease of the lower urinary tract at all. This can often be easily distinguished, and we shall speak of it elsewhere.

In all these cases in which infection of the kidney is associated with obstruction and infection of the urinary passages, there appear abscesses in the substance of the kidney itself, in addition to the acute, oftentimes very intense, inflammation of the mucosa of the pelvis. These are usually situated chiefly in the cortex, and are sometimes very small, but generally conglomerated, so that they reach the size of a pea and bulge on the surface. If one tears off the capsule of the kidney, many of them are broken open and exude a greenish-yellow pus. On section, the tissue around them is grayish red and swollen, and has lost the distinctness of its markings. Often, but not always, there are grayish-yellow, opaque streaks running down through the pyramid toward the papilla, which are produced by extensions of the abscesses along the conducting tubules (Figs. 229, 230).

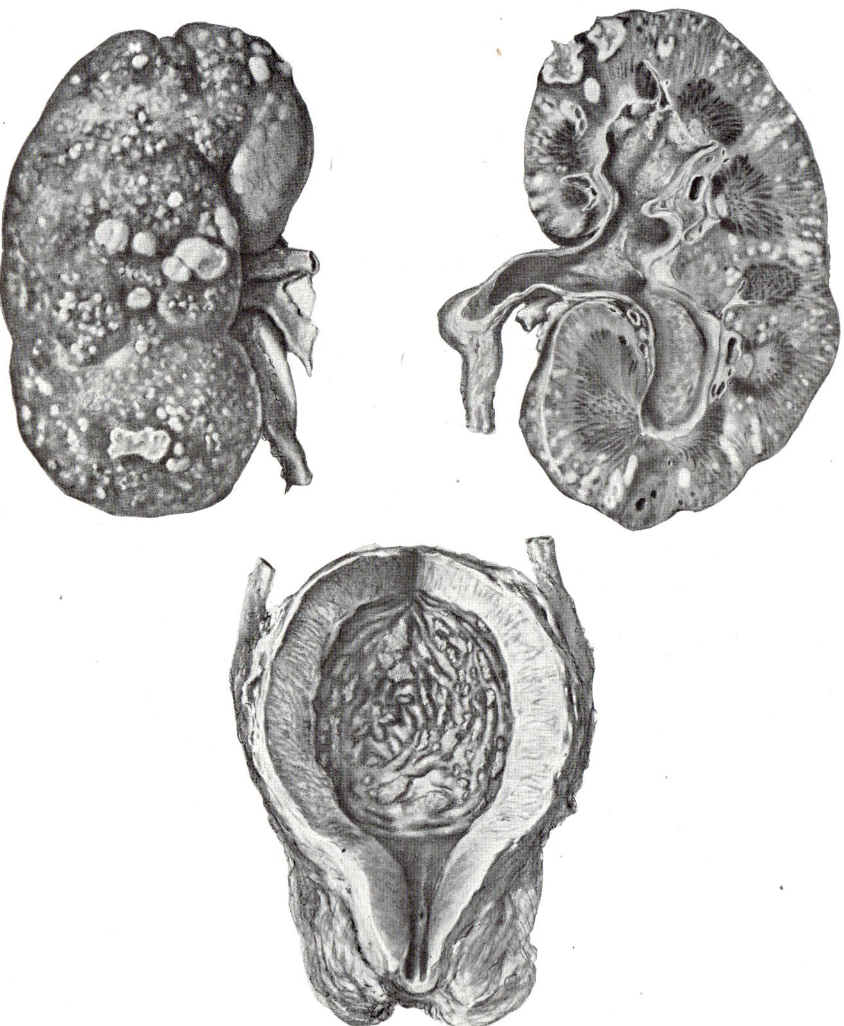

Fig. 229—Pyelonephritis, pyoureter, diphtheritic cystitis with hypertrophy of the bladder. Case of urethral stricture long treated with sounds and catheters.

Active discussion has raged for a long time as to the paths followed by bacteria, which, from an infected bladder, arrive at the production of more or less isolated abscesses in the cortex of the kidney, and many views have been proposed. It has been stated that the organisms get into the blood-stream from the bladder, and lodge finally in the kidney, which is rendered susceptible by the obstruction. Others think they pass along the lymphatics of the ureter or by the venous anastomoses between the vessels of the pelvic organs, ureter, and kidney. Neither of these last views seems to me based on probability, because they involve retrograde embolism, which is not to be lightly called to our aid.

The more common view is that the bacteria pass up the lumen of the ureter to the pelvis, and thence into the kidney. They cannot easily ascend

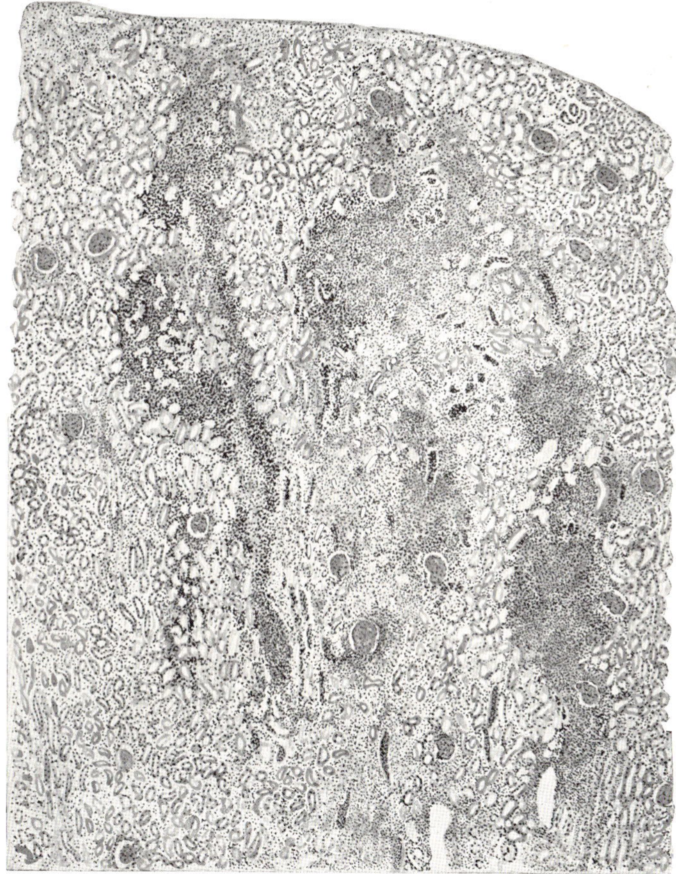

Fig. 230.—Pyelonephritis. There are beginning abscesses in the cortex, shown as areas of necrotic tubules with purulent exudate about them. Many of the tubules contained bacteria.

the ureter when it is open and flushed by the normal stream of urine, but if it is obstructed and occupied by a nearly stagnant column of urine, it is easy to believe that bacteria may spread to the kidney. This is especially true if any inflammation of the ureteral wall in its intravesical part has rendered it rigid, and thus spoiled the guard at the ureteral opening. Having attained the pelvis and produced a pyelitis, it remains to explain their entrance into the kidney. Orth looks askance at the glibly expressed belief that they wander up the tubules, but Schmidt and Aschoff have found bacteria in the tubules in animals in which they have experimentally obstructed and infected the ureters, and adopt this idea. Without it we must have recourse to the blood-vessels, of which, of course, only the arteries are available, or to the lymphatics. Muller thinks he can prove the lymphatic transmission by finding the tubules attacked and perforated on one side by exudate, which also fills the lymphatics. It is difficult, however, when the inflammation has proceeded to such a degree, to say which way it is working, and the findings of Schmidt and Aschoff, which show that the bacteria can enter the tubules, seem, after all, most convincing.

LITERATURE

Ponfick: Ziegler's Beiträge, 1910, xlix, 127; 1911, l, 1.
Orth: Lehrb. d. spez. Path., 1893, ii, 59.
Schmidt and Aschoff: Pyelonephritis, Jena, 1893.
Ebstein and Nicolaier: Virch. Arch., 1891, cxxiii, 373.
Jores: Ergeb. d. allg. Path., 1907, xi_2, 146.

CHAPTER XXIII

TYPES OF INJURY—OBSTRUCTION (Continued).—GENERAL DISTURBANCES OF CIRCULATION

Mechanism of circulatory organs. Pericardial and pleural effusions. Emphysema. Chemical influences. Effects of arterial and myocardial disease. Myocarditis. Valvular disease. General mechanism of the obstruction thus produced. Various valvular lesions and their special effects. Cardiac hypertrophy and dilatation. Decompensation; chronic passive congestion. Disturbances of conduction system in heart.

Mechanism of Circulatory Organs.—Reflection upon the general mechanism of the circulation of the blood will give one an idea of the extraordinary number of things that can fail in playing their proper part and upset the smooth working of the whole. Incidentally, it gives, too, a sense of wonder that a machine of such marvelous complexity should work at all, and not be constantly interrupted or overtaxed by the variable tasks laid upon it and the difficulties thrown in its way. It is found, however, that not only does it keep up a definite standard output of work day and night, but it will do this in spite of the most unreasonable obstacles.

The Heart.—The heart, as a bulbous muscular pump, must keep the blood moving in two circles, one through the lungs, the other through the rest of the body, for which reason it is in two halves; and it must do this promptly, having a new supply of blood ready when it has discharged one, wherefore it has its auricles. There are wonderfully perfect valves to maintain the direction, and the left side of the heart is more powerful than the right, because it drives the blood into a larger field and against greater resistance. Still, with these unequal tasks, which may vary between two beats, one side of the heart may not eject more or less blood than the other. If the right ventricle throws out so much as one drop more than the left in each beat, the lungs would be overdistended and burst within a few minutes. This perfect coördination between the two sides is even more remarkable when we think that the ventricles are formed essentially from two coils of one long muscle band, the tendinous ends of which are attached to the valves as the chordæ tendineæ, and that the tasks of the two sides are not only different, but vary differently. To be effective, the auricle must empty itself into the ventricle at the precise moment required, and the ventricle must be ready for its new load; to expel the blood with adequate force, the walls of these chambers must contract not only rhythmically, but uniformly, and to insure this rhythmic and perfect contraction there are special telegraphic connections with central stations at at least two places, from which controlling impulses are sent out—one sets the pace, the other relays the message.

The Blood-vessels.—The heart is aided in its work by the arteries, and to a less extent by the veins. They are not merely elastic tubes, in places, in the veins at least, furnished with valves, but active contractile organs, which not only drive on the blood by a sort of peristaltic contraction, but control the head of pressure with which the heart works, by narrowing or widening their own calibre. Were it not for this healthy opposition to the push of the heart, there would arise one of the vicious circles that may prove disastrous to the whole circulation; not only would the arterial blood escape into the distensible veins through the capillaries, but the back pressure into the coronaries, upon which the nutrition of the heart depends, being gone, the heart would fail at once. The fact that this controlling contraction and relaxation of the arterioles occurs locally in different regions of very different extent explains the possibility of rapid variations in pressure, which must be compensated either by extra effort of the heart or by other changes in calibre in the vessels.

Control of Blood-vessels.—The heart and blood-vessels then, work in coöperation almost as intimate as that of the two sides of the heart. This must be managed by the nervous system. There are nerves important in this respect, the accelerator and augmentor nerves, which form part of the sympathetic system, and to which the inhibitory vagus nerves act antagonistically. The blood-vessels are made to contract by vasoconstrictor fibres, which, starting from the ganglion-cells of a centre in the floor of the fourth ventricle, reach the blood-vessel walls by relays of cells through the sympathetic ganglia. They are made to dilate by inhibitory vasodilator fibres, which seem to have no definite centre in the brain and do not act rhythmically, like the vasoconstrictors, which maintain a tone in the vessels. These mechanisms which govern the vessels may be set in action reflexly by impulses conducted along sensory nerves, but probably by special fibres, some of which act to stimulate the release of vasoconstrictor impulses (pressor fibres), while others set in action vasodilator impulses (depressor fibres). From the aorta and heart there even runs a nerve whose sole function is of an afferent depressor character. Psychical stimuli, as well as those from various organs, may affect the vascular control, and in a reflex way cause the blanching or flushing of different parts of the body. Indeed, violent painful stimuli may produce sometimes such extreme relaxation of the vessels that the blood-pressure falls to a degree which proves fatal (shock). Certain chemical stimuli, such as extracts of the adrenal and pituitary glands, are known to have a powerful influence upon blood-pressure through causing changes in the calibre of the blood-vessels, and it is often suggested, though not quite proved, that the control of the balance is largely dependent on the activities of these organs of internal secretion.

Other Influences.—There are other factors of a more mechanical nature which have a very great influence upon the circulation, namely, respiration, the condition of the abdominal contents, posture and muscular activity, and many others. Respiration aids the flow of venous blood to the heart by producing a partial vacuum in the thorax during inspiration, and at the same moment increasing the intra-abdominal pressure. Most of this is done by the diaphragm, which both sucks and presses the blood out of the abdominal veins. Enteroptosis or sagging of the abdominal viscera, which pulls down the diaphragm and diminishes its excursion, annuls to a great extent this beneficial action. Great accumulations of fluid or large tumors in the abdomen bring about the same result in a different way, by pressing the diaphragm up and immobilizing it. The circulation is made easier by the recumbent posture—more difficult by the erect, but, of course, this is not felt much by the normal heart. Violent muscular exercise elicits greater activity of the heart, both to aërate the blood more rapidly and to bring it in increased quantity to the active muscles. The heart may be overtaxed by too great and prolonged effort, so that it dilates and the man falls in a faint or dies. This is really an example of the response of the heart to demands which arise from an enormously accelerated metabolism.

From all this it is seen that in the circle through which the blood is forced the conditions in each part are influenced by those in the preceding and succeeding parts. Each portion of the circle is governed by regulating mechanisms, and instantly adapts itself to new conditions, whether these are produced by changes within the stream-bed or by influences from outside, and this very adaptation, like the original change, is felt not only just in front of or just behind that point, but all around the circle. All these regulatory mechanisms act together to maintain the arterial blood-pressure at a fairly definite standard, which reaches 110 to 150 mm. of mercury during systole in the larger arteries, falling with each pulsation to 60 to 80 mm. in diastole. As the blood advances into the arterioles and capillaries, the pressure sinks and the differences between systolic and diastolic pressure disappear, so that in the veins the stream is constant, and at a pressure which still decreases toward the heart. In the pulmonary circulation its pressure is very much lower and the pulsatory variations less, but it passes with greater velocity through those capillaries than through the capillaries of the systemic organs. The importance of the maintenance of this pressure and the corresponding rapid exchange of blood are most evident in the coronary circulation of the heart and in the brain. The nice balance of this mechanism is maintained with great tenacity, and the effects of disturbing influences may often be found not in changes in the blood-flow itself, but only in the differences in the machine developed to compensate for the interference.

PATHOLOGICAL OBSTRUCTIONS

Pericardial Effusion.—Mechanical influences quite outside the circulation itself can have such effects. The accumulation of fluid in the pericardial cavity may go on gradually until the sac is enormously distended, but if it comes suddenly, as in the case of a hæmorrhage from the heart, or when one injects it experimentally in an animal, the pericardium has no time to stretch. Then the heart is greatly embarrassed because it cannot expand to allow the entrance of blood from the veins. Great distension of the veins occurs, with heightening of the blood-pressure there, while the amount of blood thrown into the aorta becomes so small that even the action of the vasoconstrictors fails to keep up the blood-pressure, little blood goes into the coronary arteries and the heart gives up its beating. Quick removal of the fluid from the pericardium may restore the normal conditions in time to start the heart once more. Moderate collections of fluid (hydropericardium or pericarditis) may cause only a tolerable overfilling of the veins and decrease in the arterial blood-flow.

Intrapleural and Pulmonary Obstruction.—Effusions of fluid into the pleura compressing the lung (*cf.* Fig. 92), tumors in the pleura, narrowing and distortion of the thorax by deformities, such as curvature of the spine (skoliosis, kyphosis, etc.), and destructive changes in the lungs themselves have a similar effect in obstructing the circulation, but act at a different point. Now the difficulty which still affects the whole blood-stream lies in forcing the blood through the compressed or reduced pulmonary stream-bed, and the burden is put upon the right ventricle. It rises at once to its increased task, and may be able to perform it by drawing on its reserve power. Often it can go on like this, forcing the obstacle and maintaining the normal circulation, in time growing in thickness and strength of wall through the increased exercise. But if it fails only partially, the blood accumulates in the veins and in the auricle, and reaches the aorta in diminished amount.

Emphysema.—One of the common obstructions acting at this point is emphysema of the lungs (see p. 419), in which the rarefaction of the lung tissue obliterates much of the stream-bed in the lung. Other changes, which, by cramping the thoracic organs or obstructing the pulmonary blood-flow, produce the same effect, will be referred to later and easily understood. This is the narrow pass for the whole circulation. Afterward in the systemic circle nothing can so readily obstruct the whole blood-flow, since there are always roundabout ways, and the closure even of large arterial trunks has practically no effect upon the blood-pressure. Even the whole aorta below the renal arteries may be ligated, with only a trifling rise in blood-pressure. Ligation of the renal arteries adds little to this; that of the splanchnic arteries has much more effect, but even this (Longcope and McClintock) is a matter of only a few millimetres of mercury. Such extreme obstructions are, of course, rare and of little importance, as far as the circulatory apparatus goes; their importance relates rather to the nutrition of the tissues which those vessels should supply.

Toxic Influences.—Chemical influences have great importance also, in so far as they affect the nervous control of the heart or arteries (atropine, adrenaline, etc.), or the muscular walls of these structures (barium, ergot, etc.), but their effects are transient and need not be considered further here.

The poisons at work in many infections act upon the heart to injure its muscle and weaken its power, or, as in the case of diphtheria, affect also the vasomotors, paralyzing their control over the vessels and thus allowing a fall in blood-pressure which may be fatal in withdrawing blood from the coronary circulation. This constitutes the underlying principle of the shock in which patients die in such intoxications.

Anatomical Changes in the Blood-vascular Apparatus.—Changes in the circulatory apparatus itself are productive of great changes in the blood-flow, nearly always in the sense of an obstruction, or diminution in the efficiency of its propulsive power. These commonly affect the elasticity and contractility of the arterial walls, the muscular power of the heart-walls, the efficiency of the valves, and the mechanism which maintains the rhythm of the heart, and may be considered in this order.

THE EFFECT OF ARTERIAL DISEASE

Disease of the arterial walls (*cf.* p. 321) results commonly in their partial rigidity. At least the elastic tissue which gives them their resiliency is broken and degenerated and greatly decreased in amount. What remains is rendered useless by the formation of stiff fibrous tissue, or even calcified patches which will not stretch. In the same way the smooth muscle, so important in changing the calibre of the vessel, and in propelling the blood by its contractions, is partly destroyed, partly splinted by the new tissue, which thickens the once delicate inner layer of the vessel, and thus changes it to a rigid tube, perfectly incapable of aiding the heart. Beside this, the lumen of these tubes is often narrowed by this process, and sometimes to an extreme degree.

The general effect is to withdraw from the heart whatever aid the vessels previously afforded in the propulsion of the blood. While this is important, it is not so great that an extreme burden is put upon the heart by its loss. Nor, except in the case of the splanchnic vessels, is the narrowing of the channels likely to cause a noteworthy rise in blood-pressure. Extra work is, of course, put upon the heart by both these factors, and the wall of the left ventricle thickens and becomes stronger in response to it, but there is still uncertainty as to the degree to which the arterial changes alone are responsible for this; probably their effect has been frequently overestimated in cases in which several factors are available in explaining high blood-pressure and the enlargement of the heart. The opinion has been expressed by many (Hasenfeld, Longcope) that rigidity and narrowing of the splanchnic vessels are by far the most important in this respect.

Of special interest are the changes in the coronary arteries of the heart, for any interference with the abundant blood supply necessary to that muscle must bring with it injuries of the heart-wall, to the detriment of the general circulation.

THE EFFECT OF MYOCARDIAL DISEASE

The arrangement of the musculature of the heart-walls (J. B. MacCallum, Mall) is such as to control with the greatest completeness the propulsion of the blood—not only does it obliterate the cavity of the ventricles, but by the contraction of the papillary muscles it insures the proper tension and perfect closure of the auriculoventricular valves. Further, special subdivisions of the muscle support the semilunar valves, and maintain their closure in such a way that even with slight imperfections of the valves leakage is much diminished by this muscular action. The heart muscle has always been regarded as a network of cells attached to one another along transverse cement lines, but in recent years there has been a tendency to look upon it as a sort of syncytium without cellular limits, the cement lines being thought to be the product of physical influences which act more intensely with the advance of age (Cohn, Aschoff, and Tawara). The muscle fibrils, with their sarcoplasmic discs, are arranged in each fibre around a central space, in which lies the nucleus surrounded by undifferentiated protoplasm. It is in this space at the poles of the nucleus that a yellowish pigment begins to accumulate in early years of life, and increases with the advance of age. With great wasting of the heart muscle this pigment may become so abundant as to give a chestnut-brown color to the whole heart (brown atrophy). As indicated elsewhere, it is one of the lipochrome pigments and takes a reddish stain with Sudan. The specific stimulus-conducting system of fibres will be described later.

Myocardial Injuries.—Myocarditis.—Degenerative and destructive changes occur in the heart muscle in the course of various infections, intoxications, and nutritive disturbances, but are not specially characteristic of any. Fat accumulates in the form of fine droplets arranged in the sarcoplasmic discs, and therefore often in longitudinal lines. This fat is, as a rule, not uniformly distributed, but is very abundant in certain little groups of fibres, while almost absent in the neighboring ones. On the whole, it is far more abundant in the inner layers of the heart-wall than the outer. This results in the peculiar mottling with minute, opaque, yellow patches, most commonly seen in the wall of the right ventricle below the orifice of the pulmonary artery, and in the papillary muscles of the left ventricle, although it may be spread all over the interior and deep in the substance of both ventricles. This is the so-called tigering or faded-leaf appearance (*cf.* Figs. 32 and 33). Ribbert thinks that this peculiar distribution is due to unequal nutrition in the regions of different minute branches of the coronary arteries. It is found most often in extreme and long-standing anæmias, protracted febrile states, and in chronic diseases, such as nephritis, associated with anæmia. The presence of the fat seems to have very little detrimental effect upon the function of the heart, or perhaps it should be said that the diseased condition of the muscle which leads to the retention of the fat does not greatly impair its activity. Dr. Welch, in studying animals kept for a long time at a fever heat, found abundant deposition of fat in their hearts, but no special functional alteration. In the same way we find a certain cloudiness of the heart muscle in such infections as typhoid, but although we may name this parenchymatous degeneration, we cannot find that it indicates much harm to the heart.

On the other hand, in a few very acute and intense infections or toxic processes, such as diphtheria and scarlet fever, there may be actual necrosis or hyaline degeneration of fibres here and there, much like that seen in the rectus abdominis in typhoid fever, and these or even slighter lesions, not easily seen as changes in the muscle, may in these diseases give rise to a wide-spread acute inflammatory reaction with focal accumulations of leucocytes, œdema, and fibrinous coagula. It is impossible that these things, involving as they do the loss of many of the muscle-fibres, should not weaken the heart. Such is its reserve power, however, that it generally continues to beat well enough in spite of them. They have been regarded by many authors (Stejskal and others) as the cause of the sudden collapse and death at the height of diphtheria (and also in peritonitis and other septic infections), but Pässler and Romberg, MacCallum, and others have shown that deaths of this sort are due rather to failure of the vasomotor control of the arteries, which allows the blood-pressure to fall and the whole heart to suffer acutely from lack of nutrition. Abscesses in the myocardium in the course of general septic infections or resulting from embolism of the coronary branches by infected fragments of endocardial vegetations (septic infarcts), and extensions into the myocardium from endocardial vegetations, produce similar effects, but they will be considered elsewhere.

Calcified foci are sometimes found which may be the outcome of the healing of such necroses. So, too, it must be admitted that scar tissue of no specific character may remain as the result of their healing, and that, therefore, these lesions may give one explanation of the origin of the so-called fibrous myocarditis. That there are other changes potent in bringing about this scarring of the heart muscle we shall see.

Tubercles and syphilitic gummata are rare in the heart, but after acute articular rheumatism, the ætiology of which is still uncertain, there appear, as Aschoff, Bracht and Wächter, and many more have shown, minute elongated nodules of peculiar structure, scattered especially in the posterior wall of the left ventricle near its base, and much more rarely situated elsewhere. These are often periarterial, and are composed of large pale epithelioid cells with large vesicular nuclei (Fig. 231). Some of the cells become very conspicuous from the size of their nucleus, and others stand out as actual giant-cells. Eosinophiles and polynuclears accompany them sparsely. Aschoff is probably correct in contending that these cells are derived from mononuclear wandering cells, and not from the muscle or connective tissue. There is no definite evidence of their influencing the muscular activity to a recognizable degree.

Affections of the coronary arteries are particularly important in producing changes in the heart muscle. In some cases fragments of the thrombotic vegetations upon the heart valves may be thrown as emboli into these vessels, suddenly obstructing a branch or the whole artery. In others arteriosclerotic thickening of the vessel-walls gradually leads to narrowing of the lumen, which may be extreme, or which may be quickly completed by the formation of a thrombus upon the degenerated plaque, obstructing the flow of blood altogether. Any of these modes of

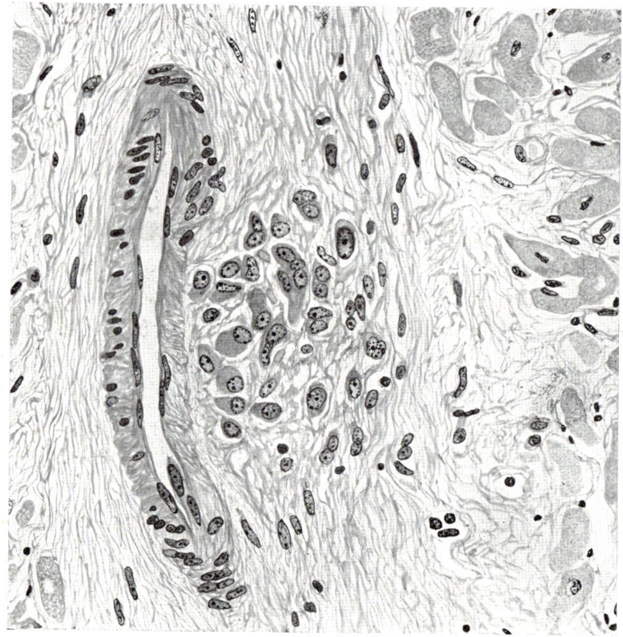

Fig. 231.—Aschoff body in the heart in acute rheumatism, showing the rather characteristic relation to the blood-vessel.

obstruction is effective in shutting off the blood supply from a certain part of the heart-wall because, although Spalteholz has shown clearly by injections that there are rather numerous anastomoses between the coronary arteries, these are insufficient to maintain the enormous supply of rapidly moving blood which the heart muscle needs. A less active organ might find it sufficient, but in the case of the heart-wall a part rather less in extent than the region supplied by the obstructed artery dies. The dead area promptly assumes the character of an anæmic infarction, and may at times occupy large parts of the walls of both ventricles, together with part of the interventricular septum. Experimental occlusion of various branches of the coronary arteries shows a variable result; often the heart stops beating at once, especially in the case of the anterior descending branch of the left artery, but in other cases, or in an animal of another kind, it may not. That human beings can often withstand extensive occlusion of the coronary arteries is familiar to every one from autopsy experience, for it is not uncommon to find large infarctions, revealed only by death from their rupture or from some other cause. Indeed,

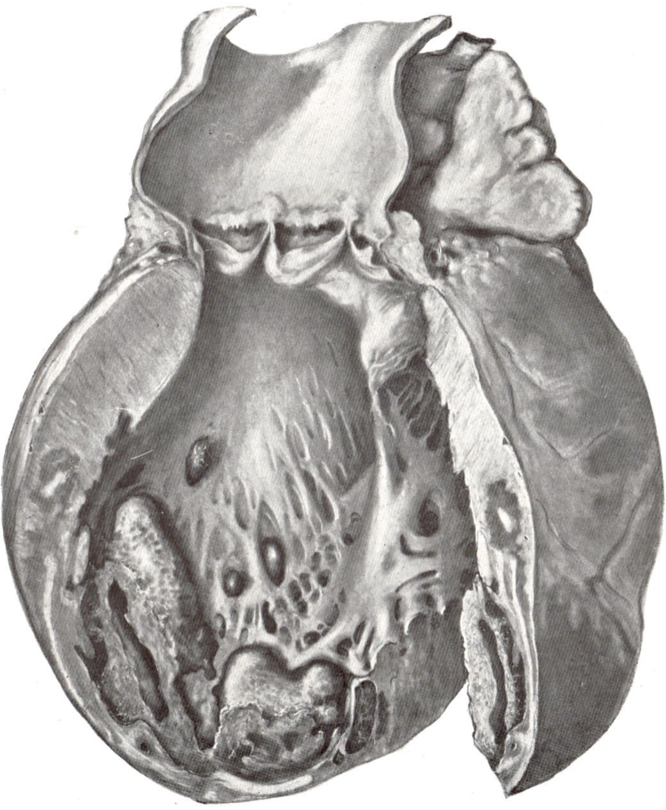

Fig. 232.—Hypertrophied heart with apical myocardial scar, aneurysmal dilatation, and extensive thrombus formation. The thrombi show central softening and excavation.

many of these heal completely into a rather thin fibrous scar, which replaces the heart-wall, becomes bulged out into an aneurysmal sac, and lined with thrombi (Fig. 232). Pericardial adhesions are generally found on their surface.

The effect of such obstructions when they concern the smaller branches is to produce little infarcts, which can be seen and felt upon the surface or in the interior of the heart as inelastic, hard, yellow, opaque masses with a halo of deep red. More common still is the discovery of various stages in the healing and scarring of such infarcts. But from finding scars in the heart-wall one cannot be sure that infarcts preëxisted—indeed, many of these scars seem to have been gradually formed by the wasting away of undernourished heart-muscle fibres and their replacement by fibrous tissue, especially in cases where no obvious obstruction or extreme narrowing of

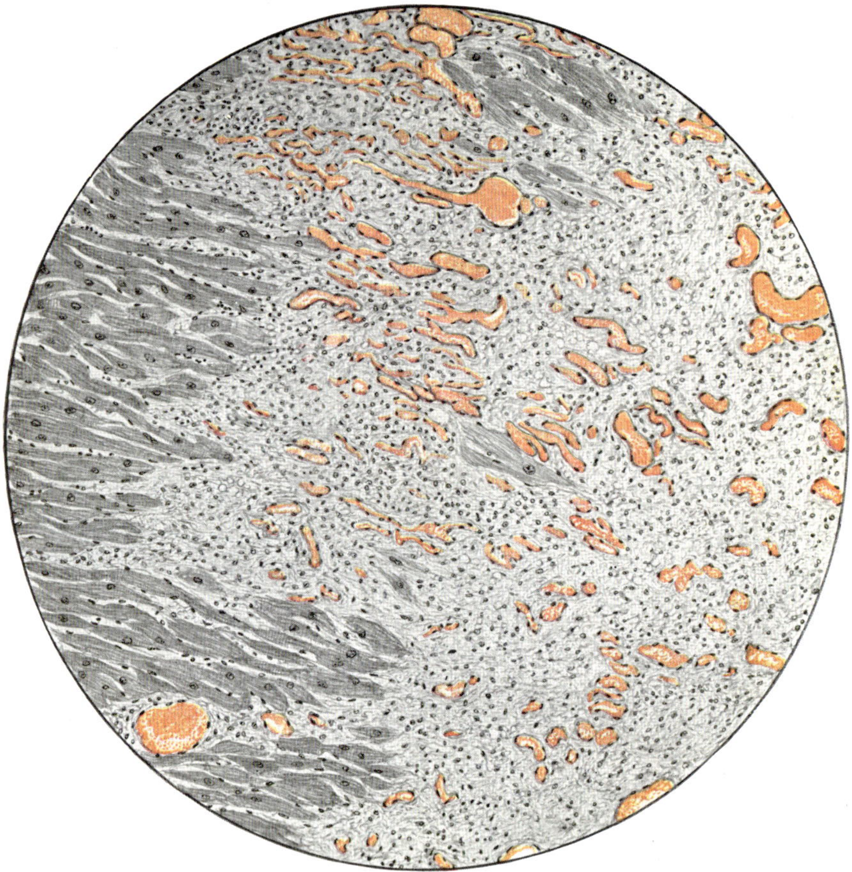

Fig. 233.—Vascular soft scar in the heart-wall. This is an early stage in the replacement of dead heart muscle by scar tissue.

the vessels can be found. And, after all, in that stage one cannot feel sure that they have not arisen through the healing of focal areas of toxic or infectious injury, which, after passing through a stage of inflammatory reaction, have ended in scars.

Thus, although from the presence of fresher stages in the form of infarcts it is sometimes possible to feel certain that the scars are due to embolic or arteriosclerotic and thrombotic occlusion of the coronary vessels, it is by no means always so. The fresher of these scars can often be felt on the surface of the heart as soft, depressed areas, which on section look gelatinous or spongy, and are grayish red and semi-translucent (Fig. 233). They are composed of a loose, soft granulation tissue, very rich in small blood-vessels, which have doubtless grown in from neighboring vascular areas. The older ones are dense, shining, tendon-like, pearly-white patches, sometimes very small and finely distributed, sometimes so large

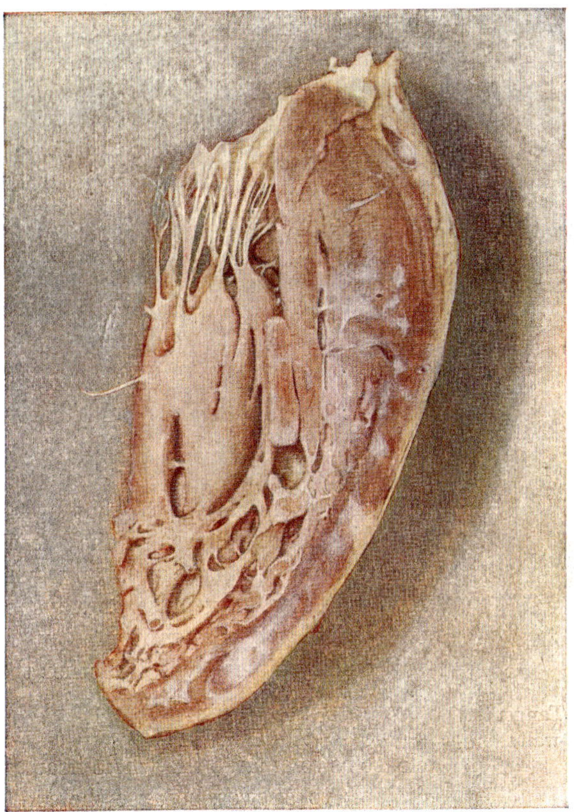

Fig. 234.—Old scars in the heart-wall (chronic fibrous myocarditis).

as to occupy much of the thickness of the wall (Fig. 234). They are often indefinite in outline, and radiate into the neighboring tissue (Fig. 235). Under the microscope they are formed of compact fibrous tissue poor in blood-vessels, but sometimes pigmented. Around their margins the muscle-fibres are frayed out, often reduced to pigmented strands (J. B. MacCallum), or swollen, with very much enlarged and deeply staining nuclei. Whenever any of these scars reaches the endocardial lining of the heart, it is covered by thrombi which doubtless began to be formed in earlier stages, when injured heart tissue was exposed to the passing blood. One may not say that all thrombi formed on the lining of the heart overlie such definite areas of destruction of the heart-wall, but nearly always, on cutting through the base of a globular intertrabecular thrombus, there is found a superficial scar. As mentioned above, it is at the apex of the heart that the conversion of the whole wall into scar tissue, thickly lined with thrombus material, is most common.

There is much dispute as to the effect of these scars, or rather of the injuries which give them origin, upon the muscular power of the heart. Unquestionably the destruction of heart muscle and its replacement by rigid scar tissue must deprive the heart of some of its strength, but such is the phenomenal reserve power of this organ that a great deal may be destroyed before the circulation is impaired. In a dog one may inject strong alcohol with a hypodermic syringe into the muscle of the heart-wall, so as to coagulate instantly a patch of the muscle; the slight fall of pressure is almost instantly made up, and this may be repeated a dozen times, until almost all the wall of the ventricle is turned into a hard, dead white mass before the circulation finally begins to fail. Aschoff and Tawara lay little stress on such scarring of the heart as a cause of the final breakdown of the circulation, and most clinical writers also agree that even extreme degrees of fibrous alteration may exist for a long time without giving rise to any symptoms. Irregular, feeble, slow pulse and dyspnœa are generally given as the symptoms, but these are not particularly distinctive. Whether the conversion of a part of the heart muscle into scar tissue is followed by hypertrophy of the rest of the muscle, so as to enlarge the whole heart, is a question difficult to answer, because the condition seldom occurs without other changes within or outside of the heart, which could also be concerned in causing cardiac hypertrophy. Exact experimental study seems not to have been carried out with reference to this point, except that Stewart has found that when myocarditis is produced by injections of adrenaline, the scarred hearts are distinctly hypertrophied and weigh more than the normal in proportion to the body weight. He thinks the action of the adrenaline, which causes the formation of scar tissue and enlargement of the muscle-fibres, results in an enlarged organ whose functional capacity is below normal. Naturally, although the scars probably occupy less space than the muscle which they replace, the increase of the

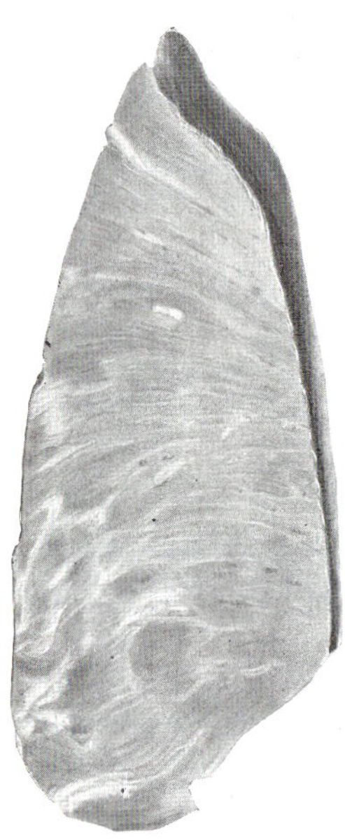

Fig. 235.—Tangential section of heart-wall showing old scars.

remaining muscle, in its attempt to carry on the work of the heart, might more than compensate for this, and result in an enlargement of the whole heart.

Fragmentation of the Heart Muscle.—In many hearts, especially those of old people, and perhaps also those of persons who have long suffered from chronic infections or from advanced circulatory decompensation, there is found wide-spread disintegration of the heart muscle, nearly every fibre being fractured transversely once or twice. These

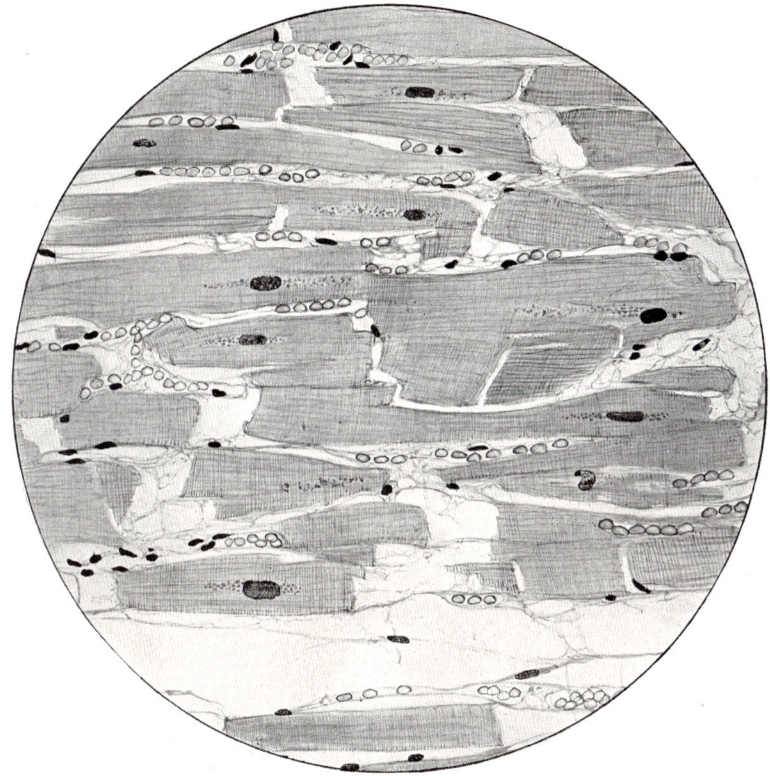

Fig. 236.—Fragmentation of the myocardium, showing simple transverse fractures.

uneven or step-like breaks seem to cross the muscle-fibre at any point, and are not essentially separations of the fibres at the so-called cement line. J. B. MacCallum distinguished simple fragmentation (Fig. 236) from a degenerative form (Fig. 237), in which the fibre breaks across a place where it was evidently in extreme extension, and where the fibrils break at different levels, so as to produce an area made up of many short lengths of individual fibrils. It seems possible to recognize the existence of this condition in many cases from the softness and flabbiness of the heart. There has been much dispute as to its significance, and since it seems incompatible with the continued activity of the heart, and yet is surrounded by no evidence of any reaction on the part of the tissues, it is generally thought to occur during the death agony, and to be produced by the final irregular contractions. Such evidence is not conclusive, however, and we must await further information.

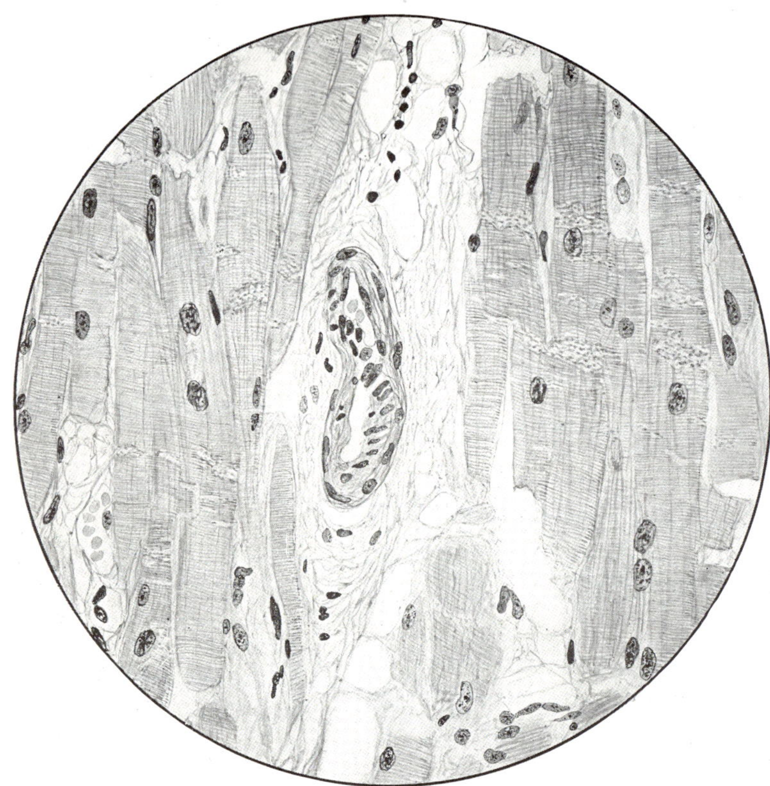

Fig. 237.—Fragmentation of the myocardium with disintegration of the fibrils (degenerative fragmentation).

LITERATURE

Hasenfeld: Dtsch. Arch. f. klin. Med., 1897, lix, 193.

Longcope and McClintock: Johns Hopkins Hosp. Bull., 1910, xxi, 270.

J. B. MacCallum: Johns Hopkins Hosp. Rep., 1900, ix, 307. Jour. Exp. Med., 1899, iv, 409.

F. P. Mall: Amer. Jour. Anat., 1911, xi, 211.

A. Cohn: Verh. Dtsch. path. Gesellsch., 1909, xiii, 182.

Aschoff and Tawara: Path. Anat., Grundlagen der Herzschwäche, Jena, 1906.

Passler and Romberg: Dtsch. Arch. f. klin. Med., 1899, lxiv.

Stejskal: Ztschr. f. klin. Med., 1902, xliv, 367.

MacCallum: Amer. Jour. Med. Sci., 1914, cxlvii, 37.

Aschoff: Verh. Dtsch. Path. Gesellsch., 1904, viii, 46.

Geipel: Münch. med. Woch., 1907, liv, 1057, and 1909, lvi_2, 2469.

Bracht and Wachter: Dtsch. Arch. f. klin. Med., 1907, xcvi, 493.

H. A. Stewart: Jour. Exp. Med., 1911, xiii, 187; Jour. Path. and Bact., 1912, xvii, 64.

Fleischer and Loeb: Arch. Inter. Med., 1909, iii, 78; 1910, vi, 427.

CARDIAC VALVULAR DISEASE AND ITS CONSEQUENCES

Mechanism of the Obstruction.—In another place (page 233) the nature of infectious endocarditis was discussed, and it was found that thrombotic vegetations on the valves might impair the accuracy of their closure; further, that the erosion and destruction of the valves would produce extreme incompetency to close the orifice. On the other hand, even if healing ensued, the valves became so stiff, distorted, and contracted by the formation of the scar tissue that they no longer reached one another, or met so imperfectly that leaks occurred. In some cases they fused into a rigid ring that greatly narrowed the orifice. This may result not only from bacterial infection, but from traumatism, arteriosclerotic changes, and as congenital malformations. Since the circulation depends so largely upon the perfect action of the valvular mechanism, it is important to study, in cases where it is defective, the changes in the rate and volume of the moving blood and the consequent changes in blood-pressure. In a mechanical model, such as that of v. Basch, these relations are complicated, but they become much more so in the living circulatory apparatus, where many compensatory mechanisms are at work. *Every valvular lesion produces an obstruction to the circulation*, either by opposing a barrier to the flow or by failing to maintain the advance effected by the contraction of the heart. Accumulation of blood, therefore, occurs behind each diseased valve, and unless exceptional compensation is available, the amount of blood actually propelled into the circulation beyond it, is reduced by the amount of that accumulation. It is not meant that any particular corpuscles or cubic centimetres of the blood remain stagnant behind the injured valve, but that, while there may be constant mixing in this region, it is as though a stream ran in and out of a lake. The vessels in that area are overfilled and distended, and the exchange of blood is slow—not like the torrent which normally sweeps the stream-bed clean at each beat.

When an obstruction or regurgitation occurs at any valve, say the aortic, the amount of blood thrown into the aorta must be constantly less than normal as long as the cavity of the ventricle retains its normal dimensions, and the wall its normal force of contraction. This may be modified by the power which the ventricle possesses of dilating to receive more blood, and expelling it with greater force, but in order to throw the normal quantity of blood into the arteries the left ventricle must receive that amount plus the amount regurgitated. This is possible only if there is an actual addition to the amount of the blood, although constriction of the arterioles may keep up the normal blood-pressure. If for a time a diminished amount, less than the normal by the quantity held back or regurgitated, circulates in narrowed vessels, there would be a rapid addition of fluid from the tissues and water taken into the stomach until the circulating amount was again normal. Indeed, one receives the impression from observing the amount of blood in the vessels at autopsy in cases of long-standing chronic passive congestion from cardiac lesions, that there is a great increase in its quantity.

The changes in the distribution of the blood may be thought of perhaps in terms of numbers, quite arbitrarily selected, to represent the amounts of blood concerned. This is, of course, entirely schematic, but it serves as a concise way of describing the probable changes.

Thus if the amount handled by any one part of the heart in one systole, say the right ventricle, be represented by 10, the left auricle will receive 10 and the left ventricle also 10. If, now, insufficiency of the mitral valve arises, a portion, say 4, is driven back from the left ventricle into the left auricle, and 6 goes on into the aorta. With the same systole 10 again reaches the left auricle and meets the 4 regurgitated from the ventricle, so that the left auricle now contains 14. That which follows will depend upon the activity of the left ventricle. If it will not receive more than the usual 10, 4 remains stagnant in the auricle, 6 is thrown into the aorta, and 4 more regurgitates. By this time 6 is thrown into the auricle from the right ventricle instead of 10, and meets with 8 of regurgitated blood, making up 14, of which 10 goes again into the ventricle. Thus the circulating blood amounts to 6, while the stagnant blood in the pulmonary circulation amounts to 4. The right ventricle forces 6 into the pulmonary circulation, already containing 4, and into which the left ventricle simultaneously forces 4.

It is usual, however, for the left ventricle under such circumstances to dilate and to exert greater force in the expulsion of the greater amount of blood received. This may be represented as follows:

When the left ventricle has thrown 6 into the aorta and there is 14 in the left auricle, the ventricle dilates at the next diastole—perhaps not enough to receive the whole 14, but enough to receive 12. Of this, it expels 8 into the aorta, while 4 is again regurgitated. The regurgitated 4 meets now with 6 driven in by the right ventricle, and 2 left behind from the 14, making in all 12. With the next diastole the ventricle receives the whole 12, regurgitates 4, and throws 8 into the aorta. By this time the amount 8 thrown out by the ventricle into the aorta reaches the auricle and meets the 4 regurgitated. The whole 12 passes into the ventricle, and thus a circulation is established in which 8 circulates while 4 is regurgitated with each systole.

These examples assume the ability of the ventricle to empty itself completely, but if, finally, it does not, a new set of conditions arises in which the ventricle itself forms part of the reservoir for stagnant blood. Many other conditions which commonly occur may be represented and discussed in this numerical way.

What has been said shows clearly enough that an increased strain is put upon the chamber of the heart behind the defect, because it is made to handle an increased amount of blood, and often, though not always, to propel it against an increased resistance.

As explained, the heart is particularly remarkable in being able to rise instantly to the emergency if an excess of work is suddenly demanded of it, and this adaptation takes place so smoothly that not a single beat is lost or disturbed. This is an evidence of its great reserve power, which is ordinarily not drawn upon, but which permits it to perform greatly increased work for a limited time, as one sees in the case of any violent muscular exertion during which the heart pumps with increased force and rapidity. But if the excessive work must be kept up for a long time, the heart-wall thickens like the muscle of a blacksmith's arm, to enable it the more easily to bear its burden. Such hypertrophied hearts and even normal hearts, when the muscle is injured or badly nourished or finally exposed to entirely excessive strain, may give way and dilate to a degree which makes their proper pumping impossible.

While these are, in outline, some of the principles concerned in the effects of valvular lesions, they come into play differently with lesions of different valves.

Aortic Insufficiency.—Regurgitation through the aortic valves may follow destruction of the valves by fresh or repeated bacterial infection,

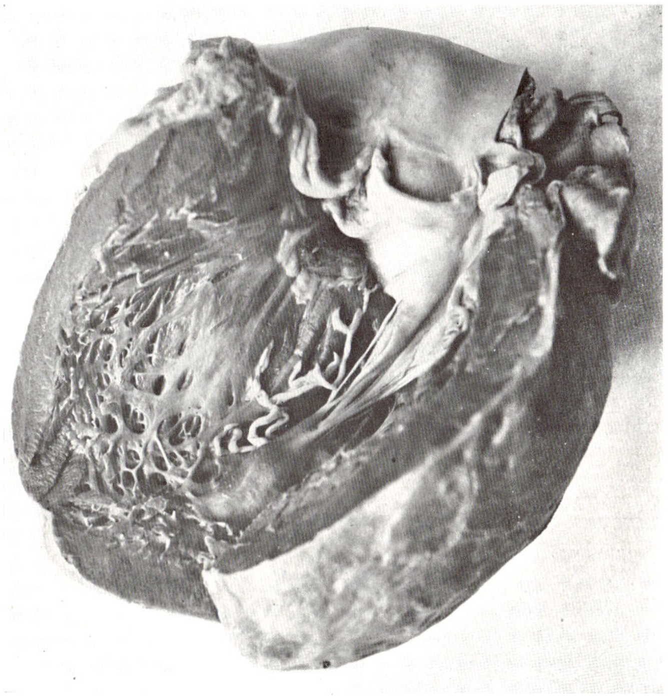

Fig. 238.—Aortic insufficiency. There is great thickening with shortening of the aortic valves, which are thereby rendered incompetent. Hypertrophy of left ventricle. Endocardial thickening beneath aortic valve. Network of soft white bands extending from the septum to the papillary muscle.

but it is most commonly the result of syphilitic infection which produces a specific type of arteriosclerosis of the aorta, and analogous scarring and retraction of the aortic valves (Fig. 238). Very often they are fused together at their base, or in other cases merely thickened into a cord-like roll at the edge, so that they are shortened, and the filmy edge which normally completes their closure is lost. At times the diseased valves rupture or tear, the fragments flapping in the stream. Experimentally one may imitate this disease by cutting through a valve with a hook, which can be pushed down the carotid artery, after which the effects are quite like those observed clinically. There need be no great disturbance of the circulation nor of the blood-pressure. The pulse is changed to a bounding, collapsing type, with a dicrotic wave low on the descending limb. This character is due to the lowering of the diastolic pressure after each beat by the rapid regurgitation of the blood, so that the aortic wall is not kept at its usual high tension. The pulse pressure is high, because the systolic pressure remains nearly normal, while the diastolic pressure cannot be kept up. With such a condition the pulse is felt in the most distal vessels like a water-hammer, and can be seen as alternate flushing and paling in the capillaries of the fingers and toes.

During diastole the regurgitant blood returns to the ventricle, making a loud diastolic murmur, and the ventricle dilates to receive it as well as the auricular blood. So perfect is the left ventricle in its power of response to the increased demand that ordinarily it succeeds in ejecting an amount into the aorta sufficient to allow of regurgitation and still maintain the normal filling of the vessels. This requires the ability to dilate and to handle the excess of blood, and generally the left ventricle is found enlarged and its wall thickened, but without necessarily producing any change in the pulmonary circulation or the right heart. Extreme defects of the valves, especially when the ring of muscle in the conus arteriosus which supports them fails, may be followed by failure on the part of the left ventricle to carry on the great excess of work without leaving a great deal of residual blood in its cavity. Then it becomes difficult for the auricle to empty itself, the pulmonary vessels remain partly filled, and the right ventricle hypertrophies in the attempt to drive its blood through them. Compensation is, however, maintained in aortic insufficiency much better than in other lesions, and death often comes unexpectedly from a final sudden failure.

Stewart has claimed that the collapsing character of the pulse is due to the rapid escape of blood, not by regurgitation, but through widened peripheral capillaries, and that in view of the very slight regurgitation the hypertrophy of the left ventricle is due to its exposure to the diastolic pressure of the aorta. These results I have not been able to accept, although the last statement implies a regurgitation during diastole.

Aortic Stenosis.—Aortic stenosis (Fig. 239), produced by thickening and fusion of the aortic valves, narrows the aortic orifice so as to offer a mechanical obstruction to the expulsion of blood; usually since the valves are incapable of closing accurately there is some regurgitation too. The blood is forced out slowly with a rasping systolic murmur, producing a pulse which, in contrast to that of aortic regurgitation, is small and rather slow. Again, the increase in effort is felt and assumed by the left ventricle, which hypertrophies in response but does not dilate. It is not until it finally fails to accomplish its momentary task of expelling the blood that residual blood plus that from the auricle overdistends it, and it becomes difficult for the auricle to empty itself. In both aortic insufficiency and stenosis it seems inevitable that the coronary circulation should be impaired in the extreme degrees of the disease, thereby weakening the heart itself.

Mitral insufficiency (Fig. 240) gives rise to rather complicated and extensive disturbances of the circulation, because the ventricles, the effective compensating mechanisms, are put at a disadvantage. Part of the blood received by the left ventricle rushes back into the auricle during systole, producing, as usual, an audible murmur. This diminishes the amount available for the aorta and distends the auricle and pulmonary veins. The right ventricle drives its blood into this partly filled pul-

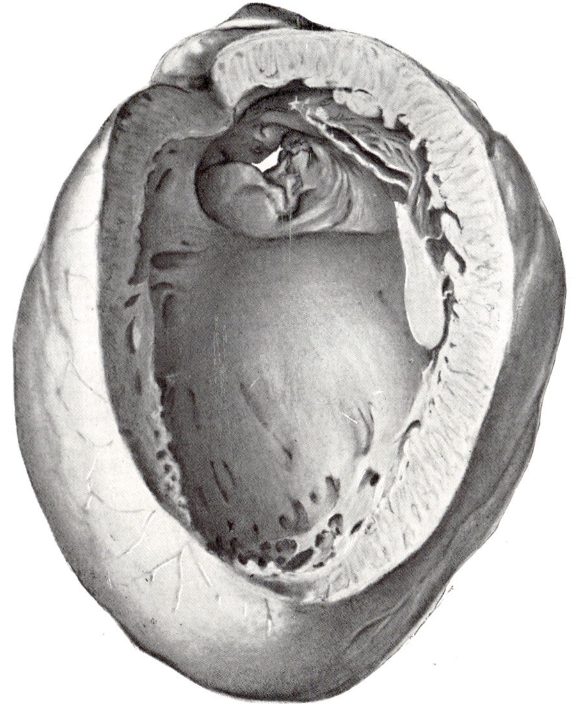

Fig. 239.—Aortic stenosis with hypertrophy of the left ventricle.

monary circulation with increased effort, and in time hypertrophies. The pulmonary circulation remains overdistended, and the left auricle, laboring with blood under higher pressure and in increased amount, dilates and hypertrophies.

The left ventricle, too, takes part in the compensatory process, and dilates to receive an excess of blood until it can, in addition to the regurgitant amount, throw out a nearly normal quantity into the aorta. Consequently the left ventricle dilates and hypertrophies. The pulsation produced by the systolic regurgitation is felt through the pulmonary circuit, and the wave impinges upon the wall of the right ventricle before its valves are closed. In a sense the right ventricle is working against the left, which doubtless contributes to the need for hypertrophy. Compensation begins to fail through the final inability of the left ventricle to expel all the blood brought to it, and the emptying of the left auricle and the pulmonary veins is embarrassed. The same obstruction is felt by the right side of the heart, and with the dilatation of the right ventricle which may follow, a relative insufficiency of the tricuspid valves can arise—that is, the tricuspid ring becomes so wide that the normal valves are too small to close it. Doubtless, however, here, as in the case of the mitral valve, the failure of the usual muscular support of the valves which helps to close the orifice contributes largely to the insufficiency. Such relative insuffi-

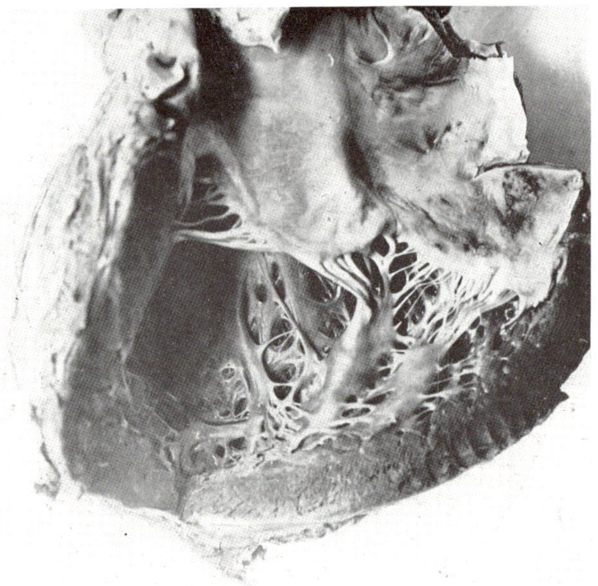

Fig. 240.—Mitral insufficiency. The valves are thickened and shortened, and the chordæ tendineæ are heavier than normal, but there was no actual stenosis.

ciency or even the difficulty which the right ventricle finds in expelling all its contents into the overdistended pulmonary circulation will impede the outflow of the systemic venous blood, and a general chronic passive congestion ensues. The patient becomes cyanotic and very short of breath, with a cough which expels sputum tinged brown by the presence of pigmented cells. Œdema of the extremities and the body and effusion into the serous sacs follow. The end is usually brought about by continued dilatation of the heart and final failure, although temporary recovery with partial disappearance of the symptoms may take place over and over. Such decompensation or break in compensation is also a feature of other forms of valvular disease.

Mitral Stenosis.—The narrowing and rigidity of the mitral valves (Fig. 241) present an obstacle to the outflow of blood from the auricle into the left ventricle. Usually the change in the valves is such that the orifice is bounded by thick, precipitous edges, which may fit together fairly well if they can move into approximation—otherwise if they are rigidly held apart there is necessarily mitral insufficiency combined with the stenosis. This is the usual condition, and is really avoided only in those rare cases in which a delicate film persists past the line of rigidity and calcification, capable of completing the closure. The narrowing of the actual

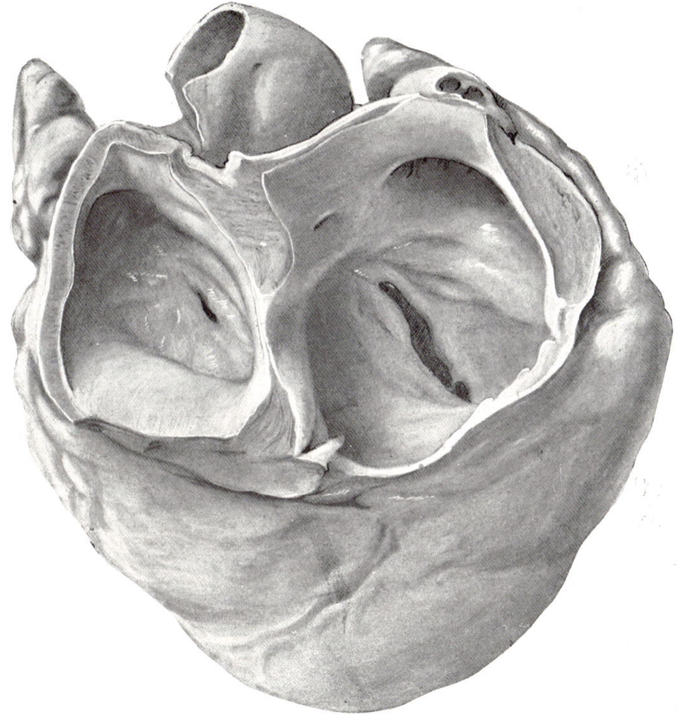

Fig. 241.—Mitral stenosis with great hypertrophy of the left auricle, which has been cut across. Stenosis of the tricuspid.

orifice through which all the blood must pass may be extreme, so that a mere crescentic slit is left with rigid margins only a few millimetres apart, and it is wonderful that life can be maintained until this is developed. Globular thrombi formed in the auricle may sometimes add to the obstruction, or even suddenly complete it by plugging the mitral orifice.

With such difficulty in expelling its blood the left auricle dilates and becomes hypertrophied. The blood is driven through the narrow hole and produces a thrill and a simultaneous presystolic rough murmur. But much of it fails to get through and accumulates in the pulmonary vessels, where the circulation is accordingly very slow and under a high pressure because of the compensatory activity of the right ventricle.

The effects of this upon the lung are described below, but the right ventricle must obviously hypertrophy. If it does so adequately, it may prevent the appearance of any symptoms except those from the lung if the stenosis is not extreme, and enough blood may be forced through to allow the left ventricle to propel a satisfactory quantity into the aorta. If the orifice is so narrowed that the left ventricle receives much less than it should handle, its wall atrophies and it shrinks to a relatively small size as compared with the enlarged and thickened left auricle and right ventricle in the same case. As in mitral insufficiency, a final break in compensation produces cyanosis, serous effusions, cough, dyspnœa, and often the coughing-up of blood from the lungs (hæmoptysis).

Pulmonary stenosis is nearly always a congenital anomaly, and is one of the commonest and most important of those found in the heart. It is generally associated with other imperfections, such as an open foramen in the septum ventriculorum. *Pulmonary insufficiency* is rare and sometimes due to malignant endocarditis.

Tricuspid regurgitation, generally due to a relative insufficiency (though sometimes caused by endocarditis), is often secondary to lesions on the left side or to obstruction in the pulmonary circulation—it causes a murmur and pulsation as well as great distension of the systemic veins. *Tricuspid stenosis* also occurs, and is accompanied by symptoms generally resembling those of mitral stenosis, *i. e.*, presystolic murmur, cyanosis, etc., but this is less significant, as it is usually associated with valvular lesions on the left side.

Indeed, valvular lesions affecting several valves at once, either to produce insufficiency or stenosis or both, are the rule rather than the exception, and hence in the calculation of the effects, complexities arise. It is possible that one lesion may partly compensate for another, although such compensation is seldom an unmixed good. Mitral stenosis may diminish the regurgitation if added to mitral insufficiency. In all cases the outcome depends largely upon the extent of the defect, and persons with definite valvular lesions go on leading an active life for years without any symptoms because the strength of the compensating ventricles is not too greatly overtaxed.

Compensation, Cardiac Hypertrophy, Dilatation, Decompensation.—It is clear, from the description of all these valvular lesions, that in each case extra work is demanded of the heart, and that while this task is sometimes assumed by the chamber directly behind the obstruction, the burden is in the end usually felt by the whole heart. When blood regurgitates into a chamber so that it must dilate to accept more than its usual quantity, it does so, and emptying itself with the next systole, it rises to the emergency by the use of its reserve power. When the systolic discharge is opposed by a stenosis, the chamber again uses its reserve power to drive out the blood, but does not necessarily dilate. Such work at high tension is possible for a time for the normal heart, as we see every day in people who make violent muscular efforts. When they are again at rest the heart subsides to its normal work and is itself unchanged. In its growth it probably merely maintains its proportion to the body musculature.

It is different with such an effort as is required of the heart by a valvular defect, because that is a constant, never-lifting burden which weighs on the ventricle wall with every beat night and day. After a time the heart-wall thickens and strengthens itself, probably chiefly by an enlargement of the muscle-fibres rather than an increase in their numbers. Its reserve force increases in proportion, and now what was an extreme effort near to the maximum limit for the normal heart is a moderate achievement for the hypertrophied one, to which still greater putting forth of strength is possible through its newly advanced reserve power.

This has not been agreed upon by all writers. Martius stated that while the absolute power of the hypertrophied heart was greater than that of the normal, nevertheless, in carrying on the increased work, it was nearer to its limit of endurance than the normal heart was with the lesser burden—in other words, its reserve power made up a relatively small part of the new strength. But Romberg and Hasenfeld seem to have proved conclusively that the hypertrophied heart is just as alert and capable as the normal in response to increased demands, although it must be remembered that the hypertrophied heart is commonly working at an increasing disadvantage.

Hypertrophy is usually thought of as the response to increased work, and it is often called a work hypertrophy. Although this does not explain it, unless perhaps we think that excessive work demands an increase in the metabolism of the cell and thus promotes growth, it is no better explained by Horvath's idea that growth depends on stretching, or by E. Albrecht's, that it is a sort of inflammatory process, or even by Loeb's theory of the imbibition of water with subsequent addition of new material. Stewart thought it due to injury of the heart muscle, followed by enlargement and scarring, in the hypertrophy produced by adrenaline injections.

The attempts at explanation of cardiac hypertrophy on other grounds than the response to increased work have been made chiefly because of the cases of so-called idiopathic hypertrophy, in which enormous enlargement of the heart appears without any valvular lesions or other evident obstruction to its work. Difficult as it is to explain these cases, the suggestion that they are of toxic or inflammatory origin seems quite unsatisfactory unless abundant scars are found in the heart muscle. Then, perhaps, the hypertrophy of the remaining muscle might effect a compensation for that which was lost. But still, and even in this case, the only acceptable explanation seems to be the increased demand upon the muscle.

Stewart has pointed out that even in experimental aortic insufficiency, where the left ventricle encompasses its new task without any increase in pressure in the auricles, the walls of the auricles hypertrophy. Whether this co-hypertrophy is quite independent of obstruction of the flow of blood or not in this particular case, the usual cause of the hypertrophy seems to be the extension of the influence of the obstruction from one chamber to another. It may be possible for the ventricle, in the case of aortic insufficiency of moderate degree, to assume all the new work, quickly expanding in each diastole to receive the original normal amount of blood from the auricle, as well as the amount regurgitated, and expelling it into the aorta, but even here, with an increase in the extent of the insufficiency of the valve, as well as the hypertrophy and power of dilatation, there might occur a disparity during which the auricle would have to make an effort, perhaps partly unsuccessful, to force all its blood into the ventricle. Then arises the need for auricular hypertrophy. But aortic insufficiency is well known to be the best compensated of valvular lesions. In mitral insufficiency the auricle must hypertrophy, the right ventricle must hypertrophy, and as soon as it fails, in the way just described, the right auricle feels the strain. Combined insufficiencies of the valves are even more certainly followed by a distribution of the excess of work all through the heart.

Thus no compensation restores the circulation to its original condition. In every case some part of the heart is working at a disadvantage, either against abnormal resistance or with an excessive proportion of the blood. Slowing of the pulse-rate may sometimes aid in compensating the first of these, while an addition to the amount of the blood in circulation may make up for the blood which lingers in the heart or in the pulmonary vessels, so that the aorta is once more normally filled. But such defects as mitral insufficiency or stenosis can hardly be completely compensated, for in all cases there remains the overfilling of the vessels of the lungs.

At best all these compensations are subject to the probable increase in the severity of the valvular lesion itself, and to the fact that their deficiencies, such as the constant congestion of the lungs in mitral disease, may be aggravated to an intolerable degree by muscular effort or psychic disturbance which would be scarcely felt by a normal person.

Failure of compensation is, then, an impending danger in all these cases, and while, as we have seen, the hypertrophied heart is stronger both in its ordinary and its reserve power than the normal, there are many ways in which it can be overtaxed. Besides muscular exertion and psychic excitation, which have been mentioned and which in general the patient with a cardiac defect must sedulously avoid, there must be mentioned all the diseased conditions of the heart muscle which have been described above, and which are particularly common in hypertrophied hearts. Those which are acutely produced in such hearts must weaken the walls through destruction of muscle-fibres. Scars and old remains of such injuries indicate rather that that danger has been survived, and probably that part of the hypertrophy has arisen to make up for the fibres whose loss they signalize. Nevertheless, such a scarred heart is weakened and subject especially to the influences which conduce to failure. Sclerosis of the coronary arteries is particularly important in restricting the nutrition of the heart-wall, and sudden complete failure of its activity may follow occlusion of these vessels by thrombi. Surprising degrees of sclerosis are survived, however, and even extensive infarctions of the wall.

Perhaps more important still in disturbing compensation in such a hypertrophied heart with valvular defects is the functional disturbance of the coronary circulation, either when, with extreme destruction of the aortic valves, the entrance of blood into the coronary arteries is deficient, or when great accumulation of blood under high pressure in the right heart and systemic veins impedes the return of the coronary blood into the right auricle. The wall of the heart suffers then a chronic passive congestion which involves malnutrition, and it fails through the action of this vicious circle.

Extraneous influences, such as chronic nephritis, extreme arteriosclerosis, pericardial effusions and adhesions, advancing pulmonary disease with obliteration of vessels, pleural adhesions, etc., may gradually heap more work on the heart until, in spite of its hypertrophy, it is unable to keep up its activity. Whether it can stop from sheer weariness and exhaustion one can hardly say, but it seems probable.

The first effect of failure of the heart-wall to meet the demand is the accumulation of blood in its cavities and its passive dilatation. Unlike the competent ventricle which expands and sucks in an excess of blood which it readily expels, the wall is overstretched and incapable of closing completely on the blood in its cavity. For some time it may continue to drive out part, dilating again to receive more, so that thus a feeble circulation is maintained. Sometimes, especially with the administration of drugs, it may recover and return to its former competency, but often it only grows weaker and finally stops beating, hugely distended with the accumulated blood. It is in the course of such dilatation that the muscle of the auriculoventricular orifices fails to support the valves by narrowing those orifices, and relative insufficiencies with regurgitation occur. Extreme distension of the veins results, with cyanosis and often with dropsy. Profound dyspnœa attends the same condition in the lungs, and the patient lies helpless and gasping, propped up in bed until death or one of the temporary recoveries relieves him. Lewis and his colleagues have recently suggested that such dyspnœa is identical with renal dyspnœa, and due to the production of acids other than carbonic acid.

Chronic Passive Congestion.—From what has been said regarding the overdistension of the pulmonary and systemic veins and the consequent slowing of the circulation of at least part of that blood, one might expect to find changes in the tissues so supplied. With increasing failure of compensation the veins become more and more dilated by the increasing pressure of the blood, and less arterial blood is driven through the tissues into them. The capillaries are widened and pulsation passes into them—the tissues assume a deep bluish color and the veins stand out tensely. In places, as in the subcutaneous tissues of the legs, they are irregularly dilated and tortuous. Everywhere there is malnutrition of the tissues, accompanied by certain pressure effects from the widening of the veins and capillaries. Neither nutritive nor gaseous exchange is carried on as it should be, and doubtless excretory products accumulate there. An almost universal result associated with the injurious effects upon the more sensitive tissues is the new formation of connective tissue in the congested and cyanotic organs.

The Lungs.—The lungs are most readily affected in mitral insufficiency and stenosis when compensation fails, and in myocardial disease. The capillaries in the alveolar walls become greatly dilated and tortuous, so that they project in loops into the alveolar cavities. Grossman and von Basch speak of a sort of rigidity of the lung produced by this overfilling. The alveolar epithelium is ill nourished, and very many of the cells are desquamated into the air-cell; fluid exudes from the tense capillaries, often with red blood-corpuscles. These quickly disintegrate, and hæmosiderin is formed from their hæmoglobin and taken up by the phagocytic epithelial

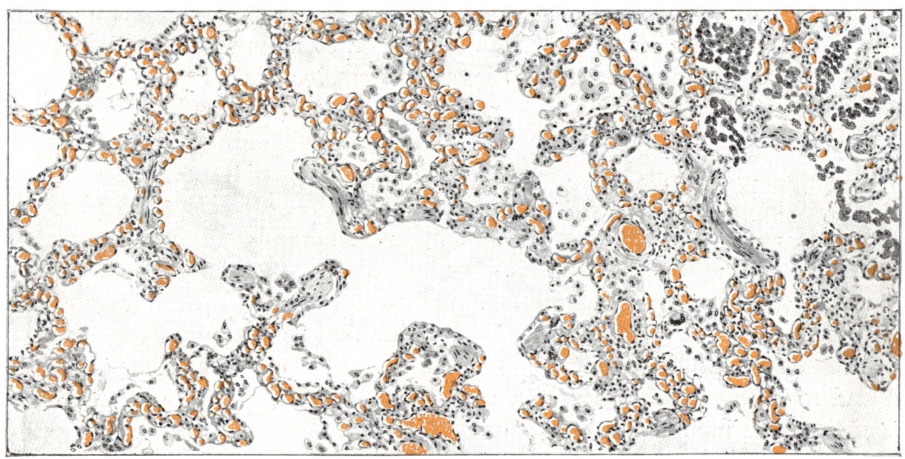

Fig. 242.—Chronic passive congestion of the lung with induration and muscular hypertrophy. Some alveoli contain the pigmented "heart failure cells."

cells. Such cells, when desquamated, are large and round, and often fairly loaded with this brown pigment in clumps and granules. They are coughed up in the sputum, and give a clinical indication of the existence of disease of the heart with pulmonary congestion, for which reason they are called heart-failure cells. In the lungs they are generally sufficiently numerous to give a distinct rusty color to the cut surface (*cf.* Fig. 13). The smooth muscle in the septa that form the vestibules in each lobule is greatly increased in bulk, and the alveolar walls in extreme cases become thickened and indurated by the appearance of new connective tissue (brown induration of the lung) (Fig. 242).

The sluggishness of the circulation which causes such general malnutrition makes it impossible for one arterial branch to supply, as in the normal, nutrition for the territory of another which may be plugged by an embolus.

Hence it is that hæmorrhagic infarctions are found in these congested lungs and practically only there.

Great dyspnœa usually accompanies such chronic passive congestion, and the explanation is not difficult in view of the inadequate aëration which the blood receives when it requires so long to send all of it through the lungs.

Such lungs at autopsy quickly lose any bluish color they may have had; instead, they are usually rather pale, sometimes dry, sometimes œdematous, and of a distinct rusty brown color, which, on the application of ferrocyanide of potassium and hydrochloric acid, turns to an intense Prussian blue (Perl's reaction for an iron-containing pigment). The consistence is altered, too, and the lung feels dense and elastic. In cases of long-standing congestion, especially in mitral stenosis, where the pressure in the pulmonary vessels has been high, arteriosclerotic patches in the pulmonary artery and its branches are common.

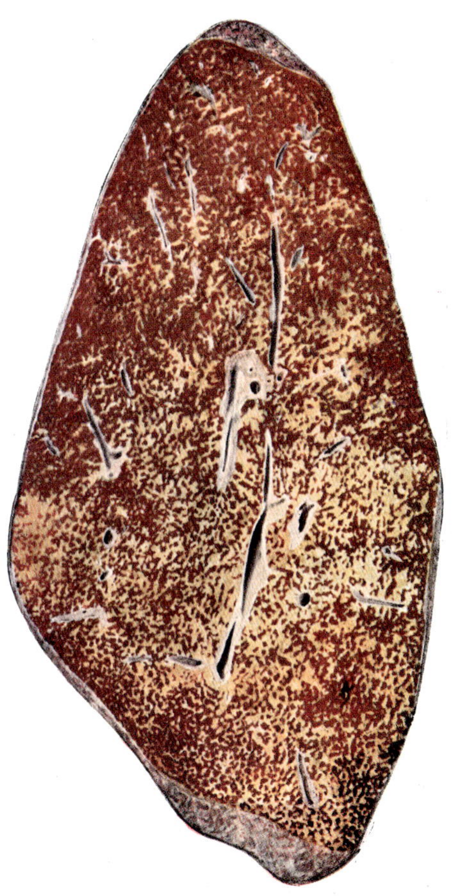

Fig. 243.—Chronic passive congestion of the liver (nutmeg liver).

The Liver.—When the systemic veins are overdistended for a long time, the liver is among the first organs to exhibit the effects. It is enlarged so that it may be felt extending below the costal margin, and often it pulsates. At autopsy it projects as a tense bluish mass in which the impress of a finger remains for a little and is slowly filled up. On cutting the great veins the liver visibly collapses and loses its uniform dark color, assuming a lobular mottling. On section this is extremely bright and distinct, the alternation of deep red and yellow or gray markings giving rise to the name "nutmeg liver" (Fig. 243).

Close examination of the cut surface with a lens, if necessary, or of a thick frozen section without staining, shows that the ordinary lobular markings are much modified by the conversion of so much of the tissue into the deep red zones. Indeed, in places, quite extensive patches may be homogeneously red, spongy, and ooze blood. The grayish yellow islands are found to surround in every case the minute twigs of the portal vein and hepatic artery, a gray zone lying directly against the vein, and then a bright yellow zone which passes sharply into the crimson. Scattered in the anastomosing, irregular crimson bands there are often sharply outlined, opaque, orange-yellow flecks. Microscopical study explains all this

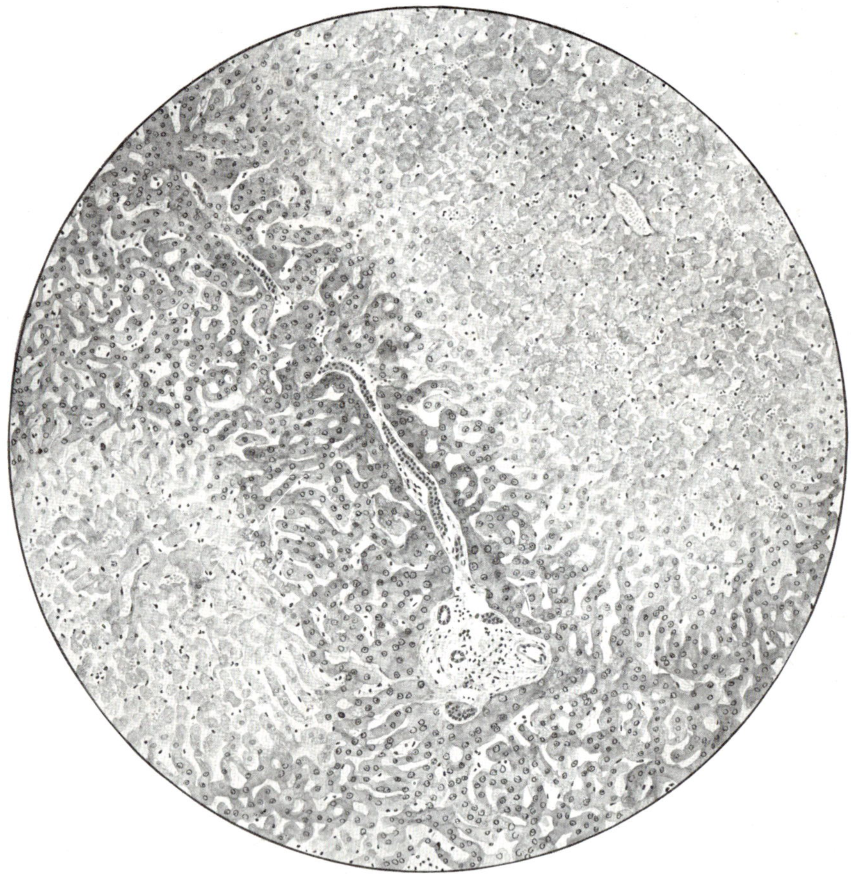

Fig. 244.—Chronic passive congestion of the liver. Necrosis of the cells about the efferent vein.

promptly. (See Fig. 147.) It is the lobule of Sabourin which is outlined and preserved in part as the pale islands—that is, for a certain distance around the afferent portal vein and hepatic artery the liver-cells are preserved. Those nearest are well preserved and show gray; further out they are injured and loaded with refractive yellow fat-globules. Still further they are dead, and in so far as patches of dead cells sometimes remain, appear as opaque, orange-colored flecks (colored somewhat by blood-pigment). But in this region the overwhelming distension of the capillaries with venous blood and the escape of that blood into the intercapillary spaces formerly occupied by the liver-cells converts the whole tissue into a blood-filled sponge in which only the framework and capillary walls remain, with some débris of cells.

Referred to the old idea of the lobule, we must say that the blood-filled portion lies about the central or efferent vein, but that, owing to the course of the capillaries (*cf.* p. 297), it maintains a distribution equidistant from the portal vein, and hence extends from lobule to lobule.

Ordinarily all this is thought to be caused by the increased pressure of the venous blood in the capillaries, which is said to be felt with especial force in the liver because it is near the heart, but I think that these dying cells (Fig. 244) in no way resemble compressed cells, such as one sees about a tumor in the liver, nor does this seem a plausible explanation from a mechanical point of view, since if the pressure in the efferent vein were higher than that in the portal vein and hepatic artery, the blood must run the other way. On the contrary, it is easier to believe that the sensitive liver-cells are badly nourished by the sluggish venous stream, and that oxygenation is especially interfered with, so that those which receive the blood-stream last suffer most severely and in time disappear, leaving a space which is then filled up with blood. On this ground the gradual transition from practically normal cells near the source of nutritive supply through fatty to necrotic cells may be explained.

Mallory regards the condition as the effect of a terminal infection with hæmorrhage into the spaces between the sinuses. Thacher has shown the remarkable inequality in the distribution of the effects of chronic passive congestion in different organs, and, indeed, one is constantly surprised by the inconsistency between the degree of change in the liver and the disturbance of the general circulation. An extreme change in the liver has been described above, but sometimes, aside from cloudy swelling or the accumulation of fat, very little alteration of the liver substance is found, although spleen and kidneys may show marked lesions.

The Spleen.—The most striking features of the change in the spleen wrought by chronic passive congestion are its deep purple color and its extreme hardness (cyanotic induration). Enlargement is usually moderate, and the great increase in the size of the spleen in connection with cirrhosis of the liver is probably due to other causes than the mere congestion. The capsule is tense and smooth, and the cut surface stands firmly at right angles to it, neither bulging nor sinking into a concavity, as in so many enlargements from other causes. Malpighian bodies, trabeculæ, and vessels stand out sharply in the background of the smooth, deep purple, splenic pulp. Microscopically (Fig. 245) one is impressed by the great clearness with which the splenic venules or sinuses are outlined. Their walls are thickened so as to present themselves as very definite membranes lined with endothelium, and every one is distended with blood. In the interstices there is a moderate increase in the connective-tissue framework, but no great accumulation of the cells of the pulp.

The kidney in such chronic congestion is sometimes little altered, since, as has been said, the effect of circulatory obstruction is often very unequally distributed. But the characteristic change is a notable swelling, with extreme rubbery hardness, such that the kidney tissue will snap away

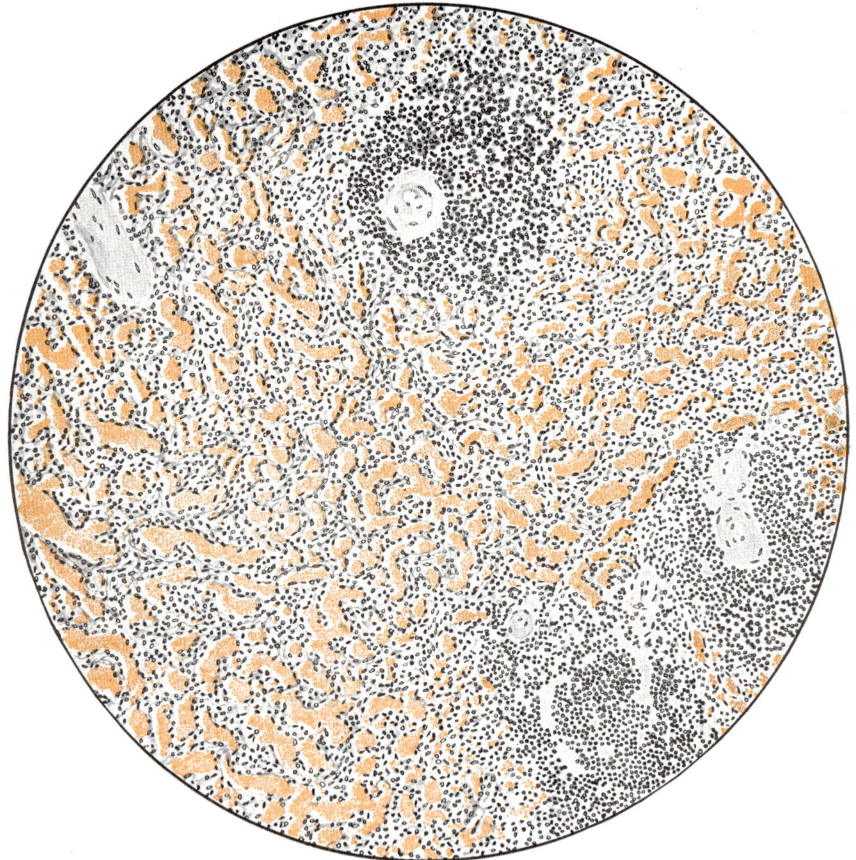

Fig. 245.—Chronic passive congestion of the spleen. Induration of the tissues between the venules renders them conspicuous.

from between the fingers and almost rebound if dropped. The whole organ is deep purplish gray in color, the surface smooth, the capsule not adherent, and on section, in the thick, grayish-purple cortex, one sees the striations with startling distinctness, the blood-vessels and glomeruli standing forth prominently in deep red, while the tubular portions are opaque and gray. The pyramids are also deeply reddened.

Microscopically little more is to be seen—the capillaries, especially of the glomeruli, are distended with blood, and there may be some coagulated fluid in Bowman's capsules or hyaline casts in the tubules. The tubular epithelium shows perhaps a moderate degree of cloudy swelling, but even this need not be marked. Interstitial connective-tissue increase may occur in extreme cases, but it is scarcely evident, as a rule, and it seems that the hardness is chiefly due to the distension with blood.

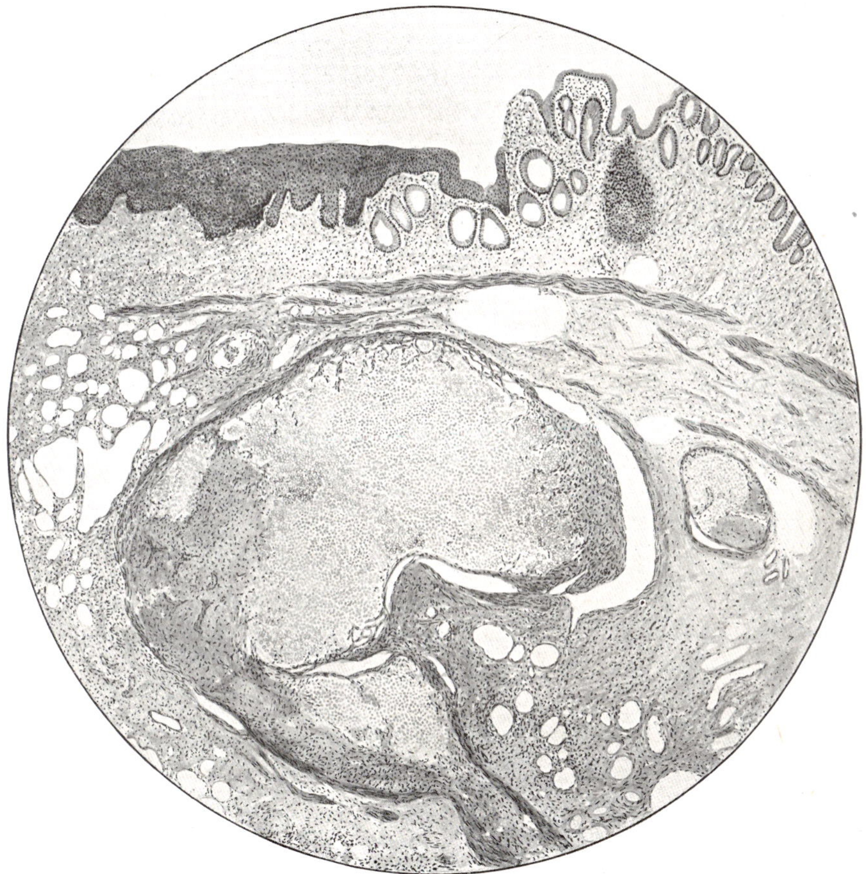

Fig. 246.—Hæmorrhoids. Vertical section showing distended vein near anus, partly occluded by a thrombus.

In contrast to this indefinite microscopical picture the functional changes are very marked. By itself chronic passive congestion can lead to the excretion of albumin and casts of various sorts in the urine, and also to distinct disturbances in the function of the kidney with regard to the excretion of water, salt, and other substances, for which, as is well known, the kidney has specific powers of secretion.

It is particularly important to estimate the part played by such congestion in producing the derangements found in cases of chronic nephritis complicated by heart disease, for they can particularly aggravate the deficiencies of an already disabled renal function. If, then, there is hope of relieving the factor of chronic passive congestion, the outlook for the patient is greatly improved.

Similar conditions of malnutrition with overdistension of the vessels are found in all other organs. In the stomach and intestine they lead to moderate digestive disturbances, often with excessive secretion of mucus and with desquamation of many epithelial cells. In the rectum the enlargement of the veins produces the painful hæmorrhoids, which often bleed and in time cause an extreme anæmia (Fig. 246). They are, however, perhaps more often due to local conditions and especially to obstinate constipation. In the limbs we find the varicose veins mentioned above, often associated with such derangements of the nutrition of the tissues that great ulcerations that refuse to heal appear over the shins.

LITERATURE

v. Basch: Allg. Phys. u. Path. des Kreislaufes, Wien, 1892.
MacCallum: Johns Hopkins Hosp. Bull., 1906, xvii, 251.
MacCallum and McClure: *Ibid.*, 260 (mitral insufficiency).
Martius: Erg. d. allg. Path., 1895, i_2, 38.
Krehl: Pathologische Physiologie, 1912, Nothnagel's Spec. Path. u. Therap., xv, Th. 1, Abth. 5.
Hasenfeld and Romberg: Arch. f. exp. Path., 1897, xxxix, 333.
Moritz and Tabora: Krehl and Marchand: Handb. d. allg. Path., 1913, ii.
Thorel: Ergeb. d. allg. Path., 1903, ix_1, 559; 1907, xi_2, 694; 1911, xiv_2, 133; 1915, $xvii_2$, 90.
MacCallum: Johns Hopkins Hosp. Bull., 1911, xxii, 197 (aortic insufficiency).
Stewart: Arch. Int. Med., 1908, i, 102 (aortic insufficiency).
Stewart: Jour. Exp. Med., 1911, xiii, 187; Jour. Path. and Bact., 1912, xvii, 64 (hypertrophy).
E. Albrecht: Die Herzmuskel, Berlin, 1903.
Aschoff and Tawara: Grundlagen der Herzschwäche, Jena, 1906.
Lewis and others: Heart, 1913, v, 45; 1914, v, 367.

PATHOLOGY OF THE CONDUCTION BUNDLES OF THE HEART

Until quite recently the study of the diseases of the heart concerned chiefly the mechanical results of distortion of the valves, of weakening of the muscle, etc., but the extraordinary discovery of His, Keith and Flack, Tawara, and others of an unsuspected connecting system of specialized strands of muscle stretching from one part of the heart to another has opened a new field for this study. It quickly became apparent that these strands, like the electric signals in an engine-room, or like nerves, controlled from a central station the activities of other parts of the heart, and at once there was hope of clearing up the obscure chapter of the disturbance of its rate and rhythm. This hope has not been disappointed, and with the aid of several new technical methods it has become possible to study with extreme accuracy all these disturbances and to explain them clearly. Most of these results have been worked out experimentally in animals, after which cases have been found in human beings which cor-

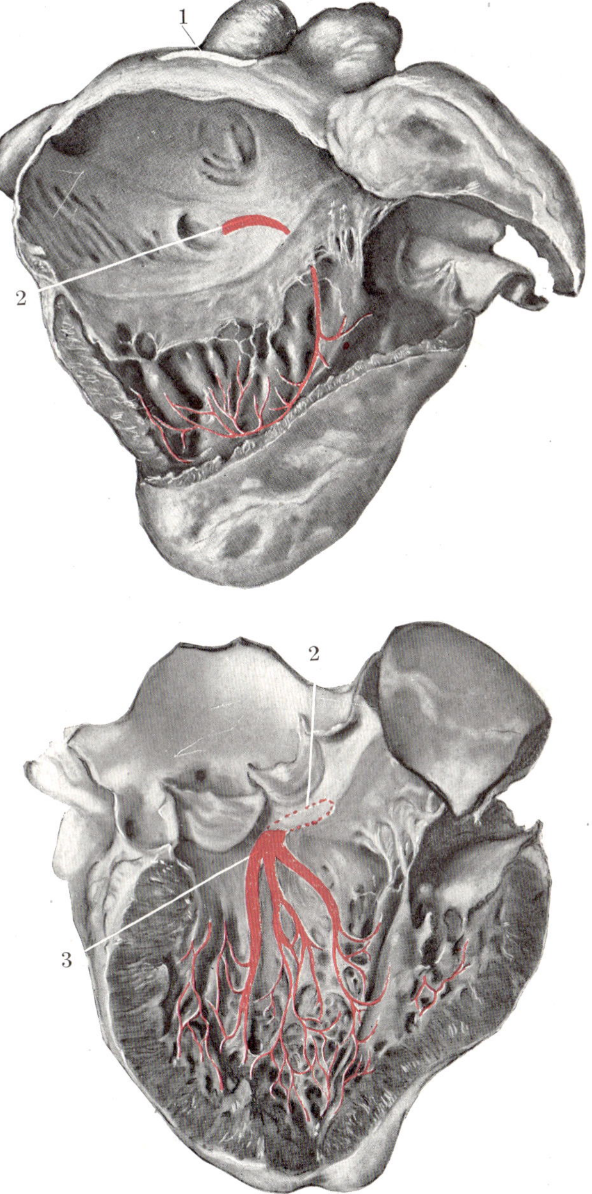

Fig. 247.—Diagrammatic representation of the conduction system: 1, Sino-auricular node; 2, atrioventricular node; 3, bundle of His.

respond so exactly to the experimental results as to make diagnosis easy and certain.

The conduction system (Fig. 247) consists of: (1) An elongated node (the sinu-auricular node of Keith and Flack), which lies in the angle between the superior vena cava and the right auricle, extending downward for a distance of one to two centimetres along the sinus terminalis; (2) a second node or mass of tissue which begins at the posterior and lower part of the right auricle, just in front of the coronary sinus, and extends along the interauricular septum forward and to the left until it reaches the septum membranaceum behind the tricuspid valve. There it follows the lower part of this septum, thus lying at the upper margin of the muscular portion of the interventricular septum, and runs forward to divide into two main branches, one of which continues under the endocardium of the right ventricle toward its apex. The other branch pierces its way into a similar situation in the left ventricle. The node, in which Aschoff has recently distinguished two parts, is the auriculoventricular node of Tawara, while the continuation across the septum membranaceum into the two branches is the bundle of His. These branches subdivide to distribute themselves throughout the muscle of the ventricles, especially stout branches passing to the papillary muscles. In spite of patient search no definite specialized connections have been found in the auricular walls between the sinu-auricular and the auriculoventricular nodes.

These nodes and bundles are composed of muscle-fibres of a peculiar kind, very narrow, striated, with numerous nuclei and rich in glycogen. In the nodes they are matted together, but in the fasciculi they lie parallel. They form no direct connection with the musculature of the heart, but unite with the Purkinje fibres, which are large, pale, faintly striated fibres lying just under the endocardium, and which in turn unite with the ordinary muscle-fibres. Numerous nerve-fibres are interwoven with the muscle-fibres of the bundle of His and of the nodes, so that it is impossible to exclude the participation of the nervous system in their activities. All these structures are enclosed in connective tissue and fat and are supplied by special arteries.

In the embryo, when the heart has the form of a curved tube, and before the ingrowth of any nerves has occurred, a sort of peristaltic contraction wave takes place. Although the ingrowth of the epicardium to form the central lamina of the auriculoventricular valves interrupts in mammals most of the connection between auricular and ventricular muscle, a portion of the continuous musculature remains and becomes specialized as the specific conduction bundle. The function of this system has been clearly shown by numerous experiments to lie in the initiation and propagation of the normal impulses which set in motion, in an orderly way, the musculature of the heart. The impulse begins normally, as shown by the experiments of Lewis and others, in the sinu-auricular node of Keith, and spreads thence to the auriculoventricular node, whence it is transmitted to the ventricle by the bundle of His. The heart muscle itself is excitable and capable of conducting the impulse; its excitability is such that, however great or slight the impulse which is capable of causing a contraction, that contraction is a maximal one. On the other hand, having once contracted, the muscle enters on a refractory phase, during which no stimulus will provoke a contraction. These peculiarities account for some of the phenomena of disturbance in rhythm to be described.

The movements of the heart normally follow one another in an orderly succession, and at a regular rate which can be accurately studied in various ways. In addition to the auscultation of the heart and the palpation of the pulse, which give only rough information, tracings are made by means of the sphygmograph or polygraph to show simultaneously the pulsations of the radial or of the apex of the heart, and of the jugular vein. Such tracings are supplemented by electrocardiographic tracings, which give

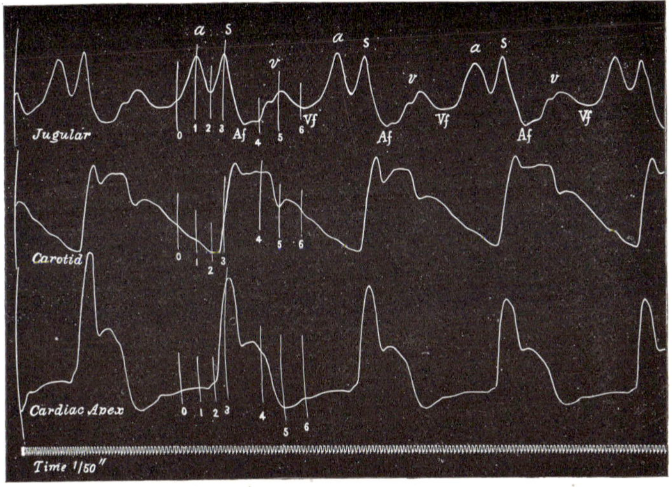

Fig. 248.—Simultaneous tracings of the jugular pulse, the carotid pulse, and the apex-beat (Bachmann, from Howell).

a clear idea of the movements of the heart. When we compare the tracings from the jugular with those from the carotid (Fig. 248), it is found possible to recognize in the jugular tracings a wave (*a*) which is due to a contraction of the auricle, a second or *c* wave (*s*), caused in part by changes in pressure in the auricle at the closure and lifting up of the tricuspid valves, and in man also by the transmitted carotid pulse, and a third (*v*) which represents the filling of the auricle and veins during the latter part of systole, with elevation of the base of the heart, after which the sudden drop is due to the opening of the tricuspid valves.

The electrocardiogram is a curve made by photographing, on a moving film, the shadow of a fine thread of silvered quartz stretched between the poles of a magnet, and connected by its ends with wires leading to electrodes attached to the two arms or one arm and a leg of the patient. The part of the heart muscle which is contracting at a given instant becomes electronegative to the rest, and the slight electrical current thus produced, passing through the silvered thread, causes it to be deflected toward one pole or other of the magnet. In the tracing there is recorded, in order, the deflection produced as the wave of excitation, *i. e.*, electronegativity, passes through the heart. The result, as shown in the figure (Fig. 249), gives an elevation for the auricular contraction (*P*); a high-pointed elevation

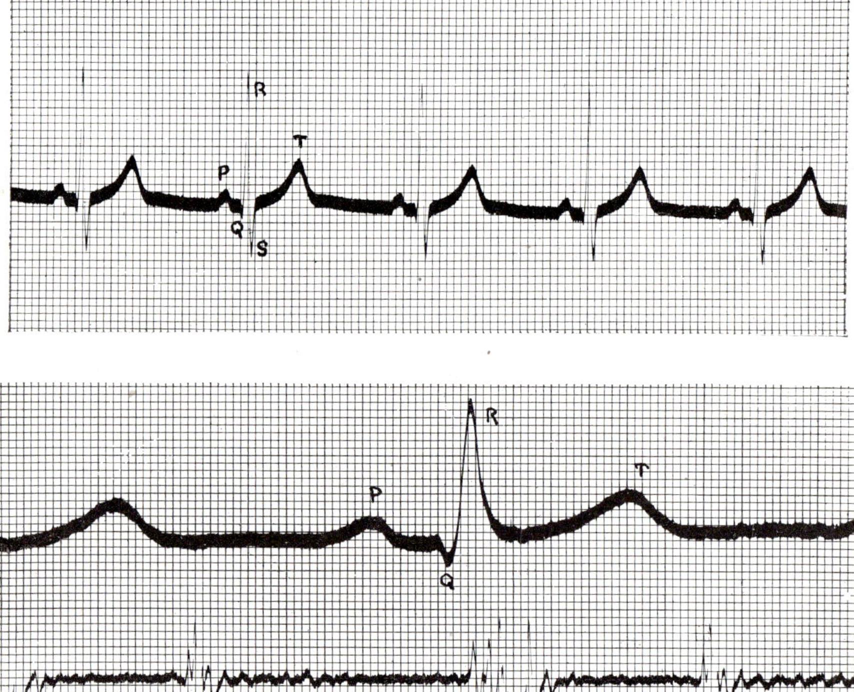

Fig. 249.*—Electrocardiogram from a normal person showing the orderly sequence of waves which have been distinguished arbitrarily by letters *P*, *R*, *T*, etc. In the second curve, which is spread over a greater space by the rapid movement of the paper, there is also a microphonographic record of the heart-sounds.

(*R*), the descending limb of which goes below the line (*S*), and later another rounded elevation (*T*). The latter three result from the ventricular contraction. This is the normal curve, and any abnormality in the rhythm is at once visible in the curve taken from the irregularly beating heart.

Irregularities in the rate and rhythm of the heart-beat may arise either (1) through changes in the rate of the impulses originating in the sinu-

*These and the following curves were kindly given me by Dr. Horatio Williams.

auricular node, and normally transmitted through the rest of the system (nomotope impulses); (2) through changes in the conducting power of the bundle of His or other part of the system, or (3) through the occurrence of abnormal impulses starting elsewhere in the system than in the sinu-auricular node, or even in the musculature of the heart, quite outside the conducting system (heterotope impulses).

1. Changes in Rate of Nomotope Impulses.—Tachycardia, in which the cycle of the heart-beat is normal, but in which the beats follow one another more rapidly than normal, arises in the sinu-auricular node after an effort, or an emotion, or in the course of fevers, tuberculosis, etc., as well as under the influence of such poisons as atropine. Probably in most cases this is due to the diminution of the activity of the vagus nerve, but in some it may be a direct action on the node. Bradycardia, in which the pulse is slowed to 45 to 50 beats per minute, generally transient, occurs in uræmia, icterus, mitral disease, convalescence from acute infections, etc., and is probably due to excitation of the pneumogastric, since it can be made to disappear by the administration of atropine, which paralyzes that nerve: jugular tracings and electrocardiograms present normal cycles although widely separated. There are also sinus arhythmias, which show normal electrocardiographic complexes irregularly spaced. They usually disappear on exertion.

2. Disturbances Due to Partial or Complete Interruption of Conduction.—(*a*) An interruption between the sinu-auricular node and the rest of the system, which would correspond to the first ligature of Stannius, has given different results in the hands of different experimenters. The heart may stop entirely or assume a different rhythm, in which impulses arise elsewhere. If the interruption is incomplete, some of the impulses may pass through so that whole cardiac cycles are missed, while others occur.

(*b*) Interruption of conduction in the bundle of His may occur in various degrees of completeness. When it is confined to a slight retardation of conduction, there are no symptoms, but the jugular tracings show a lengthening of the interval, etc. Corresponding with this, the electrocardiogram presents an elongation of the space between *P* and *R*. When the interruption is more intense, some of the impulses from the sinu-auricular node fail to reach the ventricles, so that while in the jugular tracings the elevations *a a*, which represent the auricular contractions, are equidistant from one another, some are not accompanied by the elevations *c*, *v*, that is, they are not followed by ventricular contractions. Thus a 2 : 3 rhythm or a 1:2 rhythm may be established. Complete interruption of the conduction allows the auricles to proceed in their regular contraction, while no impulses reach the ventricles from the sinu-auricular node. Then the ventricles beat about 30 times per minute, but with a rhythm quite independent of that of the auricles (idioventricular rhythm), so that in the tracings one can determine no relation between them. Under such circumstances the elevations produced by auricular and ventricular contractions are sometimes superposed, sometimes separate, or if their rates happen to be multiples they may give the impression of an incomplete dissociation. Such dissociation is commonly spoken of as heart-block (Fig. 250).

The severer grades of disturbed auriculoventricular conduction (Stokes-Adams disease) are often accompanied by crises or paroxysms of syncope or by epileptiform convulsions, due to the insufficient flooding of the brain with blood. These may pass off as the heart-rate improves, but occasionally end in death, when the slowing of the ventricular rhythm is extreme. Strangely enough such crises are rather less common in the cases of complete heart-block than in those in which dissociation is only partial.

All these conditions can be produced experimentally by gradually constricting the bundle of His, and in human beings there is generally found at autopsy some destructive lesion in the bundle. This may be a gumma or a gummatous infiltration surrounding the tract, or a scar or atheromatous

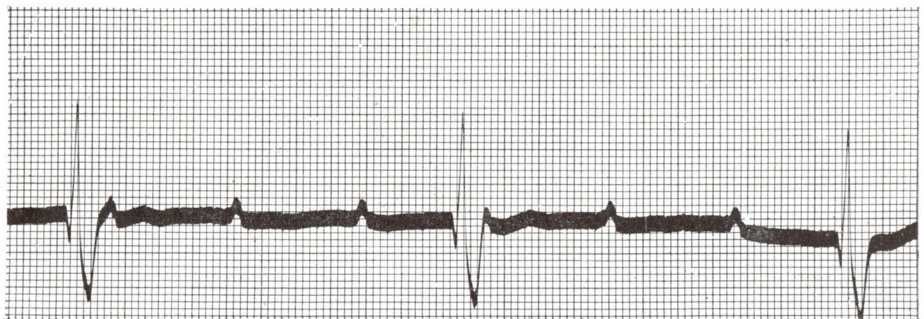

Fig. 250.—Electrocardiogram in heart-block. The auricular beats are not regularly followed by ventricular systoles, and apparently have no influence upon them.

calcified mass may extend from the neighboring valves so as to interrupt it. Cases have been described, however, in which absolutely no lesion of the bundle could be found despite the existence of heart-block. In such cases it seems possible that excitation of the pneumogastric may be responsible, for it has been shown that such excitation can greatly aggravate the effects of a slight lesion of the bundle, and also that excessive doses of digitalis can thereby produce heart-block without any injury of the bundle.

3. Arhythmias Due to Heterotope Impulses.—Arhythmias or disturbances of rhythm arising from the origination of impulses elsewhere than in the sinu-auricular node may assume several types. They depend on the fact that, although the normal source of impulses is as described, the node of Keith, still the node of Tawara, or the bundle of His, or any part of the wall of the heart itself, may give rise to such impulses, which spread then either in a normal or quite abnormal direction. It seems scarcely possible to say whether these impulses arise in the ordinary heart muscle itself or in the terminal ramifications of the conducting bundle, but at least the character of the electrocardiogram is sufficient to show that they do not originate in the main trunk of the bundle of His.

When such an impulse leads to a contraction interpolated in the ordinary rhythm, it is denominated an extra-systole (Fig. 251). The simultaneous sputtering of such impulses from many points in the heart's wall causes a disorganized, uncoördinated, waving contraction (fibrillation) which produces no impulsion of the blood. More recently it has been explained as due to the circling about of impulses in closed paths in the muscle (Garrey). Such a condition may exist in the auricles, but quickly leads to death if it occurs in the ventricles.

(*a*) Fibrillation in the auricle wall leads to complete arhythmia, or the pulsus irregularis perpetuus. Such is the tremulous quivering of the auricle wall that no contraction of the auricles is registered in the jugular curve, though minute oscillations occur in the electrocardiogram, and at occasional and irregular intervals impulses pass through to the ventricles,

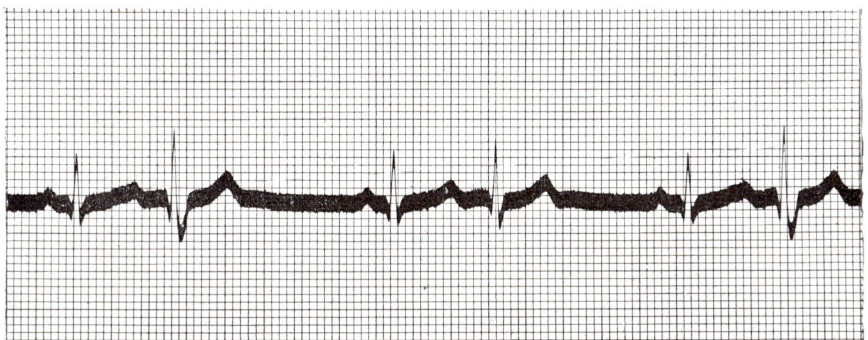

Fig. 251.—Pulsus bigeminus in which premature beats arise in the auricles.

so that their contractions are in complete disorder and show no constant rhythm. Such arhythmia is commonest in connection with disease of the mitral valve, when the auricle is distended and its wall scarred in places. Usually, but not always, it is permanent. The cause of the auricular fibrillation is not certain, however, and some authors have referred it to an affection of the sinu-auricular node.

(*b*) In other cases, again often in connection with mitral disease, extra-systoles starting in various points in the auricle are transmitted to the ventricles, and give rise to attacks of tachycardia of auricular origin. The cycles are complete, but follow one another so rapidly that in the tracings the elevations *a* and *v* may overlap, and in the electrocardiograms *P* and *T*, in which case the deflection will be the algebraic sum of the two.

(*c*) As in the auricles, impulses may arise in any part of the ventricles and give rise to effective extra-systoles which are, however, independent of the normal impulse. These may, when the heart-rate is slow, be simply interpolated between the normal heart-beats, but usually, owing to the refractory period which follows a systole, there is a compensatory rest. The next impulse from the auricle finding the ventricle in the refractory phase produces no response, and the normal cycle is missed. Thus the space between the normal cycle preceding and that following the extra-systole is that of two normal cycles. Occasionally such extra-systoles may follow one another in rapid succession, and even drive back an impulse in retrograde direction so as to affect the auricular contractions (ventricular tachycardia). Tracings from the jugular, studied together with those from the radial during the occurrence of ventricular extra-systoles, show first the normal cycle, then the elevation *c*, followed by the ineffectual elevation *a*, of the auricular contraction, and later the next normal cycle. Occasionally *a* and *c* are superposed and form one high elevation. In the electrocardiogram the extra-systole is represented by a diphasic wave the point of which is directed up when the impulse comes from the base and

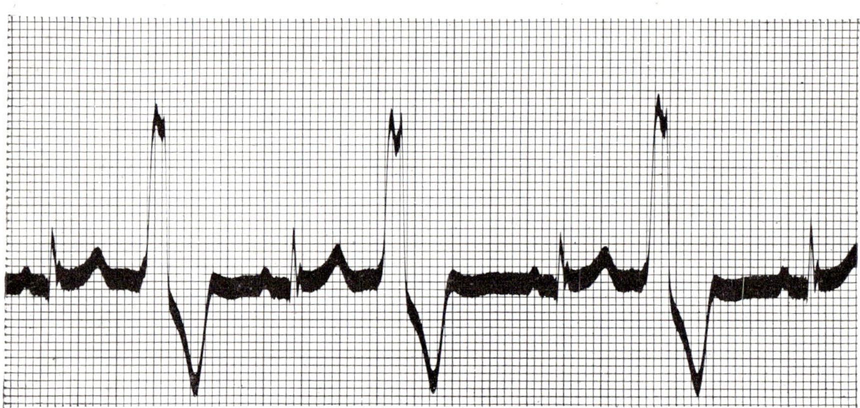

Fig. 252.—Pulsus bigeminus with premature beats or extra-systoles arising in the ventricles.

the right ventricle, downward when it arises at the apex or in the left ventricle (*cf.* Fig. 252). Lewis has shown, by the experimental production of extra-systoles from different points, that this typical form of the electrocardiogram can be actually used for diagnostic purposes. Nothing is known of the ætiology of such ventricular extra-systoles in the human being.

LITERATURE

His: Arb. a. d. Med. Klinik, Leipzig, 1, 1893, xciii.

Tawara: Reizleitungssystem des Säugetierherzens, Jena, 1906.

Aschoff: Verhandl. Dtsch. Path. Gesellsch., 1910, xiv, 3.

Hering: *Ibid.*, 36.

Lewis: Mechanism of Heart Beat, London, 1911. Lectures on the Heart, New York, 1915.

Keith and Flack: Jour. of Anat. and Physiol., 1907, xli, 172.

Josue: Localisations cardiaques, XVII Internat. Congress of Medicine, London, 1913, iii, pt. 1, 1. (General Pathology.)

CHAPTER XXIV

TYPES OF INJURY (Continued).—BACTERIAL DISEASE

General character of bacterial infection: Nature of bacterial action. Pyogenic micrococci. Streptococcus infections—of the throat, the middle ear, the digestive tract. Wound infection: Erysipelas, pneumonia, endocarditis. General septicæmia; acute splenic tumor.

GENERAL CHARACTER OF BACTERIAL INFECTIONS

As a type of injury, the harmful effects of bacteria play an exceedingly great part in the causation of disease, and must generally be reckoned with at some stage or other, even when they are not the primary cause of the ailment.

Of course, only a small number of the existing bacteria are harmful to man, and it seems that we must believe that these have gradually acquired, through long adaptation, their ability to thrive in contact with the living tissue. The rest live outside the body under all sorts of conditions, requiring in their struggle for existence heat, moisture, and nutriment. The latter they get partly from animal or vegetable matter, in which they hasten the process of decay, which depends largely upon their ferment activities. Such saprophytes may occasionally acquire the faculty of parasitic existence, and point the way trodden by those which we now think of as obligate parasites.

Many of the disease-producing organisms scattered ordinarily in small numbers in the outside world may gain entrance into the body in overwhelmingly effective numbers, merely because they have had an opportunity to multiply in some culture-medium. A few typhoid bacilli which might readily be overcome in the intestine of any healthy man can, as in a recent case, cause a fatal epidemic if they are introduced into warm food and left to multiply until it is time for the crowd to partake of refreshments.

Bacteria live in great numbers on the body surface; they are taken into the digestive tract in great quantities in the food, and penetrate readily into all the external orifices of the body. At each point there is a mechanical or chemical guard of a sort, but nevertheless there is constantly an army of them besieging each portal. The impermeability of the horny layer of the skin, the constant irrigation of the conjunctival sac, the cilia of the respiratory tract, the acid gastric juice, the irrigation of the urinary tract, the acid vaginal secretion—all act as outpost guards. Nevertheless, in each of these positions it is known that bacteria are not entirely destroyed and that there is a characteristic flora, including pathogenic forms, waiting, as it were, to break through the second line of guards. The whole upper respiratory tract is smeared with bacteria; the mouth is a perfect incubator of dozens of forms, and while the stomach and duodenum are relatively free, the lower intestine, and especially the colon, contains myriads.

Doubtless a few bacteria brought thus into the most intimate relations with the body surfaces pass into the real interior, that is, into the tissues themselves in healthy persons, but there is strong evidence to show they are rapidly overcome and destroyed by phagocytic cells and by the destructive action of the blood and tissue fluids. Were it not for these defences every one would quickly die from infection. Since infection does occur with fatal results, it is obvious that there must be failure of the defence or else the introduction of such overwhelming numbers of bacteria that defence is unsuccessful.

The chief portals of entry are, of course, the various mucosæ of the body, which are really as much exposed to bacteria as the outside skin, and the skin itself, which, through abrasions or wounds, can allow their entrance.

Having penetrated into direct relation with the tissues, most bacteria fail to multiply, but those which are adapted to such surroundings may do so, although constantly hampered by the antagonistic action of the body defences, especially such as are presented by the reaction of inflammation. Virulent bacteria in a person whose resistance is low may, however, grow rapidly and be quickly transported to other parts of the body by the lymphatic channels, or even in some cases by the blood-stream. If an intestinal loop is ruptured, pouring great quantities of infected material into the peritoneum, the bacteria are taken into the lymphatics of the diaphragm, and hence through the mediastinal lymph-channels to the retrosternal lymph-glands with the greatest celerity, and after a very few minutes may be found in the circulating blood.

Bacteria alone introduced into the tissues or body cavities are relatively easily killed. If, however, foreign bodies or dead tissue are present there, to afford a shelter against the disinfecting action of the tissue juices until multiplication to great numbers has occurred, the bacteria can more readily gain a dominating position. Bacteria in the uterine cavity in the puerperal state might be practically harmless were it not for the protected culture-medium offered by remains of detached and dead placenta, in which they reinforce themselves by growth until they can victoriously invade the uterine wall.

It is not always easy to explain the very obvious changes in the power of resistance shown to bacteria. Many external conditions, such as chilling or starvation, may aid in this, but previous disease seems even more potent in this way. Almost every one harbors pathogenic bacteria in his throat, but it requires a sudden chilling or exposure or injury to favor their invasion into the lungs and the production of pneumonia. Similarly, one sees in the lungs of a man long known to have suffered from tuberculosis, old scarred lesions at the apex, clearly stoutly resisted in their time, and fresh extensive and rapid destruction of the lower lobes, caused by the same bacteria which have seized upon a period of lowered resistance to push their advantage.

This is doubtless the explanation of the so-called secondary infections, which are so common and which underlie the statement that a "man seldom dies of the disease with which he sickens." He really dies of the secondary infection, which thrives in the body weakened by the original disease. One might say that the fatal outcome in cancerous disease is usually not from the effects of the cancer, but from the bacteria that invade the emaciated subject. And so with destructive chronic tuberculosis of the lungs, in which the hectic symptoms seem to be due rather to the streptococci and staphylococci and other bacteria which secondarily infect the cavities in those organs.

Persons who die after long illness with such affections as chronic nephritis, cardiac disease, or cirrhosis of the liver may show no special symptoms of infection other than a sudden fever at the end, but in their tissues at autopsy one finds, as pointed out by Flexner, streptococci or other bacteria which have finally invaded the failing tissue and have added the intolerable last straw. Such *terminal infections* are extremely frequent, and although they may not produce any gross lesions in the organs, they are very often represented by a terminal bronchopneumonia or diphtheritic enteritis.

Nature of Bacterial Action.—We are by no means clearly informed as to how bacteria produce their injurious effects. It is easy to say that they do so by elaborating poisons, but in reality, except in the case of a few, such as diphtheria and tetanus bacilli, which produce soluble toxins of great intensity, it is extremely difficult to demonstrate any poisons in the cultures of other bacteria, even though they are known to be exceedingly virulent. It was thought that poison might be retained within their bodies (endotoxins), and liberated only upon their death and disintegration, so that the destructive effects would depend upon their death. It is true that when these bacteria are pulverized and extracted, poisonous substances are obtained with which the symptoms of the disease may be produced, but they scarcely compare in virulence with those formed by the diphtheria and tetanus bacilli; and it seems that perhaps the whole explanation is not yet before us. It is quite conceivable, however, that bacteria in the body may produce a more active poison than when grown in artificial culture-media.

The effects upon the tissues differ widely with the different bacteria, but in general they produce the death or profound injury of the adjacent cells, and quickly call forth an inflammatory reaction. A few, such as the typhoid bacillus, although causing necrosis of the neighboring cells, do not elicit the ordinary response of the neutrophile leucocytes, but rather produce a curious reaction, in which mononuclear phagocytic cells predominate. Others, such as the tubercle bacillus, may live a long time among cells which are not only alive, but actively multiplying, only to cause in time their complete destruction. The effect seems to vary, then, with the chemical nature of the substances produced in the body of the bacteria, and these various reactions must be considered later in some detail. According to the character of the bacteria, their number, their concentration, and the resistance of the individual, infection may assume various forms. Some organisms, notably those which produce soluble toxins (diphtheria and tetanus), appear to grow only at the point of inoculation or first infection, although they distribute themselves in small numbers in the blood-stream and tissues. From this local growth they diffuse their poisons. Others, having gained a foothold, tend to spread diffusely through the tissues, causing havoc wherever they go. Such are the streptococci, while the staphylococci are accustomed to concentrate themselves at various points in the tissues, and stir up an intense concentric inflammatory reaction around themselves (*abscess formation*). Either of these forms and many others may, however, in one way or another invade the blood-vessels and pour themselves into the flowing blood. When bacteria can be recognized in the circulating blood, we call the process *septicæmia*, and this term is being found to apply properly to more and more infectious diseases as careful blood cultures are made (pneumonia, typhoid fever, endocarditis, etc.). By *pyæmia* we mean that condition associated with septicæmia or bacteriæmia in which suppurative foci are formed here and there. The student should read in this connection the interesting works of Metchnikoff, Welch, and others upon these general topics of infection and immunity which can merely be outlined here. The remarkable progress in knowledge of this region of medicine in recent years has made the general and special consideration of infection and resistance the subject not only of many text-books, but of a literature so extensive as to be almost beyond the compass of one man's reading.

LITERATURE

Metchnikoff: Immunite dans les maladie infectieuses, Paris, 1901.
Welch: "Surgical Bacteriology," Dennis' System of Surgery, Philadelphia, 1895.
Simon: Infection and Immunity, Philadelphia, 1912.
Zinsser: Infection and Resistance, New York, 1914.

The Pyogenic Micrococci.—While the bacteria belonging to this group unquestionably cause different diseases according to the special peculiarities of each, there is still a striking resemblance in their mode of action, and there are many things, such as endocarditis, lobular pneumonia, and meningitis, which may be caused by each of them in nearly the same fashion. We may, therefore, consider together in this chapter the effects produced by the Staphylococcus pyogenes aureus, the Staphylococcus albus, the Streptococcus longus or hæmolyticus, Streptococcus mitis or viridans, Streptococcus mucosus, the pneumococcus or Micrococcus lanceolatus in its various types, the gonococcus, the meningococcus or Micrococcus intracellularis meningitidis, together with other forms and varieties. No attempt will be made to describe the organisms, nor to discuss their systematic relations, which are subjects for books on bacteriology. Together with these affections there may be discussed acute rheumatic fever, the cause of which is unknown, but which resembles them in many respects.

STREPTOCOCCUS INFECTIONS

Three types of streptococcus are commonly recognized since the work of Schottmüller:

1. Streptococcus longus or hæmolyticus.
2. Streptococcus mitior or viridans.
3. Streptococcus mucosus.

To these he adds a fourth, Streptococcus putridus, which is strictly anaërobic and not hæmolytic, and occurs in puerperal endometritis. Streptococcus longus is the principal form in puerperal sepsis, wound infections, etc. It forms long chains, and in blood agar, lakes and decolorizes the blood in a halo around each colony. Streptococcus viridans and Streptococcus mucosus produce a green discoloration in blood agar, but no hæmolysis. Streptococcus mucosus forms glutinous colonies and is extremely virulent, while Streptococcus viridans tends to produce more chronic affections.

Most of the ordinary lesions seem to be produced by the Streptococcus hæmolyticus, while the type of endocarditis due to the Streptococcus viridans is perfectly distinct, and the peculiar pneumonia caused by the Streptococcus mucosus stands out sharply from the others. Nevertheless, it seems that we are hardly able as yet to outline sharply the whole field of activity of each of these organisms. We know that tonsillitis, otitis, endocarditis, etc., may be caused by each of them, but we have not yet adequate statistics to show what part each plays in any great series of cases of such common affections.

The organisms grow on mucous surfaces or penetrate into the tissues, where they produce a diffuse inflammation more rarely concentrated in the form of abscesses. They invade the lymphatics, and are carried into the blood-stream, giving rise to general bacteriæmia, or attack the walls of the blood-vessels, producing infected thrombi, from which they are continually shed into the circulating blood. Intense inflammatory reactions usually form the response to their presence, and it may be seen that a very great variety of lesions can be produced by their ability to attack any tissue in the body.

Infections of the Throat.—Since streptococci are so commonly present in the mouth and upper respiratory tract, the pharynx, with its ring of lymphoid or adenoid tissue, is a common portal of entry. Reddening of the mucosa, with a sensation of soreness of the throat, followed by swelling of the tonsils, the appearance of patches of whitish, necrotic material on the exposed surfaces, fever, and general illness are most commonly ended by recovery. Even in such cases it is probable that many streptococci pass into the general blood-stream. More severe effects of such angina are met with and may be illustrated by the case of one of our colleagues, who suffered from repeated attacks. In one of these, the tonsils became greatly swollen and reddened, with thick patches of greenish, necrotic tissue and fibrin, which, on removal, left rather deep raw ulcerations. The whole pharynx was intensely inflamed, and firm lumps appeared beneath the angle of the jaw. He was profoundly ill, and the surgeons incised the swelling, which proved to be due to infection of the adjacent lymph-glands, from which a quantity of pus containing streptococci was drained. After that he recovered, but a year later the tonsillitis suddenly recurred, the surfaces of the tonsils, as well as the whole lining of the pharynx, became intensely inflamed and covered with a necrotic false membrane. There were tumefaction and induration of the glands and high fever. He rapidly became delirious, and then comatose. A rash, like that of scarlet fever, appeared over the whole body, with pin-point hæmorrhages everywhere, and he died within seventy-two hours of the onset.

Violent streptococcal infections are an almost constant accompaniment of scarlet fever, and sometimes of diphtheria, and in the lack of knowledge of the cause of scarlet fever there are those who would ascribe it to the streptococcus. Indeed, in the case described above, the diagnosis of scarlet fever was made.

In other cases arising somewhat differently, from extension of the infection from a suppurating salivary gland, from a carious tooth, or from a peritonsillar abscess (quinsy), there may arise another form of angina, the so-called *Ludwig's angina,* in which all the loose tissues of the neck become densely infiltrated with inflammatory exudate in response to the dissemination of streptococci there. One case which we saw recently was thought to have started in an infected abrasion of the skin of the neck, but most of them arise from extension from the organs about the pharynx. The infiltration among the muscles and about the vessels and the pharynx is so dense as to be rigid and hard, so that these organs are solidly embedded. If death is postponed for a few days, there may be liquefaction of some of the necrotic tissue and exudate.

Important are the numerous cases of *streptococcal sore throat* which occur in great epidemics with high mortality, and are generally traced to some dairy in which one or more cows with udders infected with the streptococcus give a milk which is thick, yellow, and stringy, and on examination proves to be really a mixture of milk and pus, with myriads of streptococci. Several epidemics of this kind have been reported recently in this country (Pearce, Capps, and others).

The Streptococcus viridans produces tonsillitis, it seems, causing infiltration of the peritonsillar tissue, from which recovery is usually prompt. The organisms invade the blood-stream, however, for such tonsillitis appears to be the initial step in the production of the chronic type of endocarditis caused by this form.

Recently, after the paper of Kretz, in which it was attempted to show that appendicitis owed its origin to a previous tonsillitis or angina, with the transportation of the bacteria by the blood-stream, efforts have been made to show that many other local infections are of anginal origin. It seems clear, as Aschoff points out, that this is not the case with appendicitis, and each of the others must likewise be determined separately.

Infections of the Middle Ear.—Important, because so common and so destructive, these infections of the middle ear are usually caused by the streptococcus derived from the infected throat by way of the Eustachian tube. Other organisms may produce a similar condition, and apparently the staphylococci and the pneumococcus may be responsible, but the majority are streptococcal infections, of which those produced by the Streptococcus mucosus are the most severe. Infected material is often driven up the Eustachian tube in sneezing if the nose is held, or even in blowing the nose. In a case which I followed the attempt to smother a sneeze was followed by a sense of discomfort in one ear, and that, next day, by a sharp pain. The drum of the ear may be dulled a day or two later and bulge, or pus may be seen showing through it. If it is punctured, the infection may clear up, but it usually lasts a long time, and often extends into the cavities of the mastoid process of the temporal bone, which fill up with pus. Necrosis of the bone between these cavities takes place, and may extend into the other portions of the temporal bone until it reaches the dura mater, with its lateral sinus. Necrosis and infection of the dura occurred in the case mentioned, but in most instances, as one sees at autopsy, the lateral venous sinus becomes thrombosed, the thrombus being propagated often into the jugular vein and giving rise to a general bacteriæmia. Infection of the meninges beginning with the overlying temporal lobe of the brain, and the formation of an abscess in the substance of that lobe, are the common causes of death. Libman finds that bacteriæmia may depend upon the thrombosis of the jugular, and that it may be stopped by ligature of the vein.

Infections of the Digestive Tract.—Vague, and for the greater part unfounded, statements were formerly made about the part played by streptococci in the causation of dysenteries, but since the recent work of Shiga, Flexner, and others, it is clear that those affections are due to a totally different organism. Nevertheless, it still seems probable, although not proven, that some at least of the instances of terminal diphtheritic enteritis and colitis in persons dying after protracted illnesses may be due to streptococci.

Definitely of streptococcal origin are the *phlegmonous gastritis* and *phlegmonous enteritis*, in which the submucosa of the stomach or of the duodenum and jejunum is found to be enormously thickened by a tense inflammatory exudate loaded with streptococci. Invasion through some abrasion or ulceration of the mucosa, sometimes produced by a blow on the abdomen, gives origin to this condition. It is interesting from the fact that the walls of the digestive tract are rendered rigid and immovable by the exudate, and since this tract is unable to propel the intestinal contents, obstruction, with its characteristic symptoms, ensues, just as in paralytic ileus.

That the streptococcus may play an important part in appendicitis has already been mentioned.

Wound Infection.—Streptococcal infection through wounds or abrasions of the skin are perhaps not so common as those caused by the staphylococcus, but under certain circumstances, especially familiar to surgeons and pathologists, they occur and run a rapid course. A prick with a needle or a small unobserved cut during the performance of an autopsy in an infected case remains unnoticed for several hours, after which it shows a slight reaction and becomes painful. Little is to be observed at the point of the inoculation, but the whole arm aches, red lines, indicating an acute lymphangitis, run up the forearm, the epitrochlear and axillary glands swell and become very tender. A feeling of extreme illness with fever and perhaps a chill ensues. Infiltration of the loose tissues of the arm and axilla may take place and require surgical intervention, and although the body resistance is likely to overcome the bacteria, death from general septicæmia is not rare.

One instance of this sort in an artist colleague who was making a drawing at an autopsy had interesting complications. The swelling and tension in his arm were such that extensive incisions were made, in the midst of which the ulnar nerve was injured with a clamp. On recovery it was found that half of his hand was paralyzed, and some months later a second operation was undertaken to find the point of injury. The nerve was found embedded in a dense scar, which was dissected away, after which, doubtless through allowing new nerve-fibres to grow down through this obstructed point, mobility and sensation gradually but completely returned.

More extensive wounds with laceration of tissue and soiling are prone to develop streptococcus infections. Fracture of the skull extending into the accessory nasal cavities may lead to a suppurative meningitis, while compound fractures of the other bones formed, in pre-antiseptic days, the most feared of traumatic injuries. Of course, since they often developed a pyæmic condition, it is likely that other organisms, including the staphylococci, were frequently concerned, but the diffuse inflammation and septicæmia caused by the streptococcus were not uncommon. Even now, with all our vaunted knowledge of bacteriology and antiseptics, the surgeons must be careful to treat soiled and lacerated wounds in such a way that the circulation is not interfered with by suture or bandages, lest streptococci multiply in the hampered tissues and finally invade the whole body. The conditions under which soldiers in the trenches in the present war are exposed to lacerating wounds are familiar to every one, and although the tetanus bacillus and the gas bacillus add to the dangers, the most fearful streptococcus infections are described.

Erysipelas.—The hæmolytic streptococcus responsible for puerperal sepsis, etc., is also the cause of the peculiar infection of the skin, which starts from some slight wound or abrasion and which has always been known as erysipelas. It is commonly seen on the face or head, but it is also frequent in other parts of the body. Erdman, who studied 800 cases, found that 500 of them were uncomplicated cases of facial erysipelas, while far smaller numbers were affections of other parts of the body or migrating forms. It is a rapidly spreading inflammation of the skin, which becomes reddened and elevated into a dense, advancing, irregular margin, which pushes ahead, leaving the previously affected part pale again or somewhat pigmented. Where the skin is loose, it becomes œdematous and enormously swollen. Where it is stretched or tightly bound to the underlying tissues, the spread of the disease is likely to stop, and hence the treatment recommended by Wölfler, which consists in stretching the skin with strips of adhesive plaster. In the eyelids, scrotum, vulva, etc., the œdema may be such that the tense skin becomes necrotic. This is likely to occur, too, where erysipelas has started from old leg ulcers, or where it occurs in tuberculous or other wasted persons. Great blisters or bullæ are formed sometimes. The red, elevated, glistening, tense margin shows the characteristic anatomical lesion, which consists of a profuse infiltration of the crevices of the tissue and the lymph-channels with streptococci. None seem to be found in the blood-vessels, but their presence in the lymphatic canals causes an inflammatory reaction which may be perivascular in its distribution. The corium is œdematous, and there are great quantities of wandering cells, mostly of a mononuclear character. Occasionally the exudate is more nearly purulent, and abundant abscesses, loaded with streptococci, may develop in the depths of the corium; but this is a rare consequence, and usually the process continues to spread without suppurating, by the advance of the streptococci, and fades in the region already traversed. It is rather remarkable that in a streptococcal infection, which elsewhere is met with an outpouring of neutrophile leucocytes, there should be found in the skin chiefly lymphoid or small mononuclear wandering cells.

The disease affects infants as well as adults, but is less common in older children. It is particularly likely to recur, and those persons who are predisposed may have a great many attacks, which in the end cause a great thickening and induration of the skin affected. It is not limited to the external skin, but may extend to the mucosæ, involving the pharynx, the larynx (often with fatal œdema of the glottis), the middle ear, the vagina, etc. Death occurs from general septicæmia, pneumonia, etc., but most often the cases recover. Erdmann has seen 93 deaths in 800 cases. Were it not for the fact that erysipelas commonly appears as a terminal infection in persons already weakened by alcohol or disease, the deaths ascribed to it might not reach so high a number. In a case which came to autopsy recently there was found a wide-spread tuberculosis of the lymph-glands and spleen, but during the last two days of life erysipelas had set in and spread rapidly over the face and neck, causing such œdema of that side of the face that the eye was not only closed, but presented its lids as great bulging masses which projected out over the swollen cheek. The Streptococcus hæmolyticus was recovered in the blood. In other fatal cases the cloudy swelling of the viscera, the acute splenic tumor, and other characteristic features of septicæmia were found. In women, attacks of erysipelas often appear with curious regularity with the periods of menstruation. Jordan, Jochmann, Reiche, and others have described cases of erysipelas caused by the staphylococcus, and Neufeld has found the pneumococcus responsible, but these are indeed rarely of ætiological importance.

Chr. Holmes discusses, in an interesting paper, the mystery which has long hung about the pathogenesis of erysipelas, and fairly demonstrates a plausible explanation of its mode of onset. Formerly a distinction was made between spontaneous and wound erysipelas, it being recognized that after operation or lacerated wounds an erysipelatous infection was likely to start from the edges of the wound. This distinction was given up because all erysipelas was later thought to begin in some abrasion, often very inconspicuous in nature. Holmes points out the great frequency of latent infection of the nose, nasal sinuses, etc., with streptococci and pneumococci, the overwhelming preponderance of facial erysipelas, and among these cases the very large proportion starting from the nose. Further, he collects many cases in which erysipelas followed operations which lay open infected nasal sinuses, infected middle ear and mastoid cells, etc., and quite logically draws the conclusion that in all probability facial erysipelas is most commonly the result of the extension of infection from the nasal cavity. He further points out the frequency of extension of this inflammation to the eyelids, conjunctiva, and the various parts of the eye, where it may produce destructive effects.

Pneumonia.—Various forms of streptococcus may be concerned in the production of lobular pneumonia or bronchopneumonia. This is not only because the organisms are so frequently present in the apparently normal throats of persons into whose lungs they invade when resistance is lowered, but also because, in so many cases, the streptococcus is the cause of an acute pharyngitis and laryngitis which may, under favorable conditions, extend into the bronchi and lungs. The Streptococcus mucosus, which Cole prefers to regard as a form of pneumococcus, is one of the prominent causes of lobar pneumonia, and, indeed, produces extremely severe infections. For convenience in comparisons of its effects with those of the pneumococcus we may consider them together later.

Endocarditis.—With regard to the rôle of the various forms of streptococcus in the production of endocarditis, much has already been said (Chapter XIV). Since writing that chapter, however, a survey has been made of the cases of endocarditis which have come to autopsy in the last ten years, with the result that it seems relatively easy to recognize, from their gross appearance, the forms of acute endocarditis which are caused by the Streptococcus hæmolyticus, the Streptococcus viridans, the pneumococcus, the staphylococcus, and the gonococcus. This statement is perhaps exaggerated, since at best only the more typical examples can be surely recognized before cultures are made, and even then the forms of endocarditis produced by the Streptococcus hæmolyticus, Streptococcus mucosus, the pneumococcus, and the staphylococcus are so much alike that it would be hazardous to venture a guess as to the organism concerned. On the other hand, while those organisms form a group, the lesions caused by the Streptococcus viridans, by the gonococcus, and by the unknown infective agent of rheumatism are so different from them and from one another as to be pretty easily recognized. It may be useful to express this impression in the form of a table, although the student must realize that there are other organisms, such as the Micrococcus zymogenes, influenza bacillus, the meningococcus, and many others which can produce endocarditis with lesions which may be peculiar to themselves or only slightly different from the ordinary forms.

Streptococcus Hæmolyticus, Streptococcus mucosus, Staphylococcus aureus and albus, Pneumococcus	Streptococcus viridans	Gonococcus	Rheumatism
Large, soft vegetations on mitral, aortic, and sometimes on tricuspid, often causing ulceration.	Firmer yellow or greenish vegetations on mitral, extending far on auricular wall and chordæ tendineæ. Also on aortic valves. Little ulceration.	Enormous vegetations with extreme ulceration, destruction of valves.	Small, warty vegetations on mitral, aortic, and tricuspid valves, with slow thickening of valves.
Sometimes purulent invasion of myocardium.	Recurrences with thickening of the valve. General septicæmia.	Vegetations on tricuspid and pulmonary valves, also on aortic at times.	Chronic adhesive pericarditis. Peculiar myocarditis.
General septicæmia with petechiæ, embolic lesions, and cloudy swelling of the viscera.	Infarcts and minute bacterial emboli in kidneys, etc.	General septicæmia, peritonitis, joint infections. Gonococcal genital infection.	Joint inflammation. Less definite signs of active general septicæmia.
Rapid course.	Slow course.	Rapid course.	Chronic course with exacerbations.

The Streptococcus hæmolyticus, whatever its mode of entrance, is quick to gain access to the blood-stream and to localize itself on the valves. The vegetations (Fig. 253) produced there may, of course, be small at first, but they tend to grow rapidly into irregular masses which commonly extend toward the base of the valve, and in the case of the aortic valves often appear on both sides of the cusp; that is, within the sinus of Valsalva, as well as on the ventricular surface. In such a case perforation of the valve is likely to occur. Two cases have been seen recently in our series in which such large holes have been produced as to allow of regurgitation through the valve cusps. The bacteria may extend into the musculature of the septum or other part of the heart-wall, and produce a deep, abscess-like excavation. There was one example in Baltimore in which in this way an abscess, formed in the septum in continuity with a large vegetation on the aortic valve, projected beneath the pulmonary orifice, and finally ruptured there, forming a communication between the two ventricles. In another case there were vegetations on the auricular surface of the tricuspid valves so large as to make the orifice extremely narrow. They

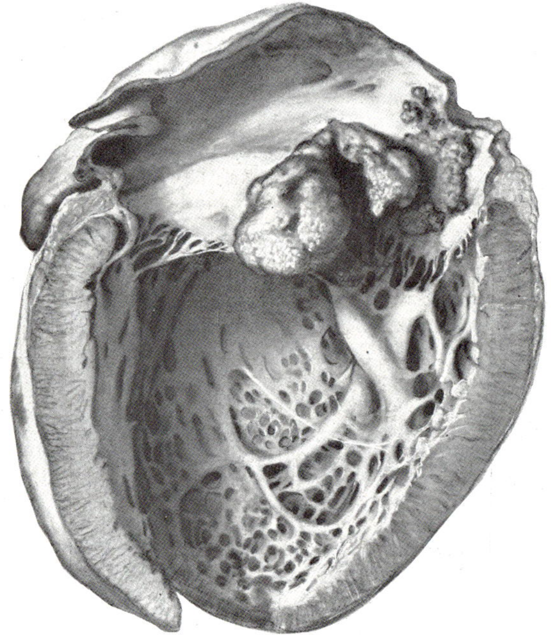

Fig. 253.—Endocarditis due to the Streptococcus hæmolyticus. Great friable vegetations on the mitral valves prone to ulceration.

bulged up as rough yellow masses into the auricle, and acted as an extreme obstruction to the flow of blood. Curiously enough, it sometimes happens that such great vegetations exist without marked circulatory disturbances or loud murmurs, but this is not always the case. They are associated with the most typical evidences of the existence of a generalized streptococcal septicæmia and often with septic infarction (Fig. 254).

The Streptococcus mitior or viridans of Schottmüller produces a type of endocarditis, already mentioned in Chapter XIV, which is slower in its progress and subject to remissions or periods of partial healing, but which, nevertheless, proceeds relentlessly to the death of the patient (Fig. 255). It has been called endocarditis lenta, or subacute bacterial endocarditis.

The distinct character of this affection was pointed out by Schottmüller, Lenhartz, Harbitz, and others, and recently Libman, in several papers, has added to the clearness of its outline. The disease begins insidiously with pains, fever, evidences of involvement of the heart valves, and progresses through several months or a year to death from cardiac decompensation, cerebral embolism, nephritis, or an intercurrent infection such as pneumonia. There may be tonsillitis, mild joint pains, and enlargement of the spleen. There is a progressive anæmia with leucocytosis, a brownish pig-

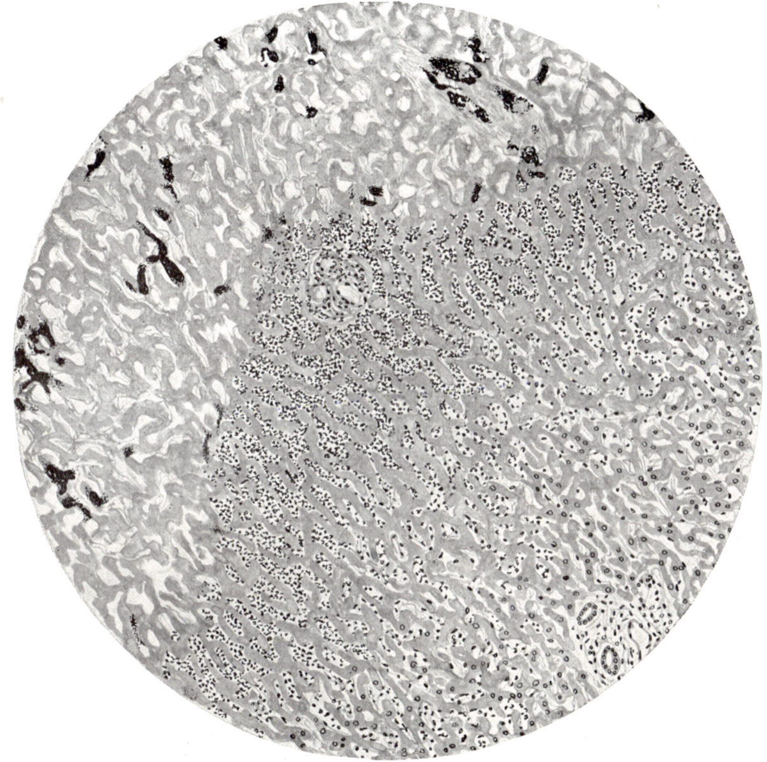

Fig. 254.—Margin of septic infarction in the liver. The capillaries in the necrotic region are crowded with streptococci.

mentation of the face in some cases, petechial hæmorrhages, and tender, erythematous nodules in the skin, sometimes with purpuric patches. Bacteria are found circulating in the blood, although in the later stages they may be absent for a time, and such stages Libman considers to be characteristic and evidence of partial or temporary healing. The symptoms are continued, however, through such bacteria-free stages possibly by the casting off of small emboli. Renal changes are almost constant, and while in the kidneys examined during the early stages they are recognizable as hyaline occlusions of the capillaries of the glomeruli, they may bring with them later much more extensive destruction of renal tissue as the result of glomerular obliteration. These lesions were discovered by Löhlein, and later described again by Baehr.

At autopsy it is found that there are old, scar-like thickenings of the affected heart valves and chordæ tendineæ, so that Libman assumes that the Streptococcus viridans produces its infective lesions on the basis of old alterations which may have been rheumatic in character. It is also conceivable that it itself might have produced the healed lesions, so that the fresher vegetations are merely a new crop in the old site. These vegetations are found especially on the mitral valve, extending down on the chordæ tendineæ and covering them, coating over the broken ends of those which are ulcerated and eaten through, as so often happens. They extend, too, far up on the wall of the left auricle, where they form a thick, rough mat. This distribution is so characteristic, especially taken together with the coarse, rough character of the vegetations and their grayish-green or pinkish-green color, that the gross appearance alone is almost enough to give the diagnosis. There is usually no pericarditis and no characteristic myocardial change.

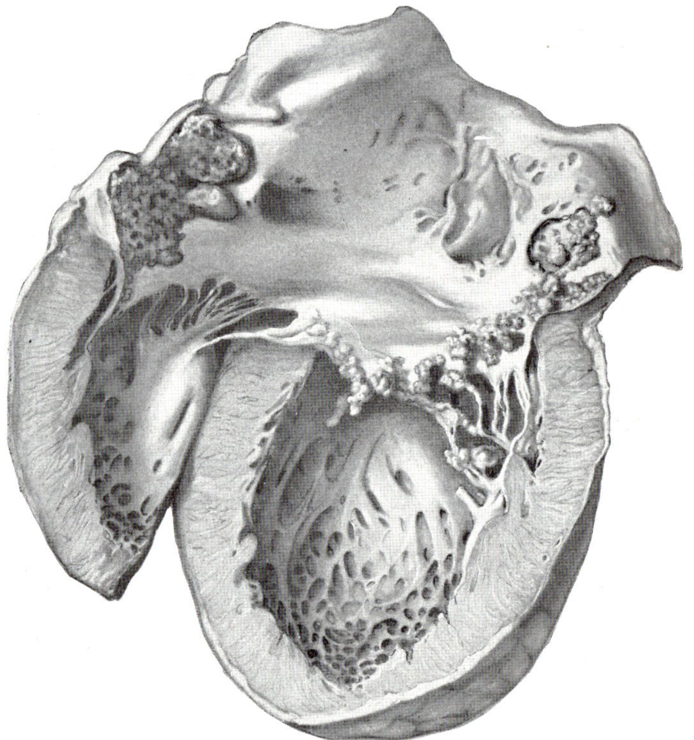

Fig. 255.—Endocarditis due to the Streptococcus viridans. Vegetations on auricle wall, mitral valve, and chordæ tendineæ.

Infarcts are to be found, of course, in the swollen spleen or in the kidneys, and sometimes in the brain, but the typical picture of the acute septic changes in all the organs is not so striking as in the endocarditis produced by the Streptococcus hæmolyticus and other more virulent organisms.

General Streptococcus Septicæmia.—Although the clinical and anatomical features of a general septicæmia or invasion of the streaming blood by bacteria have many special characters, depending on the type of organism, there is a great deal in common among them, and at autopsy one frequently recognizes the existence of a general septicæmia from the condition of the organs without being able to say whether it is due to a streptococcus, pneumococcus, staphylococcus, or some other organism. Of course, a staphylococcus septicæmia is likely to be marked by the presence of numerous abscesses, typhoid septicæmia by lesions peculiar to it; septicæmia due to Friedländer's bacillus by peculiarities of the exudate, and so on, but there are still features common to septicæmia in general.

The streptococcus seems to be able to enter readily into the blood-stream by the aid of the lymphatics, or more directly, and to grow diffusely wherever carried. It is difficult to say whether it multiplies in the circulating blood or not, but at least it becomes abundant in the blood, perhaps because it furnishes so many new sources of supply in the colonies deposited throughout the tissue.

The symptoms begin with a chill and high fever, which continues in various forms, sometimes continuously high, but more often with remissions and daily exacerbations with chills. The blood is quickly and profoundly altered. There is a great increase in the number of leucocytes, although in the severe cases, in which resistance fails, the lack of any increase or an absolute decrease in their numbers may be an index of an unfavorable outlook for the patient. The destruction of blood-corpuscles proceeds rapidly, and extreme pallor may quickly ensue. In the skin and in the retinæ the clinician is made aware of the presence of bacteria by the appearance of minute points of yellow opacity, surrounded by little flecks of hæmorrhage. These are due to the plugging of tiny blood-vessels with emboli of bacteria, or, when there is endocarditis, with fragments of the vegetations loaded with bacteria. In the skin the thickness of the tissues makes them appear as homogeneous petechial hæmorrhages, but in the conjunctiva or retina, or in the serous surfaces at autopsy, it is usually possible to distinguish a central necrotic fleck. In the skin such emboli may produce no hæmorrhage, but instead tender, nodular swellings, which on section reveal a focus of inflammatory infiltration around the obstructed vessel. Extensive purpuric hæmorrhages may spread throughout the skin, sometimes becoming confluent over considerable areas. In other cases erythematous rashes appear, resembling those of scarlatina or of measles.

In the case of streptococcus septicæmia there are found relatively few focal internal lesions produced by the lodgment of the bacteria. The most common are those in the lungs, which may take the form of bronchopneumonic patches or abscess-like infiltrations, and those in the joints, where at times there is found an intense inflammatory reaction with a purulent exudate in the synovial cavity.

In many cases these focal affections are absent. Endocarditis is, of course, focal in this regard, and, as stated, the dislodgment of fragments of the vegetations mechanically produces lesions elsewhere. But the more direct effects of the diffusion of bacteria in the blood are seen in the cloudy swelling of the liver and kidney, and such other organs as are composed of tissue capable of showing a cloudiness from changes in the water or granule contents of the cells. The nature of this is discussed elsewhere (Chapter VII). The heart muscle partakes of this dull, opaque appearance, which is intensified there, as in the liver and kidney, by the appearance in the cells of many minute globules of fat. The acute and subacute nephritis which has been described elsewhere requires time to develop, and is rather an accompaniment of those streptococcal infections which have already lasted for some time. The bone-marrow, actively exercised in the production of leucocytes, is often found to have assumed the opaque cellular appearance which is also found in anæmias, where active regeneration of the blood is required. In septicæmia death may occur before this stage of activity is reached, but if the patient survives long enough, examination of the marrow will reveal a great increase in the number of myelocytes which form the polymorphonuclear leucocytes, and also of those cells which go to form red corpuscles.

The spleen is enlarged and soft, with peculiar alterations of its substance which are discussed under the non-committal phrase *acute splenic tumor*.

Acute Splenic Tumor.—In practically all acute infectious diseases, but especially in such intense forms as the septicæmias under discussion, the spleen becomes tumefied, so that it is readily palpable beneath the margin of the ribs. Its size varies greatly, but its weight may reach 600 to 700 grams or more. The capsule is tense, but the organ is soft, so that when it is cut through the cut surface swells forward, everting the edges of the capsule (Fig. 256). One may scrape off with the knife or even with the finger a quantity of smeary, paint-like pulp. Indeed, the spleen is so soft sometimes that it spreads out on the pan or even flows as a semifluid material. The trabeculæ are sunken below the swollen surface, or else, if the cut surface has been scraped, they alone may be left as shaggy threads after the pulp has been wiped away to a considerable depth. In such extreme examples of softness it is difficult even to see the Malpighian bodies. In other cases they are much enlarged and conspicuous, sometimes with an opaque, yellowish, central fleck in each. Ordinarily the splenic pulp in such swollen spleens has a velvety or pasty appearance, and is very opaque and of a dull, pinkish-gray color. In these latter particulars the acute splenic tumor of septic conditions is very different from that of typhoid fever, which is deep red in color, and almost jelly-like in consistence, owing to the great quantities of red corpuscles held in its pulp. In order to give any idea of the nature of the change in the spleen it is necessary, first, to refer briefly to the main points in its structure, as worked out by Weidenreich, Mollier, and others. The Malpighian bodies, rather sharply marked out from the actual splenic pulp, are collections of lymphoid cells in a reticulum formed from the adventitia of the arterioles, so that they are periarterial lymphoid nodules. After leaving the Malpighian body the branches of the arteriole empty each into one of the peculiar wide venules, which, entangled together, make up the bulk of the splenic pulp. These venules have walls which are formed of peculiar, elongated endothelial cells, whose central nucleus is relatively large, causing a bulging at the middle point of the long tapered cell, which projects somewhat into the lumen. Cross-sections of the venules sometimes pass through many of the nuclei; sometimes, on the contrary, they show chiefly sections of the protoplasm of the cell. Outside these each venule is surrounded by a basketwork of elastic reticulum fibrils, which are connected with the general reticulum of the pulp. Whether there is also an intervening structureless membrane, upon which the endothelial cell lies, is not perfectly clear. Weidenreich states that there is such a membrane perforated here and there. In the spaces between these venules there lie the cells of the splenic pulp, which are of various sorts, and it is in connection with them that our information seems least precise. Many red corpuscles are normally found there, and many mononuclear cells of various forms. Polymorphonuclear leucocytes occur, but are less abundant. It is difficult to say whether any of these mononuclear cells are peculiar to the spleen, or whether they contribute largely, or at all, to the circulating blood. Morris found them swept out in numbers in the blood of the splenic vein, while others have found the reverse, *i. e.*, the mononuclear cells which entered the spleen with the arterial blood retained there, while polymorphonuclear leucocytes pass through. There seems no doubt that when the conditions demand it myelocytes can be formed in the splenic pulp, giving it some of the characteristics of the bone-marrow. Further, it is clear that the cells of the pulp are active as phagocytes, and are often found laden with pigment. This is true of the endothelial cells of the venules, just as it is of Kupffer's cells of the hepatic capillaries. As in the lymph-glands, it appears that there are large, pale reticulum cells in the splenic pulp which can act as phagocytes.

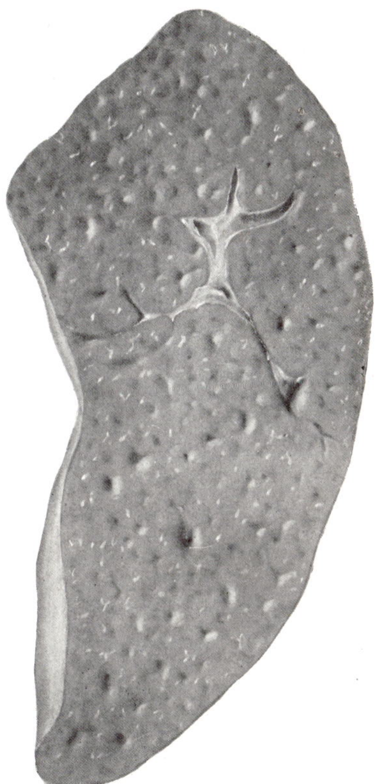

Fig. 256.—Acute splenic tumor from a case of endocarditis.

In acute splenic tumor in infectious diseases it seems that there may be a variety of changes. In some infections the Malpighian bodies seem little changed, and in the fresh spleen sink into insignificance, in contrast with the great swelling of the splenic pulp, which, on the cut surface, bulges or flows over them, so as almost to hide them from view. In other cases the prominent alteration is in these bodies.

In the acute splenic tumor accompanying streptococcus and staphylococcus septicæmia, pneumonia, etc., there is little blood in the spaces between the venules in the splenic pulp (Fig. 257). Indeed, the venules themselves seem compressed and partly emptied by the enormous increase in the number of nucleated cells between them, and it is this great accumulation of loose cells which gives the pastiness and grayish opacity to such spleens. In our ignorance of the exact nature of the process one gains the impression that this great hyperplasia is analogous to that seen under similar conditions in the bone-marrow, where hyperplasia of cells is associated in our minds with the furnishing of necessary elements to the blood. Jawein, however, regarded the swelling of the spleen as a process associated with the destruction of red corpuscles, and found that it occurred only in those intoxications and infections in which there was much blood destruction. The advent of so many cells would, for him, represent a phagocytic function.

While in the typhoid spleen this phagocytosis of red cells and other débris is a very obvious feature, and most extensively carried on, it is by no means conspicuous in the spleens of septic infections, and, indeed, one sees relatively little phagocytosis at all in

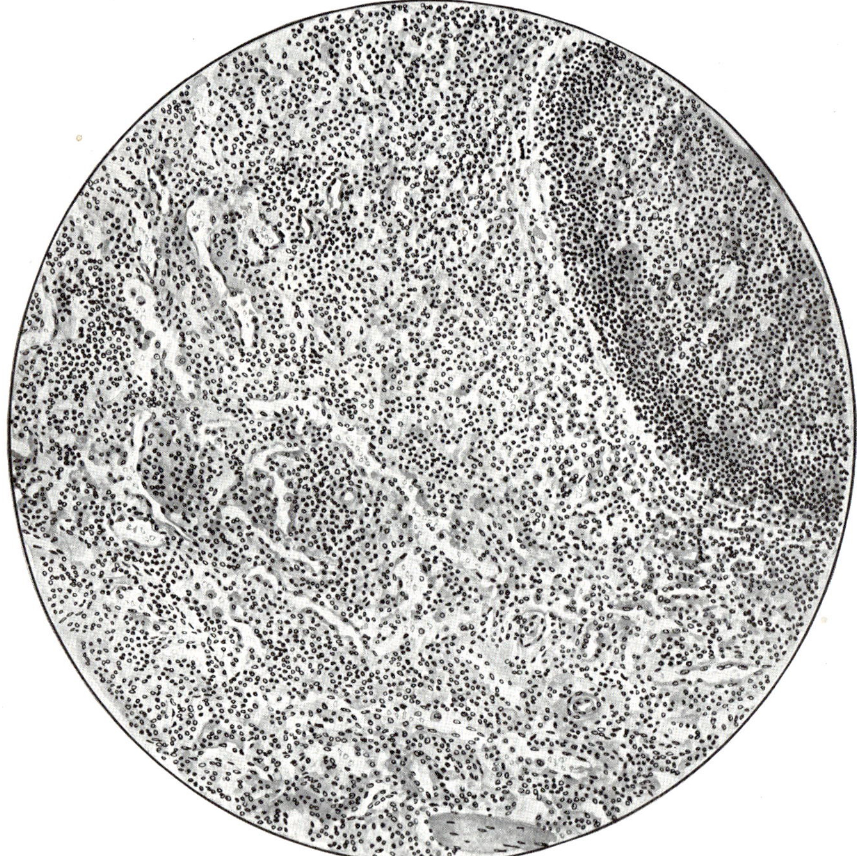

Fig. 257.—Acute splenic tumor: septicæmia associated with acute endocarditis and acute diffuse nephritis.

this pulp. Bernhardt, who studied especially the spleens of cases of scarlet fever and typhoid fever, draws this same contrast in another connection. He finds that in scarlet fever huge numbers of blood-platelets accumulate and are engulfed by phagocytic cells. Probably this occurs also in other infections, but in order to prove that these platelets are not merely the débris of red corpuscles, he shows that in typhoid fever, where there is such active phagocytosis of red corpuscles, platelets are relatively few in number in the spleen. This is another theory of phagocytosis to explain the swelling of the spleen, but hardly more completely satisfactory than that of Jawein. Occasionally one sees great numbers of polymorphonuclear leucocytes in the meshes of the splenic pulp, but this is not constant.

In diphtheria Washkewitz points out that the especial enlargement of the Malpighian bodies is due to the appearance of a central mass of large, pale phagocytic cells, which she thinks are probably derived from the lymphoid cells and not from the reticulum, as Ziegler had thought. These conspicuous pale central masses of large cells in the Malpighian bodies are by no means confined to diphtheria, but occur in many types of infections, especially in children and young people. We have reviewed the last 500 autopsies in this regard, and have found many cases in which they occur. They are all in cases of infection of one sort or another, with bronchopneumonia, tuberculosis, diphtheria, peritonitis, and many toxic processes, among which skin burns are notable. But they are not particularly a feature of the acute splenic tumor, in which the splenic pulp is especially swollen. The large cells have pale, vesicular nuclei, abundant pale-staining protoplasm, and are frequently loaded with fragments of other cells which they have engulfed. They themselves often show degenerative changes; their nuclei become fragmented, and in time the mass may come to look like a focal necrosis with clumps of broken nuclei.

It must be said that further work is required to make clear the complex nature of acute splenic tumor, which in some cases seems to be a response to the presence of the débris of red corpuscles or other cells, in others to the diffusion of a toxin or bacteria. The part of the spleen in reconstructing the blood seems to be little understood in spite of numerous studies which have been made recently, but more will be said on this point in connection with the diseases of the blood.

LITERATURE

Capps and Davis: Trans. Assoc. Amer. Phys., 1914, xxix, 279.
König: Deutsche Chirurgie, 1882, Lief 36.
Poulsen: Deutsche Zeit. f. Chir., 1893, xxxvii, 55.
Kretz: Centralbl. f. allg. Path., 1906, xvii, 887.
Libman: "Otitis," Amer. Jour. Med. Sci., 1909, cxxxviii, 409.
MacCallum: "Phlegmonous Enteritis," Johns Hopkins Hosp. Bull., 1906, xvii, 252.
Erdmann: Jour. Amer. Med. Assoc., 1913, lxi, 2048.
Jochmann: Mohr u. Staehelin, Handb. d. inneren Medizin, Berlin, 1911, i, 578, 717.
Joseph Koch: Ergeb. d. allg. Path., 1909, $xiii_1$, 135.
Fehleisen: Aetiologie des Erysipels, Berlin, 1883.
Lenhartz: "Septische Infektionen," Nothnagel, Spec. Path. u. Therap., 1899.
Holmes: Annals of Otology, Rhinology, and Laryngology, xvi, 457, 1907.
Libman: Trans. Assoc. Amer. Phys., 1912, xxvii, 157; 1913, xxviii, 309.
Schottmüller: Münch. med. Woch., 1903, l, 849.
Löhlein: Med. Klinik, 1910, vi, 375.
Baer: Jour. Exp. Med., 1912, xv, 330.
Jawein: Virch. Arch., 1900, clxi, 461.
Washkewitz: Virch. Arch., 1900, clix, 137.
Bernhardt: Ziegler's Beiträge, 1913, lv, 35.
Weidenreich: Arch. f. mikr. Anat., 1901, lviii, 247.
Mollier: Arch. f. mikr. Anat., 1911, lxxvi, 608.

CHAPTER XXV

TYPES OF INJURY.—BACTERIAL DISEASE (Continued).—STAPHYLOCOCCUS INFECTIONS

General character. Furunculosis. Paronychia, impetigo, etc. General septicæmia, pyæmia, suppurative nephritis, endocarditis, lobular pneumonia, osteomyelitis.

THE Staphylococcus pyogenes aureus, Staphylococcus albus, and other less important forms, including the Staphylococcus citreus, are concerned in these infections. Much of their peculiar effect is dependent upon their tendency to grow in clumps and to cling together, rather than to spread diffusely. Hence in the tissues there is a focal character in the lesions they produce, in contrast with the more spreading lesions of the streptococcus. For the same reason the entrance of the staphylococcus into the circulating blood results in its deposition at numerous points, where it grows into compact colonies which produce focal lesions. Unlike the streptococcus, which grows most commonly on mucous membranes, such as that of the pharynx, and enters the body thence, the staphylococci are dwellers on the skin, and infection is usually from abrasions or cracks in the skin, although, as shall be stated, infection from the genito-urinary tract is not uncommon.

Owing to the attributes just mentioned the formation of abscesses is the usual effect of the invasion of this organism, a process already described in Chapter XIV. No matter how extensive the lesions, they have the same general character of concentration which makes possible the liquefaction of the tissue and exudate.

Furunculosis.—Cultures from the skin of healthy persons show (J. Koch) a great number of staphylococci, partly saprophytic, partly truly pathogenic. The hæmolytic power of these cocci seems to be almost a measure of their pathogenic character. Even in the depths of the skin, probably in the sebaceous glands and the clefts about the roots of the hairs, there are constantly present staphylococci which grow white on culture-media (Staphylococcus epidermidis albus, Welch), and it is thought that these are responsible for stitch abscesses when sutures are made through the skin. To avoid them, subcutaneous sutures have been employed by surgeons with great success. With such a flora present, it is very easy to understand that abrasions, or even a constant rubbing which does not erode the skin, as in the case of a collar or cuff, might give an opportunity for the beginning of furunculosis which is so familiar. It depends evidently upon a predisposing lowering of resistance, which, according to Wright, may be recognized in the decreased activity of phagocytic leucocytes (lowered opsonic power of the plasma). At any rate, once begun, furuncles or boils are likely to continue to appear, sometimes in hundreds. Athletes in training, who are roughly rubbed down, are a prey to them, and, on the other hand, persons long ill with such wasting diseases as typhoid fever, are likely to have a crop of boils. The active immunization by the injection of repeated doses of killed cocci usually has an extraordinary effect in raising the resistance and completely stopping their appearance. They begin usually about a hair, and the abscess develops until the hair can be seen standing up in the middle of a small, opaque yellow fleck. From that the infection burrows deeper and spreads laterally a little under the corium, which in the thicker parts of the skin prevents for some time the complete evacuation of the pus to the outside. In time, however, through the bursting of the central necrotic cap of skin, it escapes and the hole thus left heals up by the formation of granulation tissue. The surgeon can hasten this process by stretching or bursting open the hole with as little injury as possible to the adjacent tissue. If he squeezes or cuts that adjacent tissue so as to impair its blood supply, extension of the infection is almost inevitable.

When the resistance is very low, the cocci may quickly extend to form a whole group of connected abscesses, with several projecting necrotic points side by side in the skin. The whole swollen mass is honeycombed with channels full of pus in the necrotic tissue, and the further expansion proceeds rapidly. Such a threatening affection is known as a carbuncle, and requires prompt surgical intervention. They occur anywhere, but most commonly on the back of the neck or on the lip or buttocks. Those on the upper lip are particularly to be feared, since extension along the lymphatics or thrombophlebitis extending upward through the nose to the cavernous sinus may lead to meningitis.

Infection of the finger extending about the nail (*paronychia, panaritium*) or of the palmar surface are guided in their extension by the fasciæ of the finger and hand. Involvement of the tendon-sheaths is a particularly destructive complication.

Impetigo contagiosa, a skin disease of children, appears to be caused by the staphylococcus. It produces pustules about the face, especially around the nose and mouth, which burst and dry up into a honey-yellow crust without much surrounding reaction. It may spread over the entire body, especially where the child can scratch the skin, and is contagious for other children, although not all are susceptible.

General Septicæmia.—While the Staphylococcus aureus is perhaps the most common cause of the forms of furunculosis just described, the Staphylococcus albus takes part, and in infections which become general, it, too, is quite often found. General distribution of staphylococci through the blood-stream occurs readily, even from small infected scratches or cuts, or from some other local infection, all of which may heal up and disappear before the general infection is well under way. The wide-spread character of such general infections may be most clearly brought out by describing cases which have recently come to my attention at autopsy.

A man fell in a Pullman car against some projection which caused an abrasion between his shoulders; death occurred two weeks later, and at the autopsy, although the abrasions were partly healed, huge abscesses were found among the muscles of the back; the right knee was distended with a purulent fluid, and an abscess, filled with thick greenish pus, burrowed among the muscles of the thigh.

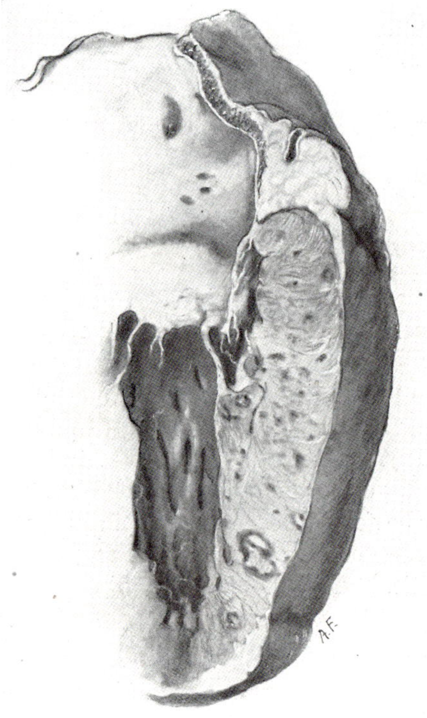

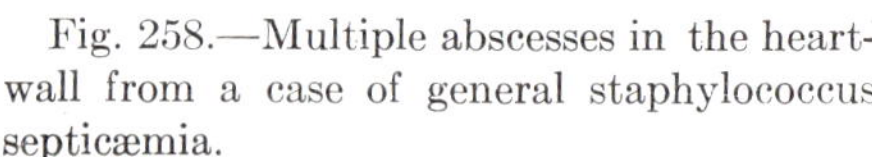

Fig. 258.—Multiple abscesses in the heart-wall from a case of general staphylococcus septicæmia.

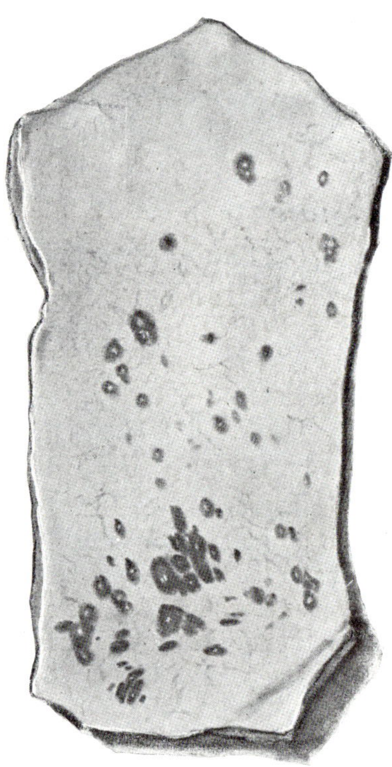

Fig. 259.—Staphylococcus septicæmia. Minute abscesses in the pericardium surrounded by hæmorrhagic flecks.

A plumber, who had cut his finger with a piece of tin some weeks before his death, making a trifling wound which had healed completely, was brought to the hospital in a condition of delirium without definite localizing symptoms. At the autopsy there was found a general infection with the Staphylococcus aureus, which was cultivated from the blood. There were small abscesses in nearly all the organs, everywhere presenting themselves as opaque yellowish spots surrounded by a zone of hæmorrhage. The heart muscle was studded everywhere with them (Fig. 258), while upon the aortic valves there were soft vegetations. The pericardium showed numerous hæmorrhagic flecks (Fig. 259), with central opacities, as did the pleural and peritoneal surfaces. Throughout the intestinal mucosa there were hæmorrhagic nodules, and similar foci appeared in the kidneys and liver. In the lungs the abscesses were larger, with central softening, and a zone of hæmorrhagic pneumonic consolidation about each.

Sometimes it is difficult to determine upon the portal of entry of the cocci, as in the case of a sailor brought off a ship to the hospital. He, too, was in a state of coma, extremely anæmic, with signs of patchy bronchopneumonic consolidation, and with abundant staphylococci in a culture from the circulating blood. At autopsy practically the same wide-spread focal lesions were found as described in the preceding case, the heart muscle

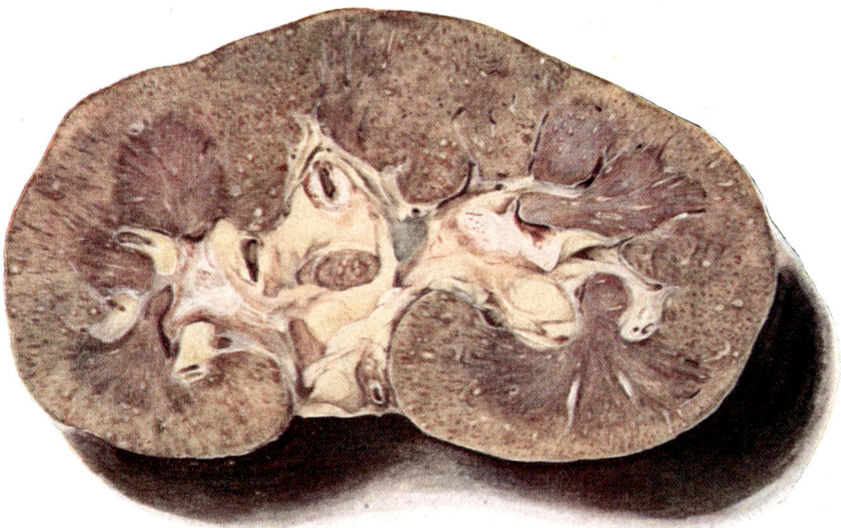

Fig. 260.—Staphylococcus septicæmia. Multiple abscesses oi the kidney.

and kidneys being especially thickly set with small abscesses (Fig. 260). No source of infection could be found after the most minute search, until a decayed canine tooth was pulled from the upper jaw, when a gush of pus came from the antrum, which evidently represented the portal of entry.

It should be noted that in such infections, especially when they are not quite so severe and rapidly fatal, localization of the bacteria in the joints with the production of a purulent synovitis is not uncommon.

Suppurative Nephritis.—Aside from their appearance as part of a general pyæmia, staphylococcus infections of the cortex and medulla of the kidney, transported there by the blood-stream, come to the attention of the surgeon more commonly than is generally thought. Jordan, Brewer, and others have described them as multiple foci, involving necrosis of the renal tissue in the cortex, and extending into the pyramids. They are probably formed in the effort of the kidney to excrete the staphylococcus brought by the blood-stream, and may develop about the bacteria, which accumulate with casts in the tubules (staphylococci are known to be abundantly excreted in the urine in general infection). Brewer looks upon them as rather of embolic origin, and therefore starting from the neighborhood of the plugged arteriole or glomerulus. They may produce multiple extensive hæmorrhagic patches of necrosis in the substance of the kidney (Fig. 261). Similarly, as the only internal lesion produced by transportation of cocci from

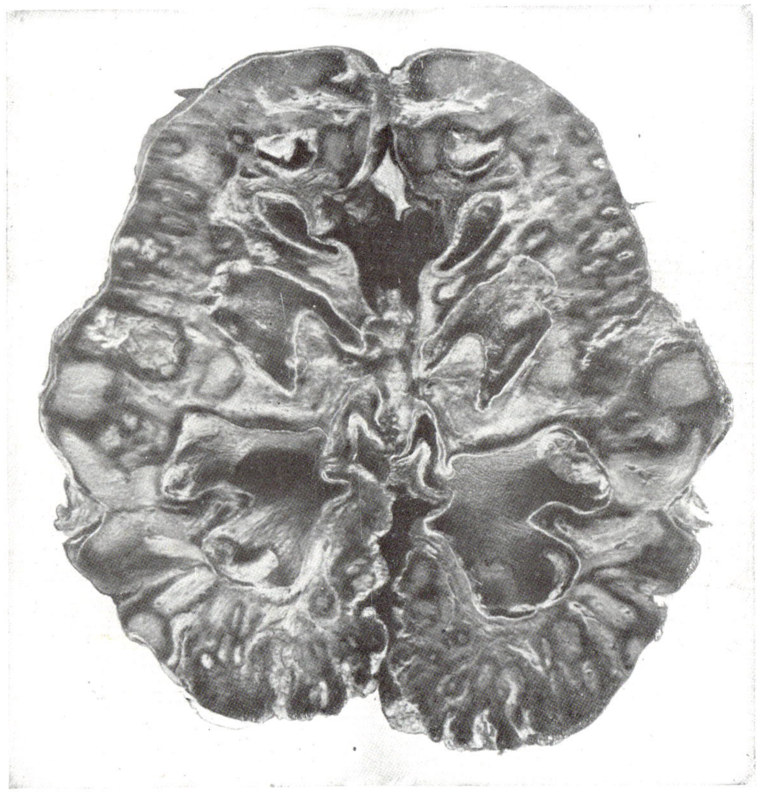

Fig. 261.—Hæmorrhagic septic infarctions of the kidney produced by the Staphylococcus aureus (Brewer).

some cutaneous infection, there may be formed a perirenal abscess which can later encroach upon the kidney.

There is always the question as to whether such hæmatogenous infections of the kidney are to be regarded as the basis for the forms of suppurative pyelonephritis associated with infections of the urinary bladder. As in the case of tuberculosis of these organs, there are those who regard the process as the result of ascending infection from the bladder, while others assume it to be hæmatogenous or indirect. It seems that both types may occur, although when abscesses appear in the kidneys as the direct continuation of an illness which begins with obstruction to the outflow of urine from the bladder, infection by catheterization, cystitis, and ureteritis, it is almost impossible to resign oneself to the idea that in those cases the bacteria enter the kidney by the blood-stream. All this can be more appropriately discussed in another place, since the staphylococcus

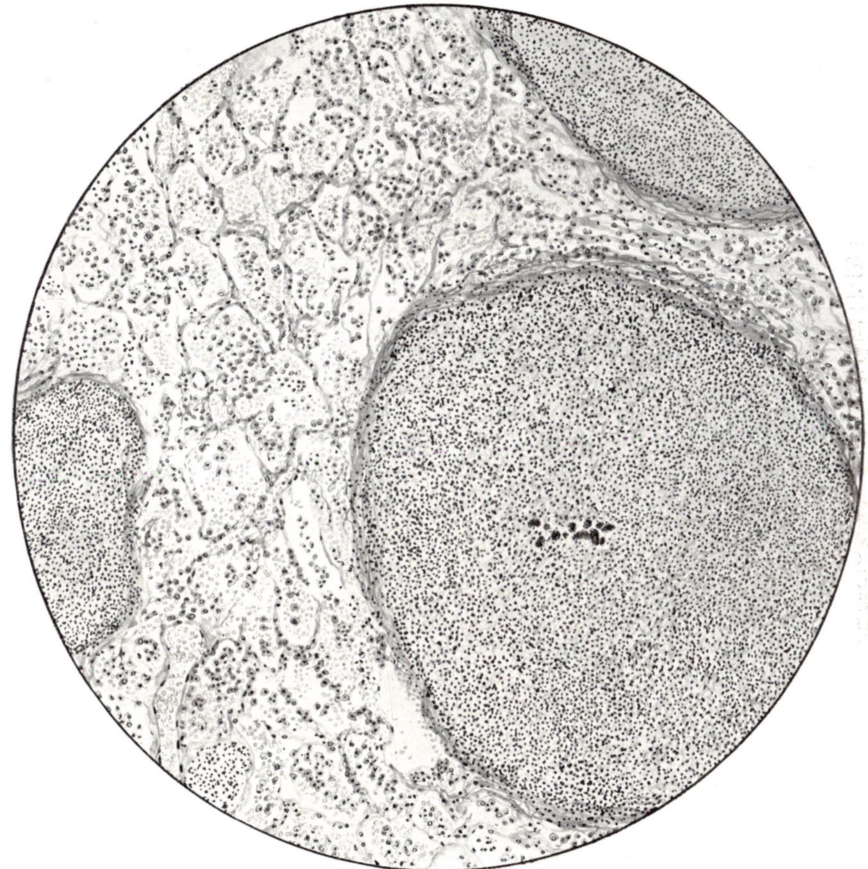

Fig. 262.—Abscesses in the lung. These abscesses were close set, and caused relatively little reaction. Usually they are isolated, hæmorrhagic, and much larger.

is not often primarily concerned in such cases. On the other hand, the chills which follow catheterization are really in most cases the expression of a general staphylococcus septicæmia of mild character initiated by the trauma in the operation.

Endocarditis is a very common accompaniment of staphylococcus infection, the mitral and aortic valves being especially affected, while the vegetations are occasionally found upon the tricuspid or upon the walls of the heart. They are usually rather large, soft thrombus masses, which readily crumble and give rise to emboli.

Lobular Pneumonia.—As in the case of streptococcal infections of the lung, there is nothing especially characteristic about many of the cases in which the staphylococcus forms the infectious cause of bronchopneumonia, except in those instances in which the concentration is such as to produce definite abscesses (Fig. 262). The mode of entrance into the lung tissue is probably in part responsible for this.

Osteomyelitis.—It is in producing a destructive lesion in the bones, involving periosteum, cortex, marrow, and even extending to the cartilages, that the staphylococcus plays one of its most characteristic rôles, although here, too, other organisms, such as the pneumococcus, the typhoid bacillus, and others may take its place and cause similar lesions. In the great majority of the cases, however, the staphylococcus is found. Here it shows particularly well its tendency to localize itself and grow in a place already injured mechanically. If several ribs or other bones are fractured in a rabbit, it is said that a subsequent injection of a culture of the Staphylococcus aureus will produce an abscess at the site of each fracture. These may be considered as points of lowered resistance, or perhaps the interruption of blood-vessels allows the bacteria to be caught there instead of being swept on by the blood-stream. In the same way in human beings a blow upon a bone appears to predispose it to the settling there of bacteria.

The organisms reach the bone either from a recognized focus of infection, or from some small infected abrasion or wound which heals and is forgotten before the disease of the bone is evident. It is the latter case which has given rise, no doubt, to the idea that there may be a primary osteomyelitis, a situation which is realized in cases of infected compound fractures. The long bones are affected far more often than the others; nevertheless osteomyelitis involving the tarsal and carpal bones, the vertebræ, the clavicles, and the bones of the pelvis is not rare. The disease occurs most frequently in children and young persons, the cases being most numerous in those between the ages of thirteen and seventeen, after which they fall off rapidly.

The cocci usually lodge in the shaft of one of the long bones in such a position as the upper third of the tibia or the lower third of the femur, and there produce an abscess in the cancellous substance of the bone which involves the cortex and the periosteum, lifting up the latter from the surface of the bone. As in other abscesses, the presence of the bacteria leads to necrosis of the tissue round about, and from the fact that this necrosis extends far wide of the clump of cocci, it may be agreed that they produce a toxic substance. (This, in fact, is well proved for the staphylococci.) The leucocytes which accumulate liquefy the necrotic tissue and attack the bony lamellæ, which they reduce to fragments. Frequently large portions of the cortex thus become necrotic and rarefied, and finally isolated from the still living bone as a sequestrum (Fig. 263) which practically floats in a pus-filled cavity. Generally it is not so completely loosened for some time, but in its extent it may amount to nearly the whole shaft of the bone.

I recall vividly one such case from my assistant time in the surgical wards, upon which I was allowed to operate. It was a boy of about twelve, whose left leg, as he was

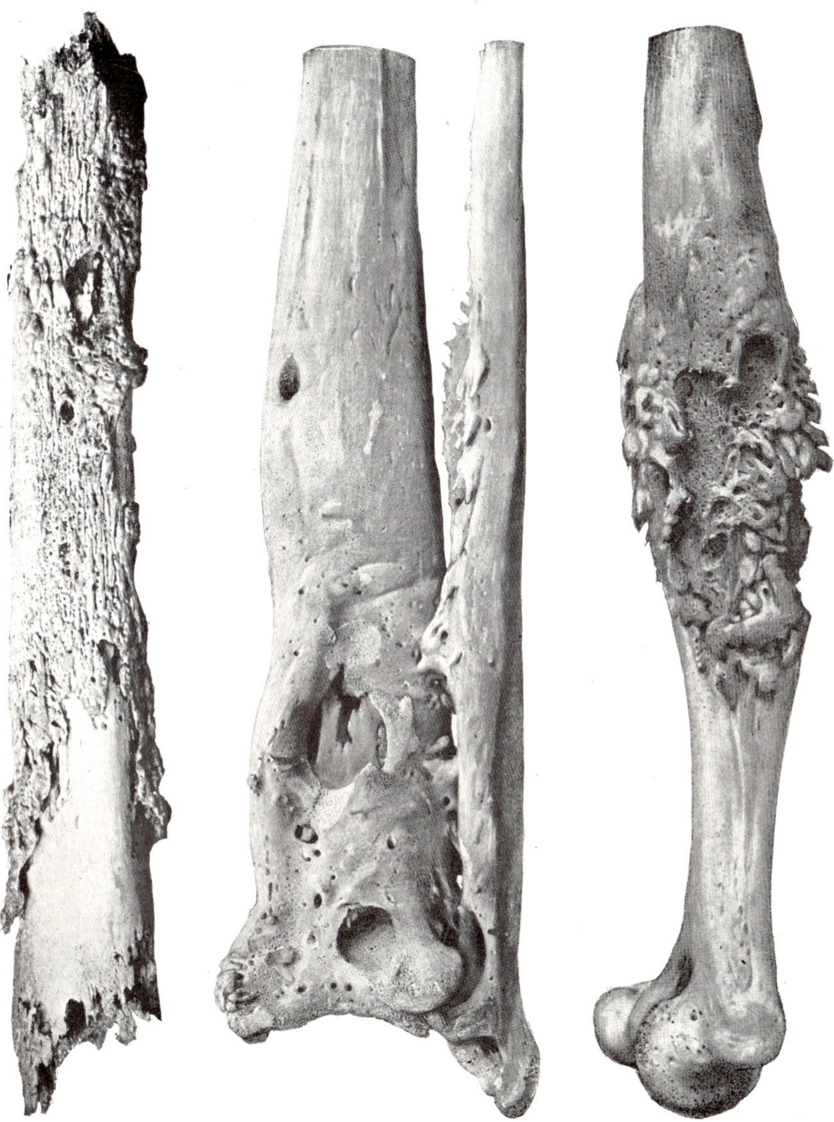

Fig. 263.—Large necrotic fragment of bone or sequestrum from the tibia in osteomyelitis.

Fig. 264.—Osteomyelitis showing the sequestrum, the involucrum with orifices which represent the sinuses, and periosteal osteophytes.

Fig. 265.—Chronic periostitis with osteophytes.

brought into the hospital, was greatly swollen below the knee, tense, and œdematous. He was suffering a great deal of pain and had a high temperature, but there was found no obvious point of infection elsewhere, from which the disease of his leg might have started. A long incision was made, and quantities of rather gritty brown pus flowed out. The periosteum had been lifted up from nearly the whole length of the tibia, and evidently had been torn to let the pus escape into the intermuscular tissues. The bone itself was already rough, and some portions of it were easily pulled away. These were ragged, as if worm-eaten. Much of the rest was chiseled or gouged away, leaving, as I remember it, the posterior half of the bone exposed in the wound which remained open. Healing occurred in a remarkable fashion by the growth of the most luxuriant granulation tissue, from the crevices in which tiny fragments of bony lamellæ were discharged for some time. Even when the skin covered most of the granulating surface, a fistula extending to the bone at one point remained for a time and discharged bony granules, but this in time healed up. This boy remained well, but it is frequently the case that before one focus is completely cleaned out and healed, another appears in some far-distant bone. Occasionally they follow one another in rapid succession, destroying or mutilating one bone after another, and ending often in the development of a general septicæmia with hundreds of small abscesses in the internal organs.

When not treated by radical surgery, the most remarkable results may ensue, especially when the infective agent is not so virulent as to lead rapidly to very extensive destruction or to general septicæmia. While in the acute forms the necrotic bone is rapidly rarefied and partly disintegrated, it may happen that in the more slowly progressing forms there is time for prolonged activity on the part of the osteoblasts which cover the bony lamellæ in the neighborhood of the focus of infection, before that surrounding bone tissue is involved in the necrosis. Then each lamella becomes greatly thickened, and the bone becomes compact as ivory (eburnation or sclerosis). It is for this reason that the necrotic sequestrum is sometimes found to be extremely dense and hard. In such subacute cases, which are more localized, the extension of the infection and inflammatory exudate to the periosteum lifts up and ruptures only a small part of it. The pus then burrows in a channel among the muscles to the skin, where it causes a bluish-red bulging, which finally ruptures like an abscess. In this way a sinus is formed through which a probe can be passed down until it scrapes upon the rough dead bone. Through this sinus fragments of bone may be discharged with the pus for a long time. If any considerable mass of the cortex has been thus converted into a loose sequestrum, extensive healing processes go on about it, even though it maintains a constant source of infection. It is true that the bacteria may die out, but even then the mass of dead bone acts as a foreign body of which the tissues cannot get rid. Instead, abundant new bone with much granulation tissue is formed about it, usually still perforated by the sinus or sinuses which extend to the skin. In time there may be produced in this way (Fig. 264) a sheath of new bone which practically represents the old shaft (the involucrum) inside which the sequestrum persists. A great part of this is formed by the periosteum, but those portions of the shaft which remain alive produce much new tissue by the aid of their endosteal cells. It is easy to understand that if that portion of the cortex of the shaft which is destined to become necrotic and sequestrated can, in the mean while, undergo sclerosis or eburnation by the new formation of layers of bone in all its Haversian systems and on the surfaces of all its lamellæ, the rest of the bone will do the same. It is for this reason that whatever remains of such a shaft is found to be heavy and dense. Indeed, if the infectious process proceeds very slowly and without gross destruction of the cortex, the whole bone may preserve its form, but become almost solid and very dense and heavy. Quite aside from the actual area of necrosis or in its absence, the inflammation which involves the periosteum results in its producing a great deal of new bone superficially applied to the shaft, so that the surface of a bone in old osteomyelitis is usually greatly roughened by such osteophytes (Fig. 265). As we shall see, a quite similar process of periosteal bone formation is frequent in other slowly progressing inflammatory affections, and is especially striking in syphilis.

When osteomyelitis caused by the staphylococcus involves the bones of the skull, or in the cases in which otitis media is due to its agency (it is very frequently active here, and the cause of nearly all the chronic forms), when metastatic abscesses occur in the brain, or when extension of the infection takes place from furunculosis of the nose or lip, acute meningitis may arise, involving the coverings of the brain and extending to the pia-arachnoid of the spinal cord. Its nature is similar to that caused by the streptococcus, pneumococcus, and other organisms, and it will more conveniently be described elsewhere. One form of meningitis is of interest, however, in this connection, namely, the purulent pachymeningitis or inflammation of the dura. That this should occur with osteomyelitis of the bones of the skull is self-evident, but one occasionally sees cases of another type in which, from an abscess in the perirectal tissue, extension of the infection occurs along the nerves, to enter the sacral foramina or even the lumbar foramina to the space outside the dura and within the spinal canal. The outer surface of the dura then becomes bathed in pus.

LITERATURE

Neisser and Lipstein: Handb. v. Kolle u. Wassermann, 1903, iii, 105.
Jos. Koch: Ergebn. d. allg. Path., 1909, xiii, 205.
Lenhartz: Nothnagel's Handb. d. spez. Path. u. Therap., 1903, iii, Teil 2, 329.
Lexer: "Osteomyelitis," Volkmann's klin. Vorträge, 173.

CHAPTER XXVI

TYPES OF INJURY. BACTERIAL DISEASE (Continued).—PNEUMOCOCCUS INFECTION

Character of organisms. Lobar pneumonia: consolidation, resolution, organization, etc. Septicæmia. Endocarditis.

Character of Organisms.—The pneumococcus or Micrococcus lanceolatus is best known on account of its preëminent relation to the clear-cut disease, lobar pneumonia. It is true that it is concerned in many other infectious processes, including otitis media, meningitis, various inflammations of the nasal sinuses, pleurisy, pericarditis, general peritonitis, and even general septicæmia, as well as the more indefinite forms of lobular or patchy pneumonia. On the other hand, a few other organisms, such as the influenza bacillus and Friedländer's capsulated bacillus, have been detected at times as the cause of unmistakable acute lobar pneumonia.

The pneumococcus is very widely distributed, and occurs in the mouths and upper respiratory tracts of most normal persons. It varies greatly in virulence, as has been shown by animal inoculations, and those cultivated from pneumonic lungs are not necessarily more virulent than those from the mouths of healthy persons. They produce a toxic substance which is hæmolytic, but which must be extracted from the dissolved bodies of the organism. It has the power of converting hæmoglobin into methæmoglobin, and can be neutralized by cholesterine. Studies of Neufeld, and especially of Cole and his assistants, have revealed the fact that there are several kinds of pneumococci which can be distinguished sharply from one another by their biological characters, although morphologically and culturally they are alike. By the aid of sera produced by inoculating living pneumococci of different strains into large animals Cole has been able to distinguish sharply at least four types, which have been found to occur in 150 cases of pneumonia in the following proportions:

Type I	57
Type II	44
Type III (Pneumococcus mucosus)	17
Type IV (heterogeneous)	32

A potent serum was obtained for Type I, a less satisfactory one for Type II. Attempts to produce a protective serum against Type III failed completely, but this organism, which is the Streptococcus mucosus of Schottmüller, is readily distinguished by its very large capsule, its stringy growth in culture, and by the glutinous exudate in the lungs in pneumonia caused by it. It produces the severest infections. Type IV is made up of a great many different strains, none of which is able to produce a very severe pneumonia. They are the forms found in the mouths of healthy persons; they are overgrown by Type I, II, or III in pneumonias caused by those types, but reappear in the mouth on convalescence after the infecting type has disappeared. Protective sera can be produced for each member of Type IV, but they are quite specific, and powerless against any other member of the group. So, too, the sera for Types I and II have no protective effect against Types III or IV, nor against one another, but are quite specific for the homologous organisms. Although infections produced by Type III are so far insusceptible of treatment by any serum, the sera for Types I and II are used in large doses, with excellent effect. Infections with Type IV are so mild as scarcely to require serum treatment. With the aid of these specific sera the organism in any case of pneumonia can be referred to its type either by inoculating mice and ascertaining which protective serum causes them to survive, or by testing the agglutination of the organisms with each serum. It is impossible to discuss here the rather indefinite toxins which have been extracted from various types of pneumococcus. The student is referred to the papers of Cole.

LOBAR PNEUMONIA

Pneumonia is an acute infectious disease which begins suddenly, usually with a sharp pain in the chest and with a chill and high fever. It proceeds with extensive consolidation of the lung, evidences of intoxication, and various metabolic disturbances, to the death of the patient or to sudden disappearance of the symptoms and rapid passing away of the consolidation (crisis), or to a slower and more gradual defervescence and relief from the symptoms of the disease (recovery by lysis). Occasionally, while the symptoms of the acute illness disappear completely and convalescence seems complete, a form of consolidation of the lung persists and is found to be due to a replacement of the exudate by fibrous tissue. Other complications which delay recovery or lead to death will be discussed later. Since most persons harbor pneumococci in their mouths, and since pneumonia seems not to be a particularly contagious disease, although rarely occurring in small epidemics, the question arises as to the mode of entry of the organisms into the lungs and the conditions under which they produce pneumonia. It is shown that many persons who do not contract diphtheria are carriers of virulent diphtheria bacilli, and the same is true, in a modified way, of other organisms. Therefore unless it should prove that those who develop pneumonia do so always from the invasion of a pneumococcus of a type different from that which they have harbored in their mouths, we must search for some predisposing cause for their invasion. It has long been known (Litten) that crushing or contusion of the thorax is frequently followed by pneumonia, and there is also the general impression that alcoholism predisposes to it, and that some sudden exposure to cold is likely to precipitate invasion of the infection. Meltzer has attempted to demonstrate with more precision that it requires local predisposing causes in the lungs to permit the bacteria to gain a foothold there. He found that a diffuse lobar pneumonia could be produced in dogs if large quantities of a liquid culture of pneumococci were blown into the bronchi and forced into the air-cells with the fluid and air-bubbles from his cannula. He suggests that in man mucus in the bronchi may be the agent which imprisons behind it a sufficient number of bacteria to gain a start and produce an effective growth. By whatever means the cocci gain a wide distribution throughout all the small bronchioles and most of the air-cells of the lobe, they are, as Ribbert has pointed out, more abundant in the terminal portion of the bronchioles and less abundant toward the outer limit of the air-cells which communicate with that bronchiole.

Ether Pneumonia.—Pneumonia which occurs after a surgical operation with general anæsthesia is not infrequent, and presents some problems of interest. It was thought to be lobular in character, and due to the aspiration of various bacteria with saliva, etc., during the anæsthesia, owing to the abolition of the normal reflexes which would prevent the access of such materials to the lungs. It proves, however, that many of these consolidations are lobar in type, and that representatives of the various groups of pneumococci are responsible for their development. These might, of course, reach the lung in the sputum, and this is rendered probable from the fact that many of the cases, at least, are due to infection with organisms of Group IV, which are known to be the forms most commonly found in the mouths of people who are not ill. It remains to decide whether this is the case regularly or whether organisms of other groups may be involved.

Anatomical Changes.—The inflammatory reaction is commonly divided into several stages. Of these, the first, the so-called *stage of engorgement*, is rarely seen at autopsy, except perhaps at the edges of an advancing consolidation, and it must be conceded that its characters are to some extent constructed from the known course of inflammation elsewhere. The capillaries of the alveolar walls are dilated with blood, and there exudes into the air-cells fluid from the blood, together with leucocytes and red corpuscles. The second stage, which is the earliest one commonly seen, is called the *stage of red hepatization* (because the lung is red and solid, like the liver). At this stage an abundant inflammatory exudate is found to have filled the alveoli and to have clotted. As in the case of a perfectly fresh clot of blood in a glass dish, which is so firm and dry that the dish can be inverted without spilling it, these clots in the air-cells are firm and dry. In sections they are seen to fill the air-cell (Fig. 266) and to be composed of a coarse-meshed network of fibrin in which are entangled numerous pneumococci, many red corpuscles, many polymorphonuclear leucocytes, and some desquamated epithelial cells. Furthermore, at this stage, and even in the earlier stage, there are seen quite numerous mononuclear wandering cells or lymphocytes. This feature has been pointed out by Pratt, and is far less characteristic of later stages. Perhaps the most distinctive thing about the exudate from the microscopical point of view is its freshness and good state of preservation. The red cells are intact, and stand out clearly with their normal hæmoglobin content; in other words, they show as yet no sign of laking or hæmolysis. The leucocytes are clearly outlined and turgid. All these cells can be seen clearly because they are relatively few in numbers and stand out distinctly in the fibrin network. Many of the leucocytes show active phagocytosis and contain several pneumococci.

In its gross appearance at this stage such a lung is very characteristic. The consolidation may involve one or more lobes, which are dense and hard and heavy. Their pleural surface has lost its normal gloss and is seen to be covered, over the consolidated area, with a delicate, scarcely perceptible layer of yellowish fibrin. On section the bronchi are reddened and may be plugged in their smaller branches with moulds of fibrin. The cut surface of the lung is usually dry, rough, and of a deep red color. The roughness is due to the slight projection from each alveolus of its plug of coagulated exudate. In sharp contrast with this flat plateau of con-

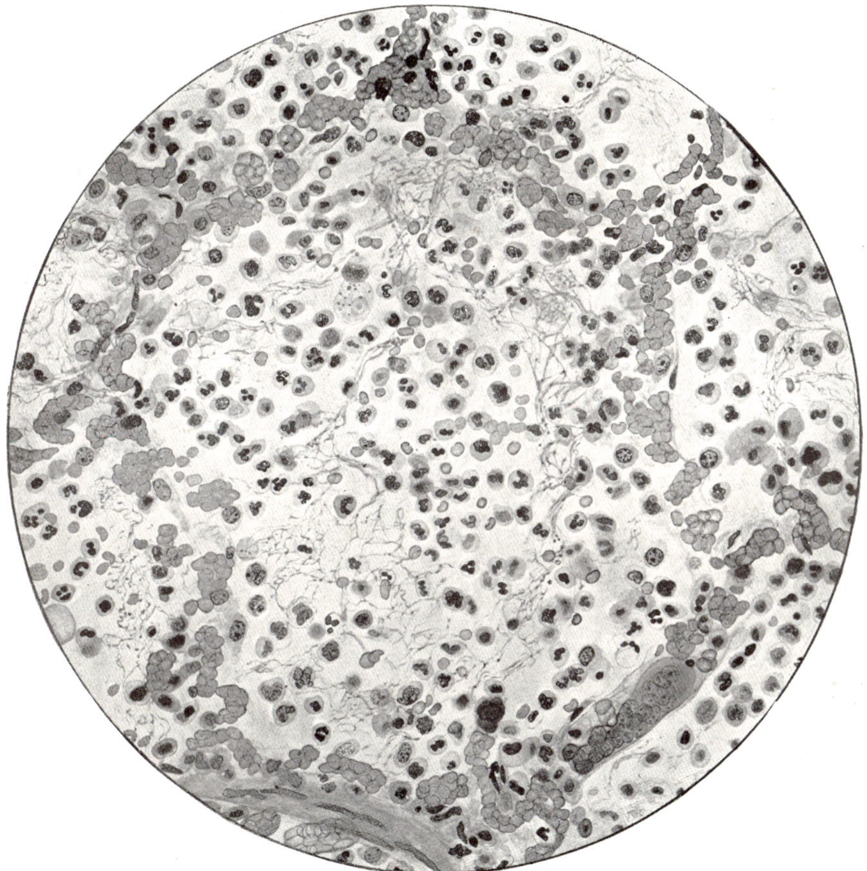

Fig. 266.—Lobar pneumonia; red hepatization. A single alveolus showing fresh exudate with well-preserved cells. A megalocaryocyte in one of the capillaries.

solidated lung, the remainder collapses and allows the escape of some of its content of air. It still crackles and crepitates under the finger, while, of course, the consolidated lobe is firm and airless. In spite of what was said about the stage of engorgement, it is rather rare to find anything but an abrupt transition from the consolidated to the unaffected lung substance.

The third stage is the *stage of gray hepatization,* although it is usual—

indeed, almost the rule—to find the consolidated lung in an intermediate condition, and of a color half-way between red and gray. The nature of that intermediate stage will be readily understood from a description of the gray hepatization.

In section the alveoli are found to be densely packed with a cellular exudate (Fig. 267). By this time, although the bacteria have increased in

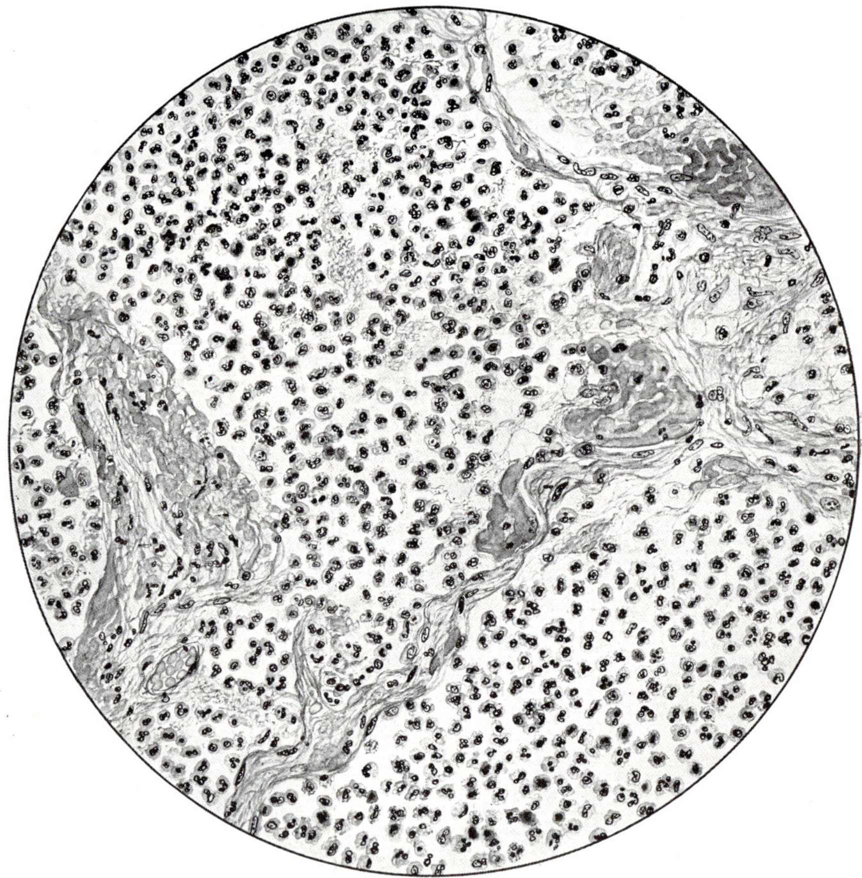

Fig. 267.—Lobar pneumonia; gray hepatization, showing retraction and consolidation of fibrin and partial disintegration of leucocytes.

number and the alveoli are crowded tightly with many more polynuclear leucocytes, which frequently contain the cocci, the fibrin is not observed to have increased specially in quantity. Instead, it is packed together, often in pretty compact masses, and scarcely shows any longer the graceful network which was to be seen in the earlier stages. Red corpuscles are hardly to be found in the advanced stage of gray hepatization, except that with careful scrutiny the shadowy outlines of those which have lost their hæmoglobin may be made out here and there among the closely crowded leucocytes. The capillaries of the alveolar wall are quite patent, as can be shown easily by injection, but they seem compressed by the mass of exudate and no longer look distended with blood. * In this stage and in the stage of red hepatization one may often find capillaries obstructed by a huge cellular mass which proves to be a megalocaryocyte from the bone-marrow, swept into the lung in the general rush of leucocytes from the marrow (Fig. 268). In both stages, too, one may make out the fact that

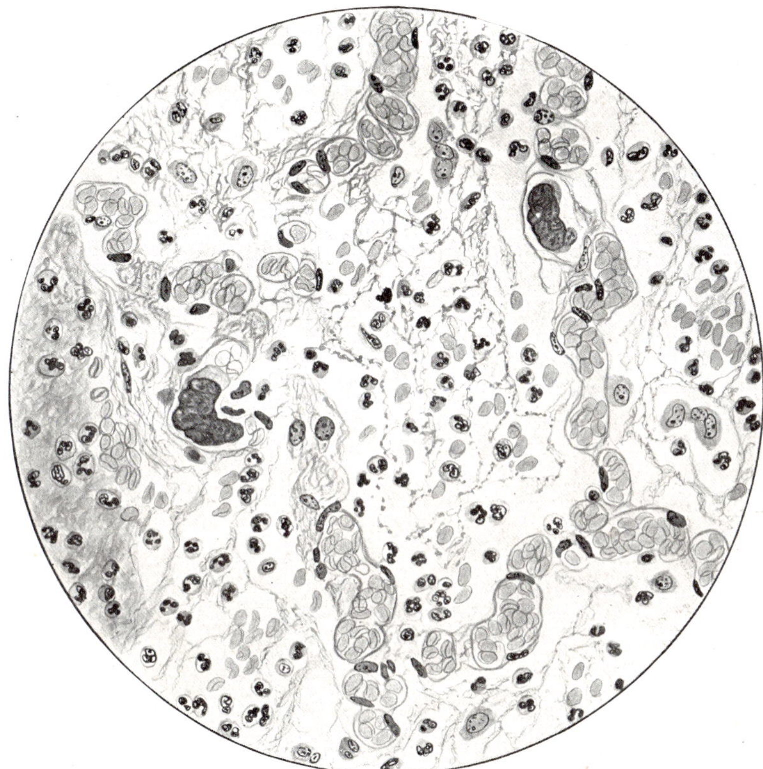

Fig. 268.—Lobar pneumonia; red hepatization, showing megalocaryocytes in the capillaries.

the fibrin threads in any one air-cell often seem to twist themselves into a thin cord, and pass directly through the alveolar wall, to spread out again into the network of the next air-cell. This is because of the presence of the so-called "pores of Cohn," which may be normal apertures in the wall,

* This was the current view, but recently Kline and Winternitz have stated that it is not true that one can easily inject the blood-channels in the consolidated lung. Instead, the area of consolidation remains almost uncolored by the mass, and the capillaries are found to be extensively plugged with fibrin. They think this may aid resolution by keeping away the blood-plasma, with its antitryptic ferment.

although it has been contended by many that they occur only in lungs somewhat altered by emphysema.

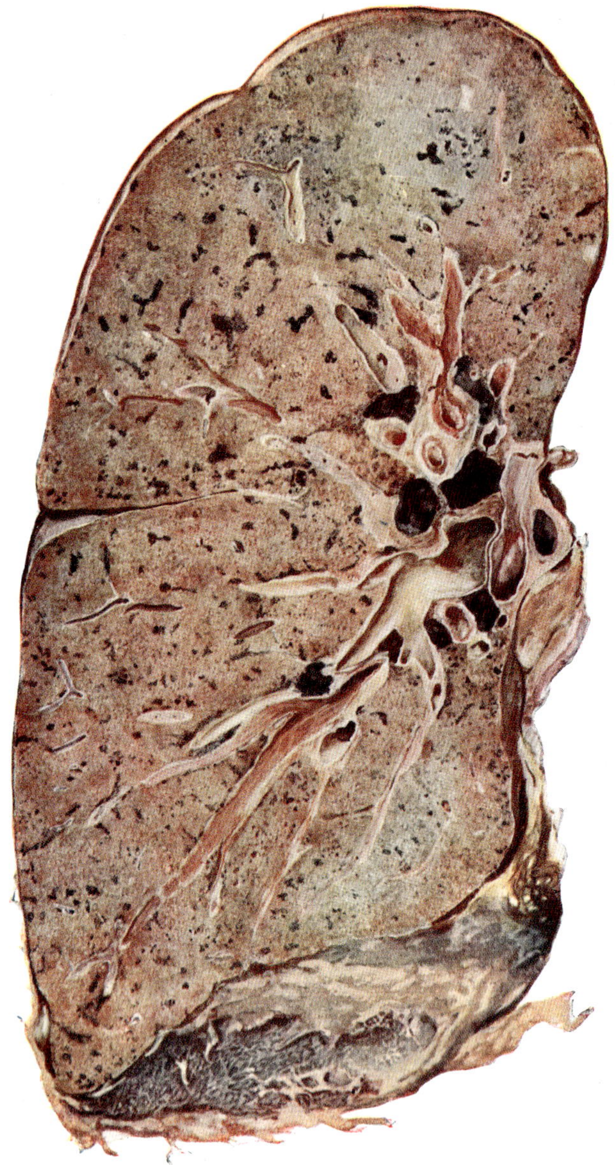

Fig. 269.—Lobar pneumonia: gross appearance of the lung in early gray hepatization with involvement of both lobes.

The most distinctive feature of the stage of gray hepatization from the microscopical point of view is the degenerated condition of the cells of the exudate. Not only have the red cells undergone laking and disintegration, but the leucocytes have lost their clear outline, if not their whole protoplasm, and have become granular, ragged, partly disintegrated cells, which, however, still show evidences of their phagocytic activity. Most of them contain fine droplets of fat, and some contain yellow pigment, evidently produced at the expense of the hæmoglobin of the broken red corpuscles. Desquamated epithelial cells are rather more abundant, and they too contain fat-droplets and pigment-granules.

In the gross appearance (Fig. 269) the lung at this stage is still more enlarged, dense, and heavy. Its surface is covered with a much thicker layer of fibrin, which can be peeled off, leaving a dull pleural membrane. Not only does this cover the consolidated lobe, but it often extends over the whole lung and the parietal pleura. Frequently there is a considerable accumulation of turbid fluid in the pleural cavity, separating the surfaces, which elsewhere may be found glued together by the exudate. On section the cut surface of the consolidated lung is found to be gray, yellowish gray, grayish white, or yellowish white, although, as mentioned, the cases in which some redness persists at death are much more common. The surface is not dry nor so rough as before, but gives the impression that the alveoli are filled with coarse plugs of softer, almost unctuous material, a condition which is doubtless due to the retraction of the fibrin setting free serum in each alveolus, and to the much greater number of leucocytes, together with the accumulation of fat-droplets in their substance. The color is easily explained by the laking of the red corpuscles, the yellowish tint being contributed, no doubt, by the hæmosiderin which is produced from their hæmoglobin, and by the fat-content of the leucocytes, aided by the generally anæmic state of the lung.

A later stage, that of *resolution*, is seldom seen at autopsy, but it can occasionally be studied when the person dies from some other cause, as, for example, the development of pneumonia in the other lung, meningitis, or pericarditis. In two cases which I have seen in this stage the change in the lung was quite wonderful. The enormously enlarged organ was in each instance very soft and friable, and had assumed a very distinct translucence, so that one could discern blood-vessels in the depths of the tissue. The alveolar contents had lost to a great extent their appearance of being in the form of plugs, and the whole lung appeared gray and jelly-like.

In section the change was not so obvious, since it apparently consisted only in a more advanced disintegration of the leucocytes and fibrin. It is well known, however, that, through the agency of the proteolytic ferments of the leucocytes themselves, the whole mass of exudate is liquefied in a few days, and while some of it is expectorated, the greater quantity is absorbed by the lymphatics and carried away.

The *stage of healing* is even more rarely to be seen. It must consist in the relining of the alveoli with alveolar epithelium after the complete removal of the exudate. It is to be noted that throughout this intense inflammatory affection of the lung there is very little infiltration of the lung tissue itself with the exudate. The alveolar walls, bronchial walls, and perivascular tissues remain throughout almost free from bacteria and exudate. It is rather as though the whole process were taking place upon a mucous membrane without any invasion into the depths, and it results that after the exudate is removed there is no damage to repair other than the loss of the epithelial cells, which are quickly made good by those which remain, so that it would be impossible to say two weeks later that that lung had been the seat of a pneumonia.

In sharp contrast to this are the effects of the streptococcus and influenza bacillus, which were used by Meltzer in his experimentally produced pneumonias in animals. In them there is far less fibrin formed, and there is a greater tendency to injury of the tissue of the lung and to its infiltration with exudate. The same difference is recognizable in the human lungs between the cases of lobular pneumonia produced by various organisms and lobar pneumonia.

Lobar pneumonia caused by the Pneumococcus mucosus differs from that produced by the members of the other types in the viscidity of the exudate and in the severity of the disease, and the same may be said of the rarer cases, in which the capsulated bacillus of Friedländer is the cause. In one case of this kind which we saw, the exudate was so glutinous that it could be lifted up from the cut surface in long strings which hung from the knife.

Complications of pneumonia, which are perhaps commoner in the case of various types of lobular pneumonia, are abscess formation, organization of the exudate, and gangrene.

Abscess Formation.—In the late stage of a severe pneumonia the consolidated tissue appears to succumb sometimes, to an especially intense injury on the part of the bacteria, so that the alveolar walls give way throughout a limited area, and the lung substance breaks down into a purulent fluid. Such an abscess-like focus may extend into the pleural cavity, producing a purulent pleurisy or empyema. One is inclined to suspect in such cases the presence of a mixed infection with streptococci or staphylococci.

Organization or Carnification.—Ordinarily, when a fibrinous exudate is thrown out on any such surface as that of the pericardium or the pleura, healing leads to its replacement by granulation tissue, which in those situations is likely to end in the formation of fibrous adhesions between the opposed surfaces. It is, therefore, rather remarkable that in pneumonia the exudate, which is apparently quite the same in character, should be completely removed without the least attempt at such replacement or organization. Possibly the rapidity with which the whole reaction proceeds is accountable for this, or there may be some other explanation. Occasionally, however, the exudate fails to be removed promptly, whether because the bacteria persist or the mechanism of autolysis fails, and blood-vessels and fibroblasts do spring up and invade the fibrinous plugs in the alveoli, finally replacing them with vascularized tissue. The origin of this vascularized tissue is interesting, since it seems not to arise from every point of the alveollar wall. This is partly because the exudate retracts and remains in contact with the walls at certain points only, but even so, it seems that the new blood-vessels fail to spring up from all these points. Instead, it may be found by reconstruction that the connective tissue

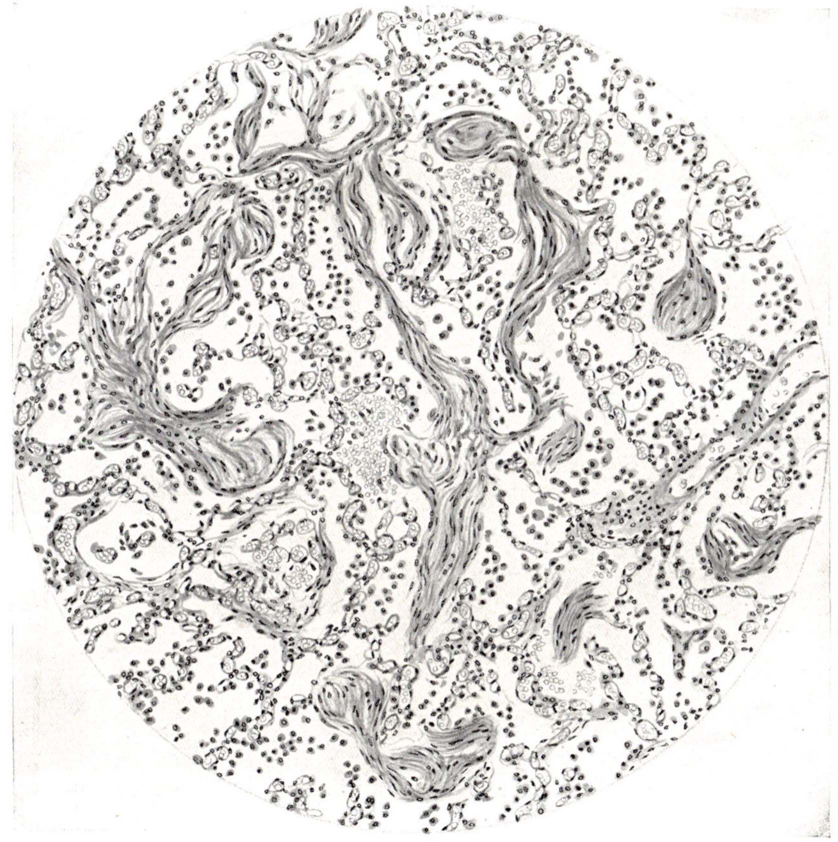

Fig. 270.—Organization following pneumonia. Strands of connective tissue extend through several alveoli and are in part covered with epithelium.

which replaces the exudate in any given lobule of the lung often springs essentially from the wall of the terminal bronchiole, or from one of those angles of the alveoli where an arteriole is surrounded by more tissue than goes to make up the alveolar wall. Then it follows the exudate, extending into each alveolus, and keeping clear of the walls (Fig. 270). Where the fibrin extends through one of the pores of Cohn the connective tissue follows, thickening itself into a stout cord and stretching the pore. Having penetrated into an alveolus belonging to another bronchiole, it extends to replace the exudate in that system. Consequently in the end it seems that a continuous network of strands of fibrous tissue stretches about in the alveoli, connected only here and there with their walls, so that if the lung substance could be dissolved away, the new connective tissue might remain as a sponge-like mould of its cavities. When the new connective tissue has replaced the exudate, or even when it has succeeded, as it often does, in forming a sort of mantle about the exudate, epithelial cells creep up from the alveolar walls and cover it. This whole process gives a dense elastic consistence to the lung, and obviously impedes greatly its expansion. Later, however, with shrinkage of the fibrous tissue, there is left much more air-space in the cavity of each alveolus, although even then the function of the lung must be greatly impaired (Fig. 271).

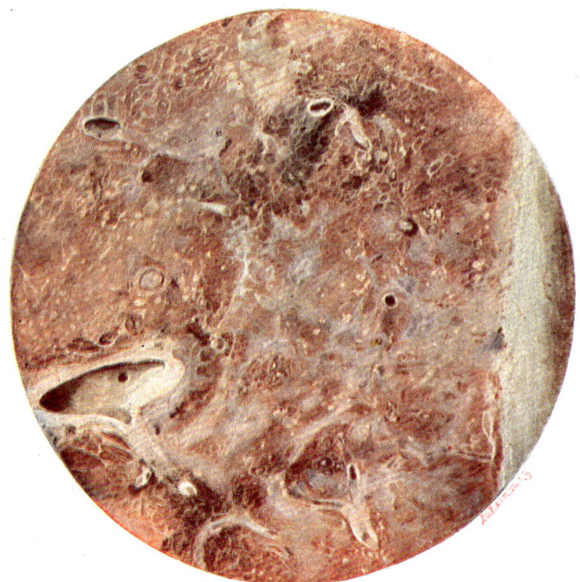

Fig. 271.—Organizing pneumonia; cut surface of lung as seen with a lens, showing scar tissue extending through the lung, and points of yellow opacity produced by fatty cells.

Gangrene.—Retarded recovery in some cases of pneumonia is accompanied by an exceedingly foul odor from the breath and sputum, which is a recognized indication of the existence of a gangrenous process in the lung. This is a commoner complication of lobular pneumonia, and is the result of a secondary infection with organisms of a different type. It has already been described in Chapter XIV.

Pneumococcus Septicæmia.—In the course of pneumonia the pneumococcus may gain access to the general blood-stream, and be recognizable in cultures from the blood. Jochmann leans to the view that this is a very frequent occurrence, since by using large quantities of blood in culture he has succeeded in discovering the organism in a large percentage of his cases. Cole, on the other hand, recognizing that occasional cocci may enter the blood-stream, has found that any considerable or even recognizable bacteriæmia occurs only in the most severe cases, and near the fatal termination of the disease.

The accompaniments of such bacteriæmia are endocarditis, meningitis, and acute arthritis, although other rarer localizations are also recognized.

Endocarditis caused by the pneumococcus resembles closely that produced by the Streptococcus hæmolyticus, or that of the staphylococcus infections. Large gray or greenish-gray soft vegetations are formed on the aortic or mitral or sometimes the tricuspid valves, and are of such friable consistence as to be a source of emboli.

Meningitis is a really common accompaniment of such endocarditis and of pneumococcus bacteriæmia in general. The distribution of the exudate is usually very general, involving the spinal cord, and extending into the ventricles.

Arthritis may take the form of a serous exudate in the joint cavity in which the pneumococcus is found, or in other cases there is found a purulent exudate with intense swelling and inflammation of the synovial membranes, erosion of the cartilages, etc.

The pneumonia itself is by no means necessarily confined to one lobe, or even to one lung. The whole of one lung may be involved, together with the development of patchy or lobular areas of pneumonia in the other. Or there may be lobar involvement of both lungs. Occasionally the spread or extension of the consolidation may be observed clinically, and in a recent summary of the cases at the Presbyterian Hospital it was noticed that before and during the extension of an area of consolidation the temperature and leucocytosis frequently sank to low levels, indicating perhaps a lowering of the powers of resistance which allowed the infection to spread.

Pleurisy has been mentioned, and it may be said further that following pneumonia, or in some cases without pneumonia, the pneumococcus gaining entrance into the pleura may cause a suppurative pleurisy or *empyema* in which great quantities of purulent fluid accumulate, compressing the lung and ultimately requiring surgical intervention.

Pericarditis of serofibrinous or fibropurulent character may be due to extension through the pleuropericardial membranes, and is a serious and often fatal complication.

Similarly, apparently by extension of the infection through the diaphragm, a generalized peritonitis may be set up. Such pneumococcal peritonitis is described in children and occurs sometimes in women. Its portal of entry is not always clear, since no lesions of the abdominal organs are found, and it may sometimes occur without pneumonia. The exudate is greenish and soft and rich in fibrin, which is loosely attached to the serous surfaces.

Portals of entry for the pneumococcus other than the lungs should be mentioned. The nasal sinuses frequently become infected from the nose, giving rise to a painful and persistent inflammation. Extension of the infection from the nares and pharynx through the Eustachian tube is the cause of those cases of otitis media which are due to the pneumococcus. From the frontal or ethmoid sinuses, as well as from the middle ear, extension may occur to the cranial cavity, with the production of meningitis.

LITERATURE

Cole and others: Jour. Exp. Med., 1912, xvi, 644–718; Archives of Int. Med., 1914, xiv, 56; N. Y. Med. Jour., 1915, ci, 1.

Wadsworth: Jour. Exp. Med., 1912, xvi, 54.

Lamar and Meltzer: Jour. Exp. Med., 1912, xv, 133.

Wollstein and Meltzer: *Loc. cit.*, 1913, xviii, 548.

MacCallum: Ziegler's Beiträge, 1902, xxxi, 440. (Organizing pneumonia.)

CHAPTER XXVII

TYPES OF INJURY.—BACTERIAL DISEASE (Continued)

Meningococcus infections: Epidemic cerebrospinal meningitis. Endocarditis.
Gonococcus infections: Urethritis and sequelæ. Salpingitis and sequelæ. Arthritis, ophthalmia, dermatitis, endocarditis, vulvovaginitis in children.
Acute rheumatism: Tonsillitis, arthritis, endocarditis, pericarditis, myocarditis.

MENINGOCOCCUS INFECTIONS

Epidemic cerebrospinal meningitis is a disease which for centuries has been known to appear first in one region and then in another far distant, and to cause an appalling number of deaths. It is not yet known how it is transmitted nor why the outbreaks should be thus isolated. It is caused by the *Diplococcus intracellularis meningitidis* of Weichselbaum (1897), otherwise spoken of briefly as the meningococcus.

The most conspicuous lesion which this organism produces is cerebrospinal meningitis, although it is also the agent concerned in the various attendant lesions and sequelæ, such as otitis media, various inflammations of the eye, lobular pneumonia, endocarditis, and occasionally joint affections. The cutaneous erythema and hæmorrhages which were formerly seen more often than now gave it the name "spotted fever." Herpes about the face and sometimes extending over other parts of the body is a very common accompaniment. Probably the organism gains entrance through the mucosa of the nose and upper respiratory tract (Weigert, Westenhoeffer), although this is not accepted by every one. Since these tissues are found to harbor the cocci which can transfer the disease to animals, the evidence seems to favor this view. There are, however, those who carry the cocci on their nasal mucosæ and do not contract the disease, but are merely a menace to others. The organisms may pass through the cribriform plate directly to the meninges, or be carried there more indirectly by the blood-stream.

There is still some doubt as to the occurrence of a general bacteriæmia, but the later work favors the idea that it is relatively common. The situation is evidently much as it is with other cocci.

The disease may take several forms: (*a*) It is fulminant, with most intense intoxication, leading to death in two or three days; (*b*) it is less violent, lasting a week or more, and sometimes ending in recovery; (*c*) it is protracted, allowing the production of chronic affections of the meninges with hydrocephalus, and causing death at last after a long illness. It is chiefly a disease of children and young people.

Meningeal Lesions.—In the very acute cases the meninges are found congested, but without any conspicuous exudate. Microscopical examination shows an exudate of a few leucocytes and red corpuscles about the vessels on the outer surface of the brain and along the spinal cord.

In the less acute cases it is found that the dura mater is little affected; it may be slightly injected, or even show traces of fibrinous exudate. It is in the soft coverings of the brain that the most striking change is found. Over the whole base, and extending up on the convex surfaces of the brain and of the cerebellum, there is a yellowish-green, opaque exudate (Fig. 272), which accumulates thickly in the sulci about the vessels, and thins out over the convexity of the convolutions. Occasionally, of course, it is

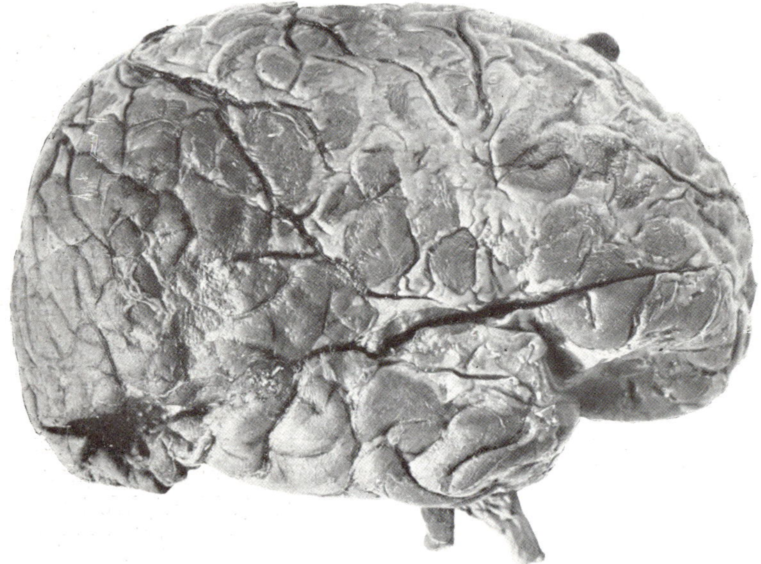

Fig. 272.—Cerebrospinal meningitis.

thick enough to cover and shroud from view the convolutions also, but usually this is at most only partial. It should be noticed, in examining such a brain, that while the exudate may be extremely abundant, it does not really lie loose on the surface of the pia-arachnoid, that is, in the subdural space. Indeed, this surface is usually pretty smooth, although the subdural fluid may be turbid. On opening the ventricles there is found, as a rule, a turbid purulent fluid, and the ependymal linings are covered with a greenish, fibrinous exudate which wraps about the choroid plexus.

The cranial nerves, including the optic and auditory nerves, are sheathed in exudate, which runs along in many cases into the substance of the eye or into the interior of the ear. Various symptoms are ascribed to a similar permeation of the other nerves with the cocci and the inflammatory exudate. In the spinal cord one finds the abundant exudate chiefly on the dorsal surface, while the anterior half of the pia may show only a slight opalescence. Often the dorsal and lumbar parts of the cord are the most involved. No gross changes are visible in brain or cord.

Microscopically it is found that the pia and arachnoid are stretched to a great thickness by the influx of cells which make up the opaque exudate (Fig. 273). There is not a great deal of fibrin. The cells are in large part polymorphonuclear leucocytes, with a few red corpuscles and lymphocytes. Attention has been directed to certain large mononuclear phagocytic cells, which are conspicuous in this exudate rather in contrast to that of streptococcus and pneumococcus meningitides where they occur, but only in small numbers. Many different ideas have been expressed as to their origin: that they arise from connective tissue; that they are wandering endothelial cells, etc. Orth has taken pains to speak especially of this, and to have his pupil, Speroni, write concerning it. It is his opinion that they are phagocytic mononuclear wandering cells which originate in the lymphocytic cells which have emigrated from the blood-vessels. The same cells occur in great numbers in the meningitis produced by the typhoid bacillus, and in describing that, some years ago, I expressed the same opinion as to their origin. These cells may contain the bodies of several other smaller cells, while the polynuclear leucocytes are perhaps more active in engulfing the cocci, which are present in great numbers. The blood-vessels often show that their endothelial lining has been lifted up in a peculiar way by the leucocytes which have wandered to that place and now form a thick subendothelial layer. This phenomenon is seen in meningitis caused by the typhoid bacillus, the streptococcus, and the pneumococcus (Fig. 274).

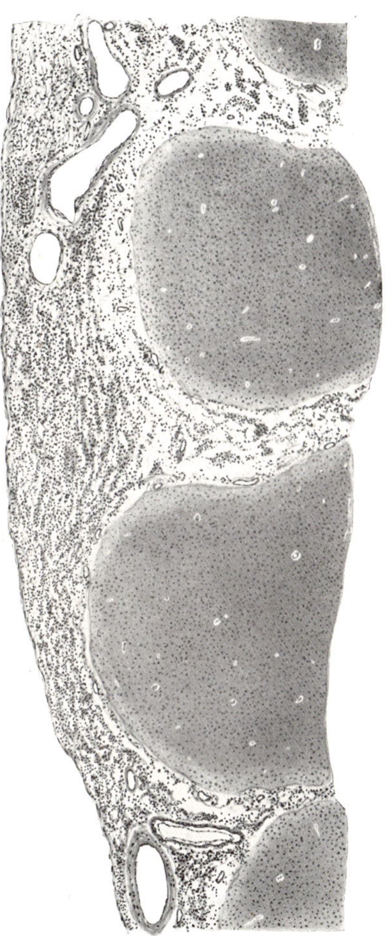

Fig. 273.—Cerebrospinal meningitis showing the limitation of the exudate by the arachnoid and its extension into sulci.

Lesions in the substance of the brain are discoverable microscopically, and are described by Councilman, Mallory and Wright. They consist in focal destruction of the nerve tissue and ganglion-cells, often with a proliferation of neuroglia and an invasion of leucocytes.

The lesions of the eye I have never seen, but Councilman describes them as due to the extension of the cocci along the optic nerve. The choroid and retina are extensively destroyed and infiltrated with exudate; the anterior chamber may become filled with pus, involving an iritis, etc. Otitis can be thought of as due to extension along the eighth nerve, or from

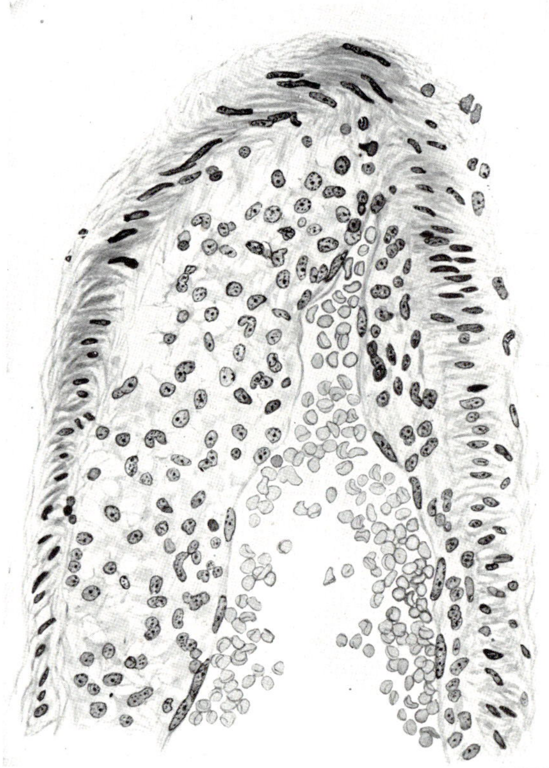

Fig. 274.—Cerebrospinal meningitis. Subendothelial accumulation of leucocytes and proliferation of deeper intimal cells in a meningeal artery.

the throat up the Eustachian tube. Here its significance is perhaps less than in other cases, where it is likely to be the cause of meningitis.

Endocarditis.—We have seen one case of endocarditis from the vegetations of which the meningococcus was recovered, but the condition must be rather rare. Councilman apparently did not see it in his long series.

Chronic Forms.—When the disease is protracted over weeks, there occurs an organization of the exudate, which may in this way form tough fibrous strands in the meninges. The fibrin is retracted and replaced by new tissue, and even in the ventricles this may occur. But the most striking result is the perpetuation and exaggeration of the hydrocephalus, which is seen in its onset in the acute stage. Probably this is in itself the cause of some of the serious symptoms of the disease, as Cushing points out. Later, however, after the lapse of weeks or months during which the exudate appears to have blocked the outflow of ventricular fluid, the ventricles may become greatly dilated at the expense of the brain substance, which is thinned out. Such patients continue to have the stiffness of the neck, the retraction of the head, and the flexion of the thighs seen in those acutely ill, and gradually waste away to mere skeletons as they lie in bed. This progressive emaciation is probably largely due to their frequent vomiting, but other explanations, for example, that it is a trophic disturbance dependent upon the changes in the nervous system, have been offered.

Flexner, Jochmann, Kolle and Wassermann, and others have produced specific immune sera by the repeated inoculation of animals with the cultures, and such sera, injected into the spinal meningeal spaces by lumbar puncture, have proven extraordinarily effective in curing the disease.

LITERATURE

C. Sternberg: Ergeb. d. Allg. Path., 1910, xiv, 136.

Jochmann: Verh. d. XXIII. Kongress f. inn. Med., 1906, 555; Mohr and Staehelin: Handb. d. inn. Med., 1911, i, 759.

Councilman, Mallory and Wright: Report State Board of Health of Massachusetts, 1898.

Flexner: Jour. Exp. Med., 1907, ix, 105, 142, 168; 1908, x, 141, 690. Jour. Amer. Med. Assoc., 1906, xlvii, 560; 1913, lx, 1937.

Orth: Deutsch. med. Woch., 1906, xxxii, 92.

Agazzi: Arch. f. Ohrenheilkunde, 1914, xcv, 1.

Westenhoeffer, Lingelsheim and others: Klinisches Jahrbuch, 1906, xv, 211.

GONOCOCCUS INFECTION

The realization of the extent to which gonococci may infect the body is a matter of very recent years. The portal of entry is, in the majority of cases, the mucosa of the genito-urinary tract, since the infection is commonly transmitted by coitus. But it may occasionally be transferred by infected clothing, towels, etc., in spite of the ease with which the organism is destroyed by drying and exposure. Especially in infants and children is this possible, and in orphan asylums and hospitals epidemics of gonorrhœal vulvovaginitis are of extremely common occurrence. In direct or indirect ways the infection can also be introduced into the mucosa of the mouth, nose, rectum, conjunctiva, and especially in the eye may produce serious results.

Gonococcal Urethritis and its Sequels in the Male.—There is, after exposure to infection through coitus, during which the organisms reach the orifice of the urethra, a short period of incubation, averaging two to eight days. Then there begins a thin, mucopurulent exudate from the urethra, which in a short time becomes definitely purulent. The orifice, with its tumefied edges, oozes thick, greenish pus, which besides desquamated epithelial cells, contains abundant leucocytes, both neutrophile and eosinophile. Gonococci are found in great numbers, many of them, if not the majority, contained in the bodies of the leucocytes, where they seem to suffer no harm. Ordinarily this inflammatory process may affect only the anterior portion of the urethra, where it passes through a florid stage, with profuse exudate, gradually to recede after several weeks. In this latter stage, which may end in healing and the disappearance of the cocci, the exudate becomes less abundant and mucoid, gluing together the edges of the meatus. But in many cases there is an extension to the posterior urethra, where healing is more difficult, and from which the important complications in other organs arise.

There are, in the course of the urethra, many accessory structures, some, such as the paraurethral channels, partaking of the character of malformations, while others, the lacunæ or glands of Littré and the glands of Cowper and various folds of mucosa, are normally present. Directly communicating with the urethra there are, of course, the more developed accessory structures—the prostate and seminal vesicles. All of these are commonly involved in the more chronic or persistent gonorrhœal infections, and serve to maintain the infection in spite of thorough disinfection of the urethra itself. In connection with the anterior urethra the follicles or glands of Littré may become converted into hard, inflamed nodules.

The mucosa in the acute inflammation is swollen, with desquamation of many epithelial cells. The gonococci penetrate among those which remain, and extend even into the subepithelial tissues. Where there are patches of stratified epithelium, such as often occur normally, the cocci obtain an especially good foothold and resist disinfection. When the process has become more chronic, especially in the posterior urethra, there appear ulcerations, with scarring and polypoid excrescences. The scarring results in strictures or stenoses (see Fig. 215) of the urethra, which cause obstruction to the outflow of urine and render catheterization necessary. Not only is cystitis a common result of this, but in attempts to pass instruments through the stricture, wounds of the adjacent tissue are produced, which may become the origin of intense infections. These may assume a phlegmonous character, or there may develop an abscess in the perineal region. The extravasation of urine into such wounded areas favors the development of the infection (Fig. 275).

Chronic gonococcal urethritis is commonly recognized by the presence of shreds or filaments of mucus with leucocytes and epithelial cells in the urine. These may contain gonococci, but often the organisms are rare and difficult to demonstrate.

Cystitis, while it can be produced by the gonococcus alone, is rarely due to that organism, but usually to secondary invaders. Ureteritis and pyelonephritis are reported as due to ascending infection with the gonococcus, but are rare.

Prostatitis and Vesiculitis.—Various types of infection of the prostate by the gonococcus are described arising in connection with posterior urethritis. These differ greatly in intensity, for while there may be a sort of catarrhal inflammation of the ducts and acini of the gland, there may, in other cases, be far more intense and destructive changes involving abscess formation. A chronic persistent inflammation with a secretion containing cocci, and leading to the enlargement, or in other cases to scarring and atrophy of the gland, is most frequent. The seminal vesicles may in the same way present acute inflammatory changes or more chronic alterations, including scarring and obliteration of their lumina.

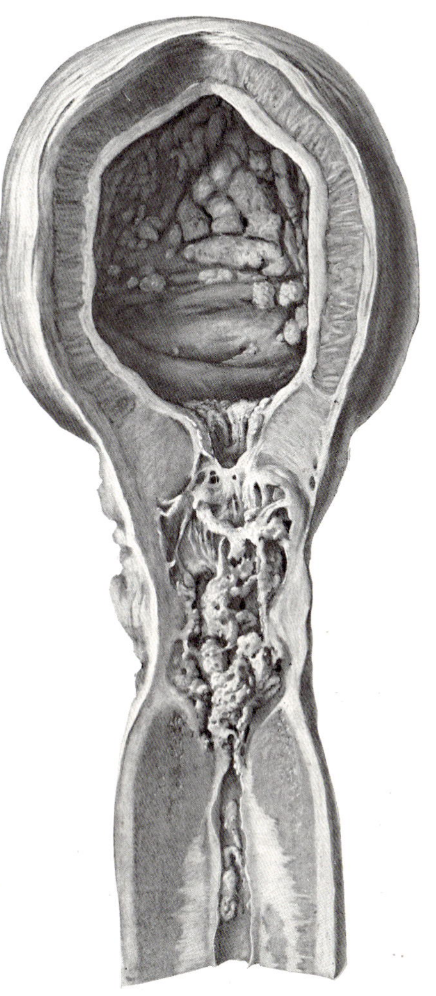

Fig. 275.—Gonorrhœal stricture after forcing of false passage. Extensive destruction and inflammation. Hypertrophy of the bladder; diphtheritic cystitis.

Epididymitis.—A common sequel of urethritis is produced by the wandering of the gonococci along the vas deferens to the epididymis, where an intense inflammation involving the neighboring tunica vaginalis, in many cases leads to great swelling and induration, and frequently to abscess formation. The gonococci can be found in the exudate, even though in some cases they cannot be recognized in the vas deferens and have produced no lesions there. Scarring and stricture or obliteration of the canal of the epididymis and of the vas deferens may lead to complete azoöspermia if the epididymis had been affected on both sides.

Gonococcal Salpingitis and Its Sequelæ.—In the female the urethra, the vagina, Bartholin's glands, and the cervix become infected and react in the same way as does the mucosa of the male genito-urinary tract. The urethra, being shorter and without complicated accessory structures, the inflammation does not lead to such serious results. A swelling of the mucosa, with the exudation of the characteristic pus, occurs. Bartholin's glands become greatly swollen and indurated, and from them there can be expressed a similar purulent exudate. These things may occur without the extension of the infection into the internal genitalia, and, indeed, in

Fig. 276.—Subacute gonorrhœal salpingitis with great thickening of the folds of mucosa by the cellular infiltration.

the vulvovaginitis of children, this more external type of inflammation, with reddening and swelling of the nymphæ, is relatively common. In the child the vagina is more intensely involved than in the adult, where its epithelium is much more resistant. Indeed, in the adult, gonorrhœal vaginitis occurs practically only as an acute process, and is then relatively unimportant. A chronic gonococcal vaginitis is uncommon. On the other hand, the cocci readily pass into the cervical canal, and establish themselves in the mucosa with its glands, extending also to those of the fundus. Slight erosions, a tumefaction of the mucosa, and the secretion of a purulent exudate mark their presence there. More important is the effect of their further wandering into the Fallopian tubes.

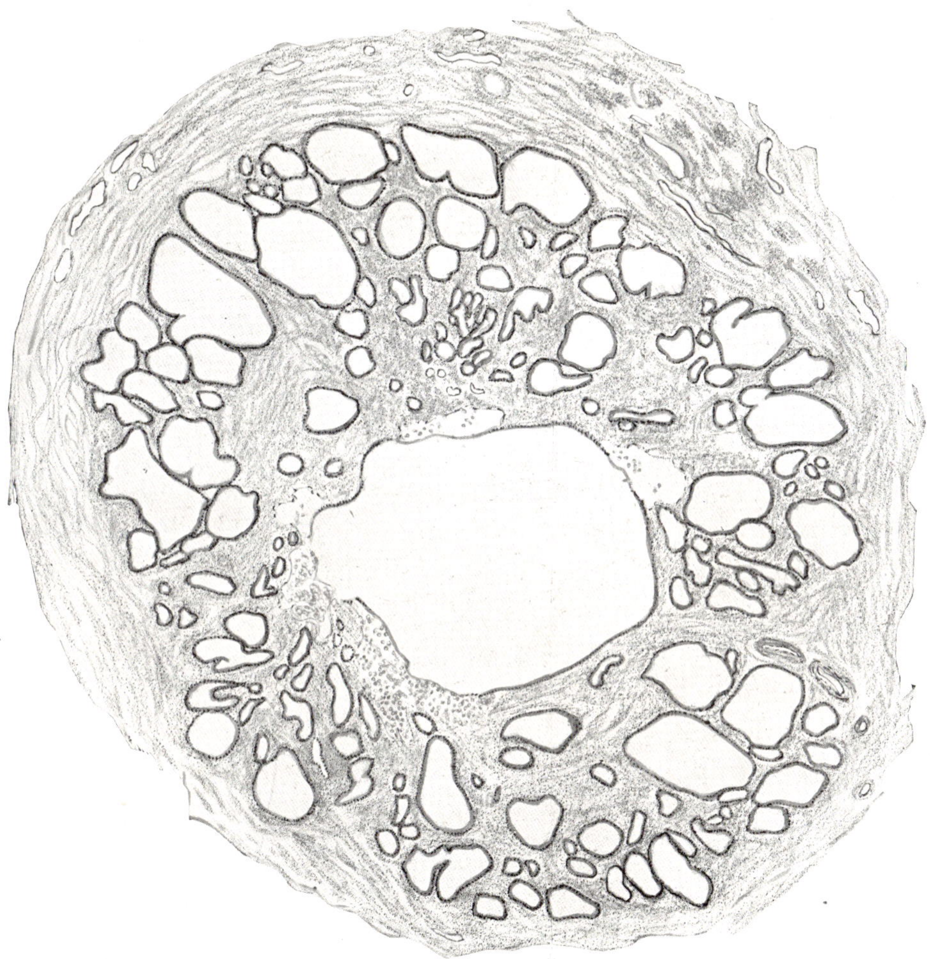

Fig. 277.—Pseudofollicular salpingitis. The appearance of closed cavities is produced by fusion of the folds of the mucosa.

Gonococcal Salpingitis.—In the acute stage the tubes become swollen, hyperæmic, and œdematous, the change being especially striking in the fimbriated extremity. In the mucosa alterations due to the presence of the organisms among the epithelial cells of the complex folds are in general similar to those in the urethra. Later chronic alterations appear, dependent upon the deeper invasion of the cocci into the tissues. Adhesions are formed about the tube, and through the organization of exudate there is occlusion of its lumen at both ends and the accumulation of a quantity of pus in its cavity. Kinking of the tube may be partly responsible for these occlusions. The progress of the infection leads to great changes in the mucosa, which in operative cases are usually seen in their subacute stages. The folds of the mucosa, ordinarily so delicate and complicated, become distended into thick lamellæ (Fig. 276), which often adhere to one another and grow together so that they cover over the intervening spaces, which then, in cross-section, look like epithelium-lined channels in the tube-wall (Fig. 277). Microscopically, these thick folds are found to be stretched by great numbers of wandering cells, among which lymphocytes and plasma cells are very numerous and conspicuous. Eosinophile cells are

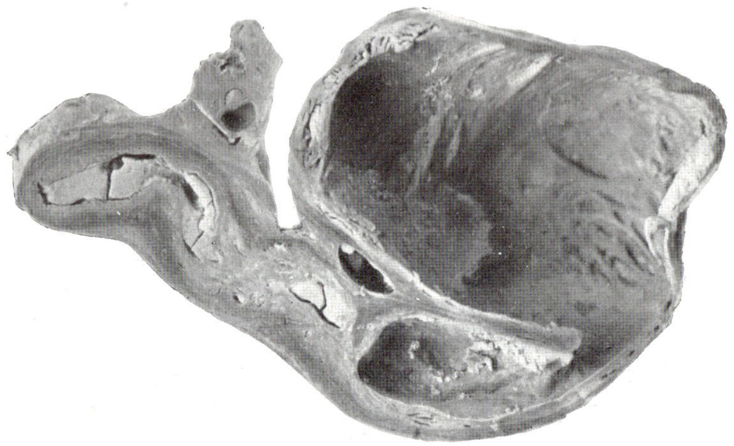

Fig. 278.—Chronic gonococcal salpingitis or pyosalpinx.

often very abundant. Schridde and Amsbacher claim that the finding of such an infiltration of lymphocytes and plasma cells is sufficient proof of the gonococcal nature of the infection, but this is, probably rightly, contradicted by Muller and Menge, who state that other organisms, such as the streptococcus, may produce the same lesions if time is allowed for the development of a subacute or chronic salpingitis. The distension of the obstructed tube with pus (pyosalpinx) may greatly separate and flatten the folds of the mucosa, and the tube itself assumes then a variety of forms, according to the arrangement of the adhesions which may attach it to the uterus, to the ovary, to the rectum, or the pelvic wall (Fig. 278). Most often it is roughly retort shaped. Rupture of such a sac may occur through violence with discharge of the pus into the peritoneum. Ordinarily, there is not produced any very severe peritonitis, and this is explained by the fact that cultures from the pus are usually sterile. In other cases the exudate may lose its purulent character after the occlusion of the ends of the tube has occurred and become more serous. Such a tube may develop into a large, thin-walled sac full of clear fluid (hydrosalpinx) (Fig. 279). Naturally, either of these results ends in the complete loss of function of the tube, and if both tubes are affected, sterility follows.

Gonococcal infections of the ovary occur in the form of abscesses or false abscesses, caused by the invasion of the cocci into freshly ruptured follicles or corpora lutea.

Gonococcal peritonitis is an outcome of the acute stage of infection of the uterus and Fallopian tubes, the cocci entering through the fimbriated extremities. It may also be produced by transfer of the organism by the blood-stream. The exudate is fibrinous or serofibrinous, and is likely to

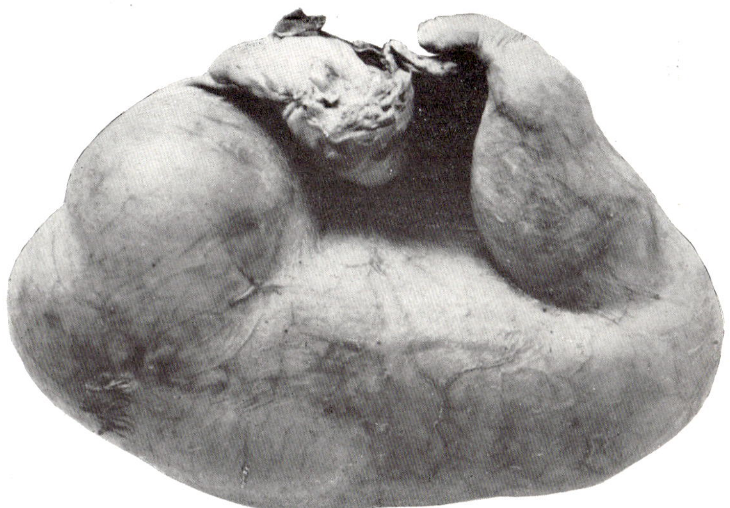

Fig. 279.—Hydrosalpinx.

lead to extensive adhesions among the loops of intestine. This condition is not of common occurrence, except in the more localized form of pelvic peritonitis, which is extremely common in association with salpingitis, and in its late stages is found to have bound the pelvic organs together by firm or lax adhesions.

Gonococcal Arthritis.—Somewhat late in the course of an acute urethritis, that is, after the inflammation has reached the posterior urethra and has lasted several weeks, there often arises a painful involvement of a joint, which is due to the transportation of the gonococci by the blood-stream to the synovial membrane. This appears to be commoner in men than in women, and usually only one joint is involved, although others may be affected in succession later. The joint most commonly infected is the knee, and the inflammation may take several forms. The mildest is that in which there is a mere accumulation of fluid without pain or marked impairment of function. More frequently there is formed a serofibrinous or even purulent exudate, with infiltration of the surrounding tissues and extreme pain, so that the joint is held flexed. Erosions of the cartilage and rarefaction of the cancellous bone may occur, and fixation of the joint with ankylosis of the bones sometimes follows. Gonococcal infection of the bones themselves is reported, but is rare.

Gonococcal Ophthalmia.—Infection of the eye with this organism is extremely serious, and often leads, even under the most careful treatment, to destruction of the eye. It occurs in infants from infection during birth from the inflamed genitalia of the mother, and this so-called *ophthalmia neonatorum,* although relatively easy to guard against or cut short by instillation of nitrate of silver into the infant's eyes, is nevertheless the cause of an enormous number of cases of blindness among children everywhere in the world. In older children—and this probably includes the cases of "late birth infections," which develop after five days postpartum—gonococcal conjunctivitis is a fairly common accompaniment of the epidemic gonococcal vulvovaginitis.

In adults such conjunctivitis is caused by the introduction of the organism into the eye with the soiled fingers, towels, etc., or, especially in physicians, by the spurting of gonorrhœal pus into the eye. It is said that there may also arise an infection of the deeper parts of the eye through transmission of the organism by the blood-stream, and in this case there are no cocci in the conjunctival sac.

The conjunctivitis begins with the injection of the blood-vessels, swelling of the lids, and the pouring-out of a thick, purulent exudate, which tends to glue the eyelids together. The conjunctiva over the bulb swells, so that the cornea is sunken beneath it. The slightest touch upon the cornea is sufficient to start an erosion there, which progresses to ulceration and often to infection of the anterior chamber, which fills up with a purulent exudate. Healing of these ulcerations is likely to cause such scars or opacities in the cornea that the eye becomes useless. But there also may be produced extensive infiltration of the iris and neighboring tissues, resulting in distorting adhesions. Indeed, the whole eye may be invaded and extensively injured by the infection.

It is conceivable that infection of the nasal sinuses or even meningitis might arise from such a process, but although de Jong and others have described cases of gonococcal meningitis, the proof of the identity of the organism which is so similar to the meningococcus is not satisfactory enough to allow these cases to be generally accepted.

Gonococcal Dermatitis.—Lesions of the skin said to be caused by the gonococcus assume many forms, among which are erythematous rashes, urticaria, erythema nodosum, hæmorrhagic and bullous exanthemata, and hyperkeratoses. Of these, perhaps the latter are most characteristic.

Gonococcal Endocarditis.—It is evidence of the transportation of the cocci by the streaming blood, and therefore of the existence of a general gonococcal septicæmia, that endocarditis may owe its origin to this organism. Gonococcal septicæmia is particularly characterized by the occurrence of the arthritis already mentioned, and of the endocarditis, and is not an absolutely fatal occurrence. Cases have been reported as recovering even after the valvular lesions were very evident, and the cocci repeatedly demonstrated in the blood.

The alterations of the heart-valves are rather characteristic, in that the vegetations are frequently extremely large and friable. They seem to effect the destruction of the valves with great rapidity, for in three cases which I have seen the valves were reduced to ragged strands, which flapped in the stream, bearing on their ends large crumbling remnants of the vegetations. Apparently the aortic and the mitral valves are most often affected, but we were impressed with the occurrence of these vegetations in our own cases on the tricuspid and pulmonary valves. Pericarditis and myocarditis of focal or diffuse character often accompany the endocarditis. The organisms are found in abundance in the vegetations.

Vulvovaginitis in Children.—With regard to the infection itself, there are some interesting features. It has been pointed out that epidemic vulvovaginitis in little children is a very common thing, and that in some orphan asylums it is never absent, but is known to produce so little real harm that it is somewhat ignored. Dr. Northrup tells me that in contrast to this familiar mild infection, the incomparably more serious effects of infection from the gonococcus from urethritis in the adult impressed him strongly in two cases. These were in two young girls, who were infected in some way from their mother, who had been infected from the acute urethritis of the father. They became profoundly ill, with circulatory collapse and symptoms that were thought to indicate appendicitis. One was operated upon and the appendix removed. Although it was normal, the whole peritoneum was intensely reddened, and there was a slight serous exudate. There were no other complications and they recovered. Recently, apparently with this idea in mind, Dr. Pearce has investigated the organisms concerned in an epidemic in a children's asylum, and has found that they do differ biologically from those isolated from urethritis in the adult. Her conclusions are in part as follows:

Two principal types of gonococci may be recognized by the methods of agglutination and complement fixation, and correspond to the adult and infant types of infection seen clinically. The gonococci isolated from cases of ophthalmia belong to the adult type. It appears that there may be many more varieties, and that these two types are not sharply marked out, but are connected by intervening forms.

LITERATURE

Jadassohn:
Ehrmann:
Scholtz:
Grosz:
Elschnig:
Schlagenhaufer:
Buschke:
Menge: } Handbuch der Geschlechtskrankheiten, 1910, i; 1912, ii, pp. 1–612. (These papers are excellent but very prolix.)

L. Pearce: Jour. Exp. Med., 1915, xxi, 289.

C. Bruck: Ergeb. d. allg. Path., 1912, xvi$_1$, 134 (literature).

Harris, Dabney, and Johnston: "Endocarditis," Johns Hopkins Hosp. Bull., 1901, xii, 68; 1902, xiii, 236.

Thayer and Blumer: *Ibid.*, 1896, vii, 57; Jour. Exp. Med., 1899, iv, 81.

Thayer: Amer. Jour. Med. Sci., 1905, lxxx, 751.

Amersbach: Ziegler's Beiträge, 1909, xlv, 341.

Wätjen: *Ibid.*, 1914, lix, 418.

ACUTE RHEUMATISM

The disease affects young people especially, causing repeated attacks of painful swelling of the joints, with fever, but usually without leaving any permanent disability of the joints. It is usually preceded by tonsillitis, and often followed by chorea, a spasmodic nervous affection which may last a long time. Nearly always there are serious changes in the heart, involving the valves, the heart muscle, and the pericardium. The cause is unknown in spite of the most careful studies, although numerous writers have described bacteria for which they claim an ætiological rôle. Of these, the majority are micrococci in pairs or in chains. Those described by Singer and by Poynton and Paine are perhaps most discussed, but it is by no means proven that they are the real cause of the disease. In our cases cultures from the blood and joint fluids, as well as smears and cultures from the vegetations on the heart valves, have usually shown no bacteria unless some terminal affection, such as pneumonia, brought bacteria to complicate the situation.

From the frequency of *tonsillitis* in the early stages it seems that the tonsils form the portal of entry for the organisms. Occasionally there is laryngitis, rhinitis, or otitis media. With the swelling of the joints there are high fever and profuse sweating. When the fever is extremely high, death is likely to ensue.

The *joints* most often affected are the knee, shoulder, and ankle, although finger-joints may be involved in those who work especially with their fingers. The swelling is very largely periarticular, and the excruciating pain is chiefly in the attachment of tendons. The joint fluid is usually clear, or contains a few leucocytes, although there is sometimes a purulent exudate. Purpuric or hæmorrhagic patches often appear in the skin, and seem to be due to changes in the walls of the blood-vessels, thought by some to be caused by embolic inflammatory processes. There are also nodes in the skin and in the periosteum, which are of inflammatory character.

The most important lesions are undoubtedly those in the *heart,* and the surprising constancy of their form and the ease with which they can be distinguished from the other infectious diseases of the heart make it seem more likely that they are caused by some peculiar infectious agent.

There is nearly always *pericarditis,* with a sticky exudate of fibrinous character, which soon brings about the firm adhesion between the two layers of the pericardium (Fig. 280). Since death generally occurs some time after repeated attacks, the pericardium is usually found densely

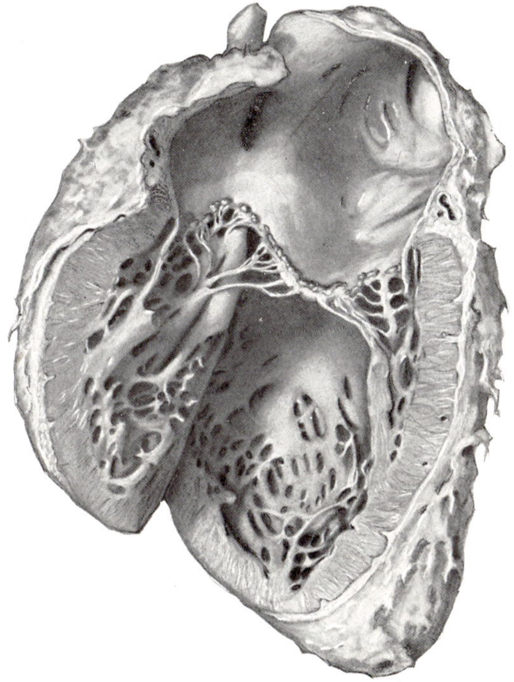

Fig. 280.—Rheumatic endocarditis; verrucose vegetations on mitral valve. Chronic adhesive pericarditis.

adherent to the heart. Vegetations appear on the valves along the line of closure, and nearly always in the form of small, warty, tough nodules, which run like a string of beads around the whole valvular orifice. They are found especially on the mitral, but also on the tricuspid and aortic valves, but seldom extend on the heart-wall or on the chordæ tendineæ. Healing of such lesions leads to the thickening and scarring of the valves, and often to extreme narrowing or stenosis of the orifices. Doubtless renewed attacks would add a new beaded string of vegetations to such scarred valves, and so might the advent of some other infection. While it seems probable that rheumatism may well be the original cause of mitral, tricuspid, and aortic stenosis and insufficiencies, it is usually difficult to prove this, especially if some other infection has supervened and produced fresh vegetations quite different in character from those of rheumatism. Thus it is common to find the characteristic distribution of fresh vegetations caused by the Streptococcus mitior or viridans on old scarred valves, which may well have been distorted by rheumatic infection of years before. Most interesting are the myocardial changes, now that their peculiarities have

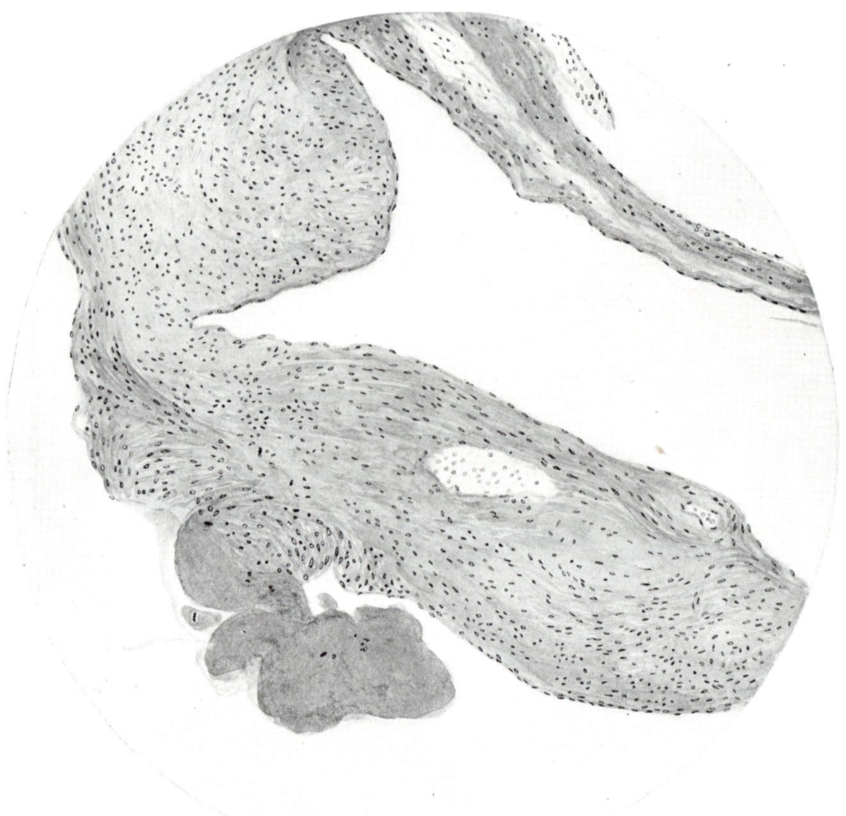

Fig. 281.—Small homogeneous hyaline vegetation, without evident bacteria, upon the mitral valve. Rheumatic endocarditis.

been pointed out by Aschoff, Horder, Bracht and Wächter, Rothschild and Thalhimer, and others. Focal collections of peculiar large cells in the neighborhood of minute vessels, or entirely surrounding them, seem to be the reaction to focal injury to the tissue. These so-called Aschoff bodies (Fig. 282) are made up of concentrically arranged wandering cells, most of which are conspicuous from their large size and their large nuclei, of which they often have several. They are much like the large cells found in

Hodgkin's disease, although usually not quite so large as those. No bacteria have been demonstrated as constantly present in these foci, but it is shown that in healing they leave behind them scars which in the end may go far toward producing the condition described as chronic fibrous myocarditis. These myocardial lesions are such constant accompaniments of the endocarditis and adhesive pericarditis that some have spoken of the rheumatic lesions of the heart as rheumatic carditis.

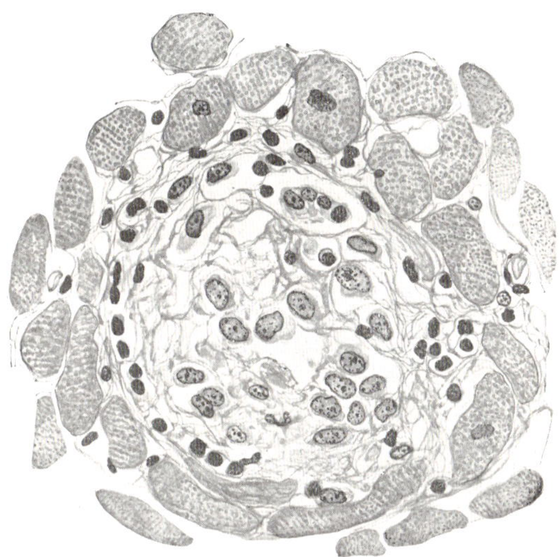

Fig. 282.—Aschoff body in the heart.

When the ætiological factor is discovered and established, it should be easy to determine its precise relation to these lesions, as well as to the accompanying purpura, iritis, chorea, tonsillitis, arthritis, etc.

LITERATURE

Wiesel: Wien. med. Woch., 1914, lxiv, 661, 746.
Poynton and Paine: Rheumatism, London, 1914.
Singer: Deut. med. Woch., 1914, xl, 788.
Rosenow: Jour. Amer. Med. Assoc., 1913, lx, 1223.
Thalhimer and Rothschild: Jour. Exp. Med., 1914, xix, 417.
Aschoff: Verh. d. Deut. Path. Gesellsch., 1904, viii, 46.
Bracht and Wächter: Deut. Arch. f. klin. Med., 1909, xcvi, 493.

CHAPTER XXVIII

TYPES OF INJURY.—BACTERIAL DISEASE (Continued)

Diphtherial infection: Diphtheria of respiratory tract. General effects upon the heart, kidneys, etc. Paralysis.
Tetanus infection: Mode of occurrence and mechanism of distribution of the toxin.

DIPHTHERIAL INFECTION

THE diphtheria bacillus is, as is well known, an organism which produces its wide-spread disturbances in the body by the agency of a soluble poison. In this respect it is paralleled by the tetanus bacillus, but by few, if any, other organisms. It can, however, in growing at the point from which it diffuses its toxin, produce a considerable local lesion, a power which is less striking in the case of the tetanus bacillus.

Diphtheria is commonly a disease of children and young people, and from the readiness with which the bacteria are transferred, is likely to occur in epidemic form. Many healthy persons have been found to harbor the bacilli in their mouths and throats, and are thus a menace to others.

The organisms may become localized in the throat, producing characteristic lesions on the mucosa of the fauces, the uvula, the tonsils, the pharynx or larynx, often extending into the trachea and even deep into the smaller bronchi. Similar lesions occur in the nose, rarely in the ear, more often in the vulva and vagina, and sometimes in the skin, especially in connection with maceration of the epidermis or skin lesions, which prepare the way, or with ulcers and wounds. Since the character of the local lesion is essentially the same everywhere, a description of the more common form in the throat will suffice.

A few days after the bacteria lodge in the mucosa, that is, after the lapse of enough time to allow them to grow and gather their forces, redness of the whole lining of the throat appears, with soreness, difficulty in swallowing, and evidences of an acute illness—fever, leucocytosis, etc. White or yellowish-white flakes appear on the reddened surface at one point or other, and spread. It is seen that the confluent patches thus form a slightly elevated, dull, opaque, membrane-like layer, which is pretty tenaciously adherent to the underlying tissue. This can be peeled off, but leaves a raw surface which oozes blood, and upon which a new false membrane quickly forms. In other places the pseudomembrane may be less adherent, and this is likely to be the case within the larynx and trachea, where it sometimes forms a complete lining, stretching for a long way (Fig. 283). Evidence of this looser connection is seen in the frequency with which children cough up the whole lining, or at least large areas of it. The reasons for the closer adherence of the false membrane to the mucosa of the pharynx and mouth than to that of the larynx and trachea must be discussed later.

While this is the ordinary type of local lesion, the diphtheria bacilli may produce much milder inflammation of a more catarrhal character, or, on the other hand, especially when there is a mixed infection and virulent streptococci add their effects, there may be the most destructive affection of tonsils, fauces, and larynx, with deep necrosis and sloughing of the tissues, together with the most violent inflammatory reaction, and with great œdema of the surrounding parts.

Occlusion of the respiratory tract, either by the great swelling produced as just described, or more commonly by the accumulation and folding together of the false membranes, can cause death by asphyxia. Indeed, in spite of tracheotomy, deaths from this cause were frequent. O'Dwyer's method of intubation went far to save children from this evil, and the timely administration of antitoxin has practically cleared away the danger.

Pathological Anatomy of the Lesion.—The diphtheria bacillus is *one* of the many agencies which can produce a diphtheritic inflammation. It has been remarked that it may also produce milder forms, but even alone it is able to produce this most severe form.

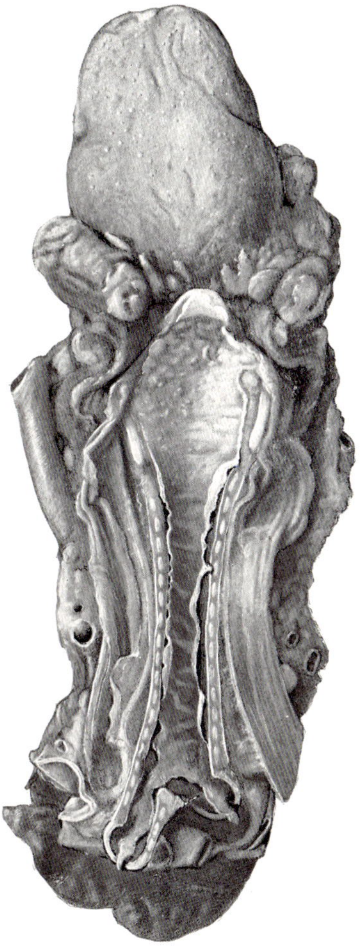

Fig. 283.—Diphtheritic membrane extending far down into the trachea. The tonsils are slightly swollen.

It may be repeated, however, that many strong alkalies or acids or salts of heavy metals, such as mercury, can produce typical diphtheritic forms of inflammation, just as many bacteria can. In other words, the term diphtheritic is used in a purely anatomical sense, to describe the nature of the lesion and not its ætiology.

The lesion consists in an effective destruction of some of the superficial cells of the mucosa, which, under the influence of these bacilli, undergo necrosis and coagulation. The destruction of the overlying cells starts and favors the pouring-out of a coagulable fluid, which permeates them and spreads on the surface. The formation of fibrin through the coagulation of this fluid not only upon the surface, but everywhere in and among the dead cells, establishes the false membrane. Leucocytes appear in great numbers and there is some hæmorrhage. Thus the first false membrane to appear is composed of the vaguely outlined coagulated bodies of the dead cells, buried in a feltwork of fibrin, together with many

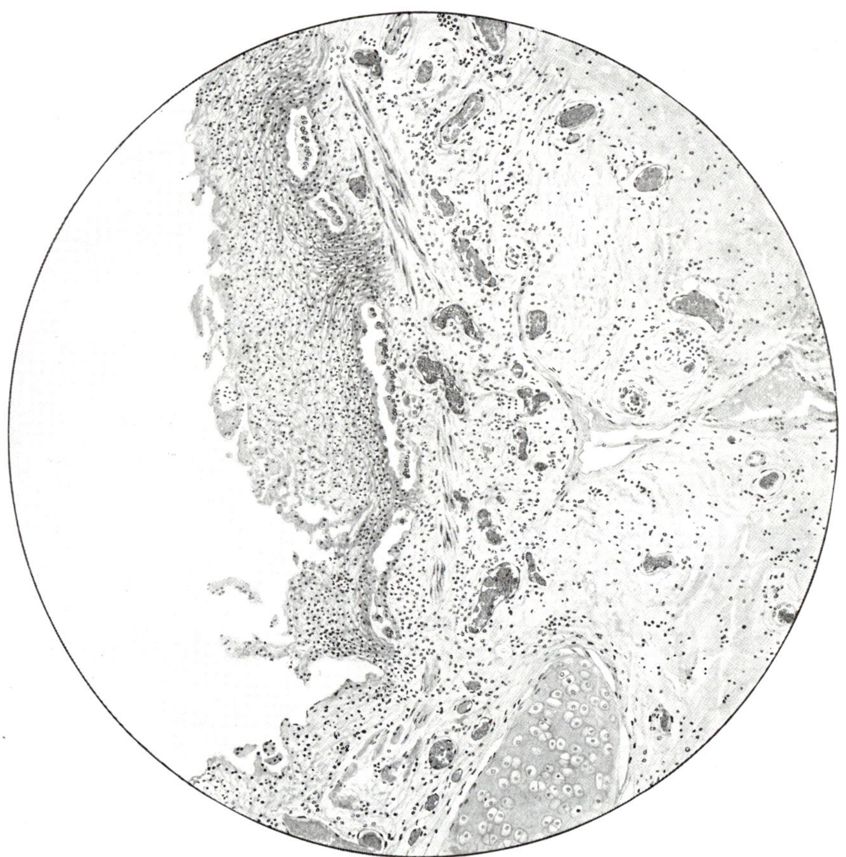

Fig. 284.—Diphtheritic membrane in a bronchus. Acute laryngeal and bronchial diphtheria. The exudate has the arrangement in arcades.

leucocytes. If this is torn off, the next membrane which forms to replace it will consist chiefly of fibrin and leucocytes, unless the growth of bacteria at the base of this fresh ulcer causes more necrotic tissue to become incorporated into the new membrane. Where the necrosis is wide-spread, the false membrane will be found firmly attached by a broad base. In the trachea (Fig. 284) and bronchi the membrane is found to be attached only at the points where the epithelial cells are necrotic and the basement membrane is destroyed. Through such places it exudes on the surface, becoming confluent over the intervening intact epithelium in a series of arcades. Beneath these arcades much of the epithelium may remain intact and serve to regenerate cells to repair the gaps after the disease is over.

The old discussion as to whether a diphtheritic membrane was to be regarded as formed by a fibrinoid degeneration of the superficial cells of the tissue, and not by fibrin from the blood, raged violently for a long time among such men as Orth and Marchand, on one side, and Neumann and his supporters, on the other. A historical review is given by Gaylord (Jour. Exp. Med., 1898, iii, 1). Even yet there are echoes of this in the acrimonious paper of Dietrich in criticism of Sudsuki (Ziegler's Beiträge, 1901, xxix, 562; xxx, 414). It seems clear enough that most of the fibrin must come from exuded plasma, but that necrotic cells embedded in it may become indistinguishable and add to the bulk of the mass. Fibrin formed through and through their dead bodies would still give its characteristic staining reaction.

Sequelæ.—While the mechanical effects of such a membrane are often serious, the more remote sequels of the infection are even more important. Bronchopneumonia is a common one, and is probably due in most cases to accompanying streptococci which pass into the bronchi.

The other things result from the diffusion of the strong toxin from the place where the bacilli are growing into the circulating blood.

Death may take place in the height of the intoxication, evidently from its direct action upon the heart and circulatory system. In the heart itself in such cases no gross changes are to be seen, and, indeed, the microscopical changes, cloudy swelling, fat infiltration, and fragmentation of the heart muscle do not offer convincing evidence of the cause of death. As has been mentioned elsewhere, Pässler and Romberg held the opinion that the effect of the poison was chiefly upon the vasomotor control of the blood-vessels, allowing them to relax so that circulation failed. I was able to confirm this by artificially maintaining the blood-pressure in the brain and coronary arteries, upon which life was greatly prolonged. But it seemed clear that the heart itself was also injured, since it would not beat quite so long as a normal heart. It is even more difficult to explain the gradual or sudden weakening of the action of the heart, with increased pulse-rate and altered rhythm, which may occur after or during convalescence. It is generally ascribed to myocardial degeneration, sometimes to derangement of the nerves which control the heart. Löw describes slight alterations of the conducting bundle of His in such cases, but is unwilling to claim this as the cause of the heart failure.

Albuminuria is common in diphtheria, and the kidneys show acute and subacute changes in most fatal cases. These rarely have the character of a glomerulonephritis, but are more commonly instances of acute interstitial nephritis.

The lesions in other organs are essentially those of any acute infection, except that the changes in the adrenals are likely to be more intense, resulting in hæmorrhages and cellular degenerations.

Paralysis of motor and to a less extent of sensory nerves is dependent upon degenerative and destructive changes in the nerves themselves, as well as in the nerve-cells. The axones disintegrate, and the myeline sheaths lose their homogeneous character, fatty globules which stain with osmic acid appearing in their place. The nerves which supply the palate and larynx, those of the extrinsic muscles of the eye and of the muscles of accommodation, suffer especially. Paresis or definite or temporary paralysis of the muscles of the extremities occur, but are less common.

Skin lesions in the height of the infection are usually in the form of an erythematous rash, but petechiæ and extensive purpuric hæmorrhages sometimes appear in the severest cases.

LITERATURE

Oertel: Pathogenese der epidemischen Diphtherie, Leipzig, 1887. Deut. Arch. f. klin. Med., 1887–8, xlii, 511.

Nuttal and Graham Smith: Bacteriology of Diphtheria, Cambridge, 1908.

Behring: Zeit. f. Hygiene u. Infektionskr., 1892, xii, 1–58.

Welch: Johns Hopkins Hosp. Bull., 1892, iii, 17.

Löw: Ziegler's Beiträge, 1910, xlix, 1.

TETANUS INFECTION

This, like diphtheria, is essentially an intoxication, since the bacteria grow only at the site of inoculation, usually in a wound into which dirt has been forced, and there produce a soluble toxin, which is diffused throughout the body. A certain latent period elapses after the infection before the symptoms appear, and the longer this lasts, the less serious are the effects. Those cases in which the incubation period is only four days are almost sure to end fatally. The effect of the poison is to produce extension and extreme rigidity of the extremities, often preceded by clenching of the jaw (hence lockjaw) and stiffness of the neck, and followed by violent contractions of the muscles of the back, such as to throw the body into a rigid backward curve (opisthotonos). When the muscles of respiration are involved, death ensues, or it may result from exhaustion. Reflex or spontaneous convulsions of great violence may occur. At autopsy no lesions are found which are characteristic of the disease. It is true that Goldscheider and Flatau, Nissl, and others, have found swelling and fragmentation of the tigroid bodies of the motor ganglion-cells and shrinkage with deep staining of the nuclei, but this condition is found under many other circumstances and is by no means specific. Tetanus must then be regarded as a functional disturbance produced by the toxin. Exactly the same phenomena can be produced in animals by the injection of the bacteria-free toxin, which is an extremely virulent poison.

In the pathogenesis of tetanus the greatest interest lies in the point of action of the poison and its mode of distribution. It is observed that there may be a local rigidity of the muscles in the neighborhood of the point of infection (local tetanus), but that while this may sometimes be the only symptom, it usually leads to a similar rigidity of the opposite extremity, and finally to an involvement of the whole body (ascending tetanus). Another form, beginning with clenching of the jaw and stiffness of the neck, quickly spreads to all the extremities (universal or descending tetanus), while a third form is that in which convulsions form a striking feature.

It was shown by Meyer and Ransom that the toxin travels from the point of inoculation up the nerves to the central nervous system, although it is also diffused to some extent by the blood and lymphatics. In the case of the local tetanus, which is less striking in man than in experimental animals, there arose some question as to the possibility of its being due to a direct effect of the toxin upon the muscles, but the experiments of Permin show clearly that if the nerve be cut shortly after the injection of the toxin, no such local rigidity appears. But the rigidity persists if the section of the nerve be performed after it is well established, probably owing to secondary changes of unknown character in the muscles themselves. Similarly, Meyer and Ransom showed that the injection of antitoxin into the nerve above the point of inoculation would block and neutralize the toxin. Further, since it might be supposed that diffusion by the blood-stream could bring the poison to the ganglion-cells of the cord, Permin has shown by experiment that if antitoxin be injected first, so as to neutralize the poison carried by the blood, a distinct local tetanus can be produced by a small dose of toxin injected into the muscles. The poison passes along the nerves rapidly, probably in the axis-cylinders, since destruction of the perineurium does not halt it, and reaches the corresponding ganglion-cells of the anterior horn. If it is limited in quantity so as to affect only this group, a local tetanus will appear. Otherwise it can spread to affect the whole spinal cord and brain, and rigidity of the muscles over the whole body follows.

In other cases in which the toxin gains more ready entrance to the blood-stream, or in which it is injected into the vein in an animal, the universal or descending type appears.

The question as to the type of nerve which conducts the poison seems not yet settled,* nor whether the anterior horn cells become spontaneously active in sending impulses to the muscles, or only excessively irritable and responsive to sensory impulses, to which they act as in reflexes. Permin showed that, by cutting all the posterior roots on one side and injecting toxin into both legs, one produces local tetanus only on the intact side, while the leg, from which no sensory impulses reach the cord, remains relaxed.

In the case of the convulsive attacks it seems that the impulses come from

* Nevertheless, Meyer and Ransom produced only pain and greatly increased reflex excitability to pain by injecting the toxin into the spinal cord or posterior roots (tetanus dolorosus), while injection into peripheral sensory nerves was without result. They therefore think the motor nerves the paths of conduction of the poison.

the brain itself, which in those cases has been affected by the poison. They can be prevented by the removal of the motor cortex in animals, and can be produced in their most extreme form in other animals by injecting the toxin into the brain or into the eye, whence it quickly passes into the brain. Tetanus is thus ordinarily the effect of the toxin upon the spinal cord, the convulsive features being due to its spread into the brain.

The enormous importance of this disease, especially in the present war, where wounds are contaminated with the highly manured soil, in which the bacilli are abundant, has led to great efforts to counteract the poison. Antitoxin, so useful in guarding against the poison, and so active in neutralizing it in the blood, cannot follow it from the circulation into the nervous system. Therefore, unless it be injected into the nervous tissue, it is relatively valueless. As stated, it will block the passage of toxin along the nerve if injected into the substance of the nerve, but it must remain difficult to diffuse it into the substance of the cord and brain in more advanced cases. The mortality remains high, although certain narcotics are useful in stopping the flow of impulses from the ganglion-cells.

LITERATURE

Permin: Mitth. a. d. Grenzgeb. d. Med. u. Chir., 1913–14, xxvii, 1.

Meyer and Ransom: Arch. f. exp. Pathol., 1903, xlix, 369.

Flatau: Flatau, Jacobsohn, and Minor: Path. Anat. des Nervensystems, Berlin, 1904, i, 1290.

A. Moschowitz: Annals of Surgery, 1900, xxxii, 416.

CHAPTER XXIX

TYPES OF INJURY.—BACTERIAL DISEASE (Continued)

Asiatic cholera: Intestinal lesions. General intoxication.
Bubonic plague: Transmission. Bubonic type. Pneumonic type.
Glanders: Acute and chronic forms.
Anthrax: Infection through skin, digestive tract, lungs.
Influenza: Epidemic distribution. Catarrhal, pneumonic, and other forms.

SEVERAL other types of bacterial infection must be considered here, some of them infections of enormous importance at certain times, when they rage as epidemics, or in tropical countries, where they exist constantly as endemic plagues, but described here only in outline.

ASIATIC CHOLERA

An epidemic disease spreading with the course of human travel, and occurring either in groups of cases or suddenly affecting a whole community. It is largely dependent upon infection of water supply or of food, and hence the rapidity of its spread in cities where the drinking-water comes from an infected source, as was the case in the Hamburg epidemic. It is endemic in India, and is the cause of hundreds of thousands of deaths every year in that country.

Taken into the stomach and intestines, the spirillum of Koch requires forty-eight hours or more to develop to a sufficient extent to cause the symptoms. Then the disease proceeds with extreme violence. There are several forms, in the mildest of which there is intense diarrhœa, which may pass off in a few days. In the so-called cholerine, there are diarrhœa, vomiting, and extreme prostration. These conditions may pass into the more severe form, in which, with great desiccation of the tissues, there are painful muscular cramps, cold sweats, stagnation of the cutaneous circulation, delirium, and collapse. In others the patient passes into coma and dies.

The stools are watery and turbid, often very slightly colored,—the so-called rice-water stools,—and contain, with flecks of mucus, myriads of the comma bacilli. There is oliguria, and in the severe cases complete anuria, lasting even many days. At autopsy the tissues are found to show very little change—the blood in the late stages is concentrated by the loss of water, and the red corpuscles are far over 5,000,000 per c.mm. The leucocytes are relatively higher. The bone-marrow is red and jelly-like. The spleen is not specially altered from normal, and contains no organisms.

The intestines do not show a marked alteration. They are half full or distended with the turbid fluid described above, and their mucosa is reddened and shows a wide-spread desquamation of epithelial cells. There seems to be no intense inflammatory reaction, although the spirilla are present in huge quantities and extend deep into the crypts and lacunæ. They seem to be limited to the mucosa, and are not found in the blood or other organs. Occasionally there is found a diphtheritic inflammation of the colon or of the vagina, but this may well be due to other organisms.

Thus, in one sense, the cholera infection approaches that of diphtheria and tetanus in that the bacteria are limited to one site. Indeed, R. Kraus, Brau, and Denier have declared that these bacilli produce a soluble toxin, and that an antitoxin may be developed by its use. Everything about the character of the disease would appear to favor the idea of the existence of a toxin different from the usual endotoxin.

LITERATURE

P. Krause and Rumpf: Handb. d. Tropenkrankheiten, Mense, 1914, iii, 242.
Th. Fahr: Ergebn. d. allg. Path., 1909, $xiii_1$, 1.
R. Koch: Arb. a. d. Kais. Gesundheitsamte, 1887, iii.

BUBONIC PLAGUE

The plague is another affection endemic in certain countries, where it is essentially a disease of rats and other rodents, but spreading with the transportation of infected materials or rats to other countries. It has occurred with the same virulence in winter weather in Manchuria as in the heat of India or Africa.

Plague is caused by the *Bacillus pestis,* discovered by Yersin and Kitasato, an organism of extraordinary virulence, capable of causing infection from the slightest inoculation, and producing a highly mortal disease, in which it becomes distributed in enormous quantities through the body. Infection can occur through the skin, through the respiratory tract, and, possibly, though this is unimportant, through the digestive tract. By far the most common are infections through the skin, either through wounds (Dürck describes infection from a rat-bite) or through the bites of infected fleas. The rather rare cases of primary plague pneumonia are often caused by the inhalation of bacilli carried in fine droplets of sputum exhaled by another person with plague pneumonia. In the great Manchurian epidemic of 1910–11 Strong tells me the cases were nearly all of the pneumonic type and were uniformly fatal. He and his assistant escaped infection by wearing thick masks of cotton.

By far the greater number of the cases in ordinary plague are not of the pneumonic type, but are characterized by buboes or suppurations of the inguinal, axillary, and other lymph-glands. In these the infection is probably caused by the bites of fleas which have infected themselves from plague-stricken rats. C. J. Martin has shown me the plugs of plague bacilli which form in the proventriculus of the flea, preventing the access of any blood to its stomach. Such a flea, constantly hungry, will bite again and again, each time transferring plague bacilli to its victims.

Bubonic Type.—After a short incubation period, painful swellings appear in the groin. In the early stage these glands are swollen and sprinkled with hæmorrhages. The lymph sinuses are packed with phagocytic cells which contain the bacilli in numbers. Necrosis follows quickly and becomes

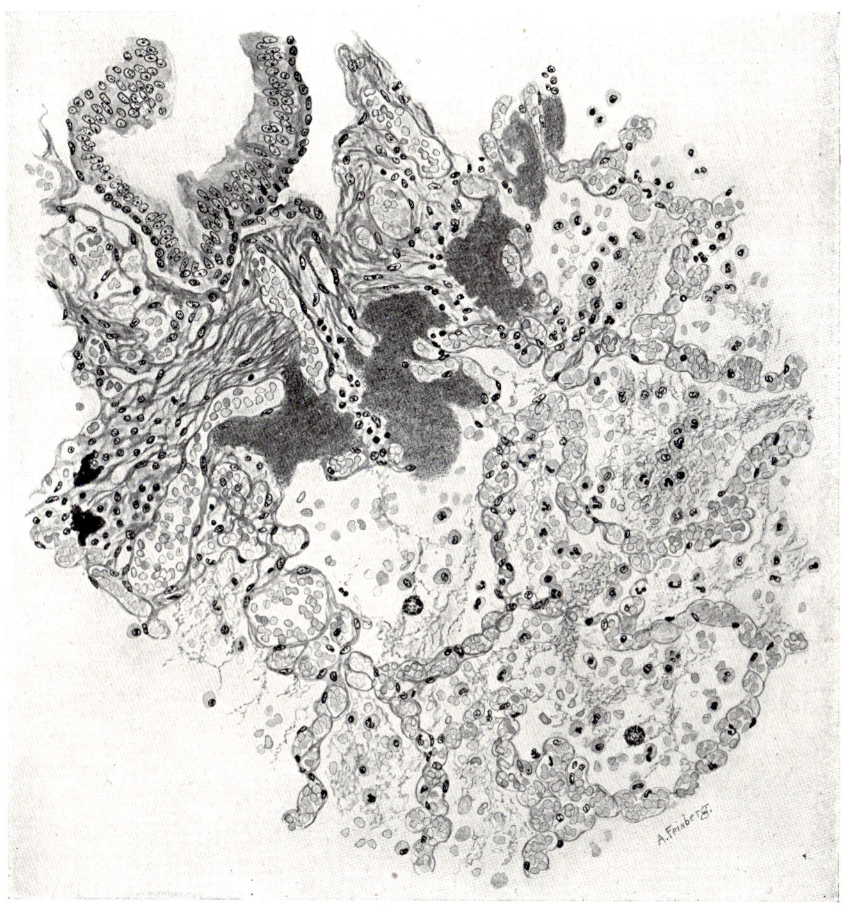

Fig. 285.—Pneumonic plague. The exudate and congestion are such as are described for the stage of engorgement in ordinary pneumonia. Great quantities of bacteria in the tissues, especially in the lymphatics of the bronchial walls.

extensive, and is associated with much hæmorrhage and outpouring of leucocytes. Dürck thinks it largely due to circulatory obstruction. The whole centre of the gland breaks down into an abscess cavity and may be discharged. Metastases of the bacilli occur to the next glands, and shortly to the lungs and other organs. In the lungs foci of necrosis of the tissue with suppuration are produced by this embolism, and the same is true for the liver. There is a great swelling and softening of the spleen with grayish opacity, caused by the new formation of cells, which Dürck thinks are endothelial cells from the sinuses. Abscesses occur there also. In the kidneys there may be definite focal necroses, abscess like in appearance, with many bacilli, or more commonly an acute hæmorrhagic nephritis with necrosis and desquamation of the epithelial cells, both in the glomerular capsules and tubules.

On the whole, the appearance is that of a fulminant general septicæmia, with the lodgment of enormous numbers of bacilli in any or all of the organs, and their transportation in quantities in the lymph and circulating blood.

Pneumonic Form.—In the bubonic form there may be found, in some cases, lobular consolidation of the lung, sometimes discrete, more often confluent. This is, in fact, the commoner type of pneumonia found in such epidemics as that of Manchuria, but Strong emphasizes the fact that the somewhat hypothetical stage of engorgement, always described for the pneumococcus pneumonia, is really the commonest phenomenon in these cases, since the affected persons die before actual hepatization can be produced (Fig. 285). He describes lobar consolidation also, in which, however, only a small part of the lung was ever found in the stage of gray hepatization, another part in that of red hepatization, while the greater part was in the stage of engorgement. Even in the gray stage there is little fibrin, while in the more usual stage of engorgement there are hardly any leucocytes, although the alveoli are filled with bacteria and fluid and desquamated epithelium, and the capillaries are greatly distended.

In the other organs there were found evidences of an intense general septicæmia, with cloudy swelling and hæmorrhages, but usually no such embolic lesions as described for the more slowly advancing bubonic form.

LITERATURE

Dürck: Ziegler's Beiträge, 1904, Suppl. vi.
Albrecht and Ghon: Beulenpest im Bombay, Wien, 1898–1900.
Strong and Teague: Philippine Journal of Science, 1912, vii, 129, 137.

GLANDERS

Primarily a disease of horses, mules, etc., infection with the *Bacillus mallei* may occur in those who handle horses or who are exposed in some way to contagion from them. In a few cases fatal infections have occurred in persons working in laboratories with cultures of the organism.

In horses the disease is largely an affection of the nasal and respiratory tracts, and frequently assumes a chronic course. Nodules appear in the nasal mucosa, especially upon the septum, which are quite firm at first, but later present a necrotic centre and develop into ulcers, which heal with extensive scar formation, recognizable by its curious stellate arrangement. Affections of the trachea and lungs, of the intestines, lymph-glands, spleen, etc., are also found in these animals (Kitt).

In man the formation of necrotizing or pustular eruptions in the nose has been described, and in such cases the destructive action of the bacilli leads before long to the ulceration and perforation of the septum of the nose, partial destruction of the turbinate bones, or even of the palate. More common are infections through the skin, which give rise to deep indurated swellings which persist until incised, or until they burst spontaneously,

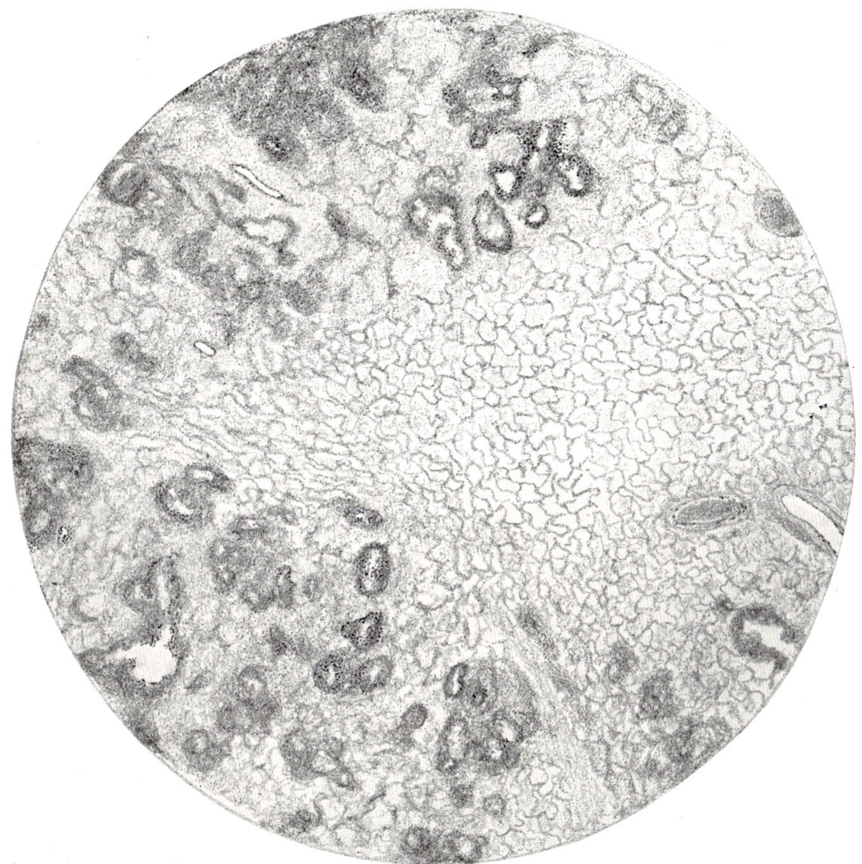

Fig. 286.—Glanders. Focus of lobular pneumonia with necrosis of the lung tissue. Low-power drawing showing only the arrangement of the consolidation and the destruction of tissue.

setting free a thick, stringy pus. Such abscesses heal very slowly, and usually a sinus persists for a long time. In other cases serpiginous ulcers are formed in the skin which extend in one or other direction, leaving behind a partly healed or scarred area. Most of the cases have presented deep muscular abscesses which evacuate the same thick pus and are slow to heal. At times the bone is attacked, and in many instances there have been necrosis and final perforation of the bones of the skull. Multiple embolic lesions in which necrotic or caseous material is formed and surrounded by a dense granulation tissue are found in various situations in the body. Pulmonary lesions are especially frequent, and assume various forms. In one case which I studied in Professor Marchand's laboratory the man had been accidentally infected by thrusting the needle of a syringe full of a culture of Bacillus mallei into his thumb. Two months later he died with what appeared to be a diffuse tuberculous pneumonia. In these lesions, however, there were found the bacilli in pure culture, and microscopically the changes were quite unlike those of tuberculosis. Instead (Fig. 286), there were foci of necrosis with débris of cells and tissue closely coagulated together, but without nuclear stain, surrounded by a zone of fragmented nuclei, and this in turn by a thick infiltration of leucocytes. The adjacent lung tissue was the seat of an organizing pneumonia, and there was extensive filling of alveoli with large mononuclear cells, as in caseous pneumonia. In this case there was nothing of the formation of nodules with giant-cells which has been so generally described in the lesions of glanders. Especially in the foci in the nasal mucosa, but also in glanders lesions elsewhere, there is said to be an extensive new formation of epithelioid cells and even of giant-cells which gives the lesions something of the character of a tubercle. As Duval points out, this occurs only with bacilli of relatively low virulence and in the more chronic cases. Otherwise the necrosis of the tissue is quickly produced and the surrounding granulation tissue is less characteristic.

LITERATURE

G. D. Robins: Studies from the Royal Victoria Hosp., Montreal, 1906, ii, No. 1.
J. H. Wright: Jour. Exp. Med., 1896, i, 577.
Th. Kitt: Path. Anat. d. Hausthiere, 1901, ii, 138, etc.
MacCallum: Ziegler's Beiträge, 1902, xxxi, 440.

ANTHRAX

A disease which affects cows, sheep, and other herbivorous animals is caused by infection with the well-known Bacillus anthracis, and is transmitted to man through contact with the sick animals, or through handling their infected hides. In certain industries which have to do with hides (tanning, etc.) or with hair or wool in the making of mattresses, paper, etc., infection may occur, sometimes almost in epidemic form (wool-sorter's disease, Hadernkrankheit).

Cattle are infected especially in pastures which are subject to inundation, but a field once infected may remain so for a long time, and the infection be added to by the secretions of the cattle themselves, or by the soiling of the ground with the remains of cattle which have died or been slaughtered and buried there. Naturally, chances for infection occur in the stalls where such cattle are kept.

In these animals the disease may be very acute, killing within a few hours, or there may develop definite carbuncles or more diffuse œdema in the skin or in the intestinal tract. At autopsy there is found a general septicæmia—the blood-vessels are full of the bacilli, and the internal lesions in general are ecchymoses, acute splenic tumor, cloudy swelling of liver and kidneys, etc., such as might be found in other acute infections.

In man the portal of entry may be through the skin, the digestive tract, or the lungs. In the case of the skin some slight abrasion is usually the point of entrance, although it has been shown experimentally that anthrax bacilli rubbed on the intact skin can pass through the hair-follicles. A small painful red nodule appears, resembling a flea-bite, and rapidly enlarges and shows a greenish, necrotic centre, induration and reddening of the surrounding tissue, with blisters filled with yellowish or bluish fluid. This phlegmonous infiltration of the skin and subcutaneous tissue spreads quickly, and the central part dries up into a leather-like crust under which the tissue is necrotic and loaded with anthrax bacilli. Such a carbuncle is at least evidence of a certain resistance, although from it the bacilli may spread in quantities into the blood. There is another type in which, instead of a localized carbuncle, a wide-spread œdema of the skin and underlying tissue appears, with myriads of bacilli. This indicates a poorer ability to resist, and passes on to a more surely fatal outcome. In the more resistant cases the leucocytosis is high and phagocytosis is active, but in some the bacilli surround themselves with thick capsules, and are then not readily taken up by the leucocytes. It is thought that the formation of such capsules is an indication that the bacilli are gaining the upper hand in the struggle, and the prognosis is correspondingly bad. The neighboring lymph-glands become swollen and hæmorrhagic, and thence the infection becomes generalized.

In the persons who work with hair, hides, and wool, inhalation of the dust which bears the anthrax spores produces a singularly fatal form of the disease, which is primarily a lobular or lobar pneumonia, distinguishable only by the recognition of the bacilli from other types of pneumonia. Eppinger has described many cases in which he found lesions chiefly in the thoracic viscera; the pleural and pericardial surfaces were covered with a fibrinopurulent or hæmorrhagic exudate, and the lungs were partly consolidated. A lobular or confluent hepatization of the lungs with exudate of a soft or hæmorrhagic character was found, and microscopically the alveoli, as well as the lymphatics and tissue crevices, were loaded with bacilli. Neighboring lymph-glands were greatly enlarged and hæmorrhagic, and elsewhere there were the changes of a general septicæmia. Risel described in this connection great hæmorrhagic infiltration of the mediastinal tissues, as well as of the bronchial lymph-glands. In persons who have swallowed infected meat or milk there arise intestinal carbuncles, just as in cattle. These are usually single, but may be multiple, and occur most commonly in the jejunum. The lesion seems to begin in the depths of the mucosa, or in the submucosa, and appears as a red, pea-sized to plum-sized swelling, which is made up of œdematous tissue loaded with bacilli and leucocytes. The whole adjacent mucosa and submucosa become infiltrated, and the carbuncle itself ulcerates deeply. The mesenteric glands swell and are hæmorrhagic.

In all these cases there are evidences of the most intense acute general infection. Probably in no other disease do such quantities of bacteria appear in the circulating blood. So extensively do they fill the capillaries that it has even been suggested that in this disease the symptoms may be due to that obstruction. The bacilli can be recognized by staining a single drop of the circulating blood. The spleen becomes greatly swollen and soft and turgid with dark blood. Indeed, it is from this dark color and incoagulability of the blood, which give the spleen such a peculiar appearance, that the disease derives its various names (Milzbrand, charbon, anthrax). Cloudy swelling of the liver and kidneys is constant, but there may also be necrosis and disintegration of the cells in these organs.

Hæmorrhagic meningitis appears to be not uncommon, and in one of Risel's cases it formed the most striking feature. There were in the nasal mucosa ulcerated nodules extending into the submucosa, and from these a hæmorrhagic cellular exudate rich in bacilli could be traced along the lymphatic sheaths of the olfactory nerves to the brain.

LITERATURE

Risel: Zeit. f. Hygiene, 1903, xlii, 381.
Eppinger: Die Hadernkrankheit, Jena, 1894.
Koranyi: Nothnagel's Handb., 1897, Bd. v, Th. v, Abt. i.
Salmon and Smith: United States Department of Agriculture, Bureau Animal Industry, circular 71, 1904.
W. Koch: Deutsche Chirurgie, 1886, Lief 9.
Herzog: Ziegler's Beiträge, 1915, lx, 513.

INFLUENZA INFECTION

For centuries it has been recognized that there is an epidemic disease, influenza or la grippe, which sweeps over whole continents, infecting nearly every one, but causing few deaths. It is particularly marked by producing catarrhal inflammation of the upper air-passages, fever, and general prostration, but it is also capable of causing a great variety of complicating ailments. The extraordinary history of this infection may be read in Ripperger's or Leichtenstern's monographs, or in popular form in the book of Hopkirk. The last great epidemic or pandemic was that of 1889–90, which, starting in eastern Russia, quickly traversed the whole world. It was in that epidemic that Pfeiffer recognized the Bacillus influenzæ as the cause, finding it in practically pure culture in the sputum in many cases. It is a peculiar fact that, as years passed after the wake of the epidemic, the bacillus, which was so obviously predominant at that time, began to play a less important part in the sporadic cases or small epidemics, being overshadowed by other organisms. On the other hand, Jochmann thinks that the bacillus does not necessarily produce influenza, but occurs as a saprophyte or accompanying organism in other diseases. It seems as though, while the acquisition of immunity may play some part, the bacillus, so active during a great epidemic, loses its virulence and becomes relatively harmless. No new great epidemic appears until a new strain arises somewhere with fresh virulence.

Leichtenstern recognizes catarrhal, pneumonic, nervous, rheumatic, and gastro-intestinal forms of the disease, which he also divides, on another basis, into toxic and inflammatory forms.

The numerous symptoms are by no means so distinctly dependent upon recognizable anatomical changes produced by the bacillus as in many other infections. The organisms do not thrive in the circulating blood, but are evidently distributed in that way in some cases, and have been cultivated from the blood. The respiratory tract forms the portal of entry and commonest localization of the bacilli. Intense catarrhal inflammation of the nasal cavities follows, frequently extending to the larynx, trachea, and bronchi. Cough, with expectoration of much greenish sputum in nummular masses containing the bacilli, is characteristic. Lobular pneumonia, in which the exudate is soft and cellular, with little fibrin, forms a most serious feature. The intense infection of the bronchi may lead to weakening of their walls, and in those cases in which the bacilli are harbored there for a long time, bronchiectatic dilatation occurs. In several cases seen at autopsy in which there were advanced dilatations of the bronchi Boggs isolated from the foul contents the influenza bacillus. Indurative pneumonia is usually associated with these changes, and may spread quite widely through the lung. An existing tuberculous infection is rendered worse, and new tuberculosis may arise on the basis of the influenza.

Extension through the Eustachian tubes from the inflamed pharynx gives rise to the rather common influenzal otitis media. In connection with this, or through direct extension from the nose, there may be meningitis or cerebral abscess. Ordinarily other organisms, such as the pneumococcus, are also involved in such lesions. Encephalitis of a diffuse form, such as was described by Wernicke, myelitis, and neuritis occur, and indeed there may be not only mechanical effects, but psychic disturbances, such as melancholia or even dementia.

In the rheumatic form the muscles and joints are affected in such a way as to resemble acute rheumatism, especially since fever and profuse sweating are associated.

Gastro-intestinal disturbances, with diarrhœa and vomiting and with intense headache, may in severe cases pass on to a definite influenzal enteritis, with hæmorrhage and even ulcerative lesions in the stomach and intestines. Rarely peritonitis results from this, but the influenza bacillus is not clearly established as the cause.

Influenzal endocarditis and pericarditis are described, and thrombosis of various veins and arteries, but, in general, circulatory disturbances, except slowing of the heart, are not common.

In many cases the bacilli persist in the mucosæ for a long time, causing chronic bronchitis. The patients are troubled by various symptoms referable to as many parts of the body, and pass as cases of gout, rheumatism, neurasthenia, etc. Recrudescences of the acute inflammatory affection are to be expected at intervals by these people.

LITERATURE

Leichtenstern: Influenza, Wien, 1912, A. Hölder.
Ripperger: Influenza, München, 1892, Münch. med. Woch., 1893, xl, 775.
Boggs: Amer. Jour. Med. Sci., November, 1905, cxxx, 902.
Jochmann: Ergebn. d. allg. Path., 1909, xiii, 107.
Lord: Boston Med. and Surg. Jour., May, 1905, clii, 537, 574.

CHAPTER XXX

TYPES OF INJURY.—BACTERIAL DISEASE (Continued)

Typhoid infection: General relations. Intestinal, lymphatic, splenic, and other lesions. Necroses in various organs. Affections of circulatory, respiratory, and nervous system.
Paratyphoid infection: Relation to typhoid and enteritis infection. Acute gastro-enteritis, accessory lesions.
Dysentery: Various organisms concerned. Intestinal lesions.

TYPHOID INFECTIONS

INFECTION with the Bacillus typhosus ordinarily produces characteristic lesions only in man, although Greenbaum has succeeded experimentally in setting up similar effects in the organs of chimpanzees by inoculation. In the smaller laboratory animals a general septicæmia may follow infection, but there are none of the destructive anatomical changes observed in man.

In man, although attention has long been concentrated upon the more local manifestations, there occurs a general septicæmia in which the bacilli are readily demonstrated in the blood in the earlier days of the disease, less readily or not at all in the later stages. While in most cases the local alterations of the intestines are most striking, they may be completely absent, so that it seems that the less conspicuous changes due to the general distribution of the bacilli are more constant and characteristic features.

The bacilli gain entrance by way of the digestive tract, being introduced with drinking-water, vegetables grown on infected ground or watered with infected water, and infected milk and other food into which the bacilli may have been introduced in the process of preparation. Even ice and oysters seem to have been the source of infection in epidemics. Flies may carry the bacilli from exposed fæces, etc., to food. Since persons who have recovered from typhoid fever may harbor the bacteria in bile, urine, and fæces for many years, they become a menace to others, and especially when they act as cooks the danger of their transferring the bacilli to food is very great. Thus a recent epidemic in the Sloan Hospital was traced to a cook who was a typhoid-bacillus carrier. Another, reported in the Journal of the American Medical Association in 1915, was traced in the same way to the cook who prepared a large panful of spaghetti, even though it was cooked in another place and not again touched by her. It was shown that in the spaghetti, which had stood overnight, there had been a great growth of the bacilli, which in the cooking were scarcely warmed in the centre of the mass.

Typhoid fever is essentially a disease of unsanitary conditions of life, and disappears in proportion as the food and water supplies are kept clean.

Infection with the Bacillus typhosus produces in man a protracted febrile disease, which begins usually one or two weeks after infection and lasts for five or six weeks or more. There are localized changes in the intestines, especially in the lymphoid structures, in the abdominal lymph-glands, the spleen, and bone-marrow. There is a general cloudy swelling of the organs, with wide-spread focal necroses, and other less constant lesions.

Intestinal Lesions.—In the first week of the disease the lymphoid nodules of the intestines, including, of course, the Peyer's patches, become swollen and stand up above the surrounding mucosa (Fig. 287). This may be caused partly by hyperæmia, but is chiefly due to an increase in the numbers of lymphoid and other cells. The change is most evident in those Peyer's patches and solitary nodules in the lower part of the ileum, becoming less marked, and finally fading away toward the upper part of the intestine. In the colon the degree of swelling varies greatly—sometimes it is imperceptible; in other cases it is extreme and overshadows the slighter changes in the ileum. On gross inspection it appears that this swelling is sharply limited to the lymphoid structures, which thus become very conspicuous and prominent, but it may be concluded, both from the microscopical examination in this stage and from the later ulceration, that the alteration in the tissue extends beyond their limits. There is a catarrhal inflammation of the rest of the mucosa, which may be evident as a moderate hyperæmia, but is often inconspicuous.

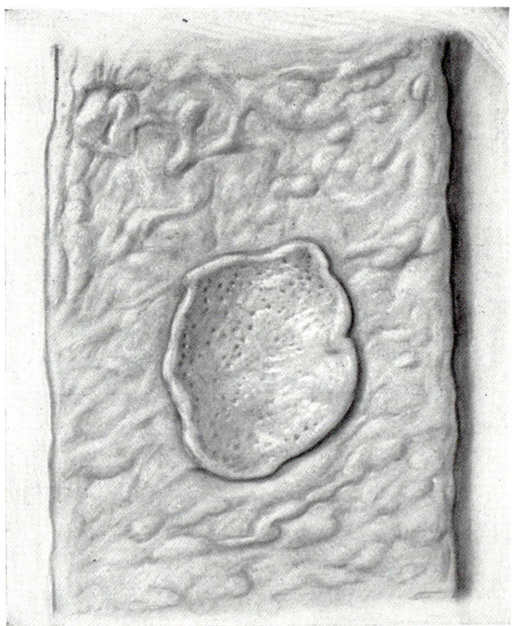

Fig. 287.—Typhoid fever. Swollen Peyer's patch.

Later, in the second week in most cases, the superficial parts of the swollen Peyer's patches and nodules lose their reddish-gray color and the velvety smoothness of their surface, and in smaller or larger areas become opaque and dry-looking, and in these areas become stained a brownish-green from the intestinal contents. This is the formation of the slough, which is an expression of the partial necrosis of the swollen patch. Sometimes the change progresses rapidly and goes deep, involving all but the margin of the patch. In the nodules the necrotic slough appears as a little, rough, greenish plug embedded in the top, and surrounded by the hyperæmic margin. From the outside the Peyer's patches can be recognized, as a rule, by their darker color and by the injection of the subserous bloodvessels, but, as a rule, the solitary nodules scarcely show through at this stage.

Not all the swollen Peyer's patches or solitary nodules advance to this stage. Indeed, in every case at autopsy it is usual to find some, perhaps even the majority, which have proceeded no further than the swelling, as far as the unaided eye can see. It is quite common to find the advanced change only in those situated rather low in the intestine, near the ileocæcal valve, although it is quite true that there are other cases in which all the lymphoid areas throughout the greater part of the ileum have run the whole gamut of changes. In persons who recover and in whom these swollen lymphoid structures which have not progressed to necrosis return to normal, there must be a process of resolution somewhat analogous to that in pneumonia. Still later other changes occur in those Peyer's patches which present necrotic areas. The greenish mass retracts a little from the edge and loosens all around its margin. The crevice goes deeper toward the middle (Fig. 288), and soon the whole slough is dislodged and falls into the lumen of the intestines, leaving an excavation or ulcer of corresponding depth (Fig. 290). If the slough is completely removed, it leaves a clean ulcer, the bottom of which is usually formed by the muscular layers of the wall, which show plainly the parallel arrangement of their fibres. Sometimes the ulcer is more shallow, and then its floor is part of the infiltrated submucosa—at other times it is deeper and may even extend quite through to the subserous tissue, in which case complete perforation is likely to occur. One may find such ulcers on the point of perforation with only a thin, easily torn film of the necrotic wall remaining. From the outside this appears as an opaque, greenish gray patch surrounded by a dark hæmorrhagic zone.

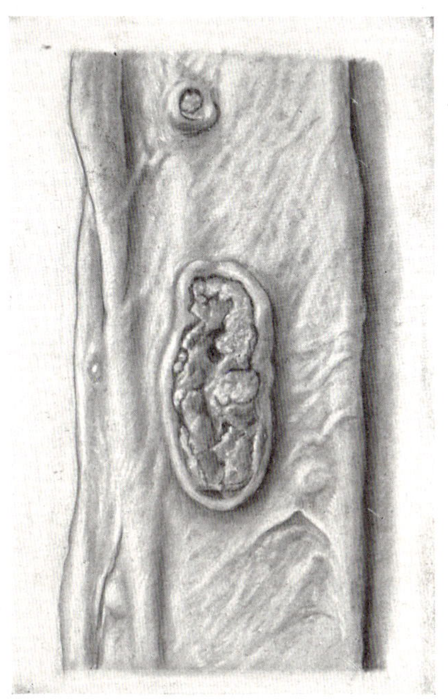

Fig. 288.—Typhoid fever. Swollen Peyer's patches with beginning separation of the slough.

It has already been said that the ulcer need not excavate the whole of the swollen patch. One frequently finds several small and rather deep ulcers in one Peyer's patch, separated from one another by partitions of still living tissue. On the other hand, the ulceration may extend quite beyond the margin of the lymphoid tissue, so as to correspond no longer

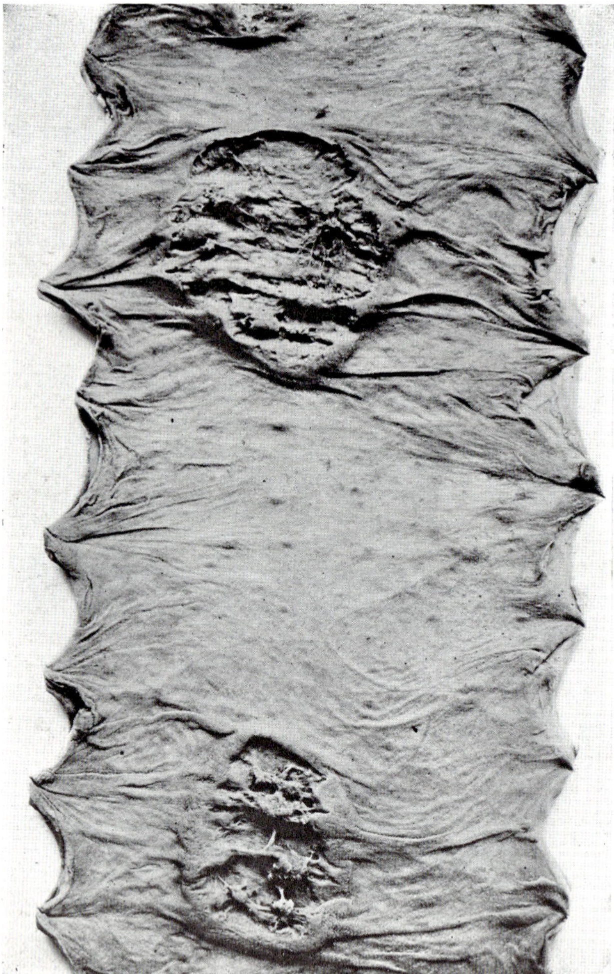

Fig. 289.—Typhoid ulcers after the discharge of most of the necrotic tissue.

with the original form, and in the neighborhood of the ileocæcal valve it is common to find neighboring ulcers confluent to such a degree that only small islands of mucosa are left. Higher up it is usual to find the ulcers more limited to the outlines of the Peyer's patches and solitary nodules. Quite similar processes take place in the colon and in the vermiform appendix, and it is not uncommon to have a perforation in the base of an ulcer in the latter situation. Since these perforations occur rapidly without time for any adhesions to form between the intestinal loop and other tissues, a general peritonitis is the common result. Naturally, in this respect perforations in the free moving ileum are more serious and likely to be fatal than those in the appendix, where localizing agencies are more available.

In many cases there is bleeding from the ulcerated intestinal wall, the blood escaping with the stools sometimes in such quantities that the patient dies from its loss. It is rare that one can find any vessel which can be shown to have been the source of the hæmorrhage.

After the ulcer is cleaned of its slough, healing begins by the formation of a layer of granulation tissue in the base, soon followed by the growth of a single smooth layer of epithelium across its surface. The depression into which this epithelium must grow is before long made up to its original level by the new formation of lymphoid tissue, and it becomes impossible to tell where the ulcer had been. No great scar formation occurs, and there seems never to be a stricture of the intestine due to the healing of a typhoid ulcer.

The nature of these lesions is rather different from any of the effects of bacterial invasion met with so far, and is to be understood only in the light of the general effect of the typhoid bacillus upon the body. The bacteria hitherto studied have been found to produce a reaction on the part of the bone-marrow, which liberates into the circulating blood great numbers of polymorphonuclear leucocytes. Such a leucocytosis fitted well with the mechanism of ordinary inflammation, and even though we recognized the presence of many mononuclear wandering cells in all stages, and especially in the more chronic forms of inflammation, the polynuclear neutrophiles dominated the scene in fresh inflammations. In typhoid fever there is no such leucocytosis—the total number of leucocytes per cubic millimetre is rather decreased, and the lymphocytes become relatively numerous. Even in the presence of secondary infections, which in normal persons produce a leucocytosis, the bone-marrow seems incapable of responding actively, and there is only a halting leucocytosis.

In the typhoid lesions the bacilli are found—indeed, they are carried everywhere in the circulating blood, but their presence rather repels the polymorphonuclears. Nor is it possible, as in the case of the staphylococcus, to demonstrate the bacilli as the central point about which the lesion is concentrated. Instead, one finds clumps of bacilli in the tissues without any striking reaction about them, and elsewhere foci of coagulative necrosis, with few or no bacilli.

In the earliest stages of medullary swelling (Fig. 290) the Peyer's patches and solitary nodules show an increase of the lymphoid cells, which become scattered into the adjacent mucosa and into the submucosa underneath. But the lymphocytes, many of which seem to have emigrated from the blood-vessels, are soon rendered less conspicuous, and separated by the appearance of great numbers of large pale cells with rather pale vesicular nuclei. It is about these cells, which occur in all typhoid lesions, that violent discussion has raged, especially with regard to their origin. They are most actively phagocytic, and engulf the injured lymphocytes until soon the latter are found only in groups, while the large cells, each of which may contain two or three bodies of lymphocytes, occupy most of the field.

Hoffmann and Billroth described these cells and noted their phagocytic capacity. Mallory decides that, since they behave like endothelial cells, they are endothelial cells, and without further ado calls them endothelial cells throughout. Marchand, more cautious, thinks that they may be partly derived from the reticulum cells, partly from the endothelium of the lymphatics. Saltykow thinks that he can trace them from the endothelial cells of the lymph sinuses, but finds them mixed in the sinuses with lymphoid cells of various types. It is a matter most difficult to decide by the fallible methods of tracing transitions, and especially difficult in this case, since it is so rare a piece of fortune to be able to study the typhoid lesions in their earliest stages.

The cells seem to be mobile not only because they are phagocytic, but because they are found in abundance far in the tissue of the submucosa, away from the reticulum

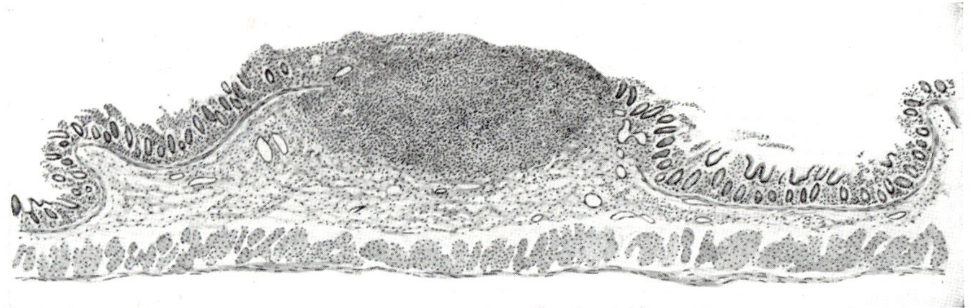

Fig. 290.—Typhoid fever. Beginning swelling of a lymph-nodule in small intestine.

of the lymphoid tissue and from the lymphatic channels. They are not peculiar to typhoid fever, but occur in identical form in tuberculosis and other affections.

It seems, indeed, that they are indistinguishable from other large mononuclear wandering cells, and that the conception of the lesions in typhoid fever becomes far simpler if we look upon them as a form of reaction in which the wandering cells which come into the neighborhood of the bacilli are the various types of wandering mononuclear cells instead of polynuclear leucocytes. That endothelial cells can act as phagocytes is unquestionable, but that the whole reaction to the presence of the typhoid bacilli should be ascribed to endothelial cells makes typhoid fever a disease without an analogue. While it is perfectly clear that in the spleen the endothelial cells of the venous sinuses are in typhoid fever, as in other conditions, actively engaged in phagocytosis, it is not so clear in other situations, such as the substance of the lymphoid tissue or the submucosa of the intestine, that the phagocytic cells are derived from the endothelium. Confusion arises perhaps from the persistence of the idea that all crevices in the tissues are lined, if only incompletely, with endothelial cells. It is my belief, on the contrary, that endothelial cells are not thus scattered everywhere, but that they form the specialized lining of closed blood-channels and lymphatic channels. The lymph-sinuses of the lymph-gland in connection with the lymphatic trunks are lined with continuous endothelium, but these cells are not scattered everywhere among the elements of the lymphoid tissue. This specific position, as the lining tissue of channels, is even more clearly seen in such tissue as the submucosa, where it is not confused by the great mass of lymphoid cells. How such lining cells could scatter themselves in such quantities and wander everywhere through the tissue without completely disorganizing the blood- and

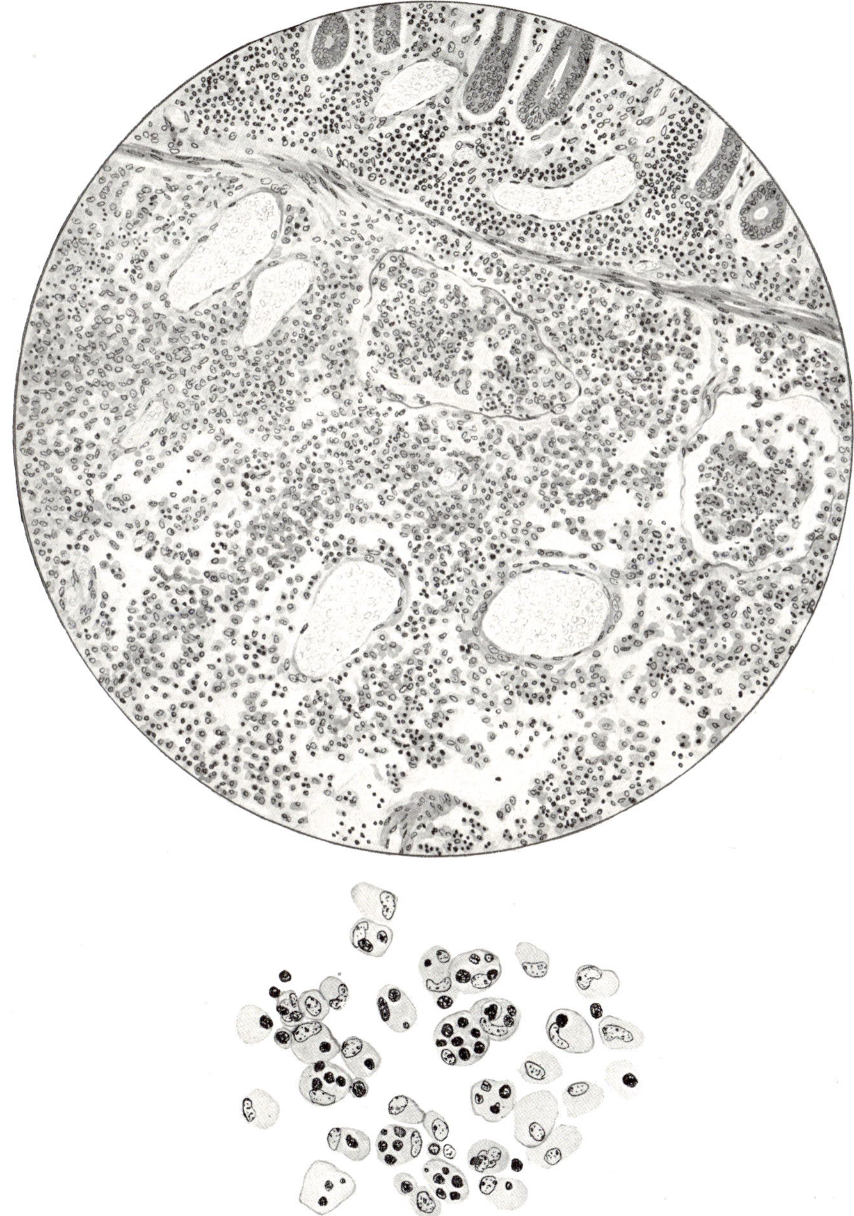

Fig. 291.—Edge of swollen patch in early stage of typhoid fever. The large phagocytic cells are accumulated in the submucosa, and there are two lymphatic channels distended with them. In the detail some of these phagocytes are shown with their content of injured lymphocytes.

lymph-channels is not clear. On the other hand, one finds lymphocytes emigrating actively through the vessel-walls in typhoid fever, and in the tissue assuming, exactly as Maximow described for his polyblasts, larger and larger forms. They do exactly the same thing in other more chronic inflammation, and there we believe that the whole group of cells, from the lymphocyte to the largest macrophage, may arise as members of one group of mononuclear wandering cells, recognizing that many of them may have led this wandering life for a long time instead of having recently emigrated from the blood-stream. Instead, therefore, of calling them endothelial cells, I prefer to speak of the large phagocytic cells briefly as macrophages, and to regard them as members of the familiar, if much misunderstood, group of mononuclear wandering cells which are present in some stage of their development and wandering career everywhere through the tissues, and are especially ready to swallow up injured cells and fragments of cellular débris.

The accumulation of the wandering cells, and especially of the pale macrophages, goes far to obliterate the architecture of the Peyer's patch and convert it into a continuous mass of cells. On the surface various bacteria are found. Some of these may invade the interior, but this is es-

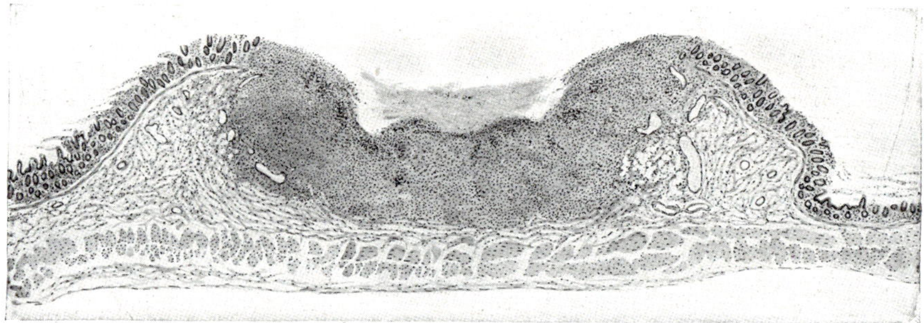

Fig. 292.—Typhoid fever. Later stage, with superficial slough and beginning ulceration.

pecially true of the typhoid bacilli, which are found in clumps in the tissue. Foci of coagulative necrosis appear irregularly, and not in any especial relation with the bacilli, and becoming confluent, form the slough (Fig. 292). There is no leucocytic reaction to the presence of these patches of dead tissue—a zone of fragmented nuclei may mark them out. Some authors have thought them due to the diffusion of a poison produced by the bacilli; others ascribe them to anæmia produced (Orth) by compression of the blood-vessels or (Mallory) by thrombosis of the small arterioles and venules. Mallory describes many such thrombosed vessels, the thrombus being caused sometimes by the clumping of injured endothelial cells within the vessel, at other times by the lifting-up of the lining endothelium by cells and fibrin accumulated beneath it.

At this stage, when the necrosis becomes confluent, nearly all the cells of the compact mass, even at a distance from the necrosis, show signs of degeneration and disintegration. Doubtless many macrophages burdened with lymphocytes and other materials fall into fragments, which are swallowed in their turn by other phagocytic cells.

The lymphatic channels are often packed with cells, which they transport to the sinuses of the nearest lymph-gland. The stroma of the neighboring mucosa presents changes almost exactly like those in the lymphoid nodules and in the submucosa, through the muscle, and in the subserous tissue one finds the fixed tissue elements spread apart by the abundant wandering cells.

Lymphatic Glands.—The mesenteric lymph-glands become greatly swollen, soft, and often hæmorrhagic. The retroperitoneal glands take

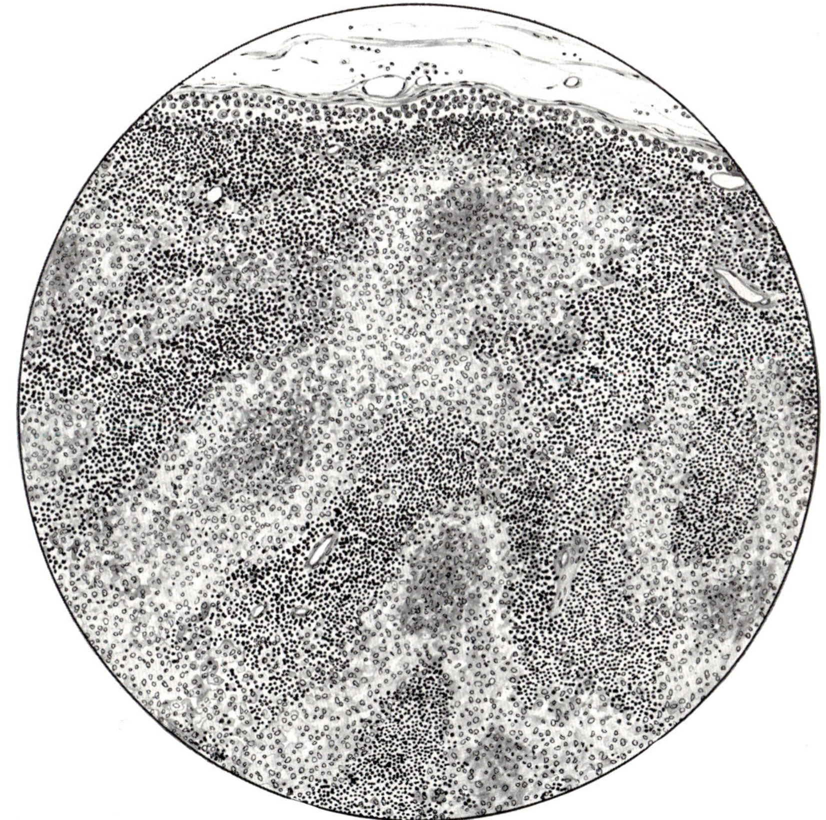

Fig. 293.—Mesenteric lymph-node in typhoid fever. The sinuses are filled with large mononuclear cells, among which are necrotic clumps.

some slight part in this, but the glands most affected are those which drain the most involved part of the intestine (Fig. 293). Bacilli are scattered in their sinuses and tissues. The lymph-cords show exactly the same changes as are seen in the Peyer's patches. The sinuses are enormously widened and packed with cells, which are mostly macrophages, although there are many lymphocytes. Probably most of these cells are swept into this situation from the intestinal lesions, but some may appear in the gland itself. Necroses quite like those described are found beginning in the mass of cells which fills the sinus, and extending thence to the lymph-cords. Sometimes nearly the whole gland becomes necrotic. From the glands great quantities of the large cells and others can be swept on into the thoracic duct, and thus into the subclavian vein. In one instance (Verh. Dtsch. Path. Gesellsch., 1903, ix) I found them transported in this way in such quantities as to plug many branches of the pulmonary artery.

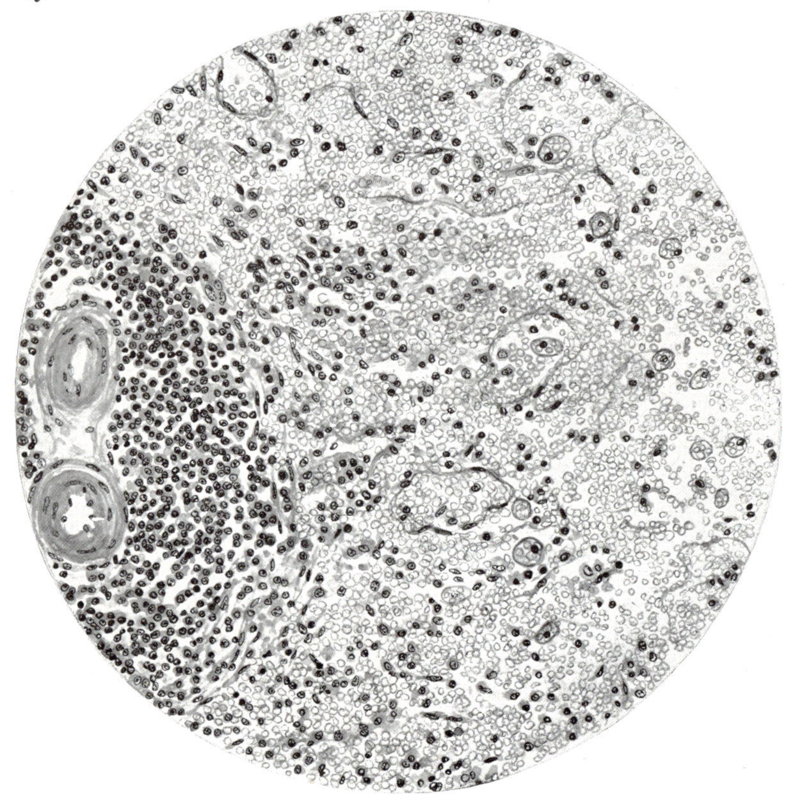

Fig. 294.—Acute splenic tumor in typhoid fever. The splenic pulp shows great accumulations of blood with phagocytic cells containing red corpuscles.

The Spleen.—The acute splenic tumor, which is very constant in typhoid fever, differs from that found in other infections in the extreme abundance of red corpuscles, both loose in the splenic pulp and engulfed in numbers by large phagocytic cells (Fig. 294). The presence of these "red-corpuscle-carrying cells" is, of course, the result of the profuse scattering of red corpuscles out of the venules into the pulp. Many of them are clearly the endothelial cells of the splenic venules. Others correspond to the macrophages seen elsewhere. There are relatively few nucleated cells in such a pulp, and if the hæmoglobin is washed out by fixation of the piece of spleen in alcohol, the tissue looks rarefied under the microscope. Necroses occur in the splenic pulp, exactly as they do in the lymph-glands and Peyer's patches. The result of these changes is the great enlargement of the spleen, which sometimes weighs 900 grams. The organ becomes extremely soft, and may rupture during life, with alarming or fatal hæmorrhage. At autopsy it is usually like a semifluid mass of deep-red color, and on section the relatively unchanged Malpighian bodies are scarcely to be seen through the overflowing splenic pulp. In other cases the splenic pulp may contain many more macrophages than are shown in the drawing.

Blood and Bone-marrow.—The blood contains bacilli through most of the course of the disease. The leucocytes are low, with usually a relative increase of the mononuclear cells. Platelets are decreased in number. In the course of the disease, especially in its later stages, there may arise a severe anæmia. The bone-marrow responds to the infection by the production of abundant lymphoid cells and others resembling plasma cells, but the formation of granulated myelocytes, the forerunners of the neutrophile leucocytes, appears to be in abeyance. Everywhere through the marrow there are found the macrophages, which show here, as in the Peyer's patches, a great avidity for the injured bodies of other cells. Necroses occur, just as they do in the spleen and the lymphoid apparatus (Longcope).

Liver and Gall-bladder.—The liver is always swollen, and on section appears dull, opaque, and inelastic. It forms a typical example of cloudy swelling, and microscopically the cells present the changes characteristic of that condition. Occasionally in the fresh-cut surface, or through the capsule, one can see minute, opaque, yellowish spots, which sometimes reach a diameter of 1 to 2 mm. These are focal necroses, which are constantly present in the liver in this disease, although they are usually so small as to be scarcely made out with certainty with the naked eye. Mallory describes two types—one produced in the lymphoid tissue, which occurs in the so-called portal spaces, and which shows changes identical with those in the Peyer's patches; the other occurring anywhere within the lobule, and involving the destruction of a group of liver-cells. The first type must be uncommon or very inconspicuous. The second is the type found in every typhoid liver. The foci consist of compact masses of distorted and fragmented cells, bound together with fibrin, and pretty sharply marked out from the surrounding tissue. Mallory regards these foci as anæmic areas caused by the plugging of the capillaries of the liver by macrophages which have been swept in with the portal blood. These large cells, lodging in the capillaries, soon become surrounded by thrombi, which continue the occlusion. Fränkel and others have thought the necroses due rather to the direct action of the toxin upon the liver-cells, with secondary invasion of wandering cells.

It has always been difficult to believe that the occlusion of the capillaries, even if it occur on all sides of such a minute mass of tissue, should cause the death of the liver-cells in these tiny areas, since they might receive enough nutrition from the adjacent capillaries. In a series of dogs we have injected corn-starch in suspension so as to plug a great many capillaries, but without producing necroses, except perhaps in one case, where the capillaries became distended into great spaces filled with the granules and the liver-cells were compressed and displaced. Even then it was scarcely possible to demonstrate actual necrosis of the cells.

Something analogous to this seems to occur in the typhoid liver, in which, in the necrotic and coagulated patches, one does not find many actual necrotic liver-cells. We have had an opportunity to study the beginning of the lesions in the liver of a man who had been ill only a few days, and in whom the autopsy was performed one hour after death, and it becomes perfectly clear that these foci are not primarily areas of necrosis of the liver-cells at all, but accumulations of the large mononuclear cells swept in by the portal stream, which distend the capillaries to a huge size and push aside the liver-cells (Fig. 295). Even in the middle of such a mass, that is, between two such distended capillaries, the liver-cells are found to be alive. It is possible that they may be so included as to be involved in the necroses, but most of them are pushed aside, and the necrosis, when it appears, is essentially the degeneration and disintegration of a mass of macrophages which has packed itself into the widened capillaries at a point in the liver tissue from which the liver-cells have been for the most part dislodged, and has there become matted together by fibrin. When the areas become larger by the constant accumulation of the cells floating in the blood, it is no longer possible to determine how they were formed, but from the early stages one many convince oneself that the coagulative necrosis is primarily an affair of the wandering cells, and that the liver-cells are only accidentally involved in the mass.

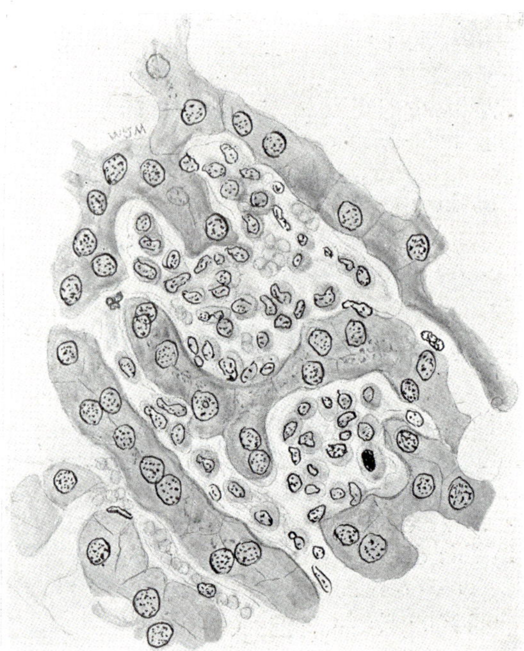

Fig. 295.—Typhoid fever. Focal necrosis in the liver. Coagulum with many wandering cells but little evident remains of liver-cells.

Rarely large necroses or abscess-like foci occur in the liver.

The gall-bladder may become infected with the bacilli, probably by way of the bile-ducts, either from the intestines or from the liver, although it is perfectly possible that they might arrive there by the blood-stream. They may cause no trouble, but may remain and multiply there for many years. Such persons are among the typhoid carriers mentioned above. Occasionally there are attacks of pain in the region of the gall-bladder during

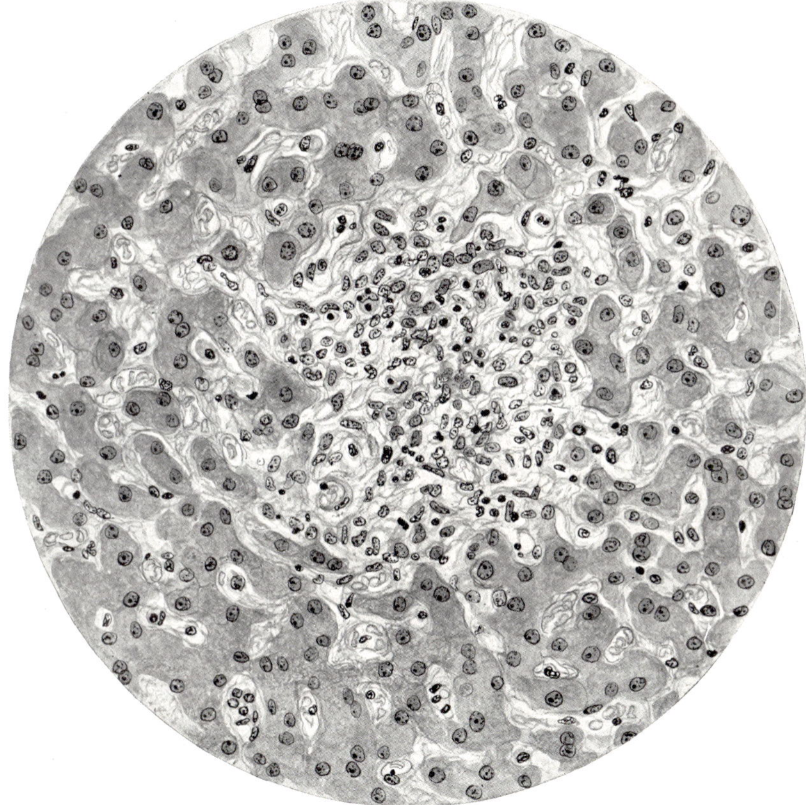

Fig. 296.—Typhoid fever. Larger focus in liver in which the area is occupied by phagocytic cells, the liver-cells having been displaced or destroyed.

the fever, but more frequent are the cases of acute or chronic cholecystitis occurring some time after recovery. In Hunner's case, eighteen years had elapsed since the attack of typhoid fever. The exudate is sometimes purulent, but more commonly mucoid, and is usually associated with gall-stones. Cushing was able to cultivate the Bacillus typhosus from the centres of the gall-stones, as well as from the bile, and thought that agglutinated bacilli might constitute the nucleus upon which gall-stones could form. The evidence in this question has been discussed elsewhere (Chapter XX).

Kidneys and Bladder.—The kidneys show a cloudy swelling of the cortex comparable to that of the liver. Œdema with great pallor is sometimes observed. Actual acute nephritis with exudative changes is, in my experience, rare. The bacilli pass through the kidney evidently through lesions of some sort, and appear in the urine. Although the bladder and ureters are not commonly affected, catarrhal or diphtheritic cystitis may occur. The urine continues to show the presence of bacilli for a long time in some cases.

Respiratory Organs.—Lobar and lobular pneumonia may accompany typhoid fever, the former rarely, the latter as a common terminal affection. Lobar pneumonia caused by the Bacillus typhosus is of a peculiarly hæmorrhagic character. Usually the pneumococcus is the causative agent when this complication occurs, and there may be a combined septicæmia with both organisms (Robinson). In the bronchopneumonia the typhoid bacillus may cause the lesions, and appear in the sputum, but probably in most cases other organisms are concerned.

In the pharynx and larynx there is sometimes an extensive diphtheritic and hæmorrhagic inflammation in a late stage of the disease.

Circulatory Apparatus.—The heart muscle is soft and flabby and opaque, and may contain a little fat. Endocarditis is uncommon, but has been described, the vegetations containing the bacilli. There are instances in which the peripheral arteries, especially the arteries of the brain, have been occluded by thrombi. In other cases thrombosis of brachial or femoral arteries has led to gangrene. Thayer has examined the arteries in many cases after typhoid fever, and finds, in rather a high percentage, evidences of beginning arteriosclerosis. This is, however, not peculiar to this infection.

Thrombosis of the veins is far more common than that of the arteries. It occurs usually in the left femoral and saphenous veins, and causes the extremely painful swelling of the leg which has long been known as "milk-leg," or *phlegmasia alba dolens*. With the organization of the clot and its recanalization, together with the development of collateral channels, the œdema disappears and the leg can again be used. Other veins may also be affected.

Muscles.—A wide-spread hyaline degeneration of the substance of the muscle-fibres, first described by Zenker, is often found, especially in the abdominal muscles and in the muscles of the thigh. (See Fig. 39.) The muscle-fibres lose their striations, and are divided into irregular, formless clumps within the sarcolemma. Rupture of such injured muscles gives rise to gross hæmorrhages, and if one observes a great hæmorrhage within the sheath of the rectus abdominis, suspicion is at once directed to a typhoid infection, although the condition is not peculiar to typhoid.

Bones and Joints.—After convalescence, or even many years later, there sometimes arise painful, abscess-like swellings over the ribs or the tibiæ, or, indeed, over any bone. Incision allows the escape of a thick, stringy, purulent fluid, and it is found that an abscess cavity extends down through the periosteum or into the bone. The periosteum is greatly thickened and uplifted from the bone, and there may be necrosis and sequestration of part of the bone. Mixed infections occur, but the typhoid bacillus is found and may cause these changes alone. Such infections are very persistent, and unless thoroughly cleaned out, fail to heal. Typhoid arthritis occurs, but is very rare.

Skin.—Prominent among the changes in the skin is the roseola or typhoid rash. Slightly raised, flat, rose-colored spots appear early in the disease, and are an evidence of the diffuse septicæmic character of the disease. The bacilli have been cultivated from these rose spots, and Fränkel, in sections, found branched colonies of the bacilli in what he thought were the lymph-vessels of the papillæ. Purpuric spots, diffuse erythema, etc., may also occur. Furunculosis, so common in the later stages, is due to a secondary staphylococcus infection.

Nervous System.—The disease has its name from the stuporous conditions produced by the infection. Nevertheless, actual cerebral changes, recognizable anatomically, are rare. I have described one case of purulent leptomeningitis due to the Bacillus typhosus alone, and Cole has collected many others from the literature. The exudate resembles that in the epidemic cerebrospinal form, but is richer still in macrophages which contain the débris of cells. Here it seemed especially clear that these large cells are to be regarded as part of the army of mononuclear wandering phagocytes. Local and multiple neuritis occurs, but is not serious, and quickly disappears in convalescence.

Genital Organs.—Typhoid bacilli have been cultivated from the uterus in cases in which typhoid fever occurred during pregnancy. Lesions of the placenta of hæmorrhagic type give one explanation for the transmission of the bacilli to the fœtus, but it seems that this may occur without obvious placental changes. Lynch shows that the effect is a fœtal septicæmia, and that the child dies *in utero* or soon after birth. Mastitis is a rare sequel of typhoid fever. McCrae has recorded three cases.

In rare cases orchitis follows convalescence and may lead to indurative atrophy or abscess formation.

Parotitis.—Owing to the prolonged illness and the stuporous condition, the mouths of these patients become foul unless continually cleansed. Parotitis may arise by extension of infection along the duct, or by lodgment of bacilli carried there by the blood. Suppuration may destroy much of the gland and extend into the adjacent tissue or into the neck. In these cases there is commonly a mixed infection.

LITERATURE

General.—Osler: Principles and Practice of Medicine, New York, Sixth Edition, 1905. "Studies in Typhoid Fever," Johns Hopkins Hosp. Reports, 1895, v; 1902, x.

Curschmann: Nothnagel, Spec. Path. u. Ther., 1902, Bd. iii, Th. 1.

General.—Hoffmann: Veränderungen der Organe beim abdominal Typhus, Leipzig, 1869.
Brouardel and Thoinot: La Fièvre Typhoïde, Paris, 1905.
Mallory: Jour. Exp. Med., 1898, iii, 611.
Posselt: Ergebn. d. allg. Path., 1912, xvi_1, 184.
Typhoid Septicæmia.—Rüdiger: Trans. Chicago Path. Society, 1903, v, 187.
Cole: Johns Hopkins Hosp. Bull., 1901, xii, 203.
Lartigau: New York Med. Jour., 1900, lxxi, 944.
Roseola.—E. Fränkel: Zeit. f. Hygiene, 1900, xxxiv, 482.
Typhoid Cholecystitis.—Cushing: Johns Hopkins Hosp. Bull., 1898, ix, 91, 257.
Hunner: *Ibid.*, 1899, x, 163.
Placental Transmission.—Lynch: Johns Hopkins Hosp. Reports, x, 283.
Typhoid Meningitis.—Cole and MacCallum: Johns Hopkins Hosp. Reports, 1904, xii, 411.
Bone Lesions.—Parsons: Johns Hopkins Hosp. Reports, 1895, v, 417.
Miscellaneous.—McCrae: *Ibid.*, 1902, xiii, 20.
A. L. Mason: Boston Med. and Surg. Jour., 1897, cxxxvi, 449, 468.
Longcope: Centralbl. f. Bakt. u. Paras., Abt. i, 1905, xxxvii, Ref. 23.
Robinson: Bull. Ayer Clinical Labt., 1906, iii, 96.

PARATYPHOID INFECTIONS

In discussing the effects of poisons upon the tissues reference was made to the outbreaks of severe gastro-intestinal disturbances produced by the eating of infected or partly decomposed meat, and it was then shown that such epidemics of what seems to be a form of poisoning are really commonly due to infection with some member of that group of bacilli, of which the Bacillus enteritidis of Gärtner is the type. These are somewhat allied to the Bacillus typhosus, and it has been more recently recognized that there are at least two types of bacilli which are not only members of this family, but produce at times a disease practically indistinguishable from a mild attack of typhoid fever. These are the paratyphoid bacilli A and B, of which A is an acid producer, B an alkali producer. Of these, the latter occurs far more frequently and is so like the Bacillus enteritidis of Gärtner as to be most easily distinguished by the agglutination reactions. They were first described in America by Gwyn.

The infection occurs by the gastro-intestinal tract, probably from eating from an animal infected before slaughtering, meat which, upon standing, has become far richer in bacilli. Two chief types of infection occur—the acute gastro-enteritis and the typhoid form. The acute gastro-enteritis represents at least a part of the cases of *cholera nostras,* and is distinguishable from true cholera by bacteriological study only, although, of course, the attendant circumstances may make the diagnosis easy. There is intense diarrhœa with desiccation of all the tissues and collapse, sometimes leading to death. At autopsy no changes are found except some general swelling and reddening of the gastro-intestinal mucosa.

The second type, probably long mistaken for typhoid fever, is, in fact, almost precisely like that disease in its clinical symptoms, details such as the roseola, laryngitis, etc., being exactly repeated. There are also quite similar complications, such as paratyphoid meningitis, cholecystitis, cystitis, pyelitis, etc. Few cases have been studied at autopsy, and these are reviewed by Burckhardt. In a large proportion of them there were found swelling in the lymphoid structures of the intestines, and ulceration resembling, even in histological detail, the lesions of typhoid fever. Others showed no affection of the intestine whatever (Longcope). In the cases with ulceration there was swelling of the mesenteric glands, whose sinuses were filled with phagocytic cells and presented necroses here and there. The spleen showed no characteristic alterations, but necroses (so-called lymphomata) were found in the liver. From these cases the Bacillus paratyphosus B was isolated in pure culture from the organs, the bile, and the circulating blood, and recognized by its cultural characteristics and by its agglutination properties. Two cases studied at autopsy in which there was infection with paratyphoid A showed in one case ulcers in the intestine, in the other case none.

In most cases the course is mild and brief, but the complications, especially cystitis and pyelonephritis or pyelitis, may persist a very long time, with constant discharge of the bacilli, which are far more destructive in those situations than the typhoid bacillus.

It is evident that much more light will be shed on these infections shortly, and already the literature concerning them is abundant, if somewhat unsatisfactory.

LITERATURE

J. L. Burckhardt: Centralbl. f. allg. Path., 1912, xxiii, 49.
Johnston, Hewlett, Longcope: Amer. Jour. Med. Sci., 1902, cxxiv, 187.
Gwyn: Johns Hopkins Hosp. Bull., 1898, ix, 54.
Pratt: Boston Med. and Surg. Jour., 1903, cxlviii, 137.
Schottmüller: Mohr and Staehelin, 1911, i, 519. Zeitschr. f. Hygiene, 1901, xxxvi, 368.

DYSENTERY INFECTIONS

The bacilli responsible for the causation of the endemic and epidemic dysentery which prevails so widely in the tropics and in occasional epidemics in temperate zones were recognized by the aid of the agglutination reaction with the patient's serum. Four types, differing in this agglutination and in certain biological characters, are recognized, and known as the Shiga-Kruse, Flexner, Y type of His and Russel, and the type of Strong. Of these, the Shiga-Kruse type seems to be most widely disseminated, and produces a distinct toxin. The Flexner type has only a very slight power of toxin production.

Epidemics arise in the rainy season, especially where there are sudden variations of temperature, and in the hot seasons in more temperate zones. The bacilli are disseminated by people who have partially or completely recovered from a previous attack, but still carry and discharge the organism. They are distributed in drinking-water, in food, by direct and indirect contact, by flies, dust, etc. The unsanitary mode of life in many parts of the tropics and in many cities favors their rapid spread.

The disease is chiefly an infection of the colon, although the lower part of the ileum may also be involved. It begins with hyperæmia of the mucosa and the secretion of abundant slimy, clear, mucoid fluid, which is later streaked with blood. The swollen mucosa shows points and streaks of

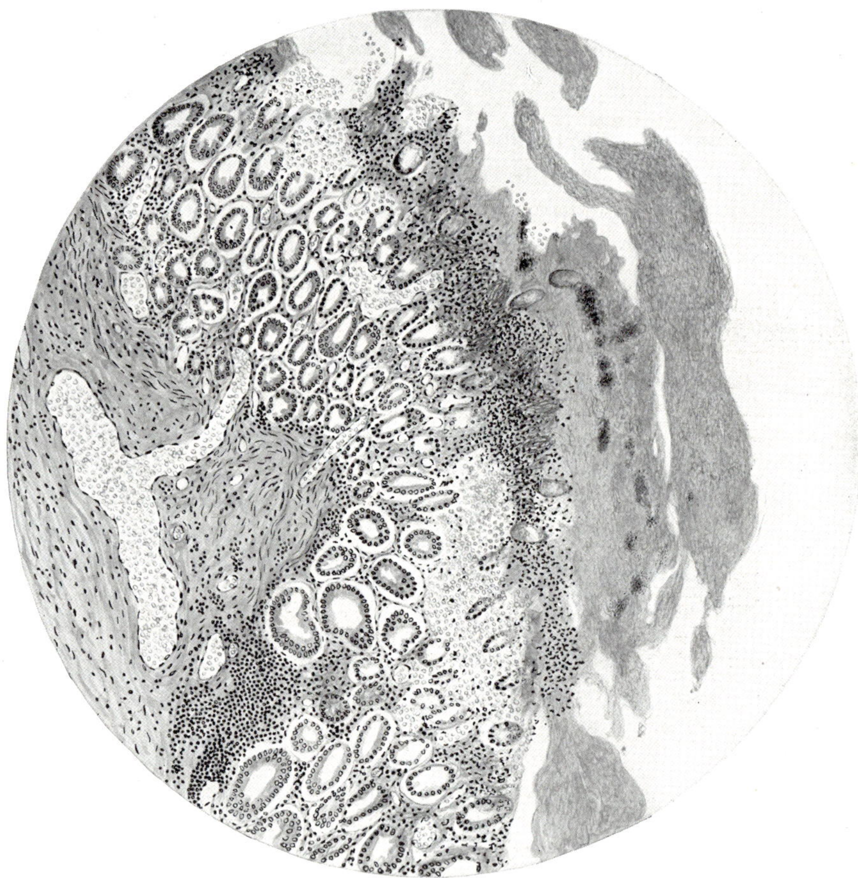

Fig. 297.—Dysentery. Diphtheritic and hæmorrhagic inflammation of the intestine involving the crests of the folds of the mucosa. The pseudomembrane is still adherent, and there is extensive hæmorrhage beneath it.

hæmorrhage, and soon there appear chaff-like, opaque flecks on the crests of the folds (Fig. 297). Even at this stage, when these flecks indicate the death of the surface of the mucosa, resolution or healing may take place, but usually the diphtheritic character of the lesion becomes more evident and progresses to ulceration. The more prominent parts of all the folds become covered with a thick, dull layer of exudate, which constitutes a false membrane and is continuous with the densely coagulated dead layer of mucosa (Fig. 298). All around, hæmorrhage and an intense inflammatory reaction with œdema appear. With the sloughing off of this layer irregular ulcers are left. These vary in size and depth, and while sometimes quite large sheets of dead and coagulated mucosa and exudate escape with the stools, at other times the ulcers are more localized, but penetrate deeper into the submucosa, the musculature, or even the subserous tissues (Fig. 299). Perforations occur, but are rare. The presence of this process excites the most violent diarrhœa, with tenesmus and the passage of liquid, mucoid, and blood-tinged stools. So constant is the passage of fluid stools, and so violent the continual straining, that the patient becomes exhausted. Vomiting may begin; the skin is covered with sweat; the voice hoarse and eyes sunken, and the whole condition cholera like. Such patients may die in collapse. If the attack is not fatal, there may be relapses from time to time, lasting over a long period, and finally the disease settles into a milder chronic process. The ulcers heal by the formation of granulation tissue, over which a smooth layer of epithelium grows without the new formation of glands. Much scar tissue develops in the gut wall in the base of such ulcers, and contracts so as to constrict or kink the intestine. Very narrow strictures may be formed thus. The ulcers are irregular in extent and outline, and are often confluent, leaving islands of mucosa which stand out above the new epithelium as pedunculated polypoid masses. In one case which I saw there were long bridges of mucosa which had been undermined and which, in

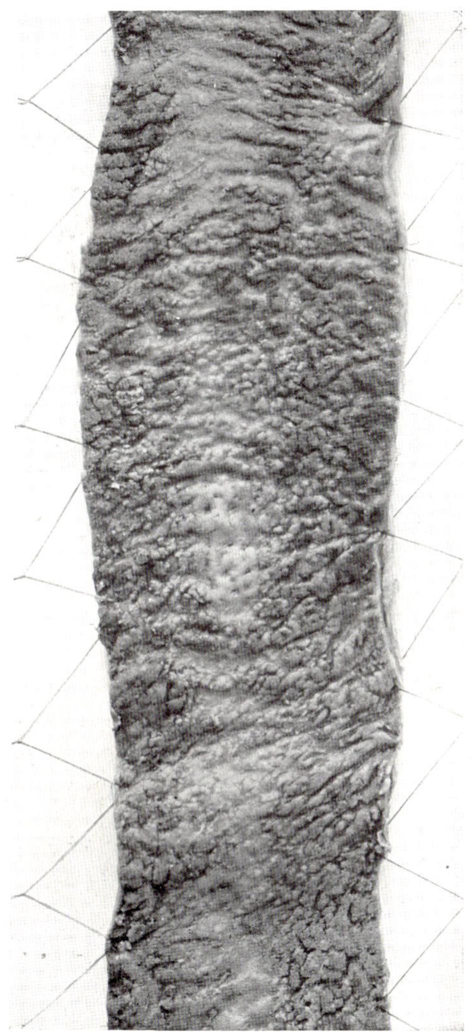

Fig. 298.—Acute diphtheritic and hæmorrhagic dysentery. Colon of a child, showing abundant pseudomembrane on the crests of the folds of the mucosa.

some places, having broken away at one end, hung in the intestine like long pendulous polypi.

Even in the acute disease the other organs are not much changed; there is no septicæmia, and therefore there are no cutaneous changes. There is no acute splenic tumor and no pronounced cloudy swelling of the viscera. The bacilli are found in the swollen mesenteric glands and also in the

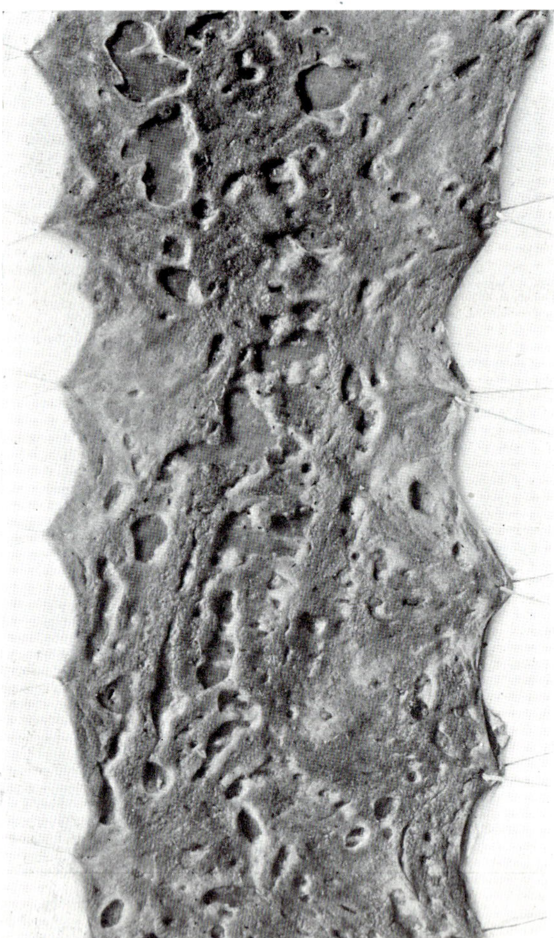

Fig. 299.—Dysentery in a child. Extensive ulceration of the colon, which involved also the ileum to a less extent.

spleen and liver, but not elsewhere. Painful joint changes are not uncommon, consisting in effusions into the joints, especially those of the foot, knee, and hip. When the pain and swelling subside in one joint, another may become affected, and with each there is a rise in temperature. They recover their normal condition without any inflammatory residue. Transient paralyses, which sometimes involve muscular atrophy, also occur.

In children in summer epidemics it has been shown by Basset and Duval, Knox and Wollstein, that the Shiga-Kruse bacillus is the causative agent of the dysentery, which is practically identical with that of adults, and in which the mortality is high. It has long been known that in asylums and prisons outbreaks of dysentery were due to some such infection, doubtless introduced, as we now appreciate, by a bacillus carrier. Kruse spoke of this as pseudodysentery, which was unfortunate, since it has been shown that these cases were due to the Shiga-Kruse bacillus (Vedder and Duval).

As stated, the blood of dysentery patients acquires, after eight to ten days, the power of agglutinating bacilli of the same type. But the serum of those infected with the Shiga-Kruse type will agglutinate the Flexner and Y types, while sera from patients infected with those types, although agglutinating one another, do not agglutinate the Shiga-Kruse type. Since the Shiga-Kruse bacillus produces, by autolysis, a rather strong toxin, an antitoxic serum has been produced, active against it, but useless against the other types, which produce little toxin, and therefore do not lend themselves to serum production.

LITERATURE

Shiga: Centralbl. f. Bakt. u. Paras., 1898, Abt. 1, xxiii, 599. *Ibid.*, 1898, xxiv, 817. Osler and McCrae, Modern Medicine, 1913, i, 766.

Flexner: Univ. of Penn. Med. Bull., 1901, xiv, 190. Trans. Cong. Amer. Phys. and Surg., 1900, v, 61. Studies of Diarrhœal Diseases of Infancy, New York, 1904.

Duval and Bassett: American Medicine, 1902, iv, 417.

Whitmore: Philippine Jour. of Science, 1911, vi, 215.

Vedder and Duval: Jour. Exp. Med., 1901–05, vi, 181.

Kruse: Deut. med. Woch., 1900, xxvi, 637.

Lentz: Kolle and Wassermann, 1909, 2 Ergnzbd., 391.

Ruge: Mense: Hand. d. Tropenkrankheiten, 1914, iii, 158.

Kossel, Singer: Münch. med. Woch., 1915, lxiii, 85, 183.

CHAPTER XXXI

TYPES OF INJURY.—BACTERIAL DISEASE (Continued)

Leprosy: Nodular and anæsthetic forms. The bacillus and transmission. Lesions of the internal organs. Affections of nerves and their sequelæ.
Actinomycosis: General character of the disease and organism. Related organisms. Mode of infection. The destructive lesions.

LEPROSY

Known in detail in ancient times as a contagious disease of destructive character and quite incurable, leprosy has spread over practically all the countries of the world, and lepers are now, as in the time of Moses, objects of horror and aversion.

The disease is the result of infection with the Bacillus lepræ, discovered by Hansen in 1874, and is a slowly developing affection, of extreme chronicity, in which nearly all the tissues become invaded by the bacilli. It occurs in at least two main forms, although there are many combinations and modifications of these types. One is the tubercular or nodular leprosy, in which the skin, especially in the exposed parts, is lifted up over firm nodules, which in time break through and ulcerate. The other is the so-called anæsthetic leprosy, in which, without much change in the skin, disease of the nerves leads to a loss of sensation, which is followed by trophic changes in the extremities and by mutilations from unnoticed injuries. The lepers live for a long time and becomes fearfully deformed, dying finally from the disease itself, or from some intercurrent affection.

The bacillus, which is acid-fast and resembles somewhat the tubercle bacillus, is transmitted from one person to another, but only after prolonged and most intimate contact, aided by malnutrition and an unhygienic mode of life. There has long been a theory (J. Hutchinson) that the infection comes from eating fish, but there is little to support this idea. The difficulty with which infection actually occurs is seen in the fact that, although these patients distribute quantities of the bacilli in nasal secretions, exudate from ulcers, etc., doctors and nurses and others who have to do with them are rarely affected. Indeed, it has been stated that it is chiefly through coitus that infection is transmitted. From the fact that the incubation period lasts over months or years, it is difficult to form a clear judgment on this point.

In all cases the bacilli are extremely abundant in the tissues, and are usually found to be contained in phagocytic cells, although many are also free in crevices of the tissues or in blood-vessels or lymphatics, or have invaded cells which probably were not active as phagocytes. The so-called lepra cells, which are large, phagocytic wandering cells stuffed with bacilli, have been ignored by Unna, who states that the bacilli are always free in the lymphatics, and this opinion is maintained by Sticker. But any one who has studied even one case of leprosy is perfectly familiar with these conspicuous cells, and cannot dismiss their existence so lightly.

In the nodular or tubercular form one finds prominent nodes over the cheeks, nose, ears, and eyebrows (Fig. 300). The eyelashes and eyebrows fall out, and the thick, wrinkled skin gives a leonine expression to the face. The skin over these nodules is smooth, and in sections appears

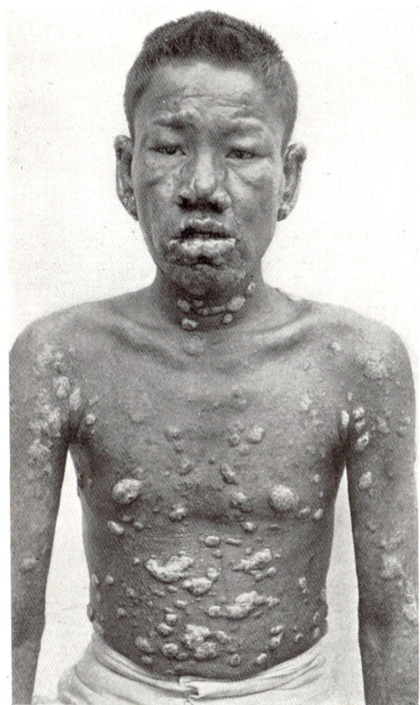
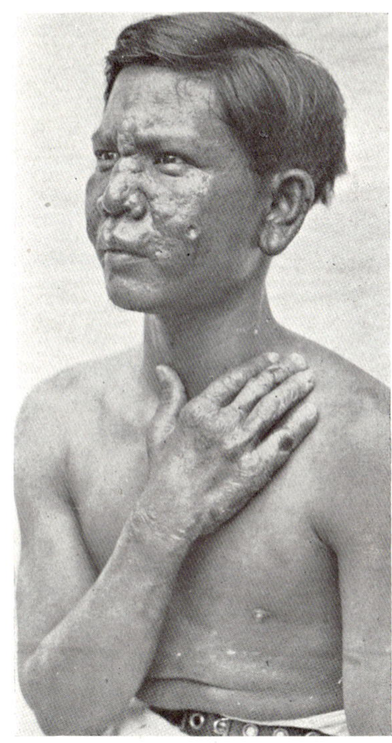

Fig. 300.—Tubercular or nodular leprosy, showing lesions on face and body.

stretched and without papillæ. Under it there is a layer of fibrous tissue without cellular infiltration, and beneath that the mass of wandering cells and bacilli which cause the swelling.

This infiltration is especially about the blood-vessels, the sebaceous and sweat-glands not being particularly involved. It is made up of abundant mononuclear cells, including many plasma cells; especially characteristic are the large pale cells with single, rather pale, vesicular nucleus and vacuolated or foamy cell protoplasm (Fig. 301). When stained with ordinary dyes, these vacuoles appear rather glistening. The cells are so numerous as to be crowded together, and are far larger than any other cells in the

* Photographs by the Bureau of Science, Manila, and kindly sent to me by Dr. B. C. Crowell.

field. Stained with fuchsin, they are found to be packed full of bacilli. It is true that the other cells also contain them, and that many are scattered loose or lie in phagocytic cells in the vessels, or even in the endothelium of the vessels. With ulceration thousands of these bacilli are set free. Scarring of such ulcers is progressive, and produces rather characteristic pale

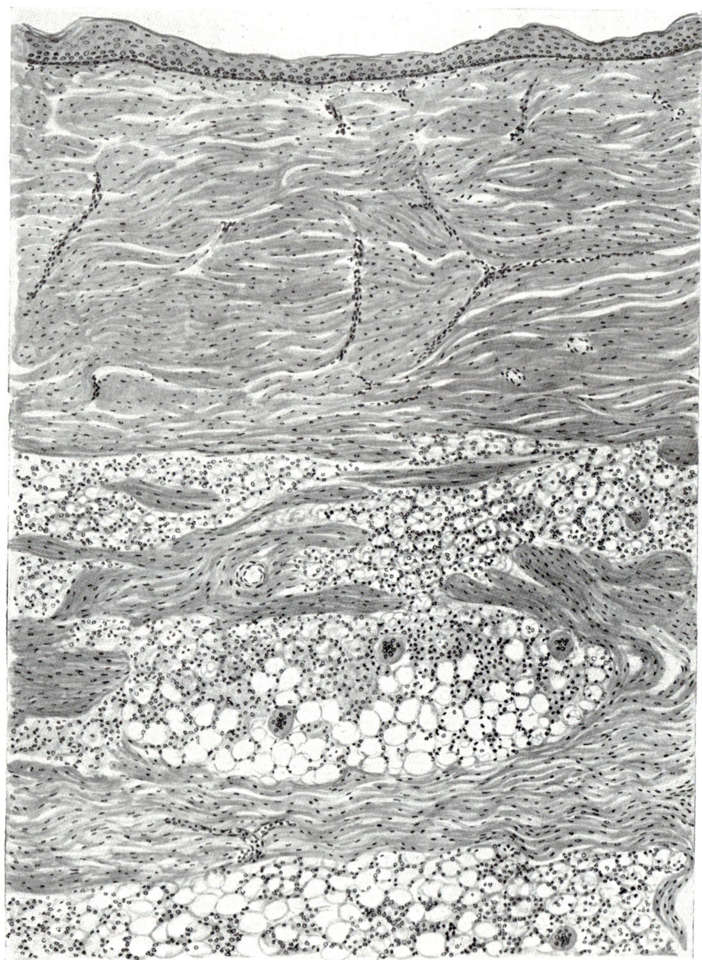

Fig. 301.—Leprosy. The section through a leprous nodule of the skin shows the obliteration of papillæ and the accumulation of giant-cells, which are loaded with bacilli, in the deeper tissues.

scars, which distort the face and stand out in contrast with the pigmented skin round about.

A quite similar infiltration with mononuclear cells, including the very large phagocytes loaded with bacilli, is to be found in many other situations. This is particularly true of the nasal mucosa over the turbinate

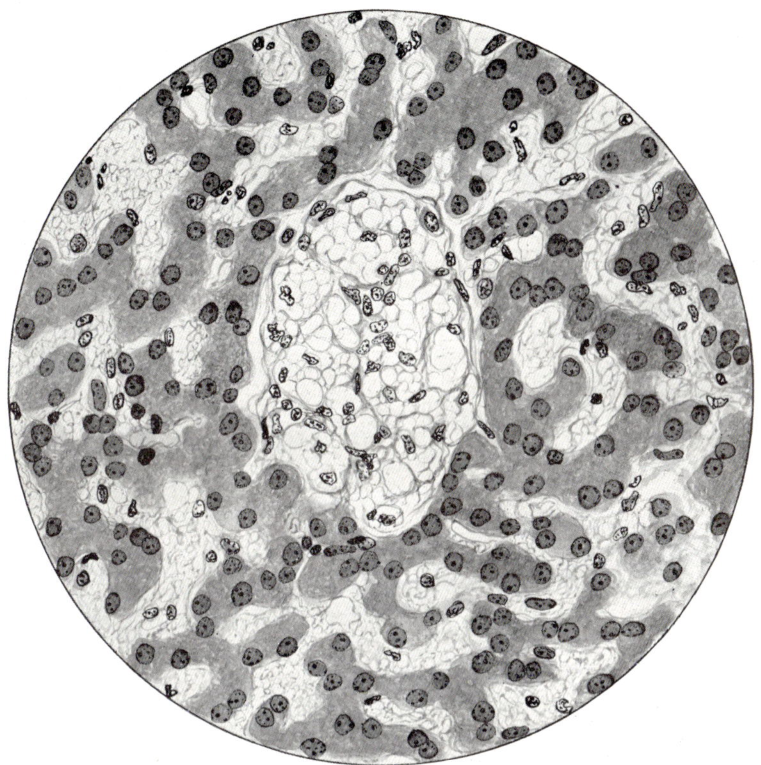

Fig 302.—Leprosy. Focal accumulation of lepra cells in the liver. These cells contain many bacilli.

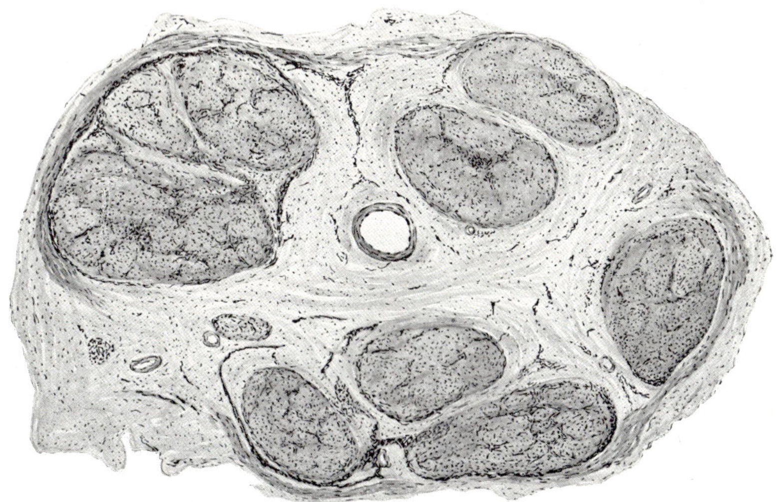

Fig. 303.—Leprous neuritis with much scar formation about the nerve-bundles.

bones and septa, where ulcerations give off quantities of bacilli; as in the skin, the surface epithelium is free from bacilli. In the conjunctiva, iris, etc., the same thing occurs. In the pharynx, larynx, trachea, and bronchi again the same thing is found, though usually to a lesser degree, but sufficient to thicken and ulcerate the vocal cords, so that the voice sinks to a rough whisper. Bacilli occur in the lungs, and some writers state that lesions are produced there which imitate in every detail those of tuberculosis. In one case which I saw at autopsy it appeared that the woman had died of an advanced pulmonary tuberculosis with cavity formation, and indeed this was true, although it might be difficult, except by demonstrating the tubercle bacilli, to be sure of the existence of a complication with tuberculosis instead of a pulmonary leprous lesion.

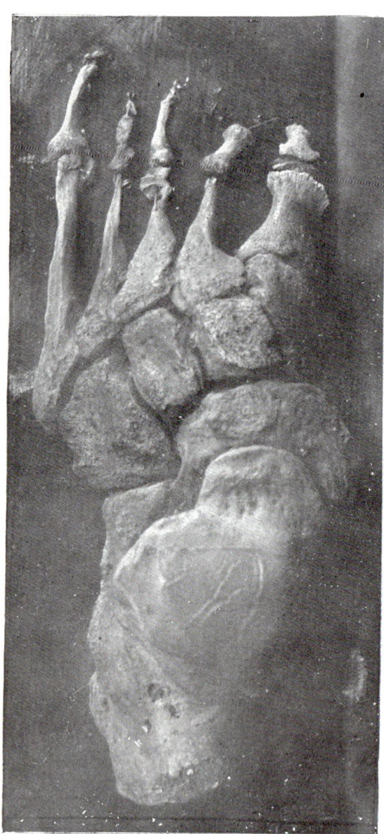

Fig. 304.—Atrophy and distortion of the bones of the foot in leprosy (Harbitz).

In the liver and spleen there are scattered everywhere small foci composed of large cells with foamy cytoplasm loaded with bacilli, and accompanied by a few other wandering cells (Fig. 302). These miliary lepromata are quite conspicuous in a microscopical section, though they cannot be seen with the naked eye. Lesions of the intestines have been described, but must be rare, since the bacilli seem not to occur in the stools. In the testes the tubules are atrophic and contain the organisms. In the kidneys the organisms are widely distributed, but there are no characteristic lesions. Destruction of the tubular epithelium leads in time to chronic nephritis, with which these patients often die. In the bones there may exist a kind of leprous osteomyelitis with lesions analogous to those of the skin, but this is much less important than the changes in the bone associated with the other types of the disease.

In the anæsthetic form the bacilli accumulate particularly in the peripheral nerves, which become embedded in a dense granulation tissue formed from the perineurium (Fig. 303). This granulation tissue is rich in bacilli, many, if not most, of which are inclosed in the same large and small wandering cells seen elsewhere. The nerve-fibres degenerate and disappear, so that in cross-section only a few are left embedded in the infected scar. Hence the loss of motor power and of sensation. Of course, there is some of this *neuritis leprosa* in the nodular form also, and it must be remembered that these are extreme types which are being distinguished, between which there are all degrees of combination. The lesion in the anæsthetic form is essentially in the peripheral nerves, although bacilli may be found in the ganglion-cells of the spinal cord and its ganglia and of the brain.

Most striking are the atrophies of the bones of the extremities which result from this interruption of the nerves which causes the phalanges to shrink and the bones to fuse into thin, pointed remnants of bone, attached to the metacarpals or metatarsals. These in their turn may atrophy and become disarranged, so that finally the hand or foot, further cramped by contractures, assumes the most distorted, claw-like appearance (Fig. 304). Harbitz, in describing these, has pointed out the fact that this is a process of mutilation not necessarily associated with ulceration and inflammation. Indeed, the most disfiguring mutilations arise from the insensibility of the hands and feet, which makes it possible for these patients to suffer from burns or other injuries without drawing away or protecting themselves. Nevertheless, it seems probable, from Harbitz's pictures, that most of these deformed extremities are the more direct result of loss of nerve impulses.

LITERATURE

Sokolowsky: Virch. Arch., 1900, clix, 521.
Babes: Histologie der Lepra, Berlin, 1898.
Kedrowski: Arch. f. Derm. u. Syphilis, 1914, cxx, 267.
Sticker: Handb. d. Tropenkrankheiten, Mense, 1914, iii, 1.
Uhlenhuth and Westphal: Centralbl. f. Bakt. u. Paras., 1901, xxix, Abt. i, 233.
Sakurane: Ziegler's Beiträge, 1902, xxxii, 563.
Harbitz: Archives of Int. Med., 1910, vi, 147.
Duval: Jour. Infectious Diseases, 1912, xi, 116.

ACTINOMYCOSIS

This disease, common in cattle, and recognized as an infectious process by Bollinger, was later described by J. Israel for man. The cattle present a tumor-like swelling, usually of the jaw, with sinuses and purulent discharge in which peculiar yellow granules or sulphur grains are found. In human beings the affection is quite commonly also a swelling of the jaw, but there are several other typical localizations, namely, in the thoracic organs, in the intestines, or in the skin. Ponfick recognized the identity of the disease in man and animals. Examination of the pus or of sections of the granulation tissue lining the sinuses shows the causative agent to be a branched organism which grows in tangled mycelia. Numerous broken portions resembling bacilli or cocci occur. The sulphur grains are knots of the mycelium with radially projecting tips, which form a layer covering the central tangle. Each of these tips is surrounded by a club-shaped or bulbous covering, of homogeneous, refractive material. The microscopical section through such a granule, therefore, shows a curved or scalloped margin of such clubs, arranged parallel or at least radially. It was from this arrangement that the name actinomyces or "Strahlenpilz" was derived.

There are many other closely allied organisms, which are commonly spoken of under the name streptothrix, and most writers make a point of applying the name actinomyces to that organism which produces the disease in man and cattle, saying that the streptothrices differ from it in not being able to produce the radiate, club-like growths. So often has this been repeated that the distinction will doubtless persist for a long time. The truth of the matter is, however, very different. Such club-bearing knots of mycelium are not formed by the organisms in culture, but only in the tissues of an animal (exceptionally in cultures in serum or animal tissue). So far from their being unable to form such clubs, those of the streptothrix group which can infect animals produce the most beautiful clubs under the proper conditions. One, commonly known as the Streptothrix asteroides, if injected into the peritoneum of a rabbit so that the infection meets with more resistance than if injected directly into the blood, will form everywhere in the organs graceful, plume-like masses of clubs in every respect similar to those of Actinomyces bovis.* Indeed, there is no valid reason for separating these organisms into two groups, and since the name streptothrix has long been preëmpted for an alga, it is necessary, according to all rules of nomenclature, to call them all actinomyces, that being the first name applied to any of the group.

It is perfectly true that not all this group have the same pathogenic powers. Some, indeed, are entirely saprophytic, while others, such as the Actinomyces asteroides, have been found in subacute abscesses in the brain, in generalized peritonitis, etc.

The Actinomyces bovis, described by Wolff, Israel, Wright, and others, is an anaërobic organism, and is recognized as the cause of the disease in both cattle and man. It has not been found in the outside world in spite of the existence of so many allied forms, and probably lives on the mucosæ of the mouth and digestive tract. It has always been thought to be introduced into the tissues by straws or splinters, but it begins to seem more probable that it merely takes advantage of the presence of such a foreign body to display its pathogenic properties. Details of the morphology of these remarkable organisms must be read in the papers cited.

Having reached the tissue, the presence of the mycelium is quickly responded to by necrosis of the cells and by the abundant accumulation of leucocytes. The process advances slowly though, and there is a most profuse formation of granulation tissue round about such an area after weeks or months; while the central part of the lesion is made up of liquid pus full of the branching organisms, the outer zones are composed of such dense fibrous tissue as to form a tumor-like mass. Lining the cavity is still fresher granulation tissue, which is now loaded with large mononuclear wandering phagocytic cells, which are themselves so full of fat-granules as to give this layer an opaque yellow color. Frequently, lying loose in the

* For that matter many bacilli—the diphtheria bacillus, Möller's grass bacillus, and others—can do the same thing under favorable circumstances.

pus in the centre, there is one of the sulphur grains with its clubs (Fig. 305). No giant-cells are found, as a rule, nor any distinctly tubercle-like nodules. The mycelium grows and advances into the tissues, destroying and liquefying it slowly with the aid of the abundant leucocytic reaction, and is attended constantly by the most tremendous formation of encapsulating connective tissue. Given such a process, it is not surprising that this

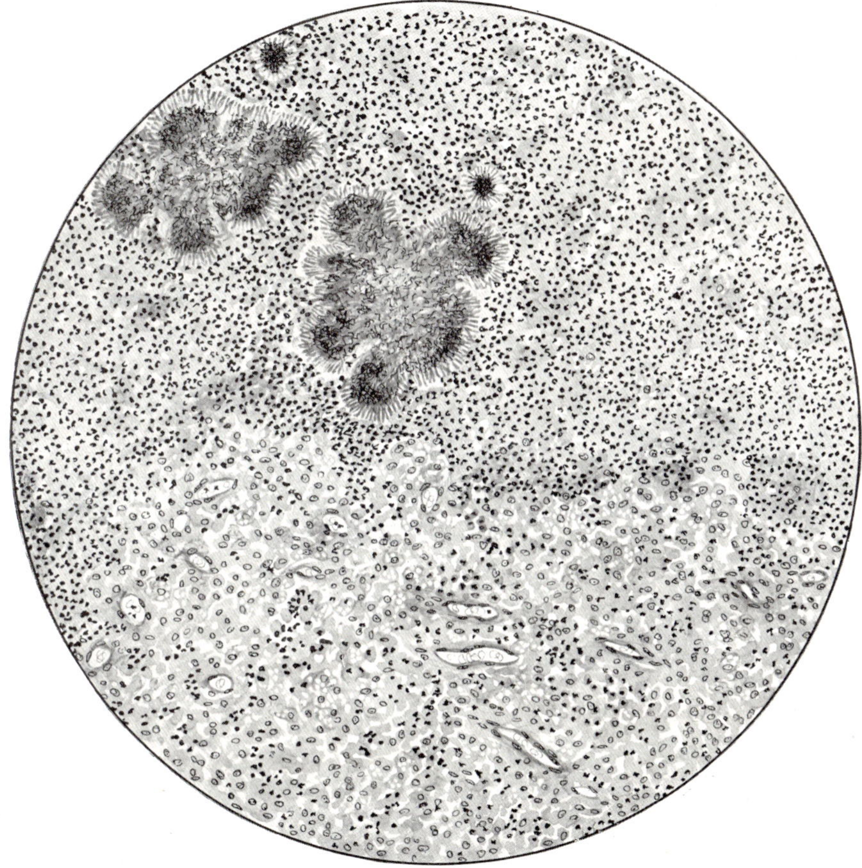

Fig. 305.—Actinomycosis. The peculiar lobulated masses of mycelium, edged with a row of clubs, are surrounded by leucocytes, outside which is a layer of granulation tissue rich in large, fat-laden phagocytic cells. Outside this is dense fibrous tissue.

becomes one of the most destructive of all diseases. The infection burrows through the tissues for great distances, completely distorting whatever it traverses, and it stops for nothing—bones are penetrated as easily as muscles, and from the lung such a mine-like advance may push through the pericardium and heart-wall into the interior of the heart.

More than half of the infections are in connection with the mouth and pharynx, and seem to begin in the gums about the teeth, although sometimes the tongue or cheek is first affected. The abscess-like lesion, with its bulwark of connective tissue, usually appears in the parotid or submaxillary region, extending thence, with destruction of the jaw, into the neck. Another group begins in the thorax, probably in the bronchi or in the substance of the lung, and extends thence, sometimes to appear in

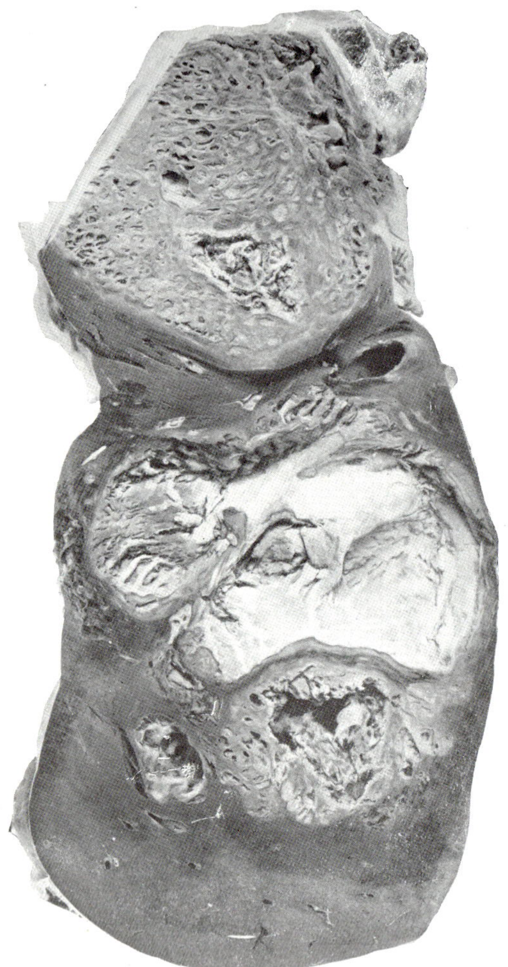

Fig. 306.—Actinomycotic abscess in liver. The figure shows the extraordinary scarring about the abscesses, which are merely loculi in a dense fibrous mass.

a sinus or series of sinuses perforating the skin. Naturally, the pleura approached by this process becomes enormously thickened. A third site of predilection is in the intestines, and especially in the ileocæcal region, where a submucous abscess soon forms a mass which progresses with adhesions to adjacent abdominal organs and to the abdominal wall, often forming long, burrowing sinuses between the muscles or reaching bones or joints. At times one finds great masses of dense fibrous tissue riddled everywhere with cavities full of pus, which represent the ramifying and anastomosing suppurating centres. Actinomycosis of the ovary and tubes has been observed in many cases. The fourth group of cases, which is much smaller, is thought to be due to infection through the skin. Here again the deeper tissues, including the fasciæ, bones, and joints, may be penetrated and destroyed.

In the course of such a chronic infection metastases into the internal organs may occur, and we find abscesses in the spleen or liver (Fig. 306) or elsewhere which may become evacuated or may, in their turn, burrow and wall themselves off. Usually, however, if the disease has progressed to that point, life is cut short by an intercurrent affection. Amyloid is often found in the organs at autopsy.

LITERATURE

Bostroem: Ziegler's Beit., 1891, ix, 1.
Ponfick: Die Actinomykose d. Menschen, Berlin, 1882.
Israel: Virch. Arch., 1879, lxxiv, 15; 1879, lxxviii, 421.
Wright: Jour. of Med. Research, 1905, xiii, 349.
Shiota: Dtsh. Zeit. f. Chir., 1909, ci, 289.
Kohler: Frankfurter Zeit. f. Path., 1914, xv, 146.
Harbitz and Grondahl: Amer. Jour. Med. Sci., September, 1911, cxlii, 386.
Dresel: Ziegler's Beit., 1915, lx, 185.
MacCallum: Centralbl. f. Bakt. u. Paras., Abth. i, Orig., 1902, xxxi, 529.
Abbott and Gildersleeve: *Ibid.*, 547.

CHAPTER XXXII

TYPES OF INJURY.—BACTERIAL DISEASE (Continued).—TUBERCULOSIS

Tuberculosis: Ætiology. Modes of infection, disposition, and susceptibility. The tubercle, tuberculous granulation tissue, acute tuberculous inflammation, distribution of the bacilli in the body. Acute miliary tuberculosis. Tuberculosis of respiratory organs, digestive tract, serous surfaces, lymph-glands, genito-urinary tract, nervous system, skin, bones, and joints.

TUBERCULOSIS

Ætiology.—The disease tuberculosis was known in practically all its forms long before the discovery, by R. Koch, of its causative agent, the tubercle bacillus. The name, based on the occurrence of small nodules or tubercula in the organs, was extended also to the bacillus when it was found. Up to that time, however, there prevailed doubt as to the unity of all the processes which we now know to be due to the invasion of this organism, and it was by no means clearly recognized that the minute nodules were of essentially the same character as the destructive lesions of chronic pulmonary consumption, nor that these were so intimately related with the acute lobar caseous pneumonia. It was vaguely recognized that a person suffering from phthisis was liable to an outbreak of tubercles in other organs, but the relation of the two conditions was not clear. Indeed, there raged for a long time a dispute, on anatomical grounds, between the supporters of the theories of the duality and the unity of tuberculosis—a dispute which seems to us of little interest since we have been taught that one ætiological factor is responsible for all.

In recent years a second dispute has arisen with regard to the unity of the ætiological agent, for it has been observed that there are human, bovine, avian, and even reptilian and piscine types of the bacillus, which differ in their biological characters and in their distribution. So marked are these differences that Koch went to the length of saying that the bovine bacillus might be neglected as a possible source of infection in man, but recent studies have shown clearly that a small but definite proportion of the cases of human tuberculosis is due to the bovine type. It is an organism more virulent to cattle than the human type, which can, accordingly, be used alive to immunize such cattle against their own form of the disease. Nevertheless, there are those who claim that, by suitable transplantations, the differences can be made to disappear, and that, in reality, the organisms are the same and only changed by environment. These matters cannot yet be regarded as settled.

The lesions produced differ in some respects in different animals, and only those of the human being can be described here.

Modes of Infection.—Tubercle bacilli are resistant to injury, and can withstand drying and other unfavorable conditions met with outside the body. They, therefore, persist in dust, dried sputum, urine, etc., as well as in such food-stuffs as milk and butter. They are discharged from the body of the consumptive most commonly in the sputum, but, according to Flügge, they are also sent forth suspended in a spray of fine droplets with the breath of such a person, especially when he coughs or sneezes. With disease of the intestinal tract or genito-urinary organs, bacilli appear in the fæces or urine. When there are tuberculous sinuses draining from some internal focus, the discharges from these canals carry abundant bacilli. The milk from tuberculous cows frequently contains them, especially when there is tuberculous disease of the udder, and it is not impossible that tuberculous lesions might be included in the meat offered for sale from diseased animals of various sorts.

The fact that the lesions produced by the tubercle bacillus are so easily recognized by their characteristic form, and commonly so sharply localized about the point at which the bacilli lodge, makes the study of the distribution of the disease in the body especially instructive. It throws light on the spread of other bacteria in infections where the tracing of the process is difficult on account of the diffuse effects of the organisms.

Still it must be constantly kept in mind that the tubercle bacilli may pass through mucous membranes or the walls of blood-vessels, and circulate like mere foreign particles without immediately producing any injury, only to set up a destructive disturbance in some far-distant spot where they finally settle. The utmost care must be taken, therefore, in interpreting the genetic relation of these lesions from their anatomical distribution as they are found at autopsy.

Congenital infection may conceivably be of two sorts—that in which either the ovum or the spermatozoön is infected, or that in which, in a tuberculous mother, tuberculous disease of the placenta forms the path of transmission of the bacilli into the body of the fœtus. In the first of these it is possible that the bacilli may be merely carried along with the sperm. In animal experiments with normal mothers and males with infected seminal vesicles, vasa deferentia, or testicles, there may be produced fœtuses in which bacilli are found, without any evidence of reaction, or offspring, with no bacilli or other sign of tuberculosis. Schmorl has found that placental tuberculosis is not uncommon, but that its results are of no great practical importance in explaining the origin of tuberculosis in later life, since if tuberculosis does appear in the suckling, it is rapidly fatal.

Infection through the skin and genitalia is also relatively unimportant, since the tubercles formed in the skin on the hands of pathologists, butchers, and others practically never give rise to pulmonary or other wide-spread tuberculosis, and genital tuberculosis is practically never primary.

The great portals of entry are the nose and the mouth, and since the further paths of the respiratory and digestive tracts cross one another, there arise some difficulties in deciding in each case how the tuberculous disease began; for bacilli breathed into the bronchi can be swept back into the pharynx and swallowed, and those which have been swallowed can rise again to the level of the larynx and be aspirated into the lungs.

There has been the most active dispute as to the relative importance of aspiration tuberculosis and deglutition tuberculosis in the production of the disease. No one denies the ready possibility of the aspiration of tubercle bacilli into the trachea or bronchi, or even into the utmost alveoli, since it is an every-day experience to find the easily recognizable coal-dust breathed in to these distant points. Nevertheless, there are many (Calmette, Klebs, Ravenel, and others) who hold that pulmonary tuberculosis in human beings is chiefly or exclusively due to entrance of the bacilli through the intestinal tract. Numerous experimental studies in animals have shown that, with the utmost care, it is impossible to be sure that bacilli introduced into the intestine have not gotten up over the brim of the larynx, and thus down into the lungs. They show that it is occasionally possible to trace lesions which show the track of the bacilli through the mesenteric glands, thoracic duct, blood, and lungs. If the animals are killed a very short time (hours or minutes) after the ingestion of the bacilli, these may be found being transported in lymph or blood, or lodged in tissues, without having as yet produced any lesions. If the animal is very resistant, pulmonary lesions are most likely to be produced.

Very important in this connection are the experiments of Findel and others of Flügge's school concerning the number of bacilli necessary to produce infection by the way of aspiration, as compared with the way of deglutition. Findel found that 19,000 times the fatal inhalation dose might be given by way of the digestive tract without producing any effect. It is pretty clear, from all the recent studies of this point, that it is possible for tubercle bacilli to pass through the intestinal mucosa without leaving a trace behind them; that they may circulate in the lymph and blood and lodge elsewhere; that they commonly, but not always, produce tubercles in the mesenteric lymph-glands in doing this. Nevertheless, it is immeasurably easier to produce pulmonary tuberculosis by the inhalation of bacilli, and we must continue to believe that the primary lesions of the lungs are set up in this way in most of the cases. Von Behring's statement with regard to intestinal infection in children did not include the idea that the bacilli thus introduced actually remained latent until pulmonary tuberculosis appeared, but rather that their absorption gave rise to a predisposition to pulmonary tuberculosis.

Susceptibility.—Much has been said as to individual predisposition to tuberculosis, and there is an impression in the minds of most people that even though actual cases of the inheritance of tuberculosis cannot be discovered, there is inherited a weakened constitution which makes the offspring of tuberculous parents especially susceptible to the disease. While this idea is rather vague, it can be shown that certain deformities of the thorax which lead to narrowing of its upper portion favor the development of apical tuberculous disease. Ill development of the circulatory organs and of the respiratory musculature may also play a part. Indeed, there is a recognizable phthisical habitus which may finally be seen in actual consumptives, but whether this is a forerunner of future tuberculosis or the effect of its unobserved existence it is difficult to say.

Hypersusceptibility of a kind may be produced by a previous tuberculous infection, and this seems to have the characters of an anaphylactic hypersensitiveness, since it expresses itself in the form of a febrile reaction. Thus a second inoculation of an animal already suffering from tuberculosis is responded to by a sudden illness with fever, respiratory disturbances, etc. This is perhaps a sort of protective reaction, because if the virulent bacilli be inoculated after a preliminary inoculation with non-virulent forms or dead bacilli, there arises this reaction, but the lesions which would ordinarily appear do not result from the second inoculation. The protective action seems to be imperfect, however, for if it be very severe on the inoculation of the second large dose, the animal may die with exceptionally acute formation of destructive lesions. An extract of the bacilli will elicit the same reaction in an animal with tuberculosis, and is used clinically under the name "tuberculin," for the recognition of some hidden tuberculous lesion.

Probably something of the same sort is present in the violent symptoms which follow upon the sudden setting free of bacilli in those cases where an old tuberculous focus gives rise to miliary tuberculosis.

Practically very important is the predisposition to tuberculous infection produced by traumatism, as seen especially in the case of the bones and joints, but also in some other situations in the body. This may be regarded as due to the establishment of a point of lowered resistance, where the bacilli easily gain a foothold. Something similar is doubtless true of the predisposing effects of an attack of measles or other infectious disease. Indeed, measles is reckoned as a very serious affection, largely on account of the frequency with which it is followed by tuberculosis. Pregnancy, diabetes mellitus, and other conditions affecting the whole body predispose in some more general way, and it is known that tuberculosis arising in the course of diabetes is usually very intense and rapidly destructive.

LITERATURE

Beitzke: Ergeb. d. allg. Path., 1910, xiv_1, 169.
Hart: *Ibid.*, 337.
Fischer: Frankf. Ztschr. f. Path., 1910, v, 395.
Findel: Ztschr. f. Hyg., 1907, lvii, 104.
Schmorl and Geipel: Münch. med. Woch., 1904, li, 1676.
Flügge: XIV. Hygien. Kong., 1907, ii, 42.

Effects of the Tubercle Bacillus on the Tissues.—The lesions produced by the tubercle bacillus are, in their ultimate analysis, essentially like those found in any acute and chronic inflammation, but the proliferative changes are so marked and come so quickly as to give a quite foreign air to them. Then, too, they have in common the peculiarity that wherever

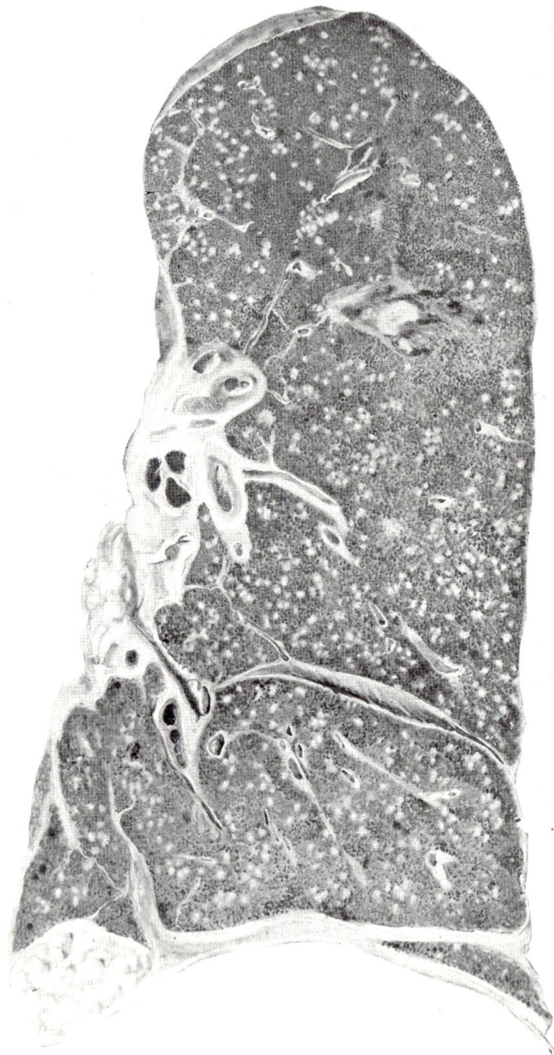

Fig. 307.—Acute miliary tuberculosis. Small tubercles scattered through the lung. There is an old caseous mass near the apex.

the bacteria are present in sufficient number with their poisons, the whole area dies and becomes coagulated.

Tubercles.—Most commonly on reaching the tissue the bacilli produce minute, translucent, grayish nodules, which, from being supposed to be of about the size of millet-seeds, were called *miliary tubercles* (Fig. 307).

We now know, however, that those were really little groups of tubercles, and that a single tubercle is a great deal smaller and scarcely visible to the naked eye. The tendency to grouping and coalescence is very strong, and such a mass, instead of being round, is really lobulated or mulberry shaped. While the tubercles are very fresh and young they remain translucent, but very soon they show a spot of yellowish opacity in the centre.

Microscopically, a fresh tubercle is a roughly concentric mass of cells, pretty sharply marked off from the surrounding tissue (Fig. 308). These cells, clustered around a central area, are sometimes arranged in laminæ,

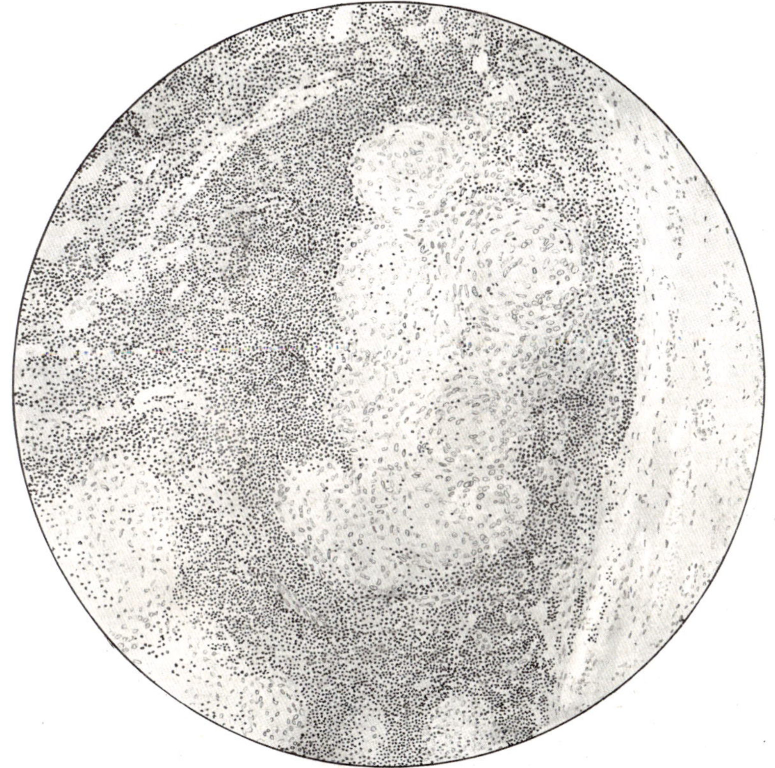

Fig. 308.—Conglomerated tubercles composed chiefly of epithelioid cells.

but are usually attached to one another in less orderly fashion to form a pale staining tissue. They have elongated vesicular nuclei, with little chromatin and a faintly outlined cell-body, which is irregular in form and branches to connect itself with its neighbors. These are the cells commonly known as epithelioid cells, which form the most constant feature of the tubercle. Often, but not always, the central part of the mass is occupied by a giant-cell, a large mass of protoplasm containing a great number of nuclei which are usually arranged around its periphery or at the opposite poles (Figs. 309 and 310).

This protoplasmic mass also gives off processes which ramify among those of the epithelioid cells. In the marginal portion of the tubercle one usually finds numbers of mononuclear wandering cells of the lymphoid type. The whole is supported by a newly formed framework or reticulum, which can be demonstrated by digesting away the cells. Usually, too, there can be shown to exist a delicate network of fibrin.

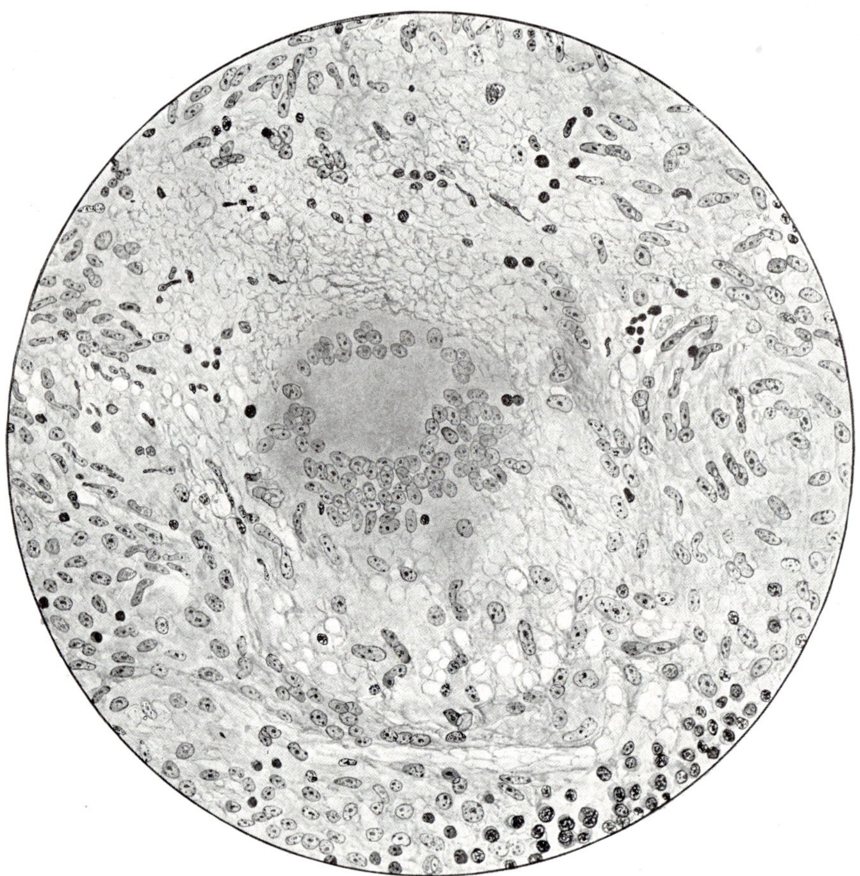

Fig. 309.—A single tubercle showing rather irregularly arranged epithelioid cells, a large giant-cell, and the peripheral lymphoid cells. The drawing shows also the reticulum of the tubercle.

Tubercle bacilli may be found in the body of the giant-cell or lying in crevices between the epithelioid cells. But there is absolutely no provision for a blood supply in such nodules, and those capillaries which were present at that point before are found to be obliterated, so that if an organ studded with tubercles be injected through the artery with blue gelatin, each tubercle will stand out as a white nodule against the blue background.

This circumstance may aid in bringing about the necrosis of the nodules, although they are so small that they might absorb enough nourishment from the surrounding fluids. More important is the action of the poison produced by the bacilli which first causes degeneration, and finally death of the cells. The epithelioid cells become distorted, their nuclei elongated and twisted, so that they lie radially and for a time take a deep stain (Fig. 311). Then, beginning sometimes in the giant-cell and involving the whole centre of the nodule, there occurs a complete disintegration of the cells, which melt together into a formless hyaline mass.

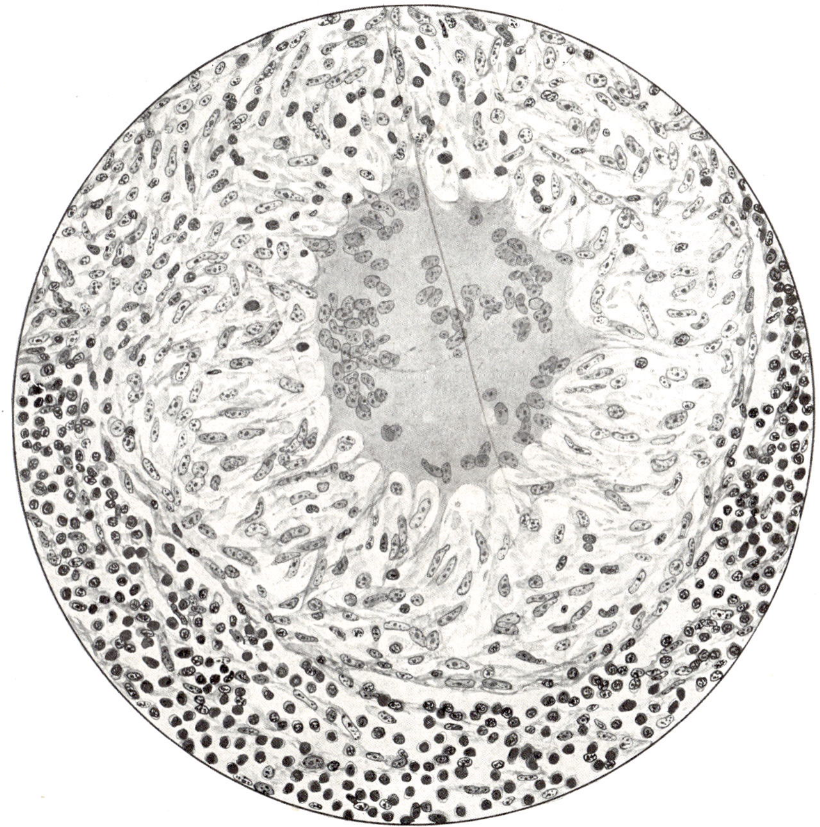

Fig. 310.—A single tubercle, rather sharply outlined with a giant-cell sending protoplasmic processes among the epithelioid cells.

There has been much dispute over the origin of the cells which constitute the tubercle. Baumgarten has always maintained that the epithelioid cells are derived from the fixed tissue, possibly the endothelial cells, while certain French authors have regarded them as wandering cells. It was shown by Wechsberg and others that the first effect of the lodgment of the bacilli is the destruction of a few adjacent cells, responded to by an inwandering of polymorphonuclear leucocytes, but that this process is soon masked by the development of the epithelioid cells. The matter is still under discussion, and Wallgren, in his detailed studies of the early development of tubercles in the liver, lays stress on the participation of lymphoid cells and polyblasts, finding that the fibroblasts play a secondary and protective rôle. He recognizes an occasional proliferation of the endothelium of the capillaries. Similarly, v. Fieandt, in studying meningeal and cerebral tubercles, finds a primary invasion of leucocytes and later a secondary invasion when they are attracted by the dead tissue. The

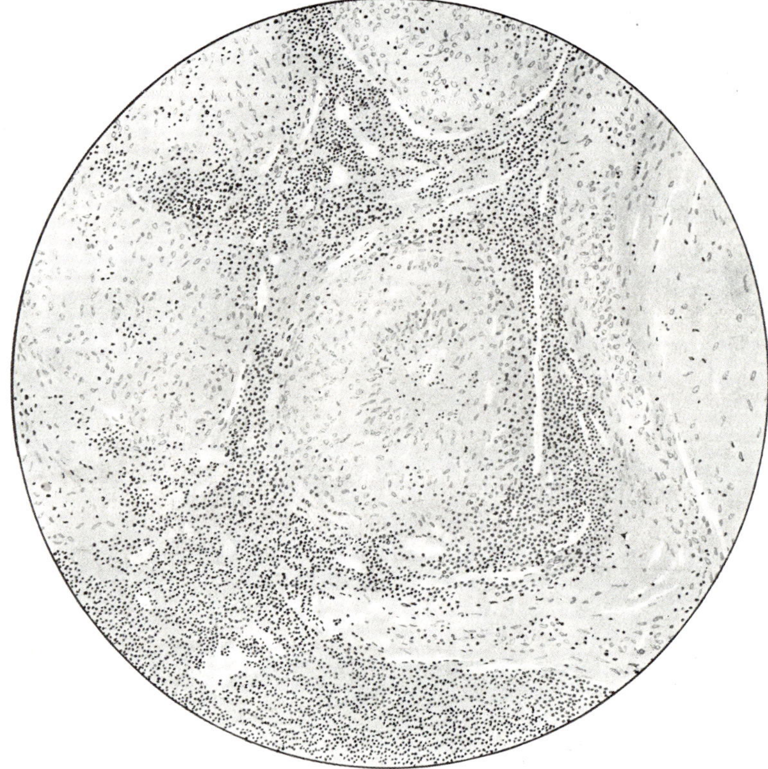

Fig. 311.—Rather older tubercles with beginning central degeneration and radial arrangement of the epithelioid cells.

part played by the polyblasts or large mononuclear wandering cells is specially important, the plasma and lymphoid cells occupying a second place. It is much later—one to two weeks after the infection—that the fibroblasts proliferate, but then they play the same part as the polyblasts, forming epithelioid and giant-cells. In the brain the glia-cells proliferate also and may form giant-cells. More recently Evans and Winternitz have applied a vital stain which distinguishes the so-called Kupffer's cells of the endothelium in the liver, and in watching the early development of tubercles have observed that these cells, which are active phagocytes, give rise to the epithelioid and giant-cells.

It seems probable that in different situations each of these explanations may be true. In the fully formed tubercle the character of the mass as a coherent tissue with the production of a reticulum strongly suggests the participation of fibroblasts. But in other cases the tubercle may be composed of rounded and evidently independent cells, which are probably wandering cells.

So, too, the formation of giant-cells offers difficulties. They might arise by division of the nucleus without division of the protoplasm, but mitoses are never seen in these nuclei, and the weight of evidence favors the idea that they result from the coalescence of many nucleated cells. All are agreed that the lymphoid cells are wandering cells which have been attracted to the tubercle.

As has been said, there is a great tendency toward coalescence in these

Fig. 312.—Large tubercles in the spleen.

tubercles, and caseation or the production of a cheese-like, necrotic substance usually takes place in the whole central part of such a mulberry-like mass. It follows that the opaque white material is left, surrounded by a scalloped margin composed of the remnants of the outermost tubercles. Tumor-like masses of cheesy material as large as a walnut are sometimes formed in this way, especially in the spleen or in the brain (solitary tubercles) (Fig. 312).

The coagulative necrosis produces at first a fairly firm material, in which all cell outlines and nuclear staining are lost. This may be softened later, often because of a secondary infection, or in other instances it may be converted into a mortar-like material or even a stony block by the deposit of calcium salts. Healing may occur in every sort of tubercle—in the large caseous ones by inspissation of the necrotic material and the formation of a dense surrounding capsule, while the fresh, translucent miliary tubercles at times are changed into hyaline fibrous nodules. It is cheering evidence of the great powers of resistance possessed by most individuals when it is found, as Naegeli and others have shown, that nearly all adults harbor somewhere a healed tuberculous lesion.

Tuberculous Granulation Tissue.—Tuberculous lesions are by no means exclusively tubercles. There may be formed, especially on a free surface, abundant highly vascular granulation tissue, which is in most places quite like ordinary granulation tissue, except in that it is perhaps more thickly infiltrated with large and small mononuclear wandering cells and contains fewer polymorphonuclear leucocytes. It is produced as a reaction to the presence of numerous tubercle bacilli, and is especially distinguished by its content of scattered epithelioid cells and giant-cells, or even well-formed tubercles (Fig. 313). Further, however, it is characterized by its strong tendency to undergo, despite its rich vascular supply, coagulative necrosis or caseation. When, as is so common, it replaces the ulcerated mucosa in lining a canal, the caseous material produced by the necrosis of its superficial layers is often sufficient to choke the canal.

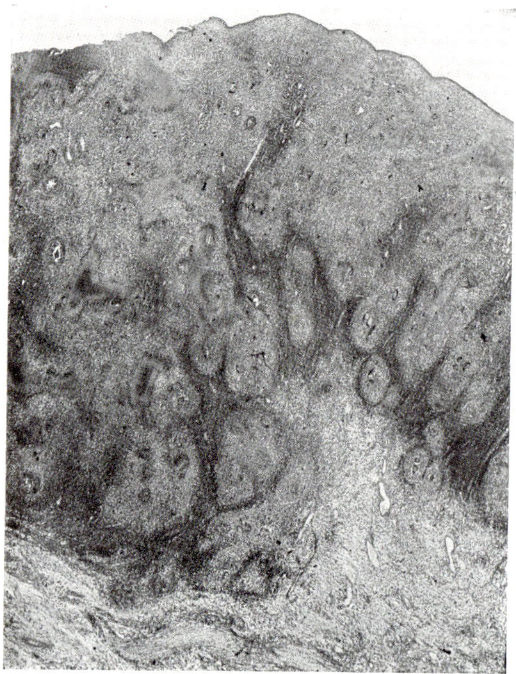

Fig. 313.—Tuberculous granulation tissue.

The tuberculous granulation tissue may, however, escape this fate in part, in persons whose resistance is high, and then contracts to form a dense fibrous layer upon which new granulations form. Sometimes the healing is complete and nothing remains but a scar or dense fibrous adhesions. An example of this is the great thickening of the capsule of the liver and spleen, regarded by many as the remains of an old tuberculous process.

The formation of tuberculous granulation tissue is most commonly the sequel to an outpouring of inflammatory exudate due to the tubercle bacilli, and in this respect it once more resembles closely the analogous tissue found after other inflammatory processes.

Acute Tuberculous Inflammation.—When the bacilli are virulent enough, or when the resistance is low enough (which, after all, is the same thing), the introduction of a considerable number into the tissue is responded to by an acute inflammatory reaction which resembles very closely that which follows the invasion of other organisms. An exudate of fluid and wandering cells with subsequent coagulation of fibrin comes from the widened blood-vessels, and in the fresher stages it may be difficult to distinguish such an exudate as clearly tuberculous. There are several peculiarities about it, however, which make the diagnosis fairly easy after the condition is well established. Polymorphonuclear leucocytes seem to be very little attracted to a tuberculous infection, and their place is taken

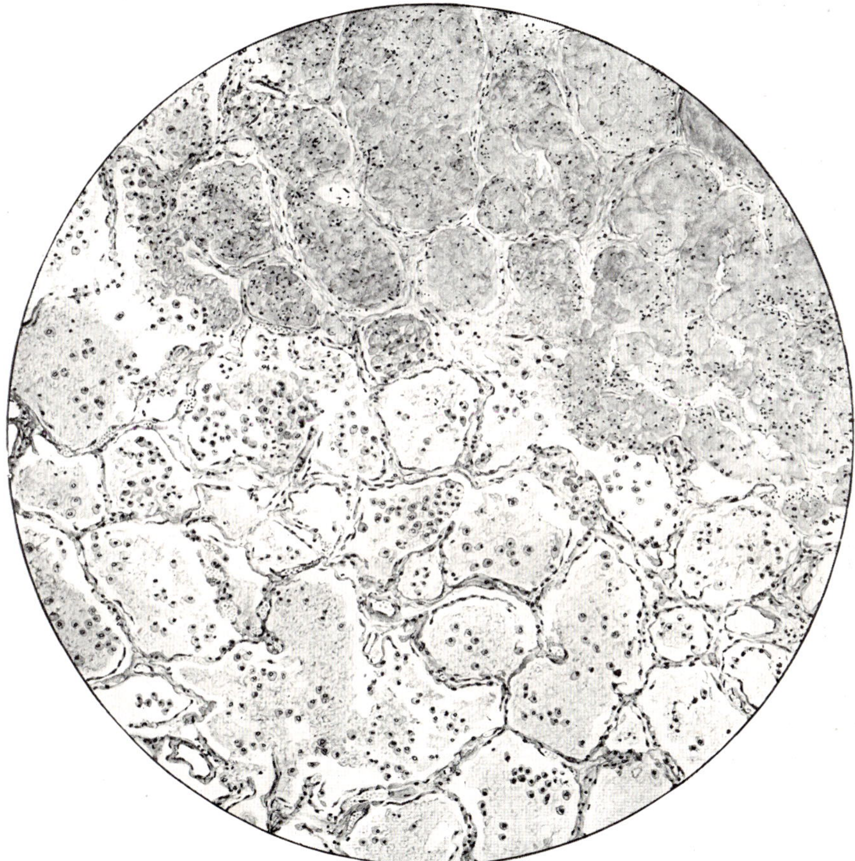

Fig. 314.—Edge of a fresh area of caseous and gelatinous pneumonia. Note the numerous large cells in the less affected alveoli.

by lymphoid cells and larger mononuclear wandering cells. Hæmorrhage is sometimes a striking feature, together with the desquamation of the lining cells of the cavity in which the process occurs. Of course, the appearance of characteristic tuberculous granulation tissue and tubercles in the attempt to organize such an exudate makes its nature clear at once. In all cases the extreme liability of exudate and included tissue to become caseous, and finally liquefied, marks out such acute tuberculous inflammations from other forms (Fig. 314). The most brilliant examples are seen in the lungs, the serous cavities of the body, and in the meninges, probably because in those situations a great number of bacilli can be readily brought into contact with the tissues.

While these are the typical effects of the tubercle bacillus, they must not be regarded as totally distinct reactions, but only as the appropriate reactions to the different degrees of intensity with which the bacilli affect the tissues. If the person lives and acquires a little more resistance, the acute inflammatory lesion is soon surrounded by tubercles and tuberculous granulation tissue which appear in its marginal portions and represent an ineffectual attempt at healing. In every case the tubercles and tuberculous granulation tissue develop as the effect of an initial injury and acute reactive inflammation which may be inconspicuous.

Distribution of Bacilli in the Body.—Having once entered the body, the bacilli may be transported by at least four methods—(1) mechanically along with air, food, secretions, etc.; (2) by growth through the tissues with the production of lesions; (3) by way of the lymphatic channels; (4) by way of the blood-stream.

The first of these is most important in the respiratory organs, where bacilli breathed in may lodge in the tissues or be wafted back again by the ciliated epithelium. Later, when lesions are established in the lungs, bacillus-holding fluid from a diseased area may be poured out into the bronchus and aspirated back into another, or it may pass out over the laryngeal mucosa. In either case new lesions can be produced in this way. So, also, in the digestive tract, the large serous cavities, the urinary organs, etc., the organisms are moved about by the contents of these cavities under the influence of gravity, secretory streams, and muscular activity. In the second case the movement of the bacilli is largely commensurate with the formation of lesions, with the gradual involvement of new tissue, and the caseation of that previously affected. The third method is often dependent upon this, since the lymphatic channels may be invaded by the spreading, caseating new tissue, but, quite aside from this, the bacilli may be carried into terminal lymphatics and swept along with the stream until they lodge somewhere—usually in the next lymph-node. Extension of a caseous tuberculous focus so as to erode through the wall of a blood-vessel is the usual basis of the fourth mode of transport (Fig. 315). It is true that actual tuberculous lesions are sometimes formed inside the vessels, but this is rare, while the extension of a caseating process through the wall of a vein or artery, so that the bacilli are shed into the passing stream, is extremely common. Great numbers of the organisms can in this way be suddenly thrown into the circulating blood before the exposed caseous material becomes covered with a protecting thrombus. It must be remembered that infusion of bacilli—(1) into the systemic veins, brings them by way of the right heart to the lungs; (2) into the pulmonary veins, distributes them into the whole systemic arterial circulation, while (3) the invasion of an artery causes a distribution only in the field to which it supplies blood. Less local in its effects is the entrance of bacilli into the thoracic duct, for that empties into the subclavian vein, and the result is the same as in the case of any systemic vein. The bacilli are very minute, however, and in any case they should theoretically be able to pass the capillaries and quickly infect any tissue supplied with blood-vessels. It happens, however, that these bacilli are quickly caught in such a passage through capillaries, so that an organ through which the blood passes acts as a very good sieve.

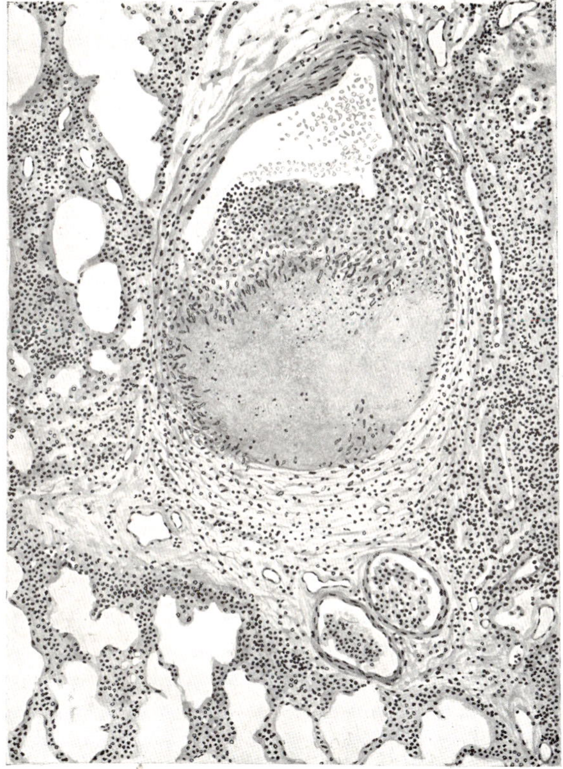

Fig. 315.—Caseous tubercle developed in the wall of the pulmonary vein, and separated from the blood by a partly organized thrombus.

In spite of the existence of so many ways by which the bacilli may be carried from one part of the body to another, tuberculous infection is generally a rather localized process, if we count all cases in which the organism gains a foothold in the tissues. This is due to the great power of annihilating these bacteria possessed by most persons, so that in the end even when they have produced distinct lesions they are killed and nothing but a scar remains to show where they have been. Still it is clear that when there is an active focus of disease they get into the blood in small numbers and are either killed or produce minute local lesions in other organs. The different size and different degree of progression of these tubercles toward caseation or healing show that the bacilli have entered the circulation a few at a time, sometimes at long intervals. Disturbances of organic function can scarcely be expected from such scattered nodules. Other organisms behave in the same way, and we are just becoming familiar with the effects of occasional intermittent escape of such bacteria as the streptococci and staphylococci into the blood-stream. With them we have been more accustomed to observe the sudden pouring into the circulation of great numbers of cocci, which in the form of an acute septicæmia cause the most profound intoxication and set up destructive processes everywhere. This happens with the tubercle bacillus also, and not only is the mechanism by which it reaches the blood-stream far more distinct than is usual in the case of the pyogenic cocci, but practically all the bacilli can be traced by the conspicuous nature of the reaction they stir up wherever they lodge. This, which is really an acute tuberculous septicæmia, is called, from its anatomical results, acute miliary tuberculosis.

Acute Miliary Tuberculosis.—The sudden introduction of thousands of bacilli into the circulating blood produces thousands of minute tubercle nodules, all of the same age. There is no reason why several such crops should not be produced, and occasionally one may distinguish such differences in size and age among the tubercles as to be able to conclude that several distinct immigrations of the bacilli have occurred. Usually, however, the occurrence of one extensive outbreak is enough to kill the person.

With sufficient diligence in the use of scissors in following the blood-vessels it is nearly always possible to find the hole through which the bacilli were discharged into the blood, and Weigert, Sigg, Schmorl, and others have gradually approached 100 per cent. The relative number and size of tubercles in the lungs and systemic circulation may give some clue to aid in this search. It is perhaps most usual to find the portal of entry in a branch of the pulmonary vein, but if this fail, the systemic veins and the thoracic duct must be surveyed. It is, of course, more likely that those veins which run through or near an extensive caseous area should be involved, and it proves especially common to find that a caseous lymph-gland attached by adhesions to the vein-wall is the source of the material. When the vein is laid open in the right place, it is found to be partly obstructed by a granular, cheesy mass, projecting into its lumen in such a way that the soft, bacillus-laden material is washed by the passing stream into the general current, or else there is a hole in the wall opening into a cavity in an adherent caseous tissue from which bacilli are swept by an eddy of the stream out into the vessel. The discharge of bacilli in either case is soon limited by the deposit of a protective covering of thrombus material on the exposed surface.

Of course, it must not be forgotten that, as Benda* and others point out, the distributing tuberculous lesion may be formed on the endothelial lining of the vessel (or even through the entrance of bacilli into the vasa vasorum), and set free new and abundant bacilli only when it has become caseous. This is specially true of the thoracic duct, which receives bacilli through its branches and comes in time to be lined with caseous, ulcerating areas from which newly grown bacilli are poured off into the blood. Rarely one may find tuberculous caseous lesions in the heart discharging bacilli into the

* Benda: Ergebn. d. allg. Path., 1900, v, 447.

blood. Intimal tubercles and erosions in the aorta and smaller arteries are uncommon, and distribute their bacilli into a limited area only.

The tubercles which are formed by this wholesale distribution may appear practically anywhere. They are sprinkled over the serous surfaces, where they are conspicuous and are scattered profusely in such organs as the spleen, liver, and lungs, where they are often easier to feel than to see. They are beautifully seen with the ophthalmoscope in the choroid of the living patient. Some tissues, such as those of the pancreas, thyroid, muscle, skin, etc., seem very little prone to develop tubercles, but even here they are found at times.

The profound intoxication, like that of typhoid fever, is doubtless due to the sudden exposure of so many bacilli through the body, so that they multiply and produce and disseminate their poisons. No doubt in advanced phthisis there may be in the lung just as many bacilli and even more caseous tissue, but there the process is localized and the caseous substance is characteristically withdrawn from relations with the blood-vessels, so that, in a sense, the poison is imprisoned.

The fact that, apart from the acute miliary form, tuberculosis is commonly a localized affection, makes it possible to refer to the lesions produced according to their situation. It will be seen, however, that, regardless of the organ involved, the same general characters are maintained.

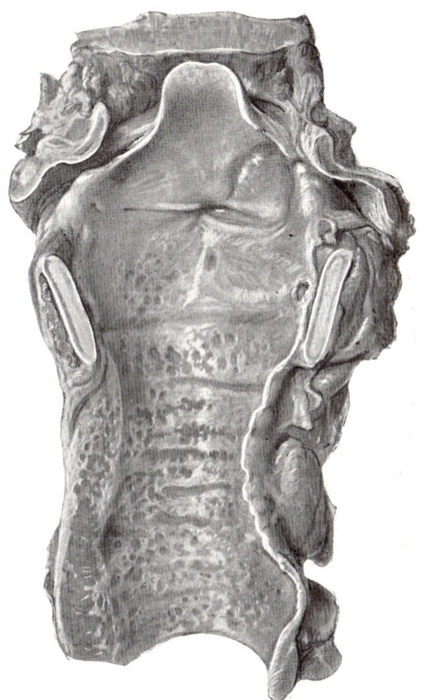

Fig. 316.—Tuberculous lenticular ulcers of the trachea.

Tuberculosis of the Upper Respiratory Tract.—The mucosa of the nose and pharynx may become infected by the breathing-in of bacilli, but probably more often by the direct introduction of the organisms from handkerchiefs, etc. Ulcers are formed and may extend to the underlying bone and to the communicating sinuses. Tuberculous ulceration of the larynx is common, and although thought to be sometimes primary, is without doubt most often caused by the passage of tuberculous sputum.

Tubercles are formed just under the epithelium and become confluent and necrotic. Ulceration of the mucosa, which results, affects chiefly the vocal cords, false cords, aryepiglottic folds, and epiglottis. The latter is sometimes completely eroded away, so that swallowing becomes very difficult. The ulceration of the vocal cords changes the voice to a husky, toneless whisper. If it extends so as to denude the cartilages of the larynx, they may become necrotic and prone to serious secondary infections. In the trachea the infection of the mucosa from the sputum leads to the formation of numerous shallow lenticular ulcerations (Fig. 316).

Tuberculosis of the Lungs.—In the *lung* the first lesion is commonly, though by no means always, in the wall of a bronchus, a centimetre or more below the apex. Why this should be so is not clear, although many explanations have been offered, based upon supposed differences in the blood supply, diminished aëration, immobility, more direct access to the bronchus of that part, etc. Freund specially emphasizes the immobility, which may be caused by a rigid first rib, and Bacmeister has found that if, in rabbits, the apical portion of the chest be held rigidly immobile in a wire basket, intravenous inoculation of bacilli produces an apical tuberculous lesion.

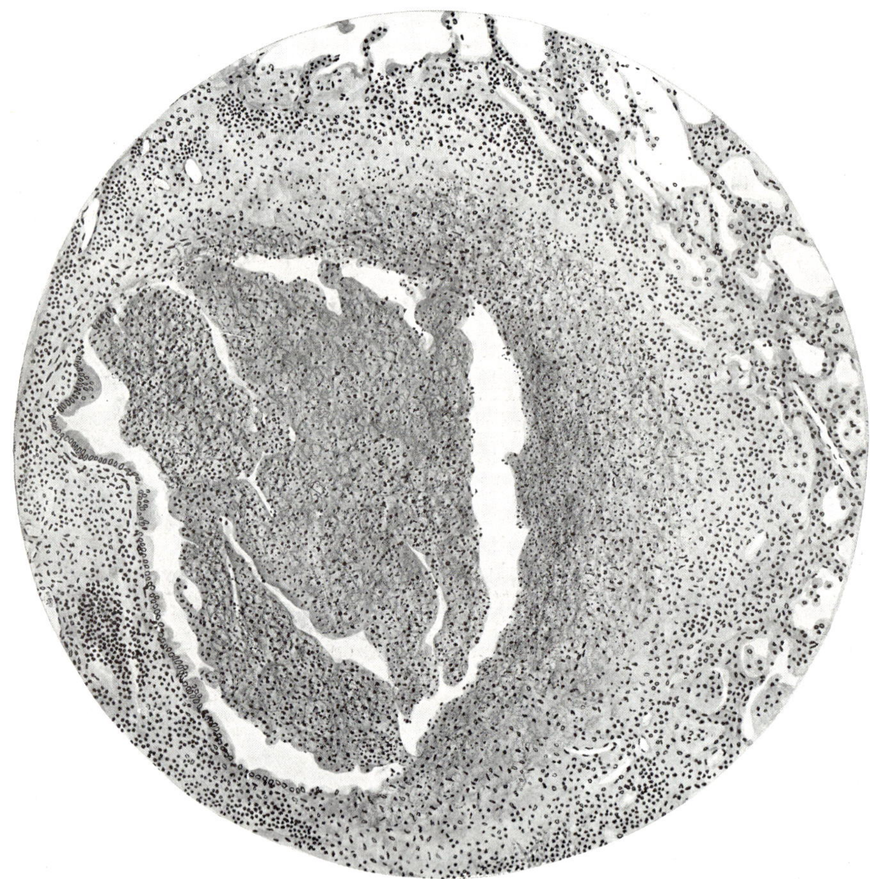

Fig. 317.—Caseous tuberculous bronchitis and peribronchitis. The mucosa on one side is still well preserved.

The apical or subapical lesion was shown by Birch-Hirschfeld to be the formation of a tuberculous granulation tissue in the wall of the bronchus. This quickly becomes caseous and softened (Fig. 317), and is discharged through the bronchus, not, however, before the bacilli have extended their growth into the adjacent alveoli, where they form numerous tubercles. In such a case a cavity is the central feature in a mass of airless lung substance in which the air-cells are occupied or obliterated by conglomerated and partly caseous tubercles, embedded in a radiating fibrous tissue. If the development of the focus has been rapid enough, it may be possible to see that some of this occlusion of the air-cells has been produced by a cellular inflammatory exudate, which becomes caseous and surrounded by epithelioid cells, so that it comes to look like caseous conglomerate tubercles.

In many other cases the whole lesion heals and there is found accidentally at autopsy an irregular or pyramidal mass of deeply pigmented scar tissue, sometimes containing desiccated and encapsulated cheesy nodules, but devoid of any resemblance to normal lung tissue. It may be hardened by a deposit of lime salts, or still later bone may develop there, with a distinct cancellous arrangement and marrow cavities with marrow. Most often, however, the patch is contracted and reduced to mere fibrous tissue in which no clear evidence of a tuberculous origin can be found. It appears, then, as a flat, scale-like scar occupying the surface of the apex of the lung. It is somewhat difficult to prove, however, that such subpleural scars are really the remains of tuberculous lesions, or, at least, of such lesions as are seen in their active form in the subapical tissue. Grober tries to explain them, and, indeed, the apical tuberculosis in general, as being due to the passage of bacilli from the tonsils by way of the cervical lymph-channels to the dome of the pleura, and thence to the apex of the lung, but this view has not been generally accepted, and requires confirmation.

While the establishment of a tuberculous focus with subsequent cavity formation near the apex is extremely common, it is not the only way in which the disease can begin in the lung. The same process may take place in one of the lower lobes, or simultaneously in several places. In the opposite lung, by infection from that first involved, hundreds of lesions may be simultaneously produced. Or in the entire absence of any primary lesion there, miliary tubercles may be showered over both lungs, from a focus somewhere else in the body. Especially in children is it common to find caseous softening of the bronchial lymph-glands, which, by eroding through the bronchial wall, pour bacilli into its lumen and set up at once wholesale tuberculous disease of the lung.

But in spite of these occasional cases, the every-day type of tuberculosis of the lungs in adults is that in which there is found a cavity in the upper lobe, with all the sequelæ which we must now describe.

Since the cavity is formed by the caseation and hollowing out of the bronchial wall and the surrounding tissue, it is always widely open into the bronchus (Fig. 318). Secondary connections with other bronchi are formed wherever these are cut across as the cavity enlarges, and through all these openings the fluid contents pass out into the trachea and are coughed up. It is clearly unavoidable that in such violent coughing some of this turbid fluid loaded with bacilli should be drawn into other bronchi, and thus into parts of the lung not yet diseased. The result is to produce, all through the lower parts of that organ and in the opposite lung, patches of tuberculous bronchopneumonia, exactly as the inhalation of material infected with

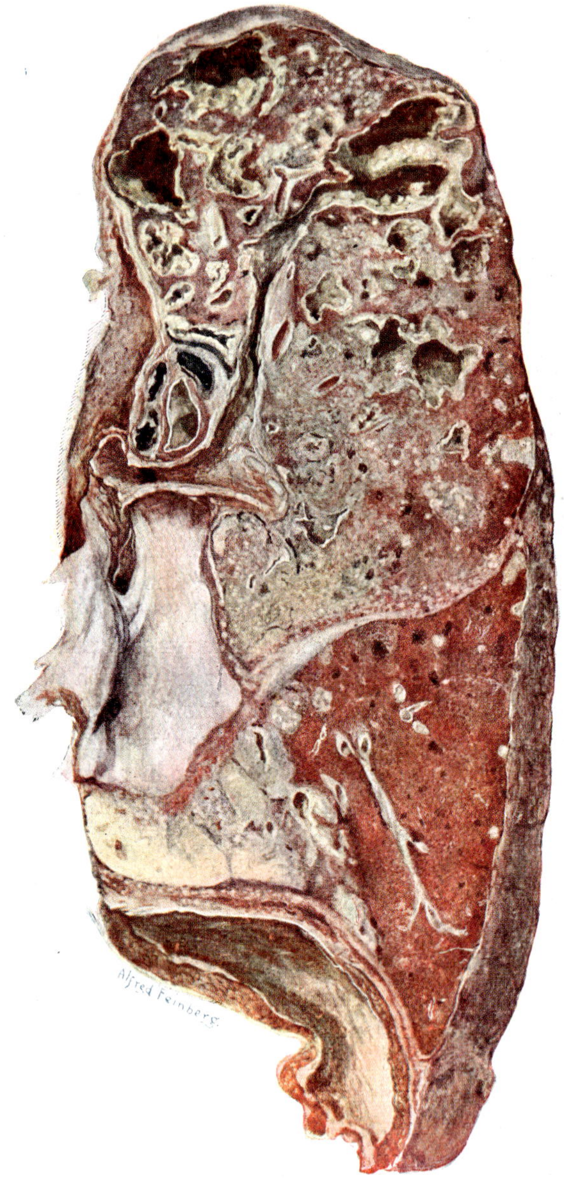

Fig. 318.—Chronic pulmonary tuberculosis with cavity formation and aspiration of tubercle bacilli by way of the bronchus, which opens into a cavity. Conglomerate patches of caseous pneumonia in upper lobes. Pleurisy with many small tubercles.

other virulent organisms produces little clusters of solid, airless alveoli about the ends of the bronchioles. In the beginning these parts of the lung may be pale or congested, and rough, dry, grayish-red areas stand out a little above the cut surface. At that stage the alveoli are found full of fibrinous exudate, with many leucocytes and some red corpuscles. Mononuclear cells prevail over the polynuclear, and there quickly appear great numbers of large pale cells with vesicular nuclei which are generally stated to be epithelial cells shed from the alveolar walls, although Orth maintains that they are large mononuclear wandering cells. The process is a true pneumonia, even though the type of wandering cells is somewhat different from that seen with pneumococcus infection. In the neighborhood (see

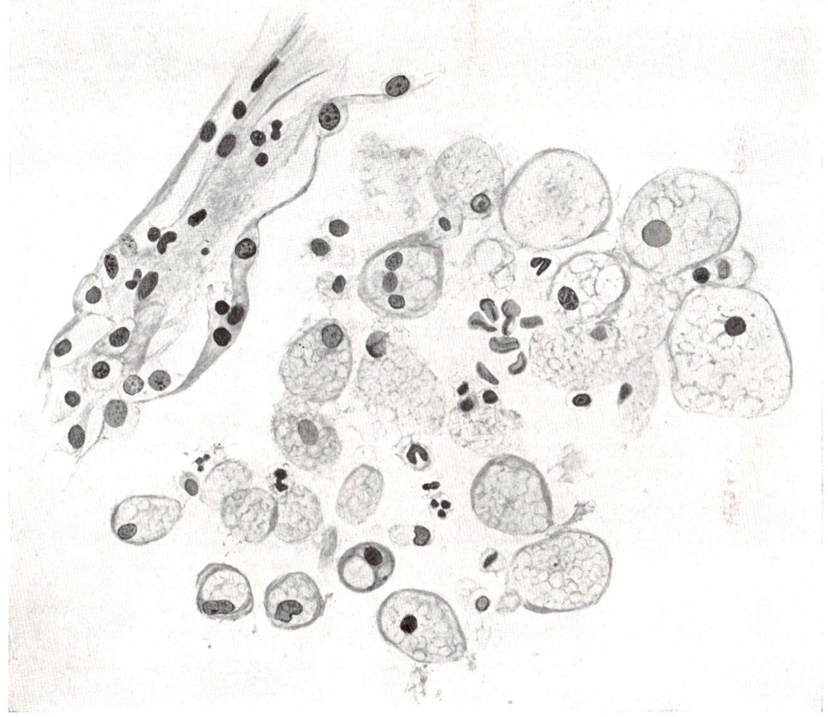

Fig. 319.—Large cells found in the alveoli in the neighborhood of areas of caseous pneumonia. They are seen to contain fat-globules.

Fig. 314) the alveoli are filled with a thick, glutinous fluid, in which float many more of the desquamated epithelial cells, which often become conspicuously yellow from their content of neutral and anisotropic fat (Fig. 319). At a slightly later stage nearly the whole consolidated area turns white and becomes soft and cheesy, and, although the outlines of the alveolar walls, undisturbed in their position, can long be discerned in virtue of their highly resistant elastic tissue, every cell dies, loses its nuclear staining, and is disintegrated. The bronchial walls become caseous also, and among such areas of *caseous and gelatinous lobular pneumonia* they may be seen coursing through the tissue as conspicuous tubes with thick, opaque, yellowish-white walls (caseous bronchitis) (Fig. 320).

Occasionally, when very great numbers of tubercle bacilli are introduced

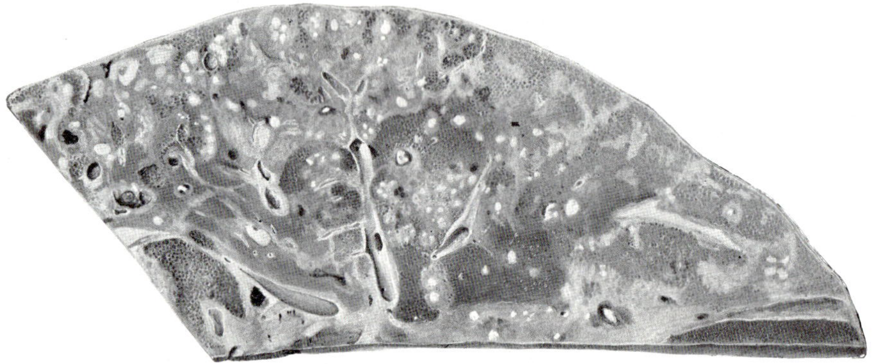

Fig. 320.—Caseous lobular pneumonia with caseous bronchitis.

into the bronchioles at one time, a *lobar caseous pneumonia* follows (Fig. 321). In such a case a whole lobe or even a whole lung may be uniformly consolidated, so that if it were seen in an early stage, it might be confused

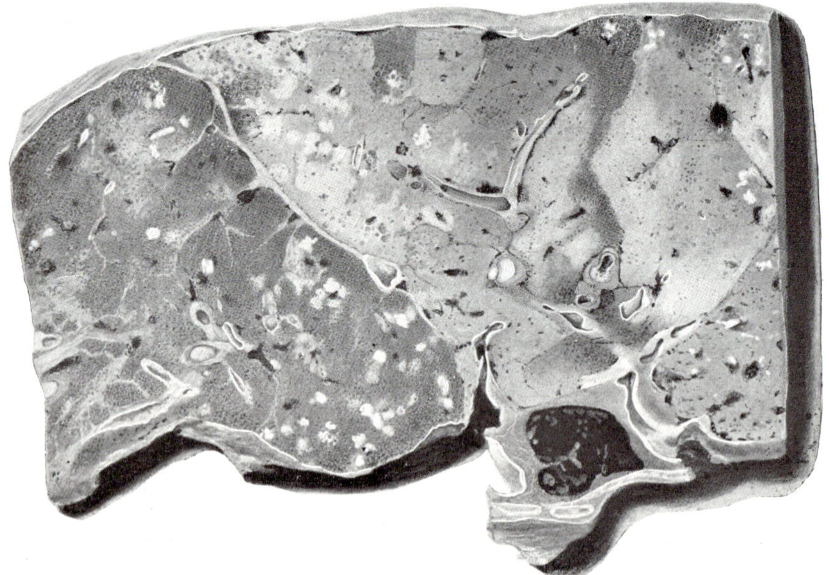

Fig. 321.—Caseous lobar and lobular pneumonia.

with an ordinary lobar pneumonia. The character of the exudate, with its predominant mononuclear cells and the gelatinous, translucent appearance of the adjacent lung tissue, which is not so intensely affected, serve even then to distinguish it, and the subsequent caseation *en masse* makes the

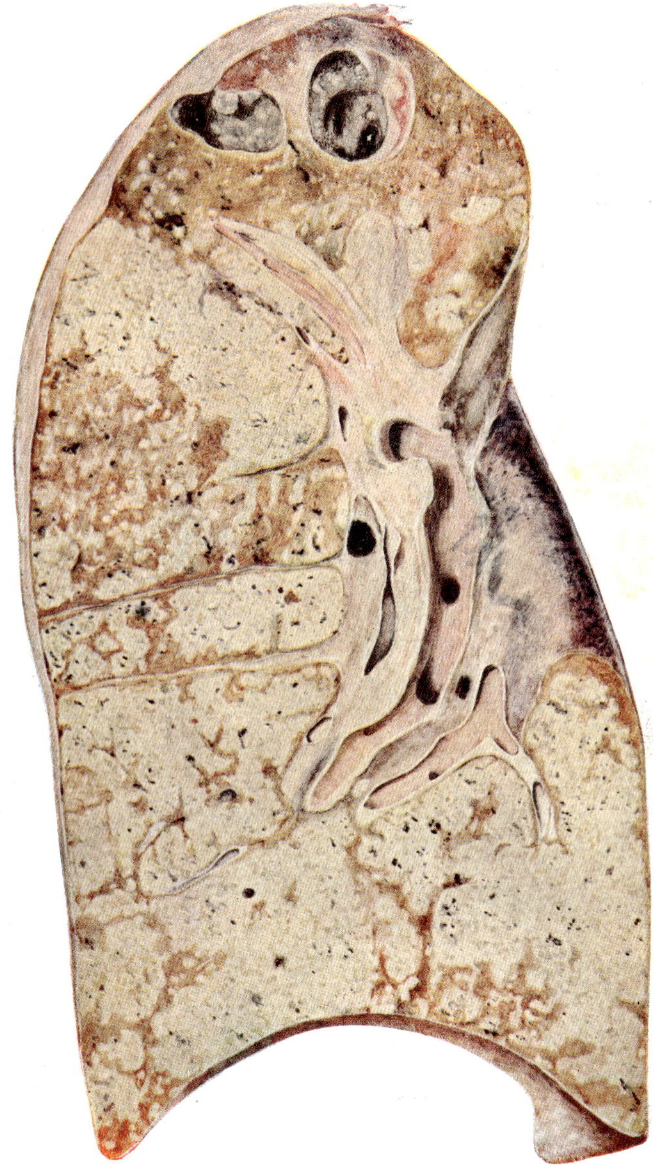

Fig. 322.—Caseous and gelatinous pneumonia. The consolidation and caseation are practically lobar in their distribution.

differentiation clear (Fig. 322). In a lung studied recently only the tissue immediately about the great vessels and bronchi remained alive. Practically all the rest had assumed the consistence of cream-cheese and was perfectly opaque and yellowish white (Fig. 323). Naturally, the softening and discharge of such necrotic material will leave huge cavities in the lung, and the rapidity with which the organ is destroyed in this way has given rise to the name *phthisis florida*, or galloping consumption. Fränkel and Troje first clearly described this form of the disease, and drew attention to its clinical features, which resemble those of a frank lobar pneumonia until, with the protracted course, there appear signs of breaking down of the lung and the discharge of a green sputum full of shreds of elastic tissue.

Even small lobular areas of consolidation become caseous and spill their contents, when they have become fluid enough, into the bronchi. This liquefaction seems to be partly the work of the enzymes of the surrounding cells, but partly the consequence of a secondary infection—at least there are always found numbers of other organisms in a cavity of any size.*

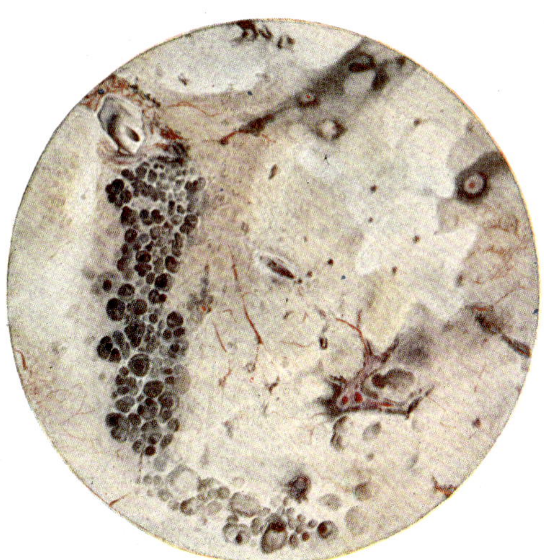

Fig. 323.—Caseous pneumonia (lens enlargement).

Were it to proceed unchecked, such destructive tuberculosis would eat away the whole lung very shortly, but from the beginning there are efforts at building up a cellular barrier against the extension of the caseation, and these efforts, pushed to their utmost and lasting over months and years, bring about the scarring and fibrous induration of the lung so characteristic of the more chronic sorts of phthisis.

In the pneumonic patches, before the central parts where the bacilli are most numerous have become necrotic, a loose wall is formed all around in the outskirts of the exudate by its organization. This process, so rare in lobar pneumonia, commoner in bronchopneumonia, is practically the rule here. New formation of epithelioid cells and of fibroblasts springs up in the walls of these alveoli, and shortly a definite tuberculous granulation tissue, including abortive and well-formed tubercles, surrounds the rapidly caseating area. This wall becomes firmer and more resistant, although itself prone to caseation and disintegration, and even in advance of the

* In this connection it should be stated that streptococci, pneumococci, etc., are sometimes the chief agents in bringing about the lobular pneumonia which results from the aspiration of the contents of a cavern. In such a case both symptoms and anatomical changes are modified.

caseating process it is backed up constantly by new tissue formed in the same way outside (Fig. 324). At this stage one could scarcely say whether this is a conglomerate tubercle, caseous in its centre, or a pneumonic area, caseous but surrounded by a wall of tuberculous tissue. Outside such a place, and even at quite a distance, the walls of the air-cells become thickened and firm. Such *indurative pneumonia* is most pronounced when the

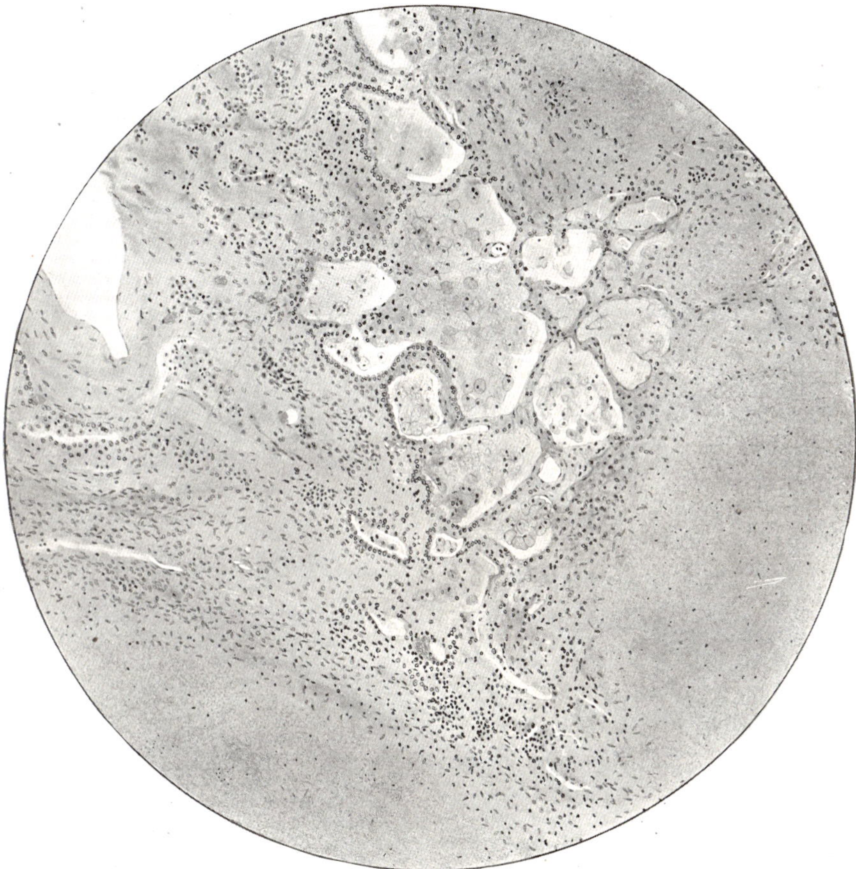

Fig. 324.—Caseous and gelatinous pneumonia; beginning encapsulation of the caseous areas.

spread of the tuberculosis has been most successfully combated over a long time.

The appearance of a tuberculous cavity or vomica in the lung might be constructed from what has been said. The bronchus may have shallow ulcers in its mucous lining, but it is not widened.* It suddenly comes to an

* There is a common statement that bronchiectasis is most frequent in tuberculosis. This is not true of the rapidly advancing forms of phthisis, although it is found in the old scarred and indurated lungs, where healing is going on with retraction of the scars.

eroded rough end, where it opens into the cavity. The cavity may reach an enormous size, occupying a whole lobe or even nearly the whole lung, in which case the organ comes to be a mere sac whose wall is formed by the thickened pleura. If this in its turn is perforated, the contents of the cavity, including air, escape into the pleura unless it has been obliterated by adhesions. The cavity usually contains a thick, opaque, greenish-yellow, somewhat glutinous fluid, which is full of bacteria, leucocytes, cellular débris, fragments of elastic tissue, etc. If it be cleaned out, the wall is still covered by an opaque, yellowish-white, caseous necrotic layer, beneath which is a tuberculous granulation tissue (see Fig. 318). All bronchi and most of the blood-vessels which lay in the area of cavity formation, are interrupted, but some of the blood-vessels are still found stretching across from wall to wall, or standing up as high ridges against one side. If they be cut across, many of them prove to be solid cords, but others still have a central lumen, from which one can squeeze a drop of blood. This persistence is due to an obliterating endarteritis which thickens the wall, and especially the intimal layer, on the approach of the tuberculous inflammation. Sometimes loose cords of these vessels hanging in the cavity show that they have finally been corroded all the way through, but no hæmorrhage has occurred. In other cases, when the patient has died from a sudden tremendous coughing up of blood, the cavity is found full of blood-clot, and study of its walls usually shows an artery approached too suddenly to allow time for obliteration. Then, as its wall is weakened by the advancing caseation, it bulges out into a little sac or aneurysm which bursts with some effort of coughing.

In all such cases the pleura is thickened and covered with a fibrinous exudate. Tubercles are to be found in the granulation tissue which lies beneath this exudate, and frequently there are quite dense adhesions, especially over the region where the cavity approaches the surface. The lymph-glands in the lung, and especially those at the hilum, contain tubercles or larger caseous areas. All this makes up, as we have said, one of the commonest combinations found in the lungs of consumptives at autopsy, namely, a cavity at the apex opening widely into the bronchus and surrounded by consolidated fibrous lung tissue studded with caseous foci, and, below this, numerous patches of pneumonic consolidation, varying in age from the freshest to the completely caseous area, walled round by organized exudate and tuberculous granulation tissue.

Aside from the pneumonic patches following bronchial transportation, there is a great variety of anatomical lesions in the lung which are due to the passage of bacilli along the lymphatics or blood-vessels, or to the direct extension of the infection through the lung tissue. In all these cases the lesion consists in the formation of tubercles and tuberculous granulation tissue, without much outpouring of cellular inflammatory exudate. Tubercles produced in the lung by bacilli brought with the blood-stream develop in the alveolar wall, but soon project into the alveolus so as to fill it or become conglomerated with adjacent nodules. Sometimes they are so small that their point of origin can be clearly determined. Such tubercles may be scattered in any indefinite order through the lung. When carried by the lymphatic channels, the bacilli produce similar tubercles in strings or clusters along the interlobular septa (Fig. 325), in the bronchial walls, or in the walls of the blood-vessels. Sometimes this can be plainly seen, but when, in advanced stages, they cluster around bronchi and are caseous, it is hard to say whether they were not small bronchopneumonic patches. There is one common type of tuberculous lesion secondary usually to an apical cavity formation, in

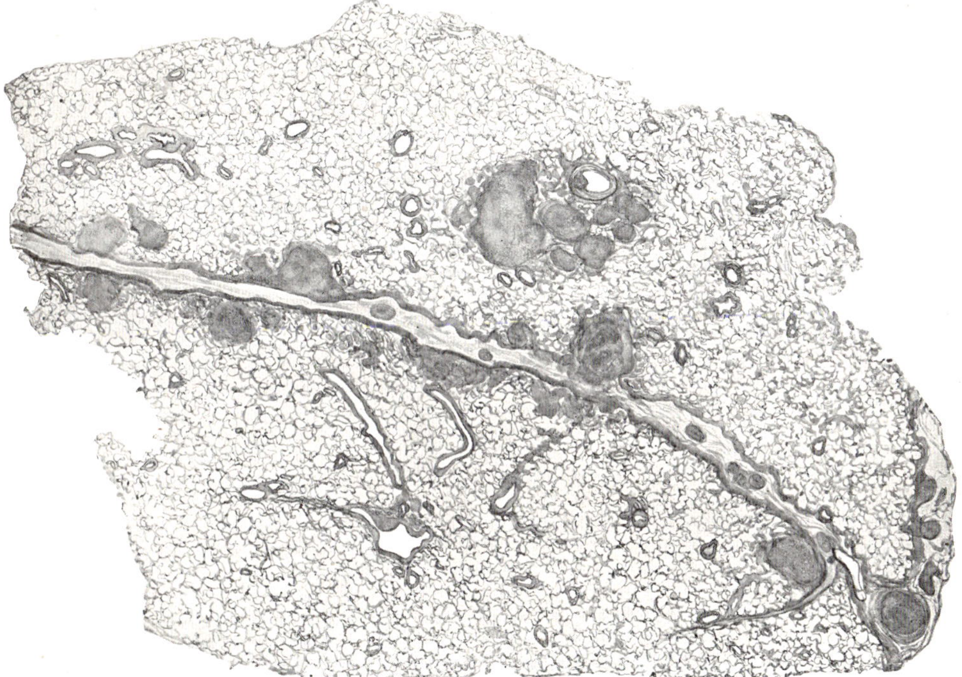

Fig. 325.—Distribution of tubercle bacilli by lymphatics, with development of tubercles in the interlobar septa.

which large and small firm masses are felt in the otherwise air-containing lung (Fig. 326). On section these are found to be quite sharply outlined and edged by a border of gray, caseating tubercles. The whole mass, measuring sometimes 5 cm. in diameter, is radially arranged, and its inner part, back of the progressing margin of fresh tubercles, is a solid, pigmented fibrous tissue with still some tubercles and caseous points, but giving the impression of having been formed by the healing or obsolescence of tuberculous tissue, which is still advancing rapidly at the margin into the healthy lung substance. Some such process as this seems to occur in many cases about the early apical lesions, and it is a process which is undoubtedly of great importance in the ordinary spread of any focus of the disease in the lung.

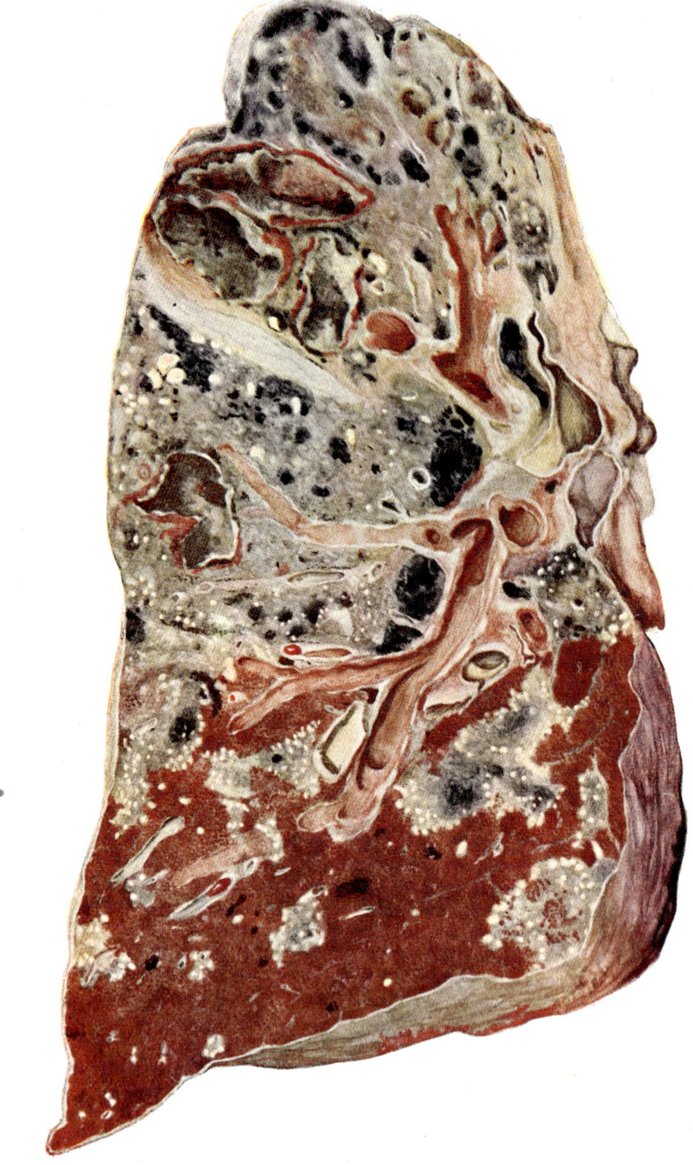

Fig. 326.—Pulmonary phthisis with cavity formation. There are extensive masses of pigmented scarred tuberculous tissue the advancing margin of which is made up of fresh tubercles.

The rate of progression, while perhaps about the same in the majority of cases, is capable of great variation, so that, on the one hand, we find a man dying a few weeks after the first symptoms appear, on the other, a man who has had pulmonary tuberculosis for many years and finally dies from something else, revealing extensive scarred and almost healed lesions in his lungs.

This scarring may consist in the permanent encapsulation of each caseous area, leaving air-containing and functional lung substance between, but more often it extends far and wide, and a whole lobe, or even the whole lung, bound as it usually is in thick pleural adhesions, is distorted and indurated and greatly contracted. On section such a lung reveals cavities at the ends of short wide stumps of bronchi, separated by a gray pigmented tissue with only islands of recognizable alveoli here and there. Microscopically the alveolar walls in these islands are greatly thickened by connective tissue, and on account of their rigidity the epithelial cells have become cubical or even columnar. In other places, and especially near the edges of the lung, the alveoli which remain are enormously dilated and thin walled (collateral or compensating emphysema). Even quite large cavities may be cleaned out and relined by a smooth layer of epithelium, a step toward healing which must indicate the most tenacious resistance on the part of the host.

It is important to indicate the functional disturbances produced by the disease. The formation of even very many minute tubercles in the lungs as part of a generalized miliary tuberculosis need not cause any great disturbance of respiration, but with wide-spread pneumonic consolidation the case is different. So, too, with extensive cavity formation and such scarring of the lung as has been described there is quite naturally a great diminution of the respiratory surface. The bed of the blood-stream through the lungs is largely obliterated, and the remaining lung substance is over-distended, so that one might expect to find hypertrophy of the right side of the heart caused by the effort to force the blood through. Curiously enough, this is seldom the case except in those individuals in whom the disease has been held in check for years and the lungs are extensively scarred.

Disturbances of temperature regulation (fever in the afternoon, etc.) are common in pulmonary phthisis, but it seems that the most intense symptoms of this kind are due to secondary invaders of all sorts (pyogenic cocci and bacteria of every other type, yeasts, moulds, and even insect larvæ), which may get into the cavities and grow there.

Changes in the general metabolism are of regular occurrence—the consumptive wastes away and becomes anæmic; the metabolism of fat is disturbed, so that it accumulates especially in the liver, and there are general, though somewhat intangible, evidences of poisoning, doubtless from the absorption of toxic substances which the bacilli produce.

Up to the present it does not seem certain that any great degree of immunity is produced in those persons who have withstood one infection.

Persons with pulmonary phthisis almost invariably infect themselves further. The lymph-glands at the hilum of the lung inevitably contain tubercles, and other more distant nodes may also be infected. The outpouring of tuberculous sputum very often sets up ulcer formation in the trachea and larynx, while, especially in children who do not expectorate and in adults who swallow their sputum, the intestines and sometimes even the stomach develop ulcers. These are the obvious ways for the bacilli to spread, but in every such autopsy one finds a few scattered tubercles in nearly all the organs, which must indicate the entrance of bacilli into the blood-stream. Although it cannot always be traced, the point of entrance is usually quite clear when the invasion is extensive enough to produce an unmistakable acute miliary tuberculosis. Localized disease in some distant organ, as in a bone or in the kidney or epididymis, may be started in this way, and, on the contrary, primary disease of the lymph-glands or of a bone may in the end give rise to pulmonary tuberculosis.

LITERATURE

Birch-Hirschfeld: Deutsch. Arch. f. klin Med., 1899, lxiv, 58.
Fränkel and Troje: Zeitsch. f. klin. Med., 1894, xxiv, 30.
Dürck: Erg. d. allg. Path., 1897, ii, 196; 1901, vi, 84.
Pertik: *Ibid.*, 1904, $viii_2$, 1.

Tuberculosis of the Digestive Organs.—From what was said above, it is evident that while tubercle bacilli may be taken into the digestive tract with the food, it is still questionable whether their entrance into the body by that path is of great importance in the production of pulmonary and general tuberculosis. Isolated primary tuberculosis of the intestine can rarely be demonstrated in adults, although commoner in children. Indeed, as a consequence of the study of the results of a great many investigators Beitzke concludes that in tuberculous children about 25 per cent. of the cases show a primary intestinal infection. The result is infection of the mesenteric lymph-glands, or even of the ductus thoracicus, or, on the other hand, the transportation of the bacilli by the portal blood to the liver, where tubercles may be formed. Miliary tuberculosis is apparently rarely or never the direct outcome of primary intestinal tuberculosis, but if a partial immunity be set up or if the bacteria be relatively non-virulent, pulmonary tuberculosis may follow. Thus while it is recognized that pulmonary tuberculosis may follow an intestinal absorption or intestinal tuberculosis, the readiness with which it is produced by aspiration leaves this method of infection in a place of secondary importance, which in adults, at least, is probably very slight.

Tuberculous lesions of the mouth, pharynx, œsophagus, and stomach occur, but are quite rare. They arise by direct infection of the mucosa, or sometimes, as in the case of the œsophagus, from invasion by caseous glands or other tissues from without. In the stomach the lesions are miliary and conglomerate tubercles in the mucosa, or ragged and precipitous ulcers.

The liver regularly presents very minute miliary tubercles when there is a general distribution of the bacilli by the blood-stream. In some cases these become conglomerate, and even quite large and centrally caseous. A type of cirrhosis of the liver results from the presence of these nodules, or at least occurs commonly in association with them. The most interesting form is that in which caseous nodules appear near the bile-ducts, and after the discharge of their contents into the ducts become deeply bile stained. Tuberculosis of the pancreas is not often observed, and usually consists in the presence of miliary tubercles.

It is in the intestine, however, that the bacilli cause their greatest ravages, and the lesions there are of interest not only in themselves, but because they may lead to other extensions of the disease. Aside from the rare instance of isolated primary tuberculosis in adults and those in children, in which the bacilli are probably swallowed in quantities in the milk, the intestinal lesions are usually caused by the swallowing of sputum from tuberculous cavities in the lungs. The mucus of the sputum protects the bacilli in their passage through the acid gastric juice, so that they reach the intestine alive.

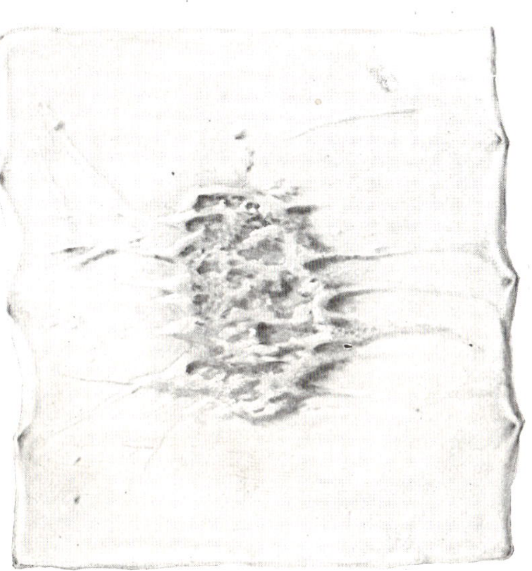

Fig. 327.—Tuberculous ulcer of the ileum.

Intestinal Tuberculosis.—The lesions in the intestine are predominantly ulcerative, and are found in their greatest intensity in the small intestine above the ileocæcal valve. Often enough, however, they both extend far up in the small intestine, and are found in numbers in the colon. They have, therefore, broadly, the same general distribution as the ulcers in typhoid fever, but they are not nearly so sharply limited to the Peyer's patches and solitary nodules. Even though the bacilli may lodge there, they soon produce an ulceration which extends wide of those structures and involves indifferently the surrounding mucosa. Indeed, the ulcers have a rather strong tendency to encircle the whole gut, whence they are often called girdle ulcers. Their beginnings can be seen as swollen, conglomerate nodules with central caseation, but the softening and discharge of this yellow, opaque central substance into the intestine leaves an ulcer which, when it has reached a larger size, is characteristic enough and very unlike the typhoid ulcer in its details. The margin is ragged, nodular and irregular, thickened, and undermined (Fig. 327). The base is generally covered with yellow necrotic material, but this is sometimes cleaned off so as to reveal the tuberculous granulation tissue which really lines the ulcer, and which is generally studded with palpable nodules. The submucosa or musculature may be exposed, or the ulcer may perforate the whole wall.

Such ulcers can generally be located from the outside by the congestion of the vessels in that spot, and especially by the crop of minute gray tubercles which spring up in the subserous tissue and cluster along the lymphatic channels. Evidently from the mucosa the bacilli are carried into these lymph-channels, and the tubercles are actually formed inside them in such a way as to block the lumen. It is for that reason that these lymphatics become so conspicuous as they run over the surface of the intestine to the mesentery (Fig. 328). Sometimes they are greatly distended with clear fluid, or even with opaque white chyle, and are beaded or like a string of sausages, because they are obstructed at intervals. In such a case they can often be traced through the mesentery to the lymph-gland, into which they empty and which usually shows tuberculous lesions too.

Microscopically (Fig. 330), the tuberculous granulation tissue is found not only lining the base of the ulcer, but formed in the submucosa wide of the actually undermined part, and through the crevices of the muscle layer even into the subserous tissue. It often shows patches of caseation and abortive tubercles, but the tubercles are usually rather indefinite in their structure.

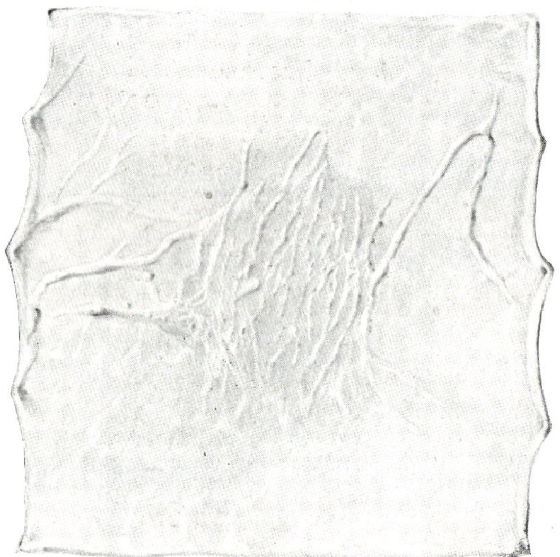

Fig. 328.—The same ulcer of the ileum from the outside, showing the chains of tubercles along the lymphatic channels.

There is one form of intestinal tuberculosis which is rather sharply localized about the ileocæcal valve and there produces a great mass of hard, tuberculous scar tissue, which may constrict the intestinal lumen until only a large probe will pass. In one such case seen recently that whole stretch of the intestine was removed by the surgeon and the young man has been quite well ever since. More common is the localized ulcerative tuberculosis of the rectum, which, extending in the form of a sinus to the skin at the anus, gives rise to the so-called anal fistula. In nearly all these cases the granular lining of the sinus is found to be tuberculous.

It follows, from the anatomical relations, that if tuberculous ulcers extend in the intestinal wall so as to present bacillus-holding tissue on the peritoneal surface, or if tuberculous disease of the lungs reaches the pleura, or if tuberculous and caseous lymph-glands approach or break into either of these cavities or the pericardium, it will not be difficult for the bacilli to gain access there and to be spread over an extensive surface by the active movements of the contained organs. It is usually in this way that tuberculous pleurisy, pericarditis, and peritonitis arise, although those surfaces may, like other tissues, be involved in a general miliary tuberculosis.

Tuberculous Peritonitis.—The principles followed in the pleura and pericardium are so well exemplified by the conditions found in tuberculous peritonitis that a description of the latter will suffice. The varied types of tuberculous disease of the peritoneum seem to depend upon the number and virulence of the organisms introduced and the resistance of the host, for in some cases there is an extensive destruction of tissue, while in others there is rather the formation of adhesions and scars which may in time lose much of their distinctive tuberculous character.

The organisms may enter the peritoneum with the blood-stream, as in the production of acute miliary tuberculosis, when they will be deposited in the omentum and subserous tissues. Or they may be directly poured into the cavity from exposed caseous masses, when, for example, a tuberculous focus in a lymph-gland or in the kidney or a neighboring bone forms a communication with the peritoneum. Caseous disease of the

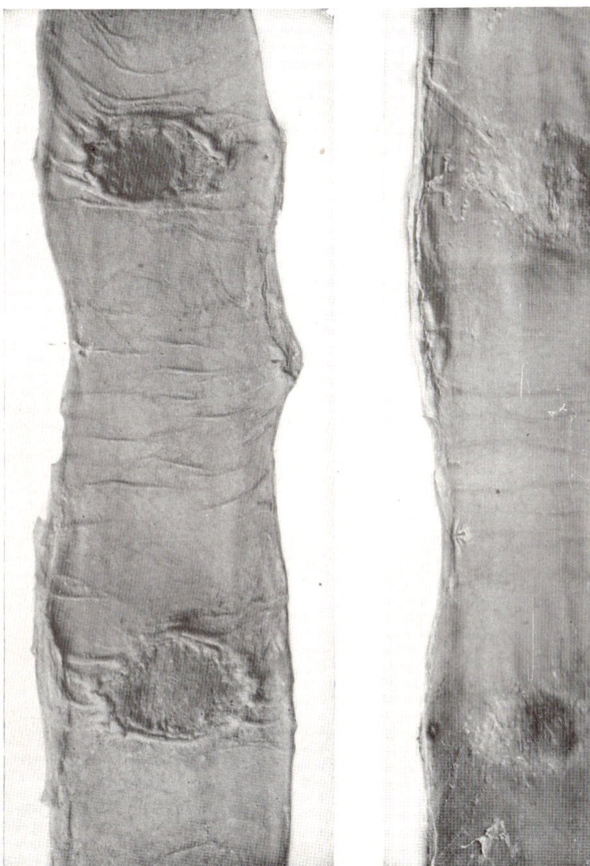

Fig. 329.—Tuberculous erosions of the lower ileum. Both sides of the intestine are shown at the same level.

Fallopian tubes is a prominent source of infection in women, and in some instances a generalized peritoneal tuberculosis may arise in the same way from tuberculous ulceration of the intestine. The latter, however, more commonly causes rather a localized peritonitis with adhesions. The bacilli are distributed by the prevalent streams in the abdominal cavity, and reach the vault of the diaphragm and the floor of the pelvis in great numbers. Sometimes their effects in the form of tubercles are seen in hernial sacs. In the earliest stages minute gray, translucent tubercles may be scattered everywhere over the surface of the peritoneum and of the omentum, without disturbing the normal gloss.

In other cases the tubercles are quickly covered by an exudate of fibrin, sometimes nearly dry, sometimes with the effusion of a very great amount of clear or slightly turbid fluid, sufficient to float up the intestinal coils and prevent them from being glued together. A soft, friable, vascular granulation tissue springs up and replaces the fibrin, so as to

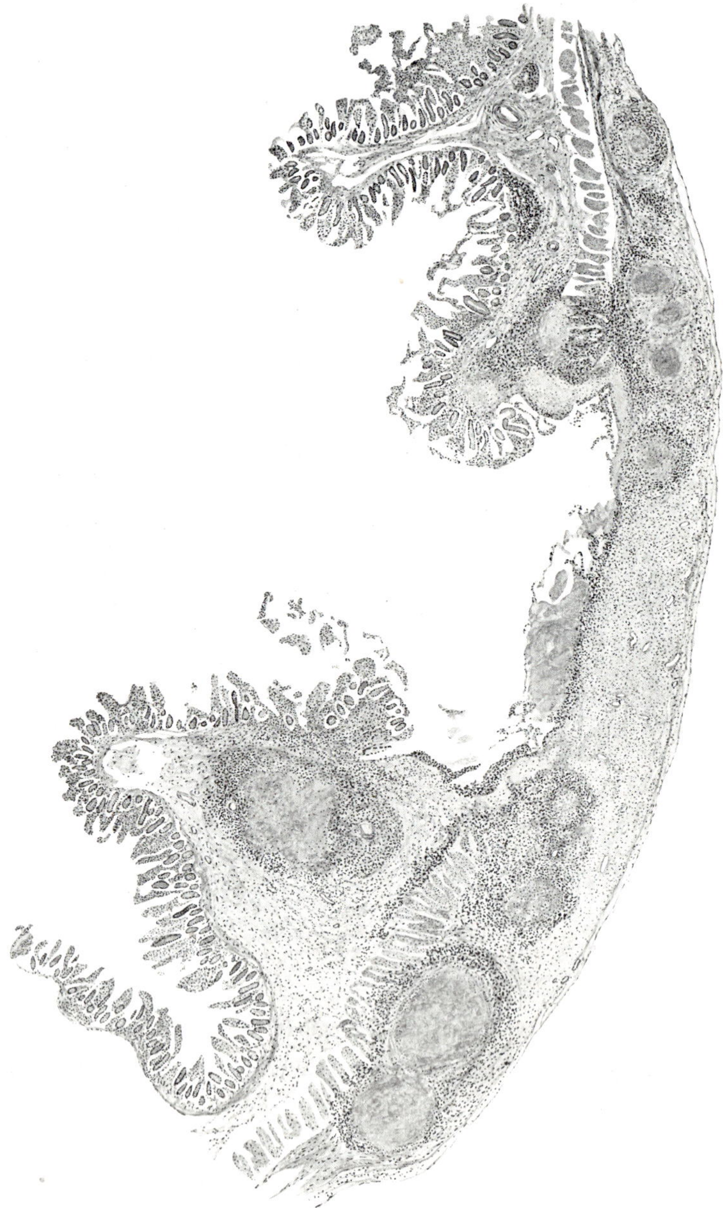

Fig. 330.—A tuberculous ulcer of the ileum, with undermined edges. The ulcer has penetrated the muscularis, and there are tubercles in the submucosa and in the thickened subserous tissue.

form organized adhesions in the cases where there is no fluid, and in these adhesions the tubercles become larger and centrally caseous. The omentum is retracted and folded so as to form a solid, prismatic mass, which can readily be felt stretching across the abdomen. In its substance tubercles and caseous areas are embedded with the fat lobules in a tuberculous granulation tissue. With the lapse of time the adhesions become dense and tough, so as to bind the abdominal contents inextricably together into a matted mass. Over the liver and spleen, and especially between the liver and the diaphragm, quite large caseous areas may form in these adhesions, and even the tearing apart of the intestines may open cavities and canals filled with soft caseous material. Withal the intestinal mucosa may be quite intact.

In those cases, however, in which the peritoneal infection is due to the exposure of

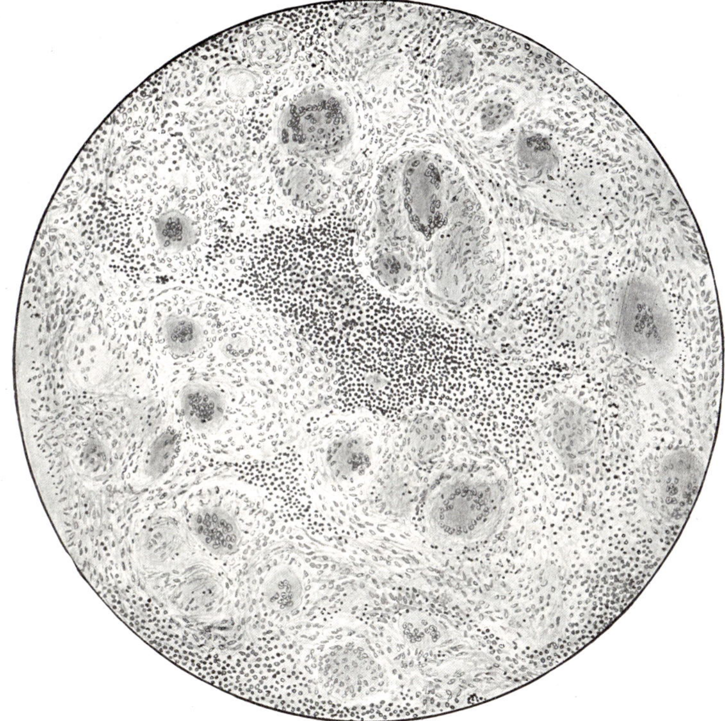

Fig. 331.—Scattered tubercles in a lymph-gland.

caseous tubercles outside intestinal ulcers, the affected areas are usually bound together, so that finally perforation of the ulcer produces only localized fæcal abscesses in the adhesions, or fistulous communications between adjacent coils. Where the resistance is high, the intestines may be found matted together by adhesions which are loose and fibrous and which show only here and there scattered encapsulated tubercles.

In other cases large encapsulated and sometimes pedunculated tubercles may occur in association with old adhesions, or even without much other change in the peritoneum. All these things indicate the possibility of healing, and, indeed, the idea has been widely entertained that those thick fibrous plates which are often found partly covering the liver and spleen (the so-called iced liver) may perhaps be due to a healed tuberculosis, even though they show no distinct anatomical evidences of their origin. In the acute forms, where there is much fluid exudate, definite advances toward healing may sometimes be attained by opening the peritoneum and removing the exudate. This has been explained by Wright on the ground that the accumulated fluid has exhausted its bactericidal power, and that the advent of fresh fluid and cellular exudate brings with it new powers of destroying the organisms.

The distribution of the tubercle bacilli is particularly well followed in the study of the lesions of the lymph-nodes, for these organs act as sieves in the course of the lymph-channels along which the bacilli are so commonly carried. For this reason changes produced and registered in these nodes are of assistance as a clue to the portal of entry of the organisms.

Tuberculosis of Lymph-glands.—The lesions are quite the same in character as elsewhere. The bacilli lodge in the sinuses of the gland or are carried into the lymph-cords, and produce tubercles often with associated tuberculous granulation tissue and an inwandering of many large mononuclear phagocytic cells (Fig. 331). The tubercles are sometimes discrete and remain so, but more often they become conglomerated and suffer extensive caseation, so that almost the whole gland may be reduced to a soft, cheesy mass. Healing occurs through hyaline changes and scarring, generally with the deposit of calcium in coarse grains, or in such a way as to convert the whole gland into something like an irregular pebble tightly bound up in a fibrous capsule.

Fig. 332.—Pocket of caseous cervical lymph-glands.

All these lesions are most common in the bronchial glands, but are very frequent in the mesenteric nodes also, where, especially in children, very great enlargement may take place and is sometimes known as *tabes mesenterica*.

From tuberculous foci in the tonsils and upper air-passages the cervical chain of glands may be infected and caseous. In such a case they become matted together by fibrous growth and present a great swelling along the side of the neck (Fig. 332). The caseous material may sometimes burrow out to the skin, so that a discharging sinus is established. More rarely a similar condition is met with in the axilla or groin, sometimes as the result of peripheral tuberculous infections. The thoracic duct, receiving bacilli from tuberculous abdominal glands, may develop caseating tubercles along its lining and thus contribute to the formation of an acute miliary tuberculosis.

In the spleen there occur miliary and conglomerate tubercles, often rather loose and cellular in their structure, and without the coherent tissue formation seen elsewhere. In this organ, too, there arise very large caseous solitary tubercles with dense fibrous capsule (see Fig. 307).

Tuberculosis of the Genito-urinary Tract.—The development of the tuberculous lesions and their anatomical form, as well as their ultimate fate, are quite the same in these organs as elsewhere, but the mode of entrance of the bacilli and their further distribution have long been debatable.

As has been stated, direct introduction of bacilli by coitus is rarely shown to be productive of genital tuberculosis. Infection of the genito-urinary tract is practically limited to the deposition there of bacilli brought into the blood-stream, but even then there are favorable and unfavorable localizations. In general miliary tuberculosis tubercles can develop nearly everywhere. When fewer bacilli are in circulation, however, and the development of a tuberculous focus depends in some degree upon favorable conditions in an organ, we find that the kidney, the epididymis, and sometimes the Fallopian tubes are the most susceptible to the infection. It is in them that the oldest lesions are found, and it is from these primary foci of disease that bacilli spread to infect the rest of the genito-urinary tract. Walker and Sawamura find that the initial lesion is practically never in the bladder or ureters, in the prostate, seminal vesicles, vasa deferentia, or testis, but that all these structures are readily enough infected secondarily, when great quantities of bacilli are poured into them from a caseous kidney or epididymis. So, also, in the female the ovary and uterus are rarely affected primarily, while the tissue of the Fallopian tube seems specially susceptible and later distributes bacilli in quantity elsewhere.

With these results in mind there are relatively few difficulties in explaining the distribution of the disease. With regard to the genital glands in the male, it is not impossible that tuberculosis of prostate and seminal vesicles should arise by infection from the bladder, and that the disease should extend along the vas deferens to the epididymis, but the reverse direction is more common. More dispute has arisen as to the possibility of an ascending tuberculous infection of the kidney from tuberculous disease of the bladder, in a way analogous to that admittedly followed in the ascending suppurative pyelonephritis following cystitis. *A priori* this would seem the most plausible explanation when one finds, at autopsy, an old caseous focus in the epididymis, tuberculosis of the prostate and bladder and of the ureter, pelvis, and kidney on one or both sides. But although isolated tuberculosis of the kidney and also ulceration of the bladder occur, it becomes impossible to tell their relation when they are combined. Naturally, those cases speak most strongly in favor of the ascending infection in which an extensive ulceration of the bladder is combined with beginning tuberculous disease in the calyces of the kidney, but these are rare.

Materials pass out of the bladder into the ureter only when, through ulceration, the valve-like ureteral orifice is destroyed, or when, through obstruction, the bladder *contracts* against a quantity of urine which cannot readily escape. In hundreds of experimental infections of the bladder in animals, however, such ascending infection has been produced only a few times. Lymphatic transportation along the ureters seems not to occur, and the great weight of the evidence from experimental studies is in favor of the primary hæmatogenous infection of the kidney with secondary infection of the bladder.

Tuberculosis of the Kidney.—In generalized miliary tuberculosis minute tubercles are found in the cortex of the kidney, beginning, as Benda states, in the glomerular capillaries, where masses of bacilli are lodged as emboli. Doubtless they may be formed also about the other capillaries, and in their growth and conglomeration they soon extend in a direction parallel with that of the conducting tubules, to form gray streaks, often with an opaque yellow centre, reaching from the cortex into the pyramid.

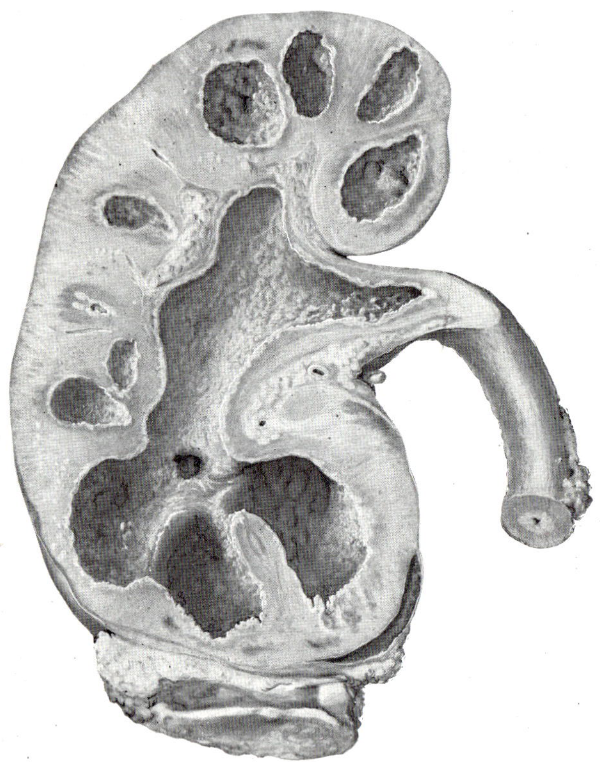

Fig. 333.—Renal phthisis. The tuberculous process has excavated the calyces of the kidney far into the cortex. There is great thickening of the ureter.

Probably tubercles are also formed by bacilli which lodge in the tubules in the course of excretion (Aschoff), and these may take part in the production of the more extensive caseous areas which arise in the margin between cortex and pyramid (Israel). Such caseous areas grow until they destroy much of the kidney substance and discharge their contents into the pelvis. In other cases the caseating area begins in the papillary part of the pyramid, usually up in an angle of the calyx, and from there the process of erosion extends deeply into the kidney. These are the cases which specially suggest an origin from an ascending infection. In any event the late result is the great destruction of the kidney substance. What remains of the pelvis is ulcerated; the papillæ have disappeared, and the calyces are represented by irregular cavities lined by caseous granulation tissue and excavated deep into the kidney (Fig. 333). The organ may be enormously enlarged and finally appear as a lobulated, sacculated mass in the walls of which hardly any kidney substance remains. If the capsule is perforated, a perirenal tuberculous infection occurs, and the extension of the caseating process, preceded, as always, by the formation of tuberculous granulation tissue, can go on until a fistulous tract is opened into the peritoneum or out through the skin. Healing must be very rare, but one finds occasionally shrunken kidneys with encapsulated, mortar-like, or stony masses of probable tuberculous origin. In persons whose resistance is great the caseation is often limited by the enormous production of scar tissue, so that the kidney, while greatly enlarged, contains relatively small pyramidal cavities surrounded by thick walls of fibrous tissue.

It is perhaps unnecessary to describe in any detail the tuberculous lesions in the rest of the genito-urinary tract, since in each case they are due to the development of tubercles in or under the mucosa, soon becoming associated with abundant granulation tissue which undergoes caseation but causes great thickening of the walls of these organs.

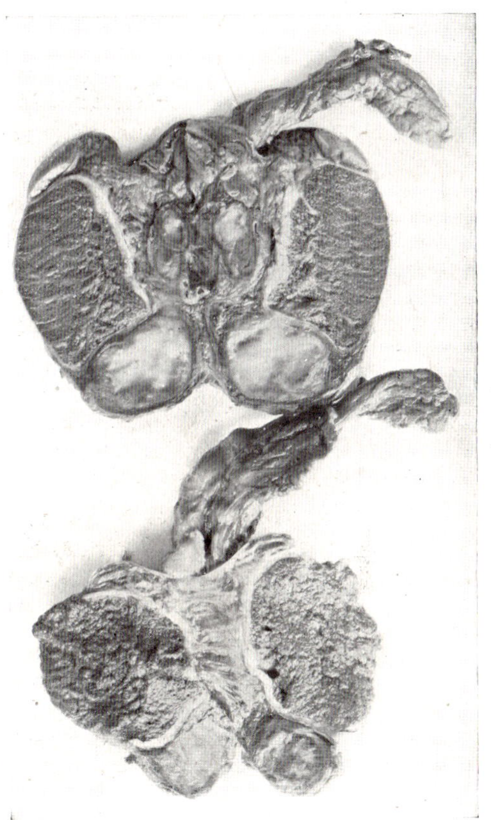

Fig. 334.—Tuberculosis of epididymis (bilateral).

The *ureter* becomes a wide but rigid tube, with ragged ulcerated lining, and is easily felt through the abdominal wall. In the bladder miliary and conglomerate tubercles occur in the mucosa, especially of the trigonum, followed later by shallow, ragged ulcerations with nodular base. The *seminal vesicles* show tubercles in the mucosa, or the wall is thickened and the lumen choked with the product of its caseation. Distinct tubercles are not usually seen in the *prostate*, but the gland becomes enlarged and riddled with caseous patches. The *vasa deferentia* are enlarged and filled with caseous material, so as to be impervious, and in quite the same way the tuberculous *epididymis* (Fig. 334) forms a great caseous mass which may discharge by fistulæ through the skin of the scrotum. Invasion into the *testicle* may take the same form, or there are scattered tubercles.

In the *ovary* tubercles may be found in preformed cysts or in the tissue itself, the caseation and softening of which produce a cavity. The *Fallopian tubes* behave much like the seminal vesicles—their walls are sometimes thickened and studded with small tubercles, which, when on the outside, appear really as a form of localized tuberculous peritonitis. The tube may later become distended and obstructed with caseous substance. In the *uterus* caseation of the endometrium of the fundus is not very rare.

LITERATURE

Benda: Orth's Festschrift, Berlin, 1903, 520.
Sawamura: Deutsch. Arch. f. Chir., 1910, ciii, 203.
Walker: Johns Hopkins Hosp. Reports, 1911, xvi, 1.

Tuberculosis of the Nervous System.—The central nervous system does not escape tuberculous infection, which is usually carried to it by the blood-stream, although occasionally it may be due to direct extension from a caseous focus in neighboring bony structures. In the substance of the brain or cord caseating tubercles of every size appear. These may be multiple, and are found scattered everywhere as yellow, opaque, caseous nodules surrounded by a hæmorrhagic zone. It is in the brain that there occur sometimes tumor-like caseous masses of great size, which are merely enormously overgrown caseous tubercles. These "solitary tubercles" cause great disturbances both through the destruction of tissue and the pressure which they produce. In the spinal cord they are especially sure to interrupt important conducting tracts.

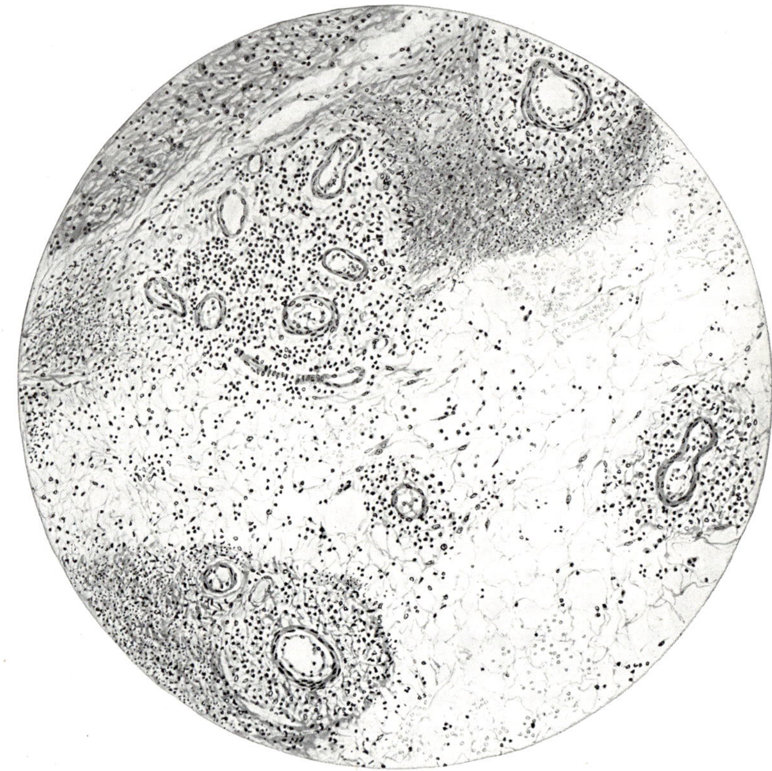

Fig. 335.—A portion of the meninges from a case of tuberculous meningitis, showing the formation of a thick wall of tuberculous tissue in the adventitia of each vessel.

When the bacilli are not thus localized in certain areas in the brain, they may be carried into the meninges and there produce miliary tubercles, or more commonly a combination of tubercles, with an effusion of cellular and fluid exudate which constitutes tuberculous meningitis. This is often spoken of as basilar meningitis, since the exudate is likely to be found especially over the pons, the floor of the third ventricle, and the optic chiasm. Nevertheless, it extends into the fissures over the surface of the brain, and on pulling open the Sylvian fissure, one can nearly always find tubercles along the blood-vessels with the yellowish exudate about them.

The ependymal lining of the ventricles usually presents similar minute tubercles on its surface, and the ventricles are often distended with a turbid, flaky fluid constituting an inflammatory hydrocephalus. In the meninges the tuberculous lesions develop in the walls of the vessels, where they may be seen in sections (Fig. 335) as eccentric thickenings affecting especially the adventitial coat, but causing also an obliterative growth of the intima. The media is generally passively invaded and destroyed by the growth of the mass. Such tubercles are usually not sharply defined, like those miliary tubercles seen in the liver or a lymph-gland, but appear as irregular collections of epithelioid cells by no means concentrically arranged. Ordinarily the person dies before any extensive caseation occurs, and generally the tubercles are found translucent. They are in the most acute cases surrounded on all sides by an exudate which distends the meshes of the pia, and even overflows on its surface. This exudate is rich in fibrin and full of mononuclear wandering cells, many of which are of the lymphoid form, while the large, pale phagocytic forms with abundant protoplasm are very numerous and give a special character to the exudate. Polymorphonuclear leucocytes are in the minority, if they are present at all.

Tuberculosis of the Ductless Glands.—Among the organs of internal secretion the only instance in which we know that tuberculous disease is of practical importance is that of the adrenal glands. Miliary and conglomerate tubercles occur there, but more commonly extensive caseous areas develop which can involve the whole gland on both sides and destroy it completely. In such cases Addison's disease, of which we shall speak in another place, generally follows.

Tuberculosis of the Skin.—In the skin there are certain definitely tuberculous conditions, among which *lupus vulgaris* is the most common, in which the bacilli may be found producing tubercles and tuberculous granulation tissue. Recently in a case of generalized miliary tuberculosis I have seen numerous papules and vesicles scattered all over the body and containing tubercle bacilli. There are other lesions of the skin, however, such as *lichen scrophulosorum*, which are known as tuberculides, and which, though always associated with tuberculosis, have yet been studied without avail in the search for bacilli or tuberculous tissue. They have been thought to be due to diffused toxins, or even to be the expression of an anaphylactic reaction.

Tuberculosis of Bones and Joints.—This subject is so far reaching in its details that no attempt can be made here to give more than the barest outline. For the rest, surgical works must be consulted.

The bacilli are brought to the bones and joints by the blood-stream or by extension from a neighboring lesion. It is especially in the bones that

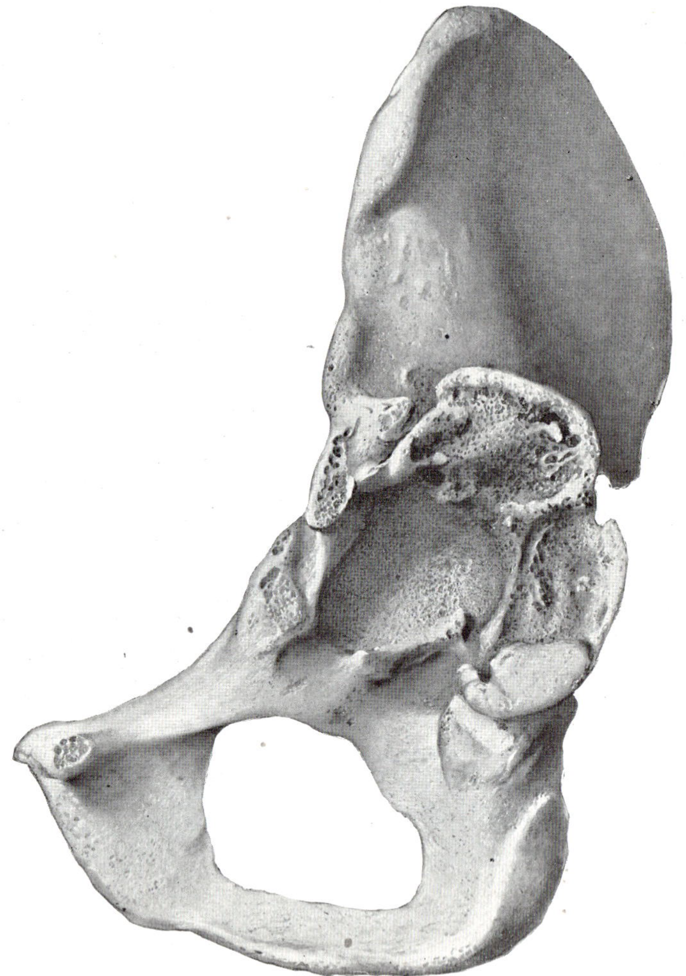

Fig. 336.—An old healed tuberculous lesion of the hip which has left the acetabulum greatly distorted and with numerous exostoses.

traumatism aids in the development of the infection by forming a point of lowered resistance where the bacteria can gain a foothold. Accordingly, it is not uncommon to find lesions formed in the bones in the apparent absence of tuberculosis elsewhere.

Tuberculous lesions usually begin, as Guillemain has maintained in opposition to König, in the bone, rather than in the synovial cavities of the joints, and it is the cancellous bone which is usually first involved—practically never the shafts of long bones. Miliary tubercles may, of course, occur, but far more important is the tuberculous osteomyelitis, which is not part of a general miliary tuberculosis. This begins in one of the short bones, such as a vertebra or tarsal bone, or in the epiphyseal ends of the long bones, and is doubtless the result of the lodgment of the bacilli in a small vessel. Miliary and conglomerate tubercles with tuberculous granulation tissue form in the cancellous bone, and caseation occurs more or less rapidly. Some authors distinguish as "fungous" forms those in which the granulation tissue persists a long time without caseation. In any case the bone lamellæ are destroyed or remain as splinters. Hardly any new bone formation occurs around the focus—indeed, it is not uncommon to find a great rarefaction with replacement of the marrow by fat. Such a caseous area often extends in pyramidal or rounded form to the joint surface, whereupon the joint becomes infected also; the cartilage becomes necrotic, uplifted, and softened. At first, miliary tubercles may appear on the synovial membranes, with effusion of fluid. Later the joint is lined by a tuberculous granulation tissue, and the condition may last for a long time, with persistence of the fluid, induration of the tissues around the joint, formation of polypoid clusters of fat tissue and of small hyaline bodies, like rice grains, in its cavity. Irregular erosions of the surfaces occur, and indeed there follow the most extensive excavations into the bone, with collapse and wide destruction of the mechanism of the joint. Fistulæ are burrowed out through the surrounding muscles and fasciæ to the skin, through which caseous débris and spicules of bone are discharged. Such destructive processes are very common in the hip-joint and especially in children. The whole head of the femur may be destroyed and the bone dislocated. To relieve the tenderness and pain the leg is drawn up and rotated inward, and through disuse it atrophies. When the joint disease heals, there remains the condition so often seen in people in the street who walk with the affected leg held stiffly bent and with the aid of a crutch.

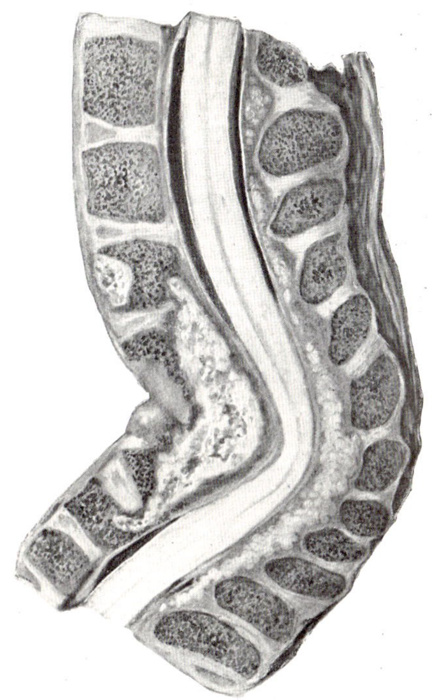

Fig. 337.—Tuberculosis of the vertebræ, with caseation and collapse of the centra which causes compression of the spinal cord.

Tuberculosis of a vertebra proceeds in practically the same way (Fig. 337). When caseation has advanced far enough to soften the bone, the affected centrum is crushed together by the weight of the body, and an angular deformity of the spine ensues. The burrowing of the material produced in this process under the sheath of the psoas muscle, to appear below Poupart's ligament, gives rise to the so-called psoas abscess. A similar thing can happen in the case of other bones, and we have seen recently an extensive burrowing from the region of a tuberculous knee-joint.

Tuberculosis of the bones of the face and of the ribs is generally in the beginning a periosteal affection which erodes the bone and produces accumulations of caseous material—the so-called "cold abscess." In the fingers there may be central caseation in the diaphysis of the phalanges, with secondary new-growth of bone outside. The enlargement of the internal cavity and the repetition of the reparatory process result finally in a spindle-shaped enlargement of the bony shell (spina ventosa).

LITERATURE

Härtel: "Tuberc. Peritonitis," Ergeb. d. Chir., 1913, vi, 370.

Fedor Krause: "Tuberculosis of Bones," Deut. Chirurgie, 1899. Lief 28a.

F. König: Tuberculose d. Knochen u. Gelenke, Berlin, 1884.

CHAPTER XXXIII

TYPES OF INJURY.—INFECTIONS OF UNCERTAIN NATURE

Typhus: Epidemic distribution. Indefinite anatomical lesions. Experimental studies, transmission by lice. A bacillus recently discovered.
Acute poliomyelitis: Infectious nature. The organism. Febrile illness, subsequent paralysis. Lesions of nervous system.

TYPHUS INFECTION

The disease has long been recognized as occurring in great epidemics with high mortality. In 1819 and 1846 it raged with especial violence in England and Ireland, although extensive epidemics had been more common in Russia and the Balkan countries. It is a disease which associates itself with the crowding and unsanitary conditions of war and famine. It was common in prisons. We are even now hearing daily of its ravages in Servia, where all the favoring conditions exist.

In spite of the unfortunate choice of name (Typhus exanthematicus), it has nothing whatever to do with typhoid fever (typhus abdominalis). The distinction between the two diseases was clearly made by W. W. Gerhard in a vivid description which is to be found in the American Journal of the Medical Sciences, 1836, after Louis had described the lesions of typhoid.

Typhus is an acute infectious disease marked by high fever, intense illness and weakness, an outbreak of a macular or papular eruption which is often hæmorrhagic, laryngitis, with cough or the more serious symptoms of lobular pneumonia. Death occurs with symptoms of general intoxication and circulatory collapse.

Lesions.—At autopsy, so far, no characteristic lesions whatever have been found, although the organs show in general evidence of the existence of an acute infection. In one autopsy in the small epidemic which occurred in Baltimore in 1901, we found cloudy swelling of the liver and kidney, moderate enlargement of the spleen, and hyperplasia of the bone-marrow. There were no changes in the intestines of any sort. This has been about the result of the autopsies described by others.

Dr. Zinsser tells me that the cases which he observed in Servia during the spring began with malaise, conjunctivitis, and dry mouth, and that only after five or six days was the diagnosis made clear by the appearance of the exanthem. In most instances this was not markedly hæmorrhagic. Death occurred usually, not in the acute stages, but later, after these symptoms had passed off and the irregular fever had fallen. In 20 autopsies nothing was found except extreme swelling and softness of the spleen.

This organ was, at times, so tense and soft as to burst in the hand. Bronchopneumonia was an uncommon occurrence.

Brill has recognized the existence of a disease in New York which has all the characteristics of mild typhus infection, and there is in Mexico another affection, called *tabardillo,* which is quite similar.

Experimental work in recent years has done a good deal to clear up the nature and relation of these infections, although it is by no means finished. Nicolle, Goldberger and Anderson, Ricketts, and Wilder have studied especially the transmission, using monkeys as test animals. Nicolle and his associates found that they could transmit the typhus found in Tunis to monkeys by inoculating the blood of patients. Further, that while it became evident that infection is not transferred directly, nor through bedding, clothes, etc., nor by fleas or bed-bugs, it could be shown that the body-louse (Pediculus vestimentorum), becomes infected by biting those who have the disease and transmits it in full virulence by biting others. Goldberger and Anderson, and Ricketts, were able to confirm this in Mexico by allowing such infected lice to bite monkeys or by grinding them and injecting a suspension of their bodies subcutaneously. The monkeys develop a fever and sometimes die, but do not show the roseola which is so characteristic of human infection. Nevertheless they become immune and after recovery are insusceptible even to injections of blood from a typhus patient. All this is also true of Brill's disease, and Goldberger and Anderson think it therefore identical with Mexican and European typhus. They found in Mexico that the causative agent is too large to pass through a Berkefeld filter, but could not associate it with any particular element of the blood. They found, however, a bacillus in the blood which they could not cultivate. The question remains undecided, therefore, whether the virus which causes the disease is merely transferred by the louse, or undergoes some stage of development in its body. Even the fact that the lice appear not to be able to transfer the infection until a period of four or five days has elapsed may mean that only after that period has the organism multiplied to a sufficient quantity for infection, and not that it has undergone part of a definite life cycle within the louse.

The general impression of typhus fever at this stage was that it resembled closely such other diseases as are transmitted by insects and would probably turn out to be caused by a parasite of protozoan character. We have, however, in the plague, a good example of a bacterial disease transmitted by fleas.

Quite recently, Plotz, of Mount Sinai Hospital, New York City, has stated that he finds in a great proportion of cases of Brill's disease and of imported typhus fever an anaërobic, Gram-staining bacillus in the circulating blood which produces the disease on being inoculated in pure culture into animals, and which is agglutinated by the blood-serum of the patients. Practically every postulate for the recognition of the cause of a disease has been fulfilled by Plotz in connection with this bacillus, and it is to be hoped that the problem is solved. It is too soon, however, to judge, and there are those who find the results inconclusive.

LITERATURE

Curschmann: Das Fleckfieber, Nothnagel's Spec. Path. u. Ther., 1900, iii, Th. 2.
Virchow: Virch. Arch., 1849, Bd. ii, 143; iii, 154.
Nicolle, Comte, and Conseil: Comptes Rendus Acad. de Sci., 1909, cxlix, 157, 486.
Goldberger and Anderson: Hygienic Laboratory Bull., 1912, No. 86. Public Health Reports, 1910, xxv, 177; *ibid.*, 1912, xxvii, 71.
Ricketts and Wilder: Jour. Amer. Med. Assn., 1910, liv, 463.
N. E. Brill: Amer. Jour. Med. Sci., 1910, cxxxix, 484; 1911, cxlii, 196.
Friedmann: Arch. of Int. Med., 1911, viii, 427.
Plotz, Olitsky, Baehr: N. Y. Path. Soc., 1915, xv, 41; Jour. Infect. Dis., 1915, xvii, 1.

ACUTE POLIOMYELITIS (HEINE-MEDIN'S DISEASE)

Recent studies have shown that this disease of children, which was formerly regarded as a type of paralysis with sudden and unheralded onset, is really an acute infectious disease which is transmitted from person to person, occurs in epidemics, and can be reproduced by inoculation in monkeys (Popper and Landsteiner, Flexner). Indeed, it has been shown that the causative agent is small enough to pass through a porcelain filter (Flexner, Landsteiner), that it can be grown in pure culture, and that it will produce the disease in animals (Flexner, Noguchi). The precise nature of the organism and its relations to other living beings are not made clear, but it is said to be an extremely minute, coccus-like form sometimes appearing in chains and causing a clouding of the fluid medium. It can be isolated from the infected brain and cord and can be shown to be present in the nasal mucosa of inoculated monkeys and persons ill of the disease. It seems that all the postulates for the proof of the relation of an organism to a disease have been fulfilled in this case.

The disease begins, usually in children, with vomiting, fever, leucocytosis, and general malaise. Pain in the back, neck, and extremities is nearly always present and is sometimes extreme, so that the child winces and cries out on being moved. After several days' illness, paralyses suddenly appear and extend to involve one or both legs or a leg and arm or even all the extremities, together with the trunk muscles. Paralyses of the muscles supplied by the cranial nerves are not frequent. When the respiratory muscles are thus involved, death ensues.

The paralysis is most commonly of the flaccid type but in some cases it is spastic. The mortality is fairly high but many cases recover with permanent paralysis. Atrophy of the muscles with subsequent contractures lead to the most crippling deformities. On the other hand, there are many so-called abortive cases in which, after the initial febrile symptoms are over, recovery takes place without any paralysis. Survival of the disease leaves an immunity, and the serum of such immune individuals has a protective effect in animals inoculated with the disease-producing agent. It is through the discovery of the existence of such an immunity that one may recognize those persons who have passed through an abortive attack.

Transmission.—Doubtless they, as well as those more seriously affected, can act as carriers and transmitters of the disease, and it was partly through the recognition of this fact that the chain of events could be made complete in the explanation of the epidemic occurrence of this affection. An attempt was made to show that the transfer of infection was effected by the bites of stable flies, but further study has proved that this is not true. Flexner has shown that it is difficult to inoculate monkeys successfully, but that repeated apparently ineffectual inoculations may finally produce the disease. The subdural inoculation of material from the brain or cord of a case of poliomyelitis is the most effective means of transmission, but monkeys can also be infected through the nasal mucosa. When the virus is injected into the blood, it requires a much longer time to develop. It seems, therefore, that the organisms must gain access to the cerebrospinal fluid, either by direct transmission from the nasal passages or possibly along the lymphatics of the nerve-sheaths. Perhaps the tonsils and digestive tract may play some part as portals of entry.

Lesions.—The chief lesions are found in the central nervous system, and commonly the predominant changes are found in the anterior part of the spinal cord. There are such variations, however, that Müller has proposed a division into cerebral, bulbar and spinal forms. Peabody, Draper and Dochez suggest what seems a better division, into affections of the upper and of the lower neurone, but this too is open to objections. It is useful in separating the spastic cases which are affections of the upper motor neurone from those with flaccid paralysis in which the anterior horn ganglion-cells are especially attacked. The changes begin, as can be studied in experimental animals and in the cases which end fatally in the early stages, with hyperæmia of the pia and of the blood-vessels which pass into the cord through the anterior fissure and with the accumulation of lymphocytes and polymorphonuclear leucocytes about them (Fig. 338). This process quickly extends into the substance of the cord, and not only in the gray matter of the anterior horns, as was formerly thought, but everywhere, the small arterioles and venules are found surrounded with a mantle of such cells. Isolated groups of leucocytes are scattered through the tissue. Destructive changes become apparent in the ganglion-cells, perhaps especially in those of the anterior horn, and they are soon found to be in the process of disintegration or shrinkage. There is disintegration and fusion of the tigroid bodies and later the nucleus in each cell shrinks and becomes deeply stained or fades away and disappears. Direct invasion of phagocytic cells into the bodies of such ganglion-cells is often observed and the remains are surrounded by a cluster of them. Many writers try to show that the mechanical effect of the inflammation causes the injury to the ganglion-cells, but it seems more probable that it is the direct result of the presence of the infective agent.

With recovery, the injured ganglion-cells disappear completely, and after the fading of the inflammatory reaction the place is occupied by a dense neuroglia scar. Quite analogous lesions are found in the medulla oblongata, where the nuclei of cranial nerves become affected, and in the higher parts of the brain as well. This is referred to as polioencephalitis (Strümpell).

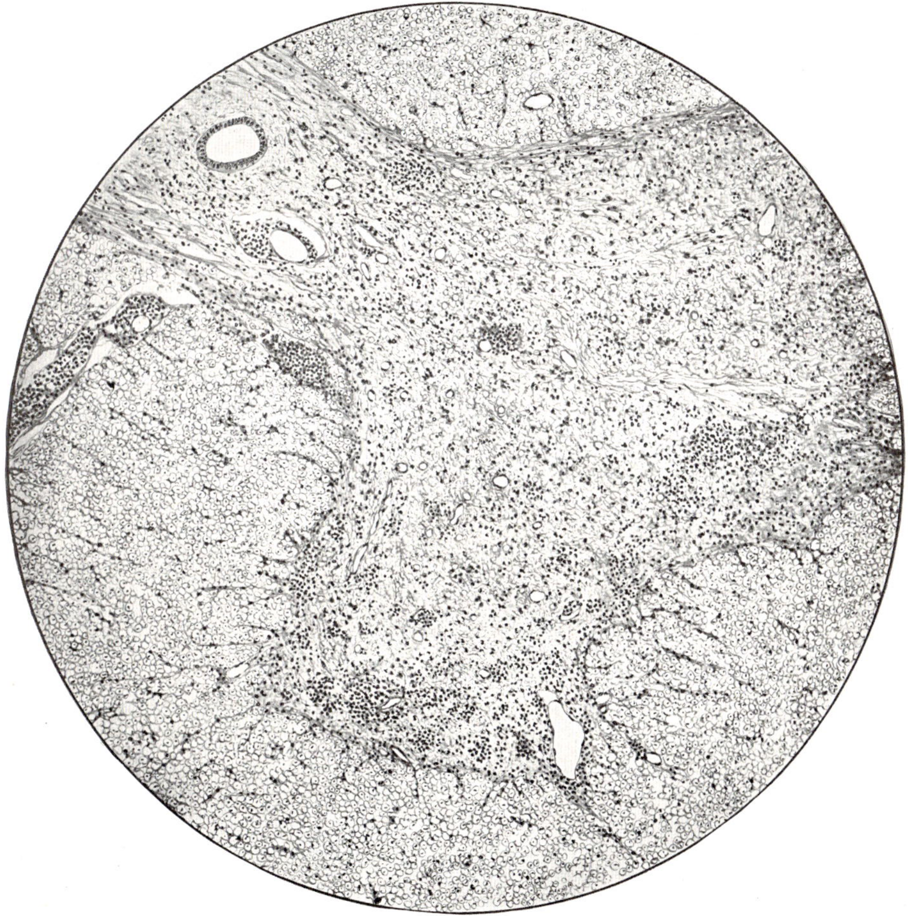

Fig. 338.—Acute poliomyelitis. Spinal cord, showing a portion of the gray matter infiltrated with leucocytes accumulated about the vessels. Ganglion-cells of the anterior horn have become indistinct or lost.

In the other organs less characteristic changes are found, but reference may be made to minute focal necroses of liver-cells with lymphocyte accumulation, and to similar changes in the lymph-glands which have been described by Peabody, Draper, and Dochez. In such lymph-glands the sinuses are filled with large phagocytic cells, as in typhoid fever. Cloudy swelling of liver and kidneys is usual.

LITERATURE

Wickman: Heine-Medinsche Krankheit, Berlin, 1907. Akute Poliomyelitis, Berlin, 1911. Transl. New York, 1913.

Harbitz and Scheel: Ak. Poliomyelitis u. verwandte Krankheiten, Christiania, 1907. Jour. Amer. Med. Assn., 1907, xlix, 1420; lix, 782. Dtsch. med. Woch., 1907, xxiii, 1992.

I. Strauss: Rep. Collective Investig. Comm. N. Y. Epidemic, 1907.

Peabody, Draper, and Dochez: Ac. Poliomyelitis, Rockefeller Inst. Monographs, 1912, No. 4.

Flexner, with Lewis, Noguchi, and Amoss: Many papers in Jour. Exp. Med., 1913, xviii, 461; 1914, xix, 411; xx, 249; 1915, xxi, 91, etc. Jour. Amer. Med. Assn., 1913, lx, 362, etc.

CHAPTER XXXIV

TYPES OF INJURY.—SPIROCHÆTAL INFECTION

Syphilis: Ætiology and distribution. Course of the disease. Nature of different stages. Immunity and transmission. Primary stage, secondary lesions, tertiary stage. Lymph-glands, blood, digestive tract, liver, respiratory tract, bones and joints, heart and blood-vessels, nervous system.

SYPHILIS

Ætiology and Distribution.—Syphilis is an infectious disease caused by invasion of the Spirochæta pallida, an organism discovered by Schaudinn and Hoffman in 1905. The disease itself had been studied in great detail throughout centuries, and numerous other supposed causes had been described, but the discovery of the true ætiological factor has caused a great flood of light to be shed upon it during the few years which have followed.

The infection is not one which remains local—instead, it gives rise in each case to a generalized distribution of the organisms with numerous local manifestations, often due to concentration of the spirochætæ in those places.

First introduced through an abrasion of the skin or through a mucous surface, it produces within a short time a general septicæmia, which in turn gives rise to the local lesions, almost countless in their variety.

The organism is not limited to man as its host, although until the recent experimental work, it seems to have been practically so limited. It is now known that anthropoid apes, and indeed most of the monkey tribe, even to the lower forms, are susceptible, and that with proper precautions rabbits, sheep, goats, and other animals may be successfully inoculated. Not in all these animals do the lesions present themselves in form and order like those found in the human being, but all the postulates necessary to prove the relation of the organism to the disease, whether produced experimentally or not, have been complied with, including the isolation and pure culture of the spirochætæ in an artificial medium.

Ordinarily the disease is transmitted by coitus, but it is also quite frequently traceable to extragenital infection, as through kissing, the use of infected utensils, towels, etc., or through shaving with an infected razor. The danger to surgeons and dentists of infecting their fingers through cuts or abrasions during an operation upon a syphilitic is considerable.

Course of the Disease.—Syphilis is usually a very slowly progressing disease, and except in the so-called "syphilis maligna," it advances pretty regularly through a series of stages first clearly recognized by Ricord. Thus, after an incubation period of varying duration (8 to 40 days), there appears a characteristic local lesion which often ulcerates at the point of inoculation. Regional lymph-glands become infected and swollen.

After a second incubation period of varying length, often eight to ten weeks after the first infection, there appear in the skin and mucous surfaces new manifestations caused by a distribution of the spirochætæ by the blood and their multiplication in certain places. These are the lesions of the secondary stage, and here the greatest variety of form is shown. Lymph-glands in general are enlarged, and some other tissues, such as the iris, cerebral vessels, testes, etc., may be involved. The secondary lesions usually heal without leaving any great destruction behind them.

After another period, which may stretch out over very many years during which the patient has supposed himself cured, the destructive lesions of the tertiary stage appear. These arise in any situation in the internal organs or the skin—no tissue seems exempt. Characteristic is the formation of tubercle-like nodules, often of large size and firm consistence (*gummata*), becoming caseous internally and ending, after wide destruction of tissue, in healing which leaves behind a most extensive scar. Or a less characteristic, wide-spread, cellular granulation tissue may in the same way lead to destruction of the tissue and distortion from scar formation. Following the tertiary stage there may appear still other lesions involving especially injury and scarring in the central nervous system (tabes and progressive paralysis), which have long been suspected of being syphilitic and spoken of as parasyphilitic affections. Recently the spirochætæ have been demonstrated in these tissues (Noguchi) and the matter set upon a firm basis. Even successful treatment by specific medication has been carried out. Such lesions are often said to constitute a quaternary stage of the disease.

Thus, syphilis is seen to be a generalized infection of extraordinary chronicity and tenacity in which, at some periods, the whole blood and tissues of the host are infected with the spirochætæ, while during years they seem to disappear or remain hidden somewhere only to multiply again at some point and produce new changes. There is a certain regularity in the progression of the different stages, although the length of time required for the appearance of each varies extremely.

It was at one time thought (Ricord) that a person who had once had syphilis was quite immune from further infection, and also that while materials from the primary lesion or initial sclerosis as well as those from secondary lesions were highly infective, the tertiary lesion were non-infective. All of this has proven untrue. Finger and Landsteiner showed that a gumma contains living spirochætæ which can produce an initial lesion followed by secondary rashes when inoculated, and they and others have also shown that while a certain increased resistance may appear after the first infection a new inoculation may be successful in any stage of the disease (superinfection). There are many instances in which a whole series of chancres or primary lesions has appeared as the result of successive exposures to infection.

It must be said, however, at this point, that inoculation of the person's own spirochætæ, or of spirochætæ of foreign origin, when it causes new lesions to develop in a person already syphilitic, produces not always chancres but lesions which belong to the stage of the disease in which he is. Thus fresh inoculation of a man harboring tertiary lesions will produce a gummatous or tertiary lesion of the skin and not a chancre, which is a lesion of the primary stage. It appears, therefore, that the stages of the disease represent different reactions to the same poison and the idea has been suggested, though perhaps not proven, that the various rashes and other skin outbreaks are largely allergic phenomena.

Congenital Infection.—Syphilis may be transmitted from infected parents to their offspring during the course of gestation, so that they are born with the disease. This is clearly not a matter of inheritance, but strictly an intra-uterine infection. As to the mode of transmission there has been much dispute, but it is clear that the infection may come from either the father or the mother. It is shown that while the spirochæta does not actually invade the sperm cell, as has been surmised, it may nevertheless accompany it mixed in the spermatic fluid or the secretions of prostate or seminal vesicles. When the mother is definitely syphilitic there is little doubt that the transmission occurs through the placenta by passage of the spirochætæ into the fœtal blood. Sometimes this seems to occur only in the late stage, during partial separation of the placenta and direct admixture of maternal and fœtal blood. Then, there may be an incubation period of apparent health after birth before the symptoms develop in the child. But the great problem is whether all infection of the offspring is placental or whether infection of the fœtus alone can occur from the father, excluding any transfer of spirochætæ from the mother through the placenta. This question is particularly suggested by the fact noticed in 1837 by Colles, that a woman might give birth to a syphilitic child and nurse it without ever showing any signs of syphilis herself, although a wet-nurse would be at once infected by the child.

This is the so-called Colles' law, and it seemed to show that the mother was immune and that the child bore the whole weight of the infection from the father. Recent studies show, however, that the mother, even though she presents no lesions, is actually infected with the spirochætæ and that she gives a positive Wassermann reaction. The so-called exceptions to Colles' law, in which such a mother is infected with syphilis and shows the typical symptoms, must be examples of superinfection, such as we mentioned above. More difficult to explain are the cases in which a mother having given birth to a syphilitic child by one husband produces healthy children by another.

Profeta's law, that a healthy child of a syphilitic mother is immune, is not true—the child may be healthy, but it is susceptible to infection from its mother.

The weight of evidence seems to be in favor of the idea that if a syphilitic child be born of a healthy mother and a syphilitic father it is because the healthy mother has been infected by the father probably by way of the uterine lining, so that no primary lesion is observed and that, after all, the placental mode of transmission may play the important part in the infection of the fœtus.

Immunity.—It may be gathered from what has been said that immunity in syphilis is by no means so definite as in such diseases as smallpox or yellow fever, but that, while there is relative insusceptibility, a new infection is possible at any stage. Evidences of the changed reaction of the body are made clear in various ways, however, and become useful in making a diagnosis. Thus the so-called Wassermann reaction depends upon the fact that the complement necessary for the laking of a sample of red corpuscles in a mixture of hæmolytic amboceptor and corpuscles, is found to have been used up if it is first treated with a mixture of syphilitic serum and a lipoid antigen represented by an extract of a known syphilitic organ or even an alcoholic extract of a normal heart, whereas when treated with normal serum and this antigen, none of the complement is absorbed and hæmolysis proceeds.

This method of deviation of complement is obviously a purely empirical discovery, although it seemed at first, when extracts of known syphilitic organs were used as the antigen, to be a very purposeful demonstration of a specific relation. Its real nature is yet to be determined, but it seems to indicate syphilitic infection very accurately.

Noguchi's method, the luetin reaction, in which an extract of a sterilized culture of spirochætæ is found to produce an inflammatory reaction in the skin of syphilitics and none in normal persons, seems to depend upon an anaphylactic sensitiveness in infected persons. It is positive in tertiary and quaternary stages and in latent forms, but seldom so in the primary and secondary stages.

LITERATURE

Noguchi: Jour. Exp. Med., 1911, xiv, 557.
Rietschel: Ergeb. d. inn. Med. u. Kinderheilk., 1913, xii, 160.
Matzenauer: Die Vererbung der Syphilis, Wien, 1903.
Neisser: Beitr. z. Path. u. Ther. d. Syphilis, Berlin, 1911. Also in: Arb. a. d. Kais. Gesundheitsamt, 1911, xxxvii.
Finger: Handbuch d. Geschlechtskrankheiten, 1912, ii, 896.
Finger u. Landsteiner: Arch. f. Derm. u. Syph., 1906, lxxviii, 335; lxxxi, 147.
Landsteiner: (Exp. Syphilis) Handb. d. Geschlechtskr., 1912, ii, 873.
Herxheimer: Ergeb. d. allg. Path., 1907, xi, 1.
Schaudinn, Hoffman: Arb. a. d. Kais. Gesundheitsamt, 1905, xxii.
Metschnikoff et Roux: Ann. Inst. Pasteur, 1903, xvii, 809.
Uhlenhuth u. Mulzer: Arb. a. d. Kais. Gesundheitsamt, 1913, xliv, 307.

Primary Stage.—The initial lesion or chancre arises, as mentioned above, at the point of infection one to four or more weeks after exposure. It is nearly always dependent upon an abrasion, although in the case of the mucous surfaces it appears that infection can occur directly. The abrasion in the skin or mucosa usually heals after a few days without leaving any trace, and it is only later that the specific lesion appears in the same place. Nevertheless, even though such an area be excised and cauterized a few hours after the exposure, it is frequently, if not always, found that transportation of the spirochætæ has already occurred, so that general infection later makes itself evident. The delay in the appearance of the first sign of the initial lesion is thought to be due to the fact that in the process of accommodating themselves to the new host many of the

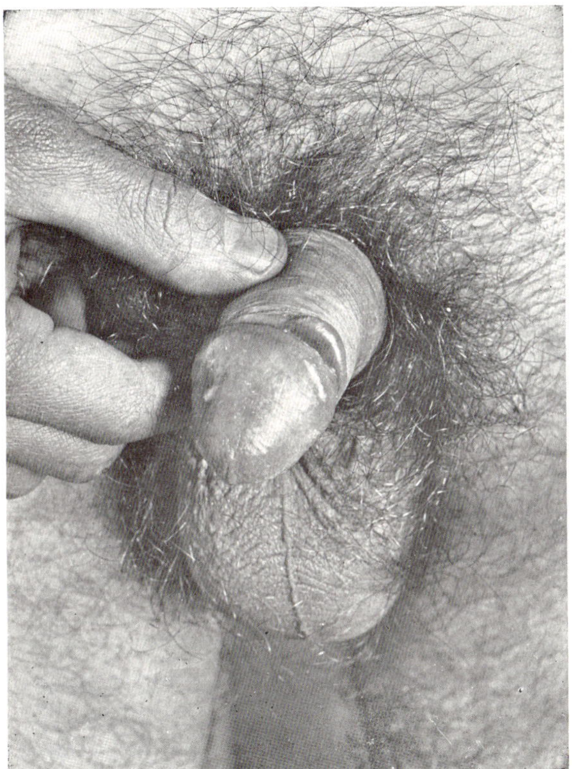

Fig. 339.—Primary syphilitic lesion of corona. Early stage (Fordyce*).

spirochætæ are destroyed, so that it requires time for those which survive to develop the lesion. This begins sometimes as a tiny vesicle, usually as a delicate thickening or induration of the surface tissue, over which, as time passes, the epithelium becomes necrotic and converted into a brownish crust which comes off, leaving a shallow ulcer. The induration extends and becomes a flattened hard mass, easily rendered bloodless by bending or by pressure, and easily movable in the surrounding tissue (Figs. 339 and

* Professor Fordyce has kindly allowed me to use photographs from his clinic for Figs. 339, 340, 342, 343, 344, 345.

340). There is a characteristic, bacon-like translucence about this mass. The ulceration may extend and become quite deep, a considerable area may be involved, and the chancre may persist for quite a time; but, in the end, it heals up, the induration disappearing and the ulcer leaving a scar. Occasionally, but not often, considerable distortion and loss of tissue may be produced.

Histologically (Fig. 341), it is found that the induration is produced by a great accumulation of cells in the skin and subcutaneous tissue. Ehrmann has shown by injections that great numbers of new blood-vessels are formed and that there is stasis in these venules from the pressure of the cells, often with hæmorrhages and the formation of blood-pigment. The accumulated cells are in part polymorphonuclear leucocytes, which are found especially in the base of the ulcer, but predominantly they are mononuclear cells of the type of lymphocytes, plasma cells, and larger mononuclears. They are assembled in great numbers about the blood-vessels whose internal layer is enormously thickened, and extend from the main mass of the induration in the form of thick mantles in and about the ad-

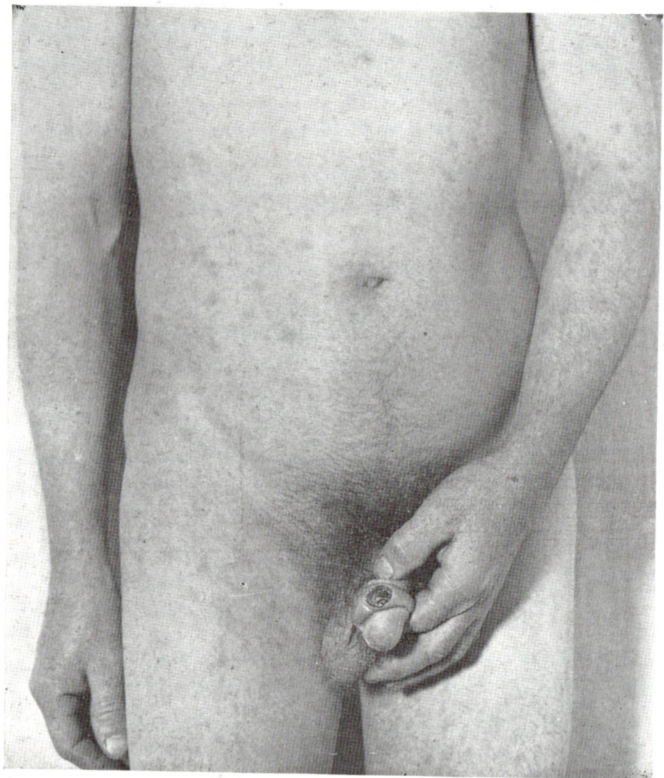

Fig. 340.—Primary syphilitic lesion of prepuce. Later stage, with crust. Secondary rash of macular character over body (Fordyce)

ventitia of such vessels. Ehrmann described the induration as largely dependent upon the alterations in the lymphatic channels, which are often choked with mononuclear cells or with proliferated masses of their own endothelial cells. In our preparations it is difficult to see any such pro-

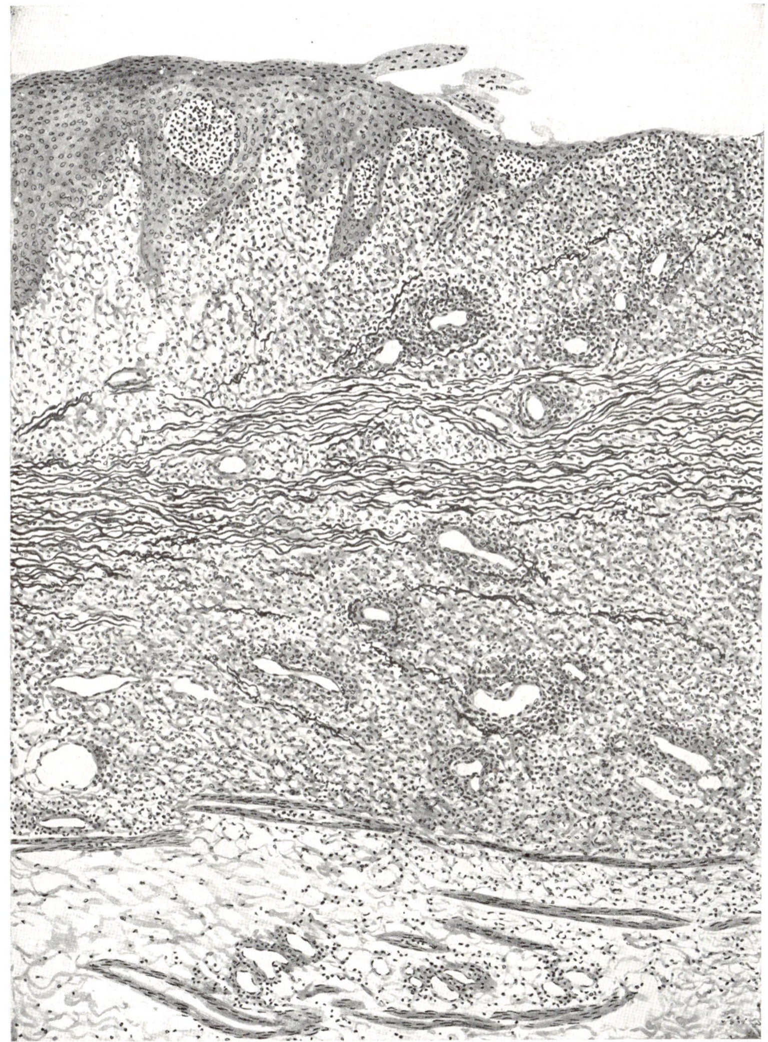

Fig. 341.—Edge of chancre, showing ulceration through the epidermis and great accumulation of mononuclear cells, especially about the vessels and lymphatics.

liferation of the endothelium of lymphatics or blood-vessels, although many of them are packed with wandering cells, but there are masses of tissue composed of large pale cells of irregular and indefinite outline with large vesicular nuclei. These are seen to be proliferated fibroblasts, and they, together with the abundant wandering cells. doubtless give the firmness and translucence to the tissue.

Leading away from the chancre are lymph-channels along the course of which little nodular accumulations of cells may be found.

The chancre may develop on the prepuce, in the coronal sulcus, on the glans penis or the frenulum, or about the orifice of the urethra, in about this order of frequency, or it may appear on the skin of the penis or of the scrotum. In the female the labia majora or minora, the orifice of the vagina, the clitoris, the vault of the vagina, or the vaginal portion of the cervix are the commonest sites. But the lip, tongue, tonsil, or the cheeks, eyelids, breast, fingers, etc., may equally be infected through the various processes of exposure mentioned above.

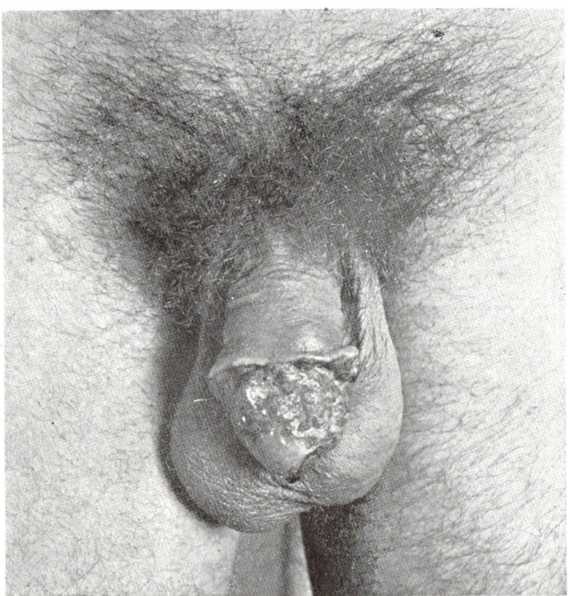

Fig. 342.—Chancroid (Fordyce).

A short time after the appearance of the chancre the regional lymph-glands swell and become hard. The inguinal glands are most commonly affected, of course. In them the spirochætæ are found just as they are in the chancre. The lymph-sinuses are filled with wandering cells, chiefly of the mononuclear type, and later there is a proliferation of the connective-tissue elements. There is little tendency to great swelling or to suppuration in such syphilitic buboes in contrast to the condition following infection with Ducrey's bacillus (soft chancre or chancroid), and that in gonorrhea.

Chancroid or Soft Chancre.—This is a type of ulceration of the genitalia transmitted by coitus or other contact and caused by a small Gram-negative streptobacillus which was described by Ducrey. The bacillus is easily cultivated and often grows in short chains. It is capable of producing a similar ulceration on inoculation in the skin of a person already infected or an uninfected one. The ulcer spreads rapidly and has a ragged outline with undermined edges (Fig. 342). There is no induration about it, but the base is rough and covered with necrotic material and bleeds easily. While the penis and labia are most commonly affected, the ulceration may extend to the skin elsewhere. Red, tender lines which are palpable run from the ulcers toward the inguinal region and are often beaded with little firm nodules. These are the inflamed lymph-channels, and the nodules or *bubonuli* are swollen collections of lymphoid tissue which may become abscesses. The inguinal lymph-glands become greatly swollen and tender (*buboes*); on incision a quantity of purulent material is evacuated and the glands are found to be matted together and excavated by the destructive process which extends from one gland to another. This lesion, like the ulcers, finally heals with an extensive scar. There are no general symptoms and no lesions in other organs.

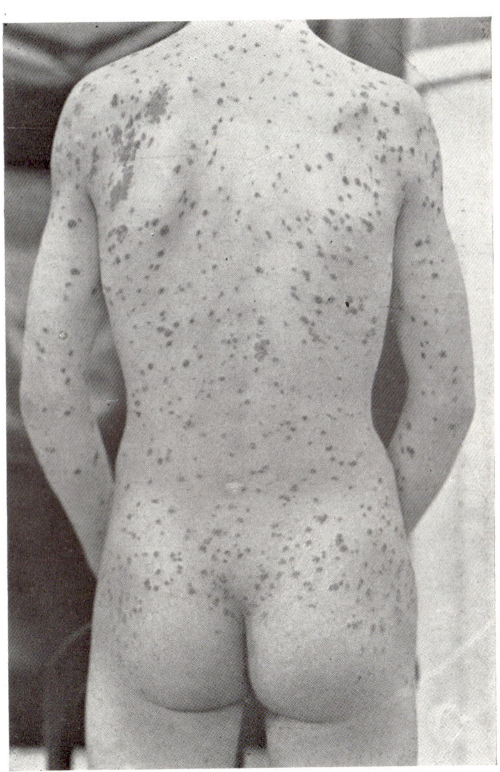

Fig. 343.—Secondary syphilitic lesion of skin. Papular syphilide (Fordyce).

Secondary Stage.—In rare cases, after the healing of the chancre no other symptoms appear, and this may be true if vigorous medication be instituted in the primary stage. But usually eight or ten weeks after the infection, that is, after a second incubation period, the secondary lesions of the skin and mucosæ make their appearance with fever, loss of appetite, muscular pains, etc. No brief description can even outline satisfactorily the extraordinary variety of these phenomena. They simulate every kind of skin disease and may be mistaken for the rashes of exanthematic diseases (measles, chickenpox, etc.), as well as those produced by various drugs (Figs. 343, 344, 345). They have a tendency to heal up and then to recur, but although they may produce the most extensive outbreak all over the body, they are seldom destructive and leave little trace of their presence.

The simplest rash is the *macular* syphilide, which begins on the trunk and may quickly appear over the whole body. It is quite like the rash of measles in some cases, and histologically presents chiefly a widening of the blood-vessels with slight accumulation of cells. Further accumulation of leucocytes and œdema is characteristic of the *papular* syphilide in which the eruption is somewhat raised. With the fading of these rashes discoloration of the skin may remain for a time. Some often develop superficial crusts due to epithelial necrosis and exudation, while others are definitely *pustular*, little abscesses forming in each lesion. Many of these syphilides have a tendency to heal in their central part while spreading and producing new lesions at the periphery. Ring-formed macular, papular, or pustular eruptions arise in this way. Scaly patches resembling psoriasis appear on the palms and soles at a later stage, and still later there may be found the rounded, terraced, elevated patches with necrotic crusts—the so-called rupial eruption. Many other forms and combinations occur, descriptions of

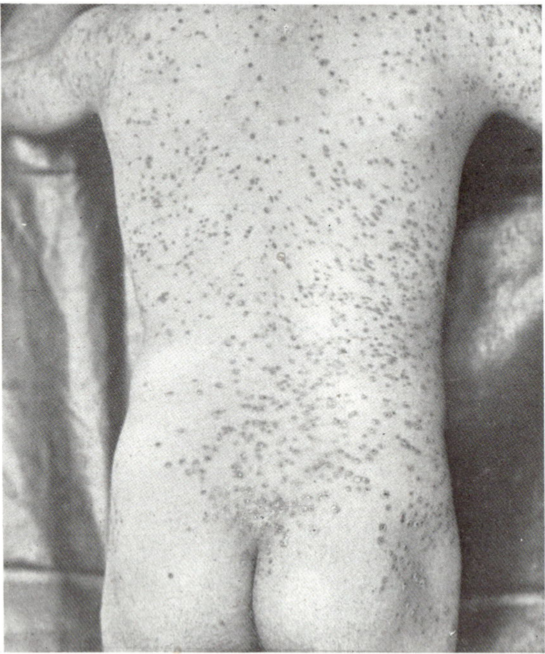

Fig. 344.—Secondary syphilis. Papulopustular syphilide. Lesions leave a pigment spot as they heal (Fordyce).

which may be found in text-books of dermatology. Not infrequent are pigmentary changes, in some of which there is a deepening of the color of the skin, in others a complete fading away of pigment in certain areas, which leaves them white in contrast with the surroundings (leucoderma). Patchy falling out of the hair (syphilitic alopecia) is also characteristic of this stage of the disease.

Soreness of the throat, with evident though slight inflammation, is common. Most characteristic, however, is the appearance of the so-called mucous patches in the mouth and throat. These are white areas in the mucosa, slightly elevated or superficially ulcerated and infiltrated with fluid and cells over which the epithelium is proliferated. They discharge the spirochætæ and are a ready source of infection. Similar patches may occur in the vagina.

Besides these lesions of the skin and mucosæ in the secondary stage, certain others are very prominent. These are the condylomata and moist papules, which as inflammatory elevations loaded with spirochætæ appear chiefly about the genitals or on the inner sides of the thighs or anal folds, or elsewhere where skin surfaces touch one another, so that sweat or other secretions and dirt are retained. They, too, form a common source of infection. The flat condyloma (to be distinguished from the pointed con-

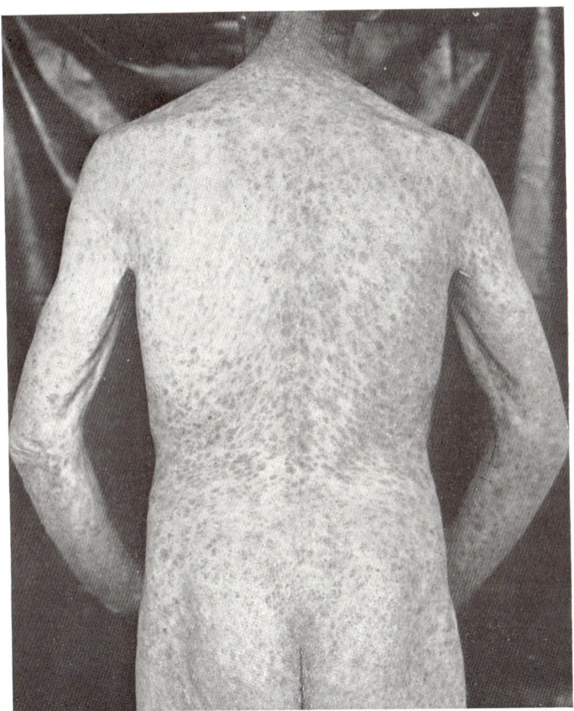

Fig. 345.—Secondary syphilis. Extensive skin rash (follicular syphilide) (Fordyce).

dyloma, which is not of syphilitic origin) is a broad, lobulated elevation covered with greatly thickened and somewhat macerated epithelium, infiltrated with leucocytes. The papillæ of the skin are enlarged by the widening of the blood-vessels and especially by the great accumulation of wandering cells.

Thus during the secondary stage the general type of manifestation of syphilis appears in the form of inflammatory processes often leading to distinct swelling of superficial tissue, with some tendency to necrosis and superficial ulceration, but generally healing and fading away. In all cases the spirochætæ are present in these lesions, and especially from those which are kept moist, the danger of transfer is great. On the whole, the cells of the mononuclear type play the greatest part in the infiltration, although the polymorphonuclears are prominent especially in the pustular forms. Giant-cells and new-formed fibroblasts are occasionally seen. The distribution of the secondary lesions gives evidence at once of their being due to the spread of the spirochætæ by the blood-stream.

The Tertiary Stage.—The most characteristic manifestation of the

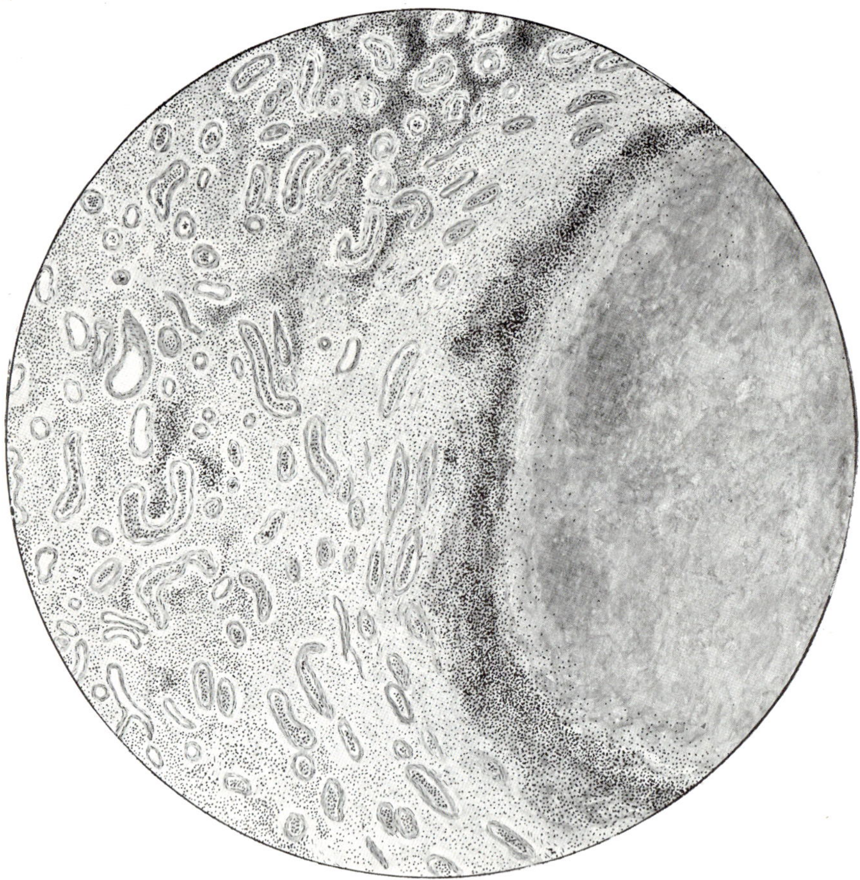

Fig. 346.—Gumma of testicle, showing caseous centre. Atrophy of adjacent tubules.

effects of the spirochætæ in this stage of the disease is the gumma, which received its name from its elastic, rubber-like consistency ("Gummigeschwulst"). Most commonly such nodules are found embedded in the tissue and surrounded on all sides by radiating fibrous tissue, which in itself is not especially peculiar. But the central portion is firm, elastic, opaque, and yellowish white, like hard cheese. This is the necrotic caseous part, analogous to that found in tubercles, but different in its elastic, firm consistency and in the slighter tendency to liquefy. In it one may sometimes discern faint outlines of preëxistent tissue now necrotic. The margin or capsule is often not specially characteristic (Fig. 346), being made up of a rather dense tissue rich in epithelioid cells, such as are found in tubercles, and closely infiltrated with mononuclear wandering cells. Giant-cells with multiple nuclei such as are found in tubercles occur, but are rarer here. Baumgarten denies their existence in gummata, claiming that they are characteristic of tubercles, and that if they do occur it is because of a coincident tuberculous infection. Such nodules may be of almost any size from minute points as small as the smallest tubercle to huge, tumor-like masses easily felt through the abdominal walls as they project from the liver, where they seem to reach their greatest size. In the miliary gummata there may be no caseation or coagulative necrosis and the nodule is

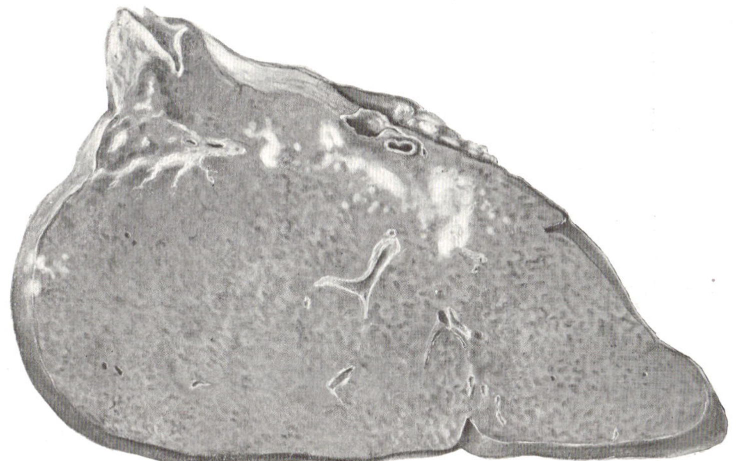

Fig. 347.—Liver, showing several fresh miliary gummata and small caseous areas.

seen as a more or less concentrically arranged group of epithelioid cells richly mingled with mononuclear wandering cells and occasionally with giant-cells. The arrangement is usually indefinite and irregular, lacking the sharpness and precision of the architecture of the miliary tubercle (Figs. 347–349).

Spirochætæ have been demonstrated by animal inoculation in larger gummata by Finger and Landsteiner, but they are not easily found in sections. How, then, is one to tell a gumma from a tubercle when it is found at the autopsy? Histologically it seems almost impossible to make an absolute differentiation between them. A section through a gumma in the lung tissue might have exactly the appearance of one from a large caseous encapsulated tubercle in the same situation. A miliary gumma in the liver might correspond exactly with some types of tubercles seen there.

Demonstration of the presence of tubercle bacilli or of spirochætæ would settle the matter, but these searches are notoriously uncertain. Better would be the inoculation of a guinea-pig with the material. The Wassermann reaction might afford decisive evidence. But as a rule the gross appearance and distribution of the lesions are found to be typical enough in each disease to allow one to discriminate—not always from the situation of any one lesion, but from its relation to other lesions throughout the body. Thus gummata are commonly found in the periosteum invading the bone;

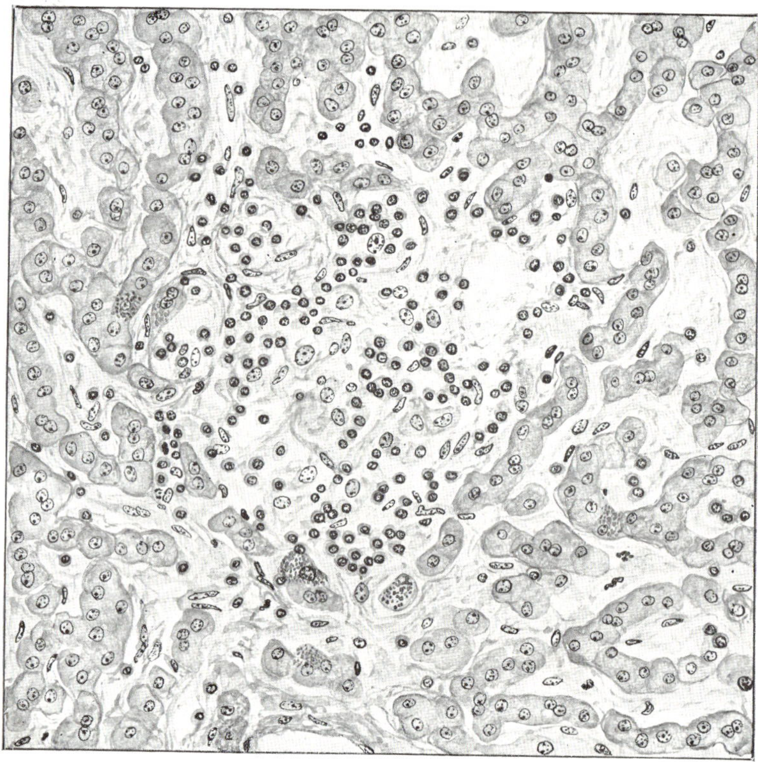

Fig. 348.—Beginning miliary gumma of liver. Necrosis of the liver-cells and wandering in of mononuclears is followed by the growth of epithelioid cells.

in the skull they are frequently found involving the meninges and extending into the substance of the brain. Such a matting together of periosteum, skull, meninges, and brain into a solid caseous mass by a tuberculous process would be rare. In the brain substance they occur and have a different consistence from that of the very similar large solitary tubercles which are found there too, but the tubercles would in all probability be associated with readily recognizable tuberculosis of the lungs, etc. This is most often the really effective aid to diagnosis, for it is not difficult to recognize well-developed and wide-spread tuberculosis. In the liver small tubercles and small gummata are similar—the condition of the other organs will generally decide their nature. Large tubercles are rare; large, partly healed gummata are common. Nevertheless we have recently had a case in which a caseous tubercle 7–8 cm. in diameter occurred in the liver. Its abundant content of tubercle bacilli and the wide distribution of tuberculous lesions elsewhere made the diagnosis pretty clear. In the testicle gummata are common, while tuberculous infection practically always begins in the epididymis, and only later may extend to involve the testicle.

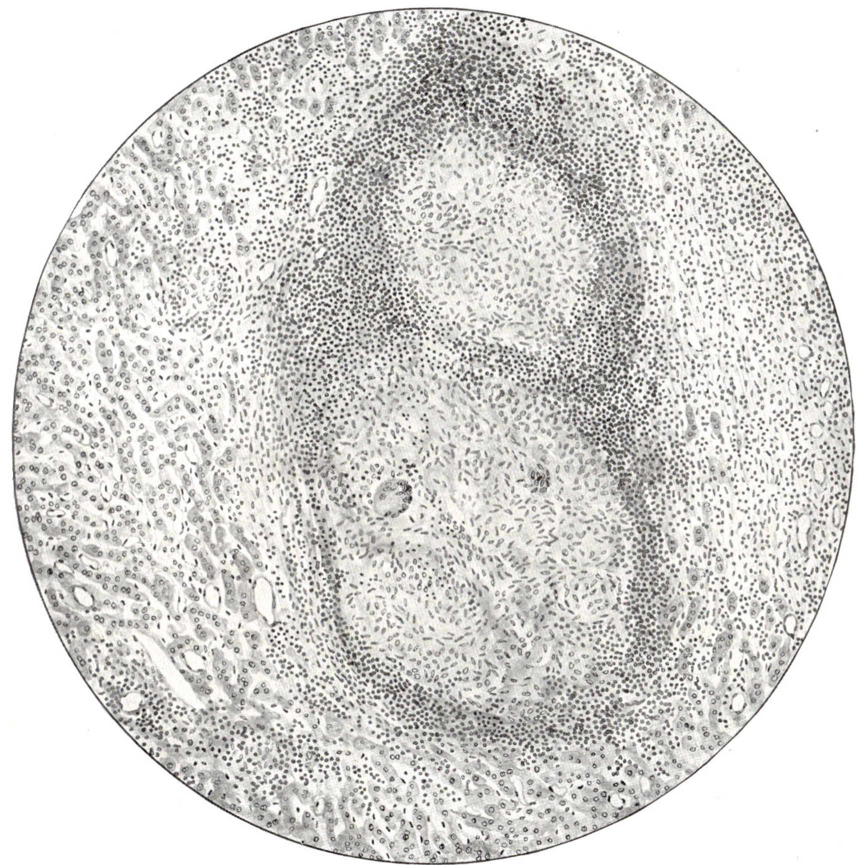

Fig. 349.—Miliary gummata of the liver with occasional giant-cells.

Gummata have a strong tendency to heal, so that they are commonly found as disappearing centres of caseous material in great radiating scars. This is far less often true of tubercles. Many other instances might be mentioned in which the attendant circumstances give the main clue to the diagnosis. The history of the case, the Wassermann reaction, the bacterial findings, the distribution of the lesions and their relation to lesions elsewhere, their size, consistence and gross appearance, their tendency to heal or to break down, and least of all their histological structure—these are the things upon which the diagnosis of syphilis in the tertiary stage may be based.

Not all tertiary lesions are distinctly gummatous, however, for there frequently arises a diffuse infiltration of tissues with wandering cells and a proliferation and new formation of connective tissue, which results in the formation of a *syphilitic granulation tissue* analogous to the tuberculous granulation tissue which plays so great a part in old tuberculous lesions. In places this tissue may have a gummatous character and undergo the same retrogressive changes (coagulative necrosis) as are seen there, but here again the tendency is toward healing, often with much distortion. Here, as elsewhere, in syphilitic processes the smaller blood-vessels generally show thickening of the intima and changes in the endothelium, which may result in their practical obstruction. About these vessels there accumulate mononuclear wandering cells in great abundance.

It will be observed in considering the development of the tertiary syphilitic lesions that they often arise in places where there were secondary lesions which had healed, and it has been suggested that they are the effect of the further growth of spirochætæ which had been left behind in the healing of the secondary syphilis. The evidence is not entirely convincing in regard to this, although there are many well-attested cases in which gummata appeared on the site of old secondary lesions. It is difficult to say whether this holds good for the gummata of internal organs.

The nature of all these processes may be exemplified in describing their occurrence in various organs.

Lymph-glands.—The regional lymph-glands, as has been said, become infected and swell slightly a few days after the appearance of the initial chancre. This swelling is never great nor does suppuration take place unless there is combined with the syphilitic infection some other, such as that characteristic of the soft chancre. Instead, the glands remain small and firm and recede after a time to their former size. In the secondary stage, that is, at the end of the second incubation period, the lymph-glands become enlarged and palpable throughout the whole body. This is so characteristic that it becomes a valuable diagnostic aid in this stage of the disease. Microscopically in both these stages the change is seen to be essentially an increase in the number of lymphocytes, and especially of larger mononuclear cells which fill the sinuses and are often phagocytic.

These large cells are also found with the lymphocytes in the lymph cords and are looked upon by most writers as endothelial or reticulum cells. Their nature is questionable in this case, as in many others in which they appear in the same way. The connective-tissue framework of the glands seems to be increased after a time.

In the tertiary stage a similar enlargement of the glands in certain localities may occur, but the most characteristic change is in the development of gummata in their substance. This is not very common and is usually found in association with gummatous lesions in the neighboring organ. Thus large gummatous masses in the bronchial glands were found in a case of syphilitic disease of the lungs, while gummata of the portal and retroperitoneal glands accompanied a fresh gummatous cirrhosis of the liver with involvement of the vena cava (Johns Hopkins Hosp. Bull., 1903, xiv, 88).

The spirochætæ are found abundantly in the swollen glands accompanying the primary and secondary stages.

Blood changes in syphilis are indefinite and not thoroughly studied; there has been much confusion as to the part played in producing them by mercurial treatment, but it seems that the infection by itself can produce a rather severe anæmia in the secondary stage. This is sometimes spoken of as syphilitic chlorosis. A moderate lymphocytosis is also found.

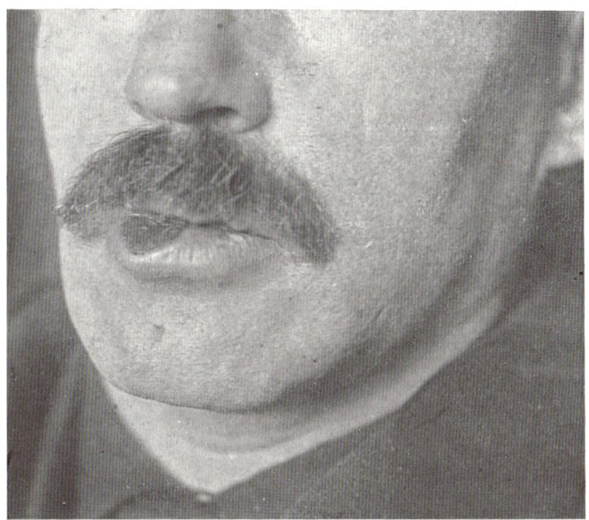

Fig. 350.—Chancre of the lip (Fordyce).

Alimentary Tract.—*The Mouth.*—It has already been mentioned that primary and secondary lesions occur in the mouth, chancres upon the tonsils, lips (Fig. 350) and tongue being relatively common among the forms of extragenital infection. Histologically and in their gross appearance they resemble those found elsewhere, and the glands which drain these regions become enlarged and very hard during the existence of the chancre.

The diagnosis is sometimes difficult, especially in the case of the chancre of the tonsil, which is often anything but characteristic.

The tertiary lesions are common and important. Gummata sometimes appear on the *lips*, but more often the whole lip becomes indurated by the formation of a diffuse infiltration throughout it of the character of the syphilitic granulation tissue. Ulceration may be most extensive, and with scarring the mouth is extremely distorted, so that, for example, the whole upper lip is destroyed, the gap extending into the nostrils and exposing the teeth and gums. With healing, the orifice of the mouth is drawn into a stiff, triangular opening. On the *tongue* actual gumma formation is more common, diffuse infiltration less so. The gummata, often multiple, arise beneath the surface and extend to the upper surface of the tongue, where they break through, forming a deep ulcer with steep walls and stiff, translucent base. Healing leaves a distorting scar.

It is important to distinguish such ulcerating gummata from epitheliomata of the tongue and from tuberculous ulcers. The epithelioma starts from the surface, usually at the margin, and extends to the floor of the mouth, growing more slowly than the gumma. Histologically it is, of course, easy to make the distinction.

The diffuse infiltration of the tongue is more serious, because it causes great enlargement and rigidity of the organ, later, in healing, leaving the surface deeply fissured but otherwise smooth. This smooth atrophy of the villi of the tongue has long been recognized as syphilitic. Particularly harmful is the rigidity of the tongue which exposes it, especially where it is enlarged, to all kinds of injuries.

Gummata are rare in the tonsils, but are more common in the hard and soft palate. Beginning usually from the nasal side from the periosteum the gummatous nodule projects both into the nose and mouth, and, soon ulcerating and discharging its contents, it produces great destruction of the bones of the nose and an open perforation from the nose into the mouth. This allows of a nasal speech (rhinolalia) and also of the passage of food and fluids through the nose. It is even worse when the soft palate is in the same way partly destroyed, for the necessary opening and closing off of the posterior nares is impossible. Gummatous ulcerations of the pharynx usually heal with less distortion, but the healing of the lesions of the soft palate and fauces is likely to produce a sort of stenosis or great narrowing of the buccopharyngeal and nasopharyngeal passages.

Œsophagus and Stomach.—Primary and secondary lesions of the œsophagus are practically unknown. Tertiary or gummatous changes have been described—gummata arising in the submucosa and rupturing to produce ulcers which in healing give rise to stricture of the canal.

In the stomach there have been found diffuse infiltrative processes in the submucosa and mucosa and also gummatous formations which on breaking down produce extensive ulcers, easily enough distinguished from the ordinary round ulcer of the stomach. Such lesions may sometimes extend into the duodenum.

Intestine.—Tertiary lesions of the small intestine are usually localized in the jejunum, or the upper ileum, where they appear as flat elevations of the character of a syphilitic granulation tissue involving submucosa and mucosa. Multiple ulcers are found which extend in the form of rings round the gut, and which in healing may produce strictures. There is a remarkable example of this in the Pathological Museum of Columbia University; but the condition must be very rare. Indeed, the only syphilitic lesions of the intestinal tract which are common are those found in the *rectum.* There, especially about the anus, chancres may appear, and secondary lesions in the form of moist papules and flat condylomata are extremely common. Various other secondary lesions involving cellular infiltration of the mucosa, abscess formation, and even fistula production occur at this stage.

But the tertiary lesions arising often very late in the disease, after all evidence of the earlier stages of the infection have disappeared, are the cause of the most disturbing changes. Anatomically they are analogous to those found elsewhere and are peculiar only in their mechanical effects. Gummata appear in the submucosa of the rectum and are soon exposed to the lumen by ulceration, and surrounded by abundant scar tissue. Without actual gumma formation there may be diffuse and wide-spread infiltration of the whole wall of the gut and especially of the submucosa, with mononuclear and epithelioid cells and this infiltrated tissue soon breaks down into extensive ulcers which partly or completely surround the lumen. A foul discharge accompanies such ulceration and the passage of fæces is painful. This is especially so when the ulceration becomes very extensive, and when, with secondary infections, fistulæ are found running into the adjacent tissues or communicating with the vagina. Later the dense scar formation about the healing and still progressive ulcers constricts the lumen of the gut (Fig. 351). Then, in addition to the pain and tenesmus, actual obstruction arises; there is alternate constipation and diarrhœa and the intestine above the stricture is dilated and hypertrophied, and ulcerated from the stagnation of fæces. The patient usually dies from some intercurrent infection, for which the

Fig. 351.—Syphilitic stricture of the rectum.

poisoning caused by this slow intestinal obstruction prepares the way. As in other cases of syphilis of long standing, amyloid infiltration of the organs is often found.

The Liver.—Little is known of any secondary syphilitic lesions in the liver. The recognized changes are essentially characteristic of the tertiary stage and consist in the formation of gummata, often with extensive inflammatory infiltration of the liver substance, and scarring. It is not usual to find fresh gummata at autopsy, but in the case illustrated in Figs. 347

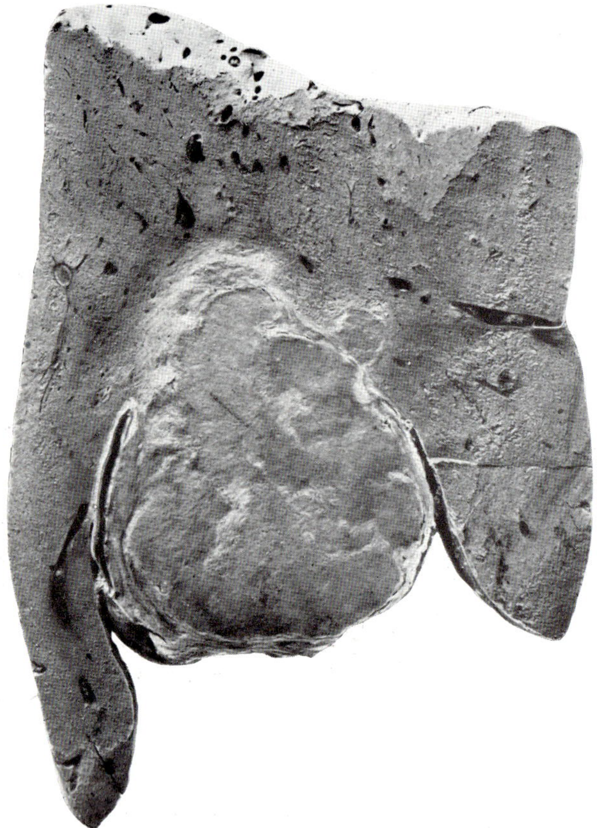

Fig. 352.—Large gumma of liver.

to 349 there were numerous groups of miliary and submiliary gummata which, in some places, were beginning to be caseous and in others were surrounded by scars. The formation of these lesions involves the destruction of the liver substance and to a less extent the pushing aside of the tissue. They are usually numerous, but sometimes they coalesce into a great tumor-like mass (Fig. 352). In one instance which I saw there was a great nodular tumor projecting from under the edge of the liver so as to be palpated through the abdominal wall. It melted away rapidly under energetic antisyphilitic treatment, which, after all, with the history, was the chief proof of its gummatous nature.

Iodides as well as mercury were given in this case, as has been done for many years. Jobling and Petersen have recently explained the action of iodides as follows. The softening and removal of caseous necrotic material from a gumma is due to a tryptic ferment. The gumma, however, persists and remains firm because it contains large quantities of antitryptic substances which are of lipoid nature, being combinations of unsaturated fatty acids. Their power of antagonizing the ferment depends upon their unsaturation, which in turn can, as is well known, be satisfied by iodine, this forming the basis of the well-known index used in estimating unsaturated fatty acids. Administration of iodine by saturating the antitryptic substances, destroys their power over the tryptic ferments, which then dissolve the caseous material.

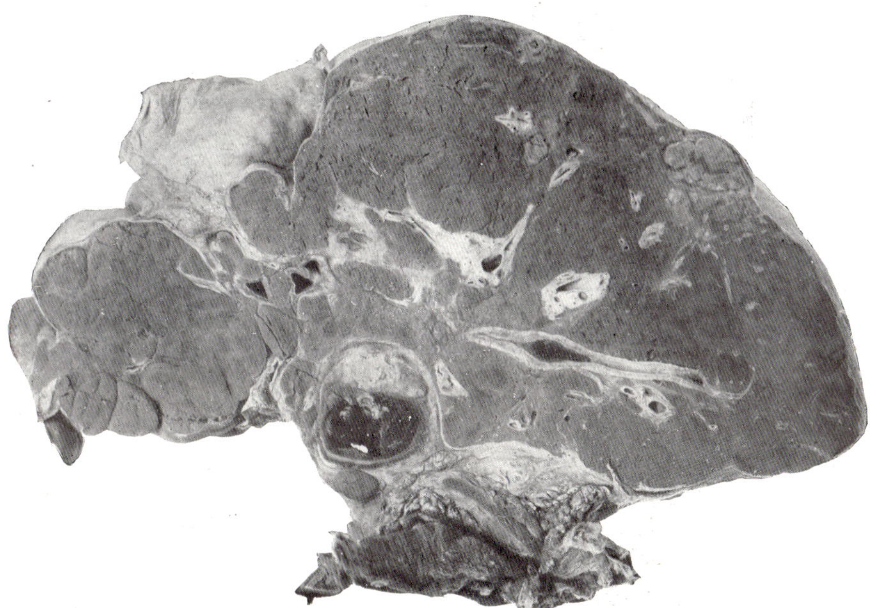

Fig. 353.—Gummata in the liver with extensive scarring. There is one large gumma in the wall of the vena cava, as it passes behind the liver, with thrombosis of the vein.

Probably the most common condition is that in which numerous distinct gummata of the consistence of Swiss cheese are formed throughout the liver, and are found as the centres of extensive radiating scars. In one such liver (Fig. 353), in a case which presented evidences of syphilis elsewhere, the organ was decreased in size and roughly and very coarsely nodular. On cutting through it, it was found to be permeated by a network of coarse bands of gray fibrous tissue which separated large masses of relatively normal-looking liver tissue, into which, however, finer bands extended. At three or four places on the cut surface there were at the nodal points of the scars firm, yellowish-white masses of caseous material up to 1 cm. in diameter. Further, as it penetrated the diaphragm, the inferior vena cava was surrounded by a large gumma originating in the liver and projecting through the diaphragm. It involved the wall of the vein and almost occluded its lumen, the closure being completed below by a great thrombus which extended down into the renal veins.

Such are the relatively fresh conditions, but generally only the broad scars remain (Fig. 354), and one finds the liver greatly distorted by the replacement of whole areas of liver substance by these scars, which have

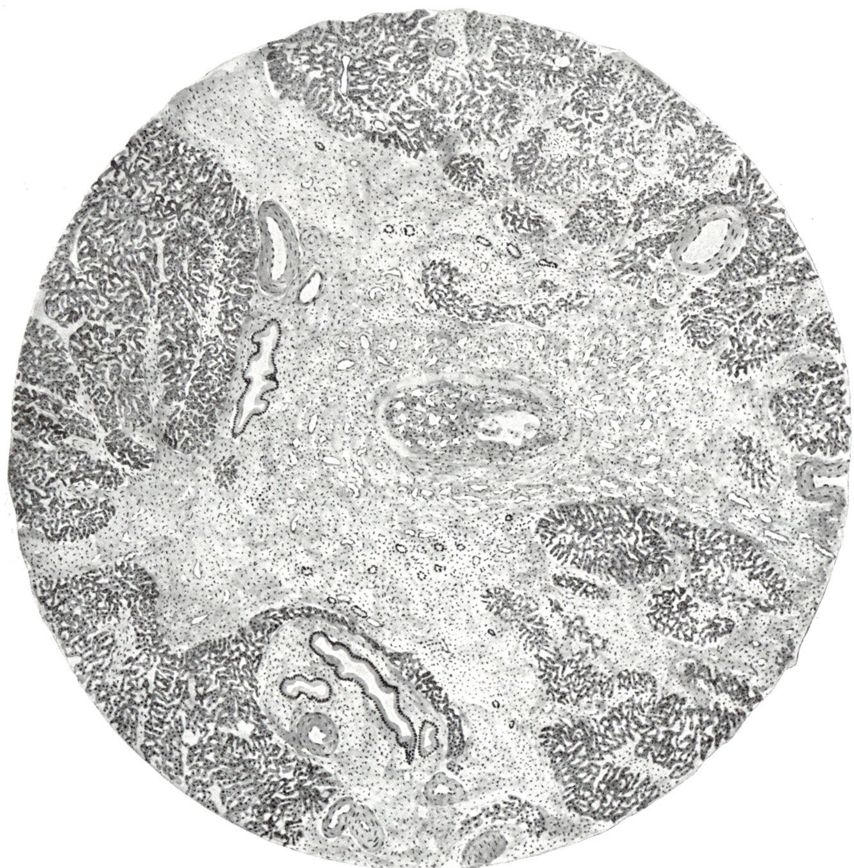

Fig. 354.—Old scar in a syphilitic liver. In the centre is a large vein which has become partly recanalized after obliteration.

retracted into the organ as though cords had been tightly tied about it, cutting deep into its substance. The rest of the liver is normal or, more usually, enlarged by a compensatory hypertrophy. Many of the features characteristic of cirrhosis of the liver, the regenerative processes, and the distortion of the circulation as well as of the liver tissue, may be found in these cases. Ascites, portal stagnation, splenic enlargement and jaundice may occur, but they vary with the varying mechanical conditions, and the presence of large gummata and scars about the portal region and bile-ducts naturally plays an important part in this regard.

Such a deeply lobed, distorted liver (Fig. 355) is almost always the result of syphilitic infection. It is not, however, the only effect which can be produced by that disease, since in other instances one may find a much finer scarring, evidently due to a more diffuse affection.

In the *salivary glands*, particularly the parotid, and in the *pancreas* gummatous and diffuse syphilitic lesions have been described in a few cases.

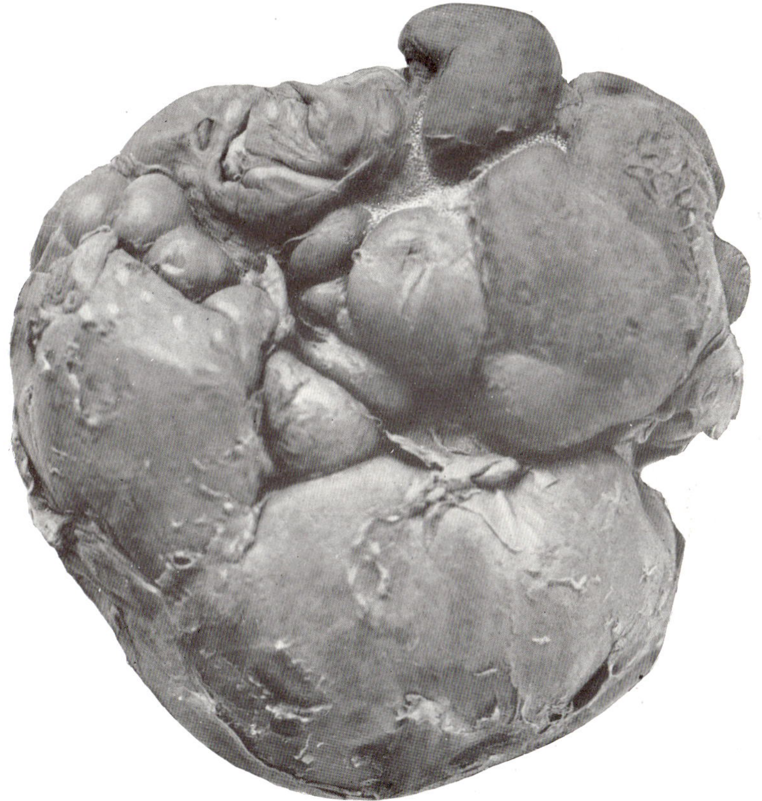

Fig. 355.—Old syphilitic cirrhosis with deep constrictions where there are scars.

In the *kidney* gummata are sometimes met with and changes leading to diffuse scarring and contraction of the kidneys due to syphilis have been said to occur. Probably they depend upon intimal lesions in the renal arteries.

The Respiratory Tract.—Syphilitic lesions are found in the upper air-passages, larynx, and trachea, and rather less commonly in the bronchi and lungs.

In the *nose*, chancres are not uncommon, appearing at the orifices of the nostrils, or the alæ nasi, or even in the interior, on the septum. They are caused as a rule by infection from the fingers or from handkerchiefs.

In the secondary stage the most common manifestation is a syphilitic erythema, or reddening, which appears in flecks, sometimes later covered by a necrotic layer of epithelium and occasionally giving rise to nosebleed. This is the basis of the coryza which is a common accompaniment of this stage of the disease. Papules and actual condylomata sometimes arise in the nose. Far more important and quite common are the lesions of the tertiary stage, which, as elsewhere, are diffuse syphilitic infiltrations or gummata. The former may produce thickening of the mucosa over the septum or turbinates, generally with ulceration, which may penetrate to the cartilage or bone, and, often through the aid of secondary infections, leads to destructive perichondritis and periostitis. Naturally this process involves the risk of extension upward to the ethmoid and sphenoid bones, and meningeal infection may follow. Sometimes great tumor-like masses are formed at the base of the septum or elsewhere. Similarly, definite gummatous lesions appear in the mucosa or in the perichondrium or periosteum of the bones which constitute the interior of the nose. Extensive deep ulcerations follow, and whole bones become necrotic sequestra. The septum may be completely destroyed, as well as the turbinates, and large portions of the vomer and the nasal bones. The nose is in this way hollowed out into a great cavity, the lining of which is a scarred and atrophic mucosa. The process is accompanied, so long as necrotic bone is present, by the most nauseating fœtor. At times, as has been mentioned above, perforation of the hard palate or destruction of the soft palate occurs. In the course of healing, the most extensive adhesions and strictures of the air-passages develop, so that sometimes the nasal cavity may be quite shut off from the pharynx. Great deformities of the face result, since, with the collapse of the nasal bones, the nose sinks into the opening produced. The mildest form of this is perhaps the saddle-nose so often seen in the streets and so common in late cases of congenital syphilis, in which the bridge of the nose is sunken and the tip turns upward, exposing the nostrils in front (Fig. 356). But in countries like Morocco, where the disease is neglected, one sees the most extreme deformities, produced by ulceration through the skin, so that the whole nasal cavity is open

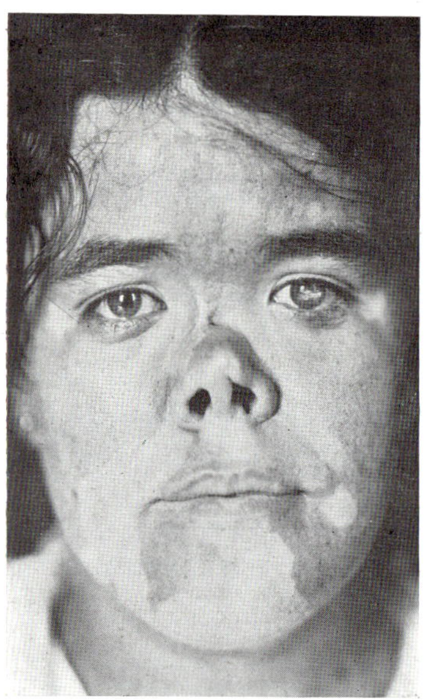

Fig. 356.—Late congenital syphilis showing "saddle nose," interstitial keratitis, and leucoderma.

to the outside and into the mouth, and all semblance of a face has disappeared.

In the nasopharynx the same series of lesions may appear, chancre of the Eustachian tube having been caused by the use of an infected Eustachian catheter.

Larynx.—The lesions of the larynx might be inferred from what has been said of the nose. Although secondary changes occur there, the tertiary phenomena are most important. In a case recently seen at autopsy there was a diffuse syphilitic infiltration of the whole interior of the larynx with ragged ulceration extending to the perichondrium and involving both sides of the cavity.

Gummatous lesions involve the arytenoid cartilages and epiglottis most commonly, but may affect any other part. The deep precipitous ulcers with abundant yellow secretion are capable of destroying the vocal cords and of leading to necrosis of the cartilages. They must be distinguished from tuberculous and cancerous ulcers in the same places. Healing leads to great deformity and stricture formation in the larynx, for which tracheotomy is sometimes necessary.

Trachea, Bronchi, and Lungs.—Tertiary lesions in the trachea and bronchi are usually in the form of syphilitic granulation tissue, although sometimes definite gummata may arise in the wall or extend from outside. The process causes much thickening of the wall with ulceration which lays bare and softens or destroys the cartilage rings.

In such a case the trachea and bronchus may collapse at an angle or be compressed. Usually healing takes place with the formation of a scar which causes a stenosis of the canal. Almost any part of the trachea may be involved, but it seems that the region of the bifurcation is most commonly affected, the stricture narrowing one main bronchus. This was the condition found in a case studied in Baltimore, and the effect upon the lung, as might have been foretold, was to produce most extensive bronchiectasis. The reasons for this are discussed elsewhere.

The clinical signs in such a case are rather definite, since the harsh stridor of the air passing the obstruction, and the prolonged expiratory sound on that side, indicate clearly the existence of a stenosis. When the stenosis appears in a branch of the main bronchus there are localized changes in the breath sounds, and the bronchial dilatation and emphysematous alterations in the lung are limited to the area which is supplied with air by that bronchus.

In the lung itself, aside from the congenital changes, the lesions due to syphilis are not very clearly nor surely recognized. Gummâta of various sizes up to tumor-like masses occur anywhere in the lung. They are grayish or reddish-gray nodules, sharply outlined, and radiating fibrous strands into the rest of the lung. One occasionally sees these masses, which in the absence of obvious tuberculosis and when other signs of syphilis exist, it seems proper to diagnose as gummata; but doubtless many of those described may have been localized encapsulated tubercles. About the large vessels at the hilum of the lung and the large bronchi gummatous indurative processes occur, with great thickening of the adventitial walls of the vessels and some constriction of the bronchi. Great scars extend out into the remainder of the lung and bronchiectasis follows the obstruction. This has been called the indurative bronchiectatic type of pulmonary syphilis. Whether pneumonic or ulcerative forms of syphilis with cavity formation really exist is uncertain. The confusion with tuberculosis, and especially the fact that syphilitics are very prone to tuberculosis, makes this point difficult to settle (Flockemann: Centrbl. f. allg. Path., 1899, x, 469).

LITERATURE

Ehrmann: Handb. d. Geschlechtskr., 1912, ii, 959–1130. Arch. f. Dermatol., 1899, xlviii, 256.

Lang: Pathologie u. Therap. der Syphilis, 2[te] Aufl., Wiesb., 1896.

Neumann: Nothnagel's spez. Path., 1899, Bd. xxiii. Exhaustive treatment of the whole subject of syphilis by Gerber, Pal, Benda, Nobl, Ebstein, Jesionek, Seifert, Harttung, Braun and others in Handb. d. Geschlechtskr., 1913, iii, 1–951.

Nonne: Syphilis u. Nervensystem, 1915, 3[te] Aufl., Berlin.

Adami: N. Y. Med. Jour., 1899, 549.

Jobling and Petersen: Action of Iodides, Arch. Int. Med., 1915, xv, 286.

Councilman: Johns Hopkins Hospital Bull., 1891, ii, p. 34 (Syphilis of lung).

v. Baumgarten: Verh. Deutsch. Path. Gesellsch., 1901, iii, 107 (Histology of gumma, with discussion).

v. Werdt: Frankf. Ztschr. f. Pathol., 1913, xii, 177 (Liver gummata).

Bones and Joints.—It is said that periosteal inflammation may form a part of the secondary stage of syphilis, but there is as yet very little anatomical evidence with regard to this. Secondary lesions of the joints are also mentioned. But the later lesions of both bones and joints are far more frequently met with and far more serious.

Tertiary lesions of the *bones* seem to affect most commonly the skull, the tibia, the fingers, and other bones which are very superficially situated, while less is known of those which occur in the more protected bones. Possibly this is due to the influence of trauma in determining the site of gummatous affections. Part of the anatomical changes due to syphilis are distinctly and characteristically gummatous, while there are others which are quite like the results of chronic inflammation of the bone produced by other causes, except perhaps in their history and in their association with other syphilitic lesions. Probably, however, the study of these chronic inflammations for spirochætæ will show more clearly their syphilitic character. Although the bone is soon involved, these are at first essentially affections of the periosteum, which is torn from the bone by an inflammatory infiltration composed chiefly of mononuclear wandering cells. With rupture of the periosteum the overlying skin may be broken through, after which the place is exposed to further infections. Such an ulceration often exposes the underlying bone, parts of which become necrotic and separate from the rest as a sequestrum which may be discharged. Syphilitic ulcers of this type are long in healing. By no means all such inflammations end in ulceration; instead, they produce a great new growth of spongy bone on the surface of the old cortex, forming in this way a convex layer which, when the bone is macerated and dried, has something of the appearance of rough pumice stone. Sometimes it is much denser and may even be very hard and solid (Fig. 357). Such osteophytes often rise in a sort of wall about the area of most intense inflammation where necrosis has actually occurred. It is this process which gives origin to many of the thickenings with rough, irregular surface which one finds so commonly on the shafts of long bones in any collection, but it must be recognized that these are not all syphilitic—other non-specific forms of periostitis can produce the same thing. In another form the new production of bone is more extensive still, and no longer limited to the activity of the periosteum; it is laid down in each Haversian system and through the cancellous bone in the interior, so that the shaft of the bone becomes dense and ivory-like and the whole bone is much heavier than normal. There is no special localization for these processes, although it is true that thickenings of the long bones, the clavicles, the sternum, etc., are particularly common.

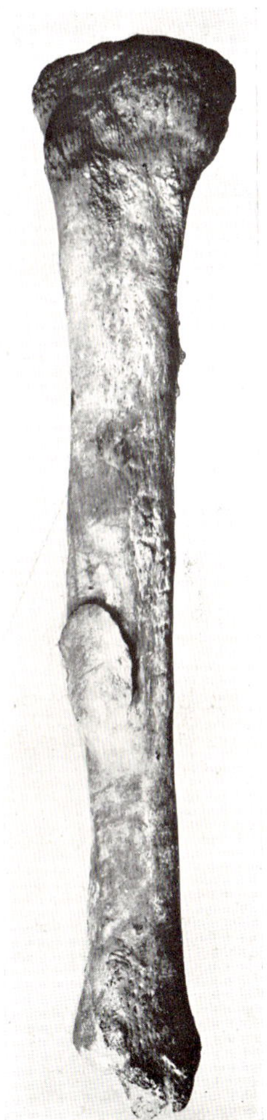

Fig. 357.—Syphilitic periostitis and osteophyte formation.

Somewhat more easily recognized and characteristic of syphilis are the gummatous lesions which may arise in connection with the periosteum or in the interior of the bone. In the first case the gummatous tissue extends along the blood-vessels into the bone, enlarging their canals and eroding the bone to a peculiar worm-eaten appearance. Sometimes, as in the skull, the periosteum can be torn off, pulling out of their canals a lot of these great cellular extensions and leaving a coarsely corroded surface. Complete destruction of the bone is easily produced by their confluence, and it is common in these cases to find the skull penetrated by a ragged hole filled by the gummatous mass which generally extends to involve the dura mater and often enough the underlying brain. But there are many cases in which the dura limits the process and the necrotic débris is discharged externally. Osteophytes from the periosteum surround such an area and make the defect seem deeper. The same gummatous nodes are often found on the shins, extending into the cortex and marrow cavity and often circumscribing and causing the necrosis of fragments of the bone. The most extensive destruction may occur in the skull (Fig. 358), and especially in old specimens derived from long untreated cases, one sees great gaps in the cranium with ragged margin and surrounded by rough osteophytes. In all these processes the simultaneous existence of rarefaction and condensation or sclerosis of the bone is to be observed. In this respect the syphilitic changes stand in contrast to the tuberculous, where rarefaction of the bone is accompanied by very little new formation.

Gummata formed in the marrow cavity are of sufficiently frequent occurrence, although they were practically overlooked until Chiari demonstrated their existence. They are gelatinous patches, often bright yellow from their content of fat, which may occur singly or in such numbers and continuity as to involve the whole marrow cavity. Generally there is no outward evidence of their existence, but the cortex may be attacked and eroded and the periosteum outside produce a new layer of bone to correspond. In this way there may be a spindle-shaped dilatation of the bone; canals or fistulæ are formed through the cortex, and, except for the absence of sequestra, the bone comes to look like the end result of an ordinary osteomyelitis.

Fig. 358.—Old syphilitic erosion of the skull. The margins in this case are smoothed off by a healing process.

Gummatous osteoperiostitis with enlargement and rarefaction and internal destruction of the bone in the phalanges, is found in the so-called syphilitic dactylitis. The finger swells and sometimes there is fracture of the weakened bone or the gummatous material is discharged through a fistula.

These, then, are the usual syphilitic affections of the bone: (*a*) periosteal gumma formation with necrosis of the underlying bone, followed by ulceration and exposure through the skin or by extensive osteophyte growth, and (*b*) gummatous osteitis or osteomyelitis with necrosis and erosion of the directly affected part and rarefaction or sclerosis of the surrounding bone. All these things may make their appearance fairly early in the disease or only after long years of apparent health.

As in the case of the bones, the joints, bursæ, and tendon-sheaths often reveal a susceptibility to syphilis only after many years of the disease. There may be an accumulation of watery exudate only, or the formation in the synovial membrane of a syphilitic granulation tissue with ulceration, and great proliferation of the adjacent unaffected membrane and synovial villi. Probably in many cases the joint affection is secondary to the appearance of gummatous infiltration of the epiphysis.

This lifts up and destroys the cartilage, and healing takes place after much loss of time through the obliteration of the cavity by fibrous tissue. In the bursæ and tendon-sheaths painless swellings due to the appearance of a lining of gummatous granulation tissue persist for a long time but yield, as do the joint affections, to specific treatment.

LITERATURE

Churchman: Am. J. Med. Sc., 1909, cxxxviii, 371.
Levin: Med. Record, 1908, lxxiv, 836.
Schmidt, M. B.: Ergeb. d. allg. Path., 1900–01, vii, 221.
Harttung: Handb. d. Geschlechtskr., 1912, iii.

Heart and Blood-vessels.—Syphilis of the blood-vessels has already been described (page 336). There it was stated that in the case of such large vessels as the aorta, gummatous or diffuse syphilitic infiltration affects the adventitia and media, being localized, almost as in the case of the bone, along nutrient vessels and that the extreme hyperplastic changes in the intima arise in response to the destruction thus produced. In smaller vessels, such as those of the meninges, practically the same thing occurs except that the gummatous mass, beginning in the adventitia and extending through the media to the intima, is relatively very large and produces a distinct nodule on the vessel.

Quite analogous changes occur in the small vessels in the interior of organs, although there it is by no means so easy to recognize the stages of the process, and the proliferation of the intima and occlusion of the vessel is likely to be the most conspicuous thing.

In the *heart*, tertiary syphilitic lesions may assume the form of distinct gummata or myocardial scars. Doubtless the latter may be due in part to narrowing of the coronary vessels by specific changes in their walls and then, of course, they are only an accompaniment of the vascular disease. Indeed, it seems that the proof of the direct syphilitic nature of the myocardial scars is not easy. The gummata may occur anywhere in the muscle, but they have a peculiar tendency to appear in and about the conducting bundle of His, and especially at the point in the septum behind the tricuspid and below the aortic valves, where it is most concentrated.

A number of proven cases of gumma formation in this situation have been described, with studies of the interruption of conductions which they cause. The dissociation of the rate of beat of the ventricles from that of the auricles (Stokes-Adams disease, or heart block) which results in this way has been described elsewhere (p. 480). Syphilitic endocarditis is a vaguely understood process except in connection with the aortic valves, where, as stated (p. 242), the deformities produced are the cause of most of the cases of aortic insufficiency.

LITERATURE

Chiari: Verh. Deutsch. path. Gesellsch., 1904, vi, 137.
Benda: *Ibid.*, 164 (Syphilis and blood-vessels).
Marchand: *Ibid.*, 197 (Discussion).
Robinson: Bull. Ayer Clin. Lab., 1907, iv, 1 (Gumma of heart).

Nervous System.—Syphilitic disease in the nervous system is essentially of the tertiary stage, unless we accept the fourth or quaternary stage for those so-called parasyphilitic conditions which we now know to be so truly syphilitic—dementia paralytica and tabes. From an anatomical point of view there are three main types, of which one includes the cases of gummatous encephalitis or meningo-encephalitis, myelitis or neuritis; the second, the various forms of syphilitic meningitis, and the third the diffuse processes described above as quaternary. But between the first two there are various gradations, and, further, it is difficult to distinguish sharply between them and others which begin in the cranial periosteum and extend into the brain.

The most common are those cases in which a gummatous mass is found in the cortex of the brain connected through the pia arachnoid with the dura and even penetrating through the skull (Fig. 359). Such a gumma may be as large as a filbert, or an irregular conglomeration of caseous masses may be much larger.

A great deal of translucent gray or grayish-red material forms the outer portions and radiates into the surrounding tissue, especially along the blood-vessels. Parts of it may be reddish-gray, but the central part is usually yellow and very opaque and firm. The difficulties in being sure as to whether such a lesion is tuberculous or gummatous have been mentioned. From the point where the gumma extends to involve the dura, that membrane may be greatly thickened on all sides by a syphilitic granulation tissue, rich in cells and showing in places a tendency to caseation.

The brain is not merely pushed away—it is invaded and infiltrated in this process, and along the vessels there is a great accumulation of mononuclear wandering cells. It has been thought generally that such a gumma may not spring from the brain substance itself, but only from the walls of the blood-vessels or the meninges. This, however, offers no limitation and one discovers gummata growing deep in the corpus callosum, or in the basal ganglia, or the pons. The medulla and substance of the spinal cord may be their seat, but it must be said that these deep-seated gummata are less common than those which are superficial and connect with the meninges.

A gumma localized in the lenticular nucleus and appearing as a fairly sharply outlined mass to the naked eye affords a good example of the histological characters of these lesions. Under the microscope it appears not nearly so sharply outlined nor so uniform in its makeup; caseous patches are scattered here and there in a kind of network in a

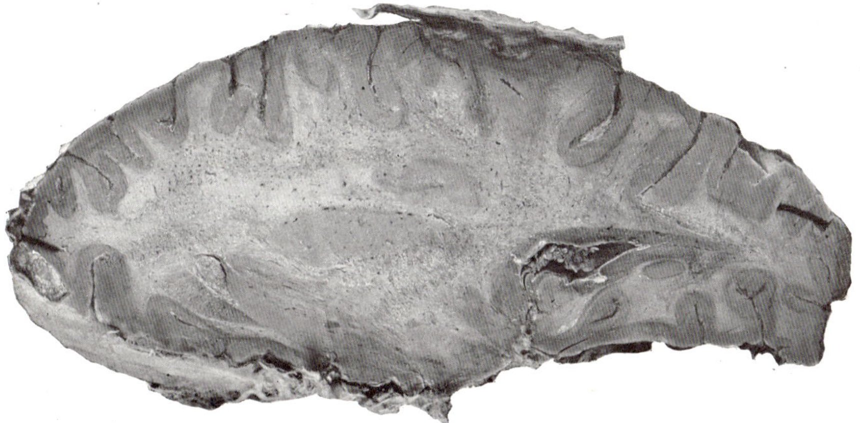

Fig. 359.—Gumma of meninges extending into the brain and producing adhesions between the brain and meninges. The skull was also invaded to some extent by the gumma.

diffuse mass of very cellular tissue (Fig. 360). On approaching from the normal brain substance the blood-vessels in the outskirts are found surrounded by lymph-spaces which are packed with loose cells. Not all of these are plasma cells. Many of them seem much larger with protoplasm which stains red; many others are lymphocytes. The intima of these vessels is often so thickened by new-formed cells as nearly to obstruct the lumen. Advancing, one reaches a tissue in which little brain substance is to be recognized; it is rich in new capillary blood-vessels and overrun by hordes of mononuclear cells of the same varieties of form as are seen in the walls of the blood-vessels. Plasma cells of typical form are there; but most of the cells are lymphocytes or else much larger cells, with granular or vacuolated cell-body and large vesicular nucleus. In places there is a condensation of the ground tissue in which the most prominent cells are like the epithelioid cells of the tubercle, with long, pale, vesicular nuclei. Often, among these are found beautiful giant-cells with many nuclei. These border on the areas of necrosis, and round them the epithelioid cells along the edge of the caseous material have become distorted and twisted into a radiate position pointing toward the caseation.

These caseous areas show throughout the shadowy remains of the continuation of the vascular infiltrated tissue which has simply been rendered necrotic. It will be seen that in no particular is this process absolutely distinguishable from tuberculosis, but at least it is more diffuse and one has less the impression of the formation of firm nodules which push aside tissue before they become caseous. This is rather an infiltrating granulation tissue, parts of which undergo caseation.

Very small or miliary gummata may be scattered all through the brain. Diffuse syphilitic infiltration or granulation tissue formation seems, however, to be very rare, although Bechterew described multiple sclerosing foci in the spinal cord in one case.

On the other hand, gummata encroach upon the cranial and spinal nerves at their roots, in some cases, and, extending from epi- to endoneurium, involve the nerve-fibres in their necrosis. Paralysis and degeneration of the nerve follow. In the peripheral nerves, gummata occur in the same way.

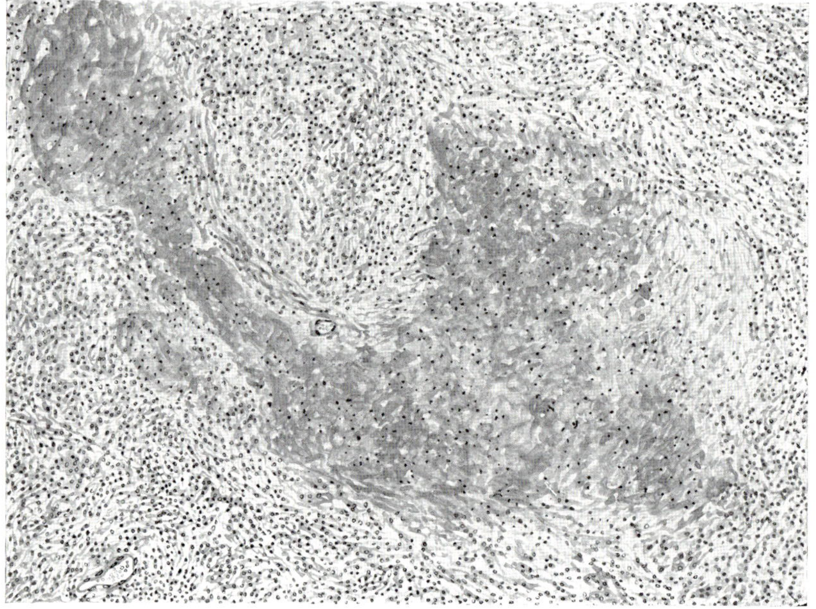

Fig. 360.—Part of a gumma of the lenticular nucleus, showing central caseation.

One case observed at autopsy in which the nerves of the upper arm were matted together in a caseous gumma, with degeneration of the distal portions, was described by Remsen.

The meningeal form, which is so apt to extend to involve the brain, affects the dura or the pia. Aside from the gumma formation just described the dura may present rather diffuse layers of granulation tissue densely infiltrated with lymphocytes and sometimes hæmorrhagic. More characteristic are the affections of the pia and arachnoid, in which one finds small gray nodules along the course of the pial blood-vessels (Fig. 361). These sometimes have opaque whitish centres and prove to be minute gummata which begin in the adventitia and quickly invade the media, inciting a similar proliferation in the intima, which is often enough to narrow very greatly or completely close the lumen. In cross-sections the tiny lumen is found at one side, and in the excentric mass the internal lamella, wrinkled on the thin side of the vessel wall, is stretched out thin and straight through the most affected part.

Sometimes the lumen is divided into two or more channels and a new elastic lamella may form, more closely placed about one or more of these. Strassmann has demonstrated the spirochætæ in these adventitial gummata.

Outside the vessels the pia is thickened and rendered opaque and yellowish by a dense infiltration of wandering cells, mostly mononuclear. This exudate is generally most abundant over the base of the brain, and especially in such regions as that of the optic chiasma. The cranial nerves passing through it were, in the case we studied (Goldsborough), roughened

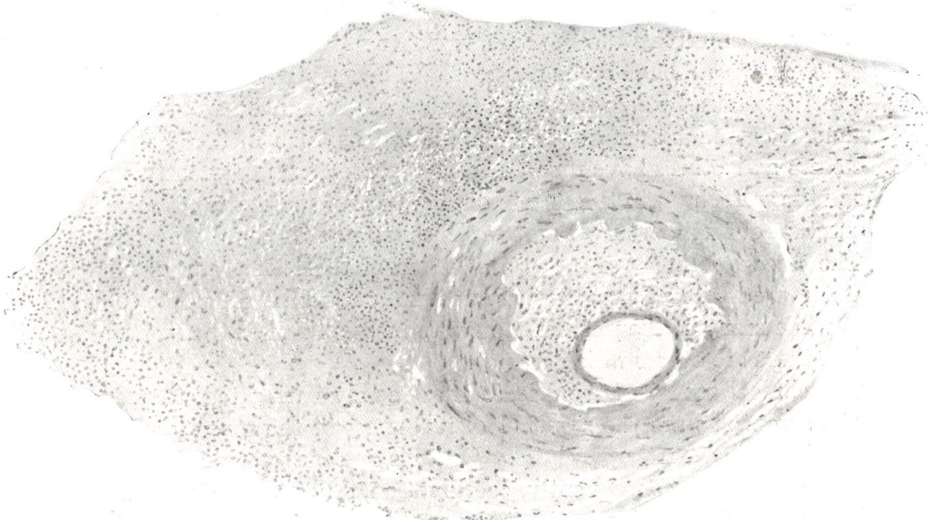

Fig. 361.—Gumma of pial blood-vessel. Syphilitic meningitis.

and swollen from the presence of small gummata which in their caseation involved the nerve-fibres.

It is manifest that all this must produce the most varied symptoms, partly the result of the general meningeal inflammation, partly due to direct irritation or paralysis of the affected nerves. Disturbances of the functions of the eye muscles, of speech, etc., are especially common.

Versé found the same process affecting the meningeal veins rather than the arteries, and demonstrated the spirochætæ in great numbers in their walls and in the adjacent tissue, or even in some cases in thrombi which occluded the veins.

LITERATURE

Nonne: Syphilis and Nervensystem, 3te Aufl., Berlin, 1915.
Strassmann: Ziegler's Beiträge, 1910, xlix, 430.
Versé: *Ibid.*, 1913, lvi, 580.
Remsen: Johns Hopkins Hosp. Bull., 1903, xiv, 280.

CHAPTER XXXV

TYPES OF INJURY.—SPIROCHÆTAL INFECTION (Continued)

Syphilis: Tabes dorsalis. General symptoms. Lesions of the nervous system, theories concerning it. Dementia paralytica, its relation to tabes; symptoms. Anatomical changes in brain and cord. Syphilitic lesions of genital organs. Orchitis. Congenital syphilis. General relations. Lesions in respiratory organs, liver, pancreas, bones, etc. Late forms of congenital syphilis.

LOCOMOTOR ATAXIA, OR TABES DORSALIS

We may consider this disease here, together with the general paralysis of the insane, even though it has not been absolutely proven to be of syphilitic origin. Statistical study has given figures which point in an unmistakable manner to syphilis as its cause. Erb found syphilis in 89.5 per cent. of the cases and others have found a similar percentage. Recently Noguchi found the spirochæta in the cord in one case out of twelve, and it seems only a question of further study to prove the constancy of the relationship.

The disease is in large part an affection of the lower sensory neurons, although we shall find that these are unequally altered in different parts, and that while many of the phenomena are to be explained as the result of this lesion, there are others which are not.

The clinical aspect of the disease is extremely variegated, though most of the symptoms are the result of disturbances of the sensory apparatus, partly irritative, partly paralytic. Reflexes and movements depending on muscle sense, and, consequently, coördination, are much disturbed.

Violent stabbing pains in the limbs or elsewhere (lightning pains) occur especially at night; sudden attacks of cramp-like pain in some internal organ—stomach, larynx, bladder, etc., are known as gastric or laryngeal or vesical crises. A period of sexual excitement is followed by impotence. The tendon reflexes are abolished; the pupils become inactive and fixed. Sensation is dulled or perverted; the patient no longer feels the floor he walks on, or feels it like so much wool. He loses his sense of the position of his extremities and must watch his feet in order to set them in the right place; inattention may result in a fall. The gait becomes peculiar and slapping. This ataxia, which has given rise to one of the names, may affect any or all of the muscles.

So-called trophic changes arise in various places. Half of the tongue atrophies; an ulcer appears in the foot and proceeds to grow deeper, painlessly, until it perforates the foot. The bones become fragile and break, and fail to heal again. Joints loosen and become disorganized; the cartilage softens and the bone is eroded, or great dislocation may occur. Disturbed nutrition of the tissues in general seems to arise and the patient dies of an intercurrent infection, although seizures, simulating apoplexy and epileptiform convulsions, may have been survived. The details of these symptoms must be read elsewhere, most clearly perhaps in Marie's "Leçons sur les maladies de la Moelle."

Lesions.—At the autopsy the lesions depend upon the stage of the disease. If the patient dies at an early period, it may be necessary to search with the microscope for any change, but if it has lasted a long time the spinal cord with its posterior nerve-roots shows a characteristic appearance. The meninges (pia arachnoid) may be thickened and cloudy in part or quite normal looking, but the posterior columns are sunken and the dorsal roots look gray and smaller than normal. On section, the dorsal columns are gray and translucent in contrast to the remaining pinkish, opaque, white matter.

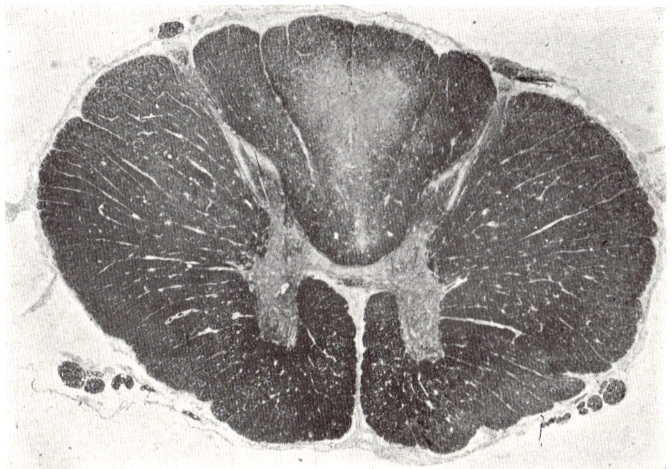

Fig. 362A.—Tabes dorsalis. Dorsal region of cord. Moderate sclerosis of posterior columns (Fordyce).

It is rarely possible to distinguish with the naked eye the exact distribution of this gray material in the dorsal columns, but with certain stains the microscope shows it well. The grayness and translucence are due to the disappearance of the lipoid myeline sheaths, as well as the axis-cylinders of the nerve-fibres and their replacement by an overgrowth of neuroglia.* If the process were fresh enough, the myeline might not have disappeared entirely, but its remnants could be made visible as black globules by the use of osmic acid, which does not blacken the normal myeline sheath. After a week or two, however, these fat-globules disappear and then the injured area can best be made apparent by the Weigert stain, which colors blue-black all the normal myeline sheaths and leaves the wasted and scarred area un-

* Observations of which Dr. Tilney has told me seem to show that much of the material employed to replace the lost nerve-fibres may be of connective-tissue origin.

stained. It is usually this unstained area which one can demonstrate in tabes (Fig. 362).

It will be recalled that the posterior roots are largely made up of central processes of the dorsal root ganglion-cells, which were at one era of development bipolar and still are in certain cranial ganglia, but which now have one T-shaped process, one branch of the T coming from the periphery, while the other enters the cord. On entering the cord in the posterior root the fibres swerve a little to the median side of the end of the posterior horn of the gray matter, which does not quite reach the surface. They pass through the zone of Lissauer, which is made up of fine fibres which also come in as part of the nerve, and turning upward a short way, sweep along with the other fibres into the posterior column and into the posterior horn. The fibres entering by the posterior root bifurcate, sending a short branch downward, a longer branch upward. Three main

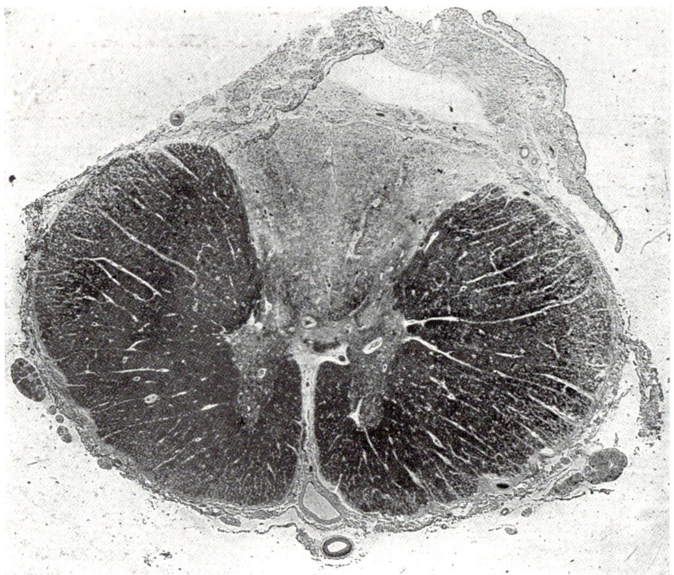

Fig. 362B.—Tabes dorsalis. Dorsal region of cord with extreme sclerosis of the posterior columns (Fordyce).

groups are generally distinguished in the distribution of these upward branches: a short group which quickly turns into the gray matter of the posterior horn, a median group which runs up in the column of Burdach—sometimes all the way, but often leaving it to turn into the gray matter and end about a cell there—and a long group which passes into the column of Goll and runs up to the nucleus of that column in the medulla or even further. It is the column of Goll which brings fibres even from the lower lumbar region.

The fibres of the dorsal root, which enter the gray matter, end in arborizations about ganglion-cells of that side, a great many of them constituting the fibre reticulum of the column of Clarke; or they pass forward to terminate about a ganglion-cell of the anterior horn, or cross by the posterior commissure to end similarly in the gray matter of the opposite side. Each fibre gives off many fine branches or collaterals which terminate in quite similar ways about the ganglion-cells of the gray matter, and thus forms abundant incidental connections at every stage in its progress upward in the cord, which are doubtless of fundamental importance in the establishment of reflex arcs.

Flechsig, Trepinski, and others have shown that, according to this distribution of the fibres, and according to the varying time at which they are matured by receiving their medullary sheaths, one may distinguish various subdivisions or tracts in the column of Burdach—a posterior, a middle, and an anterior root zone as well as a median zone which lies within the column of Goll against the median line.

In the middle root zone two types of fibres can be distinguished by their different time of myelinization, etc. Naturally these fields seen in any cross-section are only the expression of the currents of fibres at that particular level and so must change as one ascends the cord, except inasmuch as the incoming fibres deport themselves in the same way at successive levels. But if a group of fibres entering the cord becomes recognizable by any degenerative change it need not be expected that those fibres will occupy the same position in the field higher up; on the contrary they assume a new position or disappear because they have turned into the gray matter to end.

Fig. 362C. — Tabes dorsalis. Degenerative changes in the posterior nerve-root (Fordyce).

Consequently, it could only be through an exact repetition of the same degenerative change in each successive root that anything like the same distribution of degenerated fibres would be found at different levels, and even then in the higher levels the scarred remains of those entering far down and continued upward to that point would be added to those newly entering from a higher root.

The statement is generally made that in tabes dorsalis the beginning of the sclerosis or scarring is first seen in the "bandelettes externes," or parts of Burdach's column lying against the posterior horn; that the middle root zone is early involved and also the zone of Lissauer and the column of Goll, but that the anterior or ventral root zone is found intact until very late in the disease. While this is true, it must be true in any given case in different degree in different parts of the cord. The complete escape of a whole entering root, or of a series of them, from the effects of the disease at a point higher in the cord, allows intact fibres to appear in these situations, so that at those levels the areas of sclerosis are reduced to the upward prolongations which still continue from those below. And it is true that such escape of the roots may occur, just as it is true that the lesion need not be symmetrical on the two sides. But all this merely emphasizes the fact that the degenerative lesion in tabes is not like that produced by the cutting of a single dorsal root between its ganglion and the cord. The result of that would fade away into the gray matter, except in so far as a few degenerated fibres might be recognized continuing up the column of Burdach or in the column of Goll all the way to the medulla. Instead, in tabes there is a nearly constant and nearly symmetrical addition of the results of degeneration with the advent of each succeeding dorsal root. And, nevertheless, the irregularities show that the process is not to be regarded as the complete degeneration of a column or system, but as a succession of segmental degenerations accumulating their results in the cord as one passes upward. It would be most instructive to have a reconstruction of this lesion from an early case of tabes, before the whole posterior tracts had become fused in the sclerotic band, to show the topography of these repeated additions of sclerotic tissue in the cord and their relation to the changes in the roots.

It is with regard to the nature of the changes in the roots that the most persistent dispute has raged. It is agreed that while the roots are pathologically altered, the change in the portion between the dorsal root ganglion and the cord is more extreme than that in the peripheral nerves or in the ganglion-cells themselves, and consequently nearer to that seen in the cord itself. The following views have been expressed, most of which will doubtless disappear in the light of the simple explanation which must finally come some day.

The whole lesion is due to vascular obstruction; it is the effect of injury or destruction of peripheral ganglionic elements, which may also be responsible for ascending degenerations after amputations (Marie); it is a systematic degeneration of tracts in the cord itself corresponding with their developmental characters (Flechsig, Trepinski); it is the effect of destruction of the cells of the spinal root ganglia; it is the effect of meningeal inflammation about the entering roots which causes their compression and destruction (Nageotte); it is the effect of direct or indirect action of the syphilitic poison on the nerve roots, affecting less the ganglia, but producing the degenerative changes described (Redlich, Obersteiner). This is partly based on analogy with similar affections found in ergot poisoning and pellagra.

Of all these, the last seems most likely to prevail, in view of the intimate relation of the disease to syphilis and the finding of the spirochætæ in at least one case in the spinal cord. But, as can be seen, the pathogenesis of the disease is far from clear and must be much more precisely worked out before we can accept any view as final.

In the end one finds practically all of the posterior columns in the lumbar and dorsal regions reduced to a scar-like mass of neuroglia, the only exceptions, up to an advanced stage, being the ventral root zone and the medial zone. Lissauer's zone, the column of Clarke in the gray matter and the column of Goll, with most if not all of the column of Burdach, are thus degenerated. In the cervical region the lesion is less extensive and reduces itself toward the column of Goll. Since these tracts are so intimately concerned with muscle sense and with the reflex arcs it is not surprising that ataxia, the loss of the sense of position, failure in the discrimination of weights, etc., should be prominent features of the disease.

Tactile sensation, temperature sense, etc., which are so largely concerned in the short relayed tracts in the cord and in the other ascending tracts not involved in this process, are less affected. The cells of Clarke's column connecting with the cerebello-spinal tract must, however, lose some of their relations, since the fibres entering with the dorsal roots which arborize round them are destroyed.

It is difficult to explain the various "trophic" disturbances which are found in the tissues, such as the bone and joint changes mentioned above and the alterations in nails, skin, etc., which are so frequent. It seems quite possible, however, with regard to the "Charcot's joints," or tabetic arthro-

Fig. 363.—So-called Charcot joint. Syphilitic arthropathy involving the lumbar vertebræ and causing dislocation of the spine.

pathy (Fig. 363), that this is directly a syphilitic lesion, as held by Strümpell, Stargardt, and others, rather than a trophic disturbance dependent upon the nervous affection. For a discussion of this disease the student is referred to the following:

LITERATURE

Zoepffel: Berl. klin. Woch., 1911, xlviii, 2032.
Stargardt: Arch. f. Psychiatrie, 1912, xlix, 936.
Redlich: Pathol. d. tabischen Hinterstrangserkrankungen, Jena, 1897
Schæffer, K.: Handb. d. Neurologie, Lewandowski, 1911, vol. ii.
Marie, P.: Mal. de la Moelle, Paris, 1892.
Schmaus and Sacki: Ergeb. d. allg. Path., 1900, v, 268; 1904, ix, 217.

DEMENTIA PARALYTICA (GENERAL PARESIS, PROGRESSIVE PARALYSIS OF THE INSANE)

Another affection long known to be in some way associated with syphilis and, like tabes, spoken of as parasyphilitic, is now shown by the aid of the Wassermann reaction and by the demonstration of the spirochætæ in the brain to be definitely a syphilitic disease. It has been suggested by Möbius and others that this is a disease practically identical with tabes dorsalis except in that it is localized in the brain; and it seems that in a sense this is true, although the difference in localization makes a great difference in the disease as far as the manifestations are concerned; indeed, the lesions of the spinal cord in this condition are rather different from those found in tabes, and the symptoms resulting from them are also different.

Clinically, dementia paralytica is a most dramatic illness whose mental symptoms vary somewhat with the character of the individual. It is remarkable, however, to observe how, under this infection, all minds are planed down to the same low level. It usually begins insidiously, with drowsiness, lapses of attention, peculiarities of conduct, and accentuation of predominant personal characteristics, and proceeds to graver departures from civilized custom which are often shown in their true light in the police court.

Confusion of ideas and failure of memory, together with loss of self-restraint, are soon accompanied by delusions of grandeur in which the patient becomes most extravagant in his belief in his own powers and possessions.

Even at the beginning of this stage his condition may not have been recognized, and he is at the risk of committing mistakes in business or otherwise which may cost him dear.

In later stages memory is lost to an astounding degree; the patient lives only in the moment, totally forgetful of what happened an hour ago; writing becomes characteristically disturbed and finally impossible; speech is slow, blurred, and full of mistakes, the delusions take the place of everything else and are occasionally interrupted by violent maniacal outbreaks or by apoplectiform or epileptoid convulsions, from which the patient usually recovers without any after-effects. With all this, and to the end of life in the most miserable bodily and mental disruption, he is in a state of glowing content. This euphoria, or sense of well-being, is enough to compensate for most of the horror of the disease, but in other cases there is deep depression or complete mental dulling.

Aside from the mental derangement there are bodily evidences of the ailment—the pupils are irregular in form or size and usually rigid, as in locomotor ataxia. Paresis of many muscles may appear, and after the disease is well advanced contractures in these muscles hold the extremities in a helpless rigidity, so that the patient is permanently bedridden. Bed-sores of great extent are likely to appear in such cases. Loss of tactile and pain sense is common and readily results through inattention, in injuries such as burns and lacerations. The so-called trophic disturbances are found here as in tabes—perforating ulcers of the foot, great hæmorrhages in the outer ear following a slight injury, disorganization of the joints, great porosity and fragility of the bones, with fractures after trifling blows. Extreme emaciation alternates with periods of obesity, but in the end the weight usually goes down until, at death, the patient seems almost a skeleton.

Death occurs after one to three years, though sometimes there are remissions during which mental and bodily health seems pretty good and death comes only six or eight years after the onset. It may be the result of great emaciation and gradual exhaustion, but most commonly it is brought about by an intercurrent infection, especially bronchopneumonia, to which these demented people, with their dulled sensation and disturbed reflexes, are particularly exposed from the aspiration of saliva or food into

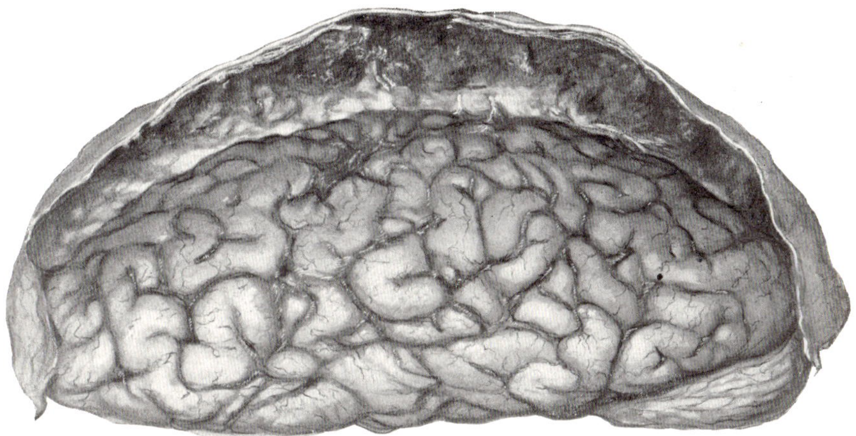

Fig. 364.—Chronic hæmorrhagic internal pachymeningitis.

the bronchi. In any case they are more than usually susceptible to infection in their state of disturbed nutrition.

At autopsy the most striking changes are in the brain and meninges. The dura is often lined over one or both halves of the brain with a thick, blood-stained layer of new tissue, which it is often possible to separate into several sheets, the deeper of which are stained a dull rusty brown by the pigment formed from the extravasated blood (Fig. 364). This hæmorrhagic pachymeningitis is not peculiar to general paresis, but is found in many other conditions.

The pia arachnoid is usually opaque and grayish white or very œdematous. Not infrequently it stretches across quite wide sulci, which are then partly filled with fluid, and sometimes the surface of the brain presents a great depression full of yellowish fluid, through and over which the arachnoid stretches. All these things are the result of the atrophy and shrinkage of the cerebral substance, the decrease in the bulk of the convolutions throwing wide the sulci (Fig. 365). The whole brain is a good deal decreased in size—on an average by 150 grams, but the two sides may be asymmetrical. The cerebral ventricles are often widened and contain an excess of fluid. Their lining is roughened by the appearance of minute gray, sand-like nodules which are outgrowths of neuroglia which push the ependyma before them. This "ependymitis granularis" also occurs in other conditions.

Microscopically, alterations are found especially in the more anterior portions of the cerebral cortex. The meninges are found to be thickened and infiltrated with mononuclear wandering cells, among which plasma cells are prominent. They are often intimately adherent to the brain substance. The vascular prolongations are accompanied by mantles of

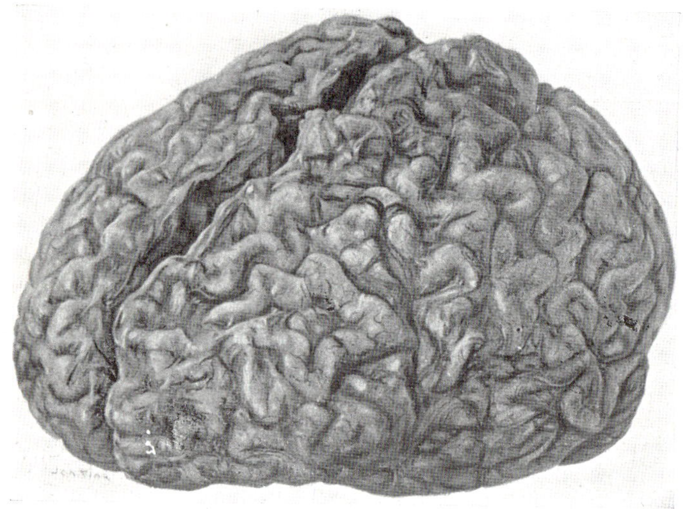

Fig. 365.—General paresis. Surface of the brain, showing atrophy of the convolutions (from Weygandt).

the same plasma cells and other smaller mononuclears, and even about the smallest vessels, which seem dilated and increased in number, the spaces are filled with these cells.

The nerve-cells of the cortex are in all stages of degeneration, shrinkage, and disintegration, and great numbers of them have disappeared. Those which remain have lost their protoplasmic processes in many cases and often their axone fibre. They are also greatly disarranged, so that the normal layers and vertical rows are no longer to be made out, but the cells lie confused and sparsely scattered in the cortex. Naturally the fibres, and especially the tangential association fibres and collaterals, are greatly reduced in number. The radial fibres seem more resistant, but even they are markedly diminished. In consequence of these losses the cerebral convolutions shrink and fall apart. But in the place of the lost cells and fibres a great new growth of neuroglia springs up. Abundant neuroglia cells, including the so-called spider cells, appear, together with a relatively dense network of neuroglia fibres. This is especially concentrated on the exposed surface and in those places where the brain substance is invaginated by the nutrient vessels. Every vessel is thus surrounded by a network of fibres. Sometimes there are even projecting brush-like masses on the outer surface, which aid in causing the adhesion of the meninges. The superficial layer, normally rather indistinct, here becomes a dense felt-work of neuroglia fibres extending a little way into the cortex and devoid of nerve-cells.

The spirochætæ found by Noguchi and Moore in paretic brains were scattered in the cerebral substance, not particularly in association with the vessels and not in this external neuroglial layer. The cerebrospinal fluid is rich in lymphocytes and contains also plasma cells. It is rich in globulins and gives the Wassermann reaction in extreme dilution.

In the remainder of the brain the lesions are very similar, with widespread loss of nerve-cells and fibres. This is well seen in the basal ganglia, the pons and medulla, as well as in the cerebellum, whose peculiar cortical cells may be greatly reduced.

In the spinal cord, tract degenerations are found in limited areas of the posterior column, generally together with descending degenerations of the pyramidal tracts. Doubtless, while the posterior tract degeneration depends upon the same ætiological factor as the changes in the brain, the descending degenerations may be due to lesions in the motor cortex. These are the changes in the so-called tabo-paresis, which, as has been said, does not correspond precisely with tabes in symptoms or anatomical basis.

LITERATURE

Kraepelin: Lehrb. d. Psychiatrie, Leipzig, 1909, General Paresis (Translation Nerv. and Mental Dis., Monogr., 1913, series No. 14).

Alzheimer: Histol. Stud. z. Differential Diag. d. Prog. Paralyse, Habilitationschrift, 1904.

Weygandt: Psychiatrie, München, 1902.

Noguchi and Moore: Jour. Exp. Med., 1913, xvii, 232

SYPHILIS OF THE GENITAL ORGANS

Of the syphilitic lesions of the male or female genitalia, aside from the primary chancres and the condylomatous and other affections of the secondary stage which have already been mentioned, the gummatous and interstitial changes in the testicle are the most common and important. Gummatous and other lesions have been described in the vagina, uterus, tubes, and ovaries, and also in the vas deferens, seminal vesicles, etc., but these are such rare occurrences and so imperfectly studied that we may turn at once to the testicular affections.

Most characteristic are those in which a definite gumma arises in the testis, taking its origin in the interstitial tissue and pushing aside the testicular tubules. In this respect it differs from the tuberculous process, which begins usually in the epididymis, and which, if it does affect the testis, does so by causing the formation of tubercles within or in direct relation to the tubules. The elastic tissue elements are destroyed thereby, although in the gummatous orchitis they remain intact. The gumma has the characters seen elsewhere and often shows the presence of giant-cells in the marginal portions. Such gummata, at first grayish-red on section, later become opaque yellowish and caseous (Fig. 366). They may extend to and through the tunica albuginea and sometimes reach a great size, so as to be mistaken for tumors, and excised. With antisyphilitic treatment they disappear, leaving an extensive scar. In a specimen before me, while the gumma is at the height of its course, the surrounding testicular tissue is very œdematous, the tubules being spread wide apart not only

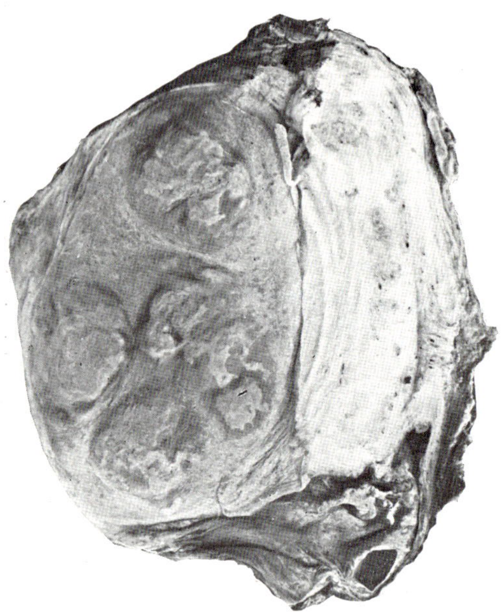

Fig. 366.—Gummata of testicle. There are several large firm caseous nodules embedded in the enlarged testicle and surrounded by scar tissue.

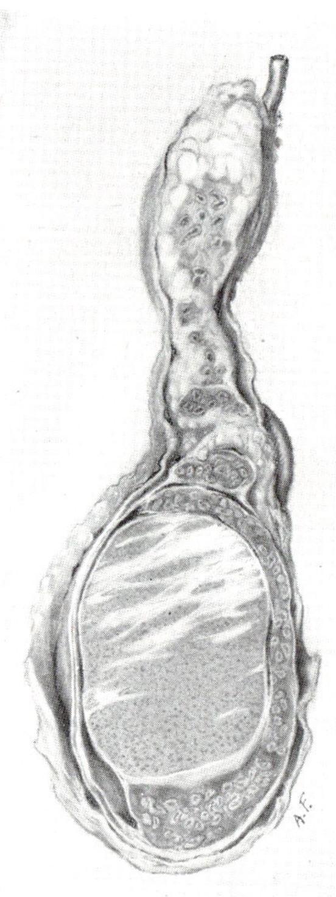

Fig. 367.—Syphilitic fibrous orchitis.

by this accumulation of fluid, but also by the infiltration of great numbers of mononuclear wandering cells. In nearly every tubule there are evidences of degeneration and disappearance of the spermatogenic cells, and in most there is already great thickening and hyaline degeneration of the connective-tissue wall. Undoubtedly these tubules would have lost their functional activity and merged later into a scar.

The other form, the so-called orchitis fibrosa (Fig. 367), has long been regarded as definitely syphilitic, and clear evidence of syphilis when found at autopsy. Except in such stages as described above, in connection with active gummata it seems to be known in the form of extensive scars through the testicle, which shine on section as pearly white streaks against the dull brown of the remaining testicular substance. In these scars are found the hyaline, thickened remnants of testicular tubules and some infiltration of wandering cells. But, as Chiari, Hansemann, and others pointed out in discussing Baumgarten's paper, there is no real proof that all such scars are syphilitic. They may, as well, result from the orchitis which follows trauma, gonorrhœa, mumps, and many other things. The literature is contradictory on the validity of the evidence of the syphilitic nature of these scars, but perhaps with the newer surer methods of diagnosis the matter will soon be made clear.

LITERATURE

Baumgarten, Chiari, Orth, Hansemann, and others: Verh. Deutsch. path. Gesellsch., 1900, iii, 107 (Syphilis of testicle).

CONGENITAL SYPHILIS

The term congenital syphilis is to be preferred to hereditary syphilis inasmuch as it appears that the disease is not transmitted as a hereditary characteristic (dependent upon the chromosomes of the uniting germ cells), but rather as an infection transmitted to the fœtus in the course of its development, either by spirochætæ which accompany the sperm cell and probably infect the mother, or by spirochætæ from the tissues of the mother, herself previously infected. In all these cases, except perhaps in late postconceptional syphilis, in which both placenta and child may possibly escape, the placenta is the seat of syphilitic alterations which are of rather vague character, since actual gummata are only unconvincingly described and are at least rare. There are found diffuse infiltrations of the placenta with wandering cells, vascular changes both in the placenta and in the umbilical cord, distinguished, as elsewhere, by thickening of adventitia and intima, and, thirdly, curious modifications of the villi, consisting of new formation of loose connective tissue about the central blood-vessels, such as to cause a great bulbous swelling of each villus and hence a marked enlargement of the placenta. On this account, a striking disproportion between the size of the placenta and that of the child is always suggestive of syphilis.

None of these changes is, however, of absolutely diagnostic importance.

Evidently the spirochætæ can enter the fœtal blood readily enough from such diseased placentæ, and finding in the fœtal tissues a specially suitable medium for growth, proceed to multiply to an extent never approached in the tissues of the adult in acquired syphilis. They are to be demonstrated in perfectly astounding numbers by the Levaditi method of silver staining in most of the tissues of the syphilitic new-born, where they lie scattered everywhere among the cells, generally without producing any very evident change about them. The lesions which they produce are essentially like those of the tertiary stage, although some are evidently of the secondary type. Primary lesions do not occur. These tertiary lesions consist most commonly of diffuse inflammation, with the formation of a great deal of scar-like connective tissue throughout the organ; rarely there are actual gummata, and often the effect seems to be shown in the retardation and impairment of the normal growth and development of the organ.

The effects of syphilitic infection in the parents upon the children seem to become somewhat weakened with the advance of time and with successive pregnancies. The first pregnancies after infection end as a rule in early miscarriages; often the fœtus is found in an extreme state of maceration, as though it had been dead a long time. In the later pregnancies the child may be born alive with lesions of syphilis, and die soon. Still later it may survive and even show no sign of disease at first, but pretty surely in childhood or adolescence or even in later life the stigmata or characteristic and destructive marks of the disease appear somewhere, either in the form of a finished process, or as a progressive disease which may lead to the deformity or death of the patient. It is evident that this so-called "syphilis tardive" forms an interminable subject with quite as many variegated possibilities as in the acquired form.

Indeed, practically all of the effects of acquired syphilis appear in the congenital retarded form, even including tabes and general paresis, and none of them shall be discussed again here. The following concerns those which are peculiar to the congenital form.

The new-born syphilitic child or dead fœtus commonly shows some affections of the skin, such as the plantar and palmar pemphigus, in which the skin of the palms and soles is lifted up in bullæ or blisters filled with fluid; another type shows extensive scaling off of the epidermis, sometimes over great areas (specific ichthyosis).

There may be ulcerative lesions over the buttocks and thighs which later heal to form inconspicuous scars. Papules and areas of infiltration on the lips, especially at the angles of the mouth, burst later and ulcerate, healing afterward to form radiating scars—the so-called *rhagades*. The same thing happens in the peri-anal region.

Coryza or "snuffles" is a practically constant accompaniment and is extremely serious to the nursing child, since it cannot breathe through its nose while it suckles. On this account it may practically starve to death. In still-born infants, or in those which die shortly after birth, the lungs show in many cases a peculiar change, generally spoken of loosely as white pneumonia or *pneumonia alba*. There has been much dispute about the nature of this, and while some have tried to separate a desquamative from an interstitial form, others have found these two processes combined.

The lungs are enlarged and heavy, the consolidation, usually patchy, is smooth, pale, and elastic. Microscopically (Fig. 368), in all the cases I have seen, there has been a combination of great thickening of the alveolar septa with some desquamation of the epithelium and in places an infiltration with leucocytes and mononuclear wandering cells. The epithelial lining cells are cubical in form from the lack of distension, and while many are desquamated into the air-cells, there seems to be no very great multiplication on their part. On the other hand, the connective tissue of the lung is enormously increased in bulk about vessels and bronchi and in the alveolar walls themselves. These are so thick that the alveoli look like

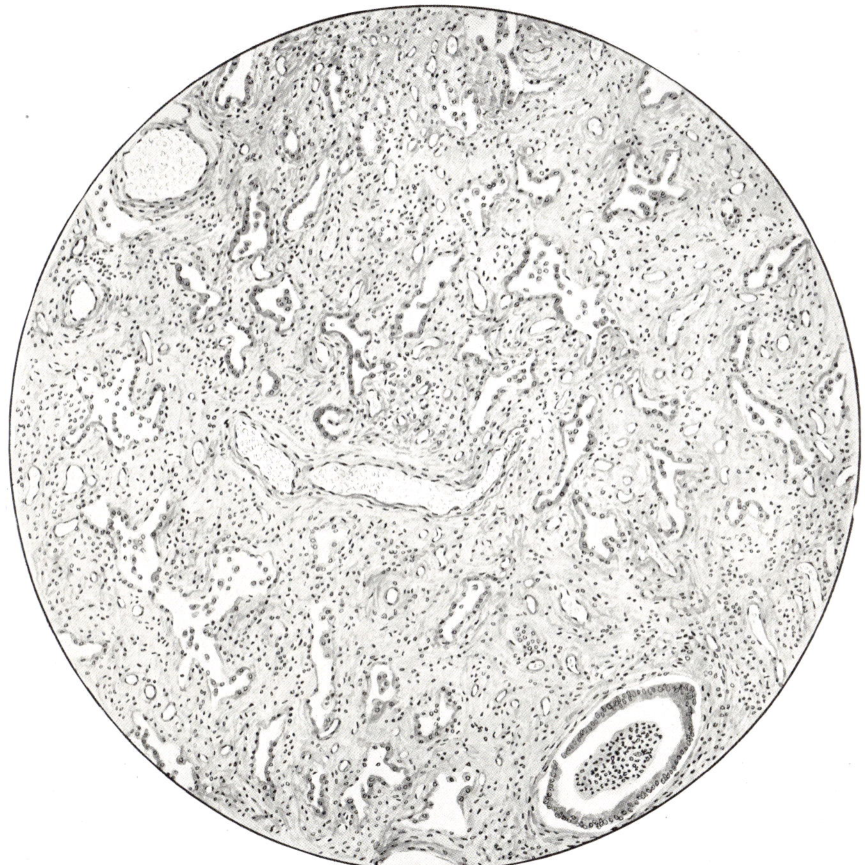

Fig. 368.—Congenital syphilis of the lung: pneumonia alba. There is great interstitial growth of connective tissue with infiltration of wandering cells and thickening of the alveolar epithelium.

glandular spaces in a solid tissue; the capillaries are wide and seem very abundant as they run from side to side of the septa. The connective tissue forms a loose network, evidently rather œdematous, in which the connective-tissue cells are scattered, sparsely mingled with a good number of mononuclear wandering cells. In rather rare cases distinct gummata have been seen in the lungs.

In the *liver* there occurs a variety of lesions. The organ is generally enlarged and firm, sometimes it has a normal dark-red appearance on section, sometimes it is pale grayish-brown and rather translucent, with numerous scattered foci of opaque yellow. Perhaps the commonest change is a general retardation of its development, so that at birth it still appears as an organ actively engaged in blood formation. The capillaries are wide and in places distended with groups of blood-cells of all sorts,

Fig. 369.—Congenital syphilis of the liver. The liver-cell strands are separated by fibrous tissue, and there are accumulations of wandering cells in places. Such foci may later become caseous.

myelocytes, lymphocytes, eosinophiles, and particularly nucleated red corpuscles. In other places the liver-cell columns are widened into bulbous masses of protoplasm in which are grouped numerous large nuclei, evidently indicating a continued new formation of liver-cells. There is nothing clearly specific about such an anatomical picture—the same thing may be found in a normal fœtus of a rather earlier stage of development, but the abundant distribution of spirochætæ through the tissue determines its syphilitic nature.

More destructive are the cases in which the whole lobular arrangement of the liver-cells is rendered indistinct by the diffuse new growth of fibrous tissue everywhere through the organ. The liver-cell strands are reduced to small distorted bands of protoplasm containing many nuclei, sometimes clustered almost as in a giant-cell, and separated everywhere by a loose fibrous tissue in which run the isolated capillaries. In the case illustrated (Fig. 369) there are numerous foci of necrosis, in which there are crowded abundant leucocytes and fragmented nuclei. These evidently form one type at least of what are called miliary gummata, although there is nothing very specific in their appearance. They, like the rest of the liver, contain

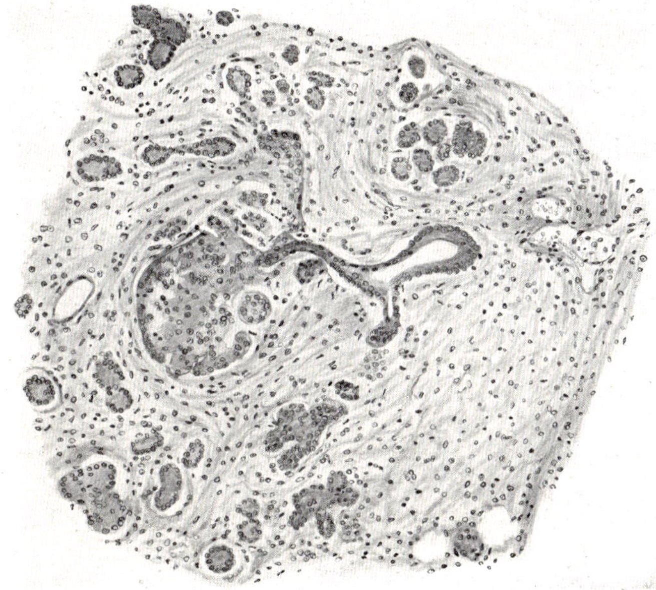

Fig. 370.—Congenital syphilis. Pancreas of child with excessive interstitial connective tissue separating acini. The island of Langerhans is still in connection with a duct.

quantities of spirochætæ. Occasionally one finds more definite concentrically arranged miliary gummata, like small tubercles in the liver, and these have been well described by Hecker. More rarely there are larger caseous gummatous nodules surrounded by scar tissue and ending in a lobulated cirrhotic deformity of the liver.

The *pancreas,* so rarely involved in acquired syphilis, is commonly affected by the congenital form. Again there are rarely gummata of definite form, but very commonly diffuse granulation tissue growth and retardation of development (Fig. 370). One finds the pancreas slightly enlarged and gray and firm. On section the acini are spread apart and apparently incompletely differentiated, the islands of Langerhans often appearing, as in the fœtus, in persistent connection with the branches of the pancreatic duct. Focal necrosis of a more or less suggestive gummatous character is often found in the interstitial tissue.

Similarly, congenital syphilitic disease in the *kidneys* produces rarely definite gummata, but often patches of atrophy and destruction of tubules and glomeruli with scarring. The same peculiarity is true of the *testicle*, in which the gumma common in the acquired form is replaced by atrophy or maldevelopment of the tubules, often with interstitial connective-tissue formation, which leaves the organ distorted, small, and hard.

In the *bones* the syphilitic osteochondritis first described by Wegner is a most definite and characteristic lesion found practically always in the syphilitic new-born, although it does not affect equally all the bones, being most distinctly developed in the epiphyseal ends of the long bones about the knee. The epiphyseal line, which ordinarily forms a perfectly even, thin, pearly gray line between cartilage and bone, loses this delicate aspect and becomes thick, jagged and opaque yellowish-white (Fig. 371). Often it has a granular, mortar-like appearance and it is seen that it no longer marks the line of continuity of the cartilage with the bone, but that instead it is really a cleft between the two, filled with a fine yellowish gritty substance. Sometimes the epiphysis is quite dislocated and separated from the bone along this line.

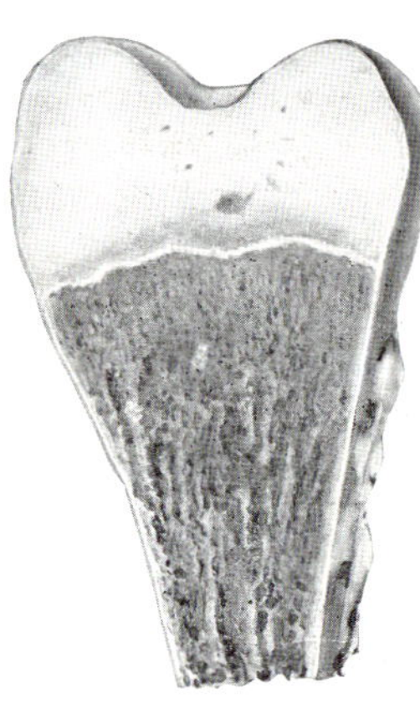

Fig. 371.—Syphilitic osteochondritis. The line of ossification is irregular and is conspicuously opaque.

Microscopically (Figs. 372, 373) the reasons for this are seen: Along the line of ossification on the side of the bone there is developed a layer of granulation tissue essentially gummatous in its character, and prone to necrosis and disintegration; it involves the most recently formed bone, and stops the process of bone formation by causing the necrosis of this layer, all of which collapses together in a débris of minute bony fragments (Fig. 374). Round about, from the periosteum and perichondrium, there are reparatory new growths of slight extent, and later, if the child survives, all this débris is removed and healing takes place in such a way as to readjust lamellated bone to cartilage and allow bone formation to proceed as before, although one may imagine that in all such cases a good deal of disturbance in the development of the bone must result.

There are many other lesions to be found in such new-born syphilitic children, but they all proceed on the same principles and these may suffice to illustrate.

Late Forms of Congenital Syphilis.—Very important and difficult to comprehend are the syphilitic lesions which appear after the lapse of months or years in children born of syphilitic parents, which at birth may not have shown any signs of disease.

Fournier, in his book on "La Syphilis Tardive," includes practically every ailment that flesh is heir to under this heading, so that at first it must seem fanciful; but while one remains skeptical about some of the phenomena referred to syphilis, good proof is brought for most of them.

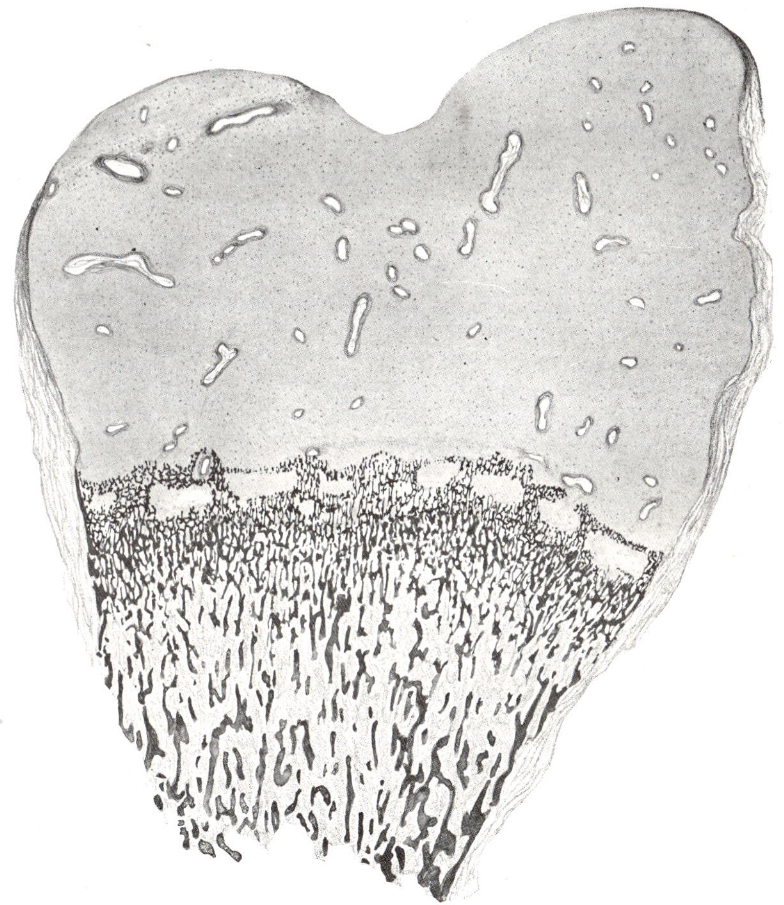

Fig. 372.—Syphilitic osteochondritis, showing slight distortion of the line of ossification.

The scars and deformities or stigmata of syphilis are recognizable, as well as the active progressive disease, and often serve to indicate the character of some other more obscure process which is still going on. Various deformities due to retardation of development leading even to dwarfism are regarded as syphilitic. These as they affect the skull produce irregularities of form and asymmetries, or a hydrocephalic dilatation which might seem due to other possible causes.

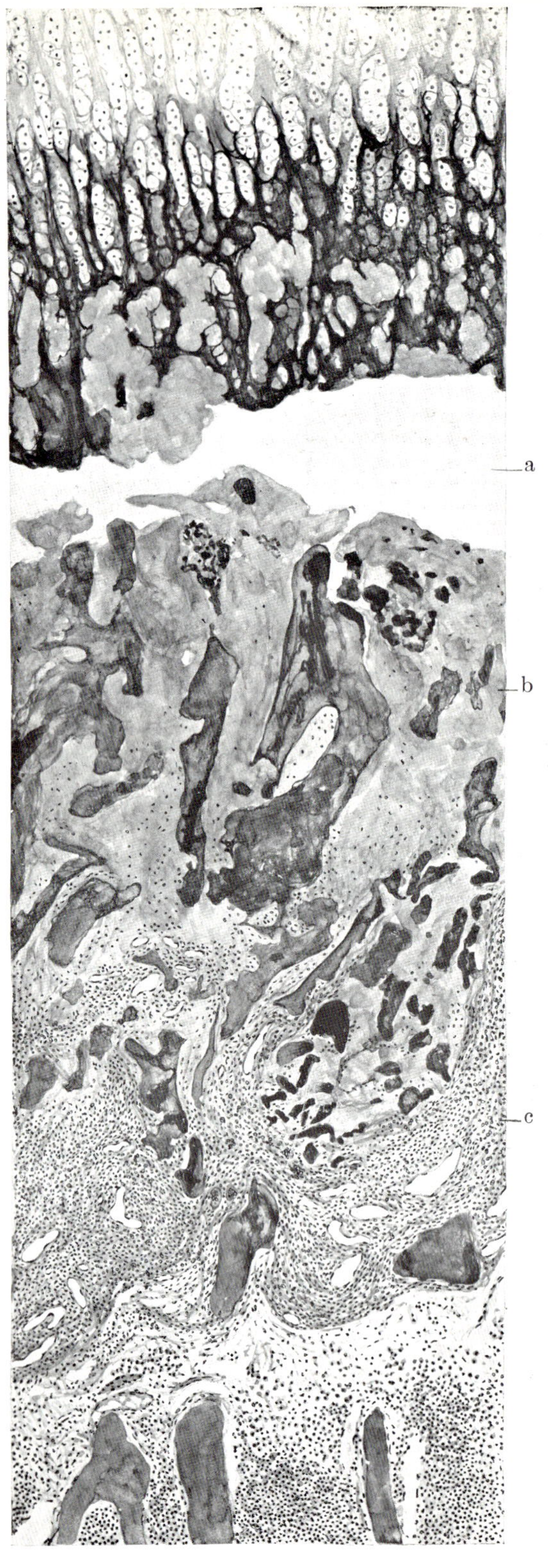

Fig. 373.—Syphilitic osteochondritis. Section showing the changes mentioned, and also separation of the epiphysis (*a*). About the comminuted fragments of calcified cartilage and bone is a cellular granulation tissue (*c*) with extensive necrosis (*b*) toward the line of fracture.

Perfectly distinct, however, are the malformations of the nose, gummatous destruction of the nasal bones producing saddle-nose, while even greater deformity is caused by collapse of the cartilaginous part of the septum, which allows the tip of the nose to telescope into the rest, so that there is a fold of skin on each side.

Various changes in ears and eyes occur with deafness and impairment of

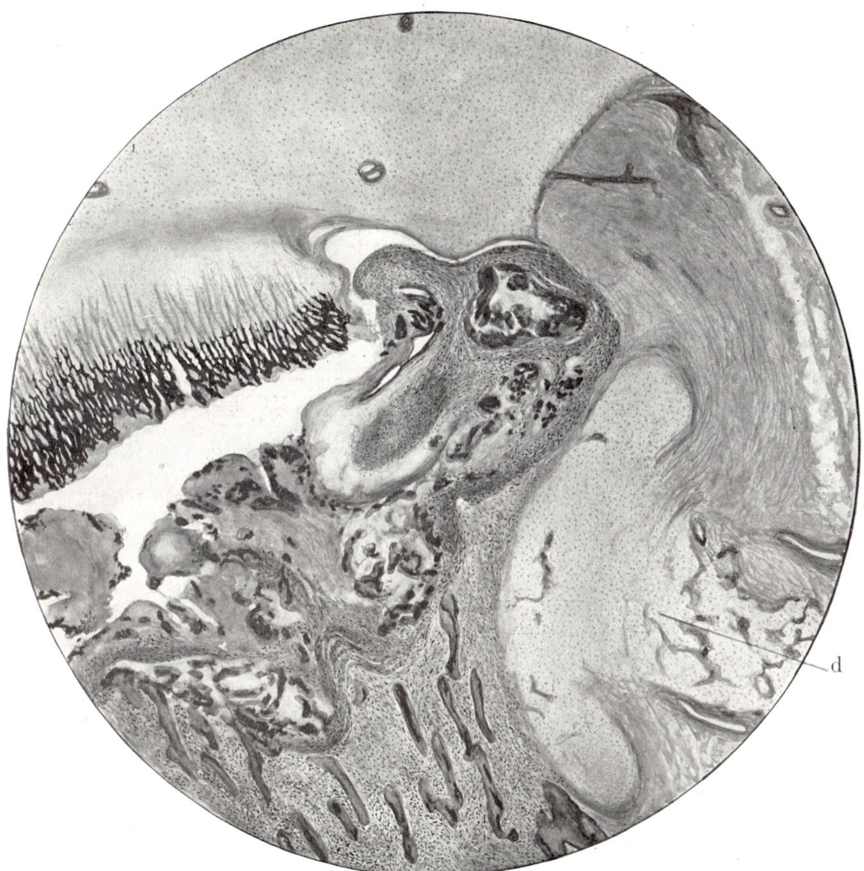

Fig. 374.—Syphilitic osteochondritis. Another section from the same case, showing extensive efforts at healing, with the formation of new cartilage and cancellous bone (*d*).

vision. Of these, the commonest and most easily recognized is the interstitial keratitis, which gives a steamy opacity to the cornea and which may obstruct vision very completely, or finally clear away entirely.

In the teeth there are many deformities ascribed to syphilis, all rather difficult to explain and none surely indicative of syphilis unless it be possibly the true Hutchinson's teeth. The change that Hutchinson described affecting most obviously the upper incisors, is such that the teeth are rather tapered, usually stand wide apart, and have a single semicircular recess in the biting edge.

In the skeleton the lesions of late congenital syphilis are practically those of the tertiary stage of the acquired form, including chronic forms of periostitis, arthritis, etc. But the atrophy, or rather maldevelopment, of bones which produces the extreme delicacy and small size of the skeleton in some of these cases is rather different, as is also the extraordinary local or partial gigantism, which is of similar origin and follows the great local overgrowth of bone.

Lesions of the nervous system and of the various other organs of the body are like those of acquired syphilis, except that they seem to be intensified in these patients, inasmuch as the infection has begun with the beginning of their lives and affected their resistance throughout.

LITERATURE

Volk: Placentarsyphilis, Ergeb. d. allg. Path., 1904, viii, 509.
Schwab: La Syphilis, 1905, Juli.
E. Fournier: L'heredosyphilis tardive, Paris, 1907.
G. Herxheimer: Ergeb. d. allg. Path., 1908, xii, 499.
Hecker: Deutsches Arch. f. kl. Med., 1898, lxi, 1.
Hochsinger: Studien über hered. Syphilis, Leipzig u. Wien, 1898 and 1904.

GENERAL DISCUSSION OF BACTERIAL INFECTIONS

Naturally there are a great many other infectious diseases caused by bacteria which have not been mentioned, although in some cases they assume a considerable importance. Those which have been discussed have been chosen merely as the commonest to serve as examples or types of the processes involved.

It must be observed that the diseases caused by bacteria have many features in common, although they are in some respects so different. In most if not all cases, one receives the impression that the bacteria are leading a life to which they have adapted themselves, but it is by no means always possible to find them in their natural surroundings. Occasionally man seems to be the more or less accidental host of bacteria which have adapted themselves to a parasitic life in some other animal.

As parasites these bacteria do harm or are ready to do harm if opportunity offers. It is well known that hundreds of kinds of bacteria live on the exposed or hidden surfaces of the body without causing any injury, but even our most accustomed commensal, the colon bacillus, will, if the opportunity presents itself, take advantage of some disturbance which weakens resistance and set up a cystitis or pyelonephritis or cholecystitis. The extraordinary powers of resistance which keep out such bacteria or destroy them after a short struggle when they have penetrated into the tissues must always seem wonderful. It is precisely in this connection that all the work of the last decades upon immunity and resistance is especially important, for with regard to the invasion of other, non-bacterial organisms, it is only exceptionally so satisfactory.

It is true that while there can be no doubt of the bacterial nature of many of these infective agents, it is not easy to decide about others. Strict devotion to a classification on the basis of systematic biology should perhaps make us hesitate to group together such infections as typhoid fever or plague and actinomycosis or syphilis. Most writers speak of the actinomyces groups as more nearly related to the rather higher fungi, and perhaps this is true. But then there are indications that many of the best accepted bacteria, such as the diphtheria bacillus, tubercle bacillus, etc., may at times possess some of these characteristics. Syphilis is caused by an organism which differs from ordinary bacteria in its size and flexibility and may well be regarded as a protozoan parasite. In the case of others, such as typhus, which has recently been forced into the group of bacterial diseases, and of all the somewhat similar exanthematic diseases, we are still so ignorant of the ætiological factor that an attempt at biological classification is useless. In poliomyelitis the peculiar minute organism receives no niche in the biological system even at the hands of its discoverers. If, then, we leave the grouping in a confused state, it is because a definite classification would rest on a very insecure basis.

The types have been chosen to illustrate the more prominent forms of behavior of the parasite with respect to the host and of the host with respect to the parasite.

While the members of the groups of pyogenic micrococci tend to spread through the body, destroying cells wherever their injurious influences are concentrated enough, and inciting a response in the form of a typical acute inflammation, the members of the diphtheria-tetanus groups grow locally and diffuse far and wide a violent poison. Again, anthrax and plague spread everywhere and cause necrosis and inflammation, while typhoid, spreading quite as widely, produces a peculiar reaction calling out a different group of phagocytes and destroying the tissues in a more insidious way. Tuberculosis, actinomycosis, and syphilis have methods of attack, slow and met by vigorous fortification, but destructive in the end without the appearance of much of the ordinary type of inflammation. In the group which follows, in which the organisms have not been recognized at all, we shall find it more difficult to explain all the lesions.

CHAPTER XXXVI

TYPES OF INJURY.—EXANTHEMATIC DISEASES

Introduction. Measles: Susceptibility, ætiology, course of the disease and pathological anatomy. Scarlet fever: Ætiology; complicating streptococcus infection, transmission, course and pathological anatomy. Scarlatinal nephritis. Smallpox: Relation to vaccinia; vaccination; ætiology; symptoms and pathological anatomy.

EXANTHEMATIC DISEASES

There follows some description of the more important of a series of diseases which we recognize as extremely easily communicable and therefore undoubtedly due to an infection, but in which, in spite of the most earnest efforts, no living organism has been demonstrated with the certainty which we demand. It is true that many supposed parasites have been found, as, for example, the cytorhyctes in the skin in small-pox, which are looked upon with confidence by their discoverers as the specific factors, but their descriptions do not carry conviction. It has been well said that if there is any doubt about a parasite when you see it, it is usually not a parasite. Whatever the nature of these organisms, they must multiply with great rapidity and disseminate themselves quickly through the body by way of the blood-stream. Indeed, the diseases can probably be transmitted in each case by inoculation of blood, as has been shown by Hektoen to be true for measles. Doubtless, too, the organisms are very small and perhaps, in most cases, capable of going through a porcelain filter. The diseases have in common the occurrence of an eruption on the skin, or exanthem, which no doubt indicates the presence of the organism there, but since such eruptions are found in other infectious diseases and even in various intoxications it does not really form a good basis for their classification. There are many such diseases, including chicken-pox, rubeola or German measles, Duke's fourth disease, erythema infectiosum, etc., but the most important are those which follow. Doubtless before long their ætiology will be cleared up and we shall be able to form a better idea of the way in which the lesions are produced.

MEASLES

This is a disease of childhood because susceptibility is practically universal and the opportunity for infection so general that few children escape. There are few adults to infect, since nearly all have had the disease in childhood. In this is implied the fact that one attack confers immunity. The disease may be transferred in utero if the mother is ill with it when the child is about to be born. The child of a mother who has never had measles may contract it almost immediately after birth, while the child of an immune mother is born with an immunity which lasts one or two months. The mother's milk confers no protection. While such a situation prevails in most civilized countries, it is well known that in isolated lands, such as the South Sea Islands, where the disease was unknown, the advent of the infection with early explorers was followed by terrific epidemics which killed off many of the natives. Ordinarily not considered a serious disease, measles nevertheless becomes so in virtue of the fact that severe tuberculous infection frequently appears as a sequel.

Nothing whatever is known of the nature of the causative agent except that it spreads rapidly in the body and is present in the circulating blood in such quantities that injection of the blood into normal persons will produce the disease in typical form (Hektoen). The most painstaking efforts have failed to reveal any recognizable living agent, although it is practically certain that it exists in each sample of blood and in the tissues.

Transmission is ordinarily direct from person to person, probably by means of the respiratory tract, the infection presumably being carried in a spray from the coughing child.

The period of incubation is eight to nine days; the rash appears after about fourteen days. There are thus several days in which prodromal symptoms of headache, malaise, and nasal and bronchial catarrh prevail. Conjunctivitis, intense coryza with reddening of the pharynx and larynx, and, a little later, bronchitis, are characteristic and constant features. The so-called Koplik's spots in the mouth are minute white flecks surrounded by bluish and then red zones. They appear early and have a diagnostic importance.

The exanthem or rash appears first on the face and then spreads over the rest of the body. It is slightly elevated, grayish-red, and distributed in flecks which are sometimes very small but usually conglomerated into larger patches which reach 1 cm. in diameter. It is common to observe a crescentic form in these patches. There are fever and leucocytosis and the catarrhal symptoms continue. With the lapse of a few days the rash fades and there may be desquamation of branny scales. The bronchitis clears up also unless there are further complications in the form of lobular pneumonia or other secondary infection.

Pathological Anatomy.—Sections of the skin which pass through the macules show a moderate œdema and hyperæmia with some accumulation of lymphocytes about the blood-vessels. But there is no necrosis nor intense inflammatory reaction. The lobular pneumonia which is extremely common in the late stages of measles has been described by Steinhaus, Jochmann, Hecht, and others. In our cases it has assumed the form of a fine consolidation occupying only a few alveoli at the very tips of the bronchioles and, indeed, Steinhaus refers to this, but he emphasizes particularly its interstitial character, saying that the causative agent appears to be carried in the walls of the bronchi and to cause infiltration there, rather than by spreading quickly in the alveolar lumina. The exudate is rich in fibrin, and Jochmann has observed also that the walls of the bronchioles become thickened by the presence of the fibrinous exudate, and that if this becomes organized, a sort of obliterative bronchiolitis may appear in which the lumen of the bronchiole is occluded by a plug of new connective tissue. Hecht finds in measles and certain other infections the development in the alveoli of great giant-cells which result from the fusion or imperfect division of the alveolar epithelium. This is, in general, a not uncommon type of lobular pneumonia in children, and may be associated with bronchial occlusions.

The other organs, beside the lungs and skin, are not characteristically affected in measles. There is usually a moderate acute splenic tumor and general enlargement of the lymphoid apparatus. The conjunctivitis, rhinitis, etc., are probably caused by the specific agent, but bacteria are so regularly associated that the affection is not peculiar. Otitis media is a not infrequent sequel.

LITERATURE

von Jürgensen and von Pirquet: Masern, Nothnagel's Handb., Wien, 1911, iv.
Steinhaus: Ziegler's Beitr., 1901, xxix, 524.
Jochmann: *Ibid.*, 1904, xxxvi, 340.
Hecht: *Ibid.*, 1910, xlviii, 263.
Brücker: Jahrb. f. Kinderheilk., 1902, lvi, 725.
Koplik: Archives of Pediatrics, 1896, xiii, 918.

SCARLET FEVER

This is generally looked upon as a more serious disease than measles, not only in itself but because of the complications which accompany it and the secondary affections which appear after recovery seems well established. It is very readily transmitted from one person to another and therefore occurs in epidemics.

Ætiology.—Nothing whatever is known of the infectious agent which causes this disease. It is true that Mallory has described peculiar rosette-like bodies in the skin and that Gamaleia and others have seen similar things, but these cannot be found in skin excised from the living patient, and, on the other hand, they can be found in the skin at autopsy in persons who have died of other diseases. Their ætiological relation to scarlet fever is at least doubtful.

Further, it is known that there is always an intense infection of the throat with virulent streptococci or pneumococci, and there are those who maintain that scarlet fever is nothing more than a streptococcus infection. Indeed, one sees not infrequently intense streptococcus septicæmias which, beginning in the throat, develop all the prominent symptoms of scarlatina. Two such cases have been mentioned in another chapter, and in one of them there remains even yet uncertainty as to whether the patient died of scarlet fever or of a streptococcus infection. But while infection with the streptococcus confers no immunity from another attack, and rather predisposes toward reinfection, one attack of scarlet fever results in a lasting immunity. Besides, scarlet fever is not the only disease which is so intimately associated with a streptococcus infection—the same situation occurs with measles, small-pox, etc., and it would be equally reasonable to insist that they too are merely forms of streptococcus infection. There are other considerations, too, which make it seem certain that the cause of this disease is a special animate virus, which is quite different from the streptococcus.

The disease may be transmitted by the nasal and pharyngeal secretion or by objects soiled with it or with the scales from the skin. Of course, this is the traditional guesswork, since the organism is not known, but at least those modes of transmission seem likely, and Stickler actually produced the disease by subcutaneous injection of pharyngeal mucus in the attempt to imitate inoculation as then practised in smallpox. Krumwiede, Nicoll and Pratt were unable to transmit the disease to monkeys in this way or even by the injection of blood from scarlatina patients. On the other hand, scarlatinal infections in surgical incisions, or in cuts or scratches received during an autopsy on the body of a person dead of scarlet fever, are well known, and the case of Leube, who thus infected himself, is famous.

The infectious agent seems to cling to clothing and other objects and to remain alive for a long time. Hence the cases of infection from apparel which has been stored for years in a trunk.

Course of the Disease.—The disease begins suddenly, after three or four days of incubation, with sore throat, fever and swelling of the lymph-glands at the angle of the jaw and of the tonsils. With increase in the intensity of the angina and the appearance of whitish flecks of exudate on the red background there comes vomiting. Soon there appears on the face, and later over the whole body, the characteristic red rash which is made up of flecks much finer than in the case of measles and more closely set; the whole face and skin has a flushed red color. In all cases the angina represents a streptococcus infection, but there are some which proceed to recovery without much further evidence of bacterial infection, while in other cases there are phenomena of the most intense sort which appear to be largely due to the streptococci. Escherich, therefore, divides the cases into toxic and infectious types. In the more severe cases the angina becomes far more intense. The tonsils swell to the point of meeting in the mid-line and become partly necrotic. Considerable areas of mucosa of the fauces and the walls of the pharynx become covered with a false membrane of greenish color, the removal of which reveals deep ulcerations with foul base. The scarlatinal angina is thus an extremely destructive process. The neighboring lymph-glands in the neck are swollen to a great size and, if incised, sometimes exude a greenish pus, sometimes show their central parts as firm, necrotic masses which are later discharged. Such *scarlatinal buboes* may occur in this way in the early stages of the disease or appear much later after the acute symptoms have passed.

Pathological Anatomy.—Laryngeal and tracheal inflammation is found only in the severest cases and then the occurrence of bronchopneumonia is likely. This lobular pneumonia commonly becomes confluent and leads to the production of abscesses in the lung. Extension into the pleural cavity results in empyema which may readily end fatally.

In the heart there may be no evident gross lesions even though the child die with signs directly indicating its involvement.

Stegemann shows that even in the early days of the disease there are changes in the heart ganglia, including degeneration and necrosis of the nerve-cells and infiltration with lymphocytes, and ascribes paralysis of the heart to these lesions. Later, in more protracted cases, there is similar infiltration of the heart-muscle and conduction bundle.

There are no specific changes in the nervous system nor indeed can any be recognized in the other organs during the acute stage. It is true that necroses have been found in the liver, which is commonly the seat of cloudy swelling, and it is thought that these necroses may sometimes lead to a form of cirrhosis. The spleen is moderately swollen, markedly so only in cases where the streptococcus infection is predominant. There are occasionally acute inflammations of the joints, with effusion of sterile fluid into the synovial cavities; but these disappear without leaving any disabilities.

Rach has studied the histology of the skin rash and has shown that in each fleck there is a focus of acute inflammatory exudation, with outpouring of polynuclear leucocytes and red corpuscles into the substance of the skin about the blood-vessels. This extends into the epidermis, where there may appear small blebs filled with leucocytes. Later there occurs a thickening and dislocation of the epidermis which forms the well-known chaffy scales. A similar influence disturbing the growth of the nails produces a transverse groove which, with the passage of time, gradually advances to the free edge of the nail.

There is a definite leucocytosis with a rather high percentage of eosinophile cells. The red corpuscles decrease for a time to about 3,000,000 per c.mm. Death may occur in the acute stage from general intoxication, with cardiac collapse, or from various lesions produced in the respiratory tract by the streptococcus in association with the main infectious agent, or the patient may recover and progress to complete health.

Nevertheless, in many cases in which the symptoms have passed away and recovery is apparently well established, new symptoms appear in about the third week. Of these, a fresh swelling of the lymph-glands and signs of acute nephritis are the most prominent. These are not due to a second complicating disease, as is the case with the tuberculosis which so commonly follows measles, but are late manifestations of the scarlatina itself. They appear to have about the same relation to the acute phenomena as the secondary lesions of syphilis bear to the primary lesions (Escherich), and evidently indicate the latent presence of the organism in the body during the period of apparent recovery. The enlargement of the lymph-glands seems independent of that which occurred in the primary stage and appears suddenly with pain. Usually it lasts only a short time and recedes after a few days, rarely ending in suppuration.

The *nephritis* is more serious. This has already been discussed in the chapter on Nephritis, but it may be pointed out again that there appear to be two forms—one in which the function of the kidney is not very greatly disturbed, except in the more severe cases, and in which the lesion consists essentially in the exudation of many wandering cells, chiefly of the character of lymphocytes and plasma cells, into the interstices between the tubules. This is the so-called acute interstitial nephritis which has been described by Councilman and others. The second form is predominantly a glomerulonephritis in which the kidneys are found to be swollen and pale or mottled, often with opaque yellowish flecks. On section the glomeruli project as grayish translucent dots. There may be ecchymoses in the substance of the kidney. Microscopically there are to be found all the changes previously described, which lead to obliteration of the glomerulus, by hæmorrhage into the capsule with organization, proliferation of the capsular epithelium, and occlusion of the capillaries of the tuft by thrombi or by massed endothelial cells. It is in the scarlatinal forms that the production of crescentic masses of capsular epithelium about the glomerular tuft is well seen, although of course this occurs in other types of nephritis. Degenerative changes in the tubular epithelium with destruction and desquamation of cells accompany the glomerular changes. Later, with the collapse of tubules, much loose connective tissue appears between the elements of the cortex, and in time the kidney may be extensively scarred. But in many cases complete recovery from all these injuries occurs, and if there is opportunity to examine the kidney of such a person much later in life, it is probable that only isolated scars may be found as the remains of the early injury. In other words, it is by no means inevitable that the occurrence of an acute scarlatinal nephritis should result in the production of a progressive chronic diffuse nephritis. The contrary is rather more probable. During such an acute and subacute scarlatinal nephritis the function of the kidney may be intensely disturbed. The secretion of chlorides and of water is diminished and there is generalized œdema. There is usually marked albuminuria and generally blood is passed in the urine. The blood pressure is quickly heightened, and hypertrophy of the heart appears rapidly. Uræmic symptoms frequently occur, and may be severe enough to cause death.

LITERATURE

Escherich and Schick: Scharlach, Wien, 1912 (Excellent paper with literature).
Stegemann: Jahrb. f. Kinderheilk., 1914, lxxx, 491.
Krumwiede and others: Archives of Int. Med., 1914, xiii, 909.
Williams, A. W.: Amer. Jour. Obst., 1908, lviii, 152.
Rach: Ziegler's Beitr., 1910, xlvii, 455.
Schridde: *Ibid.*, 1913, lv, 345.
Mallory: Jour. Med. Res., 1904, x, 483.
Field: Jour. Exp. Med., 1905, vii, 343.

SMALL-POX

Small-pox is allied to measles and scarlet fever in the sense that it is a febrile disease strikingly characterized by the appearance of an exanthem or skin eruption. This, however, is scarcely a satisfactory basis for classification, and it may well be that when we learn the nature of the ætiological factors in these diseases their relations will seem less intimate. Chicken-pox or varicella is a disease of milder character, but resembles small-pox much more closely than do the other exanthemata. A mild form of small-pox lacking the general distribution of the lesions is vaccinia. This is thought to be produced by a modified form of the same virus as small-pox. The inoculation of small-pox in cattle and rabbits and other animals produces vaccinia and not small-pox. Why under these circumstances the condition vaccinia retains its characters when inoculated into human beings is not yet clear. If small-pox be inoculated into human beings, as was done at the instance of Lady Mary Wortley Montague, before the discovery of vaccinia, a mild and localized affection is produced which protects against a severer attack of small-pox, but may sometimes be transmitted to other persons as true and severe small-pox.

The disease has occurred in extensive and very fatal epidemics, and when introduced into countries where it had not existed before, has in some cases exterminated the whole population. Even yet it rages at times with extreme violence. In 1798 Jenner published his observations on the disease of cows (cow-pox) which was often accidentally transmitted to milkmaids and others and which protected against the rather prevalent small-pox. He instituted vaccination, with the life-saving results which are so well known to-day. Even yet, however, there are many persons of meagre intelligence who oppose the use of vaccination, and on account of their influence there are always unvaccinated individuals who are susceptible and thus make possible the occurrence of the disease.

Ætiology.—We are not definitely informed as to the cause of small-pox. Numerous writers have recognized in the epithelial cells of the pocks minute bodies which they have regarded as protozoan parasites. They were first seen by Weigert and then described by others. Guarnieri named them *Cytoryctes variolæ,* and Councilman and his co-workers have described them more fully, having found them in all their cases. Calkins has worked out a life-history by comparing the various stages, but tells me that he would now modify some of these conclusions. The details must be read in their papers, but, in brief, they find a minute form in the cytoplasm of the epithelial cell which grows to a large size and finally splits up into many small forms which invade the cytoplasm of another epithelial cell. Some of these small forms gain entrance into the nuclei of other cells and there pass through more complex stages of development which are thought to produce sexual forms, and finally from these sporoblasts which disseminate multitudes of small spores that may transmit the infection.

Much has been written in opposition to the assumption that these living parasites are the cause of the disease, just as in the case of the Negri bodies in rabies, but the authors, who have had much experience with the disease, are confident of this relation. The matter must await further study of a biological nature. It is possible to transmit the infection through any number of generations, and Lambert and Steinhardt have shown that the virus of vaccinia may be propagated in culture in connection with pieces of skin and greatly increased in amount.

In all cases of small-pox, except perhaps the very mild or abortive forms, there is an accompanying infection with streptococci. It will be remembered that this associated streptococcus infection is characteristic of scarlet fever and of diphtheria also, so that it by no means excludes the idea of a separate and specific ætiological factor. Many of the lesions of small-pox, especially in the internal organs, are ascribed to the effects of the streptococci.

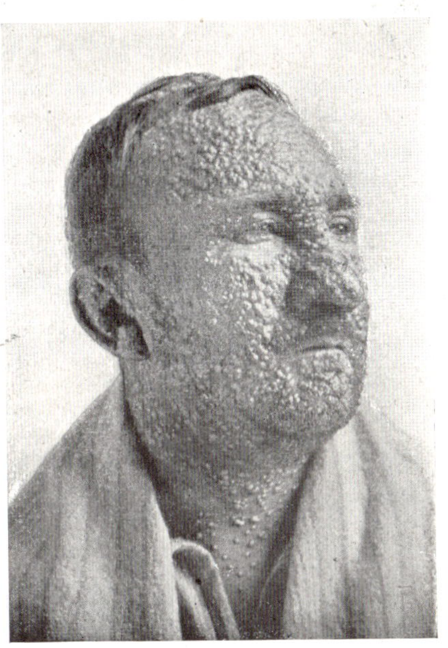

Fig. 375.—Small-pox. Tenth day of eruption (Welch and Schamberg).

Symptoms.—The disease begins abruptly with a chill or with headache and malaise and in a short time becomes recognizable by the appearance of shotty nodules in the skin which develop rapidly and reach their acme about the tenth day (Fig. 375). These at first feel like little firm points, but soon become vesicular, and from that quickly assume the yellowish opacity which reveals their pustular character. Practically all of them show a little central depression or dell, but occasionally this is obliterated, for reasons to be discussed. The pocks, or pustules, are usually about 3 mm. in diameter, but they may become confluent into irregular patches. They develop in no particular relation to hairs or sweat-glands. After the height of their growth is reached they do not burst spontaneously, but dry up into crusts which adhere for a time and finally fall off.

Pathological Anatomy.—Microscopical study in various stages shows that the lesions begin in the lower layers of the epidermis itself, just above the lowermost or Malpighian layer. The corium underneath is at first not affected and may escape completely. The epithelial cells of the prickle-cell layer swell up and become greatly vacuolated. Their nuclei swell and become distorted or shriveled, only the margin remaining. The periphery of the cell becomes compact and fuses with that of the next cell. The vacuoles rupture into one another and soon the area is occupied by a reticulum of fibres which are derived from the remains of the peripheral parts of the cells and extend from the uplifted roof to the underlying base of the cavity thus formed (Fig. 376). Such is a vesicle, due to the death and degeneration of the epithelial cells and the accumulation of fluid among their remains. Fibrin is to be found in the later stages, but at this period leucocytes are few in the exudate. Later they appear and give the purulent character to the fluid exudate. It is the reticulum of fibrils left from the degenerating epithelial cells which holds down the middle of the roof of

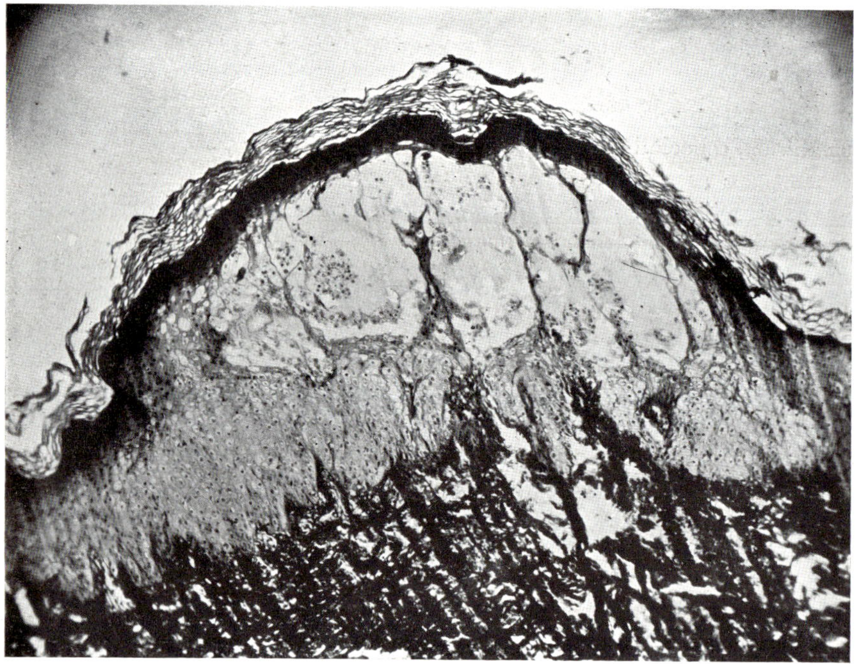

Fig. 376.—Small-pox pustule. The pustule is formed in the substance of the epidermis. Strands of persistent epithelial cells cross it (Dr. James).

the pustule and gives the appearance of the dell. If, with the rapid accumulation of exudate, the fibrils are ruptured, the surface of the pock may become convex.

After the height of the process is over, new epithelium grows from the sides over the remaining Malpighian layer which usually forms the bottom of the pustule, or over the exposed corium if that layer has been destroyed, but also along the under side of the uplifted roof of the pock. Shortly, it happens that the exudate enclosed now between two layers of epidermis of which the upper becomes completely dried up, also dries up and is rubbed off as a crust with the adherent upper layer of epithelium. A depression is thus left lined with epidermis. If the Malpighian layer has remained intact, no deep pitting results, but if the necrosis has extended into the corium, the healing of the pock leaves a pit.

Various modifications in the eruption occur and the disease is roughly divided accordingly into mild forms, in which there are hardly any skin lesions or symptoms; abortive forms, in which the lesions of the skin quickly recede and disappear; hæmorrhagic pustular forms, in which hæmorrhage occurs in and about the pustules; and purpuric forms, in which more extensive hæmorrhage into the skin forms a feature more conspicuous even than the pustules. The last is an extremely severe form in which death may occur before the eruption is well developed.

In the internal organs the changes are partly due to the specific cause of the disease, but are partly the effect of the accompanying streptococcus infection.

In the mucosæ of the mouth and other body orifices and in that of the trachea and digestive tract, there occur specific lesions of the character of those in the skin and with the same degeneration and necrosis of the epithelium, but since there is no protective horny layer to allow of the development of definite pocks, they result in the separation of the epithelial cells, the infiltration of the tissue with leucocytes, and the production of indefinite small ulcers.

In the testes and bone-marrow more readily recognizable specific lesions occur. In the testes these are found as nodules in the substance, more numerous just under the tunica albuginea. They are formed by a focal infiltration of wandering cells among the tubules. After a time the tubules involved become necrotic and invaded by the mononuclear cells. Such nodules appear in section as opaque, yellowish spots with a halo of hæmorrhage, and heal with the formation of small scars.

In the bone-marrow very similar lesions are found with central necrosis involving the blood-forming cells and marginal infiltration of mononuclear elements. The formation of polynuclear leucocytes is seen to be in abeyance in the bone-marrow and many degenerated forms are found. In the later stages of the disease the mononuclear types hold a predominant place among the emigrating cells on this account. Chiari has described this lesion as osteomyelitis variolosa, but it obviously does not resemble other forms of osteomyelitis.

In the liver there is intense cloudy swelling, and focal necroses are occasionally found. The organ is ordinarily much enlarged. In the kidneys there is no characteristic lesion, but degenerative changes appear in the epithelium of the tubules and occasionally there is acute glomerulonephritis. Interstitial accumulations of mononuclear cells are relatively common. Similar non-specific changes may be found in other organs, but it remains a question as to whether they are not produced by the streptococci. This is true also of the degenerative changes in the heart-muscle, which are like those seen in other acute infections, and perhaps also of the swelling of the lymph-nodes and spleen. In the lymph-nodes, the changes in the lymph sinuses include the appearance of many large phagocytic cells, together with abundant smaller mononuclear cells.

In most cases there is an acute bronchitis and in many there occurs a rather severe lobular pneumonia which may be confluent in character. This is often the actual cause of death and is probably to be ascribed to the bacterial infection.

LITERATURE

Weigert: Anat. Beitr. zur Lehre von den Pocken, Breslau, i, 1874; ii, 1875.
Councilman and others: Jour. Med. Research, 1904, xi, 1–360, Lit.
Calkins: *Ibid.*, 136.
Councilman and Beardsley: Osler and McCrae, Modern Medicine, 1913, i, 783.
Steinhardt and Lambert: Jour. of Infect. Dis., 1914, xiv, 87.

CHAPTER XXXVII

TYPES OF INJURY.—DISEASES DUE TO ANIMAL PARASITES

Introduction. General relation of parasites to host. Table of main zoölogical divisions. Amœbic infections: Types of parasites and life-history; intestinal infection; liver abscesses; abscess of lung. Pyorrhœa alveolaris. Malaria: Types and life-history of parasites; symptoms and pathological anatomy; Blackwater fever. Trypanosome infections: biology; sleeping sickness.

It has been seen that, through the invasion of the lowliest forms of plant life and their adaptation to a parasitic existence in the animal body, many diseases arise. This is not less true of members of several of the great groups of the animal kingdom which have undergone biological alterations in the course of a parasitic mode of existence, involving in many cases anatomical changes which separate them from their closest relatives. The animals which have thus come to live as parasites belong to the protozoa, the worms, and to a less extent to the arthropods. The student must be referred for a discussion of their anatomy and their systematic relations to one another and to the related free living forms, to works on zoölogy and parasitology, perhaps particularly to the volumes of Brumpt and Braun. Only a few types can be mentioned here in their relation to common parasitic diseases of man.

General Relation of Parasite to Host.—Those parasites which live on the body surface are more nearly capable of maintaining their existence apart from their host than the obligate parasites which spend their lives in the interior of the body. The latter may go through their whole life-history in the body of one animal, or may pass a stage of it as free living creatures in the outer world; but most of them with or without such a period of freedom are compelled to pass through an important epoch of their development as parasites in a totally different animal. This alternation of generations is a most wide-spread phenomenon and leads to great complexities in the life-history of such parasites. So difficult to unravel are these metamorphoses and changes of host that the whole story of great numbers of parasites is still unknown, and that of even the most familiar has been revealed only recently. Thus the common tapeworm lives as a mature worm in man, while its larval form is found in the ox; the Bothriocephalus of man passes its larval stage in various fish; the filaria which

46

invades the blood and lymphatics of man is larval in a mosquito, and so on. Naturally, in order that the transfer from one animal to the other should be made at the proper time, extraordinary adaptations have come about. In blood-sucking insects which act as intermediate host, the larvæ, or spores, as though by an intelligent decision, lodge themselves in the salivary glands, and nowhere else in the body, and are consequently inoculated into the blood of the next host. The effect of the specific adaptation is further seen in the complete dependence of the parasite upon one particular kind of intermediate host, as well as its particular kind of main host. Malarial organisms sucked into the stomach of a culex mosquito must die there although they develop in an anopheles, and after they have made the anopheles infective for man they perish if by mistake it bites a cow, and injects them into the cow's blood. Many nematodes, or round worms, bring forth active larvæ instead of eggs, and sometimes these are left to fend for themselves and attack their new host by their own activities. In this, some pursue a most devious course, as when the ankylostoma, necator, and strongyloides larvæ penetrate into the skin of man and are swept by the blood into the lungs and bronchi whence they reach the intestine. Others, like ascaris, oxyuris, and trichocephalus, round-worm parasites of the intestines, lead a simpler life, their eggs being transferred with water or vegetables to another person's alimentary tract, or more directly to that of the patient himself, producing an intense infection. Of their life in these hosts, and the duration of their stay, some idea may be derived from the examples given.

Parasites act mechanically in several ways to injure the host. In the case of many of the worms which pass their larval stage in man (Tænia echinococcus, etc.), the great bulk of the cystic larva may occasion mechanical injury, especially in the brain, which lies in a confined space. The ordinary round worms (ascaris) produce many symptoms by mechanical irritation of the intestine and by wandering into such channels as the bile-ducts or the Eustachian tube or the appendix, where they cause obstruction. Strongyles, and the trematode, schistosomum, which live in the blood-vessels, may cause serious obstruction, disturbing the nutrition of the tissues. *Toxic* action is clearly associated with the uncinaria and bothriocephalus which produce profound anæmia, and Schaumann and Tallquist have isolated a hæmolytic substance from the bothriocephalus. In other cases, as with malaria, the anæmia is produced in a more mechanical way by the destruction of the corpuscles in which the parasites live. The trichocephalus and the uncinaria actually suck the blood from the intestinal wall. Inflammatory reaction following upon tissue destruction is characteristic of infection with the trichina, amœbæ, and other organisms, and those which lodge in the tissues and remain there, commonly set up the new formation of much fibrous tissue in their neighborhood.

The following table will serve to indicate briefly the relations of these organisms.

PROTOZOA:

- Rhizopoda: Amœbæ causing dysentery, etc.
- Sporozoa: *Gregarinida.*
  - *Myxosporidia* (Parasites of fishes).
  - *Coccidia* (Occasional parasites of man).
  - *Sarcosporidia* (Occasional parasites of man).
  - *Microsporidia.*
  - *Hæmosporidia* (Malarial parasites).
- Infusoria:
  - *Flagellata:*
    - Spirochæta (Relapsing fever).
    - Treponema (Syphilis).
    - Leishmannia (Kala azar).
    - Trypanosoma (Sleeping sickness).
    - Trichomonas, etc.
  - *Ciliata:*
    - Balantidium, etc. (Dysentery).

WORMS:

- *Cestoda* (Tapeworms):
  - Tænia.
  - Bothriocephalus.
- *Trematoda* (Fluke worms):
  - Distoma.
  - Opisthorchis.
  - Schistosomum, etc.
- *Nematoda* (Round worms):
  - Filaria.
  - Trichocephalus.
  - Trichinella.
  - Ankylostomum (Hook worm).
  - Ascaris.
  - Oxyuris, etc.

ARTHROPODS:

- *Arachnoidea:*
  - Acarina: Ixodes (Tick).
    - Sarcoptes (Itch mite, etc.).
- *Insecta:*
  - Rhyncota: Pediculi (Lice).
    - Cimex (Bedbug).
  - Diptera: Pulex (Flea).
    - Musca (Fly).
    - Culex, Anopheles } Mosquitos.

AMŒBIC INFECTIONS

There are known to zoölogists great numbers of amœbæ, most of which are free living; a few are parasitic in various animals, and among these are certain forms which infect man. Craig, in his recent paper, enumerates all the genera and species and points out that, although forms of Vahlkampfia and Trimastigamœba may be of interest as occurring in such a way as to be confused with the parasitic forms, it is only in the genera Craigia and Entamœba that true parasites of man are found. Chief interest is attached to the genus Entamœba, which, together with about 40 other species, contains the forms *Entamœba coli* and *E. histolytica.* Briefly, it may be said that E. coli is a harmless commensal in the intestine of man. It is found in a great proportion of healthy people who have never had dysentery, and is distinguished from E. histolytica as follows. It averages 30 microns in diameter, is grayish and dull-looking, without clearly defined ectoplasm, and possesses a large nucleus. Its movements are sluggish, and when it becomes encapsulated it divides into eight young entamœbæ. The Entamœba histolytica is a distinct parasite in the intestine of man, and produces there and in other organs most intense destructive changes. It is recognizable by its larger size (20–60 microns) and by the striking contrast between its granular cytoplasm and its glassy, refractive, colorless ectoplasm. This latter is usually in active motion, throwing out and retracting pseudopods into which the remainder of the body streams. It multiplies also by fission, and when it undergoes encapsulation divides into four new amœbæ. The Entamœba tetragena is identical with this.

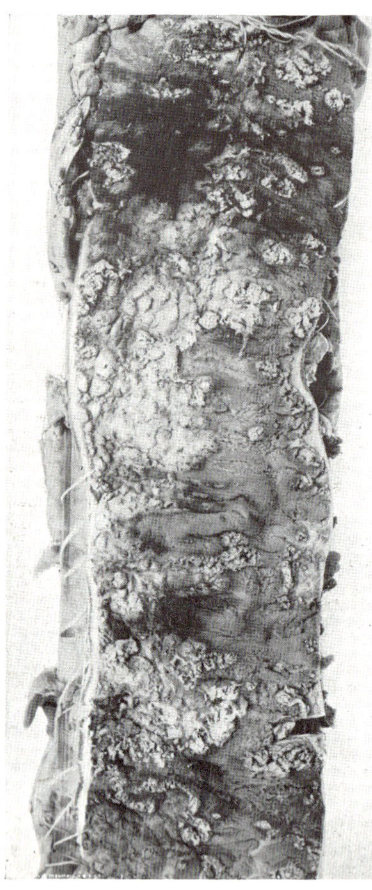

Fig. 377.—Amœbic colitis. There are numerous confluent and discrete elevated necrotic patches and many small ragged ulcerations.

The pathogenic amœbæ are doubtless introduced into the digestive system with uncooked vegetables or contaminated water. It has been shown by experiment that they are pathogenic for cats also. They have probably not been cultivated outside the body.

Intestinal Infection.—In the intestine the amœbæ finds their way into the crypts of the mucosa of the colon and there produce small areas of necrosis from which further invasion into the submucosa occurs. In most cases the mucosa of the colon is the only area affected, the invasion taking place especially in the upper part of the large intestine. It is rare to find any lesions in the lowermost part of the ileum or in the appendix.

The earliest changes appear as elevations in the mucosa, with hyperæmia or hæmorrhagic halo and a central plug of yellowish, necrotic material. Sometimes these elevations become quite large before the necrotic tissue is discharged, and I have seen cases in which the whole mucosa was covered with such patches without definite ulceration (Fig. 377). Usually, however, the softened substance falls away and reveals ulcers which show a great tendency to undermine the mucosa and to coalesce with one another, leaving bridges of mucosa between them. This is not always the case: numerous large or small discrete ragged ulcers may be formed instead;

but when it occurs extensively, as it does in some cases, the undermined mucosa dies and is found hanging in long shreds or sheets from the wall (Fig. 378). In one case observed recently at autopsy nearly the whole mucosa was thus destroyed, and great blackened, ragged films of mucosa were found hanging in the lumen. As a rule, the process is rather slow, and attempts at healing take place, so that the intestine tends to become greatly thickened by the formation of granulation tissue rather than to be perforated. Nevertheless, perforation does sometimes occur and is usually met by adhesions, so that only local abscesses are produced. Narrowing of the gut may follow such ulceration and healing.

Microscopically one may find in the earliest stages minute ulcers involving the mucosa alone, with amœbæ in the margins of the tissue (Fig. 379), but more commonly the ulcer is found to extend in the submucosa and to

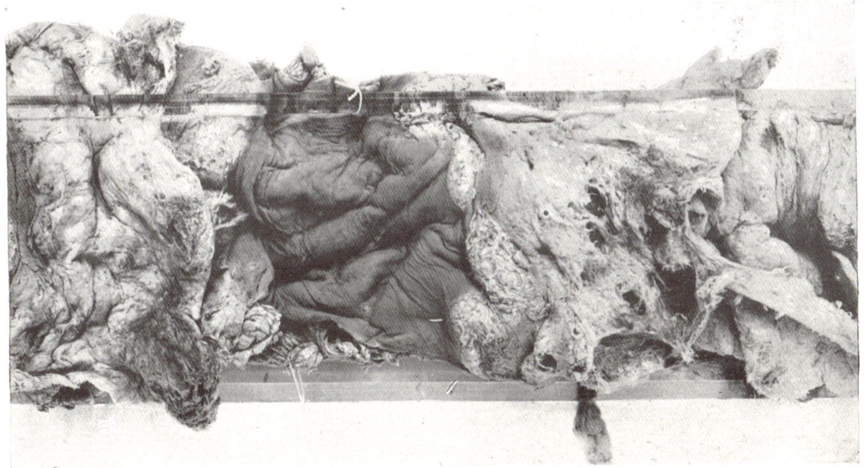

Fig. 378.—Amœbic colitis. Two large ulcerated areas over which the mucosa has been undermined and hangs in necrotic shreds.

be partly filled with disintegrated tissue with fragmented nuclei. On account of the exposure to the intestinal contents many bacteria are present and there is some inflammatory reaction, but this is by no means so prominent as in the case of the bacterial forms of dysenteric ulceration. In the edges of the necrotic tissue the amœbæ are found lying in the crevices. Often they can be traced far into the submucosa or down into the interstices of the muscle or even into the subserous tissues, and when they are found, those in advance are usually not surrounded by any reaction nor by any evident changes in the tissues. At times they are observed underneath the endothelium of the branches of the portal vein, and in many cases I have found them lying free in the lumen of such venules together with the blood-cells. This is important, since it explains readily their transportation to the liver. The reparative changes are quite like those seen in any other ulcer, but it is evident that they are frustrated by new necrosis of the tissue and must be repeated constantly.

There is practically no difficulty in recognizing the amœbæ which are found invading the tissue as the cause of the disease, although the clinician may run the risk, in the examination of the fæces, of mistaking the harmless and common E. coli for the pathogenic form.

Such ulcerative dysentery causes diarrhœa, with much tenesmus or painful straining, and the stools are made up of small amounts of mucus flecked with blood. Such mucus may contain the amœbæ, but they are found more abundantly after a saline cathartic is given. The infection is extremely persistent and often drags on for months or even years.

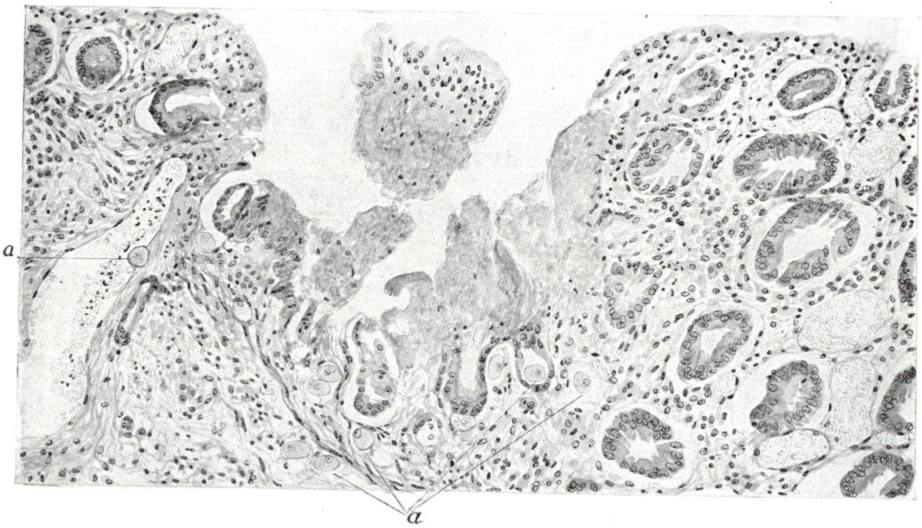

Fig. 379.—Beginning amœbic ulceration of the mucosa of the colon. Amœbæ (*a*) are seen in the crypts, in the stroma of the mucosa and submucosa, and in one case beneath the endothelium of a vein.

Liver Abscesses.—Of the sequelæ of amœbic dysentery, the commonest is the development of abscess of the liver. It is known that amœbæ enter the branches of the portal veins in the intestine, and are swept into the liver, where they lodge in the capillaries and produce effects similar in principle to those set up in the intestine. The amœbæ in the intestine take into their cytoplasm red corpuscles and bacteria as well as the débris of tissue-cells, and it is not surprising, therefore, that there are sometimes evidences of bacterial infection in the liver also. But usually it seems that these bacteria are digested, for the abscesses are likely to be sterile except for the presence of the amœbæ themselves. Although the lesions are commonly called abscesses, they are really not quite like the abscesses produced by pyogenic bacteria, inasmuch as the amœbæ cause the necrosis and liquefaction of tissue without any very pronounced inflammatory reaction. The contents of such abscesses, therefore, consist chiefly of the débris of liver tissue, with relatively slight admixture of leucocytes. Ordinarily only one such abscess is found, but in about one-third of the cases the abscesses are multiple, two or three rather large cavities being found in different parts of the organ (Fig. 380). Rarely there are hundreds of small foci. The drawing shows well the appearance of the rapidly forming fresh abscesses, of which there were several in this case, together with numerous very small ones. A description of the case may serve to present the fresher stages. The small abscesses (from which the contents can be squeezed out like paint) appear as opaque, yellowish-white areas occupying the space of one or two lobules. The large ones have a definite cavity lined with yellowish-

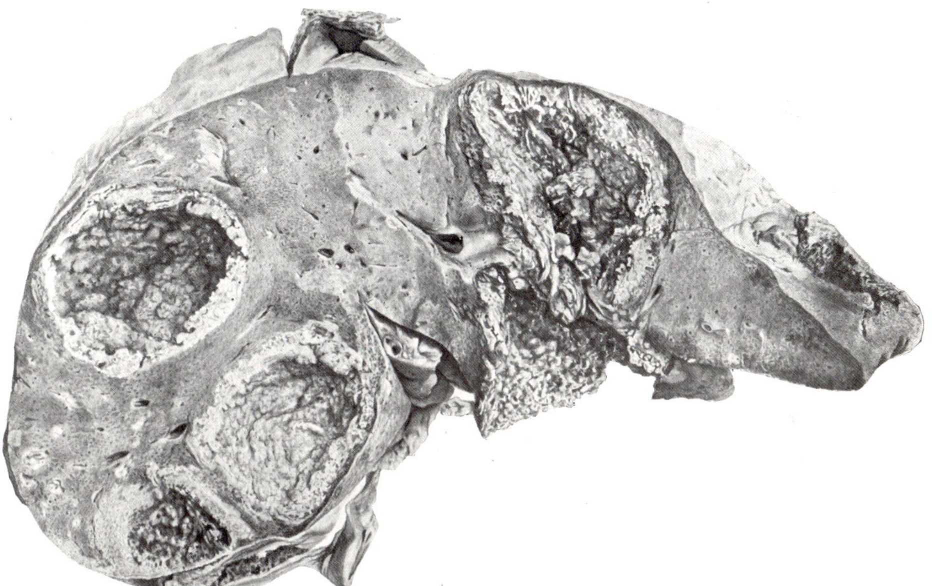

Fig. 380.—Multiple amœbic abscesses of liver (Mense's Handb. d. Tropenkrankheiten).

white necrotic material resembling badly made custard. In the cavity one may find a similar substance or a turbid fluid with shreds of necrotic tissue hanging from the wall. In one abscess in this case there was a clear, straw-yellow fluid. The surrounding tissue ends abruptly in the necrotic lining of the abscess, but from the rapid extension of the cavity and the accumulation of fluid it becomes much compressed. The effect of this pressure is to stop the outflow of blood from regions drained by branches of the hepatic vein which pass by the abscess, and thus to produce local areas of passive congestion. The same thing is to be observed in the neighborhood of metastatic tumor nodules in the liver. Other areas become anæmic from the compression of branches of the portal vein.

Far more commonly one finds the abscesses in a more advanced state in which it is no longer possible to recognize necrotic curdled liver tissue in the contents. Then they are filled with thick, creamy, gelatinous, purulent fluid or with a more pasty tenacious opaque material, which is often stained greenish from the admixture of bile from some duct which has been invaded. In these abscesses efforts at healing have been made in the adjacent liver tissue which result in the formation of a thick wall of granulation tissue. After that, the advance of the abscess through the liver tissue is far slower. Even when a distinct wall is formed, shreds and long strands of necrotic liver tissue may be found hanging in the cavity. Later still, the amœbæ may die out, most of the fluid be absorbed from the pus, and the wall

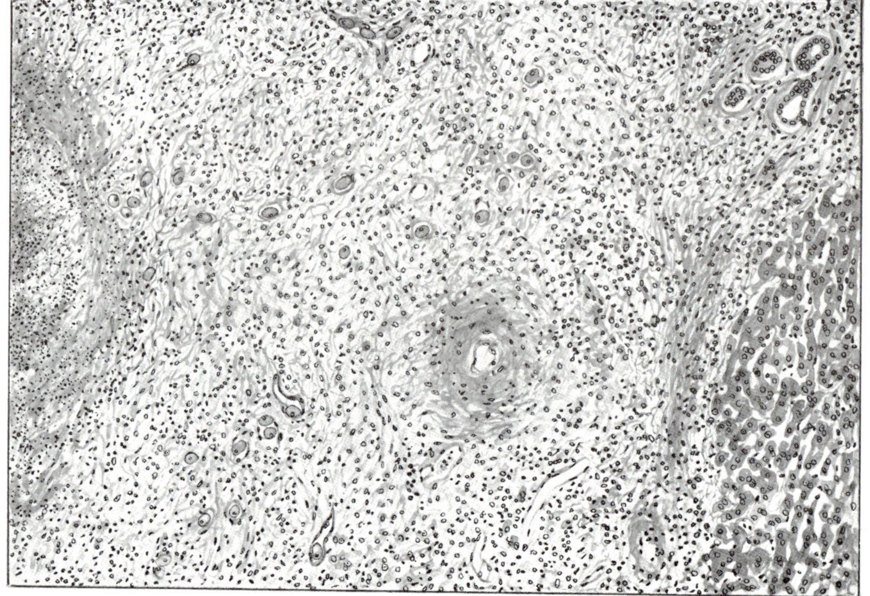

Fig. 381.—Subacute amœbic abscess of the liver. The amœbæ are seen in the crevices of the loose connective tissue which is forming round the abscess.

contract down around the mortar-like material which remains. Usually this becomes pigmented with an orange-yellow pigment derived from extravasated blood. Finally the whole may be replaced by a pigmented scar. But although one occasionally sees this spontaneous healing, it occurs in my experience usually in those cases in which another abscess has formed elsewhere in the liver or in the lung, or in which rupture of the abscess has taken place either spontaneously or through surgical intervention.

The affection is a very serious one, and the mortality is high even with modern treatment. The growth and extension of the abscesses often bring them to the surface of the liver, so that other tissues are invaded and rupture occurs in one or other direction. The commonest site is in the dome of the right lobe, whence extension can occur through the diaphragm into the substance of the adherent lung, with rupture and discharge of the pus (now stained brownish-red, "anchovy sauce appearance") through the bronchus, so that it is coughed up and expectorated. This is the most frequent and favorable outcome. But extension and rupture may also occur into the free pleural cavity or the pericardium, into the peritoneal cavity or adherent colon or stomach or duodenum, or even through the outer skin. More rarely the portal vein or vena cava receives the contents of the abscess.

Histologically the appearances vary with the age of the abscess. In the very fresh ones the form of many liver-cells can still be seen, there is œdema of the surrounding tissue, the amœbæ are found in the edge of the living tissue, and there are a few mononuclear wandering cells whose nuclei are mingled with the fragmented nuclei of the tissue. Later the necrotic lining of the cavity loses its recognizable constituents and shows only a mass of nuclear fragments with a few leucocytes (Fig. 381). The amœbæ are still found only in the margin of the living tissue unless the abscess has been opened to the air. This is because of their need of oxygen, and it is observed by surgeons that when an amœbic abscess is opened, no amœbæ are to be found in the pus which escapes, but only in scrapings of the wall. Next day, however, after the cavity has been exposed to the air, the pus which escapes is full of active amœbæ. When the dense connective tissue with its lining of partly necrotic granulation tissue is formed the amœbæ wander in the crevices of that tissue.

These abscesses may reach a great size before rupture or evacuation takes place and may contain several litres of pus. They consequently destroy much of the liver tissue and occasionally one may find efforts at its regeneration.

Abscesses of the lung of quite the same character are produced by transportation of the amœbæ from the liver, apparently by way of the hepatic veins rather than by direct extension. Indeed, Bunting was able to trace in one of our cases emboli containing amœbæ from a thrombus in the hepatic vein which also contained them, and to show that this embolism of the pulmonary arteries had produced an amœbic abscess in the lung. By this time the original amœbic ulcers in the intestine were healed.

In the so-called **Rigg's disease,** or **pyorrhœa alveolaris**, the Entamœba buccalis has been thought to be the ætiological factor and is found in great numbers in the pus which forms in the cavities between the loosened gums and the roots of the teeth. Such cavities extend down into the alveolar process of the jaw, which is eroded away. The good effects of emetine in curing the disease seem to show that the amœbæ are responsible for its existence.

LITERATURE

Craig: American Medicine, 1905, ix, 854. Arch. Int. Med., 1914, xiii, 737.
Schaudinn: Arb. a. d. Kais. Gesundheitsamte, 1903, xix, 547.

Councilman and Lafleur: Johns Hopkins Hosp. Rep., 1891, ii, 395.
Musgrave and Clegg: Bull. Gov. Laboratories, Manila, 1904, xviii.
Sachs: Arch. f. kl. Chir., 1876, xix, 235.
Kruse and Pasquale: Zeitsch. f. Hyg. u. Infektionskr., 1894, xvi, 1.
MacCallum: Handb. d. Tropenkrankheiten, Mense, 1906, iii, 22.
Bunting: Arch. f. Schiffs- u. Tropenhygiene, 1906, x, 73.
Woolley and Musgrave: Bureau of Gov. Laboratories, Manila, 1905, xxxii, 31.
Futcher: Jour. Amer. Med. Assoc., 1903, xli, 480.
Bass and Johns: Jour. Amer. Med. Assoc., 1915, lxiv, 553.

MALARIA

Since the discovery by Laveran in 1880 of the protozoan parasites which cause this disease, it has been possible to give a precise reason for the existence of three different types of malarial fever in man, since it is found that there are three different species of parasite. These can be recognized through differences in their morphology and by the differences in the time required for them to become mature, which decides the type of fever. Tertian malaria is that in which there is a chill every other day. In quartan malaria the chill comes on every third day, while in the æstivo-autumnal forms chills and the associated fever appear at irregular intervals.

The *tertian parasite* (Plasmodium vivax) is found in the red blood-corpuscles in the form of a pale, amœboid body growing rapidly to a rather large size and accumulating yellowish-brown pigment in fine granules which dance actively. It causes swelling and pallor of the red corpuscle which contains it, and on reaching maturity divides into 18 to 20 segments leaving the pigment in the centre of the rosette. Flagellated forms are seen. It requires forty-eight hours to develop from the earliest small hyaline form without pigment to the point of segmentation.

The *quartan parasite* (Plasmodium malariæ) appears also as a small hyaline body in the red corpuscles; it grows more slowly, requiring seventy-two hours to complete its development up to the point of segmentation, and is throughout smaller and more dense and refractive than the tertian form. It produces blackish pigment in coarser granules and is more quiescent than the tertian form. Finally it breaks up into a small rosette of 6 to 12 segments, having at no time caused the corpuscle to swell or become pale, but leaving it rather shrunken and deeply colored.

The *æstivo-autumnal* parasite (Plasmodium falciparum) is often at first ring-formed, but later becomes an amœboid body with brownish pigment. It develops in twenty-four to forty-eight hours and forms 8 to 10 segments, but these are rarely seen in the circulating blood, although they are to be found in the spleen and perhaps other internal organs. In its more mature form the organism is often found in the circulating blood in the shape of a rounded crescent, across the concavity of which the remainder of the corpuscle is seen to stretch. Such crescents may or may not give rise to the flagellated forms.

In studying the related forms, Proteosoma and Halteridium, in birds, I was able to show that when these parasites were removed from the circulation the maturer forms, which were inconspicuous before, proceeded to enter upon a sexual cycle. During the existence of any of the types as parasites in the blood-corpuscles of the circulating blood, they merely continue the asexual cycle, wherein they grow in the corpuscle for a certain time, after which they divide by fission into many small segments which burst out of the corpuscle and enter others, starting the cycle afresh.

The sexual cycle has a different purpose. Under the microscope the mature forms are seen to break out of the blood-corpuscles into the plasma. Some remain quiescent; others, after violent convulsions of the protoplasm, throw out long, active flagella which beat about and soon become separate free-swimming threads, like spermatozoa. These make their way to the quiescent forms, and of the little swarm which hovers about each of these female forms, or macrogametes, it is seen that one and only one buries itself in the protoplasm, while the rest perish. The flagella, or microgametes, are really analogous to spermatozoa. A short time after the fertilization the zygote, or fertilized form, becomes very active and wanders about. At this point Ross, in India, discovered that there appeared pigmented cysts in the walls of the stomach of those mosquitoes which have bitten persons ill with malaria, and formed the idea that the process of fertilization and formation of a motile zygote described above must occur in the mosquito's stomach, and that the development of cysts in the walls of that organ must be due to the fact that this new active zygote could push its way into that situation and there become encapsulated. After that, Ross found that minute transparent spores were produced in great numbers in such cysts and liberated into the body cavity of the mosquito. Thence they wandered into the epithelial cells of the salivary gland of the mosquito, and were injected into the blood of the next person bitten, together with the salivary secretion. There the spores or sporozoites entered the red corpuscles exactly as did the hyaline segments from the rosette of the asexual stage. Hence, since an important part of the development occurs in the body of the mosquito, which is thus a host of the parasite, it seems certain that transmission to human beings must always occur in this way. Further, it is learned that while a form of culex transmits the proteosoma to birds, it is incapable of transmitting any human form of the parasite. For these another mosquito (anopheles) is the specific host and transmitting agent.

To recapitulate briefly, the malarial parasite passes part of its existence in the blood-corpuscles of man, where it goes through a round of development ending in segmentation and the infection of other corpuscles by the segments which are set free. The other part of its existence is passed in the body of the mosquito. In the mosquito's stomach the elaboration of the sexual forms, conjugation, and the development of the actively motile zygote take place. There follows penetration of the stomach wall by the zygote, its encapsulation and the formation of tiny spores or sporozoites, which, wandering through the body cavity into the salivary glands, are injected by the bite of the mosquito into the human body, infect the corpuscles, and start again the asexual cycle.

Symptoms.—The evil effects of infection in the human being are therefore dependent upon the asexual cycle alone. The liberation of the segments involves the bursting and destruction of the red corpuscle, the spilling of the remaining hæmoglobin and of the malarial pigment into the plasma, and the wandering of the motile segments to new corpuscles. This is accompanied by a sudden and extreme rise in temperature with a chill. According to the length of the cycle of development the chills are spaced twenty-four, forty-eight, or seventy-two hours apart. But this is

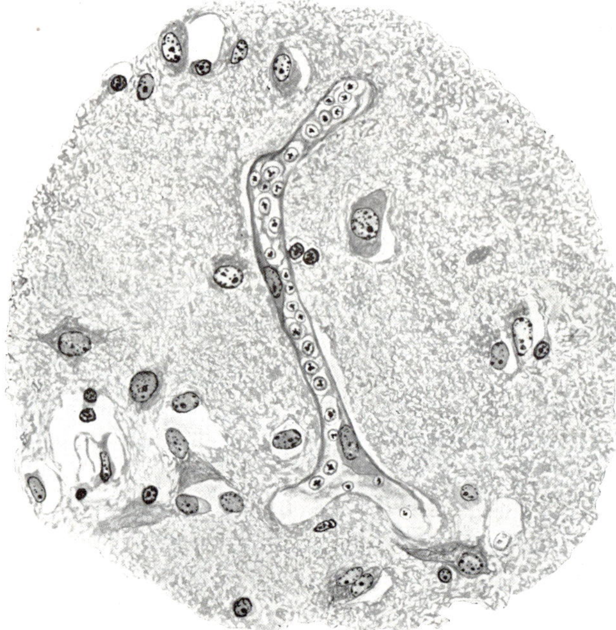

Fig. 382.—Malaria. Capillary in the brain filled with parasites of the æstivo-autumnal type.

only because large groups of parasites reach maturity at those moments. If, for example, in the tertian infection the parasites are not all of the same age, but fall into two groups which mature at different times, there may be a chill every day. The liberation of hæmoglobin and of malarial pigment, which is a kind of melanin, results in the pigmentation of the organs with hæmosiderin and melanin, and the associated destruction of red corpuscles produces an anæmia which may reach a profound degree. There is, as a rule, a marked diminution in the number of leukocytes, although there may at times be a leucocytosis during the chills. The relative number of lymphocytes is increased.

The severer symptoms of the disease, aside from the anæmia and general evidences of poisoning which may constitute what is commonly spoken of as cachexia, are dependent upon the great accumulation of the parasites in the brain or in the gastro-intestinal mucosa. There are, of course, other phenomena due to injuries to the liver and kidneys, but the symptoms of general intoxication are sometimes combined with coma when the brain is especially affected, or with choleriform diarrhœa when the intestinal capillaries are loaded with parasites. In all cases the spleen becomes enlarged, and when the infection has lasted a long time, it may be enormous and very hard.

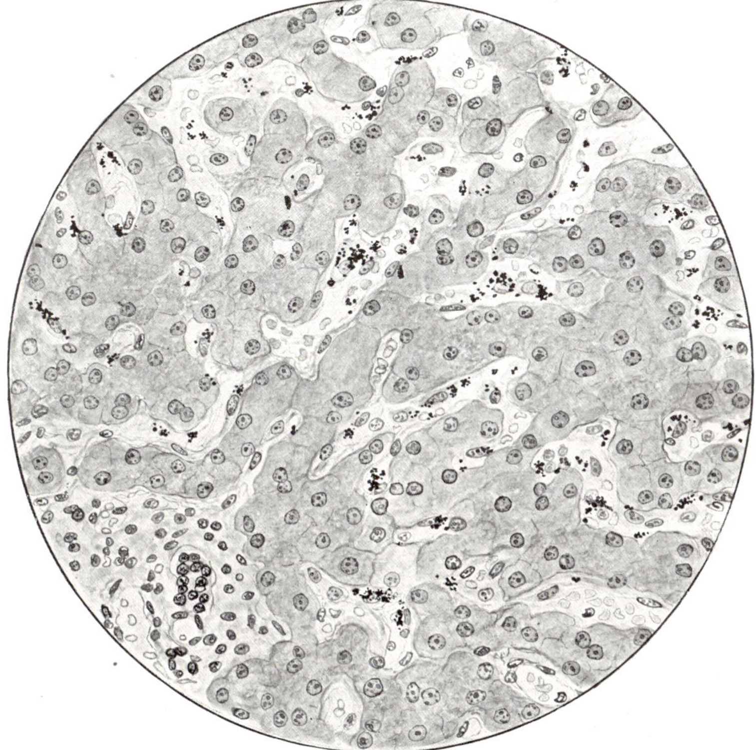

Fig. 383.—Malaria. Liver from a case of malaria of long standing. Endothelial cells and wandering cells in the capillaries are loaded with clumps of pigment.

Pathological Anatomy.—At autopsy there is a distinct slaty or blackish pigmentation affecting especially the spleen, the liver, the brain, and sometimes the intestinal mucosa. It is due not only to the parasites themselves, with their grains of pigment, but more especially to the quantities of pigment set free from other parasites and now held in innumerable phagocytic cells, both of the type of wandering macrophages and of the endothelial cells of the capillaries. This pigmentation is the most characteristic feature in the autopsies performed upon cases which have died after protracted infections.

In the *brain*, the endothelial cells of the capillaries in the brain substance may show such pigment, but in intense infections one often finds that the capillaries are actually plugged with masses of corpuscles bearing parasites, together with phagocytic cells and occasional free parasites (Fig. 382).

In the intestine the same condition may prevail, the capillaries of the mucosa being rendered impermeable by the mass of these cells.

In the liver Barker has described focal necroses. I have not found these in other cases, but there are always parasites in the capillaries and much pigment is present, especially in the stellate cells of Kupfer and in the endothelial cells in general (Fig. 383).

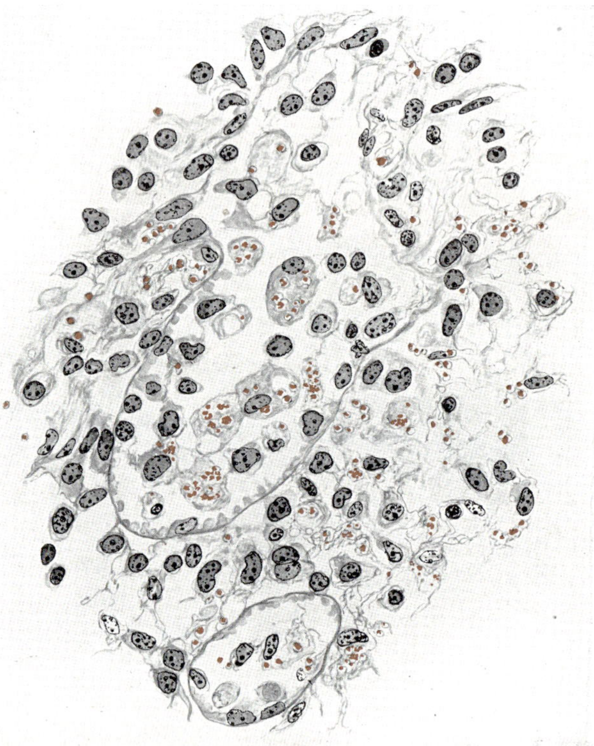

Fig. 384.—Malaria. Splenic pulp in æstivo-autumnal infection showing many pigmented parasites either free or enclosed in large phagocytic cells.

The spleen is particularly rich in the parasites and, indeed, in the case of the æstivo-autumnal form, the segmenting forms are to be found only there. The endothelial cells of the splenic sinuses are loaded with pigment and with fragments of cells and parasites (Fig. 384). These cells become so enlarged and so distended with this material that they finally burst, the débris being taken up by other phagocytic cells which are less engorged. Mononuclear wandering cells of other types take part in this process as well. Here, as in the liver, much of the pigment is the iron-containing hæmosiderin derived from the hæmoglobin set free in the destruction of the red corpuscles. In later stages there is found a great increase in the amount of connective tissue throughout the organ, doubtless caused to grow by the presence of so much pigment and the long-continued infection.

The bone-marrow is likewise pigmented, and while showing little new formation of polynuclear leucocytes, is rich in large phagocytic endothelial and reticular cells which have acted as macrophages.

Many other changes in the organs, such as cirrhosis of the liver, chronic nephritis, etc., have been ascribed to the action of the malarial parasite, but it seems that the evidence in these cases is not quite decisive.

LITERATURE

Thayer and Hewetson: Malarial Fevers of Baltimore, Johns Hopkins Hosp. Rep., 1895, vol. v, 3 (Early literature).
Thayer: Lectures on the Malarial Fevers, New York, 1897.
Barker: Johns Hopkins Hosp. Rep., 1895, vol. v, 219.
Laveran: Bull. de l'Acad. de med. de Paris, 1880, ix, 1268. Compt. Rend. de l'Acad. des Sc., 1881, xlii, 627.
Ross: Malaria, Nobel Lecture for 1902, Stockholm, 1904.
MacCallum: Jour. Exp. Med., 1898, iii, 103. Lancet, 1897, ii, 1240.
Elting: (Inoculation) Zeitschr. f. kl. Med., 1899, xxxvi, 491.
Daniels: Proc. Roy. Soc., 1899, lxiv, 443.
Bastianelli and Bignami; Grassi; Celli: Ann. d'Igiene Sperimentale, 1899, ix, 245. (Beautiful plates.)
Nuttall: Centbl. f. Bakt. u. Paras., I. Abth., 1899 and 1900, xxv–xxvii.
Schaudinn: Arb. a. d. Kaiserl. Gesundheitsamt, 1904, xx, Heft 3.
Ewing: Jour. Exp. Med., 1900, v, 419.

HÆMOGLOBINURIC OR BLACKWATER FEVER

In persons who have had malaria or who are still infected with the parasites there may occur a violent and rapidly fatal disease in which the most striking symptom is the passage of red or almost black urine, the color being due to the presence of hæmoglobin. Diminution of the urine to complete anuria may follow. There are general evidences of intoxication, with the most rapid and extreme blood destruction, which quickly leads to profound anæmia. The spleen is greatly swollen and tender, there is vomiting and intense icterus and fever. Recovery may occur without conferring any immunity, but rather predisposing to another attack, or the patient may die from suppression of urine or from exhaustion.

The condition has every appearance of being due to the action of some intense poison which produces hæmolysis, but no such poison has been demonstrated. In some patients the administration of quinine will bring on an attack, but there are many cases in which it occurs although no quinine has been given. There are several hypotheses as to its nature: That it is an especially intense manifestation of malaria; that it is due to quinine and, lastly, that it is caused by some specific infectious agent as yet undiscovered. Most writers, failing to prove any of these theories, conclude that malaria produces a condition which predisposes to blackwater fever, which may at times be induced under the circumstances by quinine. In spite of the earnest endeavors of many investigators, the matter is no more cleared up than this. The advocates of the theory that there is a specific infective agent have not proven their point.

At autopsy the spleen is found to be greatly swollen with many phagocytes and with extensive necroses. It is bright red and velvety on section, in contrast to the slaty or blackish spleen of chronic malaria. Necroses occur also in the lymphatic glands and in the liver. The kidneys are somewhat enlarged and flecked with red and black dots which are due to the hæmoglobin in the tubules. The glomeruli are usually normal, the tubules filled with irregular clumps of hæmoglobin, their epithelial cells slightly degenerated. Acute nephritis supervenes in some cases.

LITERATURE

Deaderick: Memphis Med. Monthly, 1907, xxvii, 637, *et seq.*

Whipple: Malaria, 1909, i, 215.

Deeks and James: Report on Hæmoglobinuric Fevers in the Canal Zone: Isthmian Canal Commission, 1911.

TRYPANOSOME INFECTION

Various diseases of animals and at least one disease of man are caused by the invasion of the trypanosomes, which are large flagellated organisms of elongated form with an undulant membrane rising from the blepharoplast at the posterior end and terminating in the long flagellum at the anterior end. These multiply by fission in the circulating blood and invade all the tissues, being found especially in the lymph-glands and spleen and in the central nervous system and meninges. The intermediate host is some form of biting insect—in the case of Trypanosoma lewisi of the rat it is a louse, in the *tsetse-fly disease* of cattle (nagaña) caused by T. brucei it is a fly (*Glossina*). In the *sleeping sickness* of human beings, caused by T. gambiense and T. rhodesiense, it is also a Glossina, the G. palpalis being concerned in the first and G. morsitans in the second case.

The organisms conjugate in the intestine of the fly, and smaller flagellated forms are produced in great numbers which enter the salivary glands and are inoculated into the new host by the next bite.

The infection is extremely persistent and produces in man a disease which is fatal after a prolonged illness, or, at least, in spite of every effort at cure, drags on for a very long time. The sleeping sickness, a disease essentially of Africa, is characterized by swelling of the glands and fever, later followed by disinclination to work, rapid fatigue, and a soporous condition which may pass into almost continuous sleep. Occasionally there is agitation and delirium. The victims become greatly emaciated and lie helpless until they die, with or without the help of intercurrent infections.

The organisms are found widely scattered in the tissues, and in the brain produce hyperæmia and infiltration of the meninges and perivascular tissues, somewhat resembling that in dementia paralytica.

LITERATURE

Laveran and Mesnil: Trypanosomes (Tr. by Nabarro, Chicago, 1907).

Lühe: Mense's Handb. d. Tropenkrankheiten, 1906, iii, 69.

Mense: *Ibid.*, 617.

Kinghorn, Yorke, Lloyd: Annals of Trop. Med. and Paras., 1913, vii, 183 (Rep. Sleeping Sickness Commission).

Wolbach and Binger: Jour. Med. Research, 1912, xxvii, 83.

Novy and McNeal: Jour. Infect. Dis., 1904, i, p. 1.

CHAPTER XXXVIII

TYPES OF INJURY.—DISEASES DUE TO ANIMAL PARASITES (Continued)

Cestode Infections: Tænia and bothriocephalus; T. echinococcus; echinococcus cysts in man. Trematode infections: Bilharziosis; Paragonimus and Opisthorchis. Trichiniasis: Biology of the parasite, symptomatology, pathological anatomy. Uncinariasis: Symptomatology; life-history of parasite; pathological anatomy. Infections with ascaris, oxyuris, trichocephalus, and filaria. Elephantiasis.

CESTODE INFECTIONS

Four principal types of cestode worms are concerned in the infection of human beings, as follows:

Tænia saginata, or *mediocanellata*
Tænia solium
Bothriocephalus latus
Tænia echinococcus

Each of these worms requires an intermediate host for the development of its larval form, after which the ingestion of the tissues of that host allows the formation of the mature worm in the definite host.

Tænia saginata is found in its mature form in the small intestine of man, whence ripe segments, loaded with eggs, are discharged. The eggs pass into the digestive tract of the ox, and the embryo penetrates through the intestinal wall by the aid of six hooklets at its anterior end. It is then swept everywhere by the blood-stream, and lodging in muscles develops into the cystic larval form which, if the beef be eaten uncooked, becomes the mature form once more in the human intestine. The mature tapeworm has a head with four suckers but no hooks. Its segments are characterized by having a great many lateral uterine diverticula filled with eggs.

Tænia Solium.—The mature worm, which is provided with a circle of hooks as well as four suckers on its head, is rare in the human intestine in this country. It has segments which differ from those of T. saginata in showing relatively few lateral uterine pouches. The eggs get into the intestine of the pig, and exactly as in the case of the T. saginata, pass into the muscle and organs to produce cystic larvæ (Cysticercus cellulosæ). Occasionally by self-infection the eggs can reach the intestine of man, who then becomes also the intermediate host, allowing the development of the Cysticercus cellulosæ in his organs. There is a specimen in the Baltimore museum which shows a human brain studded everywhere with cystic larval forms of the T. solium.

Bothriocephalus Latus.—The larval form of this worm is found in the muscles of several fish, including the salmon, trout, perch, ling, etc., upon the ingestion of which the mature worm develops in the human intestine. It is a large, broad worm with elongated lateral suckers and with a different arrangement of the genitalia, the genital opening being on the face of each segment instead of at the edges, as in the tænia. Its presence in the intestine causes an intense anæmia which has already been mentioned.

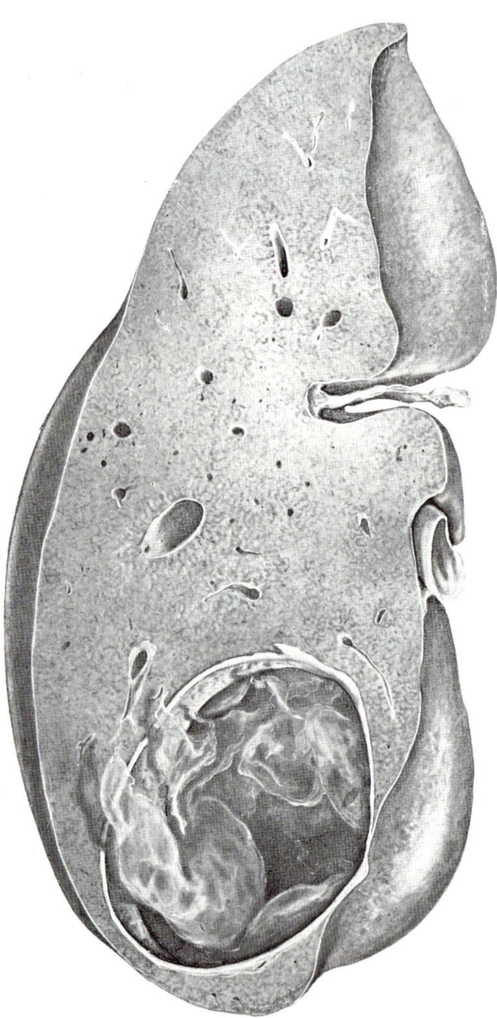

Fig. 385.—Fresh echinococcus cyst in the liver. The lining of the cyst is partly dislocated from the chitinous and fibrous wall.

Tænia Echinococcus.—In the case of this worm, of which there are two varieties, man is the intermediate host, while the mature form is a parasite of the intestine of the dog. It is a very small worm, only 3 to 6 mm. in length, in contrast to those tæniæ just described, which may reach the length of 30 to 40 feet. Many other animals can also act as the intermediate hosts. The adult is a worm with four suckers and two rows of hooks, which forms only three or four segments instead of many hundreds. From dogs, especially in such countries as Iceland, where men and dogs live in the same rooms, the eggs are transmitted to the human digestive tract. The wandering of the embryos can take them to any organ of the body, and the development of the huge cystic larva is reported for every possible situation. In the case of T. echinococcus, single cysts form, but in infection with the allied form, T. multilocularis, the larval cysts are like a ramifying spongy tissue full of small cavities. The parasite produces injury by the space it occupies (as in the brain), or by the toxic products or by the development of great numbers of secondary cysts through the rupture of the first and the liberation of the larvæ.

When the eggs hatch in the human intestine, the embryo bores through the intestinal wall and is transported by the blood-stream to its lodging place. There it grows and surrounds itself with a thin, chitinous membrane of pearly translucence which in turn is densely enclosed in a capsule produced by the reaction of the surrounding tissue. Inside the chitinous membrane the embryonic tissue grows and separates in its central part to allow

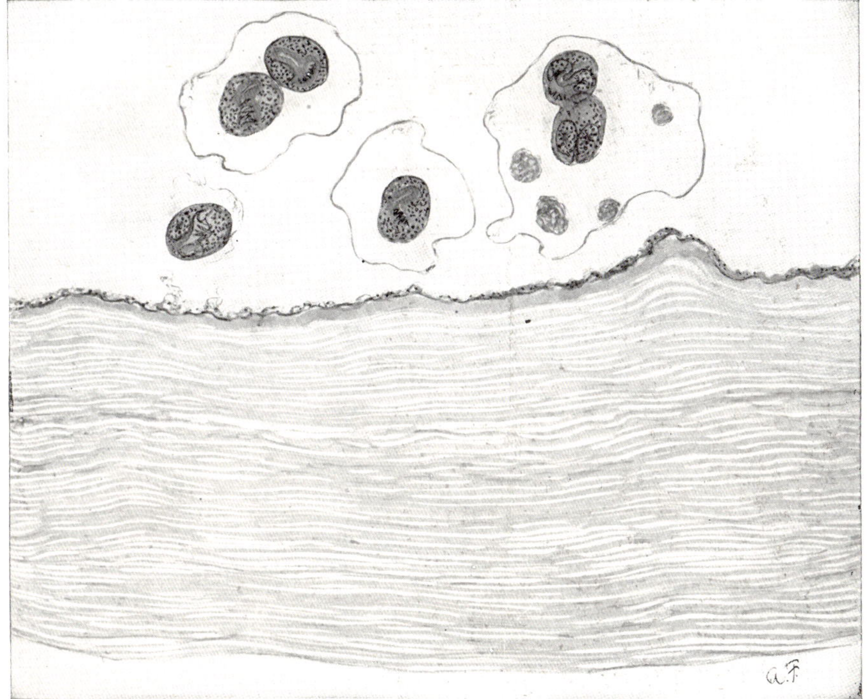

Fig. 386.—Chitinous wall of echinococcus cyst with lining membrane of the parenchyma of the worm and several daughter cysts with scolices.

of the accumulation there of a clear fluid rich in salt and albumin. It thus becomes a lining of a cyst (Fig. 385). From this lining there spring up buds which may be extremely numerous as the cyst grows larger, and are finally recognizable as the heads of new worms. Some of the buds may, however, enlarge and themselves become hollow and constitute daughter cysts in whose lining once more there may spring up little buds which give rise to new heads (Fig. 386). Such buds in the main cyst or in the daughter cyst elevate themselves in bunches on little stalks and are now seen to be invaginated, so that what is to become the head of the adult

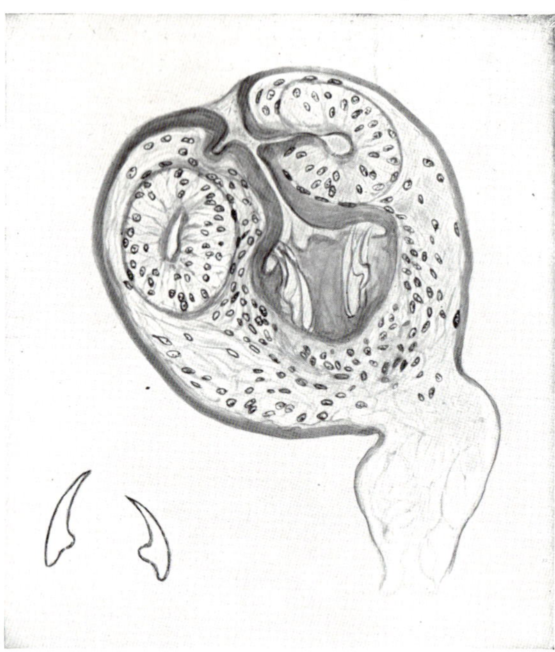

Fig. 387.—Single scolex or head from echinococcus cyst cut in median line, showing inverted suckers and rostellum of hooks. Two of the hooks are drawn separately.

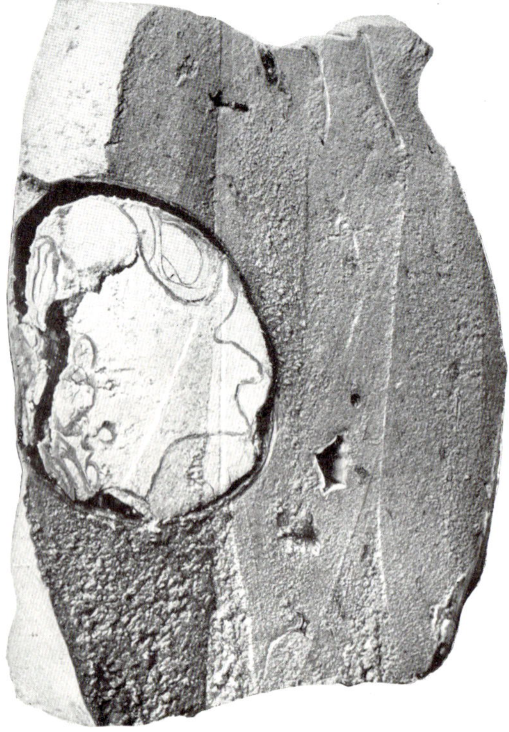

Fig. 388.—Old echinococcus cyst of liver with mortar-like contents. The chitinous lining is loosened and thrown up in folds.

worm is now turned inside out, so that in the dell at the tip of the bud one finds the crown of hooklets and four suckers facing inward (Fig. 387). With the liberation of such buds or scolices by the ingestion of the cyst material by a dog or other suitable host, the heads are quickly evaginated so that suckers and hooks present themselves in proper relations and fix themselves in the mucosa of the intestine, after which the worm proceeds to assume its mature form.

Such cysts are quite common in the liver of the pig, where they are multiple and cause huge enlargement of the organ. Later, in any organ which harbors such a cyst, if the opportunity for its ingestion by the definite host is postponed, the embryos may die and the fluid be absorbed. There remains what is easily recognizable as an obsolete echinococcus cyst, a rounded mass of mortar-like whitish material densely encapsulated with fibrous tissue, underneath which can still be discerned the wavy, laminated, translucent chitinous membrane which is in itself so peculiar as to be of diagnostic importance (Fig. 388). In the crumbly mass left after absorption of the fluid loose hooklets can be found scattered about, derived of course from the armament of the dead scolices.

The dissemination of some toxic material often gives rise to repeated attacks of urticaria and also to an alteration of the blood plasma, such that the presence of the echinococcus cyst can be recognized by complement deviation reactions.

LITERATURE

Stiles: Hygienic Laboratory, Marine Hosp. Service, Bulletins 25 and 28 (Cestode parasites of man).

Stiles and Hassal: Index catalogue of Medical and Veterinary Zoölogy, Washington, 1908.

Braun: Thierische Parasiten des Menschen, Würzburg, 1903 (Transl. 1906, New York).

Brumpt: Precis de Parasitologie, Paris, 1910.

Marchand: Handb. d. allg. Pathologie, 1908, i, 340.

Melnikow Raswedenkow: Echinococcus multilocularis, Ziegler's Beitr., 1901, iv, Suppl.-Heft, 5.

TREMATODE INFECTIONS

Fluke worms rarely cause disease in man in this country, but there are several wide-spread types of human disease, due to their invasion, in African and Asiatic countries. Of these, the most important is perhaps the bilharziosis caused by the invasion of the *Schistosomum hæmatobium*. The mature worms live in the branches of the portal veins, whence they distribute their eggs with the blood into the liver and indeed into all the organs of the body. The eggs are the cause of the lesions, which appear chiefly in the urinary apparatus, where they give rise to hæmaturia and to extensive destructive and proliferative changes in the tissue of the bladder and urethra and their neighborhood. Extraordinary new formation of papillary masses takes place in these organs, and this tissue, which undergoes necrosis and disintegration, is found to be loaded with the eggs. Abscesses and fistulæ form in connection with the urethra and extend to the skin. Similarly in the rectum, polypoid thickenings of the mucosa are formed about the eggs, and break down with intense inflammatory reaction and with the production of symptoms which lead to great straining at stool, often followed by prolapse of the rectum. This disease is to be found especially in Egypt and other African countries. In China, Japan, and Siberia other trematodes are found. In Formosa especially the *Paragonimus Westermanni* becomes a parasite of man, lodging in the lung, where it produces abscess-like cavities with intense pulmonary symptoms, including hæmoptysis, or in the brain, where it causes death by its mechanical effects. *Opisthorchis felineus* and *Opisthorchis sinensis* are other trematodes which invade chiefly the gall-ducts, producing obstruction and jaundice, and leading to great destruction in the liver. For details consult the works on parasitic diseases.

LITERATURE

Looss: Mense's Handb. d. Tropenkrankheiten, 1905, i, 77.
Cecil: Proc. N. Y. Path. Soc., 1910–11, x, 206.

TRICHINIASIS

The trichina, or, as it is now called, *Trichinella spiralis*, was discovered by Owen in 1835 and has since been studied by Virchow, Zenker, Leuckart, and a host of others, the most compendious publication being that of Stäubli. It is a nematode, or round worm, the anatomical structure of which will be found in any book on animal parasites. It carries out its whole life cycle in one animal, but it must then pass into the digestive tract of another animal to begin another cycle. The reason for this will be found in the following brief summary of its life-history. The worm is essentially a parasite of swine, but can live in rats, mice, guinea-pigs, rabbits, dogs, cats, and many other animals as well as man. It is from eating insufficiently cooked pork that man is infected, but the pigs themselves are often infected through eating dead rats. The embryos, both male and female, are found in the muscle substance of the pig, and on being eaten by man quickly develop into mature forms when they reach the intestine. There the females penetrate into the substance of the villi and often actually enter the central lymphatic; the eggs hatch in the uterus of the worm, and the active embryos are set free from the genital opening, after which they bore their way into the lymphatics, if they are not actually deposited there by the mother. Thence they are swept in great numbers through the mesenteric lymph-glands and the thoracic duct into the blood, and are to be found there by centrifugalizing, after treating the blood with 3 per cent. acetic acid, which dissolves away the red corpuscles. They are thus carried through the whole body but choose the voluntary muscles for their permanent abode. Doubtless they have to penetrate into them from the capillary by their own activity. They lodge in every other tissue, but appear to find conditions unsuitable and never develop there; indeed, they are rarely found anywhere else than in the skeletal muscles. They are not found in the heart muscle, but are occasionally seen in the mesenteric lymph-glands and for a time are abundant in the peritoneal cavity.

Fig. 389.—Pectoral muscle with encapsulated and calcified trichinæ.

Having entered the muscle, each one penetrates into a muscle-fibre where it lies as a small, rod-like structure in the middle of the fibre. As the embryo grows the fibre loses its striations and becomes granular and swollen. The sarcolemma nuclei sink into the more or less homogeneous mass and surround the little worm. A little later the parasite, having developed until it shows the alimentary tract and a rudiment of the reproductive glands, coils itself up and becomes surrounded by a rather thick hyaline capsule which is usually elliptical (Fig. 389). There is a dispute as to the origin of this capsule, but it seems most probable that it is formed by the worm, as Leuckart thought, although there are many who think it produced by the host. But the host does not produce such a peculiar capsule for any other foreign body, and it seems specifically a part of this parasite. Fat may collect at its poles outside, and within it there are usually found a few cells at each pole. These may be included parts of the group of sarcolemma nuclei. Later, the capsule becomes

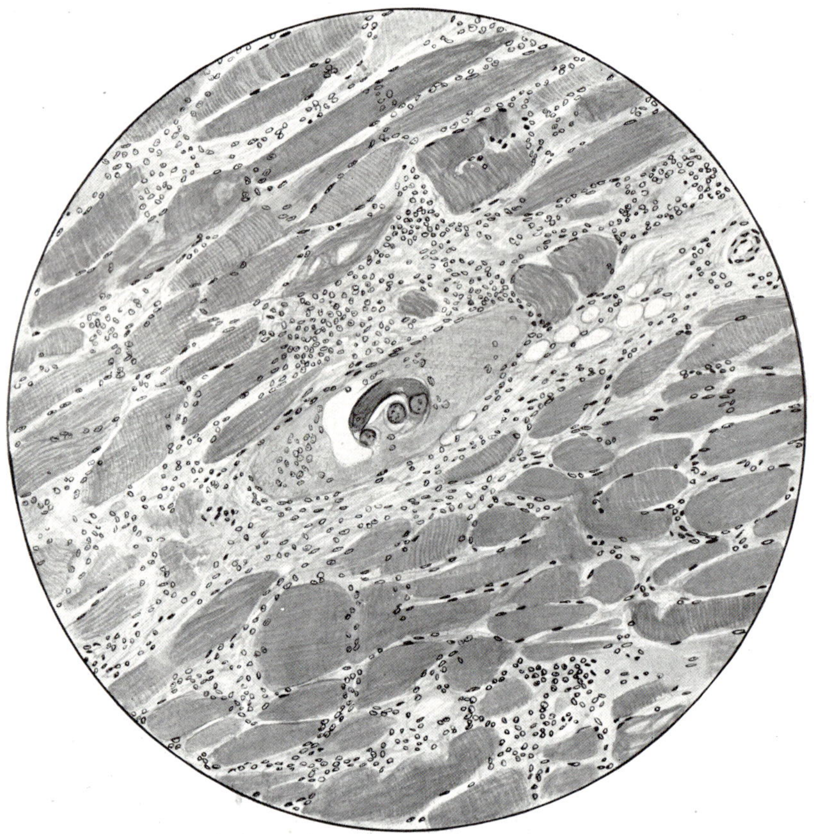

Fig. 390.—Larva of trichinæ encapsulated in muscle. There is abundant infiltration of leucocytes, most of which are eosinophiles, and many muscle-fibres are reduced to hyaline masses.

partly or completely calcified, and then the worm is likely to die or has already died. Nevertheless, they live for years in the muscle, awaiting a chance to go through the development to maturity, in their turn, in the body of another animal.

The disease trichiniasis is a serious one, and often ends fatally when much of the infected meat is eaten. Death is probably due to the intense injury produced by the penetration of the intestinal wall, although more rarely it may occur after the embryo has entered the muscle. Much care is taken by the German government to prevent the sale of infected pork, and Stäubli's book is one long outcry against American pork. The frequency with which epidemics of trichiniasis occur in Germany is, however, probably the outcome of the German habit of eating raw pork and blood sausages and makes the meat inspection futile.

The disease may simulate typhoid fever. There is fever and malaise, often with diarrhœa when the infection is intense, with œdema of the tissue below the eyes and sometimes of other parts of the body and often with profuse sweats. There is no Widal reaction, and there is a marked leucocytosis with an extraordinary increase in the eosinophile cells (Brown). Later the muscles become stiff and painful, and in the effort to relieve them there is dyspnœa, aphonia, and general immobility. With the establishment of the worms in the muscle and their encapsulation, the symptoms gradually disappear.

If a person thus infected dies, the appearance of the organs varies with the stage of the disease. In the fresher stages the intestinal mucosa is said to be swollen and reddened but without definite hæmorrhages. The lymph-glands are swollen in the mesentery and there is bronchitis, but there is usually no other organic change dependent upon the infection except, of course, the change in the skeletal muscles. The bone-marrow is hyperplastic and rich in eosinophile myelocytes.

The muscle parasites are not visible to the naked eye and there may be no sign of any change. It is only much later when, after years, they become calcified that they are visible (Fig. 390). Then they look like tiny opaque yellowish-white flecks in the muscle. Their distribution has guided the meat inspection in Germany and the diaphragm or neck muscles are chosen for study, since those places seem especially favorable for their growth.

LITERATURE

Stäubli: Trichinosis, Wiesbaden, 1909.
Askanazy: Virch. Arch., 1895, cxli, 42.
Brown: Jour. Exp. Med., 1898, iii, 315.
Herrick and Janeway: Arch. Int. Med., 1909, iii, 263.

UNCINARIASIS

Through the work of Stiles in this country and Ashford in Porto Rico the enormous importance of this infection has been made clear and Stiles has shown that, in addition to the *Anchylostomum duodenale* or *Uncinaria duodenalis*, there is another form, called by him *Necator americanus*, which is the parasite especially concerned in America and the West Indies.

All through the southern states and in tropical and sub-tropical countries around the world, the so-called "hookworm disease" is more or less prevalent. Ashford's description of it as it occurs in the "jibaro" or laborer in Porto Rico is most vivid and gives a better idea of the ravages it causes than any other I have read. The people who work in damp coffee plantations are especially affected there. Elsewhere, those who work in the soil are the ones to suffer, chiefly when they get into mud, although Stiles suspected especially the influence of sandy soils. After having walked barefoot in the mud, they have a peculiar eruption on the skin which burns and itches. Some time after that such people find themselves weak and easily tired and unable to work. They grow pale and the skin assumes a yellowish clay color. The digestion is disordered, there is constipation or diarrhœa with occasional periods of abdominal pain. The nervous system is often much affected, and in some cases actual maniacal attacks interrupt the usual stupid condition. The extreme anæmia, often with eosinophilia, becomes more profound and there is often associated with it œdema of the face or of the whole body. The patient becomes unable to walk or to help himself in any way and may die. The fæces contain numbers of the elliptical ova of the worm, but in Ashford's experience no blood. The whole affection can be cured with thymol.

Most interesting is the pathogenesis of this disease which has been worked out by Looss in Egypt. The eggs passed with fæces develop, if they find themselves in a moist place, into small active embryos. Whole areas of moist ground can be thus infected. Ashford mentions the damp ground in the shade of coffee bushes, Looss the mud in which the fellaheen work after the Nile recedes. Looss' beautiful experiments showed that if water or mud containing larvæ at this stage were applied to the skin there arose almost at once a burning and itching sensation, and by the time the water had dried all the larvæ had bored their way into the skin, leaving their shed skins as empty shells on the outside. He repeated this with a leg about to be amputated and was able to trace the larvæ into the hair follicle and thus through the skin. They do not enter sweat-glands or sebaceous glands, but Schüffner found that they could pierce the skin anywhere. Further experiments with dogs showed that they wander into the blood-vessels and are carried to the lungs, where they are too large to pass through the capillaries, but emerge into the air-cells. Thence, crawling up the bronchi, they get over into the œsophagus and reach the stomach and intestine, where after other moults they become mature worms.

Of course, the irritation felt by Looss (who thus produced a general infection in himself and long harbored the worms in his intestine) was identical with the ground itch or "*mazamorra*," which comes on after walking barefoot in infected mud or smearing the hands with it, and there seems no doubt that this is the ordinary mode of infection. Of course, the larvæ may be swallowed if muddy water or mud-covered vegetables are taken into the stomach or if, as sometimes happens to these people, a craving for bulk in their food is satisfied by eating mud or clay. But although this infection by mouth has been regarded as the chief mode of entrance it seems now, in the light of Looss' work, to be less important and perhaps even uncommon.

The mature worms attach themselves to the walls of the intestine and draw into their capacious mouths some part of the mucosa. They seem to feed upon intestinal epithelium and not to be actual blood-suckers, although there is still difference of opinion about this. Sometimes hæmorrhage can be found about the point at which they were applied, and it has been thought that much loss of blood might occur after they dropped off or changed to another place. But little blood is found in the stools, and it is not as a rule found in the intestine of the worm. The impression is, therefore, that they do not cause the profound anæmia by merely mechanically removing blood, and this is strengthened by the character of the anæmia, which is peculiar and marked by an outspoken eosinophilia. This, together with the nervous phenomena and the symptoms of general intoxication, point rather to a toxic substance produced by the worm as the cause of the anæmia.

The worms are found hanging to the wall of the small intestine and are pretty tightly attached. Hundreds of them occur in one case. Aside from the pallor, changes in the other organs are not especially characteristic. The spleen is not enlarged. The bone-marrow shows a response to the anæmia. The kidneys are found to present some exudate of blood and epithelial degeneration.

LITERATURE

Ashford and Igaravidez: Uncinariasis in Porto Rico, U. S. Senate Document No. 808, 1911 (Literature).

Stiles: "Hookworm Disease," Hygienic Labrty. Bull., No. 10, Washington, 1903.

Looss: Centbl. f. Bakt. u. Paras., Abth. i, 1901, xxix, 733.

OTHER NEMATODE INFECTIONS

Brief mention may be made of certain other very common infections with nematode worms.

Ascaris lumbricoides is the common round worm found in the intestine of children, which, by its presence in numbers, exercises an irritating influence. It does not actually fix itself to the intestinal wall, but lies free or in convoluted masses in the lumen. The effects of its wanderings into other localities have been mentioned. Apparently it may secrete a toxic material, for there are general and nervous symptoms due to its presence.

Oxyuris vermicularis, a small worm with pointed extremities, 3 to 5 mm. long, is a frequent inhabitant of the colon, where it attacks the mucosa and produces hæmorrhagic points, by its bites, and an inflammatory reaction with intense itching of the anal region. Its eggs develop on vegetables, etc., or the embryos which quickly leave the shell may be transferred to the mouth and an extensive autoinfection produced. Invasion of the oxyuris into the mucosa of the appendix has been shown to be responsible for a considerable number of cases of appendicitis (17 in a series of 129 cases, Cecil and Bulkley).

The *Trichocephalus trichiurus,* or *dispar,* is a similar worm with long, thread-like anterior end. It buries this anterior end in the mucosa of the cæcum and absorbs blood. No very marked symptoms are produced, but it can occasionally be the cause of appendicitis. More important than these is the *Filaria Bancrofti*, whose embryos are found in the circulating blood in the form of delicate, actively motile threads which appear there only at night. They are transferred by the mosquitoes (culex), in which they undergo a certain development, reaching the salivary glands or œsophagus, so that they are injected with another bite into another host. The mature worm, developing in the human body, invades and lodges itself in the lymphatic channels, where it produces great distension, hæmorrhage and inflammation. Huge masses of lymphatic varicosities are the result and much obstruction to the flow of lymph. The effect of this is evident in nearly every tropical country in the occurrence of the so-called elephantiasis, which affects the legs or the scrotum, causing huge enlargements due to lymph stasis and new formation of tissue which are traceable to the presence of the worm. Chyluria, or milky urine, and chylous ascites are also characteristic features.

LITERATURE

Braun: Thierischen Parasiten des Menschen, Würzburg, 1903.
Cecil and Bulkley: Jour. Exp. Med., 1912, xv, 225.
Opie: "Filarial Lymphatic Varix," Amer. Jour. Med. Sci., 1901, cxxii, 251.
Manson: Tropical Diseases, London, 1903, 545.
Looss: Mense's Handb. d. Tropenkrankheiten, 1905, i, 77–202.

CHAPTER XXXIX

THE EFFECTS OF INJURIES UPON THE BLOOD AND BLOOD-FORMING ORGANS

Importance of changes in blood-forming organs. The bone-marrow: its regenerative changes. The spleen. The lymphoid tissues with the hæmolymph nodes. Injuries of red corpuscles and erythrogenic tissue. Polycythæmia. Anæmia or oligocythæmia. Post-hæmorrhagic and other secondary anæmias. Pernicious anæmia. Aplastic anæmia. Hæmochromatosis. Hæmolytic icterus. Osteosclerotic anæmia. Banti's disease. Splenomegaly of Gaucher.

The fact that in the many disorders of the blood and of the blood-forming organs we are as yet in most cases ignorant of the cause, makes it seem preferable to discuss these conditions together and quite objectively. It is true, of course, that nearly all of the injuries which have already been considered cause changes in the blood and its sources, and sometimes we can trace these effects with the greatest accuracy, so as to derive enlightenment with regard to the principles which are probably concerned in the more obscure affections.

The blood, in virtue of its rapid circulation and of the powerful sifting and cleansing effect exerted upon it by the very blood-forming organs which are its source, does not show the direct effect of local injury except after very gross damage by hæmorrhage or by chemical agents. Then it becomes diluted by the inflow of fluid from the tissues, or, in the second case, it shows the effect of the chemical, as in the formation of carbon monoxide, hæmoglobin, methæmoglobin, etc.). Instead, the changes which appear in the circulating blood are essentially those which depend upon the activity of the blood-forming organs, and may consist in an incomplete new formation of cells of the same type as those which were lost, or in the introduction of greatly increased numbers of some of the cells (leucocytes), or even in the appearance of cells which are not normally present in the blood (erythroblasts, myeloblasts, etc.). Thus it is clear that we shall have to deal but little with the direct effects of injurious agents upon the blood itself. On the other hand, the changes brought about in the blood-forming organs by direct injury or through the necessity of restoring to normal the injured blood, must interest us quite as much as the remarkable changes in the blood which then follow. It is as though an army during the battle should rapidly circle back into the mother country carrying the dead and wounded, returning to the battle with ever new reserves. In time there would come a change in the character of the army, depending upon the ability of the mother country to recruit.

BLOOD-FORMING ORGANS

Leaving aside the conditions found in embryonic life, it is clear that the bone-marrow constitutes the essential seat of the formation of most of the elements of the blood, although, as we have seen in the outline given in Chapters IX and XII, the cells of the lymphoid series are furnished to the blood by the lymphoid tissues scattered everywhere throughout the body. Under stress of great need, tissue of the character of the bone-

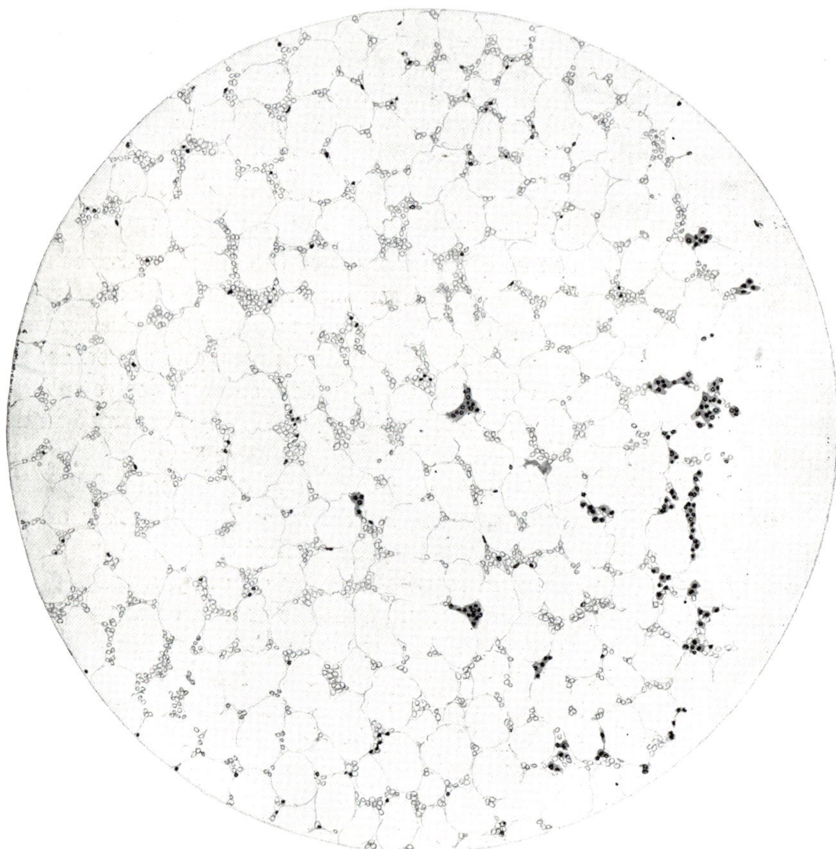

Fig. 391.—Bone-marrow from femur of normal adult, showing chiefly fat with very little myeloid tissue.

marrow appears in situations far removed from the bones, and cells swept into the general circulation may settle as colonies in the capillaries of various organs and there multiply to some extent (Tanaka). The part played by the spleen in blood formation is still disputed, and although some writers assign to it a most important rôle, others regard it as chiefly concerned in the purification of the blood. This matter must for the present be left undecided.

The Bone-marrow.—Throughout life the marrow of the cancellous framework of the short and flat bones maintains its cellular character and is active in blood formation. In childhood this is true of the marrow of the long bones too, but with advancing age fat increases in amount there and replaces the marrow, often even in the cancellous regions of the ends of the bone. The microscopical study of the marrow shows only a delicate framework with blood-vessels among the closely packed fat-holding cells. In the angles and crevices one may find a few cells of myelocyte or ery-

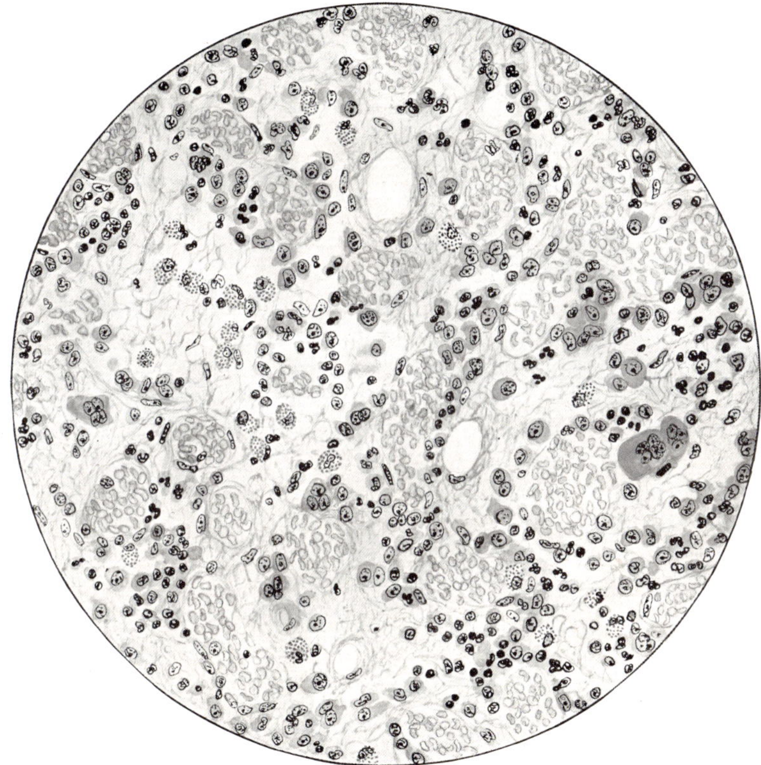

Fig. 392.—Bone-marrow from normal infant. It shows quite well-defined blood-channels, neutrophile and eosinophile myelocytes, megalocaryocytes, etc. There are numerous normoblasts which do not show well in this drawing.

throblast type (Fig. 391). It seems that these are the cells which multiply at an astounding rate when special activity of the bone-marrow is demanded. In the marrow of the child's femur (Fig. 392) or in that of the short cancellous bones a very different condition exists. There is relatively little fat, and the delicate vascular reticulum is loaded with loose cells. Of course, as mentioned before, the osteoblasts and osteoclasts which are closely applied to the bone hold aloof and are concerned only in bone formation and destruction. The capillaries are wide and variable in diameter, and it is frequently difficult to trace their endothelial outlines. Indeed, one does not receive the impression that they are stout-walled tubes capable of carrying blood safely at a considerable pressure, but rather that their walls are extremely thin if not actually lacking in places. At times it seems as though the mass of cells in the reticulum were continuous with those within the capillaries, and one must suppose that some such relation may exist, to explain the phenomenally rapid delivery of cells into the blood-stream. For a discussion of the histogenesis of the cells concerned the student is referred to the papers of Maximow, Jackson, and others.

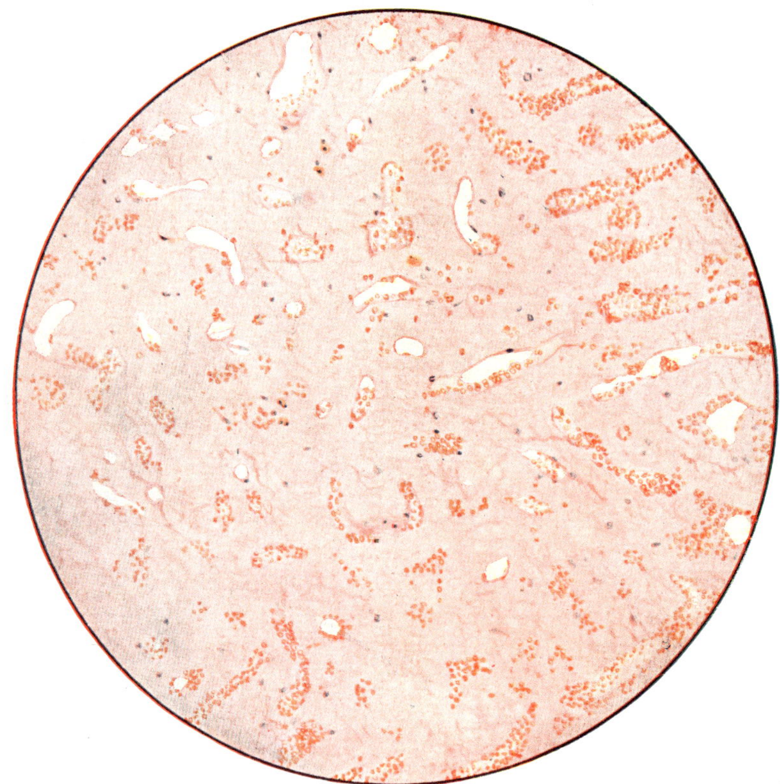

Fig. 393.—Bone-marrow of rabbit after long treatment with benzol. Practically all the blood-forming elements are destroyed.

In such cellular marrow there are found, side by side, the following kinds of cells:

1. Those concerned in the production of red corpuscles: Megaloblasts, normoblasts, and the erythrocytes themselves.

2. Those concerned in the formation of the neutrophile, eosinophile and basophile granular leucocytes: Myeloblasts without granules, myelocytes with neutrophile, eosinophile and basophile granules, and the mature leucocytes themselves with these different types of granule.

3. An indefinite but limited number of large and small lymphoid cells, situated usually about the blood-vessels and capable of giving rise to lymphocytes and to their derivatives, including plasma cells.

4. Megalocaryocytes which, by constricting off portions of their granular cytoplasm, form blood-platelets, which they discharge into the blood.

In ordinary sections these cells are so intermingled that one cannot make out their relations to one another, but Bunting puts forward the

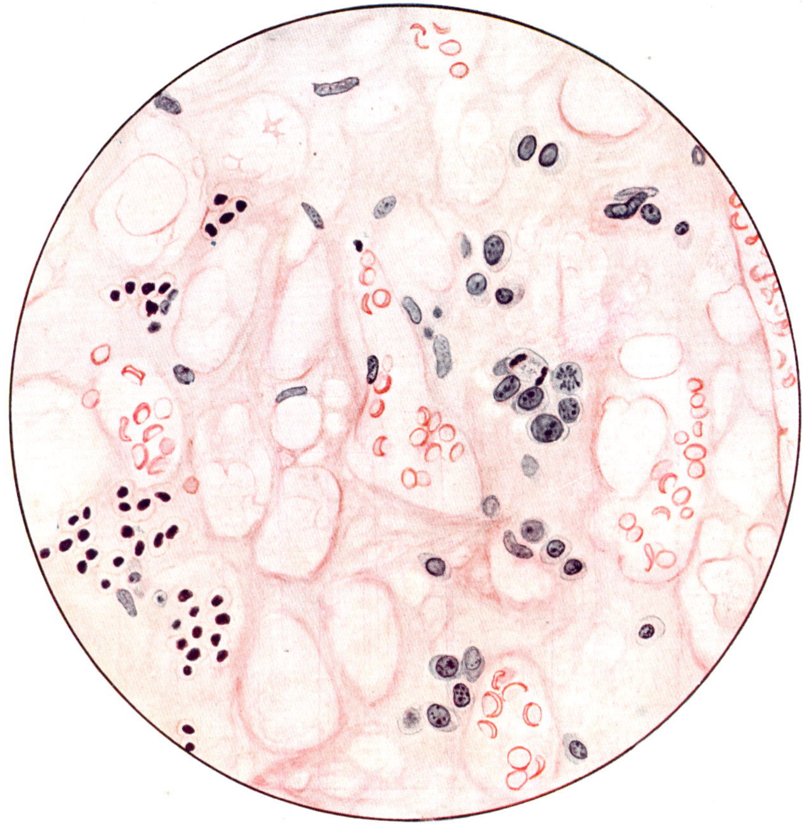

Fig. 394.—Bone-marrow of rabbit. Beginning regeneration after benzol poisoning; islands of myelocytes and normoblasts.

statement that they occur in definite groups or colonies at the margins of which the perfected cells are set free. This he has found especially striking in experimental anæmias in rabbits in which the bone-marrow had been injured by the injection of ricin or other substance used to produce the anæmia. So, too, Selling described the appearance of such colonies or pure cultures of the various cells in bone-marrow rendered practically cell-free (Fig. 393) with injections of benzol and then allowed to regenerate. These preparations I have studied and the truth of the statement is very striking. There are isolated groups composed in one case entirely of nucleated red cells (Fig. 394), in another entirely of myelocytes or of megalocaryocytes (Fig. 395), and in the later stages each of these comes to be accompanied by the mature cells which they produce (Fig. 396). Bunting explains that with further development the groups become so interwoven that it is impossible to outline them clearly, but in the bone-marrow of his rabbits made anæmic with ricin he finds such islands with a central group of megaloblasts surrounded by normoblasts and these in

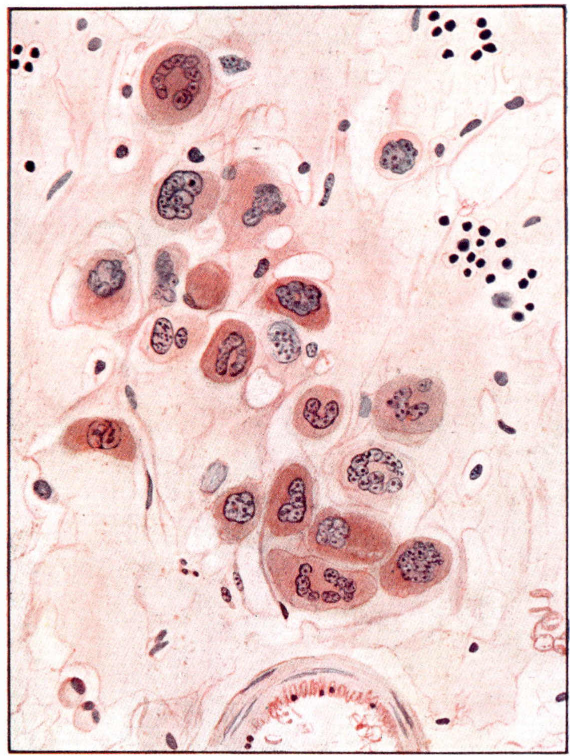

Fig. 395.—Bone-marrow of rabbit after benzol poisoning. Beginning regeneration; islands of megalocaryocytes.

turn by ordinary red corpuscles. It is on the basis of these observations that he regards the megaloblasts as normal constituents of the bone-marrow and the immediate ancestors of the normoblasts. It is well known that this is not the view of German hæmatologists (Naëgeli), who hold to Ehrlich's statement that megaloblasts are embryonic cells occurring only under pathological conditions in adult bone-marrow, and that therefore pernicious anæmia, in which they become abundant in the marrow, represents a pathological return to embryonic conditions. It seems, however, that one may convince oneself of their common occurrence in normal and regenerating bone-marrow and of the probability of Bunting's view that they represent the earlier stage in the formation of red corpuscles. The occasional sweeping of these nucleated cells into the blood will call for discussion below.

In quite the same way the myeloblasts and myelocytes of each kind grow in colonies and shed into the blood their polymorphonuclear descendants. These cells, even in their earlier non-granulated stages, give an intense blue reaction with alpha-naphthol and dimethylparaphenylene

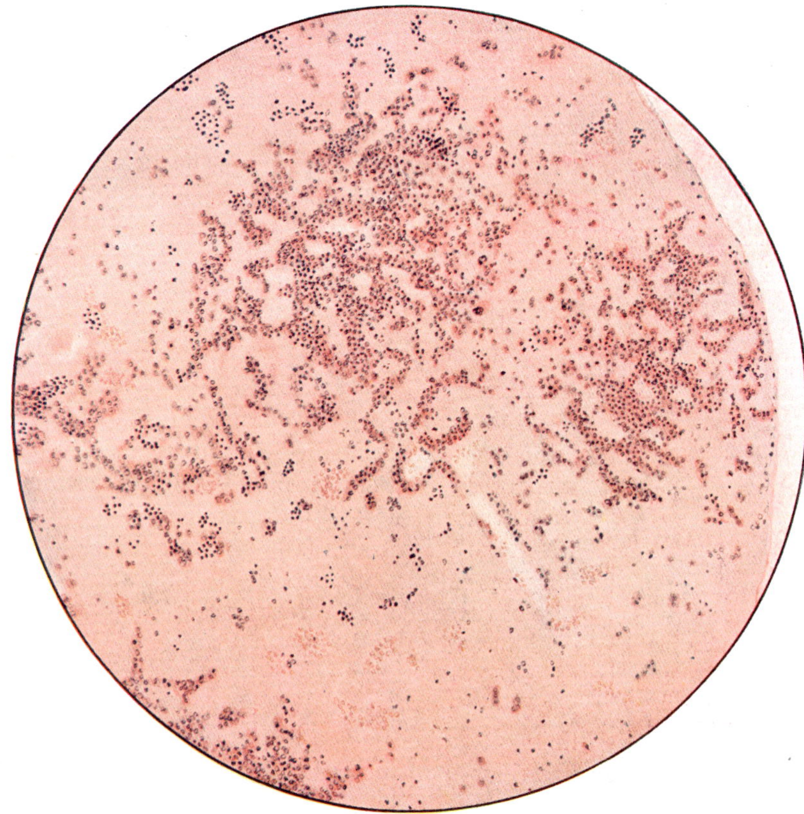

Fig. 396.—Bone-marrow of rabbit after benzol poisoning. Later stage of regeneration. Mixed islands of myelocytes, normoblasts, with occasional megalocaryocytes.

diamine, which in the presence of an oxydizing ferment produce indophenol blue (*oxydase reaction*). This reaction is also given by all the granulated leucocytes of the blood, including the large mononuclear and transitional forms of Ehrlich. The latter are thereby shown to be related to the myelocyte group rather than to the lymphoid cells, since none of the lymphocytes or related cells give the reaction. (The mast cells of the tissue fail to give it despite their basophilic granules.)

Ordinarily the lymphoid cells of the bone-marrow form an inconspicuous element of the cell mass and are sometimes collected in groups or lymph nodules. In those cases in which the injurious agent causes the isolated overproduction of lymphoid cells they may, however, increase to such an extent as to crowd aside all the other cells. Theirs is probably under ordinary circumstances the least prominent rôle among the bone-marrow cells.

The megalocaryocytes which maintain the platelet content of the blood are, like the other cells, vulnerable, and may be greatly reduced in number by toxic substances. They regenerate themselves in little colonies just as do the other cells (Fig. 395).

The Spleen.—The studies of Weidenreich and Mollier have made clear the structure of the spleen as far as concerns its vascular arrangement, but there is still much to be learned with regard to the cellular structure of the splenic pulp.

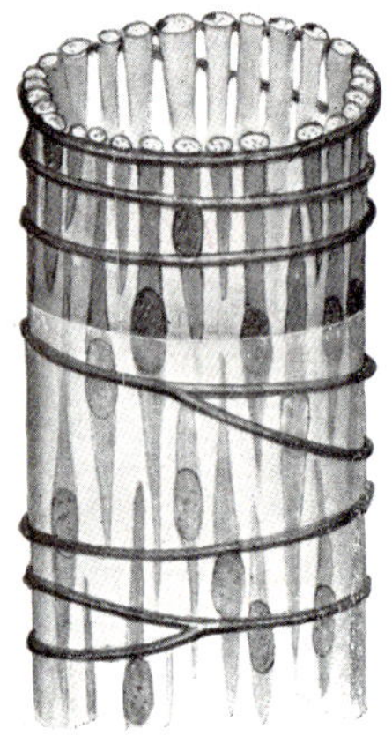

Fig. 397.—Diagrammatic drawing of splenic venule showing the elongated endothelial cells, the structureless membrane, and the circular reticulum fibres (Mollier).

The smaller branches of the splenic artery are surrounded for some distance by mantles of lymphoid tissue which constitute the Malpighian bodies. These are in every respect like nodules of lymphoid tissue found elsewhere and show the same reactions. Aside from them the tissue between the fibrous trabeculæ belongs entirely to the splenic pulp and into this the arteriole passes, to branch and empty into the wide venules, which form a sort of feltwork making up most of the pulp. In the interstices between these venules is the reticulum of the pulp, in which are held great numbers of free cells. For our purposes the most interesting features are the structure of the walls of the venules and the nature of the cells in the pulp reticulum. The walls of the venules (Fig. 397) are very loose in texture, so that it seems extremely easy for cells to wander in and out. The lining endothelial cells are quite unlike those seen elsewhere, and instead of being flat and polygonal and uniformly adherent by their edges to the edges of the next cell, they are greatly elongated, thick, and pointed at each end, with a large and prominent nucleus which projects into the lumen of the venule. In many places the cells, which lie parallel to one another and lengthwise in the venule, have their nuclei side by side, so that between these rows of nuclei the wall is formed by the bodies only of the cells. A cross-section at that point shows only the unstained bodies of the cells, like little cogs on the inside of the venule, while at another level the venule may be lined all round with the prominent nuclei (Fig. 398). Outside the venule there is a delicate cylindrical basketwork of elastic fibrils; whether there is any other structureless membrane between is still disputed.

The reticulum between the venules shows a few elongated nuclei which belong to the cells of the connective-tissue framework. In chronic passive congestion and similar conditions these are very conspicuously increased in number and the fibrous reticulum is correspondingly denser. In the meshes there are great numbers of red corpuscles, the actual quantity varying with different conditions, so that in the fibroid spleen of chronic passive congestion there are hardly any, while in the acute splenic tumor of typhoid fever they are present in overwhelming numbers. The majority of the other cells are lymphocytes, and these can be found wandering

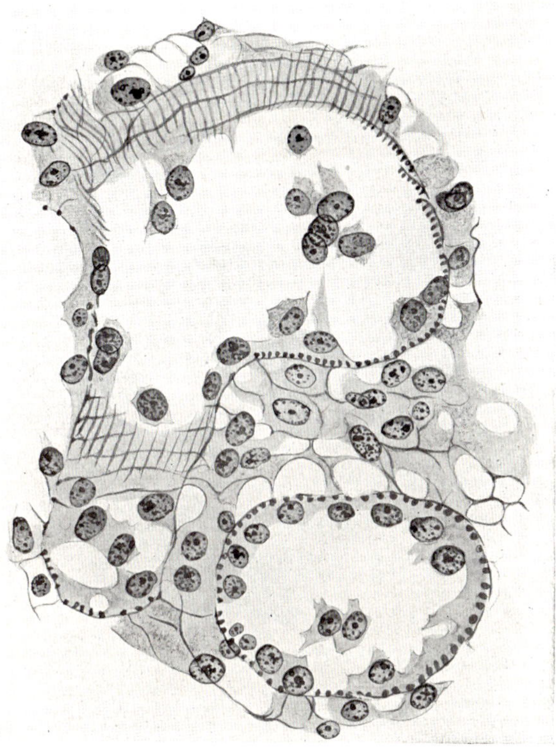

Fig. 398.—Section of spleen showing venules with endothelial cells and network of protoplasmic and reticulum strands (Mollier).

through the walls of the venules as well as within the venules themselves. There are other rather larger mononuclear cells ("pulp cells"), some of which reach the size of myelocytes. It is indeed not uncommon to find both eosinophile and neutrophile myelocytes in small numbers, but this is not a feature of perfectly normal spleens. Plasma cells, polymorphonuclear neutrophile, and eosinophile leucocytes are occasionally present, but are in very small numbers. Thus under ordinary circumstances the cells seem to be essentially of the lymphoid type. One is especially impressed with the complete ease with which all these cells pass in and out through the walls of the venules, and it is easy to understand that, under these circumstances, modifications of the passing blood might readily change the character of the splenic tissue.

As to the function of the spleen, it is even yet, after centuries of experiment and speculation (Malpighi attempted to discover this function by extirpating the spleen of a dog), impossible to say anything very definite. It is generally supposed to be an organ active in destroying injured blood-corpuscles and sifting out of the circulating blood the débris of such cells, the hæmoglobin of which it prepares for use by the liver in the formation of bile-pigments. This idea depends chiefly upon the finding of pigment in the spleen, but there is little to show that all of this cannot be equally well accomplished after the spleen is removed. It is stated by many that the spleen is an active blood-forming agent, and Pearce and his co-workers have shown, among others, that there is a temporary anæmia after splenectomy, apparently compensated for by hyperplasia of bone-marrow and lymphoid tissues. Lymphocyte production is perhaps decreased for a time by splenectomy, but is soon reinstated (Murphy). Studies of the blood of the splenic vein as contrasted with that of the artery have been referred to, but they are open to criticism and give very contradictory results. Since these methods are unsatisfactory, it is difficult to prove that the spleen actually contributes cells to the blood (although that seems probable), because new cells from any source added to the circulating blood tend to lodge in its pulp.

The Lymphoid Tissue.—The lymphoid tissue is almost universally distributed, since it occurs in conspicuous accumulations throughout the whole digestive tract, in the walls of the respiratory tract, in lymph-glands in orderly arrangement everywhere throughout the body, in the Malpighian bodies of the spleen, and in inconspicuous nodules in the skin, bone-marrow, and other organs such as the thyroid, parathyroid, adrenal, kidney, liver, pancreas. The lymphatic channels lead its cells into the blood but are interrupted by others of its masses arranged as sieves to retain impurities. Everywhere the architecture of the lymphoid tissue is the same in principle although slightly more elaborate in those places where lymph sinuses surround the more compact masses of lymphoid tissue. There is in this tissue a reticulum with many associated cells of large size and pale vesicular nucleus and, very commonly, in the follicles a central, palely staining mass of large cells related to if not identical with the reticulum cells. These have been looked upon since Flemming's work as the direct antecedents of the lymphoid cells. The latter, which are identical with the lymphocytes of the blood, are accumulated in quantities in the meshes of the reticulum. That they wander far and wide in the crevices of the tissues and develop there into larger phagocytic mononuclear wandering cells has been mentioned in a previous chapter. That the adventitial cells which lurk about the vessels, and the plasma cells which with other lymphoid cells are so abundant in the stroma of all the mucosæ and are so extensively concerned in inflammatory processes, are part of this same group has been made clear before.

Accumulations of such cells in unaccustomed situations, but still capable of reproducing themselves and increasing their numbers, are found in various conditions, dependent upon stimuli which lead to the hyperplasia of the original lymphoid tissue, just as accumulations of the cells characteristic of the bone-marrow may occur in various organs when that tissue is caused to undergo hyperplasia. Much discussion has taken place as to whether such lymphoid and myeloid foci are due to the transportation of lymphoid or myeloid cells to these situations or to an autochthonous or independent origin in the place where they are found (Meyer and Heineke, Sternberg). Probably both may occur, but from our knowledge of the possibilities of the transportation of cells and tissues and from our observations of the way in which such cells maintain themselves in good condition in the capillaries of foreign organs, it seems perhaps more probable that in most cases they are colonies descended from emigrating cells. Nevertheless, when bone with a marrow cavity is formed in a calcified area of the lung or aorta, it is hard to escape the impressions that the myeloid tissue which appears in such a marrow cavity is due to a recrudescence of the whole process of bone and bone-marrow formation.

Other lymphoid collections in the form of deep red lymph-nodes are found in the prevertebral region, neck, thorax, etc. These are the *hæmolymph nodes* whose sinuses contain blood. Aside from their supposed function of destroying injured blood-corpuscles, they seem to behave like other lymph-nodes (*cf.* Warthin).

EFFECT OF INJURIES TO THE RED CORPUSCLES AND THEIR FORMATIVE ORGANS

It is naturally impossible that there should be any extensive alterations in the red corpuscles without some accompanying changes in the closely associated white corpuscles and vice versa; nevertheless the disturbances affect so predominantly one type of cell or the other that we may confidently speak of these diseased conditions with regard to the cells chiefly affected, referring to the changes in the others as accessory.

In the normal blood the number of red corpuscles per cubic millimetre is about five million, while the number of white corpuscles taken together is about five or six thousand. Any great variation from these numbers usually indicates the influence of some abnormal condition. An increase in the number of red corpuscles or *polycythæmia* may occur, but is by no means so common as the opposite effect, a decrease in their number, *bligocythæmia*, loosely called *anæmia*.

Polycythæmia.—The rapid loss of fluid from the body, such as may occur with severe diarrhœa or Asiatic cholera or even with profuse sweating, leads to such inspissation or concentration of the blood as to raise the number of red corpuscles per cubic millimetre to six or seven million.

This is naturally a transitory phenomenon if the patient survives, since with the absorption of water from the digestive tract the blood returns to its normal concentration. There are other conditions, however, such as chronic cyanosis from cardiac insufficiency or from emphysema, in which there is a lasting polycythæmia apparently due to the actual need for more blood to nourish and oxygenate the tissues properly. This is especially marked when the chronic passive congestion has existed since infancy, as in congenital heart lesions. In persons who live at high altitudes there is a similar increase in the number of red corpuscles which appears after even a short stay in the mountains or, it is said, after or during a balloon voyage. More interesting still and more difficult to explain are those cases of *polycythæmia rubra* (Osler), or *erythræmia*, in which the blood becomes actually thick and viscous from the presence of such enormous numbers of red corpuscles (10 millions or more). There is increase in the total volume of blood, cardiac hypertrophy, great enlargement of the spleen, and hyperplasia of the bone-marrow. The cause is quite unknown and the patients go on to die of hæmorrhage or of some intercurrent infection. It is a very curious phenomenon, perhaps analogous to leukæmia, since in spite of the fact that the blood-vessels are everywhere turgid with blood, the erythroblastic tissues of the bone-marrow are found to be in process of active hyperplasia and blood formation, as though behaving quite independently of the needs of the blood which usually govern them.

Anæmia.—On the other hand, agencies which destroy and diminish the red corpuscles are extremely common, and their action far more easily understood.

Decrease in the number of red corpuscles in the blood may be brought about in a very great variety of ways which perhaps fall into the following divisions:

1. Actual loss of blood through hæmorrhage.
2. Destruction of blood and injury of the bone-marrow by poisons which are often those produced by bacteria or other parasites, often chemical substances taken as drugs or absorbed by workers in certain industries. Long-continued infections and the presence of malignant tumors are factors especially likely to bring about such results.
3. A peculiar, sharply defined disease known as *pernicious anæmia*, in which, despite the most active efforts toward regeneration, the red corpuscles continue to decrease in number.
4. *Osteosclerotic Anæmia.*—The attack may be more serious in that it is directed against the bone-marrow itself. While it is difficult to show that this is so in the case of poisons and infections which may also destroy the circulating red corpuscles, it is quite clear in those cases in which metastases from cancers of the prostate or breast occupy the whole marrow cavity of every bone to the mechanical exclusion of bone-marrow, or even in the cases of leukæmia in which the whole of the bone-

marrow is given over to the production of the forerunners of white corpuscles, so that the erythroblastic tissue is crowded out of existence. In such cases there is extreme anæmia in spite of efforts toward extramedullary blood formation.

Secondary Anæmias.—1. *Post-hæmorrhagic anæmias* depend in their severity upon the extent of the hæmorrhage and upon the frequency with which it is repeated. A single great hæmorrhage is followed by a series of symptoms due to the incomplete filling of the blood-vessels,—fainting, nausea, weakness, collapsing pulse, etc.,—but the concentration of the blood and the proportion of corpuscles immediately after the hæmorrhage is naturally exactly what it was before. Very rapidly, however, fluid passes from the tissues or from the digestive tract to dilute the blood and make up its quantity. Within a few days after such hæmorrhage the fatty bone-marrow of the long bones becomes so filled with newly formed cells that the fat is crowded out and the marrow assumes a red color and cellular consistency. In such marrow there are found abundant nucleated red cells rapidly giving rise to red corpuscles, and also quantities of myelocytes; this is not followed, however, by the pouring out of any extraordinary number of leucocytes, although the proportion of these cells in the blood is somewhat increased.

Such extensive hæmorrhages occur, of course, in mechanical injuries in which large blood-vessels are cut or torn, but they also occur in advanced pulmonary tuberculosis from the erosions of a branch of the pulmonary artery, in ulcers of the stomach or in cases of cirrhosis of the liver in which there is a rupture of the dilated veins in the œsophagus, in the rupture of an extra-uterine pregnancy, or in ordinary pregnancy at childbirth. But even more profound degrees of anæmia may be produced by slighter but frequently repeated hæmorrhages, such as those which come from recurrent nose-bleed, bleeding hæmorrhoids, and ulcerated submucous myomata of the uterus, and, possibly, in the case of certain intestinal parasites which suck the blood, although, as has already been said, this is of somewhat doubtful occurrence in human beings and the anæmia caused by these parasites seems rather due to a poison which they produce.

2. *Destruction of the blood-corpuscles* (hæmolysis) may be caused by a great variety of chemical substances, of which ricin and benzol have already been mentioned. Nitrobenzol, toluylenediamine, lead, and a host of other substances have a similar effect. Particularly interesting are the specific hæmolytic sera which have been experimentally produced, and we are even yet very imperfectly informed as to the part which similar elusive substances may play in human pathology. There are many bacteria which produce strong hæmolytic poisons, and acute infections are therefore common causes of intense anæmia. For example, the hæmolytic streptococci can cause the destruction of a great proportion of the blood-corpuscles in a brief period, and even the less actively hæmolytic *S. viridans* produces an endocarditis and general infection which runs its course with

the development of extreme grades of anæmia. The anæmia which accompanies typhoid fever, chronic tuberculosis, and syphilis is apparently due to similar processes, while in chronic nephritis and the cachexias which accompany the presence of tumors, especially perhaps when they are ulcerated, the nature of the poison is more difficult to ascertain.

The extreme anæmia brought about by malaria is in great part due to the mechanical destruction of the corpuscles by the parasites, but in the case of bothriocephalus and uncinaria it appears that a recognizable hæmolytic material can be extracted from the worms and that this is probably diffused into the blood and tissues.

Such anæmias, which together with those caused by hæmorrhage, are often called secondary, since their cause is known, resemble one another closely in the character of the blood changes. The red corpuscles may be reduced to less than a million per cubic millimetre, and tend to be rather small and pale, or poor in hæmoglobin, and show some irregularities in size or form. Normoblasts are present in the circulation, often appearing in great numbers, at intervals corresponding with what seem to be crises of activity in the bone-marrow. Megaloblasts are seldom seen. There is nearly always an accompanying leucocytosis except in the case of such diseases as typhoid fever and malaria, in which the leucocytes are decreased in number.

The changes in the bone-marrow are those already described as characteristic of hyperplasia, which appears in response to the dearth of red cells, but associated with similar hyperplastic changes in the myelocytic group (Fig. 399). When, however, the anæmia is caused by some poison which attacks the bone-marrow itself, the reparatory changes are even more striking, as shall be detailed later. In the spleen, which may be somewhat enlarged, one finds no especial change in the Malpighian bodies, but in the splenic pulp, myelocytes, erythroblastic cells, and other elements corresponding to those of the bone-marrow are to be found. Similarly in the capillaries of the liver, and sometimes outside them in the liver substance itself, such groups of cells may occur. The lymph-glands and lymphoid tissues are practically unaffected in secondary anæmias. Scattered hæmorrhages are common, and œdema of the ankles or of the tissues under the eyes forms a characteristic accompaniment. Other anatomical changes, aside from the pallor of the organs in which little or no blood pigment is deposited, are inconstant. Very often there is an accumulation of fat globules in the heart muscle and in the kidneys. The disabilities produced by such anæmia are those consequent upon diminution of the bulk of the blood and of its oxygen-carrying capacity. Weakness, faintness, etc., have been mentioned, but, curiously enough, whether from the increased efforts of the heart and more rapid circulation, or other cause, the respiratory interchange is not decreased and the nitrogenous output not characteristically altered.

A secondary anæmia is the banal result of all sort of injuries which destroy the blood-corpuscles, just as cardiac decompensation may arise from the most varied injuries to the heart. The changes in the bone-marrow are the ordinary or routine efforts of the body to repair this injury, just as new epithelium grows to cover a defect. We need not feel surprised, therefore, in finding the type of the reparatory reaction the same in all. If we can remove the cause by stopping hæmorrhage, by expelling parasites, by extirpating tumors or withdrawing chemical poisons, the rapid

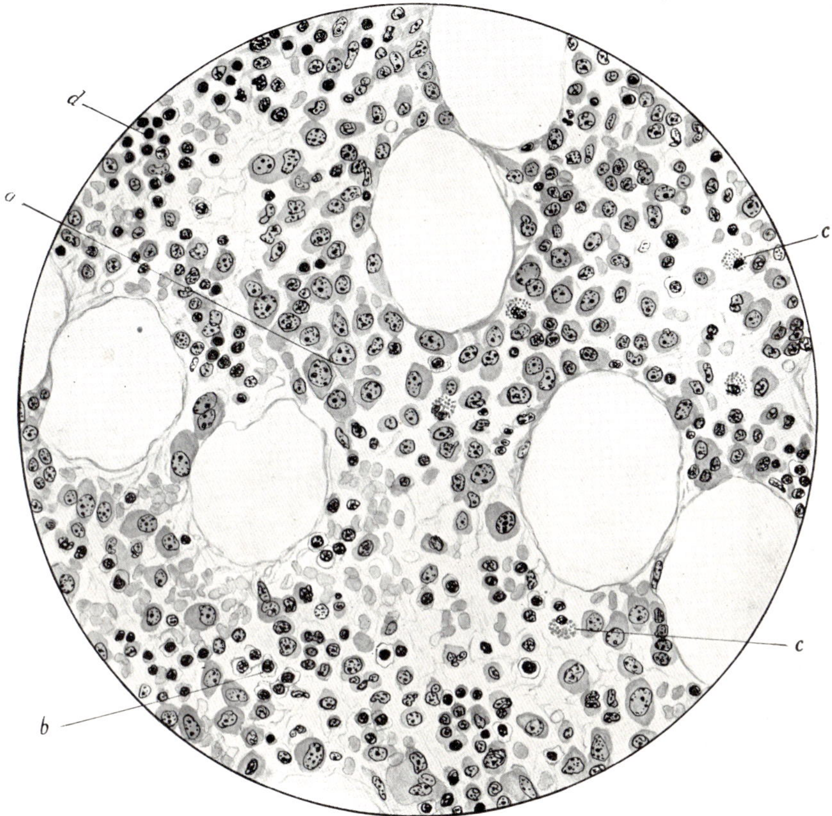

Fig. 399.—Bone-marrow in secondary anæmia, showing intense regenerative hyperplasia: (a) Myelocytes; (b) normoblasts with occasional megaloblasts; (c) eosinophile myelocytes; (d) lymphoid cells.

production of red corpuscles in the bone-marrow proceeds until the anæmic circulation once more has its normal amount of normal blood, after which it quiets down and the cellular marrow resumes its fatty character in the long bones.

Pernicious Anæmia.—This, although so difficult to distinguish from other types of severe anæmia by any single criterion, is quite obviously an independent and definite disease which we recognize with certainty, and of which we can foretell the course as surely as we can in a case of typhoid fever. It may be said that nothing is known of its cause although numerous theories have been put forward, but the complex of changes in the blood, the anatomical changes in the organs, and the symptoms and the course of the disease are monotonously uniform. From the fact that we have not discovered its cause it has often been called primary or essential anæmia, in contrast with secondary anæmias, but it seems by no means impossible that when we presently discover this cause and find that its removal allows the otherwise progressive anæmia to be repaired there will be no justification for such a name as primary anæmia. That it is different from the ordinary secondary anæmias is shown at once, however, by the condition of the blood, which is simulated closely only in the bothriocephalus anæmia. Briefly, there is extreme decrease in the number of red corpuscles, each of which, however, contains an abnormally large amount of hæmoglobin, so that, sometimes, in spite of the oligocythæmia, the hæmoglobin of the whole blood is not greatly lowered. The corpuscles are very irregular in form (poikilocytosis) and in size (anisocytosis), there being not only small forms but very large or giant corpuscles, also tinged deeply with hæmoglobin. The presence of these large forms together with the high color index is distinctive, since these do not occur in secondary anæmias where the color index is low. Nucleated red corpuscles are found sometimes in large numbers and megaloblasts are often abundant. Indeed, the finding of megaloblasts in the circulating blood is much relied on in the diagnosis of this disease. The leucocytes are decreased in number and there may be only 1500–2000 per cubic millimetre. Since the lymphoid structures in the body are unaltered, the percentage of lymphocytes rises and they may assume a proportion of as much as 60 per cent. The great decrease is in the polymorphonuclear neutrophiles. Myelocytes and myeloblasts are occasionally found. The decrease in the red cells is often such as to give the blood a peculiar watery appearance, although the high color index tends to keep it red. In actual numbers the red cells may sink far below one million. (For details of the blood changes consult the works of Cabot, Nægeli, Lazarus.) This distinctive alteration of the blood is perhaps not enough to mark out pernicious anæmia as an independent disease, but the occurrence in middle-aged people, the complete lack of any recognizable cause, the continued good nutrition of the patient, the progressive deepening of the anæmia with intermissions during which great improvement occurs, the yellow pigmentation of the skin, and the practically uniform fatal outcome are enough to establish its identity.

At autopsy the body is found well nourished, the subcutaneous fat and indeed all the fat tinged a rather deep yellow. The muscles are dark red. The diminution in the amount of blood is striking, and there may be found minute ecchymoses and local œdemas, especially in the lungs. The heart is soft, and through the myocardium there shines the yellow streaking which indicates the presence of much fat in the muscle-fibres. The liver, cortex of the kidneys, heart muscle, and the lungs are pigmented with iron-containing blood-pigment, even to the extent of assuming a rather distinct chestnut-brown color. Immersed in ferrocyanide of potassium and weak hydrochloric acid, they become gray-blue in color. The mucosa of the stomach is often atrophic and smooth and there may be achylia. Indeed, many writers have thought this to be in some way the cause of the disease, but the evidence is insufficient to uphold this view. In the mouth, too, there are often lesions of the mucosa of an inflammatory character associated with hæmorrhages which cause pain, especially when acids are taken into the mouth. On the tongue there are brownish patches

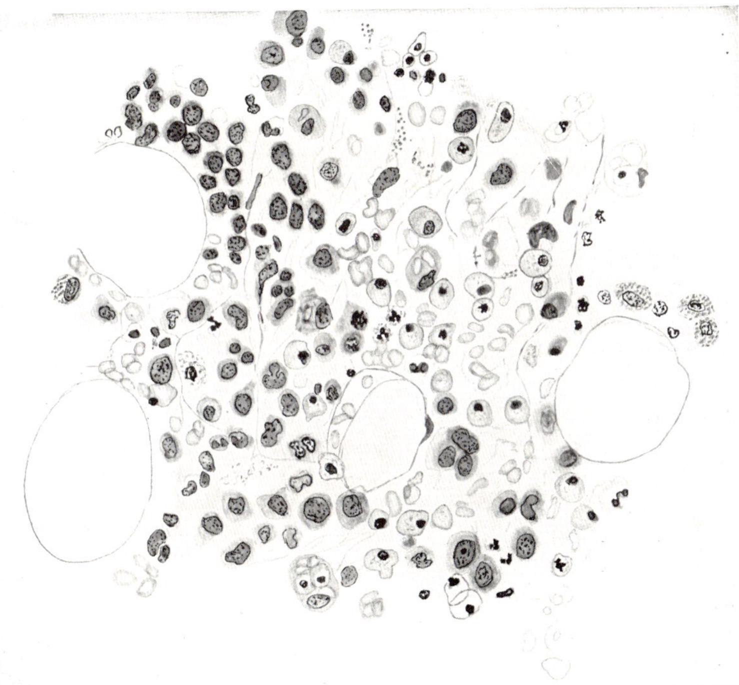

Fig. 400.—Bone-marrow in pernicious anæmia. Normoblasts and numerous megaloblasts occur, together with many neutrophile myelocytes. There are phagocytic cells and some finely granular pigment.

at the site of hæmorrhages. Hunter has especially emphasized this glossitis and regards it as the primary lesion, or portal of entry of the causative agent of the disease. The blood-forming organs show changes which are primarily distinctive of the reaction to a severe anæmia.

The *bone-marrow* is dark red and rather gelatinous. Its fat is replaced by the abundant hyperplastic tissue which in general resembles that found in secondary anæmias. The character of this can be conveyed better by a drawing than a description (Fig. 400). There is extensive new formation of myelocytes and myeloblasts. Newly formed lymphoid cells are present, and there are abundant groups or islands of erythroblastic cells among which megaloblasts are conspicuous. Ehrlich made the statement that the presence of megaloblasts in the hyperplastic bone-marrow was peculiar to pernicious anæmia and that it indicated a return to a distinctly embryonic type of erythrocyte formation, in sharp contrast with the normal formation, which is by way of the normoblasts. The appearance of megaloblasts in the blood and of megalocytes or large, deeply colored, non-nucleated red corpuscles was equally characteristic, and one must regard pernicious anæmia as a condition in which there was being formed a different sort of blood derived largely from abnormal cells, the megaloblasts, proper to embryonic life but obsolete in adult life. Nægeli and Lazarus and most

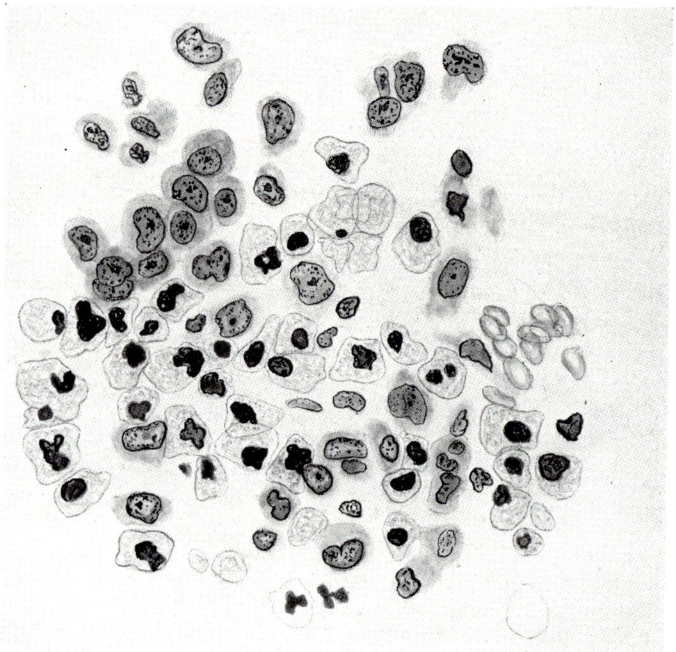

Fig. 401.—Bone-marrow in pernicious anæmia. An island or group of megaloblasts with adjacent myelocytes and a few normoblasts.

German writers have accepted this view of the obsolete nature of megaloblasts and the consequent peculiarity of the bone-marrow in pernicious anæmia. Certainly the presence of megaloblasts in the circulating blood is indicative of very severe anæmia, and although these cells occur in other forms of anæmia, they are far more common in pernicious anæmia. But any one can convince himself of the presence of megaloblasts in any hyperplastic bone-marrow, and the experiments of Bunting, in which, by repeatedly injuring the bone-marrow with ricin, he produced an anæmia practically identical with pernicious anæmia, showed further that in the bone-marrow there were quantities of megaloblasts which formed the centres of erythrogenetic islands. They formed red corpuscles by development through the intermediate normoblasts which lay peripherally. It is Bunting's idea that this is practically the normal relation, and that the erythrocytes are given off peripherally, but that in the case of such serious injury to the bone-marrow as may be produced with ricin or as exists in pernicious anæmia, not only the more peripheral normoblasts, but the central megaloblasts themselves, may be hurriedly discharged. It is quite true that in the bone-marrow of pernicious anæmia it is exceedingly difficult to outline any such groups of cells, since they are intimately intermingled with adjacent groups of other sorts of cells. Nevertheless, the relative concentration which can be made out, and the analogy with the perfectly clear-cut islands of regenerating cells in bone-marrow made aplastic with benzol, leads us to believe that Bunting's conception

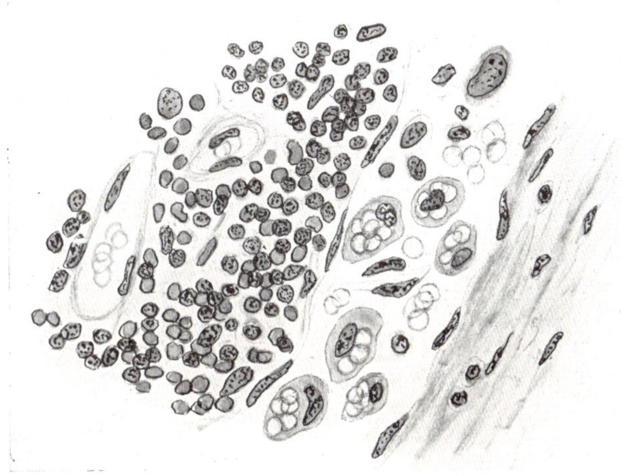

Fig. 402.—Pernicious anæmia. Lymph-gland with phagocytes in the peripheral sinus, containing red corpuscles.

is a true one (Fig. 401). Numerous large phagocytic cells are found in the sections, loaded with red corpuscles and with the shadows of such corpuscles, together with occasional fragments of nucleated cells. These have been described by Sternberg and are conspicuous also in the spleen and in the hæmolymph glands (Fig. 402). They at least indicate the activity of blood destruction.

The *spleen* is usually slightly enlarged, and in some cases, but by no means all, shows a rusty tint on its cut surface. The Malpighian bodies can be seen plainly and the splenic pulp is not very greatly increased in bulk. Occasionally the organ is larger and firmer than normal, the increase being evidently in the splenic pulp. Microscopically there is strikingly little change from the normal (Fig. 403). The venules are clearly outlined with intact endothelial cells; the intervening reticulum of the pulp is more abundantly loaded with red corpuscles than in the normal, and many of these appear to be disintegrating. The lymphoid cells which normally occupy this position seem to be relatively few. Both within and between the venules there are moderate numbers of large phagocytic cells with débris of red corpuscles in their protoplasm. The myeloid change described by Meyer and Heineke and others is by no means so conspicuous as one might be led to expect from the severity of the anæmia; indeed, it is necessary to search through the sections to find any myelocytes, and

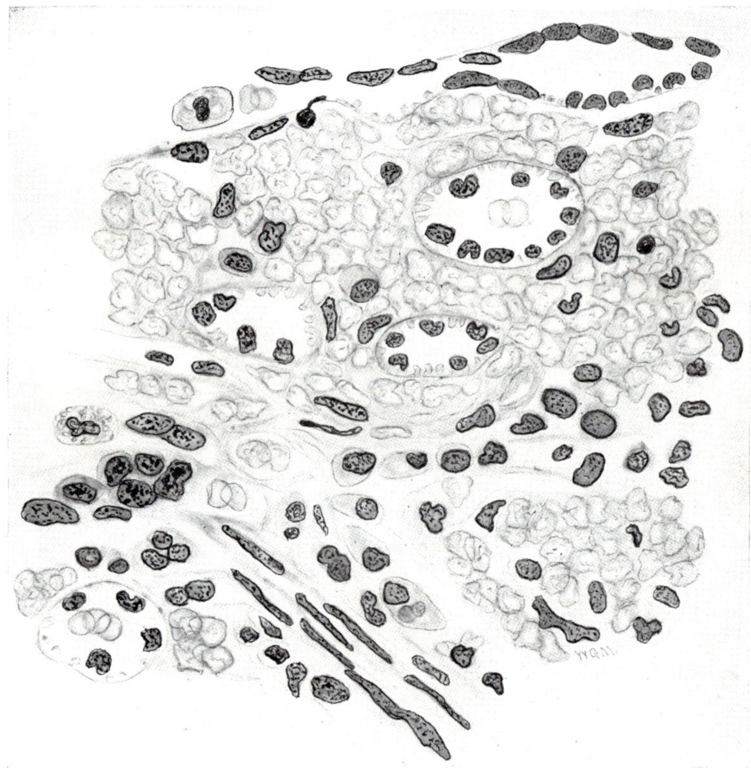

Fig. 403.—Pernicious anæmia. Spleen showing distorted red corpuscles between the venules and small group of myelocytes in the reticulum of the pulp.

then they occur only in small groups of two or three, both inside and outside the venules. Many of them are found in the margins of the Malpighian bodies or in the walls of the larger blood-vessels. Nucleated red cells are also inconspicuous, but are occasionally found in the splenic pulp. In reality, the alterations of the spleen in severe secondary anæmias may be much more marked than in this condition, both with regard to the increased number of wandering cells in the pulp and the accumulation of myeloid cells, but that is probably to be explained by the influence of the infectious or toxic process which stands as the cause of such secondary anæmia and which in itself may produce changes in the spleen (*cf.* acute splenic tumor in infectious diseases).

The lymph-glands show no striking alterations, but, as stated above, the hæmolymph glands contain in their blood-filled sinuses many of the large phagocytic cells loaded with red corpuscles. The immunity of the lymphoid tissue from alteration in pernicious anæmia is evident in some cases in the presence of a slight degree of lymphoid hyperplasia in the bone-marrow and in the relative increase in the numbers of lymphoid cells in the blood.

The liver is said by Meyer and Heineke to show accumulations of myelocytes and erythroblastic cells. Much more striking is the fine, dust-like sprinkling of iron-containing pigment in the liver-cells themselves (Fig. 52, page 120). This pigment, which is readily colored blue by the ferrocyanide method, lies about the fine bile canaliculi in the centre of each strand of liver-cells. There may be some pigment also in the endothelial cells of the capillaries but it is far less noticeable.

Another lesion characteristic of pernicious anæmia is found in the white matter of the spinal cord. Especially in the posterior tracts there occur focal areas of degeneration of the nerve-fibres and neuroglial scarring which, by interrupting these tracts, produce irregular ascending secondary degenerations. These, described by Lichtheim, Minnich, Nonne, Milne, and others, bring about very distinct sensory disturbances during life, sometimes amounting to ataxic phenomena closely resembling those of tabes.

On the whole, taking into consideration the various lesions here described, it appears that the autopsy findings in pernicious anæmia are so constant and peculiar that a diagnosis can be made with security from them alone, but when taken together with the typical course of the disease and the alterations of the blood, there remains no doubt as to the independence of the disease. It seems reasonably certain, too, that before long some simple explanation of the pathogenesis of this disease will be found.

Some mention should be made of the rather rare cases of *aplastic anæmia* which is practically identical with pernicious anæmia except in that it runs a more precipitate downward course to the fatal result because no effort toward regeneration of the blood takes place in the bone-marrow. Instead, the marrow of the long bones is found at autopsy, in spite of the most profound anæmia, to be entirely yellow and fatty without any of the cell hyperplasia seen in the ordinary cases.

In some degree allied to pernicious anæmia, although in most respects essentially different, is the curious affection *hæmochromatosis*. This has been referred to in connection with pigmentation and perhaps also in other associations. Inasmuch as it is not a form of anæmia it has no place here, but the deposition of blood pigment is so striking that it is unconsciously associated with that just described in pernicious anæmia. As a result of some process of unknown nature, and without great blood destruction, the organs become laden with hæmosiderin and hæmofuscin. Incidentally there is injury and scarring of the liver and pancreas, and usually diabetes. All these organs assume a bright chestnut-brown color. Whether the accumulation of iron is due to some inability of the mucosa of the colon to excrete the usual excess, remains to be determined.

Another form of anæmia which may be touched upon is that which accompanies the so-called *hæmolytic icterus.* It is either congenital or arises later in life and appears to be due to an excessive fragility of the red

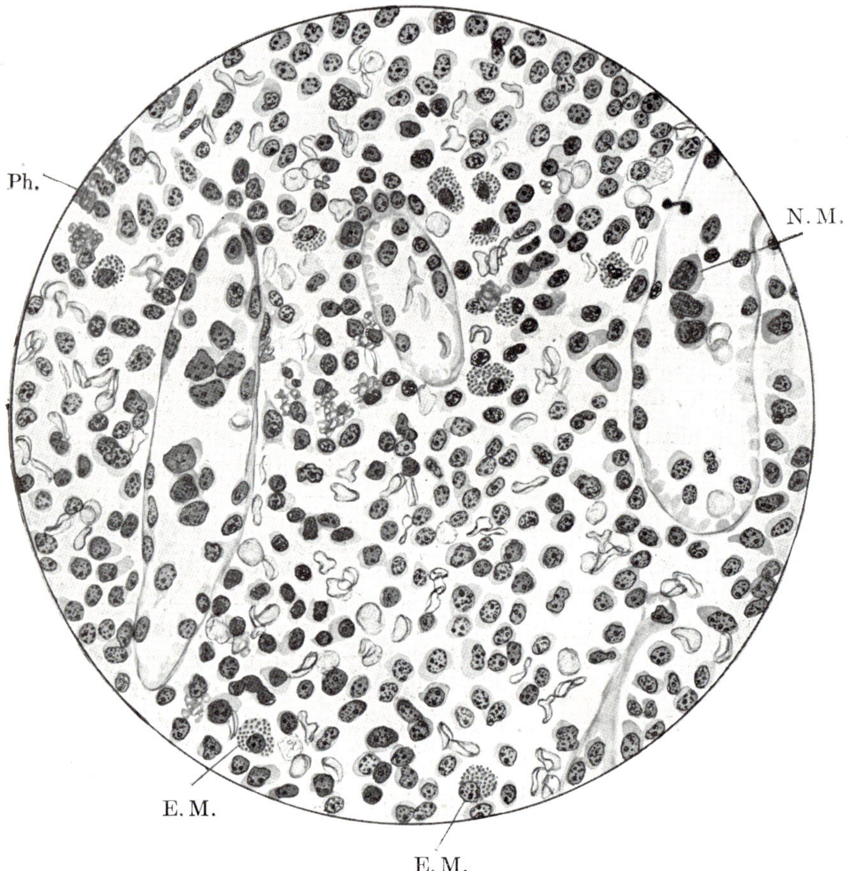

Fig. 404.—Myeloid alteration of the splenic pulp in osteosclerotic anæmia from destruction of bone-marrow by metastases from a carcinoma of the prostate. N. M., Neutrophile myelocytes; E. M., eosinophile myelocytes; Ph., pigment holding phagocytic cells.

corpuscles which, in liberating their hæmoglobin, furnish the material for the production of jaundice. There is no obstruction of the bile-passages, but the spleen becomes greatly enlarged and filled with red corpuscles. It is said that removal of the spleen brings the disease to a stop and that the corpuscles recover their normal resistance. No adequate explanation is offered for this any more than for the similar beneficial effect of extirpation of the spleen in pernicious anæmia, which seems to relieve the patient for a time.

Anæmia Following Mechanical Destruction of the Bone-marrow.—Although the technically impossible experimental destruction of all the bone-marrow has often been discussed, the only light on such a condition is furnished by those cases in which a tumor, such as a carcinoma of the prostate or breast, metastasizes to the marrow cavity of practically every bone in the body, and there, by occupying space in the rigidly enclosed

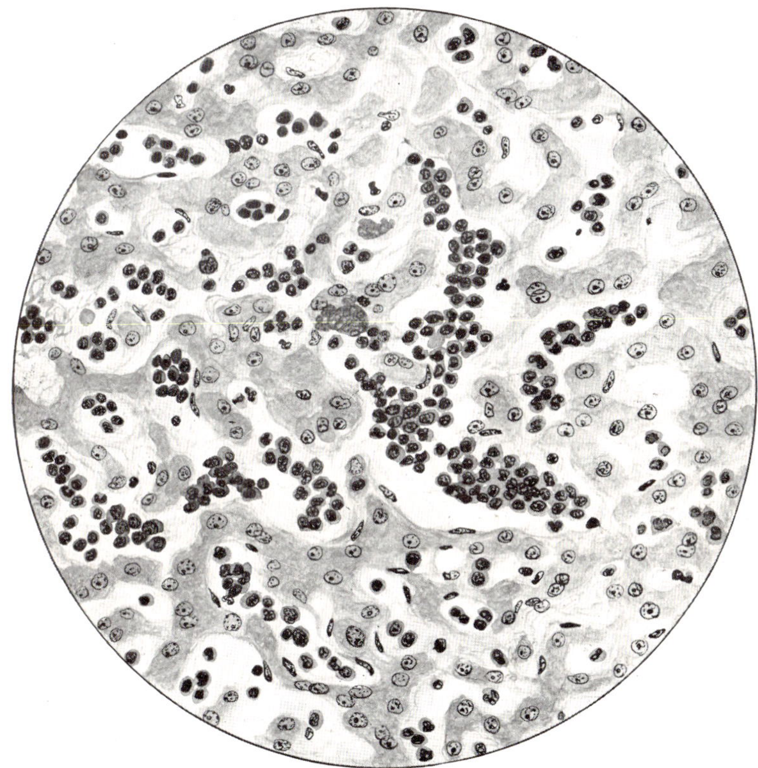

Fig. 405.—Osteosclerotic anæmia following destruction of bone-marrow by metastatic carcinoma. Clumps of myelocytes in the liver capillaries. The endothelial cells are intact.

cavity, destroys the bone-marrow. There is much uniformity in these cases, and we have recently studied two in which literally every bone was found to be completely occupied by the tumor. The cavities of all the long bones were filled with a solid tissue, for these tumors cause the formation of enormously thick laminæ of new cancellous bone which lie in a close network and contain in their meshes only the epithelial cells of the tumor. The ribs, vertebræ, pelvic and other bones were also solidly infiltrated by the bone-forming tumor. The effect was to produce the most profound anæmia in which the red blood-corpuscles sank to 600,000 per c.mm. There was a parallel reduction of the granular leucocytes. It is in such cases that the greatest need arises for extramedullary blood formation and, indeed, they furnish the best and least complicated examples of myeloid change in the spleen and liver. The development of blood in the spleen and liver in one of these cases is shown in Figs. 404 and 405.

A similar effect, as far as the red corpuscles are concerned, is produced by the crowding out of the erythrogenic tissues by the enormous overgrowth of myeloid cells in myeloid leukæmia and of the lymphoid cells in lymphoid leukæmia. Of course the destruction is by no means so complete in these cases, and the existence of the myeloid change in other

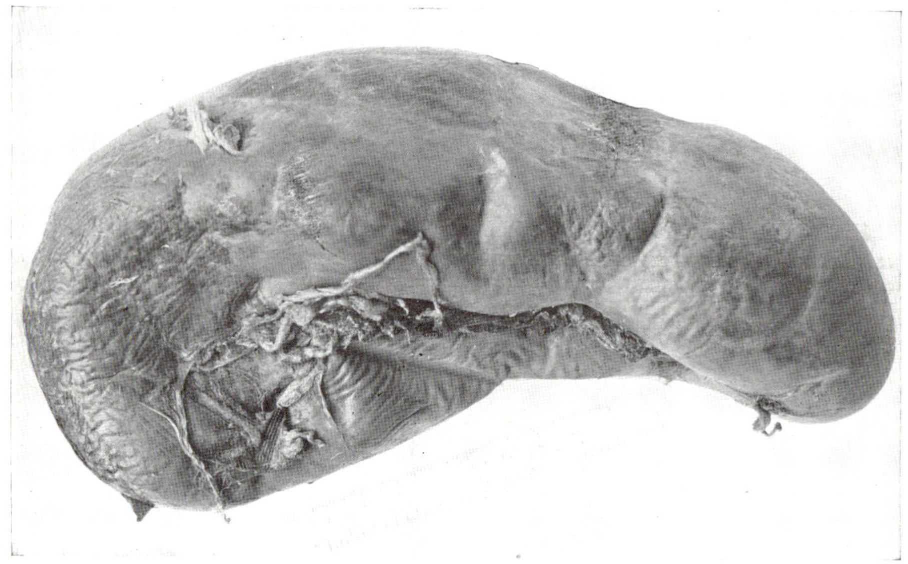

Fig. 406.—Spleen in Banti's disease.

tissues is less clearly defined since they are already overwhelmed with the hyperplastic elements from the bone-marrow itself.

Banti's Disease.—There is a form of anæmia with great swelling of the spleen and usually accompanied by hæmorrhages which has long been described by clinicians as *anœmia splenica*. Banti has studied these cases anatomically and his name is associated with the complex of lesions, although it is claimed by others that not all the cases progress, as Banti describes them, to a stage in which cirrhosis of the liver and ascites are features. Nothing is known of the cause: the spleen becomes greatly enlarged and there is a secondary type of anæmia intensified by hæmorrhages from the stomach. There may or may not be cirrhosis of the liver, but there is a peculiar and specific type of alteration in the spleen which is not like that due to chronic passive congestion nor even like the one associated with forms of cirrhosis of the liver which do not obstruct the portal blood-stream (Fig. 406). It may reach a weight of 1 to 3 kg., and during life is distended with blood. The veins are enormously enlarged and numerous huge collateral channels appear, especially in adhesions between the spleen, the stomach, and the diaphragm. There is often thrombosis of the main splenic vein, a condition which I have seen three times. When the spleen is extirpated, it shrinks and collapses with the escape of blood

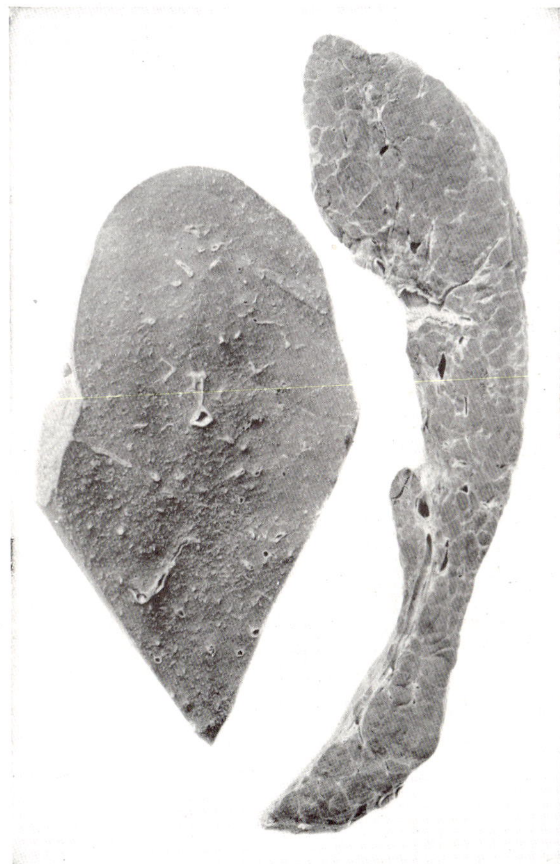

Fig. 407.—Portion of spleen and liver from case of Banti's disease. Spleen fibrous and elastic. Extreme cirrhosis of the liver.

and becomes a rather flabby elastic mass which, on section, shows a grayish-pink translucent cut surface that sinks a little below the capsule (Fig. 407). The Malpighian bodies are not visible. Microscopically there is found to be moderate atrophy and scarring of the Malpighian bodies, and in the pulp the venules are separated by quite abundant loose fibrous tissue in which there remain very few of the original pulp cells. The whole spleen is thus impoverished in cells and has assumed an empty appearance, being composed essentially of fibrous tissue in which the venules are embedded. The liver, in the late stages, is said by Banti to become distinctly cirrhotic. In our rather numerous cases it has frequently appeared normal and in few instances has shown advanced cirrhosis. The bone-marrow is moderately hyperplastic. We are thus very ignorant of this condition, but it is quite clear that it is a definite and constantly recurring disease and that it is easy to recognize the typical anatomical changes. Extirpation of the spleen appears to cure the whole malady, if it does not kill the patient through uncontrollable hæmorrhage at the operation.

There is another type of splenomegaly known as *Gaucher's splenomegaly* in which a totally different condition exists. Details must be read in the papers of Bovaird, Brill, Mandelbaum, Risel, and others, but the essential facts are that it occurs in families, affecting several children, that it produces great enlargement of the spleen without enlargement of the lymph-glands, jaundice, or ascites. There is no change in the blood, but in the spleen, lymph-glands, bone-marrow, and liver there are giant multinuclear phagocytic cells the origin of which has been much disputed. Marchand and Risel think they arise from the reticulum cells through the absorption of a hyaline foreign protein-like substance.

LITERATURE

General—Paltauf, Freund, and Sternberg: Handb. allg. Path., Krehl and Marchand, 1912, ii, 1.
Nægeli: Blutkrankheiten u. Blutdiagnostik, Leipzig, 1907.
Bone-marrow—Maximow: Arch. f. mikr. Anat., 1910, lxxvi, 1.
Jackson: Arch. f. Anat. u. Phys., Anat. Abth., 1904, 33.
Bunting: Johns Hopkins Hosp. Bull., 1905, xvi, 222. Jour. Exp. Med., 1906, viii, 625.
Myeloid metaplasia—Tanaka: Ziegler's Beitr., 1912, liii, 338, Lit.
Meyer and Heineke: Verh. Dtsch. Path. Gesellsch., 1906, ix, 224.
Sternberg: Ziegler's Beitr., 1909, xlvi, 586.
Domarus: Arch. f. exp. Path. u. Phar., 1908, lviii, 319.
Morris: Johns Hopkins Hosp. Bull., 1907, xviii, 200.
Benzol anæmia—Selling: Ziegler's Beitr., 1911, li, 576.
Oxydase reaction—Loele: Ergebn. d. allg. Path., 1913, xvi_2, 760.
Schultze: Ziegler's Beitr., 1909, xlv, 127.
Anatomy of spleen—Weidenreich: Arch. f. mikr. Anat., 1901, lviii, 247.
Mollier: *Ibid.*, 1910–11, lxxvi, 608.
Pearce, Austin, Krumbhaar, Eisenbrey: "Spleen and Blood Destruction," Jour. Exp. Med., 1912, xvi; *ibid.*, 1913, xviii; *ibid.*, 1914, xx, *et seq.*
Lymphocytes—Marchand: Verh. Dtsch. Path. Gesellsch., 1913, xvi, 5.
Polycythæmia rubra—Osler: Amer. Jour. Med. Sci., 1903, cxxvi, 187. Brit. Med. Jour., 1904, 1, 121.
Lucas: Arch. Int. Med., 1912, x, 597.
Typhoid bone-marrow—Longscope: Bull. Ayer Clin. Lab., 1905, ii, 1.
Hæmolymph nodes—Warthin: Amer. Jour. Anat., 1901, i, 63.
Pernicious anæmia—Cabot: Osler and McCrae's Modern Medicine, 1915, iv, 619.
Lazarus: Die Anæmie, Wien, 1913.
Sternberg: Verh. Dtsch. Path. Gesellsch., 1907, x, 114.

Pernicious anæmia—Ziegler: Dtsch. Arch. f. kl. Med., 1910, xcix, 431.
Aplastic anæmia—Lavenson: Amer. Jour. Med. Sci., 1907, cxxxiii, 100.
Stone: Ohio State Med. Jour., 1907, iii, 243, Lit.
Osteosclerotic anæmia—Assmann: Ziegler's Beitr., 1907, xli, 565.
Askanazy: Verhandl. Dtsch. Path. Gesellsch., 1904, vii, 58.
Hæmolytic jaundice—Guizzetti: Ziegler's Beitr., 1912, lii, 15.
Primary splenomegaly—Banti: Riforma Medica, 1901, xvii, i, 590.
Rolleston: Practitioner, 1914, xcii, 470.
Leon-Kindberg: Annales de Medicine, 1914, i, 189.
Gaucher's splenomegaly—Bovaird: Amer. Jour. Med. Sci., 1900, cxx, 377.
Brill and Mandelbaum: *Ibid.*, 1909, 1913, cxlvi, 863. Jour. Exp. Med., 1912, xvi, 797.
Marchand: Münch. med. Woch., 1907, liv, 1102.
Risel: Ziegler's Beitr., 1909, xlvi, 241.

CHAPTER XL

EFFECTS OF INJURIES TO THE BLOOD AND BLOOD-FORMING ORGANS (Continued)

Leucocytosis; Leucopenia. Lymphocytosis. Eosinophilia: Corresponding changes of hæmatopoietic organs. Independent disease of the blood-forming organs: General characters; Classification in lack of information as to ætiology. Chronic lymphoid leukæmia. Acute lymphoid leukæmia. Leucosarcoma, or chloroleucosarcoma (chloroma). Lymphoid myeloma. Pseudoleukæmia. Lymphosarcoma. Status lymphaticus.

THE blood-forming organs respond promptly in the production of white corpuscles when the occasion demands it, just as they do in the case of red corpuscles. But in this case the causes of their activity are different and it is toward the flooding of the blood with abnormally great numbers of these white corpuscles that their efforts tend, rather than to the mere replacement of those which have been destroyed in the circulation.

The appearance of an excessive number of white corpuscles in the circulation is called hyperleucocytosis, commonly shortened to *leucocytosis*, while their decrease is known as *leucopenia*. So specific are the different types of white cell of the blood that each may separately be thus affected, and it is necessary, in order to understand the nature of the change, to know not only how many white cells are present in each cubic millimetre of the blood, but in what proportion the different cells are present. Through common use the far more frequent excess in the absolute number of polymorphonuclear neutrophile leucocytes has come to be spoken of loosely as "leucocytosis" *par excellence*. But the terms lymphocytosis, eosinophilia, myelocytosis, etc., are also used to express the predominant increase in the corresponding cells, and these terms may be properly used even though the total number of leucocytes is not increased. In the following we shall use the term leucocyte to refer to any of the circulating white cells of the blood, specifying in each case the particular type meant. The details of the changes in the relative proportions and absolute numbers of leucocytes must be studied in the special works on the clinical examination of the blood, and only an outline shall be given here in connection with the description of the changes in the blood-forming tissues.

LEUCOCYTOSIS AND LEUCOPENIA

Neutrophile leucocytosis is the common outpouring of polymorphonuclear neutrophiles into the blood, so familiar in almost every sort of acute inflammatory process. These cells have to a great extent the function of attacking and engulfing bacteria and other injurious substances and of producing a proteolytic ferment which acts best in an alkaline medium. They appear in increased numbers in the course of digestion after the use of certain drugs (quinine, etc.), after hæmorrhage, during some forms of toxic injury to the tissues, but especially and in greatest abundance as a response to the invasion of bacteria. Thus in pneumonia, endocarditis, septic infection, and in nearly every sort of acute inflammatory process, the neutrophile leucocytes rise in number until the white corpuscle count reaches 20,000 to 30,000 or 40,000, or in some cases as much as 150,000, per c.mm. In such cases the other leucocytes are not correspondingly increased, and the neutrophile cells assume a proportion of 90 or 95 per cent. There are notable exceptions to this in the case of typhoid fever, measles, tuberculosis, and protozoan infections, such as malaria, in which the leucocyte count does not rise, or in the case of trichiniasis and allied parasitic infections in which the eosinophile cells are especially increased.

Lymphocytosis.—The lymphocytes are relatively and sometimes absolutely increased in number in typhoid fever and several other infections, and the important work of Murphy* has recently shown that their presence is really of the very greatest value in antagonizing such infections. Animals deprived of their lymphocytes by exposure to *x*-rays, etc., are much more susceptible to tuberculosis than normal animals, and the zone of lymphocytes which is so constantly found gathered about growing tumors is evidently of great importance, for in animals without lymphocytes implanted tumors grow rapidly, although they are destroyed in the controls. Hence we must assume that the so-called round-cell infiltration which is so striking a feature of the late stage of an inflammatory reaction and predominant in the more chronic forms, is an expression of the ability of the lymphocytes to act in the process of warding off and annulling injuries. Relative lymphocytosis occurs not only in typhoid fever but in malaria, small-pox, exophthalmic goitre, and in many affections of childhood.

Eosinophilia has been mentioned as occurring in trichiniasis, uncinariasis, and other infections with parasitic worms, in asthma, in various skin diseases, in scarlet fever, etc. Other cells, such as myelocytes, myeloblasts, and mast cells are found at times in the circulating blood but usually only in connection with leukæmias, except in certain severe infections in which myelocytes are swept into the blood in the wake of the leucocytes.

The changes in the blood-forming organs in these states of the blood are not so satisfactorily studied as one could wish. Descriptions of the spleen and bone-marrow are particularly meagre except in a few instances.

In neutrophile leucocytosis there is a strong hyperplastic reaction in the bone-marrow, which naturally consists essentially in a great new production of neutrophile myelocytes, which leads to the formation of the leucocytes. As a rule, the leucocytes are discharged so rapidly that the

* Murphy and Ellis: Jour. Exp. Med., 1914, xx, 397.

myelocytes become the most prominent feature of the bone-marrow section (Fig. 408). Undoubtedly the spleen is deeply affected in this process and commonly assumes the peculiar softness and richness in cells which has already been described as the acute splenic tumor of infectious or septic diseases. It appears that in such spleens there is a form of myeloid metaplasia combined with an accumulation of the débris of cells, and phagocytes loaded with such fragments. The lymph-glands and lymphoid tissues are

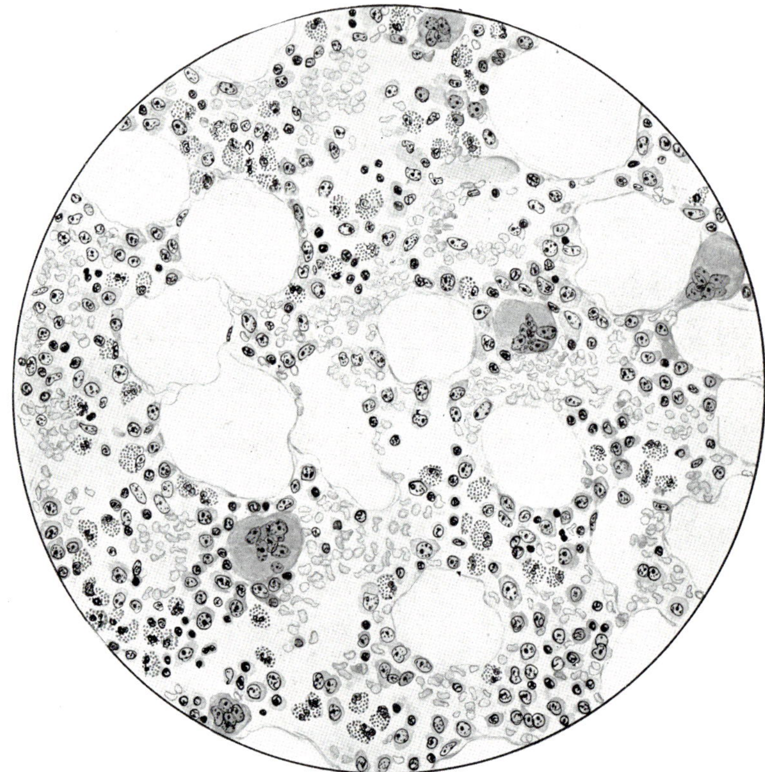

Fig. 408.—Bone-marrow from a case of staphylococcus septicæmia with leucocytosis. Myelocytes are abundant, but there are few leucocytes in the marrow.

not necessarily much affected except by local conditions in which they take up the products of inflammation.

The cause of the changes in the bone-marrow in inflammatory leucocytosis has been much discussed. It is evident that the appearance of such great numbers of leucocytes must depend upon the ability of the bone-marrow to produce them rapidly. The idea that the leucocytosis is a response to the need caused by the destruction of many of their number is scarcely different from the idea that they are drawn to the general circulation and thence to the site of the inflammation by a chemotactic substance which itself gains entrance into the circulation. That some such chemical stimulant must not only attract the leucocytes but also stir the bone-marrow to increased formation of these cells seems to be clearly shown by the extremely rapid and ready increase which takes place in infections as contrasted with the much less striking leucocytosis which appears after a severe hæmorrhage, that is, after the actual mechanical removal of the leucocytes. It is most important to realize the fact that an extremely violent poisoning, such as occurs in many severe infections,

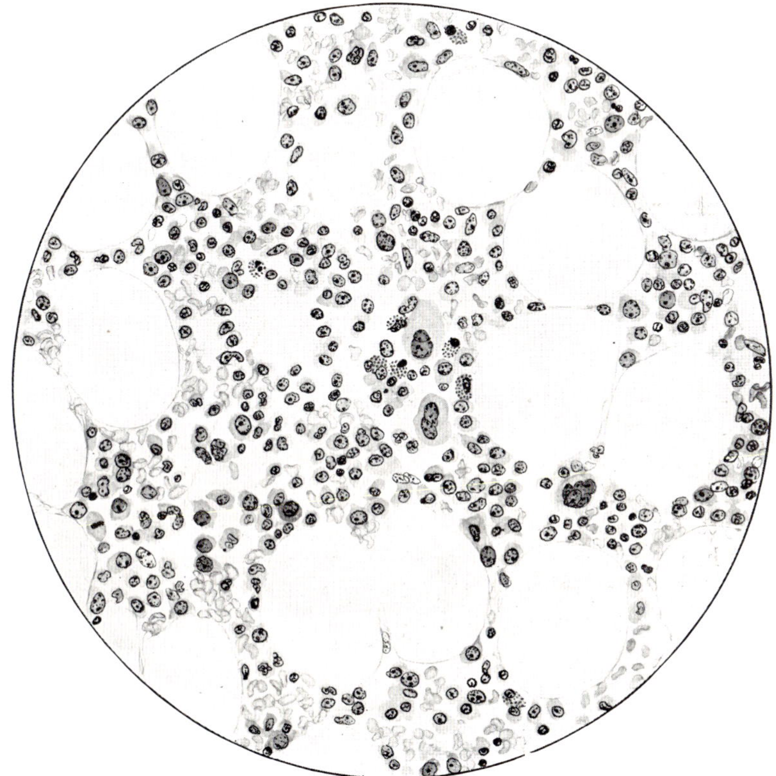

Fig. 409.—Bone-marrow in typhoid fever.

may not be followed by any leucocytosis. On the contrary, the bone-marrow seems to be so injured by the strong stimulus as to be incapable of producing the cells. It is probably exactly the same thing on a somewhat different plane when, in a debilitated old person, there is no leucocytosis in pneumonia or other infection, for then a degree of poisoning which might be readily met by a leucocytosis in a young and strong person is sufficient to paralyze the feebly reacting bone-marrow of the old man. Clearly then the prognosis in any infection may be judged to some extent by the efficiency of the leucocytic response; when there is a failure on the part of the bone-marrow to produce abundant leucocytes the disease is likely to prove fatal.

In *lymphocytosis* of infectious diseases the spleen and lymph-glands are usually enlarged, but this enlargement is generally due to local causes, as in typhoid fever, and not especially to their participation in the production of lymphocytes, although the lymphoid tissue is undoubtedly active in this way. In the bone-marrow there is very definite hyperplasia and the bone-marrow of the femur becomes red or grayish-red and cellular. Here, however, the new formation of myelocytes and neutrophile cells is found to have sunken to a relatively far less important position. It is true that the typhoid marrow still shows numerous myelocytes, but the striking feature, as Longcope has shown, is the relatively abundant new formation of lymphoid cells there. A comparison of Figs. 408 and 409 will show this. In typhoid fever the myelocytes seem unable to respond to such stimuli as usually produce neutrophile leucocytosis. The advent of pneumonia or other similar infection in the course of the disease does not necessarily bring out the corresponding leucocytosis, and, indeed, those things which usually produce an abscess have failed to do so in a person sick with typhoid fever, although the occurrence of furunculosis with typhoid fever is familiar. This, however, comes on in a late stage and corresponds with the experiment of Bauer who could produce no abscess by injecting turpentine subcutaneously during the height of the typhoid fever, although when the fever disappeared in convalescence the belated abscess appeared at the site of the injection.

In *eosinophilia* there is a relative and absolute increase in the eosinophile myelocytes of the bone-marrow. This statement is made without hesitation since it has been shown experimentally by Opie to be so, although there are as yet no conclusive reports as to the appearance of the bone-marrow in human beings in those infections (trichiniasis, etc.) in which the eosinophiles are so abundant in the blood. With regard to the analogous conditions in leukæmia we shall speak presently.

INDEPENDENT DISEASE OF THE BLOOD-FORMING ORGANS

We approach in this section a series of extraordinary affections involving the blood-forming organs, and consequently the blood, in which the morphological changes from normal are very minutely studied, but in no single one of which we know anything of the cause. The study of these diseases is made more difficult by the fact that while there are type forms which are fairly distinct, one meets with many individual cases in which there are wide variations from these types. They are affections of the lymphoid tissue on the one hand, or of myeloid tissue on the other, and such is the specific distinction between these tissues that we find no mixture of the two. They are essentially hyperplasias of the blood-forming tissues, and while in some cases this does not involve any striking change in the circulating blood, in others such quantities of new cells are emptied into the blood-stream as to be completely subversive of its ordinary composition.* Perhaps this should not be regarded as a distinction of importance between these cases, because it is said to happen that in some forms the blood, after having been normal through a long period in which disease of the myeloid or lymphoid tissue was well developed, may suddenly be flooded with an excessive number of cells representing the particular hyperplastic element. Such cases, however, are rare, although great modifications in the quantity of cells poured into the blood occur from time to time in those in which the blood shows distinct changes. It is probably correctly claimed that the classification of such diseases should be based not upon the number of cells swept into the blood, but upon their character and therefore upon the character of the hyperplasia in the blood-forming organ concerned. Still, the setting free of the cells or their retention in the place of their formation is so nearly a constant feature of each form that we must assume that there is something peculiar about the way these cells are held together in the tissue, which brings about these different results. It is difficult, if not impossible, to see in the sections of bone-marrow or lymphoid tissue anything which in one case would make the escape of cells impossible, in another facilitate it; but perhaps with finer technique this may be discerned.

In some types it appears that the hyperplasia of one sort of cell occurs strictly within the normal limits of the myeloid or lymphoid tissue, as the case may be, even though these cells may escape into the blood. In others the hyperplastic tissue extends like a tumor, so as to invade and destroy adjacent tissue, even breaking through the cortex of the bone or spreading far and wide from the normal limits of the lymphoid tissue. On account of this many authors have looked upon these hyperplasias as tumor growths. Indeed, even when there is no obvious tumor but great quantities of cells are found circulating in the blood, it seems that these cells may form colonies in other organs and there give rise to new cells of the same sort. This is the point in dispute in the question of myeloid metaplasia, other investigators holding that such colonies of cells are formed in situ by a true metaplasia, and not derived from the usual site of their formation in the blood-forming organs. The question is hard to settle satisfactorily, but in the one case the new formation of cells in an unaccustomed organ, such as the liver, would resemble the mode of distribution and proliferation of a tumor; in the other we must assume that the tissues of the capillary walls of the liver, the splenic pulp, etc., are capable of reacquiring the power of blood formation which, as all agree, they possessed during embryonic life. To me the idea of the transplant-

* Leukæmia, or leucocythæmia, was first observed almost simultaneously by Bennet in Scotland and by Virchow in Germany (1848). Virchow recognized the lymphoid nature of the cells in one type and their granular character in the other, and called them lymphatic and lienal forms. Neumann first pointed out the importance of the bone-marrow in their production.

ation and growth of cells seems more plausible, although there is some good evidence in favor of the idea of metaplasia.

It appears, then, that if we know accurately all the cellular types existent in the bone-marrow and in the lymphoid tissue, which are the blood-forming tissues concerned, and if we assume that each is capable of undergoing an independent hyperplasia, we should be able to construct a tabulation of all the possible diseases arising in this way. This has indeed been done, just as it was possible for Rokitansky to foretell what types of malformation of the heart might occur on the basis of the embryological development of that organ and then years later to meet with cases, hitherto unknown, which realized each member in his scheme. The possible existence of unknown tumors has been foretold in the same way on a histogenetic basis.

Sternberg has made such a table, which I shall quote in brief:

A—Local limited homologous hyperplasias:
- *a*—With escape of cells into the blood
  - (1)—of the lymphatic tissue . . . . *Lymphatic leukæmia.*
  - (2)—of the myeloid tissue . . . . *Mixed-cell leukæmia.*
- *b*—With slight or no escape of cells
  - (3)—of the whole lymphatic tissue (diffuse) . . . . . . *Pseudoleukæmia.*
  - (4)—of lymphatic tissue of bone-marrow (tumor-like) . . . . *Lymphatic myeloma.*
  - (5)—of myeloid tissue of bone-marrow (tumor-like). *Myeloid myeloma.*

B—Atypical growths invading surrounding tissue with heterotopic or distant nodules:
- *a*—With escape of cells into the blood
  - (6)—of the lymphatic tissue . . . . *Leucosarcoma or chloroleucosarcoma.*
  - (7)—of the myeloid tissue . . . . *Chloromyelosarcoma.*
- *b*—Without escape of cells into the blood
  - (8)—of the lymphatic tissue . . . . *Lymphosarcoma.*

B—*b*—(9) which would be an atypical growth of myeloid tissue, invasive but without escape of cells, has not yet been observed.

While this classification seems logical, it is not an ætiological classification, and therefore open to criticism. I should prefer another division, perhaps equally open to criticism, but separating as the main groups the affections of the lymphoid from those of the myeloid tissue. The subordination of the main basis of Sternberg's grouping is made for reasons explained above.

A—Hyperplasia of lymphoid tissues:
- *a*—With leukæmic blood—
  - (1)—with swelling of lymphoid tissue and lymphoid infiltration of organs . . . . *Chronic lymphoid leukæmia; Acute lymphoid leukæmia.*
  - (2)—with tumors originating in various situations and invading tissues . . . . *Leucosarcoma; Chloroleucosarcoma (Chloroma).*

b—Without leukæmic blood—
- (3)—with tumors involving bone-marrow........*Lymphoid or plasma-cell myeloma.*
- (4)—with general swelling of lymphoid tissue....*Pseudoleukæmia.*
- (5)—with regional invasive tumor-like growth.....*Lymphosarcoma.*
- (6)—with stigmata of general maldevelopment....*Status lymphaticus.*

B—Hyperplasia of myeloid tissue:

a—With leukæmic blood—
- (7)—with myeloid infiltration of organs.........*Myeloid leukæmia; Myeloblastic leukæmia.*
- (8)—with tumors of the myeloid tissue...........*Chloromyelosarcoma (Myeloid chloroma).*

b—Without leukæmic blood—
- (9)—with tumors of the myeloid tissue...........*Myeloid myeloma.*

C—(Included here though probably not related.) Tumor-like swelling of lymph-glands with nodules in spleen, liver, lungs, etc., granulomatous alteration of lymphoid tissue of specific morphology, apparently infectious in origin..*Lymphogranulomatosis or Hodgkin's disease.*

Chronic Lymphoid Leukæmia.—The onset is insidious, with painless enlargement of some of the lymph-glands and occasionally with hæmorrhages from the mucosæ. Examination of the blood shows an increase in the leucocytes without necessarily any change in the red corpuscles. Among the leucocytes the small lymphocytes occupy the important place and are proportionately greatly increased. This state may continue for years with gradually progressing anæmia, continuous intermittent increase in the number of white cells, and slow enlargement of the lymph-glands, spleen, and sometimes of the liver. The leucocytes may constitute 90 or 95 per cent. of all the white cells and there may be several hundred thousand of these per c.mm. Nægeli mentions one case in which the hæmoglobin was 25 per cent. and there were 621,000 leucocytes, of which 99.6 per cent. were lymphocytes with only 0.14 per cent. of neutrophiles. The symptoms are due chiefly to the presence of infiltrations of these lymphocytes in various places where they often produce pressure phenomena, and to hæmorrhage. In the nervous system and eyes, destructive changes may occur in this way. Dyspnœa follows similar obstruction in the lungs, which, together with the changed character of the blood, makes aëration difficult. In the skin there are sometimes tumor-like masses. Death follows from the cachectic condition itself or from acute exacerbation or intercurrent bacterial infection.

At autopsy the *lymph-glands* are found enlarged and converted into homogeneous masses of soft, grayish-white cellular tissue, without any marks remaining to indicate their structure. In one case which I watched for several years the axillary, inguinal, and retroperitoneal glands finally formed huge masses in which the separate glands had grown to the size of apples. They were so large as to hold the arms away from the sides, but showed no tendency to invade the surrounding tissue. In that case the spleen was large and hard and there were scattered infiltrations of the lymphoid cells along the portal branches in the liver (Fig. 410). The tonsils and pharyngeal lymphoid tissue may become enlarged late in the disease, but this is not invariable. The intestinal lymphoid tissue is astonishingly little affected. The *spleen* is generally enlarged, although not to the maximum degree. It may still show Malpighian bodies on section

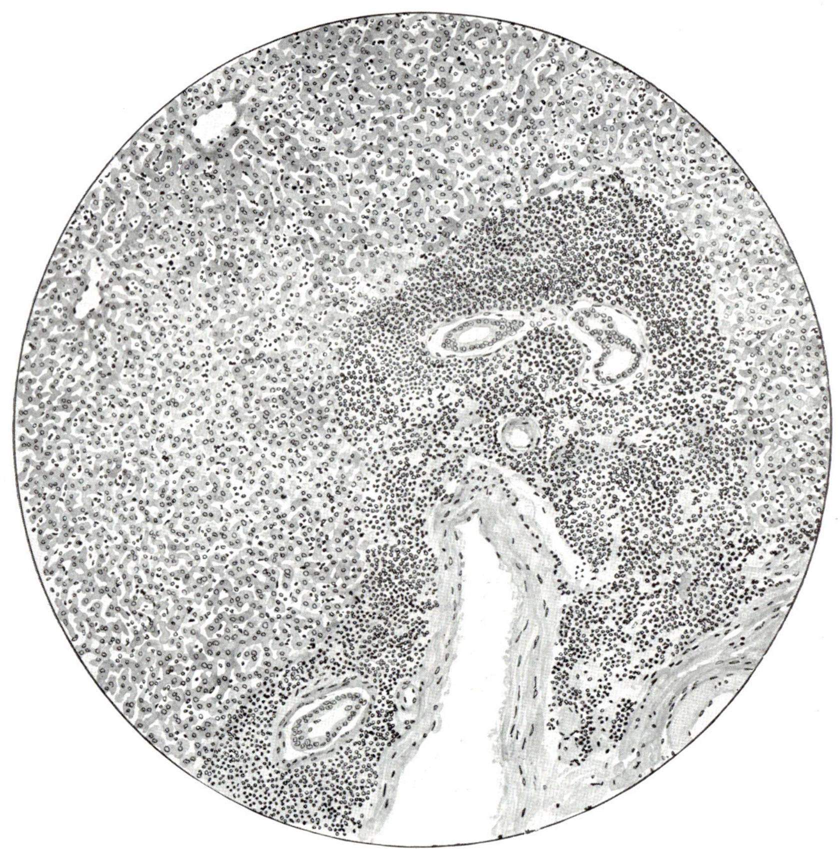

Fig. 410.—Chronic lymphoid leukæmia. Infiltration about the gall-ducts and portal vessels.

or these can become so indistinctly outlined as to merge in the rest of the tissue which is of a grayish or brownish red. The *bone-marrow* is no longer fatty in the shaft of the long bones, but forms a solid cellular tissue of gray or grayish-red color, often with patches of dark red. The liver, which is usually rather swollen, shows grayish lines accompanying the bile-ducts and portal veins. Gray infiltrations are found elsewhere too, as in the thymus, which may be markedly enlarged, or in the kidneys, adrenals, testes, etc. Following the blood-vessels in the retina are sheaths of lymphocytes with which hæmorrhages are often associated.

The histological changes are all occasioned by the extraordinary overproduction of lymphocytes from the lymphoid tissue, wherever that occurs, in the lymph-glands, lymphoid apparatus of the respiratory or digestive tracts or skin, or in the bone-marrow. It is impossible, as a rule, to make out just where it started to undergo hyperplasia in these chronic cases, although there is a better opportunity in the acute cases to be described later.

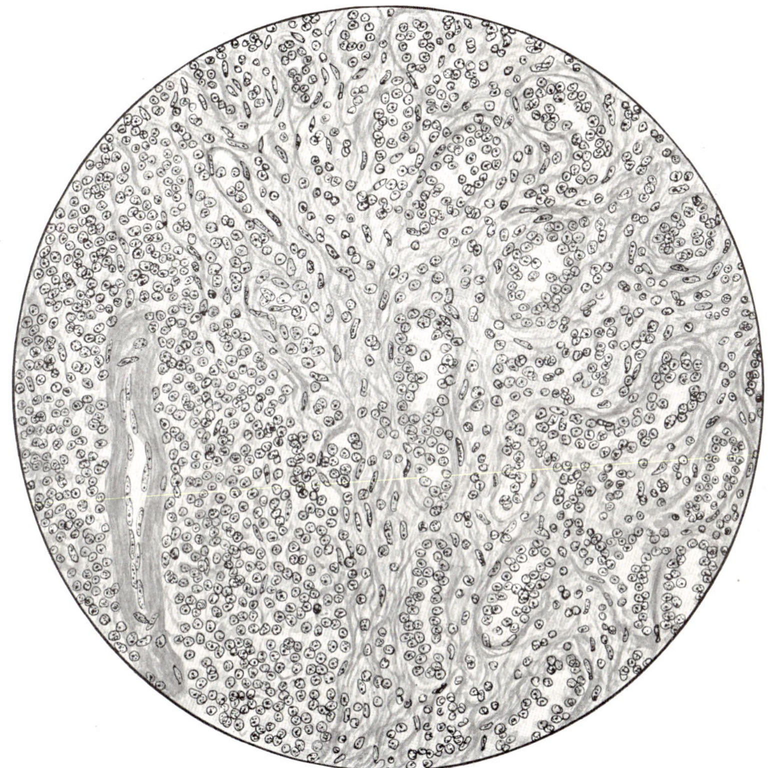

Fig. 411.—Chronic lymphoid leukæmia. Spleen showing a Malpighian body and part of the pulp in which there is much induration and infiltration with lymphoid cells.

Nægeli makes a special point of saying that such hyperplasia cannot occur in the bone-marrow lymphoid tissue alone, but that all the lymphoid tissue is equally involved.

The cells, in most of the chronic cases, are small lymphocytes. Nevertheless, in the lymphoid tissue in which they are being formed one finds almost always a mixture of these with rather larger lymphoid cells.

In the lymph-glands all signs of the original architecture with lymph-nodules and sinuses have disappeared, being swamped and covered in or pushed aside by the overwhelming growth of one kind of cell, so that the tissue appears as a solid, uniform mass of lymphocytes. In the spleen, at first sight, it seems that the same thing is true, as though the Malpighian bodies had spread to occupy everything, but closer examination shows that the structure of the pulp is still discernible and the venules and interspaces are found filled with lymphocytes. In the older cases, in which the spleen is hard, there is much new fibrous tissue between the venules. This was true in the very chronic case mentioned above and is shown in Fig. 411. In the bone-marrow there is usually almost complete replacement of the ordinary cells by spreading masses of lymphoid tissue, but in many cases there are areas of myeloid tissue left unchanged with erythroblastic and myeloblastic cells. These appear to be the dark-red patches which are visible in the gross and are no doubt responsible for the relatively good maintenance of the red cell content of the blood.

Acute Lymphoid Leukæmia.—In our experience this is a more common affection than the chronic form, and must be distinguished from it because of its more violent and severe symptoms and rapid course, and also because the cells concerned are in most cases larger. In relatively few cases only are they of the same small size as in the chronic forms. It must be noted here that certain of the cases which were formerly classed as acute lymphoid leukæmia are now known to be not lymphoid leukæmia at all, but myeloid leukæmia in which the non-granular myeloblast is the cell that is especially abundant.

In contrast to the chronic form of lymphoid leukæmia this one begins suddenly with intense symptoms: fever, hæmorrhages from the mucosæ, and rapidly developing anæmia. Hæmorrhages in the retinæ are almost constant, while those in the conjunctivæ, over the face and over the whole body, are often very extensive and gradually pass through the ordinary changes of color to become pigment spots that finally disappear. The hæmorrhages in the mouth, vagina, and digestive tract often become converted into gangrenous areas which leave deep ulcers. The tonsils and the rest of the pharyngeal adenoid tissue frequently become greatly enlarged and deeply ulcerated. The *lymph-glands* may, in some cases, even in a rather advanced stage, be relatively slightly enlarged, but usually they are palpable or even form prominent packets. In a case now under observation what seems to be the thymus has become greatly enlarged in the course of a few days. A radiograph reveals the fact, however, that this is a retrosternal mass of lymph-glands. The spleen is generally enlarged but does not reach as a rule the huge dimensions seen in some other forms. The blood in some instances shows no decrease in red corpuscles but usually the anæmia advances rapidly and in the case mentioned is already under 1,000,000. Occasionally such blood shows regenerative forms resembling those of pernicious anæmia, but often there seems to be no attempt at regeneration. The leucocytes reach high numbers, ranging from 50,000 to 250,000 or more, and the increase is represented by the lymphocytes, which may constitute 98 or 99 per cent. of the cells. As stated above, these lymphocytes are in most cases larger than those of normal blood. Death results from a terminal infection, from hæmorrhage, or from the disease itself.

At autopsy the lesions are found to resemble those of the chronic form except that since the course of the disease is so much briefer, there is not time for the development of such great accumulations of lymphoid tissue. The lymph-glands are nevertheless enlarged, and show on section a homo-

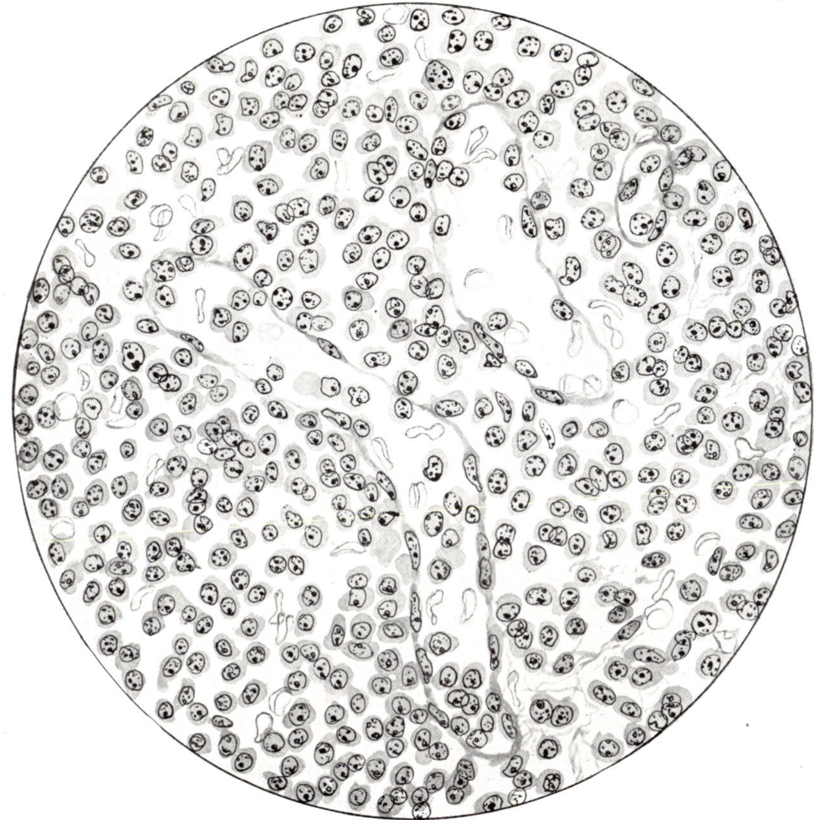

Fig. 412.—Splenic pulp in acute lymphoid leukæmia. The cells of the pulp are practically entirely replaced by large lymphoid cells.

geneous, grayish-white cellular tissue rather softer than that found in the chronic cases. The presence of hæmorrhages in these glands is very characteristic. Microscopically one may find the architecture still recognizable although the sinuses contain great quantities of lymphocytes. Occasionally, however, the whole structure appears as a mass of lymphoid cells. There are usually similar changes in the adenoid tissues of the throat, and sometimes in those of the digestive tract, so that swellings comparable to those in typhoid fever are found in the solitary nodules and

Peyer's patches. Since, with hæmorrhages, these may become ulcerated, the resemblance may be close.

The spleen is fairly firm, moderately enlarged, and dark grayish-red in color. Sometimes one can see the Malpighian bodies distinctly, but in other cases they are not to be outlined. There are occasional infarctions. Microscopically it is difficult to outline the Malpighian bodies because the splenic pulp is filled with quite similar cells. These lie in great numbers between the venules, to the exclusion of most of the other cells (Fig. 412).

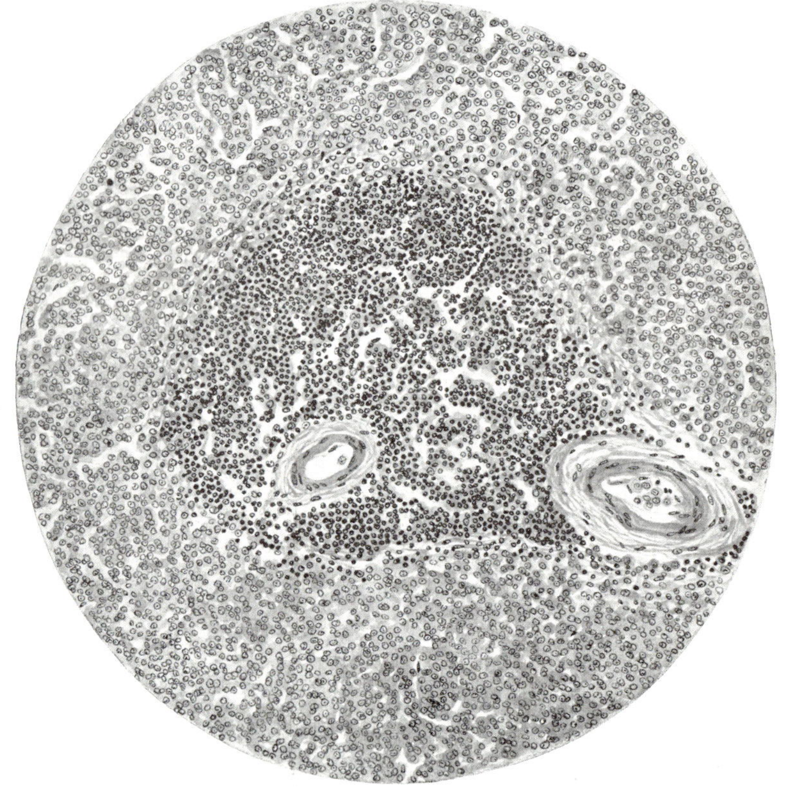

Fig. 413.—Spleen in acute lymphoid leukæmia. The splenic pulp and blood-vessels are filled with large lymphoid cells contrasting with the lymphocytes of the Malpighian bodies.

It is noteworthy that in this, as in other forms of leukæmia, the endothelium of the venules of the spleen to which so many functions have been ascribed is perfectly intact and shows no evidence of playing any part in the extraordinary changes going on round about.

In a case before me, however, the Malpighian bodies do stand out with fair distinctness because their cells are rather smaller and more closely packed than those in the pulp (Fig. 413). In the bone-marrow (Fig. 414), which is gray or grayish-red and cellular, often with red, gelatinous patches, the conditions vary. Usually practically all the myeloid elements are crowded out of existence, except perhaps in the red patches just mentioned, by the great compact swarms of lymphoid cells. Nevertheless, there are some cases in which these lymphoid cells occur at the time of death in patches only, as though they were still in process of aggression. Nægeli is very dogmatic in stating that there are, and can be, no cases in which this process begins in the bone-marrow alone—that it is essentially a systemic disease affecting all the lymphoid tissue. Nevertheless, in one

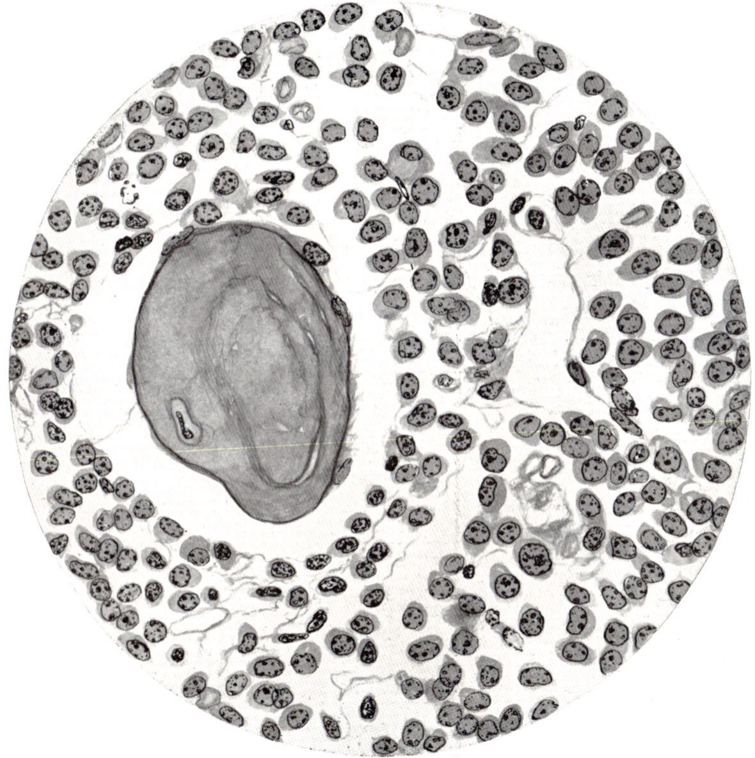

Fig. 414.—Bone-marrow in acute lymphoid leukæmia.

such case reported by Dr. Reed we found the lymphoid tissue throughout the body entirely unaffected except that, in the manner of a sieve, it had retained many of the circulating lymphocytes in its vessels. The bone-marrow was practically entirely composed of lymphocytes. Ehrlich, in studying the preparations from that case, expressed his opinion (1902) that such a leukæmia might originate from any substratum of lymphoid tissue, such as that in the skin, in the intestinal wall, or in the bone-marrow. The other changes are the effects of infiltration and localization of large quantities of lymphocytes in the organs. In the liver this deposit does not, in the brief span of the disease, reach macroscopical dimensions, but in the kidneys there have been cases in which such quantities of cells have gathered in the interstices as to enlarge the organ greatly and give it the appearance of a huge white kidney. In the nervous system and retinæ similar accumulations accompanied by hæmorrhages cause functional and anatomical disturbances. It is important to note that in neither of the forms of lymphoid leukæmia do the circulating lymphoid cells, or the cells of this sort in the tissues, give the oxydase reaction which is shown by Schultz to be characteristic of the myeloid cells. Nor, according to Longcope, are they capable of producing a proteolytic ferment. The contrast in the case of other forms of leukæmia, to be described later, is very striking.

Leucosarcoma or Chloroleucosarcoma.—This term, introduced by Sternberg, is meant to designate those cases in which a definite, tumor-like mass is developed in some organ or tissue and is composed of lymphoid cells which seem to escape into the blood-stream, giving rise to leukæmic alterations of the blood. Nægeli and others refuse to recognize this as anything distinct from lymphoid leukæmia, in which, as they say, there may be extensive, tumor-like infiltrations of the tissues. Sternberg, who finds the tumors in the dura mater, in the mediastinum, in the breast or in connection with the tissues of the orbit, denies that such growths occur in ordinary leukæmia and brings forward the cases studied by Paltauf and by Buschke and Hirschfeld in which the tumor was well developed before any changes occurred in the blood. Several cases which we have studied, even though this very point was neglected, have seemed to me to occupy so distinct a position and to begin so definitely with the formation of a localized tumor-like mass that I am inclined to accept Sternberg's nomenclature. In one of these cases there were two circumscribed "lymphomatous" nodules in the breast, which were removed by the surgeon. It was only after their removal that examination of the blood was made and revealed the presence of 250,000 lymphocytes per c.mm. Another case showed a lymphoid nodule in the cervix uteri (Fig. 415) extending to the vagina, with ulceration and bleeding. It was at first thought to be a carcinoma, but the autopsy revealed areas of infiltration of lymphoid cells in many of the organs in association with the leukæmic condition of the blood. The cells in this form also fail to show the oxydase reaction.

Intimately related to this, if not identical with it, is one of the forms of *chloroma*, so named for the green color which the tumor-like nodules show when first exposed at autopsy. There are two sorts of chloroma, one composed of large lymphoid cells, the other of myeloid cells. The lymphoid type differs in no important particular from the leucosarcoma except in its green color, and perhaps in its arising usually in connection with the periosteum, and especially with that of the bones of the face and head. The green color is inconstant, failing in some parts of the same nodule, and is not to be regarded as sufficient basis for the separation of these cases; hence Sternberg classifies them as chloroleucosarcoma. No good explanation of the bright green color has been found, and efforts at the isolation of the pigment have failed, perhaps partly because it fades very quickly on exposure and disappears. The myeloid form is named by Sternberg on the same basis chloromyelosarcoma; it will be referred to later.

Lymphoid or Plasma Cell Myeloma.—A myeloma is a growth springing up in the bone-marrow and evidently occurring as a systemic affection of the marrow-cells, since it appears simultaneously in many bones and nowhere else. Unless we assume the existence of cells which can grow only in bone-marrow, it is hard to imagine such wide-spread multiple growths as due to transportation of cells. There are again two kinds, this one composed of lymphoid cells and another, to be described later, composed of myeloid cells. In their biological behavior they are almost exactly alike. The lymphoid myeloma is gray or reddish-gray on section, while the myeloid form is deep red and soft, but both encroach upon the cortex of the bone and erode it, causing fractures at such weakened spots. In both types there occurs in the urine a peculiar albumose (Bence Jones protein), the mode of formation of which is much debated. In neither form is there any constant or characteristic alteration of the blood in the sense of a leukæmic

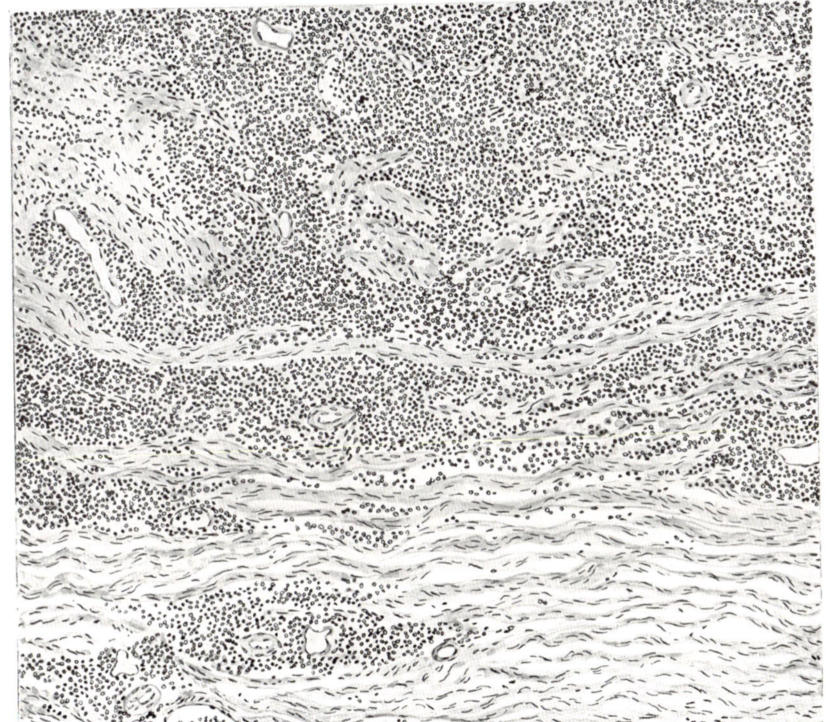

Fig. 415.—Leucosarcoma. Tumor-like nodule in the substance of the cervix uteri. This was associated with lymphoid leukæmia.

flooding with lymphoid or myeloid cells, but in one of the three cases of the lymphoid form which we observed this winter there were excessive numbers of large lymphoid cells with the morphology of plasma cells, in the circulating blood.

In two of these cases there were prominent tumors projecting from the ribs, vertebræ, and long bones. On sawing through the bones it was found that the involvement of the marrow was far greater than could be realized from the surface. Where the tumors showed, the enlargement was partly due to lifting up of the cortex, partly to its actual erosion and the protrusion

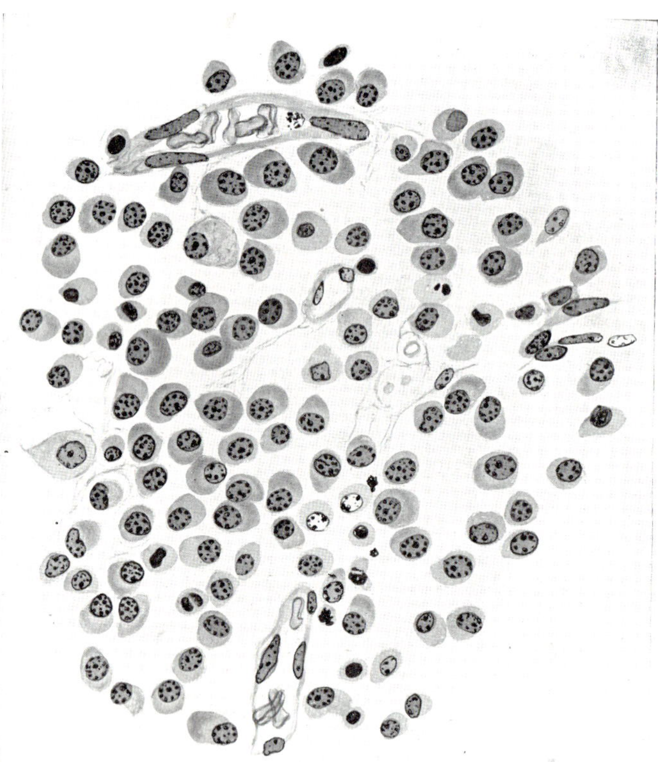

Fig. 416.—Lymphoid myeloma. The cells closely resemble plasma cells.

of the tumor. There were several fractures of the weakened bones. In the third case, in which the albumosuria was absent, there were no tumors springing from the bones, but nearly all the ribs were broken and the thorax collapsed. The marrow was entirely replaced by masses of lymphoid cells and the same was true of the marrow of the long bones where the bony cortex had become greatly thinned. There was no leukæmic change in the blood. The cells (Fig. 416) are non-granulated mononuclear cells with basophilic protoplasm, and are very similar to the plasma cells, with which they are regarded by most writers as identical.

Pseudoleukæmia.—Cohnheim employed this term to describe a case in which there was marked lymphoid hyperplasia in the lymph-glands and other lymphoid tissue but no leukæmia; in other words, a condition identical with lymphoid leukæmia, but without the blood changes. Since that time every sort of obscure affection of the lymph-glands has been called by this name, usually in the lack of any clear idea of the nature of the case, and it has been particularly confusing in the case of Hodgkin's disease. At the 1912 meeting of the German Pathological Association in Strassburg this was made the subject of discussion. Frænkel and Sternberg agreed that such a condition as Cohnheim described existed, and that it differed from lymphosarcoma and Hodgkin's disease, but that in some cases there arose a sublymphæmic condition of the blood or even a leukæmic condition, after which it could no longer be distinguished from leukæmia. In the long discussion which followed no one referred specifically to any case of this disease nor did any one seem familiar with it. It is unquestionably a very uncommon affection, and the instances which are referred to are usually those in which there has been clinical study only. Nevertheless, one does meet with cases in which there is swelling of the glands which form bulky packets, enlargement of the spleen, and no blood change. If such cases at autopsy prove to be due to a true hyperplasia of lymphoid tissue without leukæmia and without invasion of the tissues, they will fulfil the definition of pseudoleukæmia.

Lymphosarcoma.—Kundrat was the first to give a clear description of the disease which he outlined as lymphosarcomatosis. In this he recognized a more or less wide-spread growth arising from a group of lymph-glands (more rarely from a single one) or from a tract of lymphoid tissue such as occurs in the intestinal wall, pharynx, etc. Such a growth is composed of a delicate reticulum in the meshes of which lie cells of a lymphoid character. It fails to respect the capsules of the lymph-glands but grows rapidly and invades and infiltrates adjacent tissues. Isolated metastases in distant organs are rare, but the adjacent lymph-glands may be involved; otherwise the growth tends to spread in loose tissue and in film or plate form over serous surfaces. Throughout, Kundrat recognized the regional character of the growth. Where the tumor appears in the form of a metastatic nodule in such organs as the heart or kidney, the sharply outlined nodule seen with the naked eye proves to be a localized infiltration of cells between the muscle-fibres or tubules (Fig. 417). Eight cases which I was able to study seemed to fall into two groups. Three showed thoracic masses apparently derived from mediastinal lymph-glands and limited in their extension to the thorax, while five were equally limited to the abdominal cavity. They differed slightly in the form of the cells, which in the thoracic type were small (4–6 μ), while in the abdominal type they measured 8–12 μ and were associated with a few scattered phagocytic cells of large size. The thoracic type formed great masses of solid tissue surrounding the heart and compressing the lungs. In one case these had actually penetrated the heart-wall and hung in polypoid lobules in the cavity of the right ventricle. The abdominal or intestinal type, as already mentioned, either formed great ring-shaped masses at intervals along the intestine, penetrating into its lumen and obstructing it until ulceration again opened the channel, or else they infiltrated the whole wall diffusely for a long way, and by making it rigid and inactive might have caused a so-called paralytic ileus. The intestine comes to look like a stiff piece of garden hose, and the folds of mucosa are all greatly swollen and stand up stiffly (Fig. 418). In such

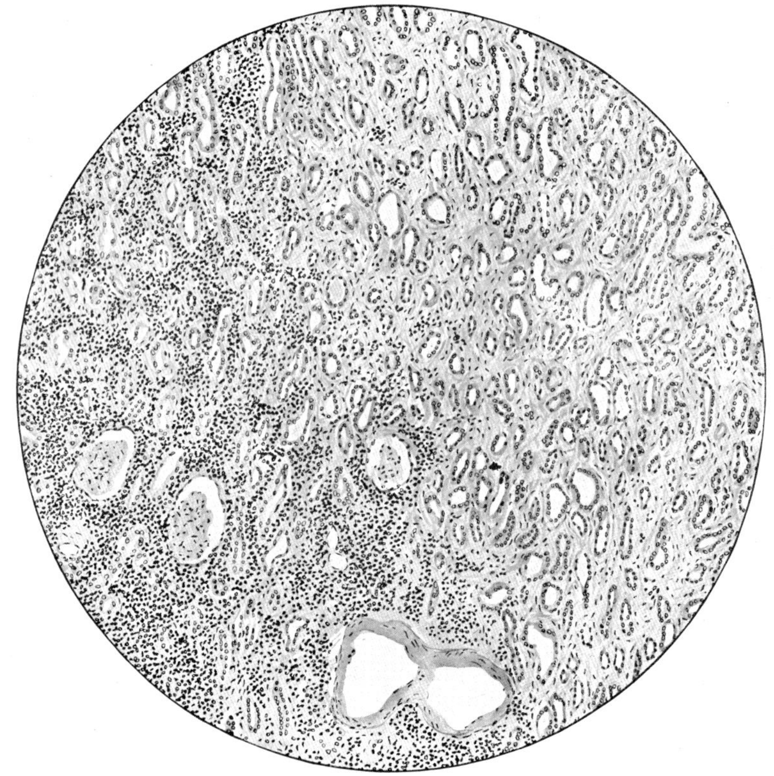

Fig. 417.—Lymphosarcoma. Infiltrating mass appearing as a quite sharply outlined nodule in the kidney. This was a case in which the intestine was probably the point of origin.

intestinal cases it is not uncommon to find organs such as the adrenal and pancreas completely buried in an infiltrating mass of the tissues. The mesenteric glands are usually greatly enlarged by a similar infiltration. The spleen shows no especial alteration in either of these types, nor do the more distant lymph-glands. It is generally stated that the bone-marrow is quite unaffected and that there are no alterations of the blood. In two of our cases there was hyperplastic bone-marrow in the long bones and there were many cells which resembled precisely those of the tumor growth, and formed solid masses of tumor tissue. Further and more modern study of the bone-marrow in such cases must be made. Lymphosarcoma arising from other groups of lymph-glands occurs as mentioned above and presents similar characteristics.

The characters which distinguish a lymphosarcoma from other conditions which resemble it in a confusing way may be best set down in a comparative form. From a single section it would probably be impossible from a study of the cells to distinguish between an involvement of a gland by chronic lymphoid leukæmia, leucosarcoma, lymphosarcoma, and small round-cell sarcoma. In chronic leukæmia the glands become enlarged but remain discrete, there is dissemination of lymphoid cells in the capil-

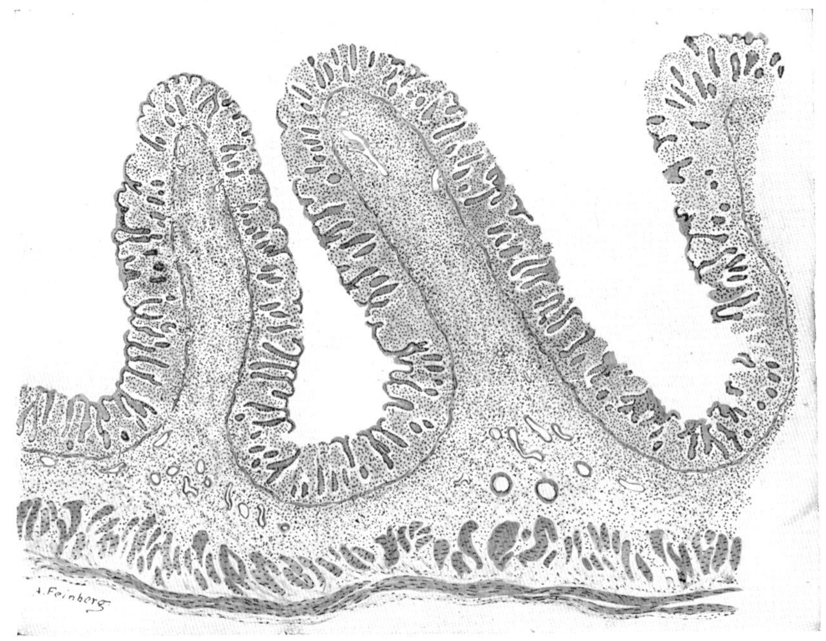

Fig. 418.—Lymphosarcoma. Infiltration of valvulæ conniventes of the jejunum.

laries of organs otherwise practically unchanged, and there is the leukæmic state of the blood. In leucosarcoma there is an invasive lymphoid tumor and there may be nodular infiltrations, but once more there is the leukæmic state of the blood. In lymphosarcoma there is an invasive or infiltrating lymphoid growth which has a peculiar regional way of spreading and is rather limited either to the thorax or the abdomen. It is much like leucosarcoma except that there is no leukæmic change of the blood. Round-cell sarcomata offer much less difficulty: they start anywhere in the connective tissue (not in the lymph-glands especially) as a single tumor nodule which invades the surroundings and metastasizes by way of the blood-stream, forming new discrete nodules in distant organs, such as the lungs,

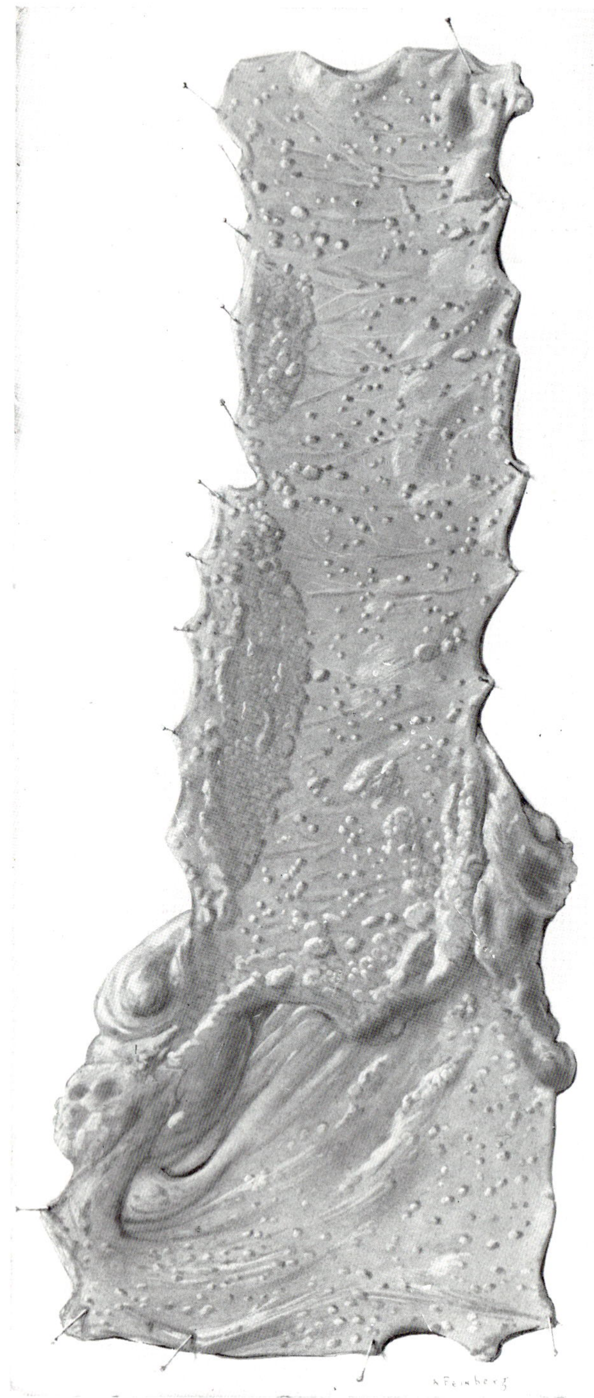

Fig. 419.—Intestine in status lymphaticus, showing great enlargement of lymphoid nodules.

liver, etc. When they lodge in a lymph-gland they produce a solid nodule with an outline, outside which some remnant of the gland may be found unchanged. All the others cause a complete replacement of the gland, although occasionally a localized lymphosarcomatous infiltration may leave the rest of the gland intact. With round-cell sarcoma there is no leukæmia.

Status Lymphaticus or Thymico-lymphaticus.—In many young persons and children who have died suddenly after some slight shock or infection which seemed insufficient to cause death, there is found, at autopsy, a general swelling of the lymphoid structures and persistence or enlargement of the thymus. Paltauf was the first to point out clearly that this lymphoid hyperplasia is only part of a general constitutional abnormality which amounts to a physical inferiority of the persons affected. The whole complex is best seen in young persons, since only part of it is as yet evident in children, while the lymphoid changes fade in old people. In men there is an incomplete development of the secondary sexual characteristics with a tendency toward the feminine type—the hair on the face is scanty or lacking, the pubic hair has the feminine distribution, being sharply limited toward the abdomen, the external genitals are small, the thighs round and arched anteriorly, and the skin smooth and velvety. In women, thorax and extremities are slender, the genitals are hypoplastic, menstruation is irregular or absent, and there may be a tendency to growth of hair on the face. In such persons the musculature may be flabby and weak, though sometimes well developed, but the heart is weak and soft and the large blood-vessels are relatively narrow and thin walled. It appears that failure of this inadequate circulatory mechanism may be one at least of the causes of sudden death and probably the most important. Emerson finds such cases most common among alcoholics and drug habitués, but it is by no means limited to mental degenerates. Persons with this constitutional abnormality are evidently far more exposed than others to destruction by the injuries and infections incidental to life, and if they reach mature age, it is through especial care or good fortune.

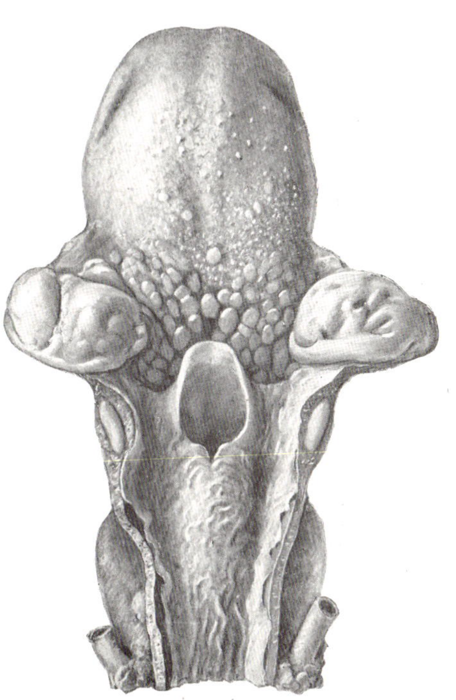

Fig. 420.—Status lymphaticus. Enlargement of tonsils and lymphoid nodules at the root of the tongue.

At autopsy one finds the lymphoid nodules throughout the digestive tract especially enlarged and prominent (Fig. 419). In the throat and at the base of the tongue the adenoid tissue is swollen too (Fig. 420), although Emerson makes little of this point. The lymph-glands in general may be larger than normal, although this is not constant. The spleen is not particularly affected except that the Malpighian bodies are enlarged. There is often red bone-marrow. The thymus is commonly persistent and often greatly enlarged, so as to weigh forty to fifty grams and extend far down over the pericardium. The narrowness and delicacy of the aorta and the smallness of the heart are striking. Wiesel has described in many cases hypoplasia of the adrenals and chromaffin system and thinks that the condition of the circulatory apparatus is connected with that. The lymphoid tissue shows no such hyperplasia as is seen in leukæmia, but maintains its architecture and the relations of lymphoid cells to germinal centres. Details of this affection should be read in the papers of Neusser, Bartel and Bauer, and others. It may be interesting to quote Neusser's division of constitutions into two categories. One, the bearer of a good heart, good blood-vessels, good bone-marrow, good sympathetic and chromaffin system, and good genitals, is like a folio edition of the genus Homo; while the other shows just the opposite, with its poor heart, poor hypoplastic vessels, poor bone-marrow, poor genitals, poor chromaffin and sympathetic system.

LITERATURE

General—Sternberg: Ergebnisse d. allg. Path., 1903, ix, II[te] Abt., 360.

Leukæmia—Nægeli: Leukæmia u. Pseudoleukæmia, Wien, 1913.
Sternberg: Ztschr. f. Heilkunde, 1904, xxv, Path. Abth., 170.
Reed: Amer. Jour. Med. Sci., 1902, cxxiv, 653.

Leucosarcoma—Sternberg: Wien. kl. Woch., 1908, xxi, 475. Ziegler's Beitr., 1915, lxi, 75.

Myeloma—Christian: Jour. Exp. Med., 1907, ix, 325.
Shennan: Edin. Med. Jour., 1913, n. s. x, 321.
Hoffman: Ziegler's Beitr., 1904, xxxv, 317.
Sternberg: Ztsch. f. Heilk., 1904, xxv, Path. Abth., 89.
Hedinger: Frankf. Ztsch. f. Path., 1911, vii, 343.
MacCallum: Jour. Exp. Med., 1901–05, vi, 53.

Pseudoleukæmia—Frænkel: Verh. d. Dtsch. Path. Gesellsch., 1912, xv, 5.
Sternberg: *Ibid.*, 22; discussion, 82.

Lymphosarcoma—Kundrat: Wien. kl. Woch., 1893, vi, 211.
Paltauf: Ergebn. d. allg. Path., 1896, iii, 652.
MacCallum: Johns Hopkins Hosp. Bull., 1907, xviii, 337. Trans. Assoc. Am. Phys., 1907, xxii, 350.

Status lymphaticus—Neusser: Diagnose des Status Thymico-lymphaticus, Wien, 1911.
Bartel: Status Thymico-lymphaticus, Leipzig, 1912.
Paltauf: Wien. kl. Woch., 1889, ii, 876; 1890, iii, 172.
Emerson: Arch. Int. Med., 1914, xiii, 169.
Zellweger: Ztsch. f. angew. Anat. u. Konstitutionslehre, 1913, i, 192.
v. Werdt: Berl. kl. Woch., 1910, xlvii, 2383.

CHAPTER XLI

EFFECTS OF INJURIES TO THE BLOOD AND BLOOD-FORMING ORGANS (Continued)

Chronic myeloid leukæmia. Acute myeloid leukæmia, myeloblastic leukæmia. Myeloid chloroma or chloromyelosarcoma. Myeloid myeloma. Hodgkin's disease or lymphogranulomatosis.

CHRONIC MYELOID LEUKÆMIA

THE beginning of this disorder is usually gradual and unnoticed, with weakness and loss of weight, after which anæmia and slight hæmorrhages appear. Many of the patients suffer no particular discomfort and show no anæmia until late in the disease, but apply for relief from a large abdominal tumor which proves to be the enormously enlarged spleen. Examination of the blood shows a very great increase in the number of white cells which are easily seen to be large granular cells. They may reach a count of over 1,000,000 per c.mm. More careful study reveals the fact that while at first the polymorphonuclear neutrophiles are still the predominant cells, there is later a great increase in the neutrophile myelocytes which usually become the most numerous cells. Eosinophile myelocytes also appear in great numbers, while eosinophile leucocytes, though absolutely increased, like the neutrophile leucocytes, do not attain to any great proportion among all the cells. Mast leucocytes with their basophile granulations and basophilic myelocytes are abundant and conspicuous. Lymphocytes are present in small numbers and form a very small proportion of the total. Normoblasts and rarely megaloblasts appear in later stages when the anæmia becomes more marked. The appearance of such blood with its huge numbers of large granular myelocytes is most astonishing even when compared with the much altered blood of the lymphoid forms of leukæmia. In late stages when the alterations have become most intense, non-granular myeloblasts may appear in considerable numbers. These, like the granular cells just mentioned, give the oxydase reaction most brilliantly, and, as might be expected, the blood in these cases is rich in proteolytic ferments. There may be no reduction in the red corpuscles until quite late in the disease. Then, partly as a result of the hæmorrhages, their number sinks and normoblasts appear in the circulation. In some cases megaloblasts are found and the form of the red corpuscles (anisocytosis, poikilocytosis) recalls that seen in pernicious anæmia. Megalocaryocytes are sometimes found.

With the advance of the disease there often occur rather extensive hæmorrhages from the mucosæ or into the retinæ or other organs. Death from apoplexy seems to be relatively common. Extensive necrotic and gangrenous processes sometimes appear here just as in the lymphoid cases.

There have been reported a few instances, such as those of Thompson and Ewing, Burckhardt, and others, in which such myeloid leukæmia with predominant myelocytes in the blood has arisen acutely and quickly led to sudden death, and in these cases evidences of hæmorrhage and necrotizing processes are most striking. They are mentioned here because there is another group of acute myeloid leukæmias to be discussed later in which myeloblasts form the predominant cell in the blood.

Fig. 421.—The spleen in chronic myeloid leukæmia.

At autopsy, in cases of chronic myeloid leukæmia, the blood is found clotted in the heart and large vessels and is so peculiar in appearance that it suggested to Virchow the name leukæmia or white blood. When it clots slowly, as in the heart, the upper part of the clot is whitish or greenish and rather opalescent on account of the great number of leucocytes. In a typical case which we have studied, the clots evidently formed more rapidly for they were of a quite uniform pale chocolate color. The most striking phenomenon at autopsy is the great enlargement of the *spleen* (Fig. 421), which is smooth and firm and often deeply notched at its edge. In some cases it is adherent to the diaphragm and abdominal wall. It stretches downward toward the right and may reach the symphysis pubis, filling a great part of the abdominal cavity and appearing to rest on the right ilium. In the case just mentioned it weighed 1550 grams but it may weigh as much as 10,000 grams. On section it is grayish-red and finely granular and opaque; the Malpighian bodies have disappeared but the trabeculæ can usually be fairly clearly seen. Sometimes, however, in the later stages it is very fibrous and dense and the whole structure assumes a rather uniform appearance. Infarcts are quite common. The *bone-marrow* in the long bones is no longer fatty but firm, opaque yellowish gray or pinkish-gray, and homogeneous. It can be cut out in blocks and is evidently a solid mass of cells. The *liver* is enlarged and rather pale but usually without any grossly visible change in the structure. However, in the case mentioned there were several opaque grayish nodules embedded in its substance and reaching 5 to 8 mm. in diameter, which proved to be masses of myeloid tissue. The other organs show no characteristic gross changes except the effects of the anæmia, which are seen in the general pallor of the organs and in accumulations of fat in the heart, kidneys, etc. The *lymph-glands* are not enlarged and with the rest of the lymphoid tissue appear to play no part in the process. Apoplectic hæmorrhages in the brain have already been mentioned. Thrombosis of various veins is not uncommon. When complicating infections occur the leucocytosis which attends them may be quite normal and the reaction about the bacteria and injured tissue typical. In such cases the whole blood picture can change so that the leukæmic character disappears, and in place of the

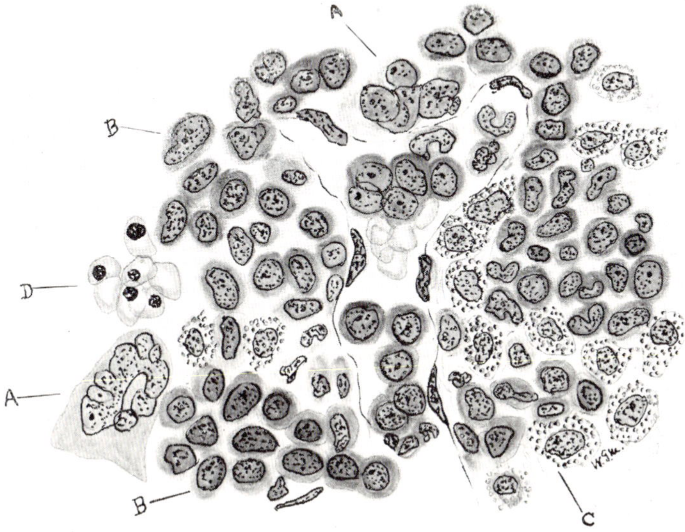

Fig. 422.—Bone-marrow in chronic myeloid leukæmia. There are very abundant neutrophile (*B*) and eosinophile (*C*) myelocytes, megalocaryocytes (*A*), and a few normoblasts (*D*).

horde of myelocytes there are found the neutrophile leucocytes. Such a change does not last, however, and when the occasion for leucocytosis is over the leukæmia returns. I have not seen such a case but it would appear to offer an interesting field for study of the nature of leukæmia.

Microscopically the *bone-marrow* is the tissue of prime interest. It appears as a solid array of cells among which the capillary vessels can be made out with some difficulty (Fig. 422). Within these vessels there are great numbers of neutrophile myelocytes, eosinophile myelocytes, leucocytes of all kinds, and red corpuscles. Outside, but evidently able to enter the blood-channels pretty easily, are masses of neutrophile myelocytes with somewhat smaller numbers of eosinophile myelocytes. Basophile myelocytes are also present in great numbers, and there are other non-granular mononuclear cells of rather large size which are probably myeloblasts. Neutrophile leucocytes are there in rather large quantities too, but there is not much to be seen of red blood-cells or of erythroblastic tissue. Normoblasts are present here and there in small groups but must be searched for. From this it seems that the progressive anæmia in this, as in other types of leukæmia, may be due to the actual crowding out of the erythroblastic tissue

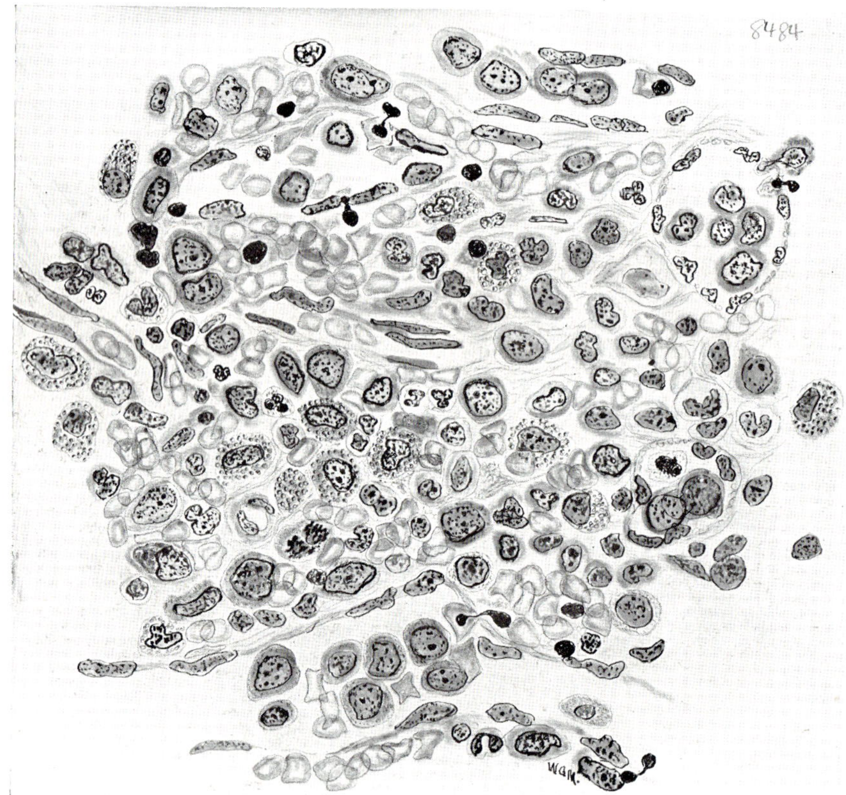

Fig. 423—Spleen in chronic myeloid leukæmia. Space between two adjacent venules, showing numerous myelocytes of neutrophile and eosinophile type. Many cells, emigrating from the venules, of which some appear to be nucleated red corpuscles.

rather than to the hæmorrhages, which are not always very evident. In this respect it would resemble the osteosclerotic anæmia mentioned above. The *spleen* (Fig. 423) in this disease, has almost the same composition in respect to the cells present as the bone-marrow; it resembles in an exaggerated way the myeloid spleen found in the osteosclerotic anæmia. As shown in the drawing, the venules of the splenic pulp (Malpighian bodies are not found) are intact and in themselves unaffected. They are full of myelocytes and in the intervening spaces myelocytes of all kinds are crowded together with some red corpuscles and a few nucleated red cells. Myeloblasts, nucleated red cells, and even lymphocytoid cells are constantly found passing through the walls of the venules which seem to be as open as so much mosquito netting.

In all the other organs the microscopical alterations consist essentially in the filling of the capillaries with myelocytes, etc., from the leukæmic blood (Fig. 424). In the liver the capillaries may be hugely distended

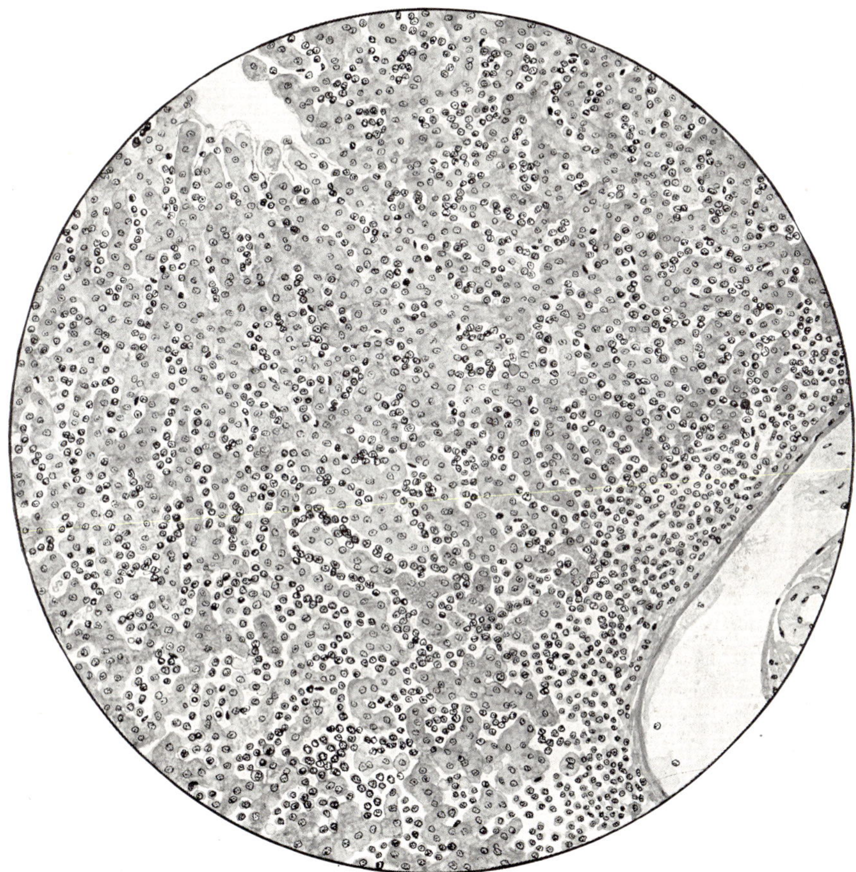

Fig. 424.—Myeloid leukæmia. General infiltration of the liver with myeloid cells.

with clumps and masses of these cells. It is interesting to note that no necroses occur in the liver-cells or even among the packed myelocytes themselves. In this the myelocytes differ from the cells found distending these capillaries in typhoid fever, which seem unused to life within the vessels and in addition carry seeds of death with them. In the nodules mentioned above there are huge pools of myeloid cells and the liver-cells are compressed into flattened rows or squeezed out of existence entirely.

Some of the wide capillaries contain megalocaryocytes in groups, and the whole area has assumed the exact appearance of bone-marrow (Fig. 425).

Other organs are also thickly infiltrated with myelocytes (Fig. 426), but as a rule show little of actual myeloid colonization. The lymph-glands

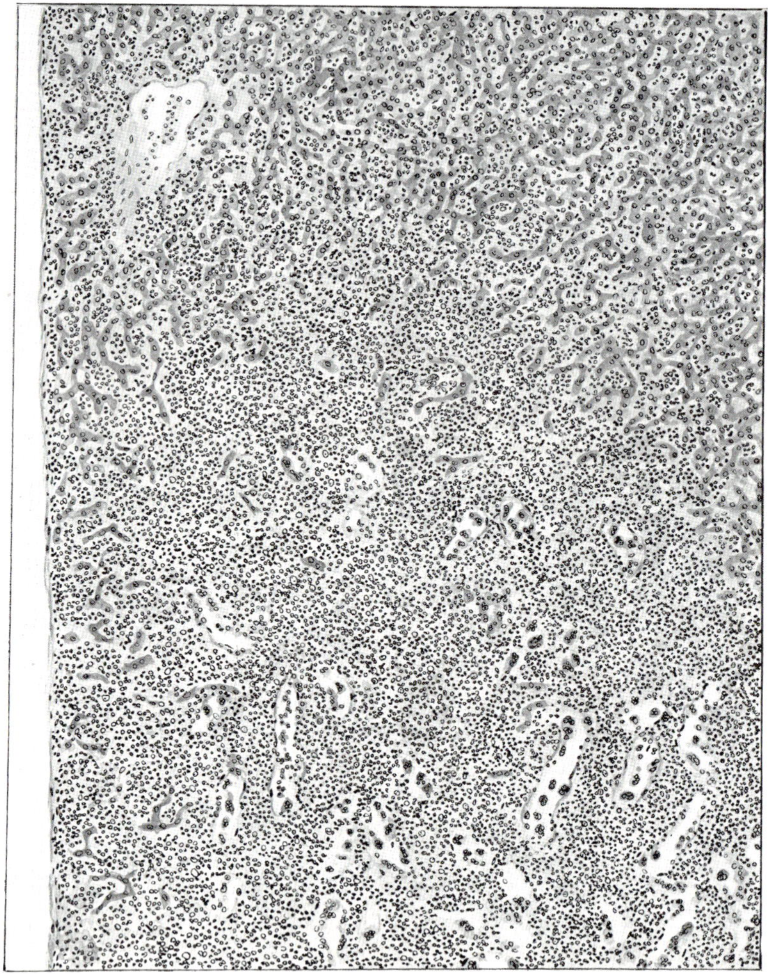

Fig. 425.— Myeloid leukæmia. Myeloid area in the liver, showing displacement of liver-cells by the abundant myelocytes, and in the endothelium-lined capillaries many megalocaryocytes.

merely participate passively in this process—occasionally their sinuses are stuffed with the cells of the blood.

The nature of the process is quite obscure as in the other forms, but it seems clear that the changes are primary in the bone-marrow, and that those of the spleen and other organs are secondary. Nevertheless it is also pretty clear that new formation of cells goes on in the myeloid accumulations of tissue in spleen and liver, although not, it seems to me, as the result of activity on the part of splenic or hepatic endothelium.

ACUTE MYELOID LEUKÆMIA.—MYELOBLASTIC LEUKÆMIA

We have already mentioned the existence of cases in all respects like the chronic myeloid leukæmia except that their fatal course is very rapid and marked by the occurrence of more extensive hæmorrhages and ulcerations of mucosæ. In another and larger group of these acute cases whose symptoms

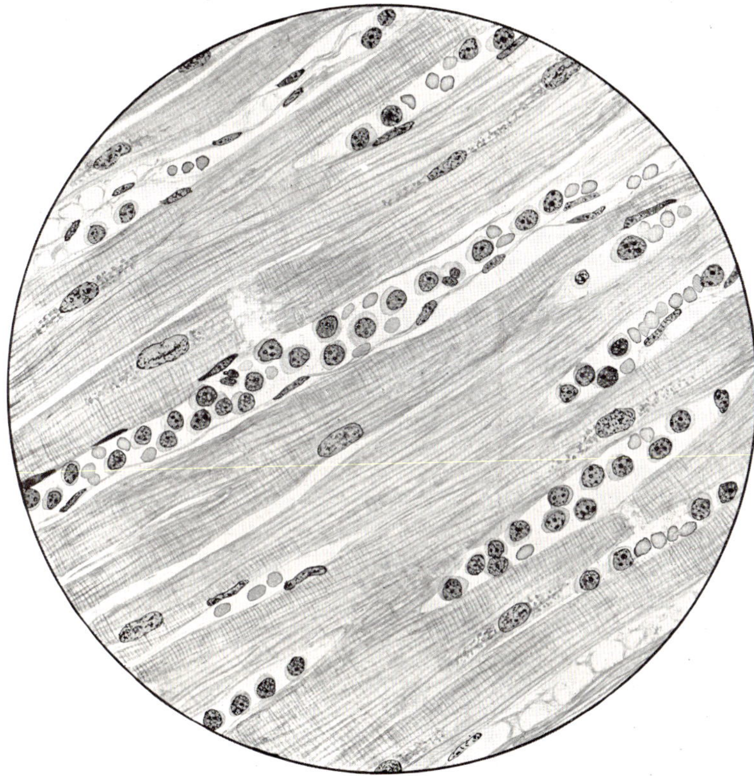

Fig. 426.—Myeloid leukæmia. Heart showing the overfilling of the capillaries with myeloid cells.

are not to be easily distinguished from those of acute lymphoid leukæmia, the differences lie in the fact that the non-granular mononuclear cells which are predominant in the blood and tissues are not lymphocytes, but myeloblasts, as shown by their possession of a proteolytic ferment action in an alkaline medium and by their positive oxydase reaction. In these cases there is a great overflooding of the blood with white cells, most of which are myeloblasts; the bone-marrow shows a myeloid hyperplasia in which they are prominent, and there are myeloid changes in the spleen and liver. Hæmorrhages, necrotic and ulcerative stomatitis, etc., are common.

Lymph-glands may be enlarged, but commonly are not. The whole condition has the appearance of an acute infectious process, and indeed infections often exist, but whether as cause or as incidental accompaniment it is difficult to say. Sternberg, however, is so impressed by this that he proposes to exclude the myeloblastic leukæmia completely from the group of leukæmias and to regard it as an infectious process—the more so since it has been shown that a number of extremely severe infections can cause the appearance of huge numbers of myeloblasts or myelocytes in the circulating blood. These, however, are not progressive processes, and the myeloid cells disappear with recovery from the infection.

The question of the relation of infection to the whole group of leukæmias is one which we can hardly discuss as yet with profit. All of them have something of the character of infections and although we have no facts to go on it seems impossible to single out one form as definitely infectious on such inadequate evidence. Only when we have a firmer knowledge of their ætiology shall we be able to make a rational classification.

MYELOID CHLOROMA. CHLOROMYELOSARCOMA

The justification for the isolation of this group is much the same as in the case of the lymphoid chloroma or chloroleukosarcoma and the same arguments have been raised against it. The peculiar feature consists in the formation of tumor-like growths within the bone-marrow or extending through the cortex of the bone to spread over the periosteal surface. Some of them spring apparently from the periosteum. They may or may not have a bright grass green color, and, as in the lymphoid chloroma, the inconstancy of this color makes it seem an inadequate basis of classification. The tumors allow the myeloid cells to escape in great numbers into the circulation and are thus accompanied by a leukæmic state of the blood. The bone-marrow, in Meixner's case, was partly red, partly occupied by masses of myelocytes which in the gross looked green. The lymph-glands were unaffected; the spleen much infiltrated with myelocytes.

MYELOID MYELOMA

In the previous chapter we spoke of multiple, rather invasive, tumor-like growths springing from the bone-marrow and composed of mononuclear cells which have been regarded as plasma cells. There are other cases, however, in which the tumors have in general the same distribution but differ in appearance, being very soft and deep red in most parts. They infiltrate and destroy the bones and give rise to repeated fractures. As in the other type there is found the Bence-Jones albumose in the urine.

Boggs and Guthrie have shown that this albumose is by no means limited to cases of myeloma, and even that it may be absent in some well-defined cases of this affection. On the other hand it is present in cases of carcinomatous invasion of the bone-marrow and in cases of chronic myeloid leukæmia. The mechanism of its production is as yet too uncertain to discuss here.

The cells which form these tumors have occasionally been demonstrated to be myelocytes or even erythroblasts (Ribbert), but in most cases they correspond with myeloblasts. In a case which I studied ten years ago I thought that their identity with myeloblasts was proven (Fig. 427). It is to be hoped that in future the oxydase reaction will be applied to these cases to settle this point definitely. No leukæmic changes occur in the blood.

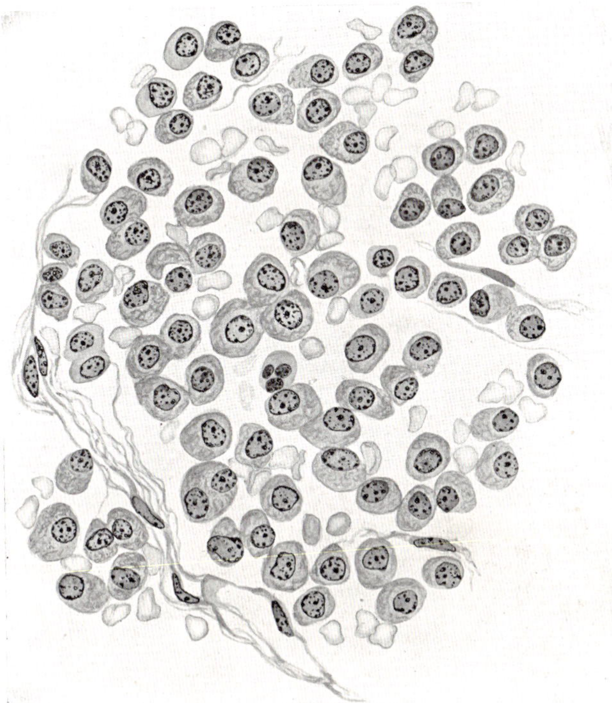

Fig. 427.—Myeloid myeloma. The cells are larger than those of the lymphoid myeloma (Fig. 416), which are drawn to the same scale. They show no definite granules, but would probably give the oxydase reaction.

HODGKIN'S DISEASE OR LYMPHOGRANULOMATOSIS

While not an example of the hyperplasia of either myeloid or lymphoid tissue, the clinical and gross anatomical difficulties in diagnosis make it desirable that Hodgkin's disease should be considered in this connection. Described by Hodgkin together with a number of other conditions in 1832, much confusion existed as to the nature of the process until the work of Sternberg, Reed, Longcope, Ziegler, and others established the fact that there is a peculiar and specific histological picture which sets it apart as a separate disease.

The affection is commonly found in rather young persons and far more frequently in men than in women. Beginning with painless swelling of the superficial lymph-glands, it progresses with gradual enlargement of these glands and signs of similar enlargement of others within the thorax or abdomen, and usually with increase in size of the spleen. Anæmia appears and may reach a profound degree. There may be evidences of mechanical pressure exerted by the enlarged glands upon the veins, producing œdema of the face or other regions, upon the trachea, leading to emphysema in some cases, or upon some part of the alimentary tract, causing characteristic effects. Death is the result of one of these mechanical influences, of some intercurrent infection, or of the anæmia and cachexia produced by the disease itself. It may be well to describe the peculiar change in the tis-

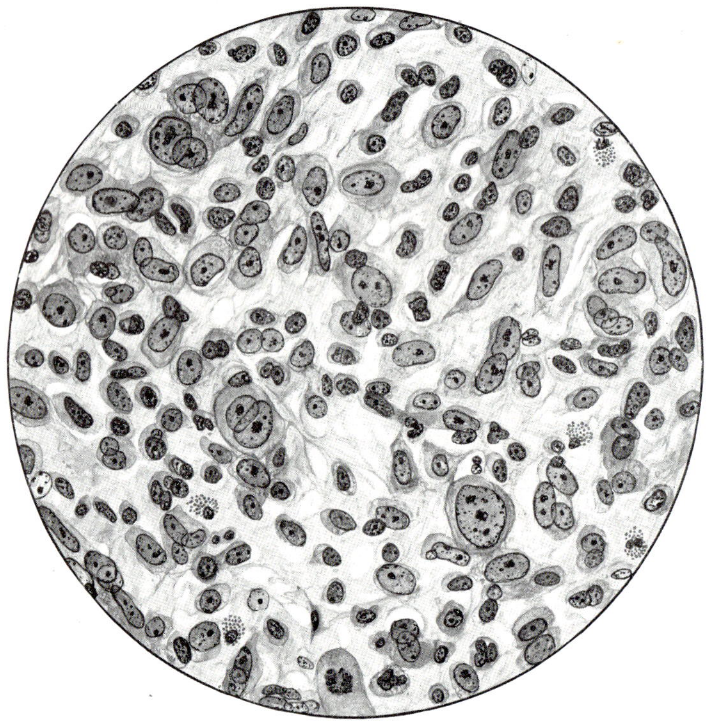

Fig. 428.—Hodgkin's disease; early stage. Lymphoid and epithelioid cells with scattered eosinophiles and large multinuclear cells.

sues, which is the same wherever it occurs, before discussing in detail the distribution of the lesions. The lesion is best seen (Fig. 428) in the lymph-glands where, in different nodules, it may be followed through the changes which it undergoes in the course of its development. In the smaller nodes the beginning of the process, as Dr. Reed pointed out, consists in a proliferation of the lymphoid cells, which is soon followed by the appearance of a coherent tissue formed of larger and paler cells with elongated vesicular and rather palely staining nucleus. These resemble the reticulum cells and have been called endothelioid cells. They lie in no particular order but they, together with the lymphoid cells and others to be described, soon spread so as to replace the normal tissue of the whole gland, obliterating the distinction between lymph-cords and sinuses. Among these cells there are found much larger ones which constitute the most characteristic feature of the lesion. These are really quite large cells, and while they vary greatly, are many times the size of the lymphocytes. Their protoplasm is clear except for scattered, irregular stainable shreds, and their outline is rather ragged. They contain one or two or several large nuclei which are rounded or indented or lobed and usually lie close together. These nuclei are very sharply outlined with a deeply staining chromatin membrane within which the nuclear substance is relatively sparsely granular. In each nucleus there is a large nucleolus, sometimes two, and these nucleoli stand out very clearly with a deep stain. Beside the lymphoid, epithelioid (or endothelioid) cells and these large cells there are usually found many eosinophile leucocytes. Dr. Reed made much of their presence, but later agreed that they might be absent without lessening the certainty with which one might recognize the tissue. Occasionally, but in my experience rarely, there are found giant-cells of another type with many rather small nuclei arranged in a ring or horseshoe. These are much closer to the sort found in foreign body giant-cells or even to those of the tubercle. The reticulum, in the meshes of which these cells lie, is of extreme delicacy and the whole mass thus forms a soft, rather translucent grayish tissue, which is quite elastic and in appearance quite homogeneous. This cellular condition is found in the earlier stages, but after a time there appears a progressive scar formation throughout the gland coincident with the disappearance of the cells. Every step in the development of this change can be followed until finally there is left a dense mass of fibrous tissue in which, here and there, are to be found pockets or nests of such cells as have been described (Fig. 429). It should be noted that this change in the gland is one which even in the earlier stages involves the whole gland and obliterates its architecture by replacing the lymph-cords and sinuses with a uniform cellular tissue. In the neighborhood of such glands tiny new glandular clumps of lymphoid tissue are formed by a regenerative process, but these are no sooner developed than they are transformed into the same new tissue. The glands first affected are usually those at the root of the neck just above the clavicle, where they form a nodular mass almost like a sort of collar. Thence those higher in the neck are quickly involved; axillary and inguinal glands are only less frequently concerned. Sometimes they are extirpated at operation and it is then found that in the earlier stages they are oval or round, discrete nodes which, unlike tuberculous glands which adhere and tend to bind themselves together in a solid mass, can be easily pulled apart. The smooth glands on section show the grayish gelatinous elastic tissue described, but in the somewhat later stage one very frequently finds in them dry, opaque, firm, yellowish-white areas of necrotic tissue with occasional hæmorrhages. The old cases still show the glands in packets, loosely bound together, but as time passes there is more tendency to adhesion. The capsule and adjacent tissue may be especially thickly infiltrated with eosinophiles in these advanced cases. In the interior of the body the bronchial, peritracheal, and mediastinal glands are extensively involved and form such masses as to compress the trachea or impede the heart-beat. I saw one case in a woman in which huge masses existed in the place of the

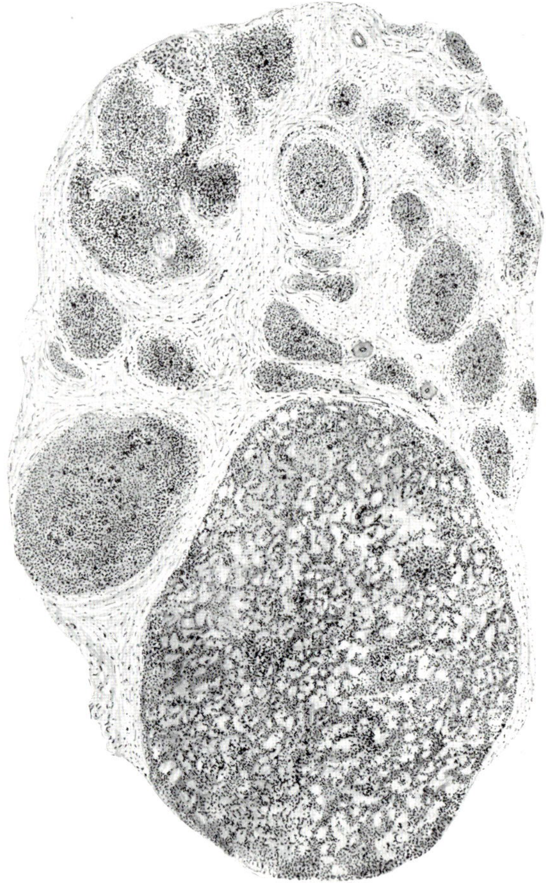

Fig. 429.—Hodgkin's disease. Partly scarred mass in which there are still areas of the characteristic tissue. The large nodule has undergone partial hyaline change.

bronchial glands at the bifurcation of the trachea. From these the tissue extended into the lungs and there were numerous large discrete nodules scattered in the lung tissue. In another, a negro boy, one lung was converted into a solid gray translucent mass closely bound by the much thickened pleura and showing no air-containing lung tissue, but only patches of collapsed alveoli in which the epithelial cells were loaded with fat. All the gray tissue was of the character just described and though already rather fibrous, showed very distinctly all the types of cells. In the abdomen, the retroperitoneal glands and perhaps more especially the peripancreatic and periportal glands are likely to be involved. The periportal glands may be large enough to compress and obstruct the common bile-duct and produce jaundice. In the liver Dr. Reed describes the wide-spread occurrence of perivascular and interlobular accumulations of the typical tissue, with its specific large cells, in strands and small nodules. This seems to be rather infrequent. On the other hand the spleen is pretty regularly involved, sometimes with mere swelling and with diffuse infiltration of the pulp; at other times, as shown in Fig. 430, with great enlargement and with numerous gray nodules composed of the characteristic tissue and pretty sharply marked off from the deep red pulp. Occasionally such foci are found in the bone-marrow, which otherwise shows no change except the hyperplasia due to secondary anæmia.

Longcope describes the invasion of the Hodgkin's tissue through the walls of the blood-vessels so as to penetrate the intima. There is, however,

Fig. 430.—Hodgkin's disease. Multiple irregular nodules of specific tissue in the spleen.

no leukæmic change in the blood from such invasion; instead there is a decrease in the red cells and usually a moderate increase in the leucocytes without much disturbance of their relative numbers. On the whole we find in this disease an affection principally of the lymph-glands, which become greatly enlarged by the development in them of a peculiar tissue which rather rapidly takes the place of the original structure. Cellular and soft at first, this tissue in the course of time loses most of its cells and becomes scarred and hard. Hence the recognition of soft and hard forms of lymph-gland involvement. The growth is not limited to the lymph-glands but may extend into the adjacent tissues, such as the lung and pleura, or appear separately as a sort of metastasis in the spleen beginning perhaps in the Malpighian bodies and extending to the pulp.

It is evident that this is not a hyperplasia of the essential lymphoid cells of the gland, nor is it anything like the myeloid hyperplasias described above. It has some of the characters of a tumor growth, but by far the greater weight of evidence is in favor of its being an infectious process involving simultaneously much of the lymphatic gland system. As to the portal of entry of the infectious agent nothing can be said. The tonsils are most often unaffected.

Nor can anything definite be said as to the nature of the causative agent. Sternberg maintained for a time that this is a peculiar form of tuberculosis, but all efforts to demonstrate tubercle bacilli or to infect guinea-pigs with the tissue were in vain, unless, of course, as was true in Dr. Reed's first case, there was a coincident infection with tuberculosis, and tuberculous lesions and those of Hodgkin's disease lay side by side. Afterward Sternberg and others thought it due to a weakened tubercle bacillus but this seems unlikely in view of the case just cited and also because a weakened tubercle bacillus ought to produce injuries less destructive than those caused by a virulent one and not necessarily fatal. Hodgkin's disease produces lesions quite unlike those of tuberculosis but is always fatal. Frænkel and Much have described certain granular Gram-positive rodlets which they find frequently and consider that they have found the cause of the disease. On the other hand, Bunting and Yates have found a pleomorphic diphtheroid bacillus which they think is the cause. It is too early to decide as to the merits of these different organisms, but the impression is strong that Hodgkin's disease is an infectious process.

LITERATURE

Myeloid Leukæmia—Nægeli: Leukämie, Wien, 1913.
Sternberg: Wien. kl. Woch., 1911, xxiv, 1623.
Herxheimer: Münch. med. Woch., 1913, lx, 2506.
Burckhardt: Frankf. Ztsch. f. Path., 1911, vi, 107.
Sternberg: Ziegler's Beitr., 1915, lxi, 89.

Myeloid Chloroma.—Meixner: Wien. kl. Woch., 1907, xx, 593.
Sternberg: Ziegler's Beitr., 1904, xxxvii, 437.
Roman: *Ibid.*, 1913, lv, 61. (Lit.)

Myeloid Myeloma.—Shennan: Edinb. Med. Jour., 1913, x, 321.
MacCallum: Jour. Exp. Med., 1901, vi, 53.
Boggs and Guthrie: Johns Hopkins Hosp. Bull., 1912, xxiii, 353; 1913, xxiv, 368.

Hodgkin's Disease.—Sternberg: Ctbl. f. d. Grenz. d. Med. u. Chir., 1899, ii, 641. Ztsch. f. Heilk., 1898, xix, 21.
Reed: Johns Hopkins Hosp. Reports, 1902, x, 133.
Longcope: Bull. Ayer Clin. Labty., 1903, i, 4.
K. Ziegler: Hodgkin'sche Krankheit, Jena, 1911.
Bunting and Yates: Jour. Amer. Med. Assoc., 1913, lxi, 1803; 1914, lxii, 516.
Discussion to Sternberg: Verh. d. D. Path. Gesellsch., 1912, xv, 22.

CHAPTER XLII

DISEASES DUE TO INJURIES OF THE ORGANS OF INTERNAL SECRETION

Pancreas. Diabetes mellitus. General character of process. Pathological anatomy. Nature of disturbance of carbohydrate metabolism. Relation of other organs. Diabetic acidosis. Résumé: Thyroid: anatomy and physiology. Myxœdema, effects of extracts. Cretinism, goitre, exophthalmic goitre, general symptoms, pathological nature of disease.

In considering the diseases which depend upon disturbance of the activities of the organs of internal secretion we must usually speak of a disease in which one of these organs is most prominently affected, because it is known that they seem to coöperate in such a way that the disabling of one disturbs the others.

Diabetes mellitus is an example of this, for while we find the pancreas most prominently concerned, we are not yet sure of the part played by adrenal, thyroid, hypophysis, etc. Nor are we sure in the case of exophthalmic goitre whether thyroid or thymus or some other organ is chiefly responsible for the disease.

The Pancreas

DIABETES MELLITUS

Diabetes mellitus is a disease occurring at almost all ages and usually more severe and quickly fatal in young persons. It is peculiar in that the carbohydrate metabolism is deranged in such a way that sugar absorbed from the intestine is no longer stored in reserve in the form of glycogen in the liver and body muscles, but circulates in the blood and is excreted in the urine. Since sugar ordinarily forms the great source of energy for the muscles and is now scarcely used by them, great changes in the general metabolism arise. Protein substances, even including those of the tissues, are consumed in an unaccustomed way to develop the necessary energy and a part split off from them in the form of sugar becomes useless because of its carbohydrate nature and is excreted with the rest in the urine.* In severe cases in spite of enormous quantities of food consumed usually with great amounts of water (polyphagia, polydipsia) the protein becomes inadequate to supply the energy demands and the fats are attacked. Being incompletely oxidized, these give rise to intermediary products, β-oxybutyric acid, aceto-acetic acid, and acetone, which are excreted

* That this is only partly true is shown by experiments with depancreatized animals in which the high sugar content of the blood is greatly decreased by muscular work.

in part, but which also act as poisons, producing the diabetic coma that so commonly leads to death. The excretion of large quantities of urine seems dependent upon the increased intake of water. Peripheral neuritis and various trophic disturbances, sometimes with gangrene of the extremities, are met with, and the patients show such an extraordinarily lowered resistance to bacterial infection that rapidly progressing tuberculosis or generalized and local infections of other sorts may become the actual cause of death.

Pathological Anatomy.—The nature of this process is not made clear by anatomical study at autopsy, for in most cases no gross changes are found in any of the organs which seem capable of explaining the complete upset of the general metabolism. Study of the blood reveals an increased amount of blood sugar. The liver is devoid of glycogen, or nearly so. That usually found in globules or granules in the protoplasm of the liver cells is gone, and the nuclei of the cells, which are swollen, now contain whatever glycogen remains in the organ. The muscles have also lost their reserve of glycogen, and this is true of all the tissues except the heart muscle, the leucocytes, and the renal epithelium, particularly, as pointed out by Baehr, that in the terminal part of the first convoluted tubules. Since the time of Claude Bernard who produced glycosuria and hyperglycæmia by injuries to the brain (piqûre) it has been known that this disease is in some way associated with disturbances of the central nervous system, and indeed, various lesions of the brain and spinal cord have been found in cases dying after prolonged glycosuria. But they are very variable lesions and although they seem to cause glycosuria, they do so by no means constantly. It is quite possible that their effects are due to changes in the hypophysis. On the other hand, most cases of outspoken diabetes present no recognizable alterations of the nervous system.

Mering and Minkowski showed that extirpation of the pancreas is followed regularly by all the phenomena of diabetes, and this led to the prevailing view of the predominant importance of the pancreas in this disease. That it was really the loss of the pancreas that produced these results and not injury to the intestine or to the nerves has been proven by the most severe tests. So long as a part of the pancreas remains well supplied with blood, even separated from all its original connections with the intestine, no diabetes appears, but as soon as that fragment is removed from the circulation, even, in suitable experiments, by a single ligature placed on its blood-vessels, hyperglycæmia and glycosuria appear at once.

Lesions may, therefore, be sought in the pancreas in cases of diabetes. It must be said that while various changes are found it usually requires a certain complaisance to ascribe the extreme diabetic symptoms to them because they are practically never destructive enough to be compared with the extirpation of the gland. Nevertheless, as we shall see, there are other things which enhance the effect of a partial destruction of the gland.

Further, it may well be that the destruction of an inconspicuous constituent of the gland will be followed by results out of proportion to the change in its gross appearance. It is well known that while the acinar parts of the pancreas secrete the pancreatic juice into the intestine by way of the duct, the islands of Langerhans have no direct connection with them or with the ducts, but are isolated groups of cells with very rich blood-supply scattered through the organ. The cells do not resemble those lining the acini in

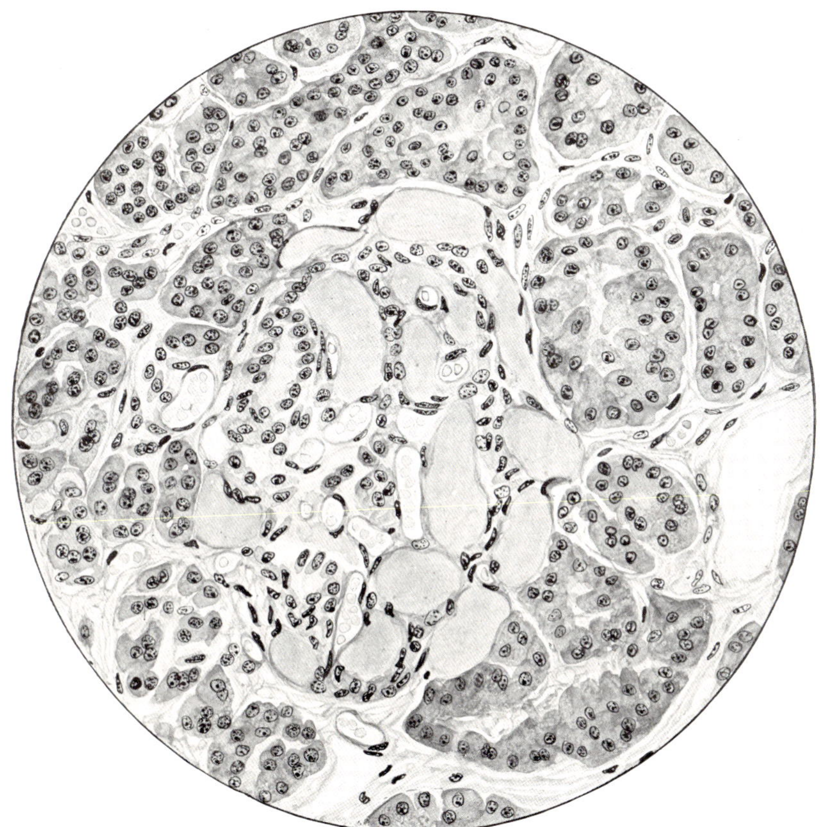

Fig. 431.—Hyaline island of Langerhans from a case of diabetes.

form or arrangement. Their protoplasmic granules are quite different and much finer and the cells are connected in an irregular network.

By special stains one may even recognize two kinds of cells in these islands distinguished by their different types of granules. The names of Opie, Schæfer, and Ssobolew are connected with the idea that these islands are responsible for maintaining at least one part of the chain of events in the metabolism of carbohydrates, and that they may be regarded as the structures in the pancreas which produce an internal secretion which is liberated into the blood. Opie described a case of severe diabetes in which practically all of the islands of Langerhans were converted into hyaline, inert masses in which living cells could no longer be seen (Fig. 431). The rest of the pancreas was normal, and naturally such an inconspicuous lesion produced no change in the gross appearance. Were this a constant finding there would be little difficulty in establishing this plausible theory of the relation of the islands to diabetes, but there are many cases of diabetes in which no such universal destruction of the islands is found. Instead, one finds very often a fine scarring of the organ analogous to cirrhosis of the liver or sometimes no recognizable change at all. Hence there are many who refuse to believe in the specific relation of the islands of Langerhans to diabetes and think rather that the whole glandular substance of the pan-

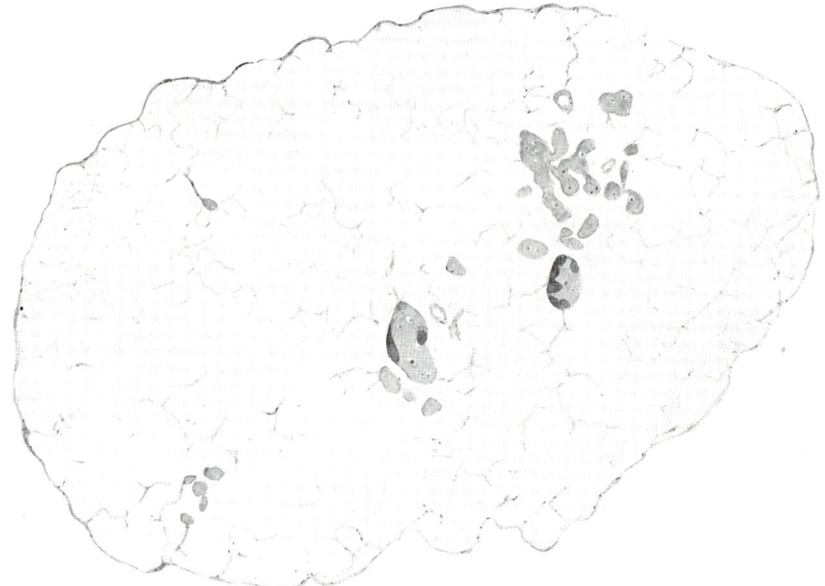

Fig. 432.—Pancreas of guinea-pig one year after ligation of the ducts. The islands of Langerhans alone remain, embedded in fat.

creas is concerned. Nevertheless Cecil, in studying a large number of cases of diabetes, found pancreatic lesions in more than 87 per cent. and showed that in these the islands of Langerhans were always affected; in about 12 per cent. the islands alone were injured.

Certain experimental studies furnish, it seems, the only unassailable evidence in this connection. The ligature of the pancreatic ducts results in atrophy of the acini, but since the islands of Langerhans have no connection with these they do not suffer and no glycosuria results. In one type of experiment, half of the pancreas was thus ligated off, and the animal survived perfectly well. After a year such an animal (dog or guinea-pig) showed the complete reduction of the ligated part to a thin, transparent film in the mesentery; extirpation of the remaining intact half of the pancreas was followed in such an experiment by transient glycosuria, but after one day of this the animal showed no symptoms whatever and could assimilate large amounts of glucose or starch. After a month, the transparent film which represented the other half of the pancreas was extirpated, and then the animal was plunged into the severest diabetes. This film contained only islands of Langerhans, as was proved in the case of the guinea-pig at least by the special stain of Bensley (MacCallum: Johns Hopkins Hosp. Bull., 1909, xx, 222; Kirkbride: J. Exp. Med., 1912, xv, 101) (Figs. 432, 433).

Other investigators have sometimes found destructive changes in the

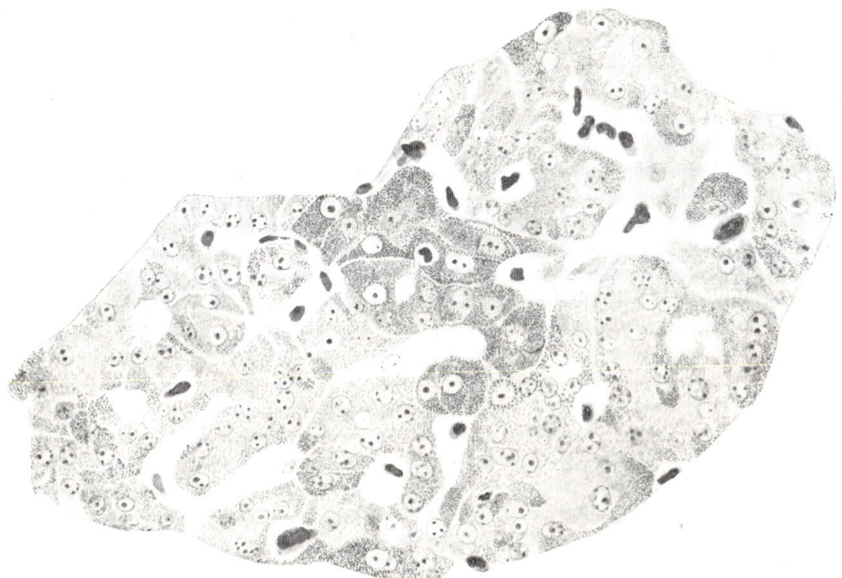

Fig. 433.—Island of Langerhans enlarged from Fig. 432. The sharp differential staining of the granules shows that the cells are intact.

islands after such obstruction of the ducts, but it seems that the weight of evidence is at present in favor of the belief that the islands are the specific organs of internal secretion.

It is true that in many cases of diabetes it is difficult if not impossible to demonstrate any lesion in the pancreas, and then it may be necessary to assume that some extra-pancreatic cause has brought about the disease, but in such studies as that of Cecil, changes in the islands are found in an overwhelming proportion of the cases.

Thus, while it is not invariably possible to demonstrate the existence of lesions of the pancreas in cases of diabetes, they are usually found; on the other hand, the whole symptom-complex can be produced by extirpation of the organ and not in any other way, although transient glycosuria may have many other causes. The rôle of the pancreas in diabetes must therefore be regarded as very important.

Nature of Disturbance of Carbohydrate Metabolism.—Experimental and physiological studies have thrown more light on the nature of the disease than has anatomical investigation.

Carbohydrates are transported in the body to the tissues, which need them as energy producers, in the form of grape-sugar or dextrose. Only monosaccharids, such as dextrose, maltose, and levulose, can be consumed by these tissues; others, such as cane-sugar, if injected into the blood are excreted unchanged. Therefore starch and allied substances and cane-sugar are hydrolyzed by the action of ferments in the intestinal tract, beginning with the ptyalin of the saliva and ending with the diastase of the pancreatic secretion, into one of these simpler sugars. Starch acted upon by diastase passes through dextrine to maltose, which is converted into dextrose by another ferment, maltase. Arrived by way of the portal vein in the liver, the dextrose is polymerized, by the action of the liver-cells, into glycogen. Doubtless the liver-cells, like the muscle cells and others capable of elaborating and storing up glycogen from dextrose, do so by the aid of a ferment, but although this may perhaps be a diastase reversing its action, the actual ferment has not been demonstrated. As far as experimental study goes it seems that only living cells are able to bring about this change.

The glycogen is set free from the liver and poured into the blood through the action of a diastatic ferment, glycogenase, which apparently occurs in all the organs and is able to convert glycogen into dextrose through several steps, in the last of which maltose becomes dextrose through the agency of the ubiquitous maltase.

Liberated in this way, the dextrose is used by the muscles as a source of energy, though the steps of this process are yet shrouded in mystery. In the end it is an oxidation, although the sugar may at first be decomposed into various intermediary substances. Taylor suggests glyoxal, lactic acid, and alcohol, as the successive steps, but this is not established. Much ingenuity and labor has been spent in the attempt to elucidate this process of "glycolysis," and the theory of O. Cohnheim is especially well known although not now generally accepted. He seemed to prove that muscle juice could cause glucose to disappear only when activated by pancreas extract, but it has been shown that this disappearance is not really oxidation of the sugar but only the assumption of another form in which it will no longer reduce copper salts.

But if we do not know the steps in the process, it is fairly clear that sugar is finally oxidized in the working muscles to carbon dioxide and water, and we can recognize the effect of this combustion in the amount of carbon dioxide exhaled as compared with the amount of oxygen consumed in the respired air.

It is well known that this "respiratory quotient" gives some idea of the character of the materials undergoing combustion, for the oxidation of carbohydrate results in the proportion $\frac{CO_2}{O} = 1$, while the combustion of proteins and fats gives a lower figure.

Upon extirpation of the pancreas this whole chain of events is at once disarranged. Probably the sugars are sufficiently well prepared in the intestine and absorbed, although the amylolytic ferment of the pancreas is no longer furnished there.

But when the sugar reaches the liver, it is not stored up as glycogen. Either the loss of the pancreas makes it impossible for the liver-cells to form and store glycogen from the sugar presented, or it allows the diastatic ferment, the glycogenase, to run riot, decomposing at once all the glycogen already lodged in the liver and forestalling the formation of any more.

Since, after the complete destruction of the pancreas, the glycogenase is so active, it seems necessary to conclude that the internal secretion of the pancreas and the glycogenase are very different things.

Set free from the liver, the dextrose circulates in excess (hyperglycæmia), and much is excreted by the kidneys (glycosuria), but none or very little is oxidized in the muscles. This is shown by the lack of any heightening of the respiratory quotient when sugar is fed to such a diabetic, and also by the fact that the amount fed reappears almost quantitatively in the urine.

This would suggest that the tissues had lost their power to consume dextrose for the liberation of energy, and indeed this is a view long held and supported by much evidence. Recent work of Knowlton and Starling, McLeod, Lüthje, and others shows, however, that the tissues of depancreatized animals if perfused with Locke's solution containing dextrose are quite as able to consume the sugar as those of normal animals. The original experiment of Starling and Knowlton with perfusion of normal and diabetic hearts seemed to show that the diabetic heart consumed less sugar than the normal. This, however, was corrected later, since it proved to be due to the increased store of glycogen in the diabetic heart, which was used instead of the sugar of the perfusion fluid. Still it may be that in the diabetic it is the blood-sugar rather than the tissue which is at fault, so that glycolysis is absent because the sugar is in a combined form which is inaccessible.

We are left then with the problem as to whether the hyperglycæmia and glycosuria arise because there is an overliberation of sugar into the blood or because the tissues are unable to consume it.

Hedon states that the introduction of the blood of the pancreatic vein of a normal dog into the portal vein of a depancreatized dog will reduce very greatly the amount of sugar in the urine and also in the blood, as though a necessary ferment were secreted by the pancreas into the blood.

If this be true, it still remains to determine whether the ferment forms glycogen, prevents the dissolution of glycogen into sugar, or causes the more distant glycolysis. The statement that it has no effect except when injected into a branch of the portal vein so as to reach the liver directly suggests that its influence is in connection with the two earlier processes.

Many observations tend to show that other factors than the mere existence of these somewhat hypothetical ferments are concerned in the control of the carbohydrate metabolism, for hyperglycæmia and glycosuria can be induced in a variety of ways. The whole mechanism of carbohydrate control seems to be, to some extent at least, under the influence of the nervous system, especially the sympathetic system. Injury to the brain and especially the so-called piqûre of Claude Bernard produces glycosuria, usually attended, however, by symptoms of asphyxia and circulatory disturbances which in themselves may have similar effects. Stimulation of the splanchnic nerves causes glycosuria without the other phenomena, but fails to do so when the adrenal glands are extirpated. From various experiments it seems that this sympathetic innervation of both adrenals comes from the left splanchnic. Massage of the adrenals or the injection of adrenaline causes glycosuria without stimulation of the nerves, and stimulation of the hepatic sympathetic plexus also does so as long as the adrenals are present, but not when they are extirpated (Nishi, McLeod).

It seems, therefore, that the secretion of the adrenal is a necessary part of the mechanism through which the impulses from the sympathetic passing to the liver promote the setting free of sugar. We may ask then whether the pancreas opposes the action of the sympathetics, since in its absence the sugar is quickly set free and still more quickly if adrenaline be injected.

Interesting relations exist between the secretions of other related organs and this condition of hyperglycæmia and glycosuria, for in the absence of the thyroid it becomes difficult to produce it in any way, while it may appear spontaneously when an excess of the secretion of thyroid or hypophysis is thrown into the circulation. In slighter degrees such modification of the sugar metabolism may be tested for by determining the sugar tolerance, that is, the amount of sugar which may be injected without producing glycosuria, or by the respiratory exchange. These relations and others have been much discussed by Eppinger, Falta, and Rüdinger, who have constructed a sort of formula which expresses them, but which ascribes all the effects to influences exercised upon one organ by another rather than to the chemical antagonisms of their secretions.

Glycosuria may also be produced by caffeine, strychnine, sensory stimuli, and asphyxia (which in its turn may be brought about by various narcotics, ether, chloroform, morphine, etc.), and by curare (Pollak). In other cases (renal poisons or phloridzin poisoning) it seems that there is no hyperglycæmia and that glycosuria arises as a result of renal changes. For information concerning the complex effects of phloridzin poisoning, Lusk's paper may be consulted.

It must not be inferred from what has been said that the carbohydrates alone are disturbed in diabetes nor that sugar is produced from carbohydrates only. Indeed, it has been shown that proteins are split up in such a way in the liver as to liberate certain molecules of sugar, and further it has been possible to determine that certain of the amino-acids which go to build up these proteins are far more capable than others of liberating sugar. Consequently some forms of meat (chicken) are found to furnish more sugar in a diabetic organism than others (beef) (Janney). Many other substances, such as glycerin, glycolaldehyde, glyceric acid, dioxyaceton, have been found to produce sugar in the perfused liver (Emden, Barrenschein).

In pancreatic diabetes when carbohydrates are quite withdrawn from the food sugar may still be excreted, and the amount of this sugar bears a constant relation to the amount of nitrogen excreted. This D:N ratio is thought to represent the relation between the amount of sugar liberated from the protein of the food or of the wasting tissues and the nitrogen of that protein. It is evident that this indicates at least a considerable waste in the proteins, inasmuch as the carbohydrate portion is excreted as such.

Although certain authors, Porges and Salomon, V. Noorden, Raubitschek, and others, claim a formation of sugar from fats, the weight of evidence does not seem to favor this idea. Lipæmia during diabetes is common, fat streaming in visible form in the blood in such a way as to make the serum milky, and accumulating in large cells in the spleen. The origin of this fat is not clearly known.

In the absence of carbohydrate utilization there occurs a peculiar imperfect consumption of fats which is analogous to that seen in the course of starvation, where for another reason no carbohydrate is supplied for energy production to the tissues. For some reason the oxidation of carbohydrates renders easier the complete combustion of fats, and in their absence this is imperfect, oxidation of the fatty acids, at any rate those with an even number of carbon atoms, takes place by the oxidation of the third carbon atom (that is, in the β position) and the splitting off of the terminal carbon atoms. In this way β-oxybutyric acid can be formed from all of these fatty acids, including palmitic, stearic, and oleic (Knoop). But for some time the β-oxybutyric acid does not appear in the urine, but, instead, diacetic acid and acetone, which are successive oxidation products derived from it. Their formulæ are as follows:

β-oxybutyric acid	CH_3—CH OH—CH_2—CO OH
Diacetic acid	CH_3—CO—CH_2—CO OH
Acetone	CH_3—CO—CH_3

These are the so-called acetone bodies, which tend to appear more readily in herbivorous and omnivorous animals than in the purely carnivorous. Diacetic acid and acetone rarely occur in any great amount in the urine, but the β-oxybutyric acid may reach 50 to 100 grams a day, or more. With such disordered fat combustion, toxic phenomena appear which are known as the symptoms of acidosis or acid intoxication. They are quite similar to those produced by the feeding of inorganic acids to rabbits or other herbivorous animals, and consist in a peculiar violent deep respiration or air hunger, and coma. These symptoms may be much relieved by the introduction of large quantities of an alkali, such as sodium bicarbonate. During the gasping for breath the blood is bright red and contains very little carbon dioxide; instead the tissues are loaded with carbon dioxide which the blood is unable to remove, presumably because the acid injected has combined with the sodium of the blood so that it is no longer able to aid in the transport of the carbon dioxide to the lungs. Ordinarily (Wells) it passes to the lungs as bicarbonate, where it is decomposed into the carbonate, liberating CO_2, and returns to the tissues for more. Exactly the same preëmption of the alkali of the blood results from the presence of the organic acids that arise from the decomposition of the fatty acids, and the diabetic dies in coma largely as a result of this kind of asphyxia, unless the alkali is supplied rapidly from the outside. In carnivorous animals ammonia is far more ready to supply the alkali than in the herbivorous ones because, from the character of their food, ammonia is more abundantly produced,

Résumé.—The loss of the function of the pancreas thus precipitates a condition in which carbohydrates are not normally utilized. They are absorbed, but neither stored in the form of glycogen nor readily dissociated in the tissues to supply energy. Proteins supply whatever is possible of the needed energy, but they too liberate from certain of their amino-acid fractions the material for sugar, which promptly becomes useless and circulates until it is excreted. Fats aid in furnishing energy to the tissues, but they too are imperfectly used and become dissociated in the process of oxidation to liberate the series of acetone bodies of which β-oxybutyric acid is the most toxic, and this, evincing part at least of its injurious action in preëmpting the blood alkalies, and thus causing tissue asphyxia, brings about the characteristic air hunger and coma in which many of the victims of severe diabetes die.

Where the pancreas exerts its function, and precisely what are its relations with the nervous system and the other organs of internal secretion, is even yet very obscure.

LITERATURE

Baehr: Ziegler's Beitr., 1913, lvi, 1.
R. L. Cecil: Jour. Exp. Med., 1909, xi, 266.
Nishi: Arch. f. exp. Path., 1909, lxi, 186.
Eppinger, Falta, and Rüdinger: Ztschr. f. klin. Med., 1908, lxvi, 1.
Lusk: Erg. d. Physiol., 1912, xii, 315; Science of Nutrition, Phila., 1909.
Pollak: Arch. f. exp. Path., 1909, lxi, 376.
Emden, Schmitz, and Wittenberg: Ztschr. f. phys. Chem., 1913, lxxxviii, 210; 1914, xci, 251.
Barrenschein: Bioch. Ztschr., 1914, lviii, 277.
Raubitschek: Pflüger's Arch., 1913, clv, 68.
McLeod: Diabetes, London, 1913.
Allen: Glycosuria and Diabetes, Cambridge, 1913.
Gigon: Ergebn. d. inn. Med. u. Kinderh., 1912, ix, 206.
Benedict and Joslin: Metabolism in Diabetes, Trans. Assoc. Amer. Physicians, 1910, xxv, 172; and 1912, xxvii, 93.
Wells: Chemical Pathology, Phila., 1914.

Disturbances of the Functions of the Thyroid Gland

The thyroid, arising from a median and two lateral rudiments from the fifth branchial arch, is composed finally of two lateral masses in some animals, of a fused organ in others, the isthmus of connection in man crossing in front of the trachea. The original duct opening at the root of the tongue is interrupted by the growth of the hyoid bone, but occasionally there are remnants of glandular tissue left about the foramen cæcum, which represents its outlet. The alveolar structure of the mature gland, its relation to blood-vessels, and its colloid secretion, and the surmises about the fate of that secretion, are discussed in all text-books of histology and physiology.

So, too, for that matter, are most of the dramatic effects of the loss of its function or its overactivity, and every one knows of its iodine content. But even so we are very ignorant of most of its relations to other organs, and the actual nature of its function is still rather obscure.

In early infantile life the alveoli are small and contain very little colloid; later they show the homogeneous colloid which may at times become inspissated into an almost solid mass, floating in the more recently secreted fluid. How the colloid leaves the alveoli and enters lymphatics or veins has not been determined, although there are many theories.

Physiology.—Destruction of the thyroid gland in animals by operative extirpation is not easy, because there are practically always numerous minute accessory nodules of thyroid tissue scattered in the neck, in the thymus, and inside the pericardium (Halsted). On this account it is difficult to produce experimentally the effects of the loss of the gland. The difficulty is increased by the fact that in some animals (cat, dog, etc.) the parathyroid glands are very closely associated with the thyroid, and if they be destroyed in the operation, the slowly developing effects of thyroidectomy will never really appear because the animal dies quickly from the loss of the parathyroids.

It is in very young animals that careful removal of the thyroids, leaving some of the parathyroids intact, produces the most remarkable changes, changes which are the counterpart of those observed in children in whom some disease has destroyed the thyroid leaving the other glands unaffected. But in adult human beings and animals similar, if less extreme, changes are also brought about.

MYXŒDEMA

The child devoid of thyroid tissue begins to show symptoms after it has ceased to nurse, and these consist essentially in the practical cessation of growth and development. The rate of metabolism is greatly decreased, the temperature is low, relatively little food is taken, and all the functions of the bodily organs are retarded. Mentally the child remains at the stage at which the destruction of the thyroid found it. Sexually it ceases to develop, and after twenty or thirty years of life it is still an infant in these respects, although the skin may be wrinkled and the hair sparse. Nothing expressed the situation better than the phrase "a sad old child" which some one has used.

Such children may become very obese, but they do not grow in stature, because the process of bone formation is retarded, not merely at the epiphyses, as in chondrodystrophy (*q. v.*), but throughout, so that a delicate small skeleton is produced in which all the cartilaginous epiphyseal lines and junctions remain as cartilage until very late in life.

In one case dissected some years ago a few of the permanent teeth had appeared, crowding inside the milk teeth, all of which were still present. The sternum was in several parts at fifteen years of age, and the three pelvic bones were still joined only by cartilage in the acetabulum. The thyroid was reduced to a minute mass of distorted alveoli about the foramen cæcum, and two extremely small cystic nodules somewhere in the position of the lateral lobes. These were smaller than the parathyroid glands, which were perfectly well preserved, and this is a common finding. The hypophysis was rather large, and gave the impression of being in process of hypertrophy.

Such a state might well be the end result of a destructive infection, such as is known to occur, without actual abscess formation, in the thyroid, or it might possibly be thought of as a congenital defect, but even then it seems more plausible to regard it as the outcome of some intra-uterine disease. This girl was an idiot with the intelligence of a young infant.

In adults the thyroid may be destroyed by operation or by disease, to a degree sufficient to produce a condition which closely resembles that seen in children, in so far as the already attained development will allow. Any further growth is stopped, and mental and sexual activity rapidly recedes, so that these people quickly becomes sexually impotent and mentally dulled. They grow sluggish and cold, appetite fails, metabolism is decreased, the skin becomes dry and scaly, and in a curious way thickened and dense. Heavy pads form in a characteristic way below the clavicles and elsewhere, and over the face and forehead the skin may feel as though there were a thick, pasty elastic infiltration in its deeper layers, so that it cannot be easily pinched up into a fold. Actually, there is said to be an accumulation of a bluish-staining semifluid material there, which was thought to have a mucoid character, and hence the name *myxœdema*, which was given long ago by Gull. The patients may or may not become very fat, heart-beat and respiration are slowed, and the carbon dioxide output is lowered.

There are all imaginable grades of this thyroid insufficiency, and the slighter ones are difficult to recognize, but in the more complete degrees the effects are overwhelming. In a relatively short time if there is no therapeutic intervention the patient sinks into a state of idiocy and physical torpor such that one is reminded rather of the life of a vegetable than that of a human being.

The proof that all this is due to the loss of the thyroid lies in the fact that the daily long-continued administration by mouth of an extract of the thyroid of some animal will restore such an inert being to life and activity. The child grows and develops and brightens into a normal person. The adult is transformed to his old self, the whole machinery quickens its rate, the skin becomes thin and moist, and the hair grows. The face loses its dull, bloated appearance, and the tongue its thickness and sluggishness, and words and ideas come back. It is as though the regulator of an engine were reset at the normal point. The same effect has sometimes been attained by the transplantation of thyroid tissue into the patient, or has appeared gradually with the increase in size through compensatory hypertrophy, of some fragment or accessory nodule left intact, or even with the growth of a metastasis from a malignant tumor of the thyroid, through the surgical extirpation of which the myxœdema arose.

In these persons, as in animals, it is found, by studying the metabolism, that the output of nitrogen in the urine is greatly decreased, that the intake of oxygen and the discharge of carbon dioxide are similarly on a lower level.

Unless the appetite is greatly decreased, there is apt to be a gradual increase in weight under these circumstances, and most of this is in the form of fat. Since the oxidation is thus decreased in the restricted metabolism of the muscles and other organs, the production of heat is diminished, and this may reach the point where the regulatory mechanism is unable to maintain the normal standard of bodily temperature, so that it falls even several degrees.

Carbohydrate metabolism is affected in such a way that it becomes practically impossible to produce an alimentary glycosuria, that is, to cause the elimination of sugar in the urine by feeding it in excessive amounts. Even those drugs and nervous disturbances which ordinarily produce glycosuria fail to do so, or succeed only when pushed to extremes. Adrenaline, which in relatively small doses produces hyperglycæmia and glycosuria, fails to do this in the absence of the thyroid, or does so only when given in far larger doses. Even the glycosuria of depancreatized animals is greatly modified by the loss of the thyroid, although not entirely abolished. It is difficult to give a satisfactory explanation of this. Falta, Rüdinger, and Eppinger regard it as the effect of the loss of the promoting influence of the thyroid upon the chromaffin system, and at the same time the loss of the normal antagonistic effect of the thyroid upon the pancreas. It seems more simple, though, to think of the thyroid secretion as something which plays a rôle in the final processes of oxidation of the sugar, acting in a sense as an antienzyme. Here, however, we tread on uncertain ground, not yet supported by enough experimental results.

CRETINISM

In certain districts, especially in the high valleys of the Alpine region, and in similar mountainous parts of other countries, a considerable proportion of the inhabitants are defective in a way very like that of the sporadic or scattered cases of myxœdema.

Unlike the myxœdema cases which occur anywhere and everywhere, regardless of environment or hereditary taint, these people, known as *cretins*, are found in regions where the condition seems to be endemic or inherent in the environment, and we can usually trace in their parents or ancestors some similar thyroid defect.

In the cases of myxœdema one may often determine the cause of the destruction of the gland, and find minute remnants of it at autopsy. In the cretins there is commonly a great enlargement of the thyroid, which none the less seems to be deficient in its function. Every grade of severity in the physical and psychical disturbance is found here also. Some cretins are able to earn a living and procreate children, others are stunted idiots. Thyroid treatment seems far less brilliant in its results with them than with the cases of myxœdema, but still accomplishes something.

The nature of this process has been earnestly studied, since it affects thousands in France, Italy, Switzerland, and Austria, but as yet without any clear result.

Bircher thought it occurred in people who live in a country formed by strata which had once been submerged under the ocean, and not in those living on strata formed under fresh water or on volcanic formations. The introduction of a new water supply from a district of different character into one of these foci (Aarau) seemed to bring with it a great decrease in the number of new cases and improvement in the old.

Bacteria have been sought in the drinking-water and found, together with many other forms of life, but it could not be proved that they bore any relation to the disease. Still the goitre could be produced, even in animals, by giving them the water from wells and springs in the affected districts, and so firmly fixed is the idea of this connection, that some of these springs are called "Kropfbrunnen," or goitre springs. But animals fed on imported food and water and kept in the district also acquire goitres. The water will produce goitre in animals kept in another country; the agency, whatever it is, will not pass through a dialyzing membrane, and therefore it must be of colloid character, but it will withstand temperatures up to 75° to 80° C. Wherefore it is agreed that it cannot be a living thing, and the problem is still to be solved. Nevertheless there are those who maintain stoutly that it is an infection (McCarrison)

GOITRE

Something has been said of goitre, which is the term long used in general to indicate an enlargement of the thyroid gland. It is not only in cretins that such enlargement occurs. There are various forms, and while one gains the impression that they are more frequently found in certain districts, such as the shores of the Great Lakes in this country, they do appear elsewhere in people and animals which have not been exposed to any recognizable peculiarity of environment. What it is in these goitre districts which produces goitre without especial signs of thyroid deficiency is as obscure as in the case of the cretins. Perhaps it is the same influence, since in the Alpine regions there are many persons afflicted with goitre who are not cretins. About Kingston, in Ontario, and about Cleveland it is especially common, and Marine states that 80 per cent. or more of the stray dogs near Cleveland have enlarged thyroids. Possibly, as he thinks, it may be due to a lack of assimilation of iodine from the food, since iodine has long been known as a remedy in this disease which is more or less efficient in diminishing the size of the gland.

There are many variations in the anatomical character of these enlargements, many combinations and progressive alterations, but there seem to be two essentially different forms which constitute the basis for all these variations.

In one of these, the so-called *colloid* or *gelatinous goitre*, the gland is fairly uniformly enlarged, because every alveolus is increased in size and distended with colloid, even to such a degree that the lining epithelium is flattened to a scale-like form. Such a goitre, on section, is rather soft and translucent, like amber, and uniform in appearance throughout, although there are often hæmorrhages or necroses, or the scars which result from these. The alveoli filled with clear colloid are often so large that they are visible to the naked eye.

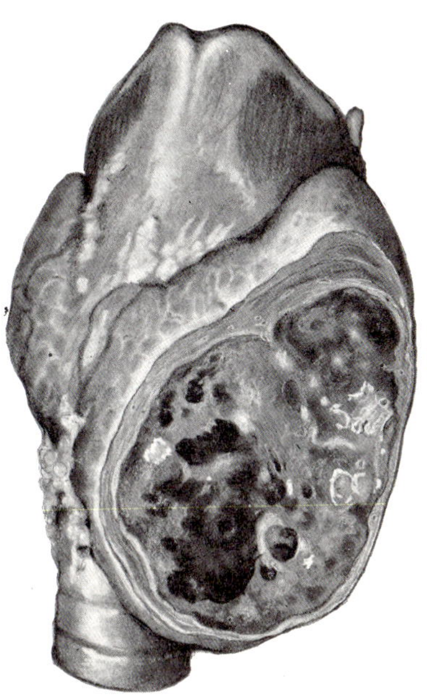

Fig. 434.—Large adenoma of thyroid. The nodule is sharply outlined and surrounded by compressed thyroid tissue. Necroses, hæmorrhages, and areas of calcification in its substance.

The other form, frequently combined with this, but also occurring alone, seems to begin in young persons about the time of puberty, and to progress very slowly. It is not a diffuse enlargement, but is produced by the presence of one or many circumscribed nodules made up of a tissue different in appearance from the surrounding thyroid, which becomes greatly compressed by the sharply outlined nodules. In their fresher state these nodules are elastic, and on section show a smooth swelling, finely granular, or velvety surface, which is grayish white or flecked with small diffuse hæmorrhages (Fig. 434). Microscopically, it is seen to be made up of many small round alveoli lined with rather high cubical epithelium, inclosing a small lumen which usually contains little or no colloid (Fig. 535). The alveoli are not, as a rule, closely packed together, but are separated by an abundant, rather œdematous looking stroma, rich in blood-vessels, from which interalveolar hæmorrhages are often seen to have arisen. In some cases the alveoli are larger and more irregular in form and filled with colloid. Indeed one occasionally finds nodules of almost the character of the colloid goitre. After they have existed for a time necroses arise in the central portion and appear as opaque yellow areas. They may become calcified, or they soften so that the nodule becomes a cyst, with turbid and blood-stained liquid contents, which in time may become, in turn, a clear yellow fluid. The rind of the nodule persists, often with extensive calcification, and is deeply pigmented with hæmosiderin from the blood which was extravasated in the interior.

These seem to be tumor-like growths or adenomata. It is true that

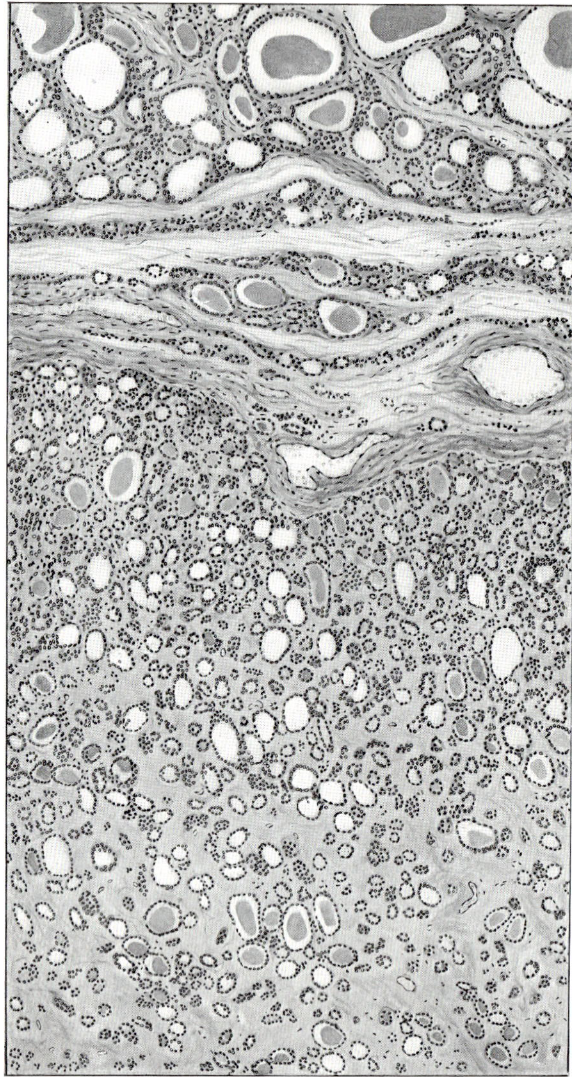

Fig. 435.—Circumscribed adenomatous nodule of the thyroid. The surrounding tissue is somewhat compressed. The alveoli of the nodule are small and round, and are embedded in abundant stroma.

their structure bears a faint resemblance to that of the fœtal thyroid in the lack of colloid, but I do not think it justifiable to call them, as Wölfler does, fœtal adenomata, since there is no evidence whatever that there is anything fœtal about them. Instead, the condition might be called *adenomatous* or *nodular goitre.*

Both of these forms, or combinations of them, even when considerable scarring has taken place, seem to be compatible with practically normal life, without any evidences of deficiency or excess of thyroid function.

If anything, it would seem that the error would be on the side of deficiency, since the colloid is found on analysis to be relatively poor in iodine (which may perhaps be taken as an indication of the efficiency of the gland), but the quantity of colloid is so increased in the first form that the total amount of iodine may exceed the normal. It leads one to the idea that the enlargement may be a compensatory phenomenon, an attempt to make up in bulk what is deficient in quality of the colloid.

It has long been recognized that there is some connection between iodine and the thyroid; poultices of burnt seaweed which contains iodine were long ago applied with effect in the attempt to reduce the size of goitres, and in a similar way iodine has been painted on the skin over them. Baumann isolated an iodine-containing protein material which he regarded as a characteristic constituent of the thyroid, while Oswald later determined that this substance is a globulin, and named it thyreoglobulin. Its iodine content varies in different glands, and indeed may be changed at will by the administration of iodine, much as the iodine content of other organs is affected, but in a far more striking degree. The lipoid contents of the gland, while showing a certain avidity for iodine, seems to play no important part in the actual iodine interchange of the gland (Howe).

Marine has shown that the iodine content of the thyroid is in inverse proportion to the activity of its efforts at hyperplasia. This hyperplasia involves the new formation of epithelium, which is thrown up into folds, and usually the diminution or dispppearance of the colloid. The administration of iodine has the remarkable effect of checking the hyperplastic epithelial growth and restoring the gland to its colloid-filled state. When the hyperplasia is already advanced, the nearest approach to the normal gland attained by giving iodine is seen in an organ whose alveoli are rather overstretched with colloid. Marine therefore looks upon such epithelial hyperplasia as a normal effort to compensate for an insufficiency due to inability to absorb or assimilate sufficient iodine. Probably the long-recognized reduction in the bulk of colloid goitres upon the application of iodine may be due to the concentration of the iodine content of the dilute colloid, and a consequent reduction in its amount.

Although the functional activity of such enlarged and distorted thyroid glands may not be strikingly disturbed, the mechanical effects upon the neighboring organs are often serious. The goitre may be so large as to be very unsightly, and impede the movements of the head, but more important than this are the results of pressure upon the trachea, the œsophagus, and the circulatory organs.

Lateral pressure upon the trachea frequently reduces its calibre to a narrow slit, with distortion and softening of the cartilages, so that extreme dyspnœa, emphysema of the lungs, etc., may ensue. Dysphagia from compression of the œsophagus is far less common, but the circulation is sometimes embarrassed, so that palpitations and tachycardia and finally cardiac hypertrophy are brought about.

Minnich, who has made a study of such goitre hearts, points out the mechanical strain offered in the lesser circulation by the effects of dyspnœa, but thinks that even more frequently the circulation is disturbed by alterations in the secretions of the thyroid, which affect the nervous regulators of the heart, diminishing especially the action of the depressor and allowing the heart to be overworked.

An interesting if rare form of enlargement of the thyroid is the so-called plunging goitre, which hangs down behind the sternum and moves up and down, in and out of the thorax, with respirations.

EXOPHTHALMIC GOITRE

Most interesting of all the diseases which affect the thyroid is this so-called Graves' or Basedow's disease, in which, at least, there are active symptoms

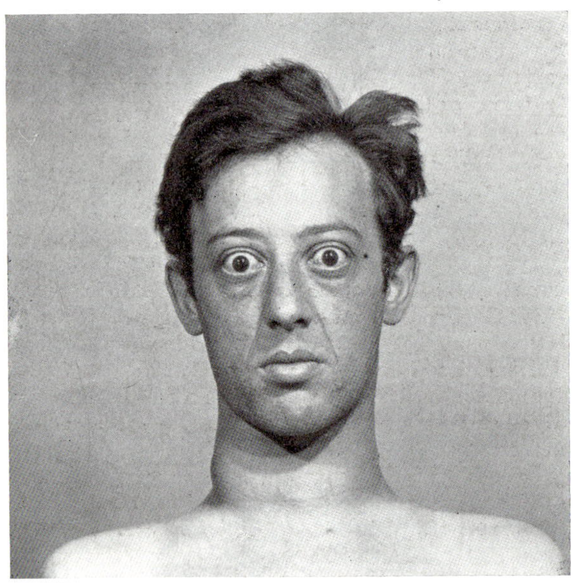

Fig. 436.—Exophthalmic goitre. The patient shows a goitre of moderate size; great exophthalmos, smooth forehead, and abnormal expression.

in place of the sluggish effects met with in the diseases following upon deficiencies in the thyroid glands. But here the nature of the relation of the symptoms to the thyroid is not so clear, although it is commonly looked upon as the effect of overactivity of the gland.

The disease is common, occurring sporadically everywhere without recognizable relation to any particular district, and much more frequently in women than in men. Extremes of age have been reported, but it is essentially an affection of young and middle-aged adults. It begins without any very obvious causes, after recovery from some infection or often after some violent emotional disturbance or fright, sometimes appearing suddenly in its full intensity, more frequently developing gradually. The more prominent disturbances of function are briefly as follows: there are nervousness and irritability, the patient being agitated and perturbed by occurrences which would produce little impression on a normal person; the skin is flushed and moist, and the patient feels hot; the heart beats very rapidly and forcibly, and the peripheral vessels are distended and thump. There is tremor; the eyes protrude abnormally, so that the eyelids may fail to cover them properly; there are disturbances in the motility of the eyelids and of the forehead (Fig. 436). There is often, though not always, enlargement of the thyroid, and finally, in spite of the good appetite, the patient wastes away. Nitrogenous metabolism is increased, as judged by the excretion of nitrogen in the urine; the calorimeter shows an increased dissipation of energy. The tolerance for sugar is lowered, and glycosuria is readily brought about or occurs spontaneously, since the storage of carbohydrate is so unstable.

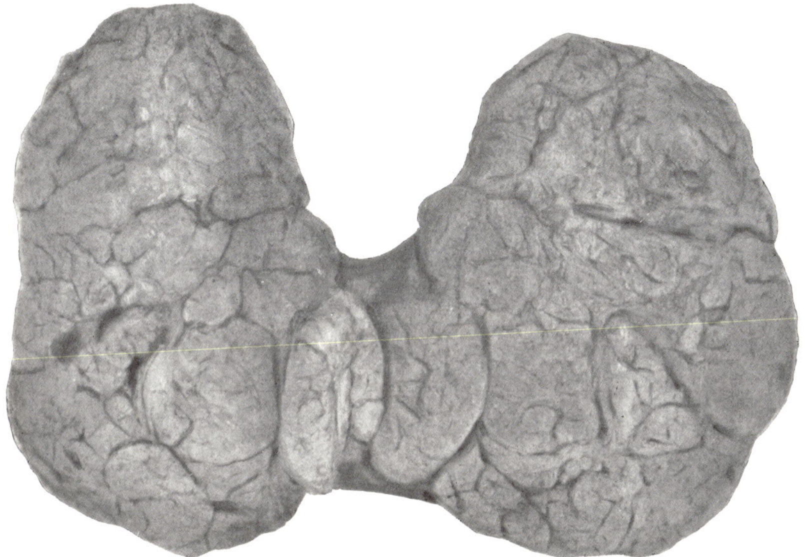

Fig. 437.—Exophthalmic goitre. Gross external appearance of the thyroid.

Such patients are more or less incapacitated, but some of them go on for years and die of an intercurrent affection. Others develop symptoms of such intensity that they die from the disease itself, often with mental derangement, with cardiac dilatation, with excessive vomiting, or with exhaustion from any of these.

At autopsy fairly constant changes are found in the thyroid, in the thymus, and in the lymphoid structures. The heart is frequently hypertrophied, but there are no very obvious changes in the other organs. The brain, in spite of most diligent search, has shown nothing constant.

The Thyroid.—Many descriptions of the thyroid alterations have been given and many subdivisions made, but it is doubtful whether these classifications have any great significance. Many stages or degrees of alteration are found in the gland, and these must be studied in detailed reports on this subject (A. Kocher, etc.). There is not always a great enlargement of the gland, and sometimes it cannot be palpated. When the thyroid is exposed at operation, it is found to be very richly supplied with blood, and over the surface course huge distended veins whose walls tear

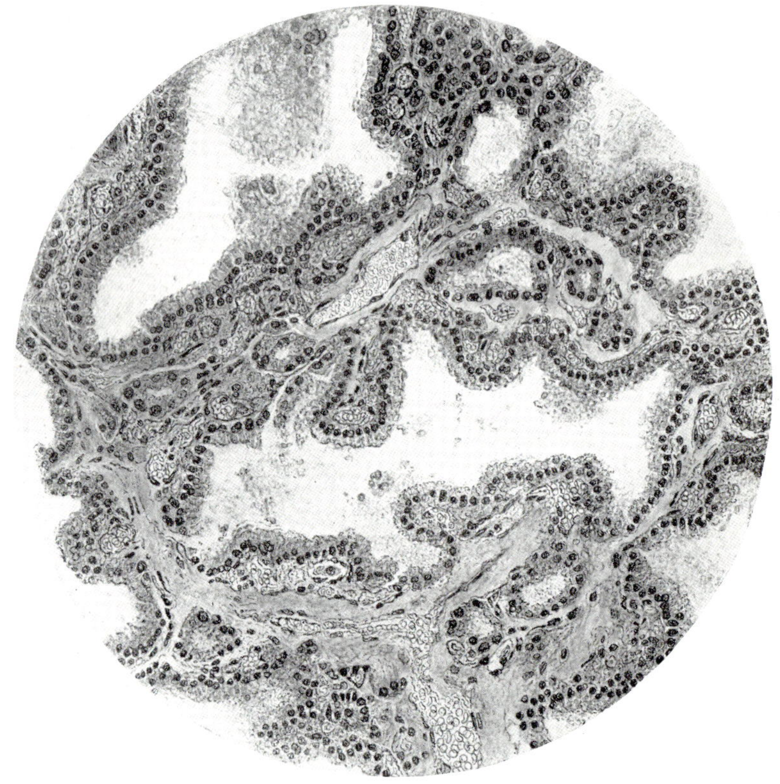

Fig. 438.—Exophthalmic goitre. Alveoli are irregular in form, lined with columnar epithelium, and almost devoid of colloid. The stroma is increased in quantity.

readily, so that the risk of hæmorrhage is great in these operations. After removal, when the blood runs out, the gland appears pale, dense, and hard, and on section its cut surface is both finely and coarsely lobulated, opaque, and of a pale, grayish-pink color (Fig. 437). Little or no colloid can be found. On the other hand, there are some cases in which colloid is abundant, so that the characteristic gross appearance of opacity is not produced.

Microscopically, there is found in the most typical cases an alteration of the gland (Fig. 438) which closely resembles that recognized as a compensatory hyperplasia in the remnant of the thyroid of a normal animal, some time after a large part of the gland has been extirpated. The alveoli are no longer uniform in size or shape, and contain little or no colloid. What they do contain is no longer homogeneous or refractive, but granular or shreddy, like a thin, coagulated fluid. The epithelium, instead of being flattened or low cubical, is high and often distinctly columnar, and is so increased in amount that it is thrown up into folds, giving to the alveolus an irregular outline, with papillary ingrowths encroaching greatly upon the cavity. Commonly many very small alveoli are associated with each larger one, and one sometimes receives the impression that many of these are merely cross-sections of the bays which project from the larger ones. The stroma is frequently but not always fortified by scar tissue, sometimes to such an extent as to suggest a cirrhotic condition. Definite lymphoid nodules are often found scattered through the gland, an appearance which, while fairly characteristic of this disease, is rarely if ever seen in the normal thyroid.

These changes may sometimes be recognized as beginning in patches scattered through the normal gland, but in most cases they appear gradually and diffusely throughout the organ. They are constantly found, in some stage of development, although in any large series one finds several cases in which, although the symptoms are definite and intense, the alveoli of the thyroid are still large and fairly uniform in outline and filled with colloid. The various modifications of this anatomical picture which involve reduplication of the epithelial lining, distortion and irregularity in the form of the cells, desquamation of the epithelium, etc., must be read in such papers as that of Kocher.

The thymus, which is ordinarily atrophied in adult life except for microscopical remnants, is found to be greatly enlarged. This has been constant in the autopsies which I have seen, and in some cases it has presented itself as an organ almost the size of one's hand. Hassal's bodies persist, and the small cells are in such excess that the ordinary distinction between medulla and cortex is obscured. Dr. Halsted discusses its importance in connection with the symptoms and the favorable effect of its extirpation.

The lymph-glands, especially in the neck, are often markedly enlarged. In some cases this increase in the bulk of the lymphoid tissue occurs throughout the body, even the solitary nodules in the intestine projecting as gray prominences. Together with this, which corresponds with the finding of new lymph-nodes in the substance of the thyroid, there is a distinct lymphocytosis (Kocher), which is reduced to normal when the thymus is removed (Capelle and Bayer).

Conceptions of Nature and Cause of the Disease.—In spite of all investigation, the nature of this disease is still in doubt. Since the statements of Möbius it has been most commonly thought of as the effect of hypersecretion or perhaps an altered secretion on the part of the thyroid, without any further curiosity being shown as to what might cause this altered activity of the thyroid. The main support for this lies in the recognition (by the acetonitrile method of Hunt) of excess of thyroid secretion in the circulating blood, in the increased nitrogenous metabolism during the disease, in the harmful effects of thyroid extract, and in the peculiar hypertrophic changes in the thyroid itself. The lack of colloid there is ascribed to the rapidity of its removal by the passing blood. Further, the view is supported by the beneficial effects of removing part of the thyroid or of ligating the thyroid arteries.

Opposed to this view are the following facts: the thyroid gland and the colloid contain less iodine than the normal gland; after extensive operative extirpation, or even in the natural course of the disease, symptoms of myxœdema which surely indicate insufficiency, may arise, while the symptoms of exophthalmic goitre are still present and intense. Nor do the symptoms of exophthalmic goitre disappear with any precision upon the removal of half or more of the gland, as they should if they were merely the result of an excessive secretion. What actually happens is that the recognized influence of the thyroid in promoting nitrogenous katabolism is halted by the loss of the gland, and for a time the patient, in spite of her other symptoms, gains weight. Nevertheless, with the compensatory growth of the thyroid the weight sinks again. Further, it is impossible to reproduce exactly the whole symptom complex by administering an excess of thyroid secretion, although some of the phenomena can thus be brought about.

On the whole, it seems clear that while the thyroid is profoundly affected, and through the disturbance of its function does cause many of the symptoms, it is not alone responsible, but forms part in a chain or circle in which notably the sympathetic system and probably the other organs of internal secretion, perhaps especially the thymus, are concerned. This is true, as we have seen, in most of the diseases which involve these organs, and in their study we are more and more impressed with their close interrelation.

Cannon has recently reported an ingenious experiment which may shed much light on the affection, although in itself it must be regarded as a purely artificial imitation of the disease. He anastomosed the phrenic nerve, which sends an impulse with every breath to the diaphragm, with the cervical sympathetic, which gives sympathetic fibres to the thyroid. After the time necessary for the functional union of the two nerves had passed, he found that the animals (cats) showed practically all the symptoms of exophthalmic goitre, tachycardia, diarrhœa, greatly increased appetite, emaciation, an increase of 150 per cent. in the nitrogenous metabolism, exophthalmos, and, while in the dark, a rhythmic expansion and contraction of the pupil with each breath.

On the basis of such experiments he thinks that in exophthalmic goitre there may be a lowering of the threshold which normally limits the passage of sympathetic stimuli to the organs, and that the overactivity of the thyroid and the consequent symptoms are due primarily to a disturbance of the central nervous system and the preponderance of the sympathetic over the autonomic stimuli. (For a discussion of the relation of sympathetic to autonomic nerve influences see Barker, Trans. Assoc. Amer. Phys., 1912, xxvii, 491.)

THYROID LITERATURE

Halsted: Jour. Exp. Med., 1912, xv, 205.
v. Eiselsberg: Krankh. d. Schilddrüse, Dtsche. Chirurgie, 1901, 38.
Marine: Arch. Int. Med., 1909, iv, 440; 1911, vii, 506.
Oswald: Chemische Beschaffenheit d. Schilddrüse, Strassburg, 1900.
Minnich: Das Kropfherz, Leipzig, 1904.
Möbius: Die Basedow'sche Krankheit, Wien, 1906.
A. Kocher: Virch. Arch., 1912, ccviii, 86.
MacCallum: Jour. Am. Med. Assoc., 1905, xlix, 1158.
Halsted: J. H. H. Bull., 1914, xxv, 223; Harvey Lectures, 1913–1914, ix, 224.
Capelle and Bayer: Beitr. z. klin. Chir., 1913, lxxxvi, 509.

CHAPTER XLIII

DISEASES DUE TO INJURIES OF THE ORGANS OF INTERNAL SECRETION (Continued)

The parathyroid: Anatomy, physiology. Tetany, hyperexcitability of nerves. Relation to calcium metabolism, pathological anatomy. Other types of tetany. Thymus: Anatomy, evolution, and involution. Hyperplasia. Thymus in exophthalmic goitre, in myasthenia gravis, in status thymico-lymphaticus; accidental involution. Adrenal: Anatomy. Function of medulla, functions of cortex. Addison's disease.

DISTURBANCES OF FUNCTION OF THE PARATHYROID GLANDS

The parathyroid glands arising from the walls of the third and fourth branchial clefts come to lie in man in various situations along the posterior edge of the thyroid, and are usually four in number. They are brown and soft, with conspicuous peripheral veins, and are composed of anastomosing strands of cells many of which have a very clear protoplasm in early youth, while in later life the predominant cells have a slightly granular cytoplasm, a few groups standing out by reason of their small dark nuclei and their bright eosinophile protoplasm. Differences in the function of these cells are not understood.

Experimental study has shown convincingly enough the complete independence of these organs, although there are still writers who claim that they are merely undeveloped portions of thyroid tissue. That they are intimately related functionally in the community of organs of internal secretion is, however, pretty certain, although it is not yet possible to outline precisely the part that they play.

Physiology.—When the parathyroids are completely extirpated, a period of twelve hours to several days elapses during which there are no symptoms, but then there appear the evidences of the so-called tetany, which may quickly reach the greatest intensity. Twitchings of various muscles appear, and soon there is a continuous quivering or vibration of the tense muscle, which can be felt as a thrill interrupted by violent convulsive jerks. The whole body becomes rigid, the jaws snap, and every muscle is thrown into violent clonic convulsions. Smooth muscle is said to be affected also, but its participation is inconspicuous. Such convulsions involve the most extreme labor on the part of the muscles, and the temperature rises to fever heat because the dissipation of heat cannot proceed rapidly enough. In the dog respiration becomes very rapid, because that is its way of dissipating heat. Death may occur in such a convulsive seizure, or the tetany may pass off for a time and recur until death follows from complete exhaustion. Sometimes a sort of continuous milder twitching persists for a long time, the animal rapidly wastes and becomes infected, and dies in a kind of cachexia.

All this depends upon the most striking and constant feature of tetany, the hyperexcitability of the motor nerves, with which there appears to be associated a similar hyperexcitability of the sensory nerves.

This hyperexcitability is easily shown, in that a muscular jerk is elicited by a galvanic shock applied over the motor nerve, so weak that it would have no effect under normal conditions. The direction of the current and the character of the shock, whether due to opening or closing of the circuit, must be considered, and the following table will give an average comparison between the shocks necessary to produce a visible muscular contraction in a normal and a tetanic animal.

	Normal Milliamperes	Tetany Milliamperes
Kathode closing	0.3	0.05
Kathode opening	6.0	0.6
Anode closing	1.8	0.8
Anode opening	2.0	0.8

It will be seen that the greatest and most characteristic change is in the reaction to the kathode opening shock; that is, where the kathode of the battery is put on the nerve and the current broken. Practically all the other symptoms seem to depend upon this hyperexcitability of the nervous system.

It was found (MacCallum and Voegtlin) that injection of a salt of calcium would abolish the hyperexcitability and cure all symptoms of tetany, even to the extent of keeping the animal alive and well for months if regularly administered, and it was suspected that a lack of calcium in the circulating fluids and tissues might explain the hyperexcitability of the nerves. As a fact, the blood and nerve tissues of animals in tetany contain a decreased amount of calcium. It was shown (MacCallum) that if an isolated extremity of a normal animal be perfused with blood from another in the height of tetany, the excitability of its nerves would be increased to the tetany level, returning to normal when again perfused with normal blood. Conversely, if one extremity of a dog in tetany be perfused with normal blood, the excitability of the nerves of that leg becomes normal, and that leg ceases to twitch, although the excitability rises and the twitchings begin again if the femoral vessels are reanastomosed with their stumps, so that the leg is again flooded with its own "tetany blood." This blood is poor in calcium, and it seems that the hyperexcitability of ganglion-cells of the central nervous system throughout, as well as the nerve endings, is produced by this, for if one remove calcium from the blood by dialysis (MacCallum and Lambert), and then perfuse an extremity with that blood, exactly the same hyperexcitability is produced. Further evidence in favor of the conception of the parathyroid as an organ presiding in some sense over the calcium metabolism is presented by Erdheim, who finds that in chronic tetany in rats, produced by extirpating almost all of the numerous scattered glands, calcium fails to be deposited in the constantly growing teeth, so that they become soft and break off. Fractured bones heal with only a soft callus, and thus fail to unite firmly. Reimplantation of parathyroid tissue restores the ability of the dentine to calcify and harden, and reëstablishes the ossification process as long as the graft lives.

The influence upon the sympathetic system is not yet worked out, although there are vague indications of hyperexcitability of those nerves after the destruction of the glands.

Metabolism in tetany has been studied, but with unsatisfactory results, and nothing which definitely illuminates the situation has been found (Cooke, Greenwald, etc.).

Tetany in Human Beings.—In human disease the parathyroid plays a part in the various forms of spontaneous and post-operative tetany, and also possibly in certain diseases which exhibit a disturbance in calcification, such as osteomalacia and rickets, although in these their rôle is by no means assured.

The simplest example is undoubtedly the post-operative tetany, in which the parathyroids may have been removed or crushed or their circulation so impaired that they are unable to function. There may remain enough uninjured tissue to reëstablish the function; if the immediate emergency be tided over, as by the administration of calcium, until it can undergo some compensation from hypertrophy, the smallest portion of intact gland substance can maintain normal conditions under favorable circumstances.

It is more difficult to understand those forms of tetany in which there is no disease of the parathyroids, but which seem to arise because conditions are produced in the blood and tissues, which cause tetany, in spite of the presence of normal glands. Such are perhaps the tetany of pregnancy and of lactation, as well as that which occurs when the pylorus is obstructed and there is stagnation of the stomach-contents, with excessive vomiting. There are other forms which seem to be due to intoxications of one sort or another, as with ergot, phosphorus, etc., or simply occur in certain localities or among certain types of workmen. Finally there is the form which affects infants, especially those which are improperly or artificially fed, and which some have thought due to inadequate absorption of calcium, others to hæmorrhages in the parathyroid glands which may have occurred at birth. On the whole, these explanations have not yet been satisfactorily established.

LITERATURE

Frankl Hochwart: Tetanie d. Erwachsenen, Wien, 1909.
Escherich: Tetanie d. Kinder, Wien, 1909.
Erdheim: Mitth. Grenz. d. Med. u. Chir., 1906, xvi, 632.
MacCallum: *Ibid.*, 1913, xxv, 941.
MacCallum and Voegtlin: Jour. Exp. Med., 1909, xi, 118.
MacCallum and Vogel: Jour. Exp. Med., 1913, xviii, 618.
MacCallum and Lambert: Jour. Exp. Med., 1914, xx, 149.
MacCallum: Ergebn. d. innere Medizin, 1913, xi, 569 (Lit.); Jour. Amer. Med. Assoc., 1912, lix, 319.

DISEASES DUE TO THE DISTURBANCES IN THE FUNCTION OF THE THYMUS

The thymus arises in man as a paired ventral outgrowth from the entoderm of the third and fourth branchial clefts, the main portion of the gland being derived from the third cleft.

Its original form is that of a flat pouch. With the gradual thickening of the walls of the sac the original lumen is obliterated, but vestiges of the original canal may be found even in the fully developed organ. In embryos of 30 to 40 mm. the rapid increase in size leads to great convolution of the surface, but although the form of the gland becomes more complicated, the parenchyma maintains its continuity. The right and left lobes remain separate, but there is no formation of isolated lobules.

Two types of cells are distinguishable in the thymus—one, resembling the lymphocyte, being concentrated in especial abundance in what thus becomes the cortex of the organ, while the other, recognized as epithelial in nature, occurs throughout, but is less masked in the central or medullary part.

Long dispute has occurred as to the nature of these cells and their origin, and the controversy is not yet finished. For many years the lymphocytic nature of the small cells was unquestioned, but their origin was attributed by one school (His, Stieda, etc.) to an early invasion of the epithelial elements by wandering mesenchymal cells, by another to a direct differentiation of the epithelial cells into lymphocytes identical with those of the blood-stream and lymphatic tissues (Beard, Kölliker, Prenant, etc.).

Stoehr, in 1906, declared that the small thymus cells were neither genetically nor functionally lymphocytes, but true epithelial cells, while more recently Hammar and Maximow have demonstrated an early invasion of the epithelial cells by migrating lymphocytes which accompany the ingrowing blood-vessels.

Morphologically and biologically the small cells resemble in almost every respect the lymphocytes.

The greater portion of the medulla and the reticular framework of the cortex are formed of derivatives of the original epithelial cells. They tend to arrange themselves in concentric fashion to form the Hassal bodies, which are not vestigial structures, but are constantly being newly formed from hypertrophic epithelial cell complexes. The protoplasm of the epithelial cells has a fibrillary character, and gives rise in places to intracellular fibrils resembling neuroglia fibrils.

There is no fibrous reticulum within the substance of the organ, and only a delicate sheath accompanying the blood-vessels. Opinion is divided as to the significance of the thymus as a blood-forming tissue, aside from its importance as a site for the production of lymphoid cells.

The thymus is thus, if we accept the prevailing view as to the lymphocytic nature of the smaller thymus cells, an organ composed of two genetically distinct types of tissue. These two types of cells, lymphoid and epithelial, are intimately commingled, and in the normal gland there constantly occurs a destruction of the lymphoid cells and phagocytosis of the degenerating cells and pyknotic nuclear fragments, by the larger epithelial cells.

Normal Evolution and Involution.—The thymus reaches its maximum development coincidentally with the maturation of the sexual organs, and then gradually atrophies. This is the normal involution, but since the work of Waldeyer it has been known that even in senescence there are regularly found the strands of thymic tissue containing presumably functioning thymic cells.

In early childhood cortex and medulla cannot be distinguished, as the lymphoid cells are predominant throughout. In later childhood the differentiation between cortex and medulla becomes more pronounced, but from adolescence on there is a progressive reduction in the amount of the parenchyma, the Hassal bodies are brought together, and the interstitial tissue and fat form a large part of the volume of the organ.

Hammar gives a table of normal weights at various ages, from which the following may be extracted:

	Grams
New-born	13.26
6–10 years	26.1
11–15 years	37.52
21–25 years	24.73
56–65 years	16.08
66–75 years	6.0

"Hyperplasia," "Abnormal Persistence" of the Thymus.—Since thymic tissue can be demonstrated in normal individuals at any age, the term abnormal persistence should be dropped, but there are cases in which the thymus fails to undergo involution at the proper time, and others in which there is a renewal of growth after involution has been established. In these latter cases it may attain a weight several times that of the normal organ.

Such hyperplastic glands are found in infants usually unassociated with general lymphoid hyperplasia, in older individuals in connection with various derangements of the organs of internal secretion, particularly thyroid, adrenals, hypophysis, and genital organs, in the so-called myasthenia gravis, and finally in individuals presenting the anatomical features included under the conception of status thymicolymphaticus.

In the form found in infants the thymus may reach a weight of 60 grams at birth, and may actually constitute an obstruction to the respiratory passages or great veins. In older persons the evidence is against the possibility of any such mechanical obstruction, although the literature is full of contradictory statements concerning thymic asthma and other effects of pressure. Nevertheless, the immediate relief of the suffocative attacks which follows the partial removal by the surgeon of the enlarged gland is pretty strong evidence in favor of the idea. There is no evidence that the enlarged thymus can interfere with the function of the vagus, phrenic, or recurrent laryngeal nerves.

The Thymus in Exophthalmic Goitre.—Reference has already been made to the enlargement of the thymus which, according to Capelle and Matti, occurs in 75 to 79 per cent. of the cases. That it is an actual enlargement is clear from the fact that its weight may greatly exceed the normal limits at the height of development. The descriptions of the histological changes are most contradictory, but it seems that they may represent an accentuation of the condition corresponding to the age at which the disease developed. In a young person (twenty-three years) the appearance was that of a child's thymus, the hyperplasia being essentially in the lymphoid elements. The interpretation of the rôle it plays and of the beneficial effects of its operative removal is as yet entirely speculative.

Hyperplasia of the thymus in Addison's disease and acromegaly and in genital hyperplasia or eunuchoidism has been frequently observed and it has been experimentally proven that the involution of the thymus is greatly delayed after castration at an early age.

Myasthenia Gravis.—In about 90 per cent. of the cases of this peculiar disease the thymus is enlarged into a bulky mass, variously regarded as a new-growth or as a simple hyperplasia. There are found lymphoid infiltrations in the skeletal muscles and sometimes in the myocardium, adrenal, and liver.

The Thymus in Status Thymico-lymphaticus.—This condition (already mentioned in Chapter XL), difficult to recognize before puberty, is more definite in adults. There is at least a certain group of individuals who are characterized—(1) By anomalies in the hair distribution; (2) by the rounded conformation of the limbs; (3) by the smooth texture of the skin; (4) by a general lymphatic hyperplasia; (5) by hypoplasia of the aorta and other arterial trunks, and (6) by hypoplasia of the adrenals and the entire chromaffin system.

It is generally assumed that enlargement of the thymus forms a part of this rather vaguely outlined condition, but it requires further study to be sure of this. Pappenheimer, analyzing 28 cases of sudden death in subjects up to thirty-five years of age with the anatomical features of status lymphaticus, found that the beginning of involution of the thymus is delayed to the third decade. The histological picture is in no sense characteristic, although Schridde claims that there is hyperplasia of the medulla with underdevelopment of the cortex. The possibility that there may have been previous involutional changes, thinning the cortex, must be remembered.

There is no proof that the thymus is concerned in the development of status lymphaticus or in the sudden death which sometimes occurs in these persons. It is more logical to believe that it is the incomplete differentiation of secondary sexual characters, which causes the failure of the thymus to undergo involution, and possibly all the other features of status lymphaticus may be best explained in this way too. Nor is there convincing evidence that the sudden death, increased susceptibility to acute infections, trauma, emotional stress, and anæsthesia, is in any way due to hyperfunction or disordered function of the thymus.

Accidental Involution.—Starvation, acute and chronic wasting disease, infections, and exposure to *x*-rays produce rapid degenerative changes in the thymus, leading often to extreme atrophy.

The histological picture produced in this condition, which Hammar has called "accidental involution," varies with the acuteness and severity of the injury and the previous state of involution of the gland. The small thymus cells suffer first, being most susceptible to injurious influences; their nuclei become pyknotic and fragmented, and the débris is taken up by the active phagocytic epithelial elements. The depletion of the cortex may lead to an inversion of the normal picture, the medulla now becoming packed with small cells or their remains. The reticular cells lose their protoplasmic connections, become rounded and vacuolated, and may contain fat-droplets. The Hassal bodies are resistant, and because of the rarefaction of the intervening parenchyma, they become concentrated together. There may occur a sort of sclerosis in this rapid destruction, in contrast to the condition seen in normal involution, in which the parenchyma merely disappears without stirring up the production of any scar tissue.

Otherwise, except in the rate of development, the accidental involution is in principle the same as the normal process.

LITERATURE

Hammar: "Fünfzig Jahre Thymus Forschung," Ergeb. d. Anat. u. Entw., 1909, xix, 1; also Zentralbl. d. exp. Med., 1912, i, 23; *Ibid.*, 1913, iii, 109; *Ibid.*, 1914, v, 55.
Wiesel: Ergebn. d. allg. Path., 1911, xv, 416.
Stöhr: Anat. Hefte, 1906, xxx, 407.
Maximow: Arch. f. mikr. Anat., 1909, lxxiv, 525.
Pappenheimer: Jour. Med. Res., 1910, xviii, 1.
Matti: Mitth. a. d. Grenzgeb. d. Med. u. Chir., 1912, xxiv, 665.
Capelle: Münch. med. Woch., 1908, lv, 1826.

DISTURBANCES IN FUNCTIONS OF THE ADRENAL GLANDS

In the adrenal glands we have organs of complex character long recognized, but only recently known to be intimately related to many other similar organs which are scattered chiefly along the course of the chains of sympathetic ganglia, and known as chromaffine bodies. These chromaffine bodies are of the same character as the medulla of the adrenal glands, which is itself enveloped in a cortical covering of very different nature. In children the so-called Zuckerkandl organ is a mass of medullary or chromaffine substance situated near the bifurcation of the aorta. The carotid glands are said to have the same chromaffine quality, absorbing chrome salts and thereby stained brown, but it is not known that they actually belong to this system. Practically the same relations exist in other animals lower than man, but in some fishes, such as the sharks and rays, the two types of tissue are not so intimately intermingled; instead, the cortical substance forms one mass between the kidneys (interrenal body), while the other tissue (the adrenal bodies) is distributed in a series of nodules with the sympathetic ganglia. On this account it is feasible to carry out on these animals isolated extirpations not possible in the higher animals, where cortex and medulla or interrenal and adrenal substances are too inextricably entangled.

In the early development the cortex arises as a new formation from a portion of the mesodermal ridge, while the medulla appears in the form of tiny groups or balls of cells which arise with the sympathetic ganglia and from common forerunners. These cells wander into the substance of the cortex and take up a central position, where they constitute the medulla. They retain the most abundant and intimate connections with the sympathetic system, receiving quantities of fibrils from the cœliac ganglia.

Accessory or aberrant masses of adrenal character occur frequently in man, as well as other animals; indeed, they are practically constant in the rat. They are usually composed of cortical material, sometimes of cells resembling the outermost or glomerular layer, sometimes and most often of cells such as form the fasciculate zone. It is rare to find an aberrant adrenal containing medullary substance. They occur in the kidney, liver, retroperitoneal tissues, ovary, testis, in the tissues accompanying the spermatic cord, and elsewhere, and are conspicuous on account of their bright yellow color.

The normal histology of the adrenal need not be described here, but attention should be called to the peculiar involution through which it passes in early life. It is a relatively large organ in the new-born infant, and in the first two weeks during which the medulla, which is then an extremely inconspicuous collection of cells, begins to grow, the innermost zone of the cortex is destroyed and converted into a highly vascular and often hæmorrhagic connective-tissue layer which collapses. Consequently it requires some time for the adrenal to reach again the size it had at birth, and this growth is partly effected by the extension of the medulla into this collapsed framework which represents the inner layer of the original cortex (Thomas, Pappenheimer and Lewis).

The medullary cells, while they are in themselves colorless and appear gray and translucent in mass, have, as stated above, the property of absorbing chromium salts and assuming a bright chestnut-brown color. The peculiarities of granule staining in the various zones are complicated, and as yet very inadequately studied.

The cortex is particularly rich in globules of anisotropic lipoids (cholesterine esters), as well as ordinary fats, which, however, as the experiments of Landau, Hueck, and Rothschild show, cannot be taken as evidence that these organs produce the lipoids, nor even that they affect the combination of cholesterine with fatty acids. Cholesterine fed to herbivorous animals is stored in quantity in the adrenal cortex. It is abundant there normally, and especially so in pregnancy, but tends to disappear with infections, narcosis, delirium tremens, etc.

Functions.—It is even yet impossible to separate accurately the functions of the cortex and medulla, and still more hopeless to distinguish the activities of the layers of the cortex. Doubtless both cortex and medulla are vitally important organs, but there seems to be evidence that the rapidly fatal effects of extirpation of the whole organ are chiefly due to the loss of the cortex, since animals survive which possess accessory masses of cortical material.

At any rate, death follows quickly the loss of both adrenals, and it is certain that this is not due to the severity of the operation. Dogs die usually within forty-eight hours, and so indeed do cats and other animals, with symptoms of profound depression, weakness, low temperature, and low blood-pressure. It is thought, however, that the low blood-pressure is only that which is to be found in any moribund animal, and appears just before death. Stewart showed that these phenomena were much postponed in pregnant or lactating animals, and that this might possibly be due to the excess of cholesterine in their blood, since the injection of cholesterine esters before and after the operation seemed to prolong life. Extirpation of one adrenal only has no especial effect, except that the remaining organ hypertrophies, the hypertrophy affecting especially the cortex. Upon the loss of both adrenals the cholesterine content of the blood increases at once. If the animal lives long enough, glycogen disappears from the liver and sugar is decreased in the blood. The fat of the body is mobilized and wasted, and the animal rapidly loses weight. Whether the change in distribution of the cholesterine causes this is uncertain, but Landau suggests that cholesterine is just as necessary to the functioning of the adrenal cortex in its relation to the medulla as the cortex is in its regulating effect upon cholesterine. It may be gathered from these vague statements that little is known even about the mechanism of the symptoms and death following adrenal extirpation. Even in the case of the rays, where the interrenal body has been extirpated alone by Biedl and Hueck, there is no agreement as to the symptoms that lead to death.

It has, of course, been suggested that death may be due to lack of adrenaline, and it is true that adrenalectomized animals may be revived repeatedly by injections of adrenaline, but nevertheless they die almost as quickly as though they received nothing.

Function of the Medulla.—Massage of the adrenal evidently forces out into the circulation some of the medullary secretion, for the effects are those of a small dose of adrenaline. This extract, presumably derived from the medullary substance, is most remarkable in its effects, which are well known (Biedl, Meyer, and Gottlieb). Injected subcutaneously or intravenously, it stimulates the heart to violent activity and raises the blood-pressure also, by causing an intense contraction of the smaller peripheral blood-vessels. It acts upon the sympathetic nerve-endings, or perhaps rather upon the substance of the neuromuscular junction, and not directly upon the muscle itself. The coronary arteries it causes to dilate. In the same way it relaxes the intestinal wall. In the eye, separated from its nervous connections, it produces, in extremely small doses, dilatation of the pupil, but has no effect in the intact eye except that after pancreatectomy it dilates the pupil when dropped on the conjunctiva.

It causes quite violent contractions of the uterus, and may produce miscarriages in animals, but this action is greatly modified or even reversed by other drugs, such as ergot. In all these cases it is evident that its effect is upon smooth muscle innervated by the sympathetic system, and in all a striking peculiarity is the transitory character of the effect of a single dose. A violent rise in blood-pressure, with constriction of the vessels and energetic heart-beat, soon passes off, possibly because adrenaline is quickly destroyed in the organism.

Perhaps the most interesting and important effects of the secretion of the chromaffine tissue, which we believe to be essentially adrenaline, are those which it exerts in connection with the organs of internal secretion. They are probably simple enough, but in the present state of our knowledge appear extremely complicated. Injections of adrenaline as well as the original application of adrenaline to the pancreas (Herter and Wakeman) produce hyperglycæmia and glycosuria. The same thing results from massage of the adrenals or from stimulation of the splanchnic nerves. There is some difference of opinion as to whether it follows splanchnic stimulation after adrenal extirpation. McLeod and others speak of the splanchnic impulses as going to the liver via the adrenals, and think that the presence of adrenal secretion is necessary to their effectiveness in liberating sugar. Freund and Marchand, however, produced hyperglycæmia by piqûre, or by splanchnic stimulation after adrenalectomy, and think the splanchnic fibres go direct to the liver. It must, of course, be remembered that there exists much other chromaffine tissue which could furnish adrenaline.

Evidently the adrenaline so acts upon the liver-cells as to cause them to bring about the rapid depolymerization of their glycogen, and does this independently of the pancreas, since the hyperglycæmia following pancreatectomy is even accentuated by injection of adrenaline.

The relation of other organs of internal secretion to this function of the adrenal is not yet entirely cleared up. In the absence of the thyroid it is less easy to produce hyperglycæmia with adrenaline, although pancreatectomy still produces it. In exophthalmic goitre, on the contrary, glycosuria is apt to occur spontaneously. Thus it appears that, with certain controlling mechanisms, this particular activity of the adrenal which brings about the pouring of immediately available carbohydrate into the blood is regulated by the nervous system through the splanchnic sympathetic nerve. Cannon has shown that, in fear or rage or pain, strong impulses are sent to the gland, and that the mechanism is well adapted to such situations, since under those conditions there is an immediate supply of dextrose to the muscles, which act violently without fatigue, the blood-pressure being at the same time correspondingly heightened, so that the animal can fight or run to the best advantage. The influence of the medulla is in all these ways so important that we are not surprised that the chromaffine tissue is scattered so widely and is so well protected.

Functions of the Cortex.—It is evident that not much more can be stated

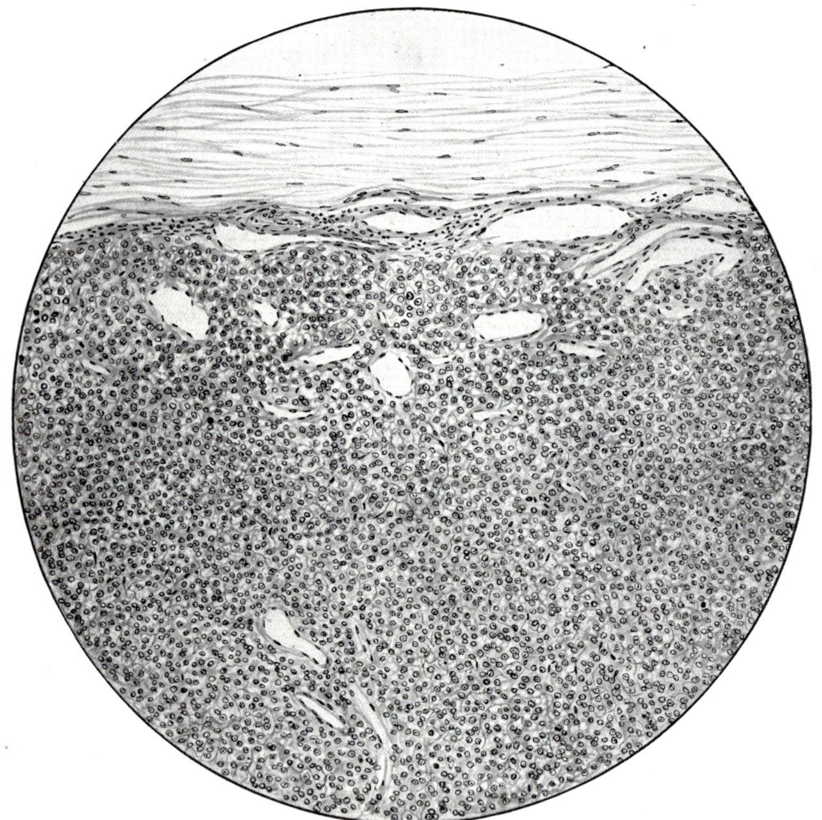

Fig. 439.—Tumor of adrenal cortex from a female child who showed masculine characters.

definitely as to the functions of the cortex in the present state of our knowledge. As a storehouse of cholesterine esters, and possibly in some sense a controller of the metabolism of these bodies, it seems to play a rôle, but there is practically nothing else to impute to it except a vague "vital importance." In a number of cases in which tumors have occupied the adrenals, composed usually of tissue resembling the cortex rather than the medulla, and containing no adrenaline, there have been signs of a peculiar precocity in sexual development. Children with such tumors (Fig. 439) may appear as mature sexually as adults. When the tumor developed in late life (after the menopause), as in a case described by Tuffier, the woman assumed male characters, heavy beard, baldness, ability to perform heavy labors without fatigue, etc. On the other hand, the gradual atrophy of the adrenal is thought to be associated with a condition of premature senility called *progeria*.

Addison's Disease.—Addison described in 1855 a symptom complex which is now known by his name, and found to depend upon chronic destructive disease of the adrenals. The patients become gradually weak and easily fatigued, the circulation is enfeebled and the blood-pressure low, the heart beats rapidly, irregularly, and feebly, there are vomiting and anorexia, and the skin becomes pigmented at first only about the usual areas of greatest pigmentation; later the whole skin may become brownish or deep bronze in color. In a state of the most extreme weakness and prostration the patient dies. The autopsy reveals most commonly a tuberculous infection which has attacked especially the adrenals and converted them into necrotic caseous masses, but there are other cases in which some other destructive process has so injured the adrenals as to leave only scars or calcified nodules in their places. In a few cases the adrenals appear normal, while there are others more numerous in which they are apparently entirely destroyed or converted into caseous material, although there have been no signs or symptoms of Addison's disease. To explain these things is not easy, and the attempt leaves us with the conviction that we are still ignorant of the exact relation of the adrenals to the disease. Wiesel, who sees in the chromaffine tissue the first part affected, although by no means denying the important rôle that the cortex may play, recalls the fact that outside the adrenal there is much chromaffine tissue in the paraganglionic nodules, so that the destruction of the adrenals does not mean the destruction of all the chromaffine tissue. In several fatal cases of outspoken Addison's disease he found that these paraganglionic masses had disappeared. If the symptoms were really due to the loss of the chromaffine tissue alone, might not Addison's disease exist with only very inconspicuous changes in the adrenals themselves, and, on the contrary, might not that portion of the total chromaffine tissue which is in the adrenals be destroyed without symptoms?

Others have found lesions in the sympathetic ganglia and in the splanchnic nerve supply, and suggest that these may occasion a cessation of the activity of the gland, just as the destruction of a motor nerve does that of its muscle. Still others (Scott, Karakascheff) have found the destructive change chiefly in the cortex of the adrenal. Discussion of all these arguments will be found in the works of Biedl, Neusser, Wiesel, Bittorf, and Bayer.

With regard to the pigmentation of the skin, the ideas are vague. Fürth has found that the ferment, tyrosinase, will produce a black pigment from adrenaline, but it is difficult to understand how, in the absence of the adrenal, such a reaction could aid in the enormous production of pigment seen in Addison's disease.

Two other questions may be briefly discussed in this place: first, the idea of Schur and Wiesel that the high blood-pressure and cardiac hypertrophy which are so common in cases of chronic nephritis are due to a coincident hypertrophy of the adrenal and especially of the chromaffine tissue. This has been supported by many who think they have been able to observe such hypertrophy and hyperadrenalinæmia, but contradicted by many others who find no evidence in favor of it, and who point out that Schur and Wiesel themselves fail to find the hypertrophy in many forms of nephritis in which the blood-pressure is high and the heart enlarged. It must await further investigation, although at present the weight of evidence is rather against this explanation.

The second question is that of the production of arteriosclerosis in the aorta of rabbits by the repeated injection of adrenaline. The lesions can apparently be produced only in rabbits, in which spontaneous lesions of the same kind are not infrequent. At any rate, dogs and other carnivorous experimental animals seem quite unsuited to this experiment, possibly just as they are for the production of arteriosclerosis by the feeding of cholesterine. The aorta in the rabbit becomes greatly deformed by the dilatations and areas of calcification. The lesion appears with necrosis and calcification in the media, and later extends to involve the intima, although some writers state that they have found primary accumulations of fat in the intima. At first it was thought that this might be due to the mechanical effect of the high blood-pressure, but the same effect is produced if another drug is given to counteract the high pressure, and thereupon the idea was adopted that a toxic action of the adrenaline was responsible for the injury. The application of these findings to the explanation of human arteriosclerosis has not yet been successfully carried out.

At the same time destructive lesions of the walls of the heart, with necrosis of the muscle and later extensive scarring and compensatory hypertrophy, are produced (Stewart).

LITERATURE

Neusser and Wiesel: Erkrank. d. Nebennieren, Wien, 1910.
Bittorf: Pathologie der Nebennieren, Jena, 1908.
Elliott: Quarterly Journal of Medicine, 1914–15, viii, 47–89.
Biedl: Innere Secretion, Berlin, 1913.
Bayer: Ergeb. d. allg. Path., 1911, xiv, 1.
Stewart: Journal of Pathology and Bacteriology, 1912, xvii, 64.
Landau: Verh. Dtsch. Path. Gesell., 1914, xvii, 573; Die Nebennierenrinde, Jena, 1915.

CHAPTER XLIV

DISEASES DUE TO INJURY TO THE ORGANS OF INTERNAL SECRETION (Continued)

Hypophysis. Structure. Properties of extracts of different lobes. Experimental extirpation. Effects of hyperactivity and hypoactivity at different periods of life. Gigantism. Acromegaly. Fröhlich's syndrome. Adiposity. Relation of genital function. Diabetes insipidus. Histological changes in hypophysis in pregnancy, acromegaly, etc. Hypertrophic pulmonary osteoarthropathy.

THE EFFECTS OF INJURY TO THE HYPOPHYSIS

Structure.—The hypophysis is a complex organ, formed, in part, of an upgrowth of the epithelium of the pharyngeal vault, in part of a downward prolongation of the floor of the third ventricle of the brain. The epithelial part becomes constricted off (although remnants are often found along the tract of a perforation in the sphenoid bone, the so-called canalis craniopharyngeus), and constitutes eventually the anterior lobe of the gland. It retains a cleft or cavity at its juncture with the posterior lobe, which is lined by epithelium and is the pars intermedia. This anterior portion is composed of strands and networks of cells which are often so loosely arranged that they seem to be in masses. But they are held in a reticulum which bears adequate blood-vessels. Many of the cells are relatively small and show no especial granulation or staining affinity (chromophobe cells), while others are granular and reveal either eosinophile or basophile granulations (chromophile cells). The cells of the pars intermedia are more apt to form alveolar cavities which often contain a colloid material. They also produce hyaline droplets, which are seen to spread into the posterior lobe. The posterior or infundibular portion, also sometimes called pars nervosa, has, in lower animals, a wide-open cavity, but in man there is none, or only a scarcely perceptible canal which extends along the stalk to the third ventricle. The structure of this lobe seems not thoroughly well known. It is said to be composed mostly of neuroglia. No distinct nerve elements are described, but there are a few cells scattered here and there. As mentioned, the hyaline soluble droplets from the pars intermedia pass readily into its meshes, and indeed Herring, whom Cushing warmly supports, declares that he can trace the passage of these hyaline droplets to their escape into the cerebrospinal fluid in the third ventricle, and thinks that this is the mode of delivery of the secretion of the gland. Cushing has demonstrated, by means to be discussed, the existence of the specific secretion of the hypophysis in the cerebral fluid.

Properties of Extracts of Different Lobes.—Extracts from the anterior lobe seem quite inactive when injected into animals. On the contrary, extracts of the posterior lobe have striking effects (Schäfer, Howell). They depress and then raise the blood-pressure, constrict the coronaries, and dilate the renal vessels, thus causing diuresis. They cause contractions of smooth muscle, as in the uterus, and give rise to a temporary increase in the production of milk. They also cause glycosuria by lowering the glucose tolerance. Such is the astonishing series of properties of extracts of the inert-looking neuroglial mass, while the extracts of the active-looking epithelial part of the gland do none of these things and seem to be perfectly without effect.

Experimental Extirpation.—Extirpation of the whole gland causes death in a few days with symptoms of collapse, extreme lowering of the temperature, apathy, etc. These symptoms appear to depend upon the loss of the anterior lobe. Perfectly clear experiments with the extirpation of each lobe alone seem not to have been accomplished, and one cannot give a clear-cut idea of their separate functions. Removal of the posterior lobe alone seems to give rise to no recognizable symptoms although, as was said, its extract is the only one with obviously active properties. Most of the experiments in which animals have remained alive were those in which the posterior lobe and a large part of the anterior lobe were removed. Such animals grow fat, become stupid, retrogress sexually, or, if very young at the time of the operation, never develop sexually beyond the infantile stage. They fail to grow like the controls, their temperature is low, they often have a transient polyuria, secreting five times as much as normal, and they develop an extraordinary sugar tolerance, so that it is practically impossible to produce alimentary glycosuria.

Apparently, then, most of the serious symptoms following destruction of the gland are due to the loss of the anterior lobe, although the posterior lobe seems responsible for the disturbances of carbohydrate metabolism and the consequent adiposity or obesity. Unsatisfactory as the experimental work is in sharply separating the functions of the parts of the gland, it will be seen that the effects of disease in human beings, which on account of the wealth of rather contradictory details we must present rather dogmatically, throw a good deal of light upon it.

Disease of the gland may be produced by primary changes in its own tissue, or through its compression or destruction by a tumor or gumma or other pathological process, or by its compression through the presence within the rigid cranial cavity of a distant lesion which heightens the pressure. In the contracted limits of the sella turcica even the growth of the anterior lobe, which might cause its hyperactivity, can in time, by compressing the posterior lobe and the outlet of the secretion, cause an insufficiency.

It is thought that the anterior lobe has an important influence upon the growth of the skeleton and upon other organs of internal secretion, but especially upon the genital organs. If it is deficient in its activity, growth is stunted and sexual development is stopped. If its activity is excessive, growth passes all normal bounds and precocious sexual development occurs. Most of the actual observations fit with this hypothesis and support it, but it must nevertheless be regarded as a mere hypothesis, since prolonged administration of extracts of the anterior lobe have not been found capable of producing any such striking effect on growth nor on sex manifestations. Possibly, therefore, it is a qualitative change in the function of the gland which is responsible for the remarkable growth phenomena, etc., rather than a mere quantitative one. The hypothesis goes on to state that if the gland is excessively active it is not constantly so, but with irregular remissions, perhaps only for one short period. If this occurs before the ossification at the epiphysis is complete, the individual grows to giant proportions; if it takes place after ossification is complete and the epiphyseal line of ossification has disappeared, then the bones enlarge and become curiously deformed in the fingers and toes and in the face, but the height is not necessarily increased. Hence the conditions gigantism and acromegaly (enlargement of the tips of the extremities). Further, the idea is of importance that while this hyperactivity leads to such astonishing results which remain as permanent changes, it may pass into a state in which the gland is inactive and supplies too little secretion for the body. Then development stops and retrogression begins.

Hyperactivity and Hypoactivity.—The following paragraphs are meant to recount in more detail the conditions illustrative of the effects of hyperactivity or insufficiency of each part of the gland. It must be remembered, however, that hyperactivity may give place to inactivity, and that signs of both may remain.

1. Hyperactivity of the anterior lobe before epiphyseal ossification is complete.
2. Hyperactivity of anterior lobe beginning after epiphyseal ossification is complete.
3. Inactivity of anterior lobe beginning before puberty.
4. Inactivity of anterior lobe beginning late in life.

1. When the gland is excessively active or enlarged and still active in the period of epiphyseal growth, its effect is to exaggerate the growth of the skeleton and of the other tissues at the same time. As a result the individual becomes a giant. An illustration taken from Cushing's work will convey more than any description (Fig. 440). This one, aged thirty-six, was rather weak, had a high sugar tolerance, was sexually impotent, and showed at autopsy a much reduced hypophysis converted into a cyst. Evidently the activity of growth under the influence of the hypophysis, which began to increase at the age of fifteen, gave place, after the ossification was complete, to glandular insufficiency. Such *gigantism* (Figs. 441, 442, 443) is not entirely limited to those in whom the activity of growth stops with the completion of ossification, but may be combined with the

effects of overgrowth which occurs after the epiphyseal lines are ossified, and thus may play a part in the changes in cases of group 2.

2. When the anterior lobe, through hyperplasia or increased activity, causes excessive growth in adult life, the result is *acromegaly* (Marie, 1886). Again an illustration of a typical case will convey more than a description (Fig. 444). The bones of the face and those of the hands and feet become

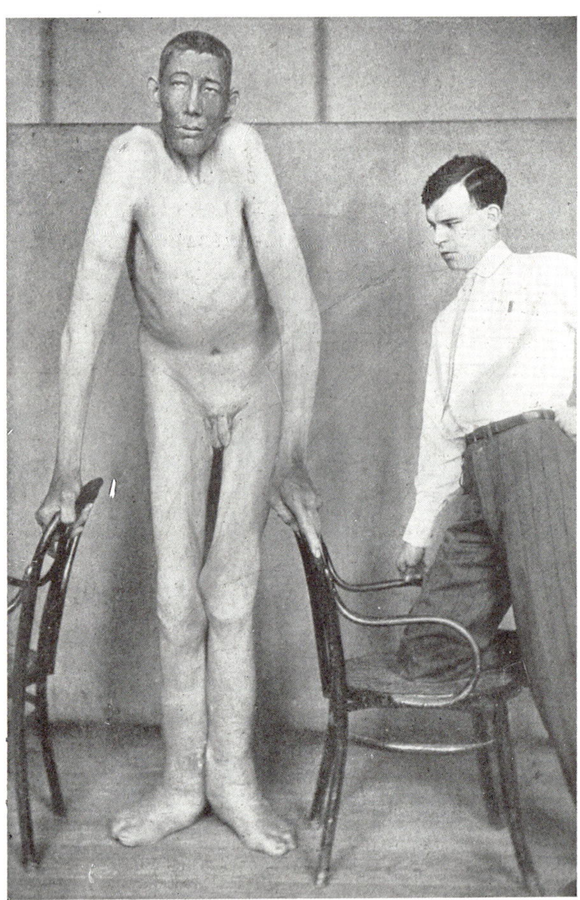

Fig. 440.—Note the narrow chest; large joints; hypotrichosis. Also the large size of the hands compared with those of Dr. Crowe, whose height is 5 feet 8 inches (Harvey Cushing).

enlarged, the jaw projects, and the soft parts of the face, hands, and feet become greatly thickened (Fig. 445). For a time there may be glycosuria, or at least a lowered sugar tolerance. The sexual function is not impaired in this stage. Some acromegalics are also giants, evidently because the stimulus to growth existed before ossification was complete, although there may have been a long interval after the increase in stature before the distorting growth of the facial bones and extremities took place. Such remissions in the activity of the gland are recognized. The condition, acromegaly, is permanent, but in most cases, owing to subsequent impairment of the hypophysis, symptoms of insufficiency (obesity, impotence, high sugar tolerance, etc.) appear.

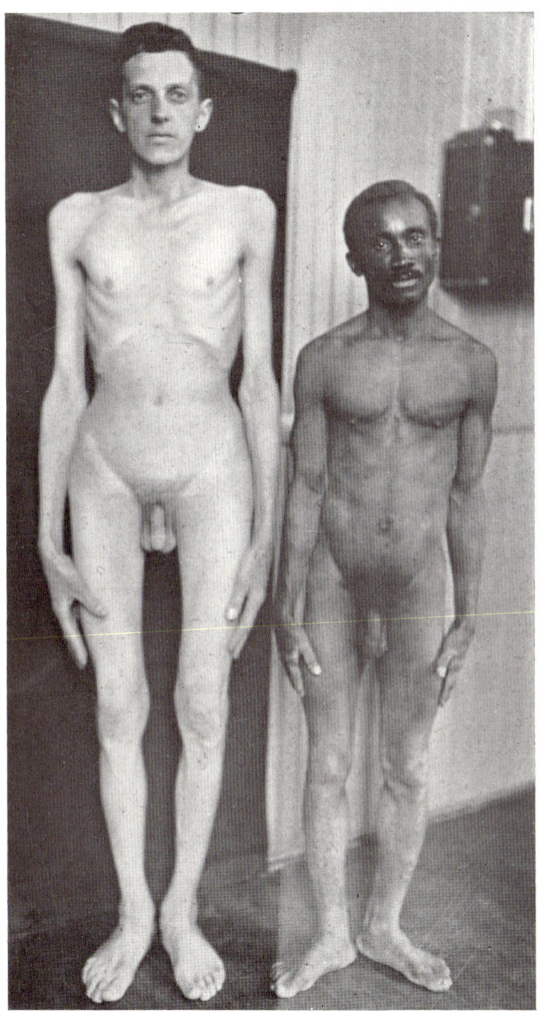

Fig. 441.—Gigantism. Man with evidences of hypophyseal disturbance, shown in contrast with a normal negro man, 5 feet 8 inches tall. Hands and feet are shown for comparison (Figs. 442 and 443).

3. Inactivity of the hypophysis beginning before puberty causes the changes observed in puppies after hypophysectomy, namely, stunting of growth, great obesity, high sugar tolerance, and failure in the development of the sexual glands and in the appearance of secondary sexual characters. Mental dullness is a frequent accompaniment.

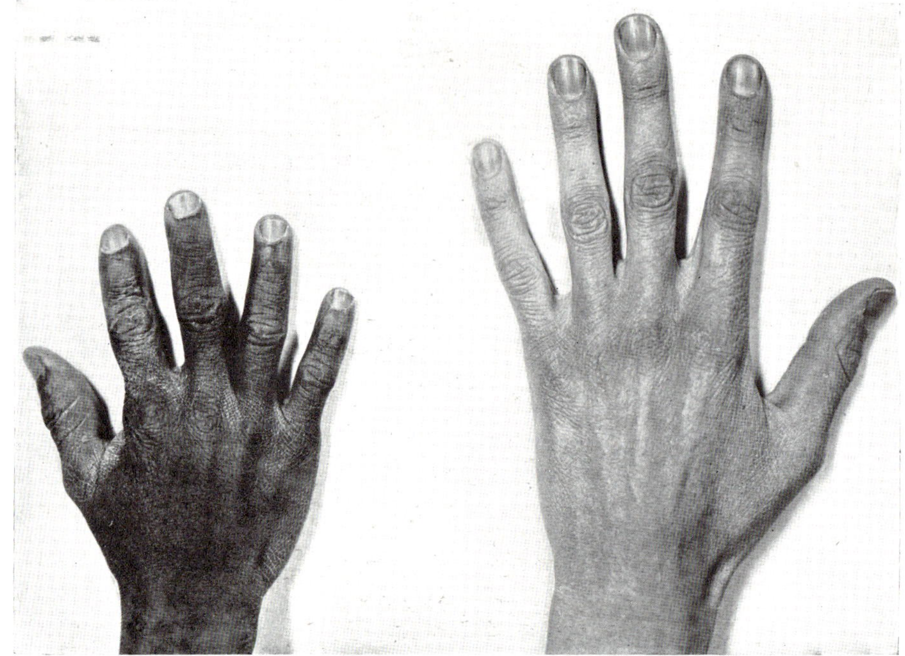

Fig. 442.—Hand of patient in Fig. 441 compared with that of a normal negro.

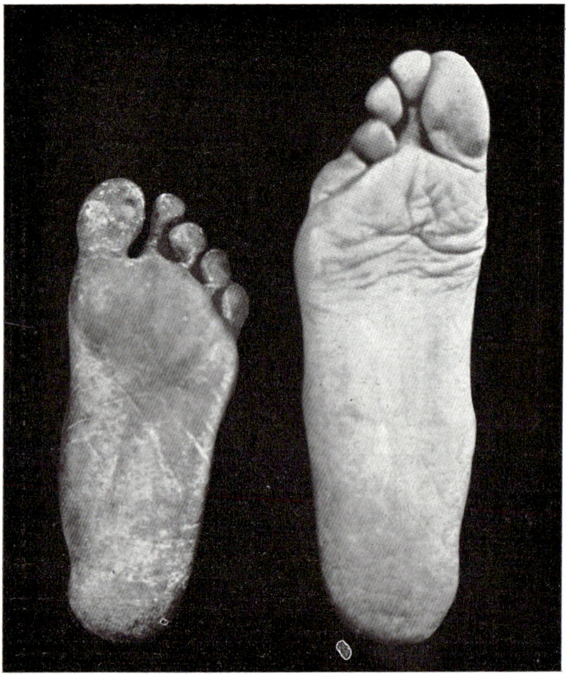

Fig. 443.—Foot of the patient in Fig. 441 compared with that of a normal negro.

Fig. 444.—Acromegaly. Great enlargement of face, with heavy features. Great increase in size of hands, with thickening of the fingers.

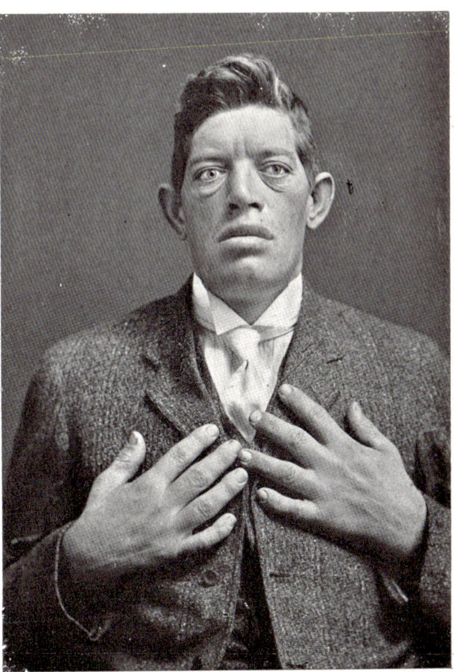

Fig. 445.—Acromegaly. This man was an acromegalic giant aged thirty-five, with blindness and large tumor of the hypophysis (Cushing).

Fröhlich's Syndrome.—These are the fat boys that one sees so frequently, fairly bursting from their clothes. They have a peculiar feminine habitus (Fig. 446), with wide hips, knockknees, and especial collections or pads of fat in the pectoral regions and on the hips (Fig. 447). Even in adult life there is no beard, and hair is scanty over the body. If there is any pubic hair, it has the feminine distribution (Fig. 449).*

4. If the deficiency of the hypophysis begins late in life, there is an approach to this condition. Naturally there is no retrogression of anatomical features of the skeleton already established, nor even of the distribution of the hair and development of the genitalia, but obesity comes on with the great heightening of the sugar tolerance, and there is gradual or rapid loss of sexual functions. It is apparently among these cases that we should class those extraordinary instances of adiposis dolorosa, or Dercum's disease, multiple lipomatosis, etc., although the relation is not clearly established (*cf.* Lyon). These are people in whom there are huge irregular accumulations of adipose

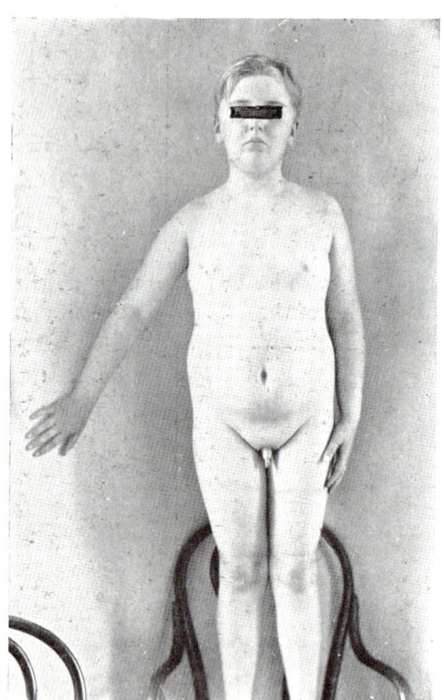

Fig. 446.—Fröhlich's syndrome. Preadolescent pituitary insufficiency in a male (Cushing).

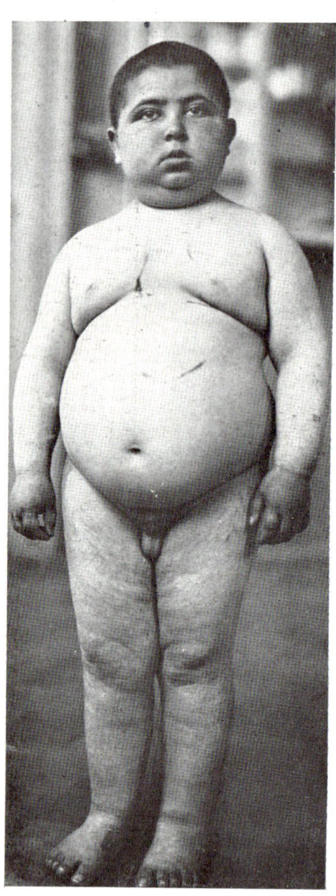

Fig. 447.—Preadolescent hypophyseal insufficiency in a male (Cushing, after Neurath).

* I am indebted to Dr. Harvey Cushing for allowing me to use the photographs of his cases.

tissue, or in whom with neuralgic and joint pains the whole adipose tissue is greatly increased (Figs. 450, 451).

The peculiar anatomical conditions which surround the hypophysis are responsible for much of the confusion which still prevails as to the part played by each division of the gland in these lesions. If the hypophysis were an organ like the thyroid, situated in loose tissue, and able to grow without compressing itself, or so placed that one part might grow without

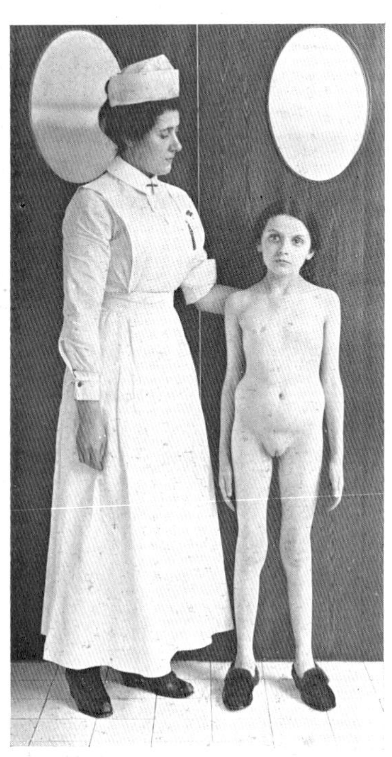

Fig. 448.—Preadolescent pituitary insufficiency in a female aged sixteen. Skeletal and sexual infantilism. Congenital pituitary tumor. The child was formerly extremely fat (Cushing).

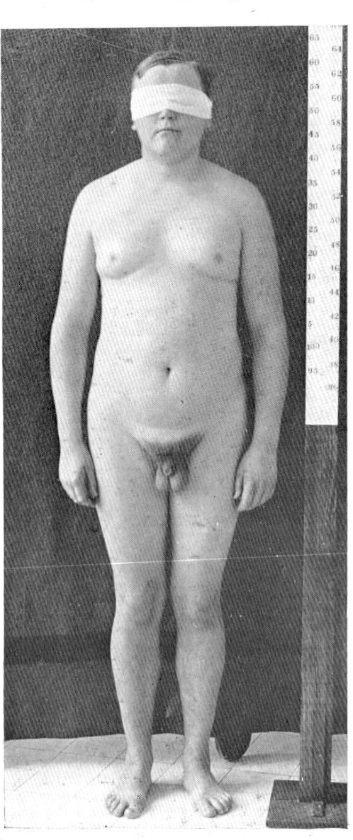

Fig. 449.—Adult pituitary insufficiency with hypophyseal tumor. Feminine habitus (Cushing).

destroying the other, it might be easier to recognize the rôle of each lobe. Furthermore, the fact that the functions of all the organs of internal secretion seem so closely interrelated makes it difficult to outline the part of each. The hypophysis seems especially closely related to the genital glands, and its destruction brings with it the loss of function of those glands, amenorrhœa, and cessation of spermatogenesis. The thyroid and adrenals are vaguely associated also, and changes are likely to be found in their structure and function when there are hypophyseal disturbances.

In these diseases of the hypophysis, except when atrophy leads to its diminution in size, there are mechanical effects produced by the enlargement of the gland itself or by the tumor which causes its destruction. These are found to be associated with either the signs of hyperactivity or those of insufficiency, but since hyperactivity is a relatively transient phenomenon and usually passes over into insufficiency, even through the very agency of the tumor formation, the mechanical effects are most commonly found in the stage of insufficiency. They are, as a consideration of the anatomical relations of the hypophysis would show, usually caused by pressure upon the optic tracts or upon the brain as a whole as it lies within the rigid cranium, or upon the hypophysis itself. There is progressive narrowing of the field of vision, hemianopsia passing on to com-

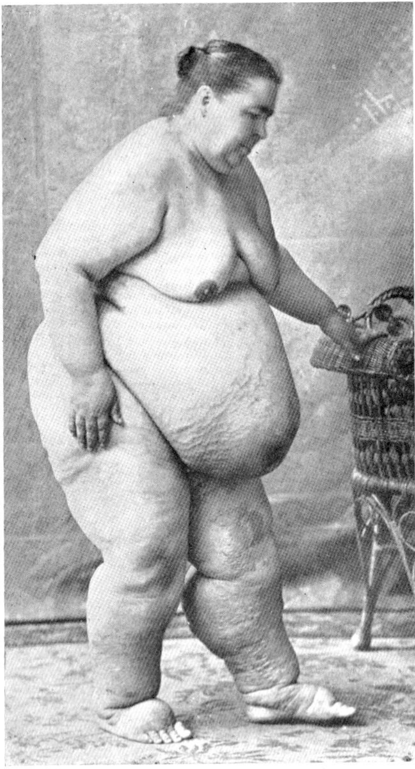

Fig. 450.—General extreme adiposity probably due to late hypophyseal disease.

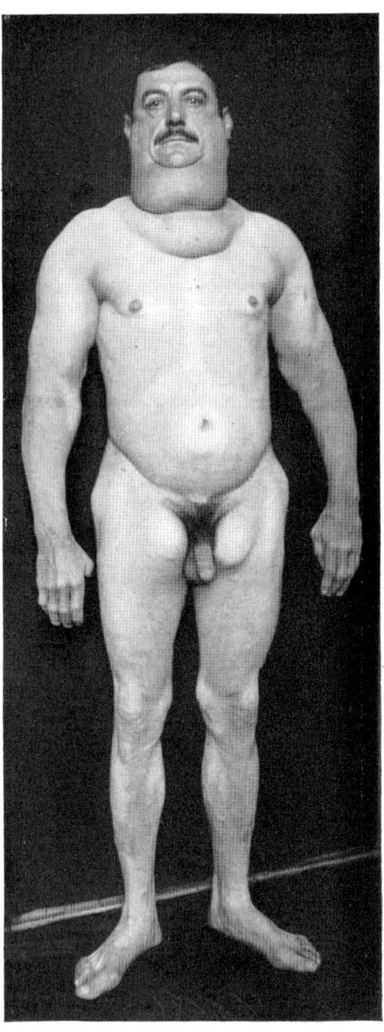

Fig. 451.—Multiple lipomatosis. There are symmetrical fatty tumors about the neck, arms, hips, and femoral regions.

plete blindness, choked disc and retinal changes, violent headache, etc. Hydrocephalus may be the cause of hypophyseal insufficiency, just as any distant intracranial tumor may, in the limited space, give rise to slight evidences of hypophyseal impairment.

Diabetes insipidus, which is a name given to a symptom complex in which extreme thirst and polyuria form the most striking features, is probably in most instances due to an injury of some sort to the hypophysis, causing its insufficiency, although it is difficult to explain why the insufficiency of the posterior lobe should cause such diuresis when the injection of its extract has exactly that effect (Berblinger).

As to the nature of the changes in the hypophysis itself, much more study is required. It has been stated that in the anterior lobe there are neutrophile or chromophobe cells which form a great proportion of the tissue, but that there are also many eosinophile and basophile cells. Erdheim and Stumme have shown that there are remarkable changes in the gland during pregnancy. It becomes much enlarged, and the chromophobe cells, which they call chief cells, are greatly enlarged and increased in importance, pushing aside the eosinophiles, which shrink, and the basophiles, which become very pale. Indeed, as the great mass of "pregnancy cells" these altered chief cells occupy practically the whole field. With the end of pregnancy and during lactation the gland undergoes gradual involution to the normal condition.

In the various phases of the hypophyseal hyperactivity or insufficiency mentioned above, it is evident that the destructive effects of tumors, cyst formation, hæmorrhages, tuberculosis, gumma formation, anæmic infarcts have nothing especially peculiar about them. They cause insufficiency by destruction of the tissue or by pressure. The cause of hyperactivity is more interesting and not yet clearly determined. Usually there is an excessive growth of the tissue of the anterior lobe in the form of a sort of tumor or glandular hyperplasia often spoken of as an adenomatous growth. Great variety exists among these. Erdheim has described eosinophile adenomata and Nothdurft a basophile one. Benda pointed out that in the cases of acromegaly the new growth found in the anterior lobe is rich in eosinophile cells, and others have agreed with him, while Cushing, in the strumas or adenomata found in cases of hypophyseal insufficiency, has found only the chief or chromophobe cells. Nevertheless it would be hazardous to state definitely that the acromegalic changes depend upon the eosinophile cells.

A sharp distinction must be drawn between acromegaly and the other condition described by Marie as *hypertrophic secondary pulmonary osteoarthropathy*, which also results in elongation of the bones of the extremities and in the formation of a rather thick periosteal new bone formation. In this the hands and feet may be greatly enlarged, but they are quite different in form from the short thick extremities of acromegaly. It is supposed to be due to the absorption of some toxic substance, since it accompanies chronic bronchiectasis, tumors of the lung and thorax, and other analogous affections.

LITERATURE

Benda: Dtsch. med. Woch., 1901, xxvii, 513, 536, 564.

Cushing: The Pituitary Body and its Disorders, Phila., 1912. Also Jour. Amer. Med. Assoc., 1909, liii, 249. With Crowe, Quart. J. Exp. Physiol., 1909, ii, 389. With Goetsch, Amer. Jour. of Physiol., 1910, xxvii, 60.

Pick: Dtsch. med. Woch., 1911, xxxvii, 1930, etc.

Erdheim: Frankf. Ztschr. f. Path., 1910, iv, 70.

Kraus: Ziegler's Beitr., 1914, lviii, 159.

Lyon: Archives of Int. Med., 1910, vi, 28.

Erdheim and Stumme: Ziegler's Beitr., 1909, xlvi, 1.

Wurmbrand: *Ibid.*, 1910, xlvii, 187.

Berblinger and Goldzieher: "Diabetes Insipidus," Verh. Dtsch. Path. Gesellsch., 1913, xvi, 272.

Simmonds and others: Verh. Dtsch. Path. Gesellsch., 1914, xvii, 184–231.

Swale Vincent: Practitioner, 1915, xciv, 147.

Marie: Rev. de Med., 1886, vi, 297; 1890, x, 1.

Thayer: New York Med. Jour., 1896, lxiii, 33.

CHAPTER XLV

INJURIES WHICH CAUSE METABOLIC DISTURBANCES AND CONSEQUENT DISEASE OF THE BONES

Chemical interchanges in growth of bone. Importance of calcium. Relation of internal secretions to bone formation. Normal ossification. Rickets. Osteomalacia, chondrodystrophia fœtalis. Scurvy and Möller-Barlow's disease; osteogenesis imperfecta; osteopsathyrosis; Paget's disease.

THE structure of the bones is so complicated, and their mode of growth involves so many chemical interchanges, that it is not surprising to find them extremely sensitive to disturbances of metabolism. In most cases we are ignorant of the ultimate causes of those disorders of the chemical interchanges of the body which bring with them visible alterations in the bones, but in some we understand at least the principles which are immediately concerned. Since mineral substances make up so great a part of the weight of the bones, we naturally turn at once to them. It is well enough known that attention to the food of horses and other domestic animals, and care that they receive enough lime and phosphorus, is necessary that their growing bones be well formed and strong. If we deprive an animal of the lime which should be in its food, its bones become porous and weak, or even quite soft, and it may be rendered helpless by the giving way and bending which can occur (Pexa, Dibbelt).

Dibbelt found that for a growth of 100 grams, a dog uses 2.2 grams of CaO. In his experiments with calcium-poor food, the deposit of lime was $\frac{1}{5}$ to $\frac{1}{200}$ of the normal, and the bones became extremely light and porous. The epiphyseal cartilages grew large and broad, and the cortex everywhere became rarefied by the enlargement of the Haversian canals into considerable cavities. The broadening of the epiphyseal line is due to the lack of provisional calcification of the cartilage and the consequent inability of the marrow capillaries to convert it into bone. In spite of the lack of calcium, however, there was abundant formation of a tissue morphologically like bone, but devoid of lime salts (osteoid tissue). Stoeltzner thinks that the formation of this osteoid tissue is dependent upon a stimulus furnished by calcium, and that osteoid tissue remains so only because it is unable to take up the calcium. He is supported by Lehnerdt, who substituted the closely allied strontium for calcium, in the food, and found, just as did Dibbelt in the extreme lack of calcium, that the cartilage cells being unchanged, were not normally invaded by marrow capillaries, and that the underlying spongy bone was replaced by a thick zone of osteoid tissue. This latter formation he states is due to a power of stimulation possessed by strontium equally with calcium, but that since strontium cannot replace calcium as a hard deposit in the new-formed tissue, it remains osteoid tissue and not bone. Dibbelt's observation seems to disprove the idea that the stimulus of calcium or strontium is necessary for the growth of the osteoid tissue. Phosphorus, which, with carbonic acid, is found in the normal lime and magnesia combinations which make up the hard part of bone, is naturally of great importance for proper bone formation. Some authors have looked upon it as a special stimulus to bone formation too, but whether it is in that rôle, or merely in its obvious part in furnishing material for the ultimate phosphates, remains to be determined. Magnesium salts are present in a much smaller proportion than those of calcium, but nevertheless play a part to which it seems not enough attention has yet been paid.

Importance of Calcium.—Direct abstraction of lime from the food does not ordinarily occur, and one must, if a disease appears which points toward an insufficiency of calcium, determine whether the failure is not

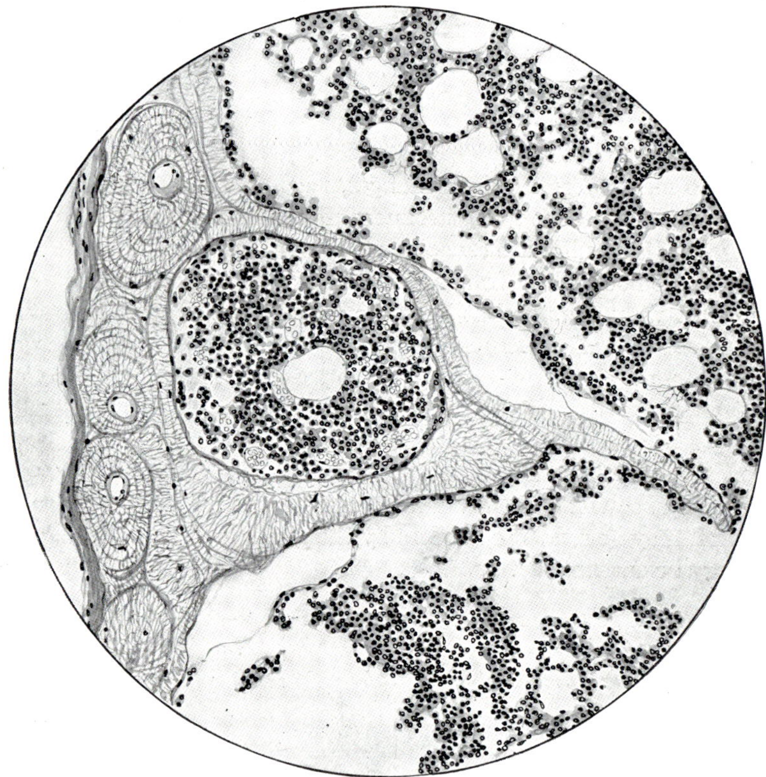

Fig. 452.—Senile osteoporosis. Section of rib showing great thinning of the cortex and atrophy of the lamellæ. With the disappearance of calcium, the lattice figures become evident in the Haversian systems.

rather in the ability of the body to absorb, retain, and deposit the calcium. It is known, of course, that, in the period of growth, and especially in childhood, the deposition of lime salts is abundant, and that the bones become progressively firmer, while in old age the reverse is true—more lime salts are absorbed from the bone than are deposited there afresh, so that the lamellæ become thinner and disappear, and in the Haversian systems of the cortex so much of the solid material is lost that the laminæ of bone assume a reticulated appearance and become relatively weak (Fig. 452). This is the senile osteoporosis which is to be regarded as a more or less normal process, but which leads to obvious atrophic changes in some bones, such as the skull and jaw bones, and to such rarefaction of the others that fractures occur with comparatively slight occasion. This is an expression of the preponderance in old age of the process of absorption of the bone over that of apposition, two processes which go on side by side through life, even during the period of most rapid growth.

Relation of Internal Secretions to Bone Formation.—We have a certain amount of vague information regarding the influence which the organs of internal secretion exert over the interchange of calcium and the other constituents of bone, and over the growth of bone itself, and much of this has already been detailed. Its vagueness consists largely in the fact that while metabolism and growth in general are largely influenced by these glands, it is more difficult to ascribe specific changes in the bones to their activity or lack of activity. Acromegaly and gigantism, in which there is such an excessive growth of bone (together with that of the soft parts), is fairly clearly associated with excessive activity of the anterior lobe of the hypophysis. Klose and Matti find that the destruction of the thymus causes great defects in bony growth, but Pappenheimer and many others dispute this. Defective metabolism and growth follows destruction of the thyroid, but there is no specific or especially pronounced change in the bones except general retardation of their development. Loss of the parathyroid is thought to disturb the calcium metabolism and to allow the tissues to become impoverished. The dentine of the teeth fails to become calcified, and the callus formed in the healing of fractures remains soft, but it has not yet been made clear that the processes of bone formation in general are characteristically affected. Still less definite statements are made about the part played by the chromaffine system and by the ovaries and testes on the course of ossification. This is one of the most obscure but also one of the most interesting chapters of human pathology, and as yet we possess only the beginnings of information on the subject. We may examine the facts, however, which are afforded by study of the several diseases in which the growth and structure of the bones are peculiarly affected (together with many changes in other organs), and attempt to realize at least where the problems lie.

Normal Ossification.—A few words as to the tissues concerned may recall what is necessary to the understanding of the pathological changes. Bones are formed either by ossification of connective-tissue membranes or by the replacement of cartilage by bone tissue. Membranous bones seem to be produced by a change in the function of certain cells which acquire the power of laying down an intercellular matrix in which they bury themselves, and which in time becomes calcified. In the cartilages of the fœtus which are covered with a layer of such altered or osteoblastic connective-tissue cells there comes a time when blood-vessels (later the nutrient vessels) push into the substance of the cartilage, carrying the perichondrial osteoblasts before them. They hollow out the cartilage, and the osteoblasts, after destroying the cartilage cells, deposit further formless material upon the remains of the matrix, bury themselves in it, and promote its calcification. Thus bone is formed. It can be most clearly studied along the line of demarcation between the epiphyseal cartilage and the advancing marrow cavity, because there the process persists for a long time, with the formation and ossification of ever new cartilage, as is necessary for the growth of the bone in length. Growth in thickness is by this time carried out by the persistent periosteal and endosteal cells in the diaphysis, which add to the mass of the cortical bone and to the lamellæ of the cancellous bone. In the epiphyseal ossification zone the process is clearly seen as follows. The most distal of the cartilage cells near the joint surface are flattened; next is a great quiescent mass of small elongated cells lying in every direction; toward the marrow cavity there is a broad belt in which they begin to be more deeply stained and to be arranged with their long axes more transversely to the long axis of the bone. Still nearer to the border zone they form straight, closely arranged columns, like grains of corn on a cob, separated by the alternating and more irregular columns of the blue-staining matrix. Quite at the line of ossification these cells swell and become large, rounded, or irregular structures (*cf.* Fig. 44). A whole phalanx of capillary loops from the bone-marrow presents itself along this row of cartilage cell columns, and each capillary, covered loosely with a mantle of osteoblasts, tends to push itself into or alongside of a column of cartilage cells. Here, in the matrix of the border zone of cartilage cell columns, there is a provisional or preliminary deposit of calcium salts in very fine granules. This calcification seems to offer some obstacle to the invasion of the vessels since in its absence blood-vessels penetrate far into the cartilage and branch there in a way which we shall discuss presently in connection with rickets.

When the conditions are all favorable, the cartilage cells themselves are broken in upon and set free from their nests in the matrix (*cf.* Fig. 44). They may be destroyed or they fall into the marrow cavity and are thought to take no further part in actual bone formation. The invading osteoblasts range themselves along the jagged remnant of matrix and once more begin their process of burying themselves in a hyaline substance which forms around and beneath them. After a time they show clearly, as they lie in the little cavity which they form for themselves, their numerous long thin processes which extend out in all directions in minute canaliculi in the homogeneous matrix. The tissue at this stage is osteoid tissue. Quickly, however, there occurs a deposit of calcium throughout and it becomes hard bone. Ordinarily there is no considerable amount of osteoid tissue at any time, but, as we shall see, there are diseases in which it persists as such. Thus finished, this cancellous bone is left behind and the capillaries with more osteoblasts advance to meet new cartilage cells. The epiphyseal bony centre is formed later in exactly the same way by the invasion of another vessel into the epiphyseal cartilage, and bone formation spreads from this centre through the cartilage in all directions. Perichondral blood-vessels invade the cartilage only rarely, except in the direct process of entering to form the epiphyseal ossification centre (and to some extent along the plane between resting and actively growing cartilage), but that too is much modified by disease. Along the epiphyseal line the process is actually maintained for many years until the bone has reached its full length, when with a final replacement of the remnant of cartilage the line is merged into the cancellous bone.

RICKETS OR RACHITIS

The weakened condition of the bones probably gave rise to the old name, rickets, for this disease, and rachitis is only a high-sounding Latinization of the English word. It is an astonishing condition which is seen at its height in children, beginning usually at the sixth month and lasting sometimes for several years, with remissions and final healing. The disease may, nevertheless, leave behind it very obvious traces of the deformities which are produced when the bones are soft and fragile. It is often remarkable to observe how completely the healing process, by the aid of the mechanical agencies which normally act on the skeleton, can restore to the normal form, bones which at one time were greatly deformed. The signs of rickets in adults are rarely very disfiguring, although in the case of the pelvis the deformity may have far reaching consequences in the obstruction of childbirth.

The disease is commonly said to pass through three stages which can be distinguished as the beginning, the florid stage, and that of healing. Different conditions with regard to the metabolism prevail in these stages. At the height of its development the following may be observed. The child is pale and sickly, the anæmia being sometimes quite profound. Such children show a lowered resistance and are prone to infections of all sorts. The lymph glands are usually enlarged, and tonsils and other adenoid tissues are everywhere swollen. The abdomen protrudes, and in many cases, if not in all, the spleen is enlarged and fairly firm. The distension of the abdomen may be in part due to atony of the intestinal walls. Flabbiness and softness of the skeletal muscles are most striking. The epiphyses, especially those of the wrists, ankles, and knees, are much enlarged. At each costochondral junction there is a hard swelling which can be felt through the skin, and the row of these nodules on each side of the sternum is often spoken of as a rickety rosary. The enlargement is especially prominent on the inside of the thorax and may be due in part to the angular inward dislocation of the bony end of the rib through respiratory efforts which are often made difficult by adenoid growths in the upper air-passages, associated with the general lymphoid swelling. Skoliosis, or curvature of the spine, bending or fracture of the long bones, and a peculiar flattening or contraction of the pelvis are due to the general softening of the bones. The anterior bowing of the tibiæ (sabre tibia), and the consequent flat foot, are particularly striking features in those children who walk about.

The skull is made square, and the forehead very prominent, by the growth of convex spongy thickenings over the frontal and parietal bosses. There is often an actual erosion deep into the bone of the skull over the back of the head as the child lies on the pillow, but Ziegler regards this "osteotabes" as a totally different affection, and he is probably right.

Most cases, if the child survives, end with the gradual restoration of the normal consistency of the bones and afterward with the far more gradual rearrangement of the bony structure and readaptation to the mechanical needs and normal form of the bones. There are some, however, in which such extreme distortion of the whole skeleton takes place in the florid stage that the deformity is never really overcome, and the patients remain permanently disabled. Such skeletons are seen in European museums showing extreme bending and twisting of the long bones, but the extremely severe cases seem at least very rare in this country. M. B. Schmidt thinks that different forms occur in different regions, those seen in Zürich having large epiphyses with straight hard diaphyses, while those seen in Strassburg have large epiphyses also, but show bent and deformed or fractured diaphyses with a thick covering of soft periosteal new bone. In this country we occasionally see the latter type, but the former is more common.

At autopsy it is rather easy to cut with a knife down through the epiphyseal end of the bone deep into the shaft, and the cut surface presents an extraordinary contrast with the normal bone (Fig. 453). It is seen that in the normal bone the line of ossification is perfectly sharp, even, and really a narrow line. In rickets it is replaced by a wide irregular band of rather

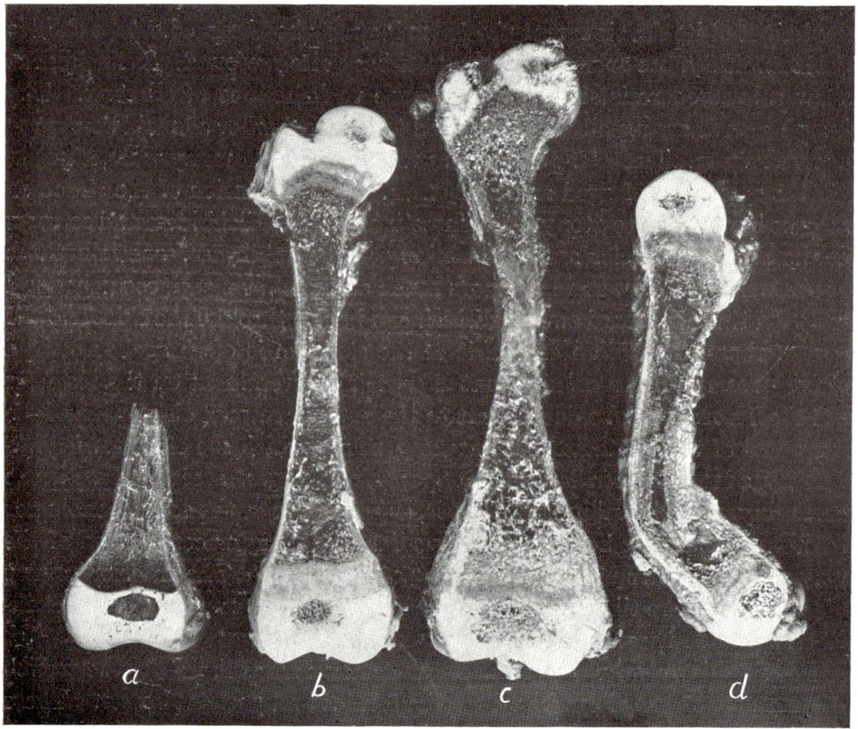

Fig. 453.—Rickets. *a*, Normal bone with clear line of ossification. *b* and *c* show broad bands of osteoid tissue instead of this line; their diaphyses are firm, delicate, and straight. *d*, Form of rickets in which the diaphysis is weakened, covered with periosteal new bone, and fractured.

soft gray translucent tissue, in which white opacities and gritty particles represent the calcified lamellæ, but throughout which islands of bluish cartilage can also be seen. The cortex of the shaft often shows soft, spongy growths both inside and outside. These changes are especially well seen in the lower end of the femur, the upper end of the tibia, etc., but to a slighter degree they are found in every bone and are very prominent in the costochondral junction of the ribs. A section through the epiphysis and shaft of such a bone shows (Fig. 454), on analysis of the confusing scene, that the border zone of the cartilage where it should abut on the advancing marrow vessels has failed to undergo the usual provisional calcification or is calcified in irregularly scattered places only. Where there is no calcification, the

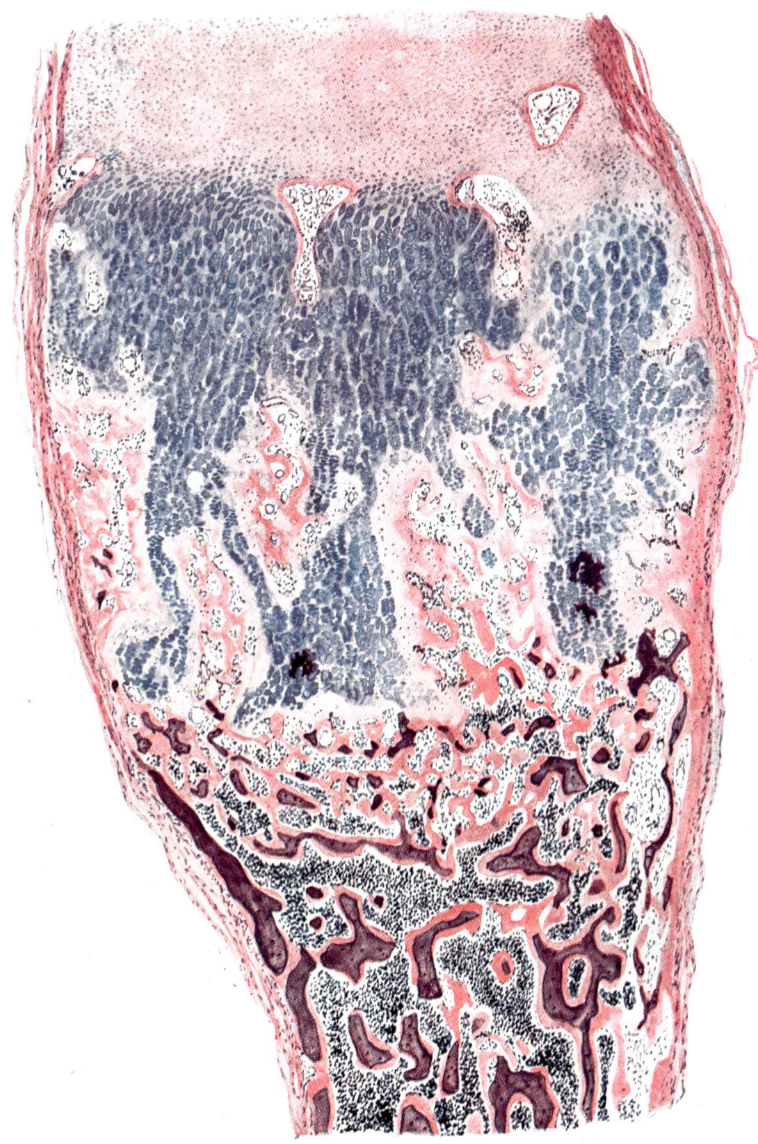

Fig. 454.—Rickets. Rib at site of line of ossification. The preparatory zone of cartilage is irregularly invaded by perichondral and marrow vessels. Calcification of cartilage lacking, except in two or three foci. Invading blood-vessels surrounded by osteoid tissue. Lamellæ of bone remain partly covered with osteoid tissue.

marrow vessels push far into the cartilage and branch here and there, leaving long tongues of the calcified cartilage projecting toward the marrow cavity. So sluggish is the process of invasion of the cartilage cells that much uncalcified cartilage is also left in these tongues or islands of tissue. Where the capillaries do lay open the cartilage cells and spread their osteoblasts on the remaining cartilage matrix, the result is the formation of highly irregular, thick laminæ, morphologically like bone (though much more bulky), but not calcified. This is the osteoid tissue described before, and this it is which makes up practically all of the thick grayish band which lies where the line of ossification should be. Where the capillaries grow far into the cartilage, they may surround themselves with zones or mantles of osteoid tissue. So too the margins of the cartilage masses left behind in the

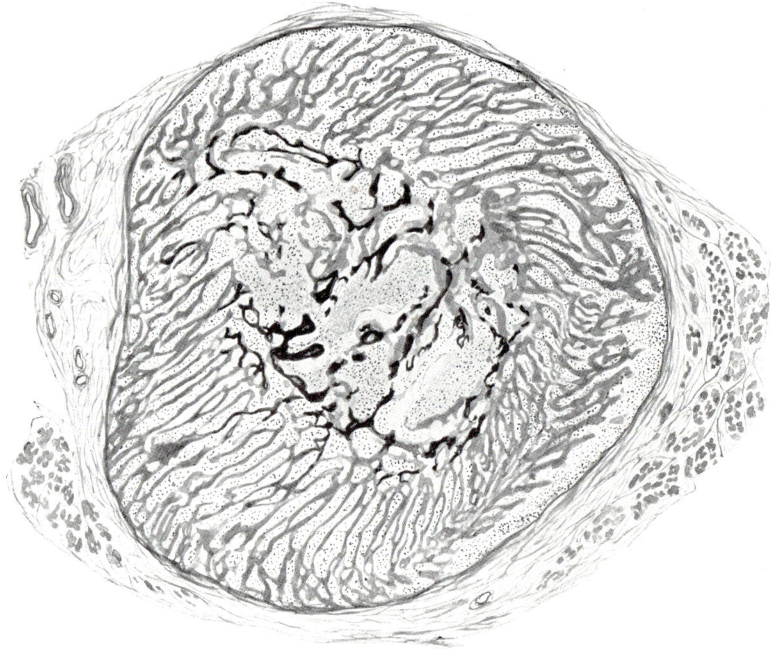

Fig. 455.—Periosteal osteoid formation about a rib in rickets.

advance of the growth become changed into osteoid tissue, and when, in healing, this becomes bone, the rest remains as a cartilage island enclosed in bone. There is much of this osteoid tissue in the shaft of the bone also, making up the superficial layers of the laminæ of the cancellous bone and of the periosteal exostoses (Fig. 455). Even in the denser bone of the cortex one finds osteoid tissue, especially about the vessels, which lie in the so-called perforating canals, but also at times occupying a quadrant or more of an otherwise well-calcified Haversian system. The point most disputed in the recent discussion of rickets and osteomalacia before the German Pathological Society was the question whether this calcium-free bone should be regarded as the result of the absorption of lime from old bone previously calcified (halisteresis), or new bone laid down calcium free. The strongest evidence seemed to be in favor of the wide-spread existence of halisteresis, although, of course, it is clear that much osteoid tissue is newly formed.

Another process characteristic of rickets is the abundant ingrowth of blood-vessels into the epiphyseal cartilage from the perichondrium. These split up the resting cartilage in every direction, and end in a network of small vessels parallel with the transverse plane of ossification. Several such layers or "stages" of vessels may be formed, and may be visible at once, although as the irregular region of ossification advances they become in turn confluent with the vessels from the marrow cavity and lose their identity. As they lie in the cartilage ("cartilage marrow canals") the matrix round them loses its blue stain and assumes the power of staining with eosin. This collagenous material soon becomes converted by the accompanying osteoblasts into osteoid tissue, which finally adds itself to the mass of osteoid tissue formed by the marrow vessels.

The marrow is in itself changed into a tissue much more fibrous than normal ("endostitis fibrosa"), and laminæ of bone or osteoid tissue may be formed in this fibrous marrow. It is easy to see that an extremely complicated condition can be produced in this way, especially when it is remembered that similar processes in modified form occur in the shaft of the bone as well. It is remarkable that any adequate return to the normal architecture of the line of ossification is possible in the course of healing. The enlargement of the epiphyses is due, not so much to any excessive production of cartilage, as to the fact that ossification is extremely sluggish and the cartilage does not become converted into the calcified and less bulky bone. The exostoses on the skull are soft, spongy masses of lenticular form composed of porous osteoid tissue which becomes partly calcified and later may be absorbed in large part or completely converted into bone.

The spleen is often enlarged, and shows an increase in the reticulum fibres without any parallel increase in connective tissue. Giant-cells occur, the Malpighian bodies are small, and the pulp hyperæmic (Hayaski). In our cases the condition is variable, and in some there is a distinct induration from an excess of connective tissue. There is atony or hypotony of the skeletal muscles, as well as of the smooth muscles of the intestines and arteries.

With regard to the mineral metabolism in rickets, Schabad and Dibbelt have shown that the excretion of calcium in the florid stage is especially high in the fæces, while the proportion in the urine sinks. There is frequently an absolute loss or negative balance, dependent upon the excessive amount discharged with the fæces. Healing is preceded by hyper-retention and a relative increase in the output of calcium in the urine. After healing, the proportions are normal. Dibbelt thinks that rickets is due to a specific disturbance of the calcium metabolism, and not merely to inability of the bone to take up calcium, since in that case the excretion of the excess would retain its relative proportions in urine and fæces. The output of phosphates is also increased.

The cause of rickets is unknown. It seems clear that the deficiency of calcium is a most important factor, and Dibbelt thinks it adequate to produce the typical lesions of rickets. Others, however, deem it necessary to assume that there are specific changes in the bone-forming tissue which make them unable to retain the calcium. The elements of unhygienic surroundings, poor food, etc., have always been emphasized as the causes of the disease, but recently attention has been turned to something more definite. Various deficiencies of the organs of internal secretion have been held responsible,—thymus (Matti), parathyroid (Erdheim thinks the parathyroid deficiency probably responsible for the allied osteomalacia), chromaffine system (Stoeltzner),—but none of these is supported by much evidence.

Infections of various sorts have also been thought capable of causing the disease. Morpurgo found it possible to produce rickety changes in rats which he infected with an organism isolated from spontaneously rickety rats, and J. Koch claims that it is possible to reproduce the skeletal changes with precision by the injection of cultures of the Streptococcus longus seu erysipelatis into the veins of young dogs.

Osteomalacia is a very similar disease which occurs in adults, especially in women, with exacerbations during pregnancy and lactation. It is thought by many to be practically identical with rickets, except in occurring in persons whose endochondral ossification is complete. Otherwise the histological modifications of the bones are nearly identical. Here the softening of bones which were quite calcified and hard a short time before must be due to halisteresis, and in section the bones show clearly the osteoid margin along each lamina of bone, covering in the still calcified central part. The most extraordinary deformities through bending of the soft bones are produced during the florid stages, when the decalcification is at its height, and this is accentuated by the greater weight of the adult body. The pressure of the heads of the femora flattens the pelvis laterally and forces the symphysis pubis forward into a sort of beak. With returning rigidity such a pelvis is, of course, incompatible with childbirth. The loss of calcium may be relatively high in each day's excreta (Holtz' case, 0.1809 gm. daily; Sauerbruch's, 0.07 to 0.17 gm. daily).

Adrenal insufficiency and ovarian hyperactivity have been looked upon as the cause of the affection, and adrenaline treatment or castration carried out with alleged good effect. But the matter is still debated. Erdheim found lesions of various sorts in the parathyroid glands, and calls attention to the parallelism between this condition and the escape of calcium in parathyroid insufficiency.

LITERATURE

Rickets.—Schmidt, Stoeltzner, Dibbelt, Schmorl: Verh. Dtsch. Path. Gesellsch., 1909, xiii, 1–54.

Ziegler: Ctbl. f. allg. Path., 1901, xii, 865.

Schmorl: Münch. med. Woch., 1909, lvi, 1256.

C. Meyer: Jahrb. f. Kinderh., 1913, lxxvii, 28.

Dibbelt: Dtsch. med. Woch., 1913, xxxix, 551.

Rickets.—Grosser: Med. Klinik, 1914, x, 577.
Aschenheim: Jahrb. f. Kinderh., 1914, lxxix, 446.
Koch: Ctbl. f. Bakt., 1. Abth. Ref., 1913, lvii, Beih. 250.
Osteomalacia.—Marinesco, Parhon, and Minea: Nouv. iconogr. de la Salpêtriére, 1911, xxiv, 1.
Erdheim: Sitz. d. k. Akad. d. Wiss., Wien, Math. Naturw. Kl., 1907, cxvi, Abth. iii, 311.
Bauer: Frankf. Ztschr. f. Path., 1911, vii, 231.

Chondrodystrophia fœtalis is a disease of the cartilage occurring in fœtal life, and leading to a partial or complete cessation of the endochondral ossification, while periosteal bone formation proceeds vigorously. The result of this is that the infant is brought into the world with extraordinarily shortened arms and legs and with other deformities, among which are distortion of the pelvis, malformation of the vertebral column and thoracic skeleton, and great enlargement of the skull, with retraction of the nose. Every one is familiar with the peculiar short-limbed dwarfs, with their large heads and characteristic faces, in which the nostrils seem directed almost straight forward. They are intelligent, active, and strong, and make their way in life, often as clowns in circuses, where their strength and agility find them occupation. They may reach an advanced age and bear children, although on account of the deformity of the pelvis these must be removed by Cæsarean section. That the disease is hereditary is seen from the fact that these are commonly also dwarfs, but cases of chondrodystrophia occur often enough in families in which no other instances are known.

The cause of the disease is quite unknown. The organs, including all the glands of internal secretion, are found to be quite normal, and all the changes are explained on the basis of the disturbances in the cartilages. Kaufmann distinguishes chondromalacic, hyperplastic, and hypoplastic alterations of the cartilage, but, as Siegert points out, all these may occur together in the same case. The epiphyseal cartilages are found abundantly penetrated by blood-vessels from the perichondrium (Fig. 456). The cartilage cells may be very small and widely separated by a rather soft fibrillar intercellular substance. Often they lie in great spaces which produce a spongy appearance. Along the line of ossification there is in patches a columnar arrangement of cells, while for the rest the cells are enlarged and totally irregular in their arrangement. In other instances the zone of columnar arrangement of cartilage cells is separated from the marrow cavity by other cartilage cells arranged in a network. Often, but not always, a lamella of periosteum with blood-vessels extends across the epiphyseal cartilage, just above the line of ossification, and causes a complete cessation of that process. Invasion of the cartilage by marrow capillaries is almost at a standstill, and usually the spaces are limited by a film of completed bone. Calcification of the cartilage is rather slight, but some remnants of blue-staining material are found in the centres of the terminal bone lamellæ. In spite of these anatomical conditions, which express the result, it is hard to say exactly why such slight obstacles are not overcome, so that growth of the cartilage into orderly columns and consequent ossification may proceed. Periosteal growth, building up and breaking down of the lamellæ of the diaphysis, and bone-marrow formation are normal. Premature synostosis of the portions of the sphenoid with one another and with the basilar portion of the occipital bone is common, and in sharp contrast with the condition in myxœdema or cretinism, in which this connection remains cartilaginous a very long time. It may be responsible in part for the retraction of the nose. There is a lumbar lordosis, and the promontory of the sacrum projects into the upper strait of the pelvis, so as to make it very narrow. In adults of this type, as in the case of a woman aged seventy-five seen at autopsy recently, ossification is quite complete, and no trace of intermediary cartilage remains. Endochondral ossification with some growth does, therefore, go on to completion, but without adding much to the length of the bones. This condition is not to be confused with cretinism, in which the whole process of ossification is retarded, nor with rickets, in which there is a period during which osteoid tissue, and not bone, is formed abundantly.

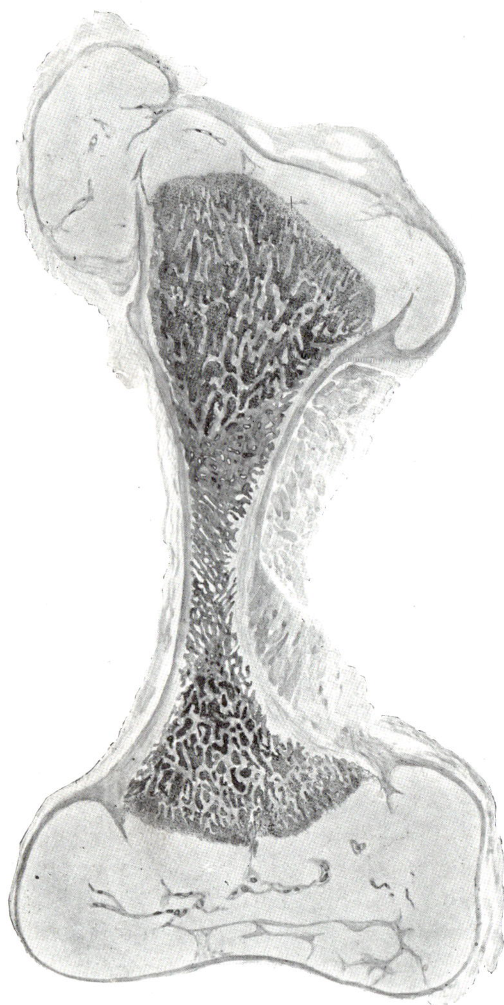

Fig. 456.—Chondrodystrophy in an infant. Median section of the femur, showing softening and displacement of the epiphyseal cartilage.

LITERATURE

Kirchberg, Marchand: Ziegler's Beitr., 1889, v, 183.
Kaufmann: Die sog. fœtale Rachitis, Berlin, 1892.
Siegert: Ergeb. d. inn. Med. u. Kinderh., 1912, viii, 64.
MacCallum: Johns Hopkins Hosp. Bull., 1915, xxvi, 182.

SCURVY AND MÖLLER-BARLOW'S DISEASE

Prolonged subsistence upon such food as salted meats, canned meat with biscuits or bread, and boiled or condensed milk, without fresh fruits, milk, vegetables, or fresh meat, is known to produce a complex disease characterized by anæmia, swelling and infection of the gums, painful hæmorrhages in the joints and under the periosteum, and purpuric hæmorrhages in the skin. This may lead to death, but can be cured by giving the so-called

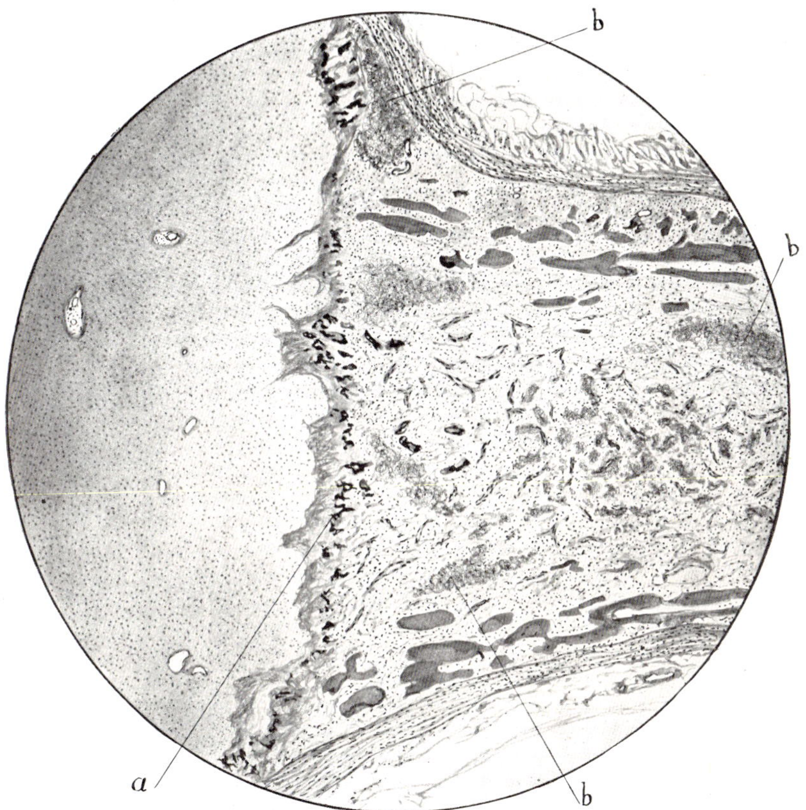

Fig. 457.—Infantile scurvy. Line of ossification of the lower end of the femur: (*a*) Calcified cartilage; (*b*) hæmorrhage in the fibrous bone-marrow. The process of ossification in almost entirely interrupted.

antiscorbutic substances which are contained in fresh fruits and vegetables and in fresh meat and milk. It is a disease which raged among sailors in times when it was difficult to carry these things, and voyages were of longer duration. In adults it is now rather rare, and occurs only among the very poor, or in conditions of isolation where fresh food is not obtainable. It is still observed in children, especially when they must be artificially fed. The scurvy or scorbutus of adults seems to be identical with the infantile scurvy or Möller-Barlow's disease of children, except in some trifling details which depend upon anatomical differences. It may be experimentally produced in animals by intentional feeding with a "scorbutic" diet, and prevented or cured by giving the antiscorbutic substances. The lesions in animals are identical with those in man.

Fig. 458.—Infantile scurvy. Section of femur showing subperiosteal hæmorrhages with periosteal bone formation. There are hæmorrhages in the bone-marrow and distortion of the line of ossification at the lower end.

Among antiscorbutic substances, lemon- and lime-juice are well known. They resist heating, are acid, and keep well. Extracts of vegetables, such as cabbage and potatoes, or dandelions are effective, but deteriorate on standing, are alkaline, and are destroyed by heating. The beneficial properties of milk are destroyed by heat. Attempts to isolate the active substance have as yet led to no clear result.

The lesions, which develop in the course of a few weeks or months of the unfavorable diet, affect chiefly the bones. The bone-marrow loses its blood-forming elements and becomes converted into an œdematous fibrous tissue in which the blood-vessels and osteoblastic cells seem relatively few. As a result, bone formation becomes almost stagnant everywhere, and since the resorption of bone goes on normally, the whole structure shortly becomes rarefied. At the epiphyseal line the lack of proper and orderly invasion of the cartilage columns is very marked (Fig. 457). Sometimes there is irregular or oblique invasion, and the zone of osteogenesis becomes broadened where there is a network of capillaries, but this is also an ineffectual method of bone formation. Usually only scattered laminæ are produced, and in some cases a sort of bony wall is formed transversely which obstructs further ossification. Hæmorrhages occur as elsewhere in the body, in the joints, underneath the periosteum, and in the substance of the bone-marrow. The periosteum may be elevated from a large part of the shaft of the bone by the effusion of blood (Fig. 458). Periosteal growth of bone tends to replace the clot, but the cortex continues to be rarefied. The disturbances of ossification do not depend on the hæmorrhages, since they precede them (Ingier).

Healing takes place after the proper food is once more given by the rearrangement of the disturbed cartilage cells in their columnar order, by the reappearance of blood-forming cells and abundant capillaries with osteoblasts in the impoverished bone-marrow, which then go on to the normal processes of ossification. The disease is quite different from rickets, in which the chief feature is the absence of calcification of the cartilage, and the consequent rapid ingrowth of capillaries which form osteoid tissue, in the lack of calcium.

LITERATURE

Schmorl: Ziegler's Beiträge, 1901, xxx, 215.
Holst and Fröhlich: Ztschr. f. Hyg., 1912, lxxii, 1.
Ingier: Frankf. Ztschr. f. Path., 1913, xiv, 1.

OSTEOGENESIS IMPERFECTA

Osteogenesis imperfecta is a condition in which, in infants and young children, multiple fractures of the ribs and long bones occur. Niklas, in describing a still-born infant in whom there were more than 60 fractures, most of them produced some time before birth, regards the process as different from osteopsathyrosis or osteogenesis imperfecta tarda, which occurs in adult life and the nature of which is still doubtful. Study of the bones in osteogenesis imperfecta shows normal cartilage with normal preparatory calcification, a normal line of ossification, with normal-looking osteoblasts. These, however, must function imperfectly, since the lamellæ of bone are extremely delicate and thin. Periosteal bone formation is greatly reduced, and many lamellæ of the cortex are disconnected and run transversely. Resorption of bone is normal in the presence of this faulty or deficient apposition—hence the numerous fractures. Niklas found a hyperplastic thyroid and ovaries, and suggests the possibility that disturbances of internal secretion may be concerned.

LITERATURE

Bamberg and Huldschinsky: Jahrb. f. Kinderheilk., 1913, lxxviii, Ergnzngsheft., 214.
Hart: Ziegler's Beiträge, 1914, lix, 207.
Niklas: *Ibid.*, 1915, lxi, 101.

PAGET'S DISEASE (OSTEITIS DEFORMANS)

In 1876 Paget described a disease in which the bones of the extremities and of the skull became greatly thickened, and to some extent softened, so that bowing of the legs occurred. The enlargement of the head was extreme, and the person sank in stature. Many cases of this disease have been studied, and although the cause is still unknown, the anatomical changes are fairly clear. It begins usually after the age of forty, and progresses slowly with some pain and tenderness in the altered bones. In some cases the changes are unilateral or limited to one or two bones. In those in which the skull and facial bones alone are affected the condition is spoken of as *leontiasis ossea*. In them the softened bone may later assume an ivory-like hardness. The tibiæ and femora commonly become thickened and bent forward. The skull (Fig. 459) may reach a thickness of two to three or even four centimetres, and, as a rule, the bone is easily cut with a knife. Since it is a disease of advanced life, there is no question of disturbance of ossification along the epiphyseal line. Instead, there are concerned especially extensive resorption of the normal bone by osteoclasts, and the excessive new formation of irregular bony lamellæ by the osteoblasts which accompany the fibrous marrow. The marrow actually loses its blood-forming elements and becomes converted into a vascular fibrous tissue which produces much soft, bone-like tissue. The architecture of the bone is disorganized, and the

Fig. 459.—Paget's disease, or osteitis deformans. Thickened skull and cross-section of femur. Marrow cavity filled with osteoid tissue.

cortex loses its dense character and sharp outline. The marrow cavity is encroached upon or filled completely, and a thick subperiosteal layer is formed (Fig. 459). In this new tissue the lamellæ run in every direction. Occasionally there are cysts or spaces in it filled with fluid, or tumor-like growths may appear. There is no halisteresis, as in osteomalacia.

Various theories have been proposed as to the causation, and many infectious agents have been held responsible, including syphilis. There is little evidence for these views. Others have thought of it as an effect of the disturbance of some internal secretion. DaCosta and his coworkers find that there is a retention of calcium, magnesium, and phosphorus, with excessive excretion of sulphur, and state that there have been analyses which show that, in spite of their softness, the bones are especially rich in calcium.

LITERATURE

Paget: Medico-Chir. Transactions, 1877, lx, 37; 1882, lxv, 225.
Higbee and Ellis: Jour. Med. Research, 1911, xxiv, 43.
Watson: Johns Hopkins Hosp. Bull., 1898, ix, 133.
Hurwitz: *Ibid.*, 1913, xxiv, 263.
DaCosta and others: Publications of Jefferson Med. College, Phila., 1915, vi, 1.

CHAPTER XLVI

ARTHRITIS DEFORMANS

Confusion as to classification; infectious, traumatic, neuropathic, and gouty forms. Arthritis deformans: terminology. 1. Proliferative arthritis deformans or progressive polyarthritis; clinical and gross pathological characters; histology. Spondylitis of Bechterew and Marie. 2. Degenerative arthritis deformans. Clinical and gross pathological changes; histology. Malum coxæ senile; spondylitis deformans.

THE recent discussion of chronic affections of the joints at the International Congress of Medicine in London showed how confused our ideas are as to the classification of these affections. We have learnt that there are many infections in the course of which recognizable organisms lodge in the tissues of the joints and produce acute or chronic forms of arthritis and periarthritis. This is particularly true of the pyogenic micrococci, and perhaps especially of the gonococcus. There are also, as is well known, articular and periarticular inflammations due to the unknown infectious agent of rheumatism (and to avoid confusion we shall use the term rheumatism for that affection only in which fever, arthritis, and peri-, endo-, and myocarditis are found, often associated with tonsillitis and chorea).

The part played by the tubercle bacillus in producing destructive and reactive changes in joints has been dwelt upon, and there are other cases in which the spirochæta of syphilis plays a similar rôle.

These are, with many others, the infectious forms of arthritis usually easily recognized to be the sequelæ of the existence of a focus of similar infection elsewhere. While this primary infectious lesion may sometimes be very evident, it is less so at other times, as, for example, those cases in which pyorrhœa alveolaris, or some nasal suppuration, is the real, though unsuspected, source of the spread of bacteria. The lesions of the joints are sometimes suppurative inflammations; sometimes there are only effusions of fluid; adhesions and even complete ankylosis of fibrous or bony character often occur. Traumatism, especially when bacteria are introdued into the joint cavity, is naturally often productive of an arthritis, and in hæmophilia and allied conditions there arises hæmorrhage into the joints which may simulate in its effects those of an inflammation.

In the course of some diseases of the spinal cord, notably tabes dorsalis and syringomyelia, there occur curious changes in some of the joints, causing complete disorganization not only of the joint structures themselves, but of the neighboring bones, with the most deforming dislocations. The tabetic arthropathies have already been mentioned, and one of them at least represented in an illustration (Fig. 363).

A fourth type is that already described and figured in speaking of gout, in which the deposition of crystalline masses of urates in the joint cartilages and in the periarticular tissues is the cause of intense inflammatory reactions (Fig. 34).

When all these forms of arthropathy have been considered, there still remain many which cannot be regarded as definitely belonging to any of those groups. These are commonly chronic and extremely persistent affections, which, although they may sometimes begin suddenly enough with pain and fever, and even in quite young people, drag on through years, and cause the most extreme deformities and disabilities, which are permanent. Indeed, they appear to be gradually progressive during all that time in producing atrophy and disorganization of the cartilages and of the bone itself, accompanied by extraordinary new formations both of cartilage and bone, as well as of scar tissue, in and about the joint.

It may as well be admitted at the beginning that, since every author who writes upon the subject seems to use a different terminology, it is extremely difficult to compare their results and to decide upon the limits of the disease and its most satisfactory subdivision. Barker has reviewed the subject, and in his tabulations he separates osteoarthritis deformans from chronic progressive polyarthritis (the rheumatoid arthritis of Garrod). German writers, such as M. B. Schmidt and Kaufmann, divide arthritis deformans into three groups: (1) *A. ulcerosa sicca*, which is often monarticular and is essentially a degenerative and destructive process; (2) *Arthritis adhæsiva*, in which many joints are involved, and while destructive in a sense, is especially characterized by the growth of granulation tissue forming adhesions and even a firm fibrous ankylosis; and (3) *Arthritis deformans*, in which atrophic or degenerative changes in the cartilage and bone are accompanied by extraordinary new formation of both bone and cartilage in such a way that the ends of the bone forming the joint become profoundly deformed and often dislocated. Nichols and Richardson regard all the cases as examples of one disease, but recognize an essentially degenerative form in contrast with another in which proliferation of connective tissue, cartilage, or bone is predominant. It seems that their proliferative form must correspond with the A. adhæsiva, while their degenerative form comprises the other two classes. In the same way in comparing their terminology with that of Barker it seems that the proliferative form is the same as the chronic progressive polyarthritis or rheumatoid arthritis, while the degenerative form is co-extensive with osteoarthritis deformans.

Proliferative Arthritis Deformans.—The first part of these, the proliferative form of arthritis deformans of Nichols, or progressive polyarthritis of other writers, begins often with fever and sudden pain in the joints, almost as in an attack of rheumatism. It affects young people as well as old, and quickly leads to lameness, disability, and stiffness of the joints. It affects many joints, including those of the knees, shoulders, etc., as well as those of the hands and feet. The joints become enlarged, but remain soft and doughy, without any irregular nodules (Fig. 460). *X*-rays show rarefaction of the bone, which may be due to a withdrawal of calcium salts, but no exostoses. If such a joint be opened, its articular surface is found partly covered with red granulation tissue and the synovial membrane generally thickened. At a later stage the cavity may be partly or completely obliterated by adhesions, and the cartilages partly replaced by new bone or by fibrous tissue. Fibrous or even bony ankylosis may occur, and in extreme cases the two bones become united with continuous marrow cavity. Partial dislocations are sometimes found, but even in such late stages there is no new formation of bony nodules about the joints.

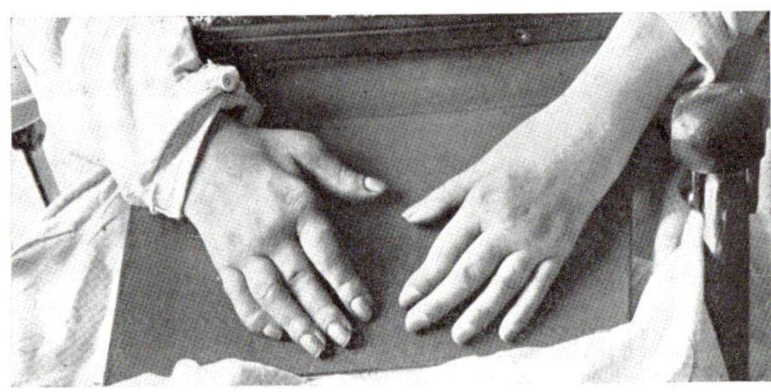

Fig. 460.—Proliferative arthritis; soft swelling of the joints of the hand.

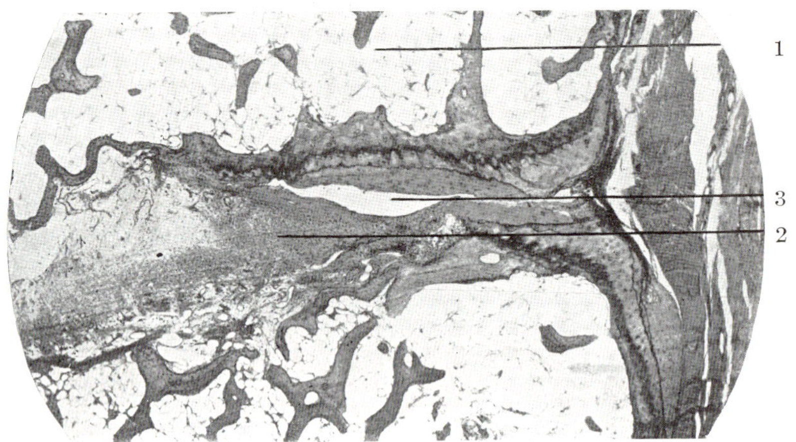

Fig. 461.—Proliferative arthritis with ankylosis of phalangeal joint. Spongy bone of the phalanx (1). Growth of fibrous tissue and fibrocartilage (2) has almost entirely obliterated the joint cavity (3) (Nichols and Richardson).

Histologically, the following is found to occur. As a result, no doubt, of some primary injury, there is formed a layer of granulation tissue on the surface of the synovial membrane and spreading over the cartilage of the articular surfaces. This reduces the extent of exposure of the cartilage, and through adhering to the similar granulation tissue of the opposite side, causes partial obliteration of the joint cavity (Fig. 461). The granulation tissue also extends into the substance of the underlying cartilage and tends to destroy it. The bone beneath shows, for a time at least, no morphological evidence of rarefaction, but the bone-marrow becomes converted into an œdematous fibrous tissue with many osteoblasts and capillaries. This invades the cartilage from below, causing its ossification as it goes, and may penetrate to join the overlying layer of granulation tissue. The activity of the osteoblasts may cause much condensation of the bone beneath the cartilage, but it also causes much new bone formation within and overspreading the cartilage, often with new cartilage formation as well, so that Nichols even pictures a bone in which, while part of the original cartilage remains, there is a layer of bone surmounted by cartilage covering it. All these things explain the tendency to the formation of dense fibrous ankylosis which may be more or less complete. One type of this disease which involves fibrous or bony ankylosis of the articular processes of the vertebræ, including the costovertebral articulations, is particularly striking. Occasionally the ligaments are ossified also. The result is the solidification of the

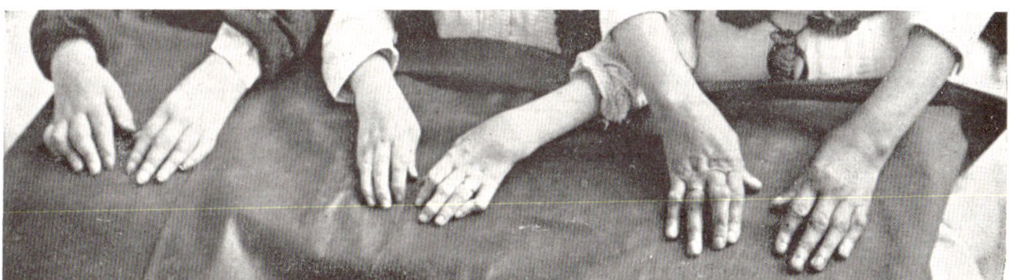

Fig. 462.—Degenerative arthritis; characteristic deformities of the hands with nodular enlargements of the joints.

spinal column into a rigid curved structure, concave throughout on the anterior aspect. In the so-called Bechterew's disease the ankylosis is limited to the spine or part of it, beginning above, but in other cases the hip- and shoulder-joints are also involved (*spondylose rhizomelique* of Marie-Strümpell).

Degenerative Arthritis Deformans.—The second group, the degenerative form of Nichols or osteoarthritis deformans of others, is more particularly found in elderly people, and is often an affection of fewer joints. It usually begins insidiously, without fever, and progresses slowly to extreme deformities and disabilities of the joints. These become enlarged by the appearance of firm or hard nodules, and are tender and painful. The joints of the hands and feet often show the most striking changes, although the knees and hips and other large joints are equally characteristically affected (Fig. 462). The hands of these patients present an especially remarkable appearance. There is flexion of the fingers, as a rule, with deflection to the ulnar side. Great knobby enlargements of the knuckles and of the terminal phalangeal joints are often associated with relatively slight enlargement of the middle joints of the fingers, so that these tend, on account of the relaxation or atrophy of their ligaments, to bend backward (Fig. 463). Between the knuckles and the wrist-joint the back of the hand over the metacarpal bones sinks into a hollow over which the skin is extremely thin, like crinkled tissue paper, shiny and translucent, so that the veins show through distinctly.

On opening one of these joints no new growth of granulation tissue is

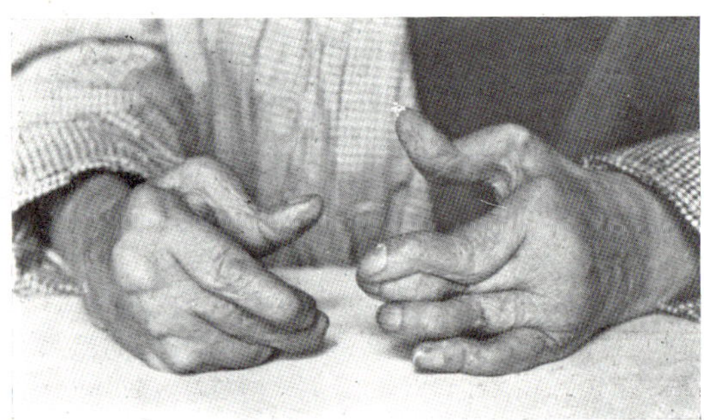

Fig. 463.—Degenerative arthritis; typical deformity of the hands, with ulnar deflection.

found, nor any tendency to ankylosis. Instead, the changes are predominantly in the cartilage and secondarily in the bone. The cartilage is at first fibrillated and plush-like, so that its shaggy surface can be smoothed over from one side to the other. This causes such softening and disintegration that it is readily eroded away, leaving deep ulcers and sometimes exposing the bone (Fig. 464). In the gross specimen this uncovered bone is in most cases found to be smooth and hard. Opposite such an ulceration of

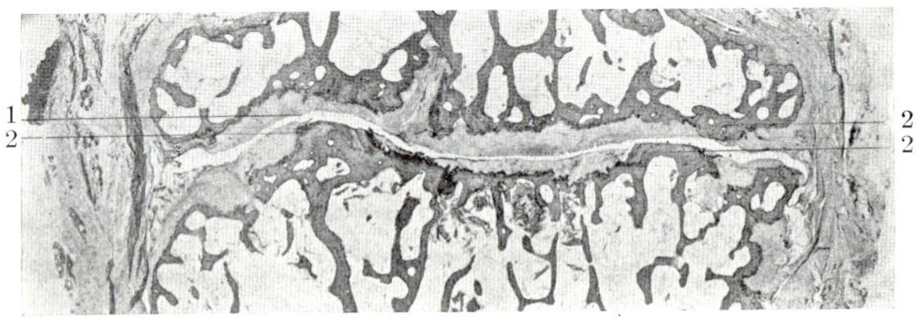

Fig. 464.—Degenerative arthritis. Phalangeal joint, showing irregular joint surface, (1) with exposed eburnated bone (2, 2) (Nichols and Richardson).

the cartilage the cartilage of the other joint surface tends to thicken itself and fill up the space, often becoming partly or completely ossified in this process. But sometimes both of the opposed surfaces are denuded of cartilage and bone grinds against bone. Ordinarily this sets up the formation of much new bone in the substance of that which is exposed, and the surface layers become very compact and hard. In such joints as move like hinges these opposing surfaces of dense bone grind upon one another until they become brilliantly polished. Sometimes this condition arises only after inequalities in one surface have been filled up by overgrowths from the other which have become bony. Then the grinding produces parallel grooves,

Fig. 465.—Arthritis deformans (degenerative form). Head of femur showing erosion and marginal osteophyte formation.

Fig. 466.—Arthritis deformans (degenerative form). Extreme erosion of the head of the femur, with polishing and exostosis formation.

which are fitted by ridges of the opposite side. In joints which work in many directions these parallel grooves do not appear (Fig. 465). Where the bone is very atrophic and unable to respond, or in retired places where the pressure is insufficient to stimulate much new bone formation, the sur-

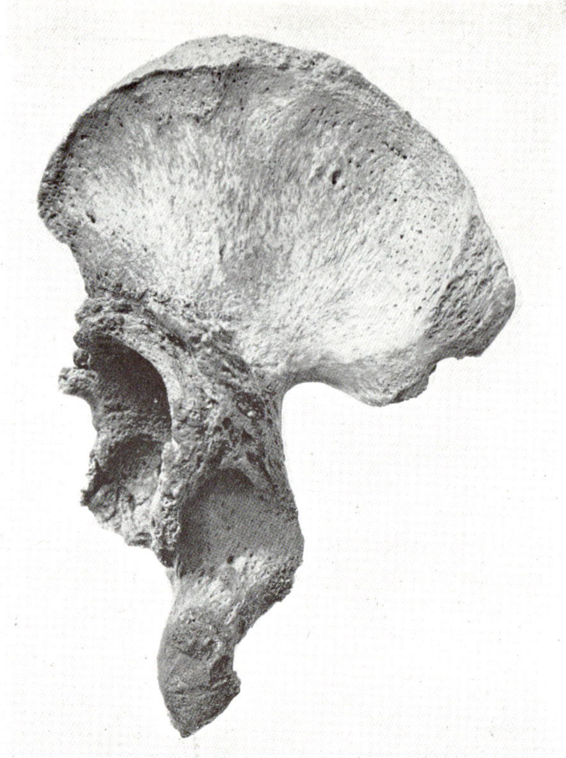

Fig. 467.—Arthritis deformans (degenerative form). Acetabulum with marginal osteophytes.

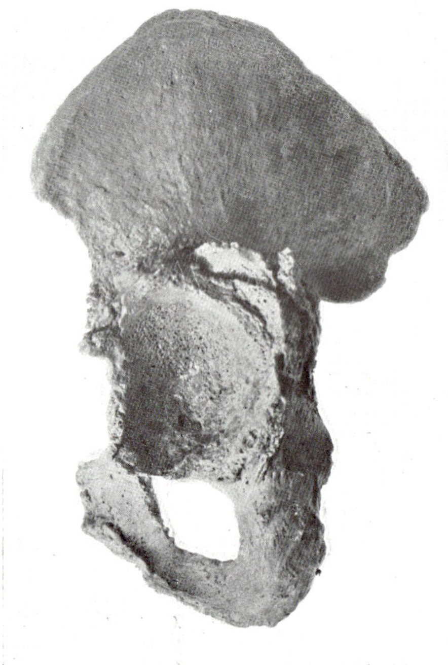

Fig. 468.—Arthritis deformans (degenerative form). Shallow acetabulum surrounded by marginal osteophytes. (Another view of Fig. 467.)

face does not become smooth and shiny, but remains porous, as though one had tried to polish pumice stone (Walkhoff).

All round the margin of the joint (Fig. 466), which is much enlarged thereby, there is usually formed a series of cartilaginous or bony nodular outgrowths. These may interlock in such a way as to limit the motion of the joint very seriously. From the capsular synovial membrane there often hang villous, branched, fat-containing masses which are spoken of as *lipoma*

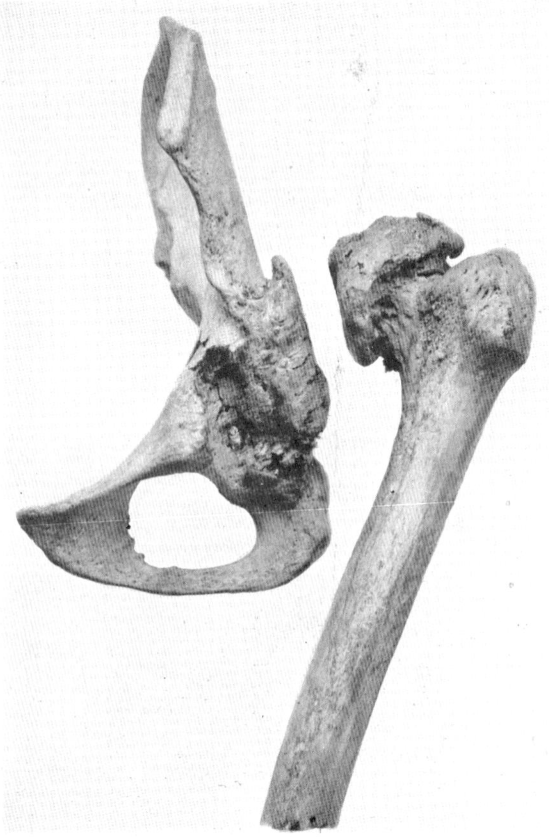

Fig. 469.—Arthritis deformans (degenerative form). Erosion of head of femur with dislocation to a new flattened joint surface on the ilium.

arborescens. In this capsule, also calcified or cartilaginous masses of tissue may form and become pedunculated. Through constriction of their stalk they may come to be free in the cavity, where they cause much disturbance (*joint mice*).

Histologically the first changes are found in the cartilage, which loses its normal elasticity and homogeneous character and becomes vertically split into fine fibrillæ. The cartilage cells degenerate and disappear. The whole layer may be ground away, exposing the bone, which has in the meanwhile, by the activity of the subchondral osteoblasts, become eburnated or condensed, so that the cancellous laminæ lie close together in a compact mass. Great proliferation of the remaining cartilage around the margin of the joint occurs, and into this cartilage the blood capillaries of the osteogenic marrow grow, converting it into bone. There is little or no formation of granulation tissue from the synovial membrane or perichondrium over the surface of the joint, and ankyloses do not occur. The erosion can go

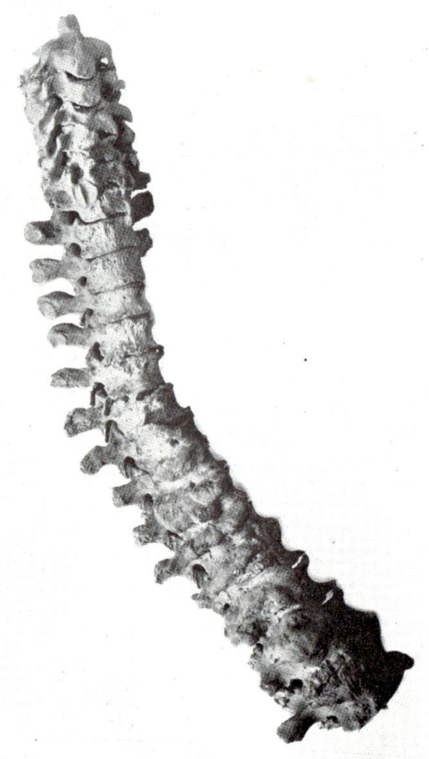

Fig. 470.—Spondylitis deformans, showing fusion of the bodies of the vertebræ by exostoses which stretch across the intervertebral discs. The smaller articulations show no ankylosis, in which this condition differs somewhat from the spondylose rhizomelique.

much further than the mere thickness of the original layer of cartilage. The exposed bone is worn away deep into the head of the epiphysis until the most extreme deformity is produced, constantly made up in a futile way by the growth of the marginal osteophytes (Fig. 467). In the hip such changes produce a flattening of the head of the femur into a mushroom-like mass fringed with hanging osteophytes which plays in the partly filled-up and very shallow acetabulum (Fig. 468), or the erosions may be more lateral and the head of the femur, now a laterally flattened mass, becomes dislocated to some point on the ilium where it lies against a new-formed acetabulum (Fig. 469). In all the more advanced cases of this type there is much rarefaction of the bones, and a dried femur is extraordinarily light as compared with one from a normal person. In one case which I observed for a long time the bones were so fragile that one of them broke on lifting the body of the woman from the bed after death. A section showed the cancellous bone to be extensively atrophied and the cortex greatly reduced in thickness.

This group comprises, beside the forms in which the joints of hands and feet are affected together with other larger articulations, those in which erosion of the cartilage and atrophy of the bones found in one hip-joint (*malum coxæ senile*), and those in which the cartilaginous intervertebral discs form the starting-point, and in which the production of exostoses and ecchondroses round the centre of the vertebræ results in a rigidity of the spinal column not dependent upon ankylosis of its smaller articulations (spondylitis deformans) (Fig. 470).

LITERATURE

Pommer: Mikr. Befunde bei Arthritis deformans, Wien, 1913.
Pribram: Spez. Path. u. Therapie v. Nothnagel, 1902, 7ter Theil, v.
Kimura: Ziegler's Beiträge, 1900, xxvii, 225.
v. Stubenrauch: Münch. med. Woch., 1914, lxi, 1494, 1565.
Barker: XVII. Internat. Cong. of Med., London, 1893, vi, Part I, 253.
Nichols and Richardson: Jour. of Med. Research, 1909, xxi, 149.
Walkhoff: Verh. Dtsch. Path. Gesellsch., 1906, ix, 229.

CHAPTER XLVII

TUMORS

General nature of tumors; difficulty of classification. Fibromata. Neurofibromata, keloids. Lipomata. Chondromata. Osteomata. (Xanthomata.) Myomata; leiomyomata, rhabdomyomata.

General Nature of Tumors.—It seems quite impossible to discuss the general nature of tumors or to attempt any definition of a tumor until after some survey of their varying anatomical characters and modes of growth is made. In the meanwhile it may be said that they are masses of tissue resembling, but not perfectly identical with, the normal tissues, which grow without any regard for the laws which govern and restrain the growth of normal tissue. They are supplied with blood-vessels and a sufficient supporting framework by the host, and derive their nourishment from the circulation of the host. Therefore, like any parasite, they are harmful to the person in whose body they grow, but the injury which they do becomes intolerable when they not only absorb this essential nourishment, but also invade and destroy the normal tissues. In olden times they were actually looked upon as parasites foreign to the body, but such a vague idea was forced to disappear when Johannes Müller showed that they were always composed of tissue of their host. If, now, we speak of a fibrous tumor as a fibroma, a fatty tumor as a lipoma, and cartilaginous or bony tumors as chondromata or osteomata, it is rather because their tissues closely resemble fibrous, fatty, cartilaginous, or bony tissue, than that we can actually trace their origin to these tissues. Our classification is, therefore, rather a tissue of assumptions than one formed on a true histogenetic basis. Probably it is true than an epithelioma *is* definitely derived from the epithelium in which it began, and the fibroma from the preëxistent connective tissue. It would be difficult to conceive of any other explanation, but the absolute proof is not at hand. Classification is at best unsatisfactory on a histogenetic basis, since so often we cannot make a good guess at the tissue which the tumor most resembles, and since then, in so many cases, we have no clue as to the point from which it actually sprang. It is greatly aided by observations on the histological characters of the new-growths, and in our ignorance of their ætiology, we adopt a subdivision in which the type of the tissue and the mode of growth form the main lines upon which separation into classes is carried out. Such a classification will be given (p. **1024**) after we have examined the tumors themselves.

FIBROMATA

A fibroma is a tumor composed of tissue which resembles more or less closely one of the many types of normal connective tissue. There is such variety in the relations of intercellular substance and cells in these normal types (tendon, fascia, areolar tissue, dermis, etc.) that it is not surprising that the fibrous tumors, which can diverge in every way from the character

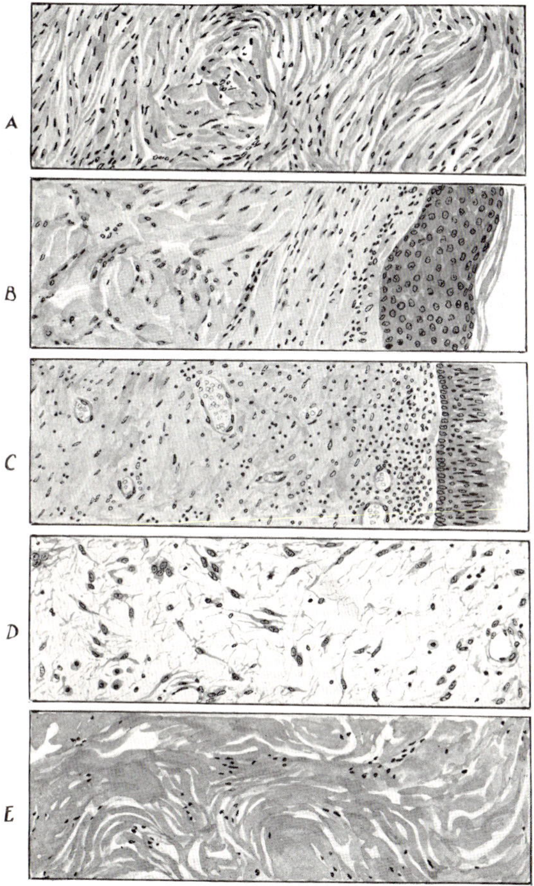

Fig. 471.—Types of fibroma. *C*, Nasal polyp or œdematous fibroma. The others (*A*, *B*, *D*, *E*) are fibromata of different consistence, formed in various situations in the body.

of the tissue from which they may be supposed to arise, may show a much greater variety. In every case one is impressed by the purposeless arrangement of the fibres, which stand in no especial relation to adjacent tissues, as they do in normal connective tissue, but are merely woven together in a mass. Some fibromata are extremely soft and loose in texture—others are dense and hard (Figs. 471 and 472). When the intercellular fibres are little developed and the tumor is made up chiefly of closely packed cells, it may be found that its growth is rapid and invasive, and that the tumor should really be called a sarcoma. This is one of the points at which mere histological examination may fail to afford a correct interpretation and the biological characters must be known. To coin for such tumors the name fibrosarcoma is probably only to add to the difficulties of classification.

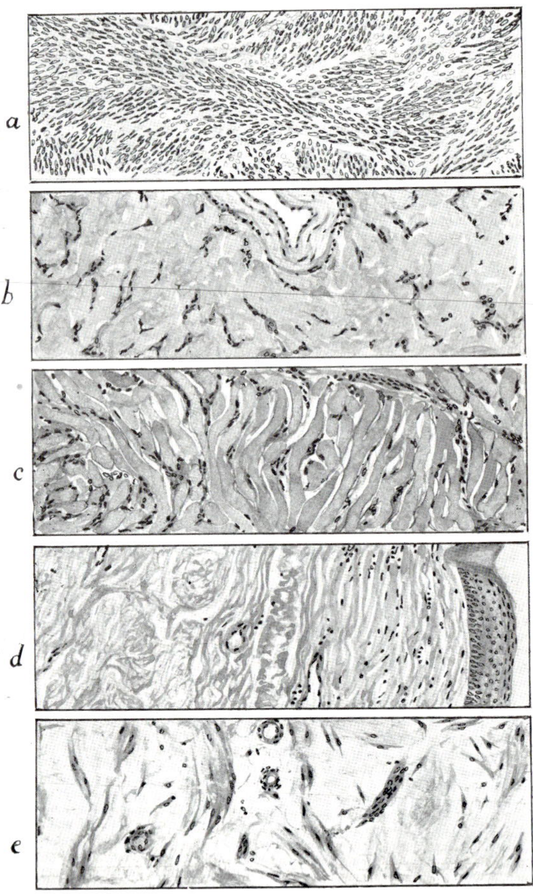

Fig. 472.—Types of fibroma: (*a*) Cellular fibroma resembling a spindle-cell sarcoma, but benign; (*d*) keloid.

Fibromata occur almost anywhere in the body and are frequently multiple. They arise most commonly in the skin, the fasciæ, and the intermuscular tissues, about the joints or in connection with nerves. In the internal organs they are found in the submucosæ, in the kidney, ovaries, etc., but in many cases, especially in the breast and uterus, the excessive growth of fibrous tissue accompanies that of other cells, such as epithelium or smooth muscle, and although such tumors are commonly spoken of as adenofibromata or fibromyomata, it seems probable that they are rather to be regarded as tumors of epithelium or muscle with merely a very abundant stroma. Fibromata of the skin are sometimes hard, solid tumors embedded deep in the skin and extending into the subcutaneous tissue (Fig. 473). One which was studied after its removal by operation formed a thick cap over the whole scalp, projecting down with thick rounded edges as far as the ears. It was so rigid and so densely connected with the skin that much

Fig. 473.—Subcutaneous hard fibroma.

skin had to be grafted to cover the skull after its extirpation. Others are soft and project above the skin surface, often hanging by a relatively thin stalk (Fig. 474). Occasionally very large tumors composed of soft fibrous tissue are found hanging by a long stalk from the labium majus or from some other site about the external genitalia. Single tumors of this sort occur, but the most characteristic form is that described as *fibroma molluscum,* in which great numbers of soft, partly pedunculated nodules are scattered over the whole body (Fig. 475). This condition is often called *von Recklinghausen's disease*, and it has been learned that it is a more complicated condition than might appear at first sight. It is congenital or hereditary, although the nodules may become conspicuous only in later life. There are areas of pigmentation scattered among them, and the nodules themselves are developed around nerves in the substance of which fibrous masses also appear. Dissection of such a mass will often reveal a cutaneous nerve embedded in loose fibrous tissue and beaded along its course by small denser fibromata which spread apart its fibres. There is also in some cases a peculiar relaxation of the skin, usually over the scalp, which allows great folds to hang down over the ears or over the face. In such folds similar nerves beaded with fibromata have been found. Fabyan found no nerves in the tumors in his case.

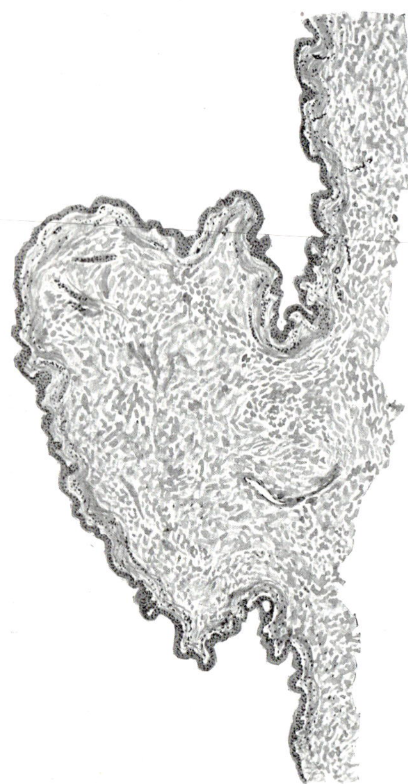

Fig. 474.—Small soft pedunculated fibroma of the skin.

Keloids are extremely dense, scar-like tumors which appear in some people (especially in negroes) in the scars of wounds. Even when the wound has been very slight great nodules may result. I have seen one or two negresses in whom puncture of the ear-lobes for earrings had set up the formation of great lobulated keloids. In other cases scratches, burns, or even healed acne pustules seem sufficient to start the growth. Extirpation leaves another scar in which, of course, the process may repeat itself. It seems that there must be some individual predisposition in such cases for, of course, this does not happen in every one. The tumors are composed of very dense fibrous tissue in which blood-vessels and cells are far apart (Fig. 472, *d*).

In the *nose* fibromata grow in clusters from the nasal septum, pushing up the Schneiderian membrane to cover them. These become extremely œdematous since they are loose in texture and hang in the cavity of the nose as translucent, rather turgid rounded bodies almost like white grapes (nasal polyps). They cause obstruction of the air-passage and are exposed to trauma. Microscopically they are found to show sparsely arranged connective-tissue cells, but are infiltrated with all sorts of wandering cells, including many eosinophiles and the most beautiful mast cells (Fig. 471, *c*).

In connection with fasciæ, ligaments, and periosteum there are found larger, dense fibrous tumors in which the cells and their abundant intercellular fibres are closely packed together in a hard mass which, on section, shows a shining, pearly white surface. These too may present softer areas, but usually the consistence is pretty uniform. Sometimes the fibres are gathered into interlacing bundles, an arrangement which is particularly common in those which are associated with the sheaths of the nerves. These tumors, often mistakenly called neuromata, are sometimes found in large numbers even along the course of the larger nerves, and not only, as in the case of von Recklinghausen's disease, as small nodules near the termination. Dr. Prudden has described one case from which specimens are preserved in the museum, and his illustrations show the extraordinarily wide distribution of the tumor masses. Here the nerve-fibres are stretched out over the nodules so as to enclose them. Such relations with the nerves seem commoner than with the blood-vessels, although there are found, in the nose and elsewhere, fibromata of extraordinary vascularity.

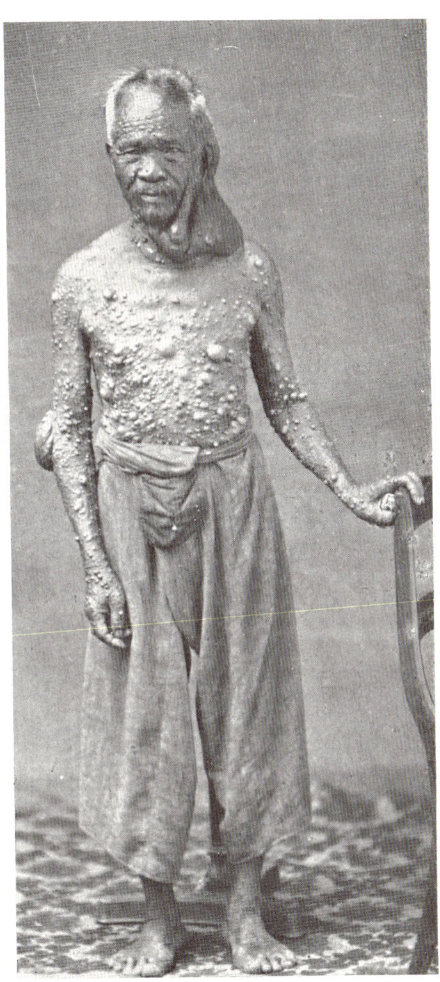

Fig. 475.—Multiple neurofibromatosis (von Recklinghausen's disease). Observe the great relaxed mass of skin which hangs from the side of the head.

Pure fibromata are rare in the uterus and in the mammary gland. In the *ovary* they occur in the form of hard nodules which may reach a great size. These show microscopically closely arranged spindle-shaped connective-tissue cells with compact intercellular fibres. In the *kidney* there are often seen rather small, round, grayish white glistening nodules embedded in the cortex or pyramids and crowding aside the tubules. These on section show an atypical fibrous tissue with varying proportions of cells and fibrous material. So too in the submucosæ of the alimentary tract firm gray nodules are found lifting up the mucosa. While some of these are true fibromata, most of them are made up of smooth muscle with a fibrous stroma.

Mention is usually made in this connection of elephantiasis and of localized giant growths, although it seems that they have little to do with tumor formation. Elephantiasis, aside from the type produced by filariæ, is probably congenital and consists in the enormous enlargement of an extremity with œdema and fibrous induration of the subcutaneous tissue and extreme thickening of the skin, which becomes very rough and folded. Many of these conditions seem to be caused by inflammatory processes, while others are related to von Recklinghausen's multiple neurofibromatosis and occur with it. Partial gigantism, in which one extremity is merely developed on a larger scale than the rest, is evidently the result of disturbances of embryonic development.

LITERATURE

Fibroma.—Gergö: Virch. Arch., 1913, ccxiii, 317.
Neurofibromata.—Harbitz: Arch. Int. Med., 1909, iii, 32.
Helmholtz and Cushing: Amer. Jour. Med. Sci., 1906, cxxxii, 355.

LIPOMATA

These are tumors composed of fat tissue and occurring in the form of circumscribed and sometimes lobulated flattened or rounded masses. Since fat tissue is not very sharply characterized histologically, it is difficult to make out differences between that which occurs in tumors and the normal fat. In some cases, however, the fat is associated with such a dense fibrous growth that the name fibrolipoma may be appropriate. In others an excessive vascular supply may suggest the name angiolipoma.

The tumors occur most commonly in the subcutaneous tissue, and especially over the back, the neck and shoulders, and the buttocks. They project as rather soft, lobulated masses which are sometimes quite tender or even spontaneously painful. They can be shelled out of their bed in the tissue and do not tend to recur. Microscopically there is merely fat in hugely dilated cells, arranged in compact lobules held together by the fibrous stroma. Coalescence of fat-cells with loss of their walls so that pools of oil are formed is an uncommon occurrence. Calcification or even ossification in necrotic areas is sometimes observed.

Other sites for lipomata are in the mesentery, the submucous and subserous tissues of the whole alimentary tract, in the kidney, heart, uterus, and even in the meninges. In the kidney the lipomata are usually rather small, but a few larger ones have been studied and have shown, beside the fat, an admixture with muscle and other elements, often with nodules of adrenal-like tissue.

Very interesting are the symmetrical multiple lipomata which have been mentioned before as related somehow with the irregular adiposis dolorosa of Dercum. The figure (Fig. 451) gives the impression better than any description. These are often tender or painful, and are associated with mental, motor, sensory, and trophic disturbances of various sorts. Lyon thinks they shade off into the more general adiposis and may prove to be due to some disturbance of internal secretions.

Lipomata are practically invariably slow-growing tumors which increase from within themselves, expanding so as to compress surrounding tissues or to project on the body surface.

LITERATURE

Lipoma.—Lyon: Arch. Int. Med., 1910, vi, 28.
Keenan and Archibald: Jour. Med. Research, 1907, xvi, 121.
Ebner: Beitr. z. kl. Chir., 1913, lxxxvi, 186.
Schridde: Ergebn. d. allg. Path., 1906, x, 674.

CHONDROMATA

Tumors composed of cartilage of a somewhat irregular and atypical character occur in connection with preëxisting cartilage in the joints, in the bones, or occasionally in the bronchi. Those which spring from the bone or skeletal cartilage appear as nodular tumors (Fig. 476) composed of elastic, pale-bluish cartilage which is covered with a fibrous envelope and divided, as a rule, into lobules by a framework of connective tissue which bears blood-vessels. They are broadly connected with the bones or cartilage, or are partly embedded in the bone, occupying much of its marrow cavity and extending through the cortex to project upon the surface. The bone is often greatly distended by such a mass, and especially in the case of the fingers becomes greatly distorted (Fig. 477). Large tumors of this kind are not uncommon in the hand, where several fingers may be converted into unwieldy lumps which become absolutely useless. In the pelvis enormous cartilaginous masses have been seen, projecting from the symphysis pubis or from the sacro-iliac synchondrosis, and so occupying the cavity of the pelvis as to obstruct childbirth. Similar tumors are described for the scapulæ, the ribs, the hyoid bone, etc.

Fig. 476.—Chondroma of phalanx.

Chondromata arising in the trachea or bronchi are often flattened clumps of tissue which, even though they lie in the spaces between the cartilaginous rings, are found to have a connection with them or with the perichondrium. In other cases large nodules have been observed blocking the bronchus or extending into the lung tissue.

Since normal cartilage is not vascular and depends for its nutrition upon the absorption of fluid from the vessels of the perichondrium, no great bulk of it can maintain itself alive. In the cartilaginous tumor, however, the tissue is in relatively small districts well supplied with nourishment from abundant blood-vessels which accompany its fibrous stroma. The intercellular substance is more variable in consistence and less dense than that of normal cartilage, and often shows a distinctly fibrillar structure. The cells vary greatly in size, and in their arrangement in groups, and thus differ markedly from those of normal cartilage (Fig. 478), but, on the whole, the resemblance is very close, and as a rule it is not easy to be sure of their tumor nature without recourse to information about the general features of the growth. Blood-vessels sometimes grow into the cartilage, as in normal endochondral ossification, and convert it into bone, so that the chondroma eventually becomes a kind of osteoma. Usually a layer of cartilage remains over the surface. In other cases extensive calcification occurs in patches, or the tumor may undergo a softening which leaves a cavity filled with a gelatinous, semi-fluid material in which large radiating cells are found. Actual cysts are formed finally if the liquefaction continues.

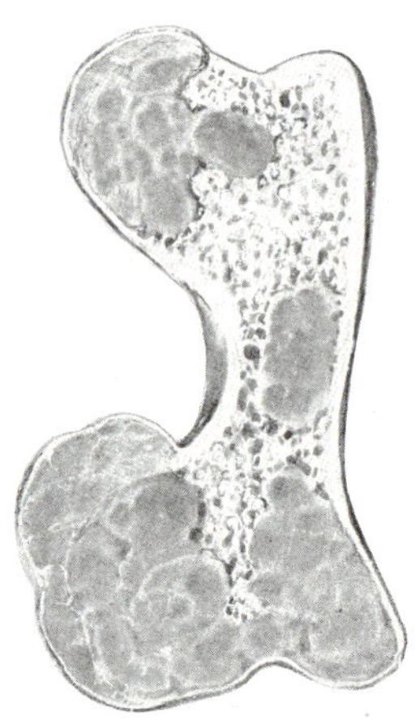

Fig. 477.—Chondroma of phalanx. The tumor appears to begin in several places, perforating the cortex and lifting up the periosteum.

Virchow and others have attempted to show that since these tumors are commonly found in young people, they may have arisen from congenitally misplaced cartilage or from disarranged cartilage islands cut off in the ordinary process of endochondral ossification. Such little islands do occur and remain unchanged. Virchow thought for a time that rickets, with its exaggerated and disorderly process of ossification, might present an especially favorable condition for such displacement of cartilage, but the cases seldom, if ever, show signs of healed rickets. It seems hardly necessary to insist upon the existence of such latent displaced cartilage islands, however, since periosteum and endosteum are so readily capable of producing cartilage whenever, as in a fracture, the new formation of tissue is required. Since we have other atypical tumor growths arising everywhere without special preparatory displacement of the tissue which exactly corresponds with them, it is not difficult to imagine the growth of a cartilaginous tumor from the cells which form bone by the way of cartilage. So, too, in the lung the new cartilage growths, which are often called ecchondroses, when they seem to represent a mere hyperplasia, are easily derived from the perichondrium.

Combination of cartilage with other tumor elements is frequently found.

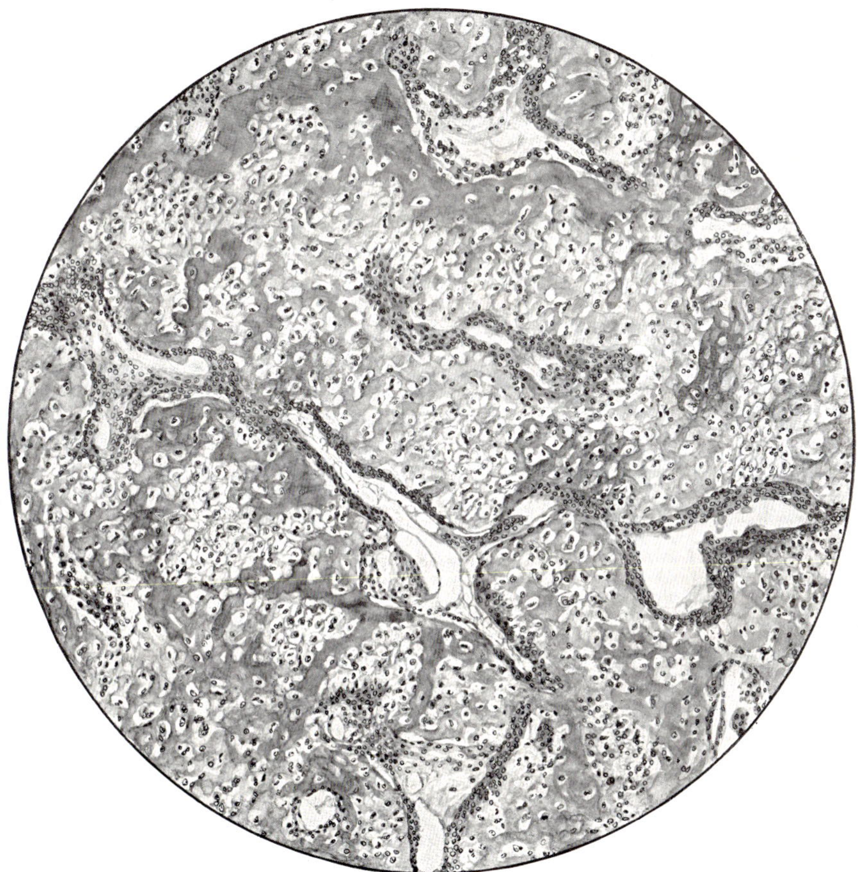

Fig. 478.—Chondroma with irregular blood-vessels and atypical bony areas.

LITERATURE

Chondroma.—Ribbert: Geschwulstlehre, Bonn, 1904.
Ehrenfried: Jour. Amer. Med. Assoc., 1915, lxiv, 1642.
Boggs: Johns Hopkins Hosp. Bull., 1913, xxiv, 210.

OSTEOMATA

It has already been stated that at many points throughout the body ossification of tissue may take place if degenerative changes and deposition of calcium salts have occurred. At points in relation with cartilage and bones, instances have already been met with in which, as, for example, in the case of arthritis deformans, rather extensive new bone formation occurs. Injuries to muscles and fasciæ and inflammations of various sorts seem capable of giving rise to some change which finally leads to bone formation. Thus it is said that cavalrymen acquire bony plates in the muscles of the insides of their thighs, and soldiers and others, similar plates in their deltoid muscles where gun or heavy burden rests. It is difficult to regard such things as tumors, since they seem to be merely an osteoplastic healing process which follows upon injury to the tissues. The so-called *progressive myositis ossificans* which, after inflammatory stages, ends in the formation of extensive bony shells in the muscles is doubtless similar in character.

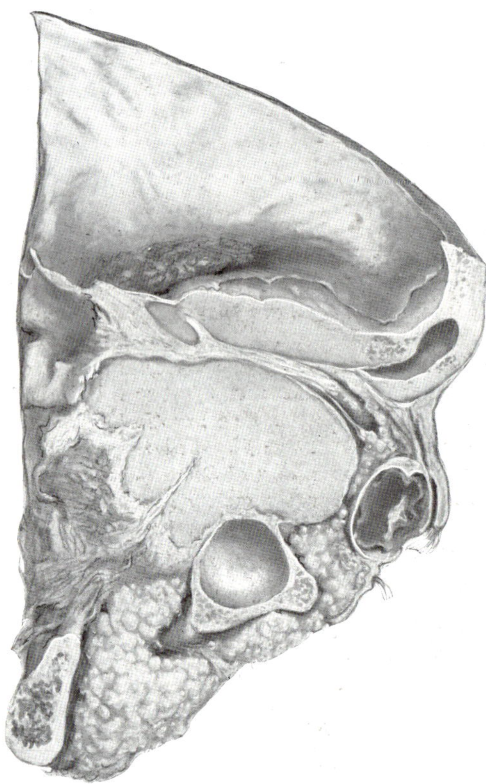

Fig. 479.—Large osteoma of very dense texture surrounding the elongated optic nerve, and dislocating the eye by extending into the orbit. The tumor bulged into the cranial cavity, and over it the brain was adherent.

More difficult to interpret properly are the multiple exostoses which appear about the epiphyses in young persons and are left along the shaft as the bone grows. They are often partly cartilaginous for a time, but in the end are bony. They can stretch some distance, and sometimes interarticulate in a way, with one another, or, by fusing, limit the motion of the extremities. These growths are often observed to occur in one family and seem to have an hereditary element. Of course, any collection of bones will be found to present at least a few examples in which extensive exostoses are found in the form of irregular, rather thin, sharp outgrowths, but these are usually recognized to be the accompaniments of an old fracture or of some long-standing inflammatory disease. Growths of this kind from the surface of a bone are called *exostoses;* those which appear in the interior of a bone, *enostoses,* while a diffuse thickening of the bone is called *hyperostosis.*

The nodules of bone found in the lungs sometimes reach a considerable size. They are thought by many to depend upon preëxisting inflammatory processes, and so too are those tiny bone masses which form in the trachea and roughen its mucosa. These are not in direct connection with the tracheal cartilage rings.

Tumor-like growths of bony consistence, usually masses more or less closely connected with the bones, may be very compact and hard, "eburnated," or soft and spongy. Much has been said of such bony growths in other connections, and it will suffice to recall attention to the rounded masses of osteoid tissue which appear on the skull in rickets and later become hardened into bone; to the extensive new bone formation in chronic osteomyelitis around the areas of infection and in the neighborhood of ulcers which overlie such bones as the tibia. Chronic syphilitic forms of periostitis in the same way lead to the production of rough periosteal growths which deform the bone. Mention may also be made of the so-called osteophytes of pregnancy, which are thin, white, chalk-like deposits on the inner surface of the skull. These seem to be reabsorbed or merged with the cranial bones later, and are probably the result of changes in the distribution of calcium which characterize the altered metabolism of pregnancy.

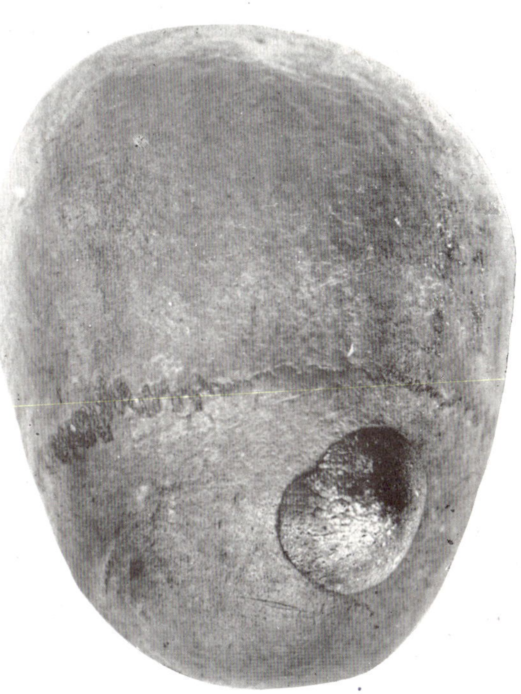

Fig. 480.—Ivory-like exostosis or osteoma of skull.

Osteomata or bony tumors in which the bone is growing independently and without a limited aim are rare. They sometimes occur in connection with the long bones and sometimes with pelvis, shoulder-girdle, etc. Occasionally they are more independent of the skeleton and arise in tendons or muscles as actual growing nodules. It appears that the bones of the skull, especially about the nose and orbit and middle ear, offer the most favorable chance for their development, and it is not infrequent to find rounded masses developing in the nasal cavity from the ethmoid or other bones or in the accessory nasal sinuses. These sometimes become loose and are known as dead osteomata. One which we studied last year showed a compact, extremely hard mass, which had grown to occupy the upper maxilla, and part of the temporal bone, projecting far into the orbit so as to displace the eye. When sawed through (with great difficulty), it presented a perfectly smooth, ivory-like surface, and was seen to project in all directions so as to occupy space in the cranial and other cavities (Fig. 479). There are other ivory-like tumors which occur like buttons on the skull, and sometimes form hemispherical masses of considerable size. They are usually a little separated from the skull around the edges so as to appear pedunculated. These cause no especial inconvenience (Fig. 480).

LITERATURE

Osteoma.—E. Brückmann: Virch. Arch., 1910, cc, 433.
Heymann: Virch. Arch., 1886, civ, 145.
Zimmermann: Dtsch. Ztschr. f. Chir., 1900, lvii, 354.
Fischer: Ergebn. d. allg. Path., 1906, x, 678.

XANTHOMA

Although commonly described with tumors, the forms of xanthoma seem hardly to be true tumors, but rather the result of local or wide-spread accumulations of lipoid substances in degenerated cells. Although this suspicion is not justified entirely by the histological study, it does seem to be upheld by the transient character of many of these growths and by their usual association with jaundice, diabetes, pregnancy, etc., all conditions in which the lipoid content of the blood is altered.

There are found—(1) xanthoma palpebrarum, in which flat, slightly elevated yellow patches are developed on the eyelids. These contain cholesterine esters with other lipoids in large cells in the cutis. These are thought by Pollitzer to be degenerated muscle cells; (2) multiple xanthoma which resembles (3) xanthoma diabeticorum in forming nodules in various places in the body, composed of somewhat similar large lipoid-laden cells, together with connective-tissue cells and a fibrous stroma. These nodules occur also in the internal organs, and are in most cases associated with jaundice.

LITERATURE

Pollitzer: N. Y. Med. Jour., 1899, lxx, 73.
Sikemeier: Frankfurter Zeitschr. f. Path., 1913, xiv, 428.

MYOMA

The term myoma is applied to tumors which are composed largely of muscle, those in which smooth muscle or non-striated muscle constitutes the predominant tissue being called leiomyomata, while the rather more complicated tumors, which contain striated muscle, are spoken of as rhabdomyomata. Since these types of tissue are not very closely related, it is not surprising to find that the corresponding tumors stand very far apart.

Leiomyomata

Tumors composed of smooth muscle occur very commonly in the walls of the uterus. Although they are found elsewhere, as in the walls of the stomach and intestine, in the bladder, kidneys, skin, etc., they are only rarely encountered in those situations and constitute a group of little importance as compared with those of the uterus.

Myomata (or fibromyomata) of the uterus, often loosely spoken of as fibroids, appear as rounded or nodular tumors situated in the uterine wall, although they frequently project from the outer surface in such a way that they seem to be attached to the uterus by a slender peduncle only. The thin layer of uterine muscle which envelopes them becomes more and more inconspicuous as they project in their growth from the uterine surface. On the other hand, there are also fibromyomata which project into the cavity of the uterus, carrying with them a very thin layer of the uterine musculature and the mucosa. They, too, become pedunculated and hang by this

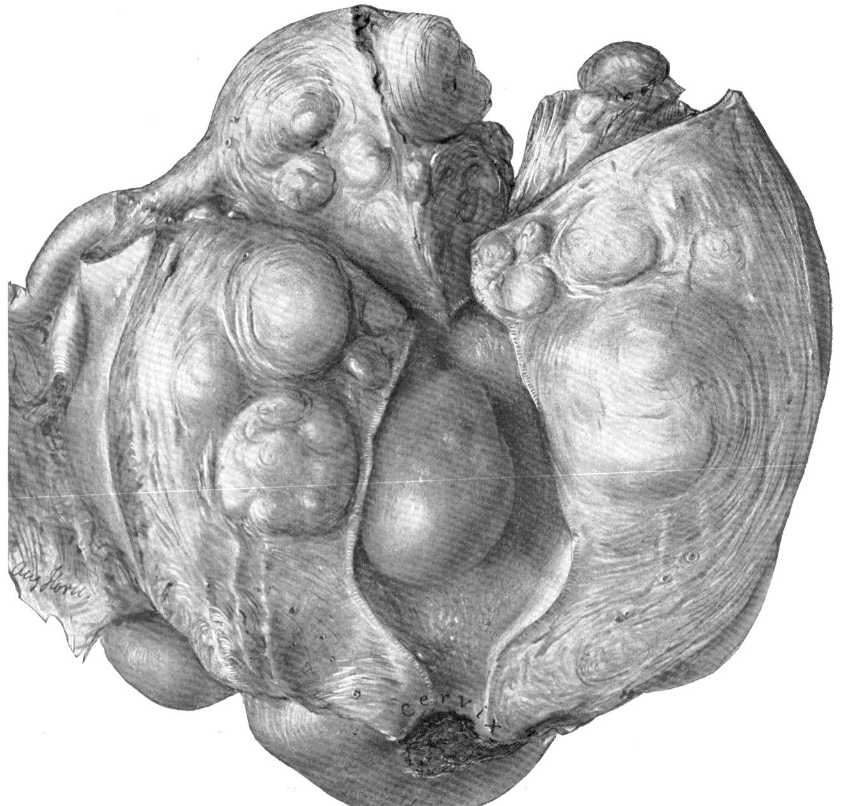

Fig. 481.—Subperitoneal, submucous, and intramural myomata of the uterus (Kelly-Cullen).

stalk in the cavity, sometimes projecting from the external os uteri. In these three positions the tumors are given the epithets intramural, subserous, and submucous.

Uterine myomata vary greatly in size, some being found embedded in the wall, and no more than 2 or 3 mm. in diameter, while others reach enormous dimensions. Often several tumors of different sizes are found in the same uterus, and these may occupy all three situations (Fig. 481). In the cases in which large submucous myomata are found, the cavity of the uterus is greatly enlarged and distorted by the presence of the mass, and indeed this is true also in those cases in which large tumors occupy an intramural position.

They are dense, hard, pearly-white masses, which on section are found to be sharply marked out from the surrounding uterine musculature by projecting above its cut surface. They are further distinguished from it by their greater density and by their poverty in blood-vessels, for whereas the uterine wall is rather reddish-gray and vascular, the tumor is usually composed of whorls of fibres intimately woven together so as to shine with a tendon-like lustre, reflected separately from each bundle, and is much more rigid than the surrounding tissue. Its blood-vessels, although sometimes rather large in the superficial zone, are quickly reduced to a very small calibre as they penetrate into the interior. Clarke has shown that this vascularization often becomes quite inadequate to nourish with blood the innermost parts, so that most extensive necroses appear, recognizable as hyaline areas or patches in which calcification or even bone formation has occurred. Great cyst-like cavities filled with brownish, turbid fluid are also found as a result of the disintegration of the tissue.

Such tumors grow by new formation of tissue from within, expanding and compressing adjacent structures, but showing no tendency to invade nor to set up, by metastasis, similar growths in distant organs. Nevertheless, they may cause great distortions in the uterus and interfere seriously with its function. Although childbirth may be possible when the tumor is not too large, or when it is situated high in the fundus of the uterus, it may readily be understood that a large tumor, especially when situated low in the uterus, can effectively obstruct parturition. Submucous myomata tend also to interfere with pregnancy and may, in case pregnancy does occur, offer a serious obstacle to the birth of the child.

The submucous myomata are especially productive of serious symptoms at all times, since the uterus tends to expel them into the vagina, exposing the surface to infection. Circulatory disturbances aid in causing the mass to soften and disintegrate, and from the putrefying tissue absorption of poisonous substances soon leads to a cachectic condition in the woman who bears such a tumor. In addition, these growths usually cause frequent hæmorrhages from the uterus, which may bring about extreme anæmia.

The many other details in the biology of these tumors may be read in the book of Kelly and Cullen on Myomata of the Uterus, in which a great wealth of material is described. One of the most interesting phenomena is the formation of vascular adhesions between large subperitoneal uterine myomata and the omentum or intestine, or other abdominal organ, after which the tumor becomes dependent upon that organ for its blood supply and may even be separated finally from all connection with the uterus (parasitic myoma).

Microscopically, fibromyomata are found to be composed of smooth muscle-fibres arranged in parallel rows in bundles which interlace in every direction. These are embedded in an abundant stroma of connective tissue which bears the blood-vessels. According to the proportion of muscle to fibrous stroma, the consistence of the tumor varies, increase in the fibrous tissue adding to its hardness. The muscle-fibres are recognizable by their rod-shaped nuclei and by their relatively plump cell-body, which takes a greenish color with Van Gieson's stain, in contrast with the bright red fibrous stroma. Of course, the actual bodies of the connective-tissue cells stain greenish yellow also, but they are rather sparsely scattered in the stroma.

Several theories as to the origin of these tumors have been advanced, but none are as yet firmly established. While it seems probable that they arise from abnormal portions of the uterine musculature itself, there are those who assert their origin from the musculature of the walls of the blood-vessels. The fact that myomata relax and soften during pregnancy, recovering their hardness afterward, seems to point to their relation to the uterine musculature.

The greatest interest has been roused by certain rather diffuse myomatous tumors which occur in the uterine wall, especially at the angle where the Fallopian tube enters, and also in the tube itself and in the round ligament. These are peculiar in containing epithelium-lined, gland-like cavities scattered in the mass of smooth muscle. They were called adenomyomata by von Recklinghausen, who ascribed them to misplaced rudiments derived from the mesonephros or Wolffian body. This view has been widely accepted. The proof is not complete, however, and R. Meyer, Lockstaedt, and others bring forward arguments against it showing that it is quite possible that such glandular tumors might arise from inclusion of uterine glands in a muscular mass. Cullen, in his volume on the subject, has shown, by careful study of 73 cases, that in 56 it was possible to trace the uterine mucosa directly into continuity with the glands of the tumor, a finding which seems to decide the matter definitely.

Myomata of the stomach and intestine are usually small nodules lying beneath the mucosa or projecting on the peritoneal surface. They show no degenerative changes, and are, as a rule, too small to cause any symptoms. Those in the vagina and in the urinary bladder are sometimes much larger, while nodules of smooth muscle in the kidneys are usually quite small. In the skin, myomata develop as subcutaneous or intracutaneous nodules arising probably from the tissue of the arrectores pilorum, although other explanations have been given.

Malignant tumors composed of smooth muscle occur. Ghon and Hintz described one which arose from the intestinal tract with secondary growths in pancreas, liver, heart, etc., and give references to the literature which show that many cases have been observed. The development of such malignant characters is most important in the case of the common uterine myomata. In those tumors there are observed changes in the microscopical appearance of the cells, leading to their extreme irregularity in size and form. Corresponding with these peculiar appearances it has been found that the tumors assume a rapid and irregular growth and give rise to secondary growths or colonies in other organs or in adjacent tissues. It seems clear that malignant tumors spring out of benign myomata which have already existed for a long time, but the question remains as to their exact origin. They may be due to the acquisition of malignant powers of growth by the smooth muscle-cells, in which case we should speak of them as malignant myomata, or the invasive tumor may be the offspring of the

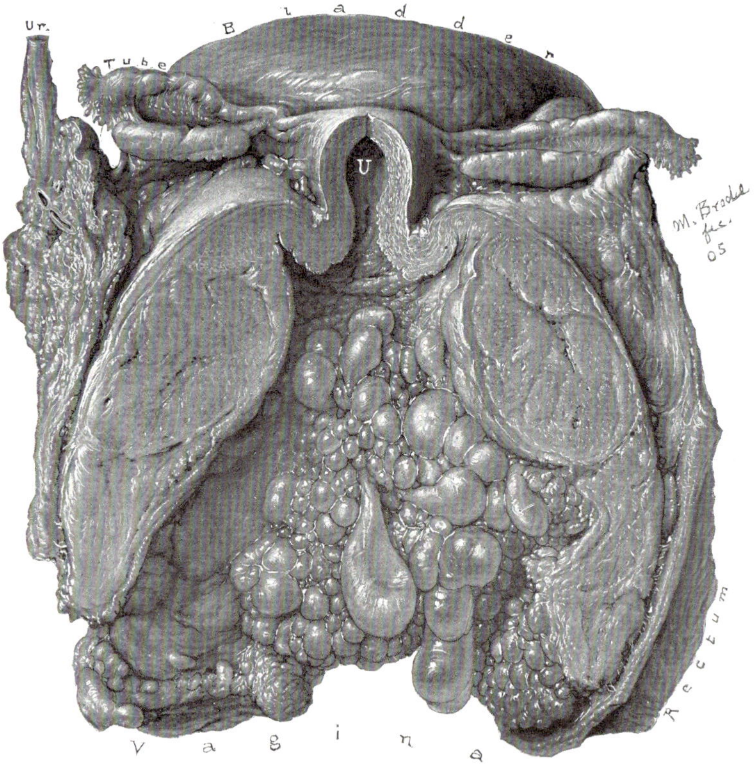

Fig. 482.—Rhabdomyoma beginning in the vaginal wall in a child, and extending into the bladder. Grape-like polypoid masses hang from the infiltrated vaginal walls (Dr. C. Cone's case, from Kelly-Noble).

stroma of the myoma, and then it would be justifiable to call the tumor a sarcoma. It is only in the latter case, in which there is a true sarcoma mixed with the muscle tissue of the myoma, that such a term as myosarcoma is justifiable. A sarcoma is not a tumor derived from muscle, but rather one arising from connective tissue.

LITERATURE

Leiomyomata.—Kelly and Cullen: Myomata of the Uterus, Phila.
Cullen: Adenomyoma of Uterus, Phila., 1908.

Leiomyomata.—Ghon and Hintz: Ziegler's Beiträge, 1909, xlv, 89.
Lubarsch: Ergebn. d. allg. Path., 1895, i, 330; 1897, ii, 574.
Aschoff: *Ibid.*, 1900, v, 97.
Zieler u. Fischer: *Ibid.*, 1906, x, 700.

Rhabdomyoma

In these tumors, which are found usually in young persons or children in such positions as the heart-wall, bladder and vagina, kidney, œsophagus, etc., the tissue frequently contains cells of various kinds, among which there are found striated muscle-fibres. It seems to be rare to find a whole

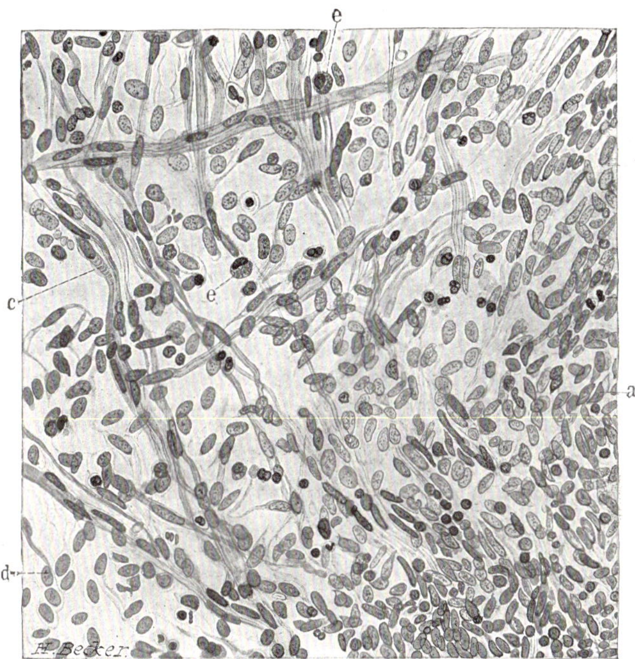

Fig. 483.—Rhabdomyoma, from same case as Fig. 482; long, ribbon-like, striated fibres (*c*) are mingled with round- and spindle-shaped cells (*a*, *d*). There are some wandering eosinophiles (*e*) (from Kelly-Noble).

tumor made up of muscle-fibres, and the admixture is often with such elements as cartilage, loose cellular connective tissue, and even epithelial structures. The suspicion is, therefore, aroused that rhabdomyomata are closely related to the mixed tumors or teratomata.

These are usually benign tumors, but in many cases they develop invasive characters and may metastasize widely. Those in the heart-wall form single or multiple nodules which often project into the cavity of the heart. Those in the bladder, of which we were able to study one case, hang in polypoid masses which often appear in the vagina as well and protrude from its orifice (Fig. 482).

Microscopically, these are soft, often œdematous tumors, which show numerous small, irregular, and spindle-shaped cells which make up a considerable part of their bulk, but scattered among these, and sometimes in compact masses, are larger elements in whose protoplasm a delicate striation is visible (Fig. 483). These do not resemble muscle-fibres closely, but show transitions to other greatly elongated cells which do resemble the earlier developmental stages of striated muscle. These are narrow, ribbon-like cells with a central space which may contain many nuclei. The protoplasm is not only longitudinally striated, but shows distinct transverse striations. The rhabdomyomata usually have an abundant content of glycogen. They are regarded by most writers as arising from a rudiment derived from an early embryonic stage, which, displaced in the course of development, has grown in its unusual situation.

LITERATURE

Seiffert: Ziegler's Beiträge, 1900, xxvii, 145.
Stumpf: *Ibid.*, 1911, l, 171.

CHAPTER XLVIII

TUMORS (Continued)

Tumors derived from elements of the nervous system: General relations to various stages in development of the nervous system. Neurocytoma, neuroblastoma, chromaffine tumors. Gliomata. Angiomata: hæmangiomata, lymphangiomata. Sarcomata: General characters. Spindle-cell, mixed-cell, round-cell, and alveolar sarcomata. Giant-cell sarcomata. Osteosarcomata. Myxomata.

TUMORS DERIVED FROM ELEMENTS OF THE NERVOUS SYSTEM

THE interpretation of tumors of the nervous system has recently undergone many changes, and certain tumors growing in other parts of the body and formerly regarded as peculiar sarcomata, have been recognized as belonging to this group.

Tumors are found composed of neuroglia in its various modifications; others contain certain ganglion-cells, often with abundant nerve-fibres, others are composed largely of antecedents of these structures capable sometimes of forming in the tumor ganglion-cells or fibres, elements of the type of the chromaffine tissue or any of the modifications of neuroglia. The type of tumor finally evolved seems to depend upon the stage in embryonic development at which the formative cells were diverted to the formation of a tumor.

Originally, the epiblastic cells which line the medullary groove are capable of developing into nervous elements or into supporting glial cells. The production of the peripheral nervous system is due to the outgrowth of nerve-fibres from this central region, but in addition to this, many of the neuro-epithelial cells wander into the interior of the body and assume certain positions in relation to the organs where they give rise to the cells and fibres of the sympathetic system. Their invasion into the interior of the rudiments of the adrenal glands results in the formation of the medulla of those glands in close relationship to the adjacent sympathetic ganglia. Similar modifications of some of these invading neurocytes in other situations lead to the formation of the analogous chromaffine bodies which are found in close association with the sympathetic ganglia in the thorax and retroperitoneal tract. It is necessary to believe that these cells may also give rise to less specialized attendant or supporting cells in each of these situations.

The relations to one another of the elements derived from the original medullary groove may be expressed as follows in a table which is partly derived from Wahl and Landau:

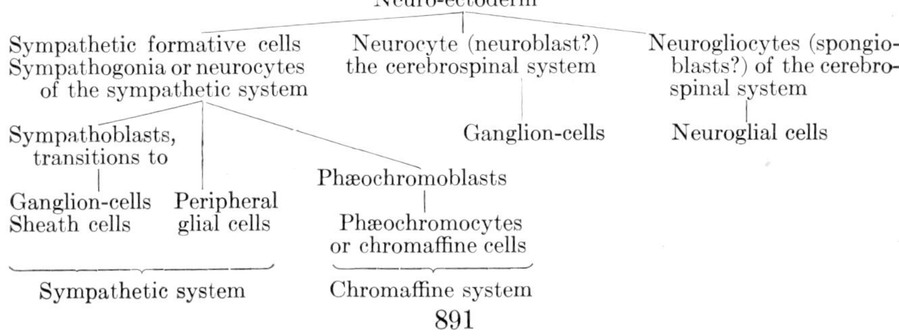

The known limitation of the power of mature nerve-cells and fibres to reproduce themselves has made it seem probable that those tumors which contain ganglion-cells and nerve-fibres must have arisen from some less differentiated stage. Indeed, since the weight of evidence is distinctly opposed to the idea that the cells of the sheath of Schwann, even if they do prove to be of nervous origin, can give rise to a new axis-cylinder, little credence is given to any report of tumors composed solely of tangles of nerve-fibres. There is probably no such tumor.

Tumors of Nerves.—The tumors which actually appear in the course of the nerves are usually derived from the supporting structures and are sometimes called false neuromata or neurofibromata. They have already been described in connection with fibromata. Those which show a cirsoid arrangement under the skin of the scalp or face are also of epineural or perineural origin, but do involve a great elongation of the nerve-fibres. Similarly the so-called amputation neuromata, which are round or nodular masses of whorled nerve-fibres, developing at the ends of nerves severed in the course of an amputation, are not tumors in the true sense. They are merely masses of twisted nerve-fibres frustrated in their attempt to grow down to the end-organ. Having excluded these growths from the group of tumors belonging strictly to the nervous system, it is found that nearly every stage in the table given above is represented by tumor formation. Wahl has discussed all these forms in an able paper in which he tabulates clearly all the tumors which have as yet been described and which can now be recognized as belonging to this group.

Neurocytoma.—Marchand has described a small tumor composed of cells resembling lymphoid cells, with fine fibrillar ground substance, which he regarded as a *neurocytoma,* or tumor derived from the undifferentiated neuroectoderm. This tumor was found in the Gasserian ganglion, and no similar growth has as yet been discovered in the sympathetic system.

Neuroblastoma.—J. H. Wright was the first to recognize clearly the existence of a group of tumors originating from the sympathetic formative cells or sympathogonia, and to these he gave the name *neuroblastoma.* These are growths which appear, as a rule, in infants and young children, although occasionally in adults, and in most cases arise from the adrenals, with abundant metastases in the liver. When they spring from other situations, such as the retroperitoneal or pelvic region, they are found to be associated with the sympathetic nervous system, and thence metastasize with great malignancy. They are often very extensive tumors, composed of small cells which are frequently arranged in characteristic rosettes, and the processes of these cells form a fine fibrillar intercellular stroma which gives none of the staining reactions of neuroglia or connective tissue.

Sympathoblastoma.—Martius has described one case in which, side by side with ganglionic elements, the tumor which lay at the root of the neck contained cells transitional in appearance between those of the neuroblastoma and ganglion-cells. He thinks, therefore, that this tumor represents Poll's sympathoblast or transitional stage.

Ganglioneuroma.—Many tumors containing ganglion-cells have been described from all parts of the body, but most often from some situation such as the retroperitoneal or pelvic or retrocervical regions, where they might have arisen in connection with the sympathetic system. These contain nerve-fibres also, though chiefly those of the non-medullated sort. The ganglion-cells are usually imperfectly developed and irregular in form, and the fibres are twisted and irregular in appearance, with, of course, no proper connection with any end-organ. While most ganglioneuromata are thought to be derived from the later developmental stages of the sympathetic system, there are some which arise in the same way in connection with the ganglia of the cerebrospinal system (Risel) or even in the brain itself. They are usually benign tumors, but a few, such as the second of Beneke's cases, show numerous metastases which seem to be derived from the smaller and less differentiated cells.

In connection with these there is sometimes a marked new formation of neuroglial elements which spring from the peripheral glial-cells, and such tumors have been called ganglioglioneuromata.

Chromaffine Tumors, Paragangliomata.—Benign and solitary tumors have been found in old people, arising usually in the adrenal medulla and containing, as a rule, sympathetic formative cells. These are composed largely of masses of cells which are sufficiently developed to give the brown staining reaction with chromic salts. No one has yet discovered a tumor which could be assigned to the earlier stage in the development of these cells (phæochromoblasts).

It is seen that practically all these active tumors are derived from some stage in the development of the sympathetic system and its allied tissues, only rare examples of ganglioneuromata derived from developmental stages of the cerebrospinal system being mentioned. In contrast with this the tumors arising from the neuroglia of the cerebrospinal system are relatively common and occupy an important place in the surgery of the nervous system.

Gliomata.—From the neuroglia there develop tumors in the brain, in the spinal cord, and in the eye. These are benign growths in the sense that they give rise to no distant colonies or metastases, but they are extremely destructive, inasmuch as they grow expansively, and in an infiltrating way, into the important structures of the nervous system. Since they are confined in the bony cavities of the skull and spinal canal, they soon cause the most serious symptoms through pressure on the brain or cord. Even though a glioma embedded in the brain may not itself increase the intracranial pressure enough to cause these well-known symptoms, it is constantly liable to sudden extravasations of blood into its substance, which are followed by apoplectiform attacks, with loss of consciousness, high blood-pressure, choked disc, and even generalized paralysis.

The gliomata of the brain may be situated at any point in the cerebrum, cerebellum, pons (Fig. 484), etc., and vary in size from very small nodules

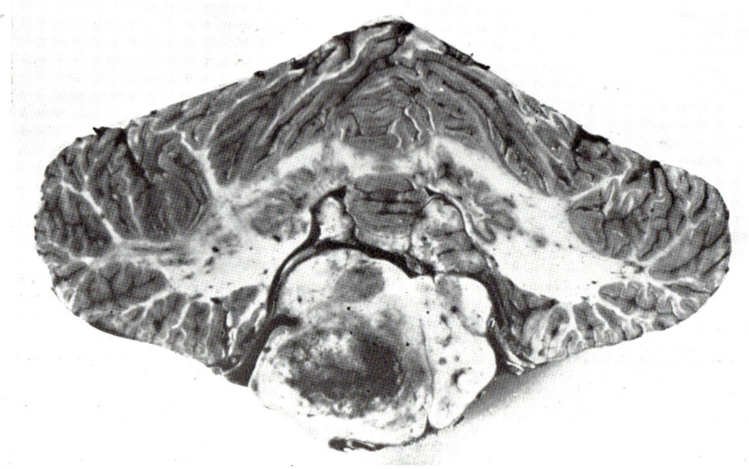

Fig. 484.—Glioma of pons with moderate hæmorrhage.

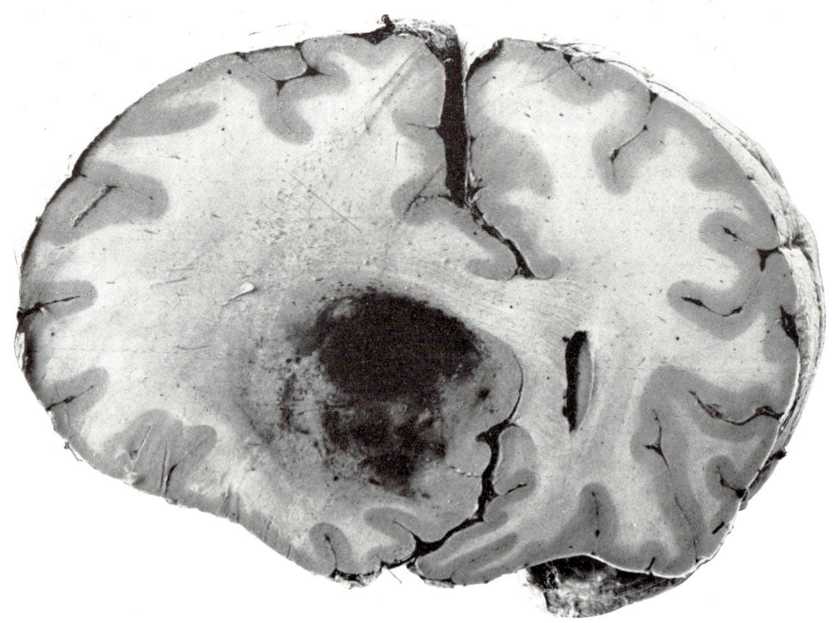

Fig. 485.—Glioma of brain with hæmorrhage.

up to huge masses which occupy nearly the whole of a hemisphere. They are rarely sharply outlined, either by their color or their consistence, but shade off insensibly into the surrounding brain substance (Fig. 485). Their position can be made out in the cut surface fairly well, however, by the swelling, the increased vascularity and translucence, and by the hæmorrhages and necroses which are usually present. There are some forms, indeed, which are so diffused through the brain substance that it is difficult to determine their outline even with the microscope. The adjacent tissue is pushed aside, and is much torn by the growth of the tumor. Nevertheless, gliomata do not, as a rule, extend to the surface of the brain and never pierce the meninges. A small group of these tumors presents an appearance

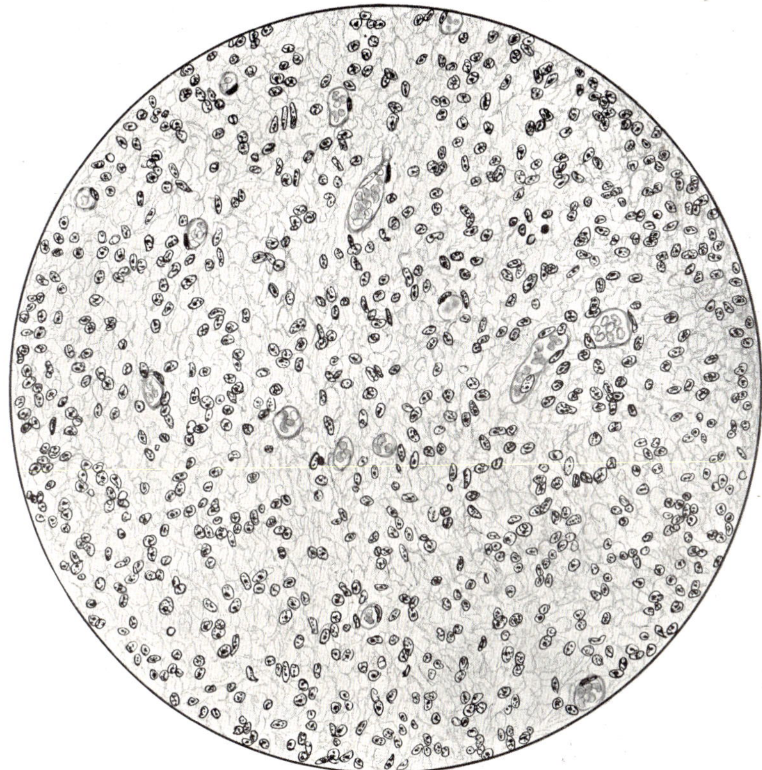

Fig. 486.—Glioma of the cerebrum composed of loosely arranged neuroglia cells and fibres.

very different from that of the common ones. Instead of being gray, translucent, soft, and rather œdematous, they are small, compact, and even quite hard. These generally project in relation to the ependyma.

Under the microscope most gliomata present a fairly uniform mass of cells of rather small size, with numerous protoplasmic processes which extend into a tangle with those of other cells and thus produce a feltwork of delicate filaments (Fig. 486). The question as to the independence of some of these neuroglia fibres seems to be unsettled in the minds of some writers, but Mallory has shown by special stains that the neuroglia fibres bear the same relation to the neuroglia cells as the collagen fibres to the cells of the connective tissue. They are differentiated products sometimes still traversing the edge of the body of the cell, sometimes lying free. Nevertheless, the actual protoplasmic processes of the cells play a considerable part in forming the fine intercellular network.

Great variety is seen in the form and arrangement of these cells. They are frequently found to have a rather abundant cytoplasm, with many long processes extending in all directions, so that they have acquired the name astrocyte or spider cell. Others are much simpler in outline and may have

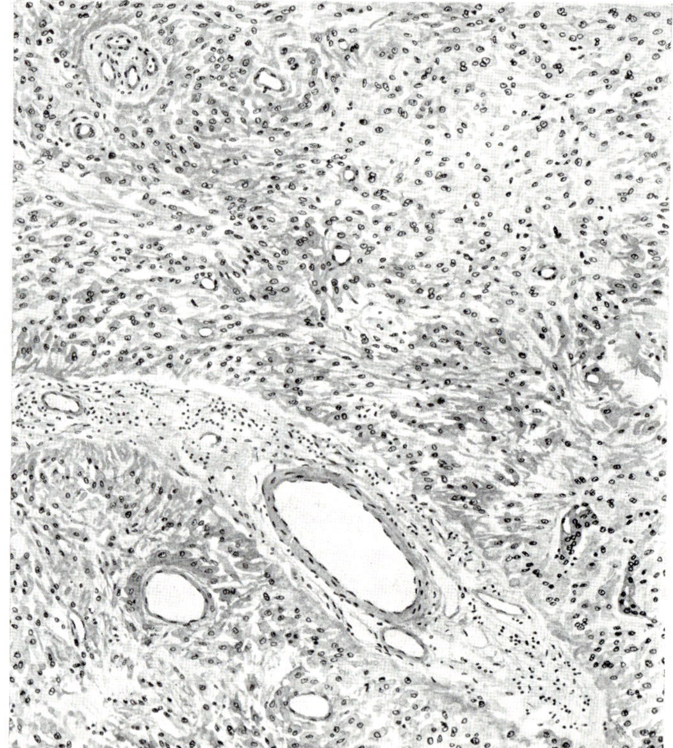

Fig. 487.—Glioma of cerebrum.

very few prolongations (Fig. 487). In many gliomata they are especially condensed about the blood-vessels; in others there are minute spaces about which cells are arranged radially with a flat or curved foot at the edge of the space, and a long, frayed-out cell-body extending peripherally to become entangled with the other cells. About larger spaces the same presentation of a smooth surface to the cavity is seen. Ganglion-cells and other nerve-cells of smaller size are quite frequently found in the substance of a glioma. It seems clear that these must be remnants of the original nervous tissue which have been caught in the advance of the tumor and surrounded (Fig. 488).

The degenerative changes, hæmorrhages, and necroses which are so frequent in these tumors have already been mentioned. They may lead to such wide-spread destruction of the tumor that only a thin rim of tumor tissue is left. It is not infrequent in such cases to find that the débris of the tumor-cells and blood has been replaced by a clear fluid, so that the whole area appears as a thin-walled cyst with only some pigment and fast vanishing traces of tumor tissue in its walls to indicate its original nature. I have seen two cysts of this kind in the cerebellum which had had time to reach this state in spite of the great destruction of the cerebellar tissue.

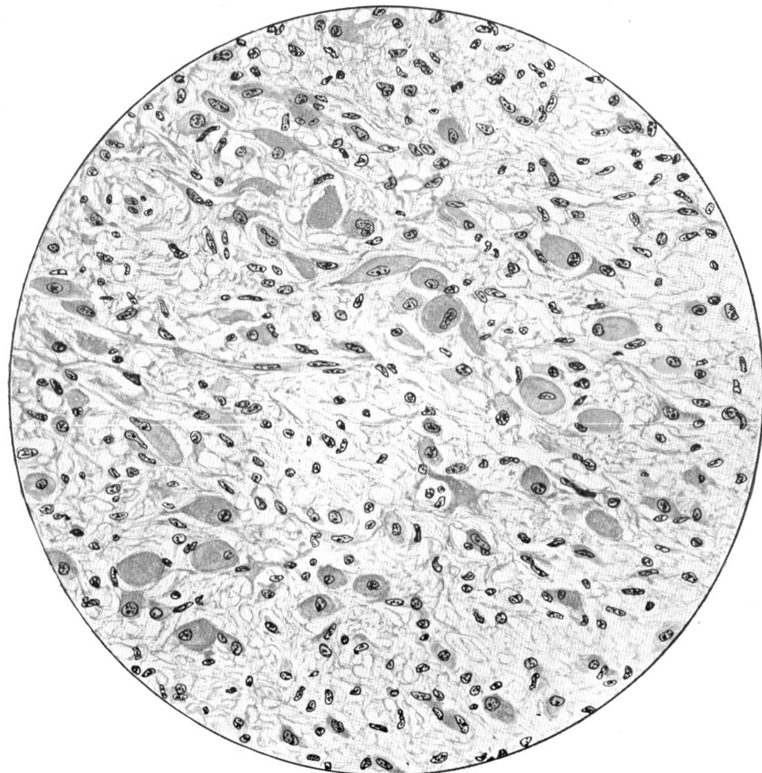

Fig. 488.—Glioma of cerebrum with inclusion of many ganglion-cells.

Gliomata developing in the pons or in the medulla may cause even more serious and quickly fatal destruction than those embedded in the brain. In the spinal cord these tumors are less common. They may exist in the form of a nodular mass, but are usually centrally placed and much elongated, forming, in the midst of the cord, a pencil-like growth which pushes aside all the nervous elements and compresses them. Many of these central tumors have a lumen and then appear as tubes. While an overgrowth of neuroglia or gliosis may occur in the cord from other causes, the presence of such tubular glioma can give rise to one, at least, of the forms of syringomyelia.

Syringomyelia is a curious affection of the spinal cord in which, as its name implies, a pipe or tube of neuroglia is embedded in the cord, and extends, sometimes, upward into the medulla. The most extraordinary symptoms follow: loss of temperature sense, and later of tactile sense, extreme contractures and deformities of the extremities and thorax, etc.

In the eye, gliomata arise from the glial constituents of the retina, or from some earlier developmental stage of the cells of the retina which can give rise to glial tissue, and grow out into the vitreous humor, pushing the retina forward. Frequently they begin near the anterior margin of the retina, and extend thence so as to occupy much or all of the cavity of the eye. Necroses are extremely frequent in the tissue, and the whole tumor may be reduced to a non-staining débris, except for the cells which immediately surround the blood-vessels. In other cases, in which there is no such necrosis, the nodular mass pushes through the sclera or through the cornea and appears in the orbit or on the surface of the eyeball. When removed by the enucleation of the eye, it tends to recur and to spread rapidly in the orbit and backward into the brain. The opposite eye is commonly involved.

The tumor itself is usually composed of small cells with little protoplasm and very few inconspicuous fibrils. There is another type first described, as far as I can determine, by Flexner, in which the cells are frequently arranged in rosettes. This tumor, he thought, should be designated *neuro-epithelioma*, since it apparently arose from an undifferentiated element of the retinal neuro-epithelium.

Ependymal Gliomata.—Several authors have described gliomatous tumors in which, on account of the presence of peculiar gland-like spaces lined with cells resembling epithelium, they have traced a relationship to the ependymal cells. Mallory was able to show that these peculiar cells have in their protoplasm certain small rodlets or granules which are characteristic of the ependymal cells, and therefore had no hesitation in regarding them as ependymal gliomata. Saxer described other tumors in which the ependymal elements occupy the predominant place and grow up into papillary masses resembling those seen on mucous surfaces. These cells are, however, of the same origin as the neuroglial elements in general.

LITERATURE

J. H. Wright: Jour. Exp. Med., 1910, xii, 556.
Landau: Frankfurter Ztschr. f. Path., 1912, xi, 26.
Wahl: Jour. Med. Research, 1914, xxx, 205.
Herde: Archiv f. kl. Chir., 1912, xcvii, 937.
Wegelin: Verh. Dtsch. Path. Gesellsch., 1912, xv, 225.
Symmers: Jour. Amer. Med. Assoc., 1913, lx, 337.
Glioma.—Landau: Frankfurter Ztschr. f. Path., 1910, v, 469.
Mallory: Jour. Med. Research, 1902, viii, 1.
Stroebe: Ziegler's Beiträge, 1895, xviii, 405.
Saxer: *Ibid.*, 1902, xxxii, 276.
Flexner: Johns Hopkins Hosp. Bull., 1891, ii, 115.

ANGIOMATA

Hæmangioma.—A hæmangioma is a tumor composed essentially of blood-channels, in contradistinction to a lymphangioma, whose cavities contain lymph instead of blood. A true hæmangioma is distinguished from a mere dilatation of capillaries or venules belonging to the general circulation by the fact that its blood-channels grow independently, without regard to the laws which govern the distribution of such vessels. It thereby forms a mass which is somewhat withdrawn from the general circulation, and although supplied with artery and vein, does not stand in any intimate anastomotic relations with the adjacent circulation. Ribbert lays great stress upon this lack of communication between the capillaries of an angioma and those of the contiguous tissue, and has proved his point by injections. Further, he insists that such tumors grow from their own vascular substance and not through the widening and assimilation of adjacent vessels. There are some border-line forms in which it is difficult to say whether one is dealing with a tumor or not, such as the plexiform or cirsoid angiomata of the scalp, which are made up of tangled masses of pulsating arteries, and others of even less tumor-like nature, such as the bluish vascular flecks seen in the skin of old people. True hæmangiomata are most commonly divided into a simple or telangiectatic form, in which the abundant capillaries, though widened, maintain fairly well their form as tubes with parallel walls, and the cavernous form, in which the character of erectile tissue is approached, with large, irregular blood-spaces opening abundantly into one another. It is not very apparent, however, where the line of division can be sharply drawn between these groups. Certainly it is difficult to determine from sections in some cases whether one should regard the tumor as verging on the cavernous or not. Doubtless if the channels were injected and a slice of the tumor rendered transparent, a most beautiful proof of this distinction might be obtained.

These tumors occur most commonly in the skin, especially on the face and scalp, but also in all other parts of the body. The more definitely simple forms through which blood runs fairly rapidly present themselves as flat or slightly elevated, bright-red patches from which the blood may be squeezed out (nævus flammeus). Many of these are found in the neighborhood of angles or fissures about the face and neck so that they have been thought to be congenital displacements. Hanes has recently reviewed the history of a peculiar hereditary form of multiple telangiectasis with numerous bluish nodules in the skin and nose from which any trifling injury would serve to start a profuse hæmorrhage. In these, the irregularly widened capillaries lay just under the thin smooth skin. Other examples of simple angiomata are found in the muscles, where they reach a considerable size. In the tongue, nose (Fig. 489), and lips they are also found, but in all these latter situations the tumor is likely to have more of the cavernous character.

Cavernous angiomata are also common in the skin, where they form most of the so-called birthmarks which are so frequently seen on the face. These are usually dark purple, and are often covered with rough, nodular skin (nævus vinosus). They are, as a rule, distributed over the region of one or more divisions of the fifth cranial nerve and seldom cross the mid-line of the face. It is said that they sometimes appear in the meninges in a

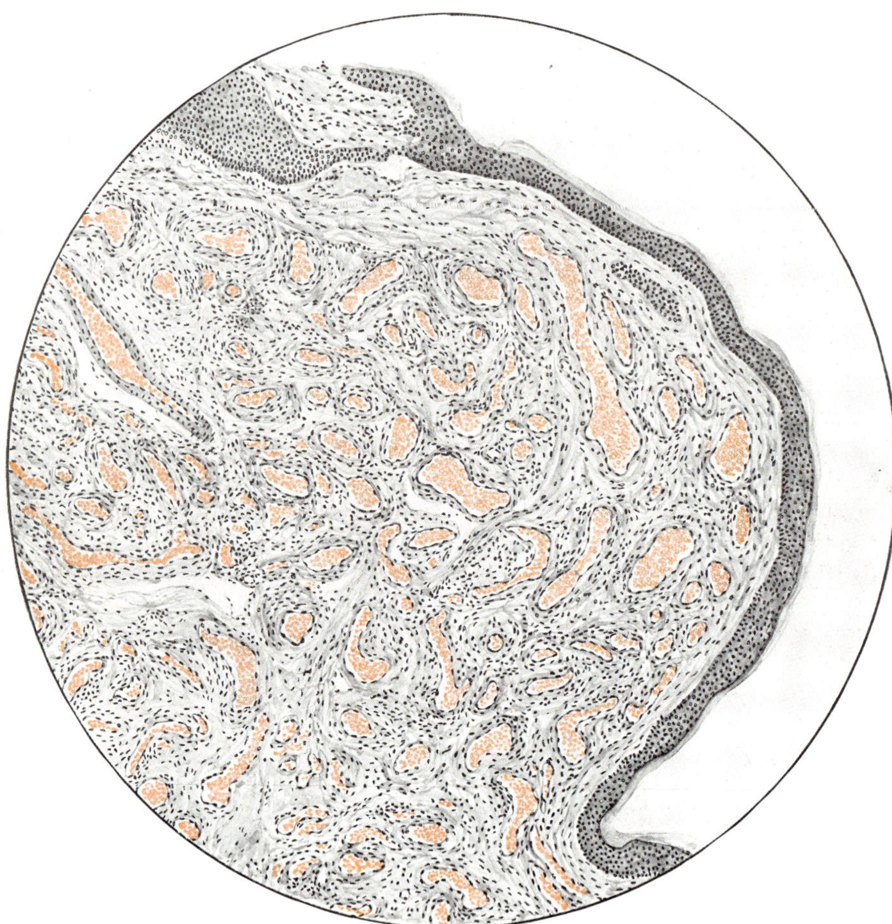

Fig. 489.—Angioma from the nose. The blood-channels are of fairly uniform calibre.

corresponding distribution, and that they may give rise to hæmorrhage there (Cushing). In the lips or tongue they form large, nodular, purple masses very prone to injury and hæmorrhage and very distorting. I have seen one or two cases of multiple cavernous hæmangiomata in the walls of the intestine (Fig. 490). Hæmorrhage may occur from these, although it had not done so in my cases. In the muscles, masses of spongy vascular tissue are found, extending between the fibres and into the intermuscular spaces. In these, too, the blood-channels are frequently irregular in form, with wide communications.

The cavernous angiomata of the liver constitute perhaps the best studied type (Fig. 491). They are found, as a rule, at autopsy, without having given rise to any symptoms, and may be very small or reach a diameter of several centimetres. Frequently there are four or five in the same liver, of

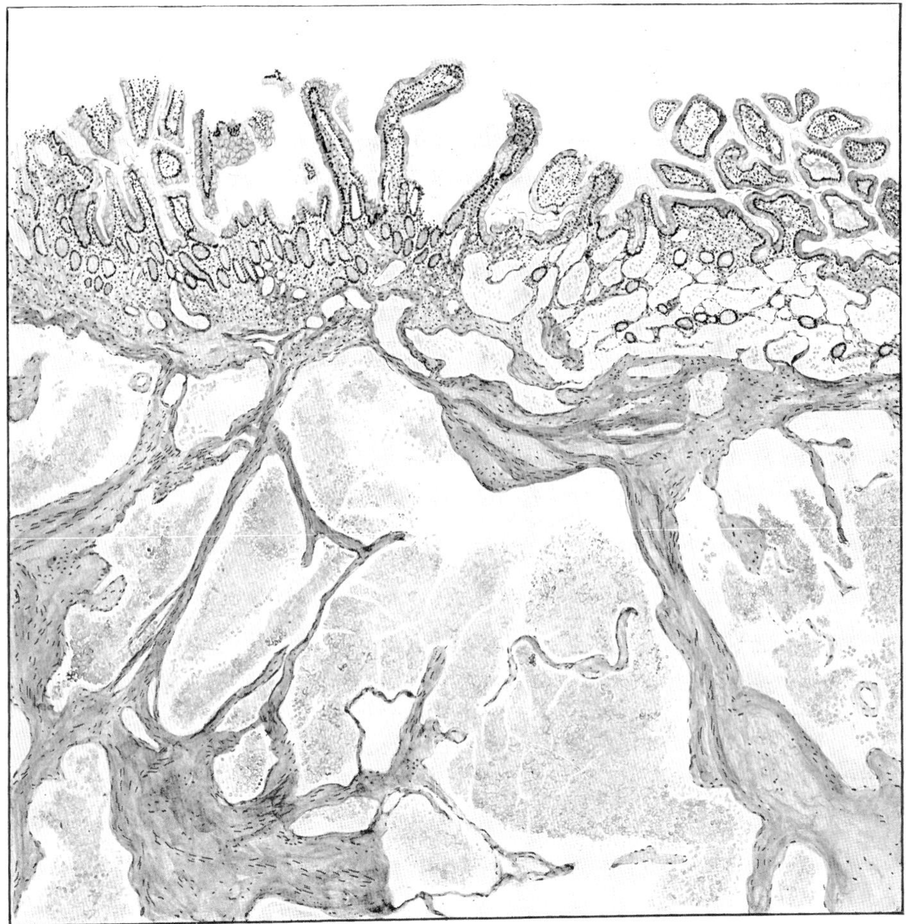

Fig. 490.—Cavernous hæmangioma of the small intestine.

which some may be visible through the capsule, while others are buried deep in the substance. On section, they appear as deep, purplish-red, sharply outlined areas, from which dark blood can be squeezed or washed out, leaving a grayish-white, spongy framework. We have recently seen at autopsy a huge angioma of the liver which was only partly surrounded by liver tissue, and hung as by a stalk from the right lobe. It measured 24 cm. in diameter, and corresponded in structure with the smaller ones. Microscopically, this framework is seen to inclose quite large spaces which open into one another, and which are evidently interposed between artery and vein. They are lined with endothelium and do not seem to communicate with the adjacent capillaries, although some of them occasionally extend into the adjacent liver substance as though forming an outpost of growth. Liver-cell strands are often found to lie in the connective tissue of the angioma, practically surrounded by it. Nevertheless, as Ribbert points out, an injection of the angioma passes very little, if at all, into the circulation of the liver.

In all these angiomata circulatory disturbances can occur. Infection may cause an inflammatory reaction in their substance, thrombosis of the blood-channels is common, and phleboliths may be formed. It is not infrequent to find parts of them scarred and obliterated by such processes with abundant pigmentation.

Ribbert's idea of their origin from a rudiment which is destined to form blood-vessels, from which they grow independently, is generally accepted, and the ideas as to their being due to mere dilatation of capillaries, or to the

Fig. 491.—Cavernous hæmangioma of the liver.

organization of hæmorrhages, should be abandoned. That they may be the result of fœtal displacement of tissue is, of course, prominent in all discussions, and applies here just as it does in the case of most other tumors. These are among the displacements or perverted formations of tissue which Albrecht separates as "Hamartomata."

In the edges of the heart valves of infants there are frequently seen minute, tense, deep-red nodules which project like tiny red berries. On section they look like cavernous hæmangiomata, but they persist only a short time, and are probably not to be regarded as tumors (Fig. 492).

Lymphangioma.—Quite analogous tumors, except that they are composed of spaces and channels containing lymph, are the lymphangiomata. They are telangiectatic or simple, cavernous, and cystic. Of these, the first type is especially common in the skin, lips, tongue, and subcutaneous or intermuscular tissue. They form nodular masses or diffuse enlargements which, on injury, may allow the escape of lymph. In the case of the tongue, they cause an enlargement which constitutes one of the forms of macroglossia, and in the extremities the diffuse distribution of such a cutaneous and subcutaneous tumor may give rise to a great enlargement which constitutes one of the numerous divergent forms of elephantiasis. In section such tumors are found to be made up of anastomosing channels or spaces lined with thin endothelium and filled with clear fluid with a few lymphoid cells. Naturally hæmorrhages into these spaces may confuse the picture and suggest the existence of a hæmangioma, but the history of the case will prevent such an error in diagnosis. In these tumors, as in the hæmangiomata, the interstitial connective tissue grows, together with the lymph-channels, to

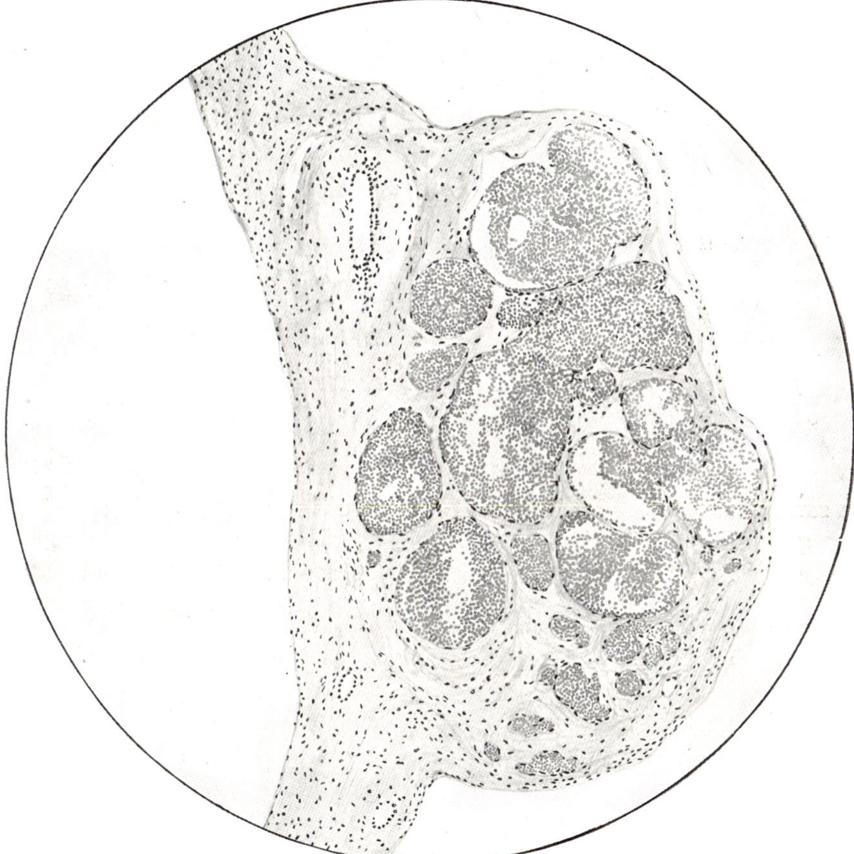

Fig. 492.—Angiomatoid nodule upon the heart-valve of an infant.

produce the tumor which again is more or less independent of communication with adjacent lymphatics. In the intestinal wall one may observe nodules of considerable size filled with clear or with milk-white fluid, and composed of cavernous arrangements of lymph-channels. It is important here to distinguish between true cavernous lymphangiomata and mere dilatations of the chyle-ducts.

The cystic lymphangiomata are, as a rule, still more circumscribed, and are composed of masses of rounded or irregular cystic structures with the same thin endothelial lining. They occur sometimes in the internal organs, as in the liver, spleen, adrenals, etc., where they are usually pretty sharply marked out from the organ itself. In the neck and sacral regions the so-called cystic hygromata are found, and are especially easily recognized as the results of developmental disarrangements of tissues. They are cystic lymphangiomata which are less circumscribed, and in the neck form large, ramifying masses which extend far up behind the ear and down between the muscles of the thorax and in the soft tissues of the shoulder. One, which we saw recently in a child, had become infected, so that all the cavities were filled with a purulent exudate which infiltrated the tissue between them. When, as in the so-called lymphangioma tuberosum multiplex of Kaposi, there are more complex strands of endothelial cells in place of simple endothelial lined channels, it is better to speak of the tumor as an endothelioma.

LITERATURE

Hæmangioma.—Ribbert: Virch. Arch., 1898, cli, 381.
Hanes: Johns Hopkins Hosp. Bull., 1909, xx, 63.
Roggenbau: Ziegler's Beiträge, 1910, xlix, 313.
Fischer and Zieler: Ergebn. d. allg. Path., 1906, x, 815.
Lymphangioma.—Sick: Virch. Arch., 1902, clxx, 9; 1903, clxxii, 445.
Fischer and Zieler: *Loc. cit.*, 842.
Paltauf: Verh. d. Dtsch. Path. Gesellsch., 1908, xi, 255.

SARCOMATA

A sarcoma is a tumor arising from connective tissue and retaining most of the general characteristics of connective tissue, but endowed with the new power of invading and actively destroying adjacent structures and of forming colonies of its own tissue in distant organs. In this respect sarcomata are typically malignant tumors.

It has been shown that benign tumors may be derived from any of the various forms of connective tissue which make up the framework of the body, and that they depart somewhat, in each instance, in the character of their cells, from the normal standard. All this is equally true of the sarcomata, and while they, too, may originate in any kind of connective tissue, their cells are far more unlike those of the normal tissue in appearance and totally unlike them in their biological characters.

It is scarcely possible to decide from the study of a microscopical preparation as to the point of origin of any sarcoma, since almost any region may be the starting-point for any type of tumor. When the tumor contains bone or cartilage, it is fairly safe to say that it sprang from some part of the skeleton, although this, too, would be indiscreet, since such tumors occasionally arise elsewhere.

The sarcomata are tumors preëminently characterized by the energy and rapidity of growth of their cells, and this in itself brings about the striking morphological differences between them and the corresponding benign tumors arising from similar situations in the connective tissue. It would doubtless be quite misleading to describe the lack of a capsule or of a dense stroma as mechanical factors favoring their rapid growth. On the contrary, they grow so quickly and irresistibly that there is no time for the formation of a dense stroma nor any opportunity for their encapsulation. There may be differences between these cells and those of a fibroma with regard to the process of mitosis. It is possible that irregularities in mitosis are associated with their precipitate growth, and that this explains the irregularities in the form of the cells sometimes met with, but in general they grow and develop in much the same way. Cultures *in vitro* from normal connective tissue and sarcoma tissue are almost indistinguishable from one another, except by most careful comparison of such things as the mitotic figures just mentioned. In both cases the cells grow out in scattered strands or isolated groups, quite unlike epithelial cells, and through their power of stretching themselves along a support and responding to tactile stimuli make considerable progress away from the point of origin. In the tumors, as they occur in the body, the impression is given in many cases that such cells form the whole compact mass, but in every case it is found that in addition there is a distinct framework of ordinary connective tissue with very abundant blood-vessels and some nerve-fibrils. Just as in all other tumors, the sarcoma elements demand this service of the normal tissues, and force the development of a mechanism for support and blood supply. Sometimes the framework is extremely delicate and seems to consist of little beside thin-walled blood-vessels (Fig. 493, *c*). In other cases it is very abundant and dense, so that the tumor-cells are separated into strands and compact masses which anastomose with one another, but appear in sections as the contents of alveolar spaces. (Fig. 493, *b*) There are also types of sarcoma in which the tumor cells themselves have the power of producing abundant intercellular fibres.

The malignant character of the tumor is evident in the infiltrating, destructive manner of its growth when it is well established, but in the beginning it may be difficult to recognize this. Nevertheless, unless the tumor is extirpated it soon reveals its true nature, and even if it is removed at operation, the tendency to recur in the same place from traces of the tissue left behind is associated with other evidence of its malignancy. Above all, the appearance of colonies of the same tissue elsewhere in the body leaves no room for doubt. It appears, then, that in order to decide upon the nature of a connective-tissue tumor which, as far as its microscopical morphology is concerned, might be a benign fibroma or a malignant sarcoma, it is necessary to know the history of the growth and its gross relations to the adjacent tissues. Even then it may be impossible to be completely sure until recurrence or metastases have appeared. It is at this point that the greatest uncertainty may exist, but ordinarily, as will be explained, the morphology of the tumors has become sufficiently well known in connection with the history of their growth to allow one to foretell the progress of the growth and to decide upon its nature.

There are great difficulties in outlining this group of tumors, since there are so many malignant growths composed of ill-characterized cells upon whose origin it is almost impossible to decide exactly. Many authors are willing to speak of malignant tumors arising from muscle, neuroglia, etc., by such names as myosarcoma and gliosarcoma. Ribbert is among those

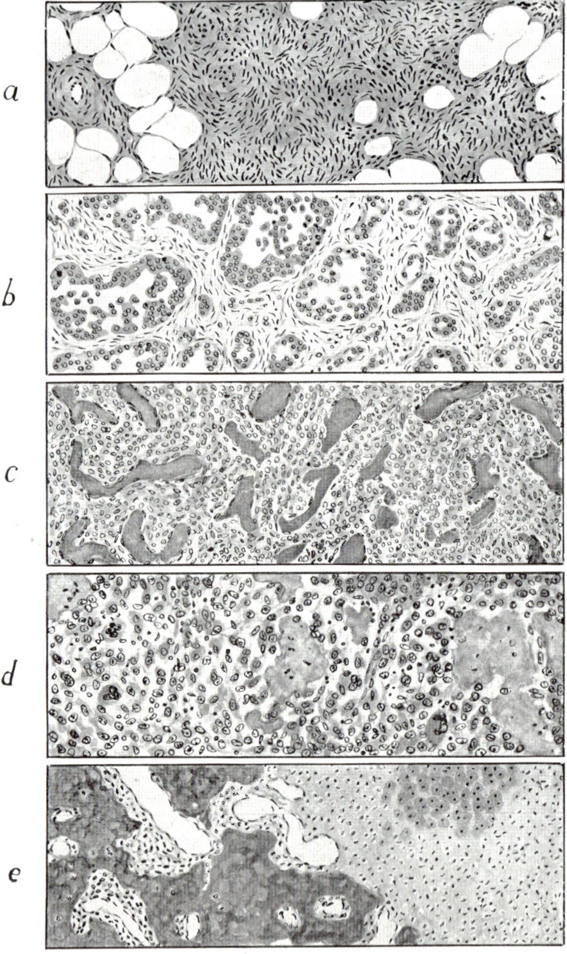

Fig. 493.—Several types of sarcoma: (*a*) Spindle-cell sarcoma from chest-wall; (*b*) alveolar sarcoma of mesentery; (*c*) spindle-cell sarcoma; the blood-vessels are injected and are seen to be very numerous; (*d*) mixed-cell sarcoma of leg metastasizing to the mediastinum; (*e*) osteosarcoma with calcified areas and cartilage.

who prefer, as it seems to me correctly, to call them malignant myomata and malignant gliomata, reserving the term sarcoma for malignant tumors clearly of connective-tissue nature. Such names can be used, however, to indicate a sarcoma in which the type of connective tissue from which it originated is still evident, as osteosarcoma, chondrosarcoma. Recently, too, there has been a tendency to treat separately, on account of their peculiar character, tumors thought to be derived from endothelium, and that group of pigmented tumors long known and still generally spoken of as melanosarcomata. In addition to these there are numerous tumors which arise from somewhat specialized cells belonging to the blood-forming apparatus and

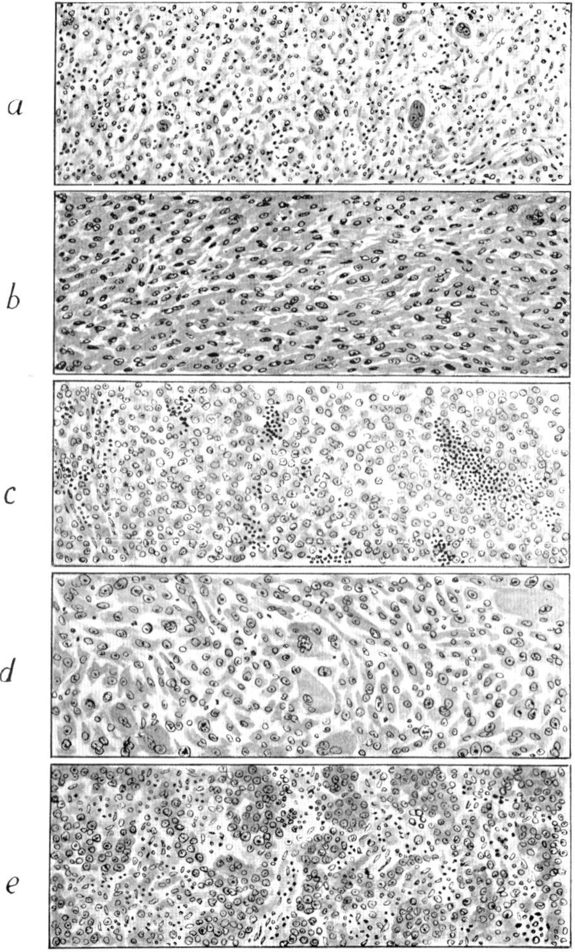

Fig. 494.—Several types of sarcoma: *a*, Mixed-cell sarcoma; *b*, coarse spindle-cell sarcoma; *c*, metastatic round-cell sarcoma; *d*, sarcoma of thyroid with giant-cells; *e*, sarcoma of ovary.

which, under various names (lymphosarcoma, leucosarcoma, myeloma, etc.), have, rightly or wrongly, been considered in connection with the diseases of that apparatus, since it is by no means quite clear that they are tumors at all. Finally, there are tumors, usually of rather complicated structure and often occurring at birth, or in the very young, which have long been designated sarcomata, but which appear to be rather of the nature of the so-called mixed tumors, which are referable to the aberrant growth of tissue displaced in the course of embryonic development. In this group there may be mentioned especially many of the malignant tumors of the testicle and the sarcomata of the kidney which grow during infancy and childhood.

Nevertheless, in spite of the nebulous state of our knowledge as to the real relations of these questionable growths, there remain many well-

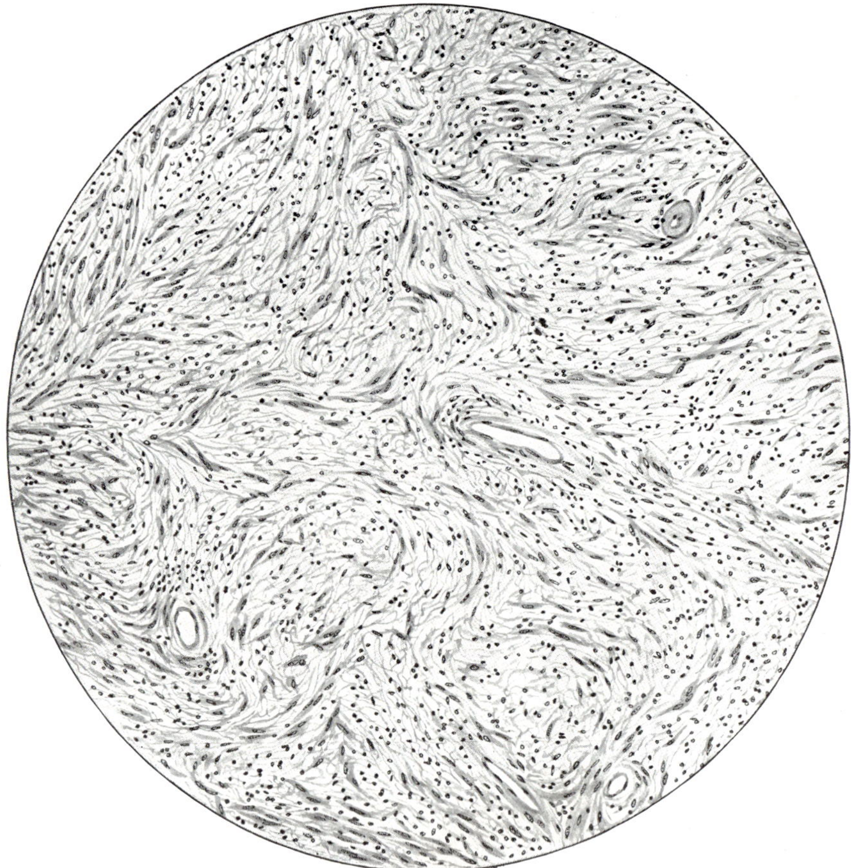

Fig. 495.—Sarcoma of tissues of the axillary plexus. The cells of the tumor are long and fusiform, and there are many wandering cells.

defined sarcomata which, in any series of cases, stand out sharply as easily recognized representatives of certain groups. They are distinguished from one another chiefly by the form of their cells and by the character of their intercellular substance, as well as their energy of growth, but there are so many transitional forms and combinations that I do not wish to draw very sharp lines between them (Fig. 494).

Of these, the commonest are the **spindle-cell sarcomata,** which originate in almost any situation. In the series which I have for study spindle-cell sarcomata arose in the breast, hand, mesosalpinx, vulva, wall of ovarian cyst, leg, liver, etc., but any connective tissue, such as fasciæ, subcutaneous tissue, or the framework of organs, may be their starting-point. They are white or gray-white, rather firm, shining, and somewhat circumscribed masses which have perhaps less tendency to metastasize widely than some of the other forms. Microscopically, they are found to be composed of smoothly arranged, elongated or spindle-shaped cells, very uniform in size and general appearance, and supported in bundles or whorls by the most delicate stroma, with wide and very thin-walled blood-vessels. The intercellular substance of the tumor itself is usually extremely scanty, so that the cells lie close together. In some cases, however, there is a good deal of fibrillar intercellular substance, the cells are less uniformly arranged and tend rather to a branched form (Fig. 495). To such tumors the name fibrosarcoma may be fittingly applied. The secondary growths or metastases may occur in the lymph-glands, which drain the area of the tumor, but they are more frequently found in the lungs (Fig. 496) and later in other internal organs which would indicate that the cells of the tumor were transported by way of the venous blood-stream (*cf.* Fig. 28). Borst emphasizes the idea that such spindle-cells are especially immature, approaching in this respect embryonic cells. It seems to me, however, that this is based merely upon the general resemblance in form to the cells of embryonic connective tissue. Their biological characters, which should be of greater weight in deciding such a question, are totally abnormal, and they have acquired powers which might distinguish them very sharply from even the most immature of embryonic cells, since they are such as to enable them to grow indefinitely

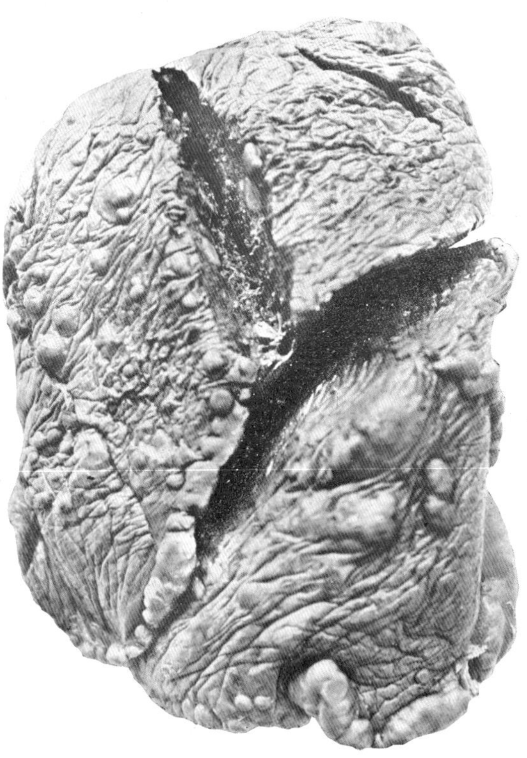

Fig. 496.—Metastatic sarcoma in the lung. Nodules are found in various parts of the pleura, but especially along the margins of the lobes.

without at any time differentiating themselves into any finite tissue which obeys the normal laws of growth. The resemblance to embryonic tissue is, therefore, most superficial, and they are rather cells which have no true analogue in the body at any stage of its development.

Nearly as common as the spindle-cell sarcomata are those in which cells of many forms and sizes occur, with many bizarre modifications of their nuclei. For want of any better term, these may be called **mixed-cell sarcomata** (Fig. 494, *a*). They arise anywhere, too, but perhaps most commonly in connection with the internal organs. I have seen them especially in the retroperitoneal region, apparently springing from the lymph-glands there, and forming huge masses, but there are before me examples from the thyroid, from the ovary, periosteum, etc. The cells are in general fusiform, but are somewhat irregularly arranged and form by no means so compact and orderly a tissue as in the pure spindle-cell type. Among these are many of much larger size, with several nuclei or one very large and deeply stained nuclear mass.

Round-cell sarcomata are in our experience relatively rare as long as we separate from them the lymphosarcomata and leucosarcomata, which have distinctive features, as already mentioned. They are tumors composed of small round cells held in a most delicate vascular stroma which in any single microscopical preparation might be difficult to distinguish from lymphosarcomata. They arise, however, as single, rather circumscribed masses springing from the connective tissue of the skin or fasciæ or intermuscular septa or elsewhere, and, aside from their local invasion and destructive growth spread, not in a regional way, as lymphosarcomata do, but exactly as other sarcomata, by the transportation of their cells, usually by the blood-stream to the distant lungs, where they form once more circumscribed and solid nodules (Fig. 497). When a regional lymph-gland is involved, it usually presents a more or less definitely outlined tumor mass embedded in its substance, and is not itself at first completely replaced by the new tissue. These round-cell sarcomata are extremely malignant, and give rise to wide-spread metastases, often passing through the lungs into the general circulation. There are some with small and some with relatively large cells.

Other distinctly sarcomatous tumors of equally cosmopolitan origin are composed of cells uniform in type, but not definitely round nor spindle-shaped. They are rather polygonal or plump cells, which form a compact tissue with abundant ramifying blood-vessels.

In these especially, but also in the other forms already described, there often occurs what seems to me to be a local necrosis of the tumor cells from lack of sufficient blood supply. This leads to a curious condition in which only those cells which are close to the blood-vessels remain alive and the rest fade into a pale-pink staining débris (Fig. 498). Consequently the tumor appears to be made up of blood-vessels each with a thick mantle of cells, and such tumors have been described as a separate type under the name angiosarcoma. The cells about the blood-vessels have been regarded as arising from a hypothetical tissue spoken of as perithelium, and the tumor, therefore, called a perithelial angiosarcoma. It is possible that tumors with this structure really exist, to which the explanation just given will not apply, but I have not seen them. The appearance is common enough, but in itself does not seem sufficient to warrant the use of a special name.

Alveolar sarcomata are those in which the tumor-cells are rounded or polygonal, rarely fusiform, and grow in groups or strands which lie in the

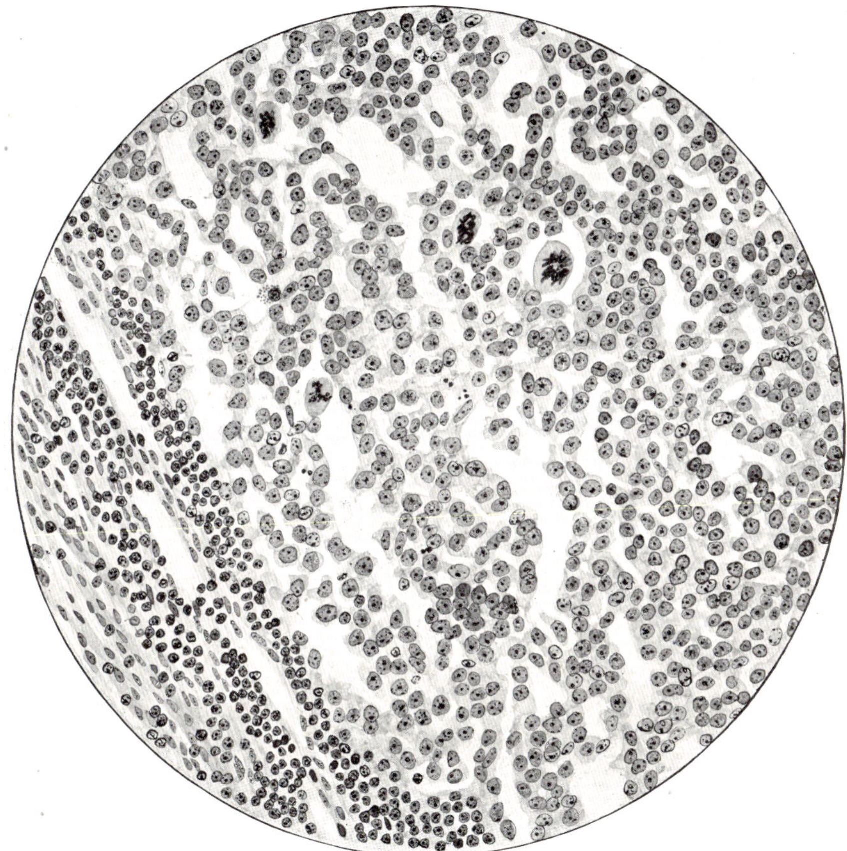

Fig. 497.—Round-cell sarcoma primary in the testicle. There are several large cells which show irregular mitotic figures.

meshes of a fairly dense stroma (Fig. 493, *c*). In a single section the cells appear to be inclosed in alveolar spaces and indeed they then resemble very closely some kinds of carcinoma. At times it is difficult if not impossible to distinguish between them from a single section, although the distribution of the tumors and the history of the case will usually decide. Efforts have been made to state histological criteria, by which it is made to appear that the cells of the sarcoma are in more intimate relation with the stroma and often pervaded by fine fibrillæ of stroma, while the carcinoma cells lie isolated in spaces lined by endothelium. I am sure that this is all based on hypothesis made to suit the case for the relation of the epithelial cells of the cancer to the connective tissue may in point of space be just as close as that of the sarcoma cells; moreover, the fibrillæ of stroma are not evident, and the cancer cells do not restrict themselves to endothelial-lined channels, but push into any cranny or crevice of the fibrous tissue. The form of the

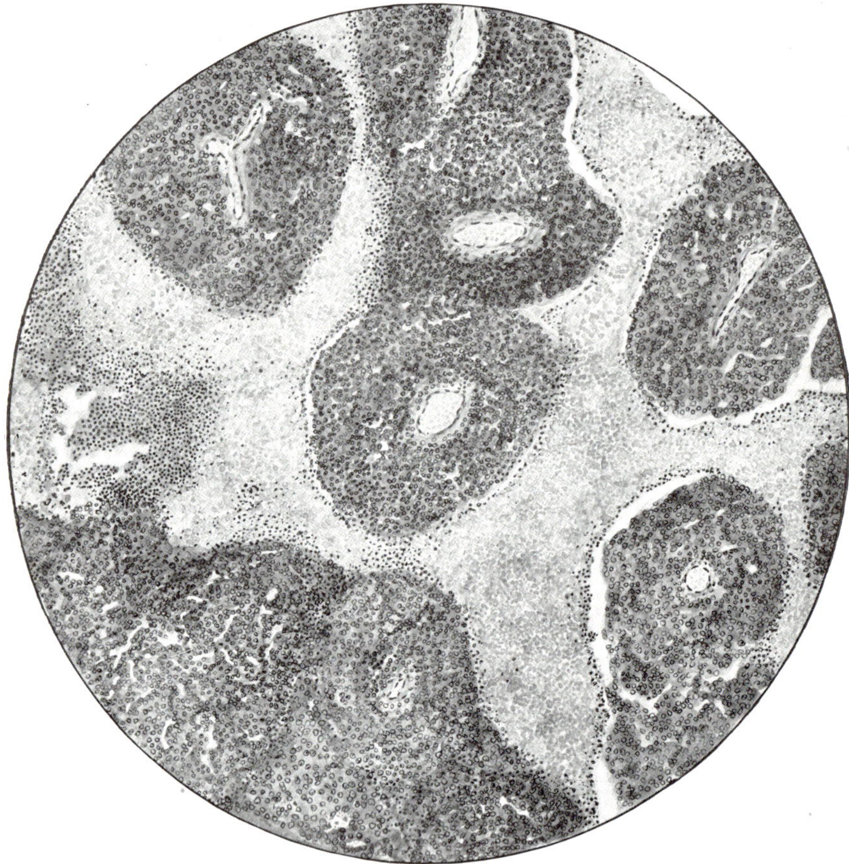

Fig. 498.—Sarcoma springing from the pelvis and showing disintegration of the cells, except in the neighborhood of the blood-vessels.

tumor cells is of no help because sarcoma cells and epithelial cells may look exactly alike. But an epithelial origin is soon found for the cancer in one or other characteristic site, whereas the alveolar sarcoma begins its growth, not in an epithelial organ, but in some such place as the dermis or the fascia or the skeletal tissues. It is quite common to find very numerous subcutaneous or intracutaneous nodules scattered over the body which reveal themselves as alveolar sarcomata, and appear to grow simultaneously. They are usually secondary to some original growth of earlier formation.

Giant-cell Sarcomata.—Although large irregular protoplasmic masses with several nuclei occur at times in many of the mixed cell sarcomata, there is a group of tumors in which typical multinucleated giant-cells form so constant and characteristic a feature that they are classed by themselves under this name.

They arise usually in connection with bone, and although many of them

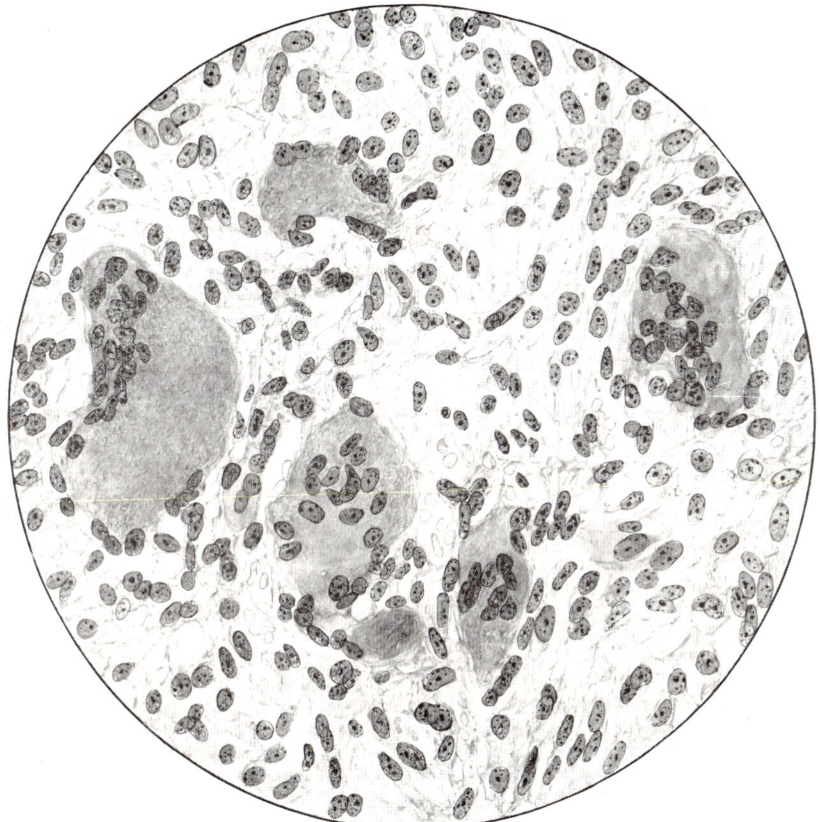

Fig. 499.—Giant-cell sarcoma springing from a bone.

are otherwise composed of spindle-shaped cells showing no tendency to cartilage or bone formation (Fig. 499), there are also tumors containing such giant-cells which definitely belong to the group of osteosarcomata. For this reason, the idea has been suggested that the giant-cells may be identical with the osteoclasts of the bone which are endosteal or periosteal cells modified by their phagocytic function. Others have thought that since giant-cell sarcomata occur also in other places, such as the breast, far from any connection with bone, the giant-cells might be regarded as comparable to the ordinary foreign body giant-cells. There is perhaps no fundamental difference between the giant-cell character of osteoblasts and that of foreign-body giant-cells, and in both cases it seems to be a morphological modification dependent upon the function of the cells and perhaps only temporary. It is, therefore, difficult to decide upon the relation of the cells of the tumor to such cells and probably dangerous to assume that any of these types of giant-cells could transmit their giant-cell character to their offspring.

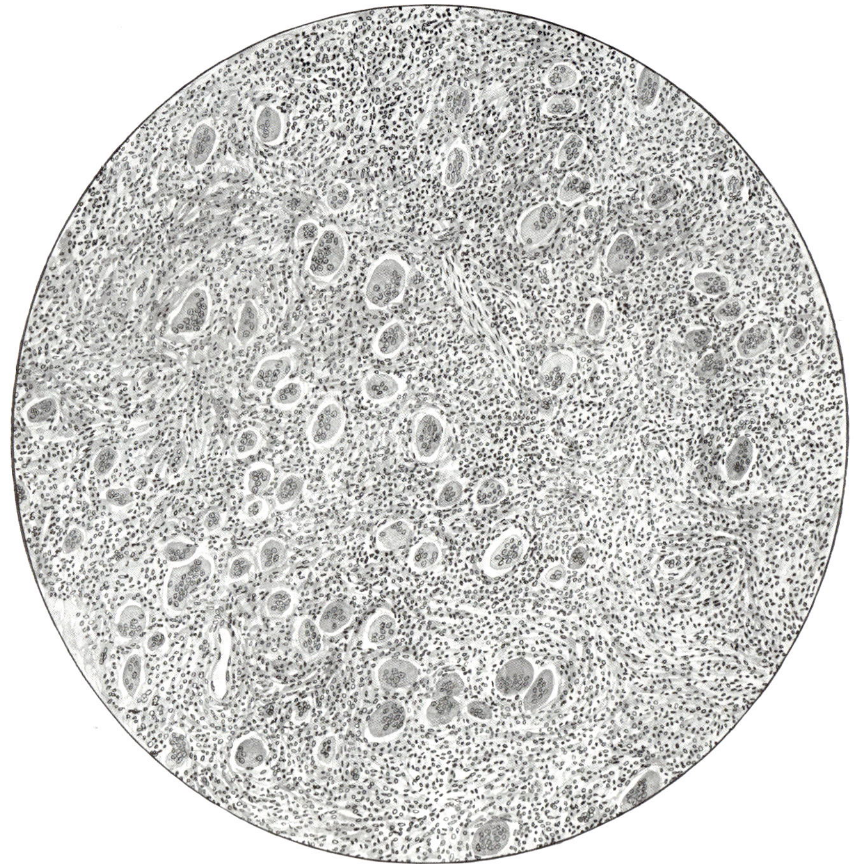

Fig. 500.—Giant-cell sarcoma (epulis) from the jaw.

The most common giant-cell sarcomata are those which grow from the alveolar process of the jaw and hang as pedunculated tumors in the cavity of the mouth. These growths, which are known by the name *epulis*, are covered for a time with the mucosa of the mouth, but tend to become ulcerated. They are usually rather small, but occasionally, as in one case which I saw, reach such a size as practically to fill the mouth. When removed, they show little tendency to recur and there are no metastases.

Microscopically the dense, hard tumor is found to be composed of interlaced spindle-cells with numerous large multinucleated giant-cells (Fig. 500).

Other giant-cell sarcomata, closely related to these, spring from the periosteum of long bones, or, still more commonly, from their endosteal lining. Expanding and eroding the cortex of the bone, they form large masses which are kept covered by a constantly new formed shell of periosteal bone. The central part may, through hæmorrhage or other disturbances of circulation,

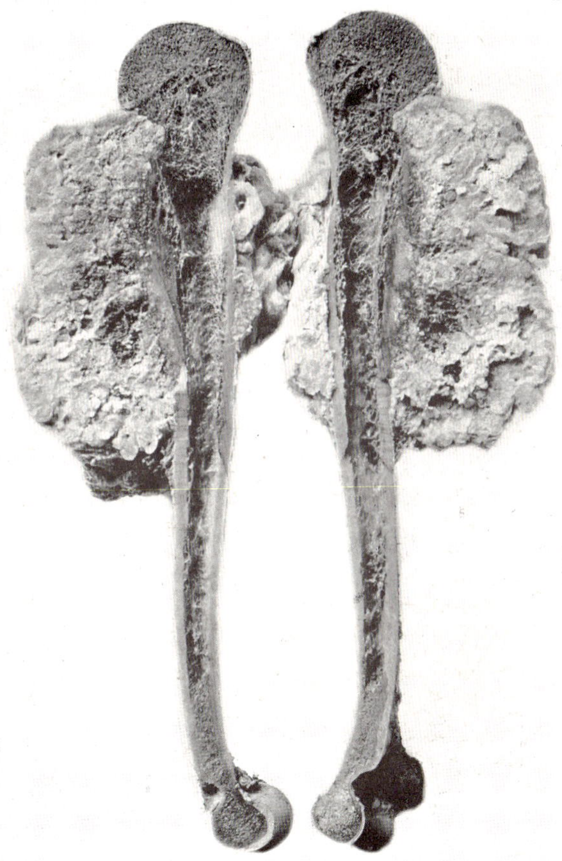

Fig. 501.—Periosteal osteosarcoma of the humerus. The marrow cavity is not invaded.

become necrotic and softened, and there may be formed a cyst-like swelling in or about the bone, in the walls of which little or no tumor tissue is left.

Osteosarcoma, Osteochondrosarcoma.—There are other sarcomata, usually forming large nodular masses about the bones, which are developed from the periosteum or from the endosteum. These, while showing to some degree the capacity of sarcomata to metastasize, have retained the power of the bone-forming cells to elaborate all the types of connective tissue concerned in the formation of bone. Hence the tumors are found to contain cartilage, osteoid tissue, and definite bone, as well as the less specialized cellular or fibrous tissue.

Those which arise from the periosteum form spindle-shaped or irregular nodular masses around the bone (Fig. 501), often with beautiful, glistening, radially arranged spicules of bone which give the tumor great rigidity. Those which start in the endosteum fill the marrow cavity, erode through the cortex of the shaft of the bone, and finally spread outside as expanding nodular tumors (Fig. 502). In either case there may be great irregularity in the form of the growth and in the character of the tissue of which it is composed. In all these tumors which arise from bone-forming cells the new-formed tissue usually presents a ground-substance of irregular or spindle-shaped cells, among which certain groups give rise to areas of cartilage or cartilage-like tissue. This becomes calcified, and, by a process resembling that of normal ossification, lamellæ of bone are formed, usually in the most irregular arrangement. In other cases, or even in the same tumors, osteoid tissue is usually formed without the intervention of cartilage, and later becomes calcified into true bone. Many tumors, however, remain as osteoid sarcomata, composed largely of osteoid tissue with relatively little bone formation. The cortex of the original bone may remain visible in the midst of such tumors, but usually shows much erosion and one or more fractures. In other cases, with the growth from inside, the dense cortex is eroded away and replaced on the outer surface of the advancing tumor. Since the replacement is less rapid than the erosion, a thin-walled dilatation of the cortex is produced and finally broken through.

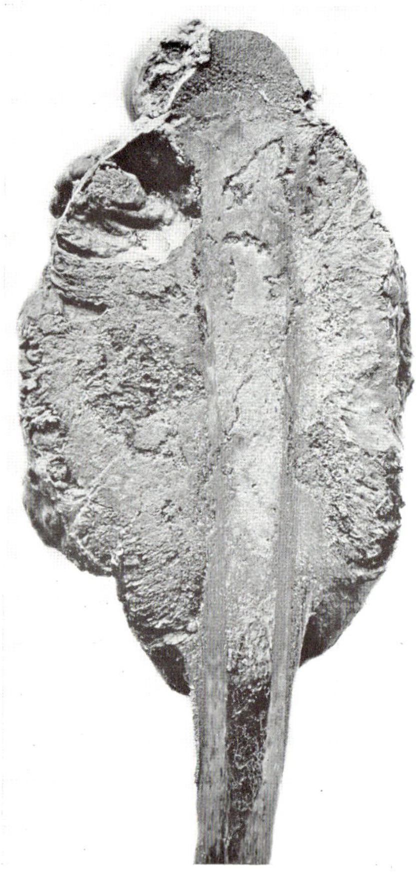

Fig. 502.—Osteosarcoma involving the marrow of the humerus, piercing the cortex in many places, and growing out radially under the periosteum.

Osteosarcomata and the allied chondrosarcomata form metastases in distant organs, such as the lungs, and, in those new situations, the secondary nodules usually show the same atypical cartilage and bone formation. They are, in general, less malignant than other sarcomata, but are by no means entirely innocent.

Sarcomata of other types may also arise in the interior of the bones, and, having eroded their way through the cortex and spread outside into a large tumor, metastasize extensively elsewhere. These appear not to grow from the active bone-forming endosteum, since they form little or no bone or cartilage, but are composed of soft cellular tissue. In one which we studied recently there had been a tumor springing from the femur for which the leg had been amputated several months before death. At autopsy enormous, soft, partly necrotic tumor masses were found in the lungs and mediastinum. These were composed of variegated cells without the least evidence of any tendency to bone formation (Fig. 493, *d*).

LITERATURE

Sarcoma.—Borst: XV. Cong. Internat. di Med., Lisbonne, 1906, Section iii.
Ackermann: Volkmann's kl. Vorträge, 1883, Nr. 233, 234.
Coenen: Beit. z. kl. Chir., 1909, lxiii, 337.
Mönckeberg: Ergebn. d. allg. Path., 1906, x, 730.

MYXOMATA

This term is used to indicate tumors which are composed of a loose connective tissue with branched cells widely separated by a viscid, opalescent, mucoid fluid, which actually contains mucin. While such tissue is not found in the adult body, it does exist in the Wharton's jelly of the umbilical cord, which tissue, therefore, stands as the prototype of the myxoma.

These tumors are found in various situations in the subcutaneous and intermuscular tissues in connection with tendons, periosteum, and joints, and especially in the heart.

Ribbert makes a point of declaring that in those frequent cases in which a complex or teratomatous tumor presents patches of mucoid tissue here and there, the myxomatous part is not to be regarded as a secondary degeneration of some other part of the tumor. In other words, he maintains the independence of the myxoma as a distinct tumor which may be combined with cartilage or with bone, etc., to form a myxochondroma or myxo-osteoma.

In the heart the soft tumor is in most cases found to hang in polypoid form from the wall of the left auricle, more rarely arising from the septum or other situation. It is covered with endothelium and composed, as in other cases, of the mucin-containing loose tissue.

In most instances myxomata are benign and well-outlined tumors, but occasionally they evince signs of malignancy and invade widely and metastasize to other organs. On the whole, they are rare tumors.

There is a form of myxomatous tumor which grows in great nodular masses in the retroperitoneal region at the root of the mesentery, and pushes aside the abdominal organs, although it does not become closely adherent to them. The nodules are encapsulated, and may be as large as a cocoanut. On removal they tend to recur, and even to produce metastases in the liver and other organs. Such tumors are not rare, and we have had an opportunity to study one of them from the Mount Sinai Hospital material, where Dr. Mandlebaum has seen four. In this case there were five large masses, one of which seemed almost entirely composed of fat. The others were elastic, translucent, and gelatinous, with little admixture of fat. Microscopically the lipoma-like tumor showed some areas of the same translucent

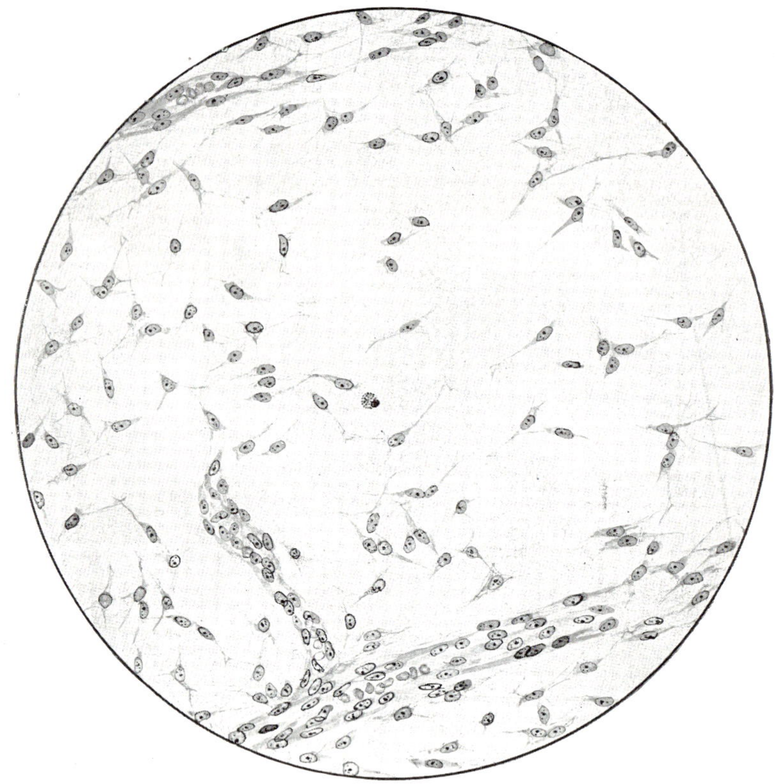

Fig. 503.—Myxoma from retroperitoneal region.

tissue. The larger gelatinous tumors were composed of an extremely loose vascular tissue in which the cells were rather small, provided with a rounded or oval vesicular nucleus, and long branching protoplasmic processes by which they held together (Fig. 503). The intercellular fluid was extremely abundant, and it was necessary to examine frozen sections, since any attempt to make a paraffin section resulted in great shriveling of the tissue. With hæmatoxylin the fluid assumes a bluish stain.

LITERATURE

Ribbert: Frankfurter Ztschr. f. Path., 1910, iv, 30.

CHAPTER XLIX

TUMORS (Continued)

Pigmented tumors: Nævi. Their relation to epithelium and connective tissue. Melanomata or melanotic sarcomata. Tumors of adrenal origin: Hypernephromata. Relation to aberrant adrenal tissue. Endotheliomata: difficulty of establishing their relation to endothelium. Endotheliomata from lymphatic endothelium; cylindromata. Pleural and peritoneal tumors. Endotheliomata of the meninges. Tumors derived from endothelium of the blood-vessels. "Perithelial" tumors.

Tumors which show the presence of brown or black pigment, and which in some cases develop an extreme malignancy, form a group whose position in the general scheme of tumors is still extremely debatable, because it is impossible to decide as to the nature of the cells from which they arise. Since they behave more in the manner of sarcomata than in that of other tumors, they may be described here, although it must be borne in mind that there is no good proof of their right to this place.

NÆVI

The simplest of these are the pigmented moles or nævi, which are flat or slightly elevated, gray or brown or almost black patches in the skin. Sometimes they are quite prominent, roughened, and irregular, and may be marked by the growth of coarse hairs (Fig. 504). There are many varieties in so far as the intensity of pigmentation and the bulk of the tumor tissue are concerned, but the structure is, in its essentials, similar in all. Occasionally, however, the tumors are exceedingly rich in blood-vessels, so that they have then the character of superficial angiomata. The overlying skin is slightly irregular in thickness and sends down quite long interpapillary processes of epithelium. The papillæ of the corium are enlarged by the presence of compact or loose masses of cells, commonly called nævus cells, which are sometimes quite colorless (Fig. 505) and sometimes deeply pigmented. It is with regard to the nature of these cells that discussion has been carried on for years, since it is most desirable that we should know whether they are derived from the epithelium or not. The following table from Dalla Favera shows fairly well the position taken by various authors on this point.

1. They arise from the epidermis (Unna, Kromayer, Marchand, Gilchrist, and many others).
2. They are of mesodermal origin, and are—
   (*a*) Young connective-tissue cells (Simon, Virchow, Riecke).

(b) They arise from proliferation of the lymphatics (v. Recklinghausen, Lubarsch, Herxheimer, and others).
(c) They spring from the endothelium and perithelium of blood-vessels (Pick, Jadassohn).
(d) They originate in the sheaths of nerve-fibres (Soldan).

3. They are specially characterized cells of mesodermal origin—chromatophores (Ribbert).

From this it will be seen what divergent views have been held by the best observers. Dalla Favera, in a paper from Marchand's institute, presents the study of 30 nævi, and brings very convincing histological pictures to

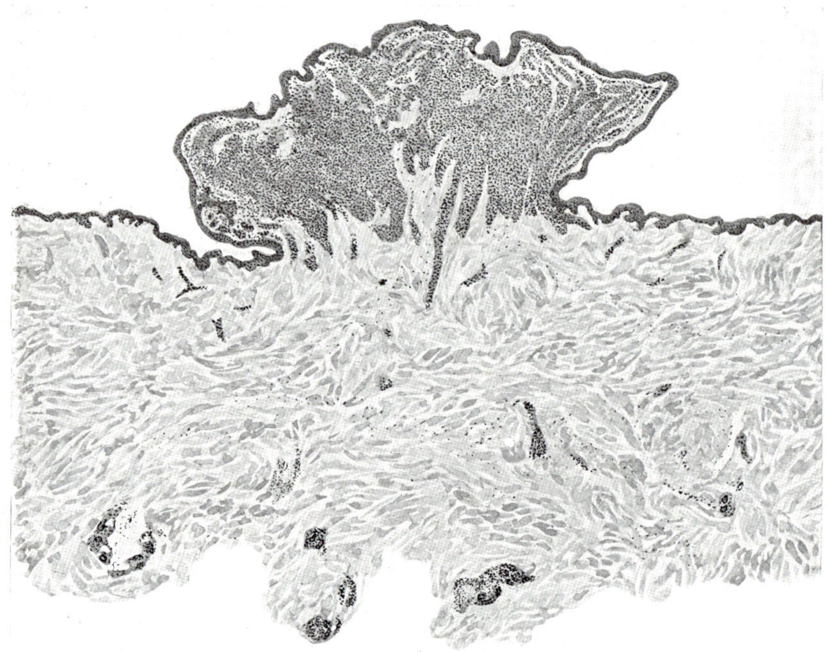

Fig. 504.—Small pedunculated nævus of skin showing the relation of the nævus cell strands to the epidermis.

prove that nævus cells originate in direct continuity with the epithelial cells, forming in little nests in cavities among those cells, and later becoming loosened and separated. Ribbert is quite as emphatic in his claim that these cells are *not* epithelial cells, since the character of their nuclei and protoplasm, and especially the possession of numerous long processes, makes that practically impossible. As chromatophores they are mesodermal cells whose duty it is to carry pigment. Similar cells are found in many lower animals, where they lie in the skin, and by changes in their form are instrumental in producing changes in its color.

Such pigmented and colorless nævi may remain for many years without much increase in size and without producing any ill effects. Through traumatism or for some other more obscure reason they may, however, begin to grow and produce a definite tumor. The pigmented tumor thus formed is a melanoma or melanotic sarcoma.

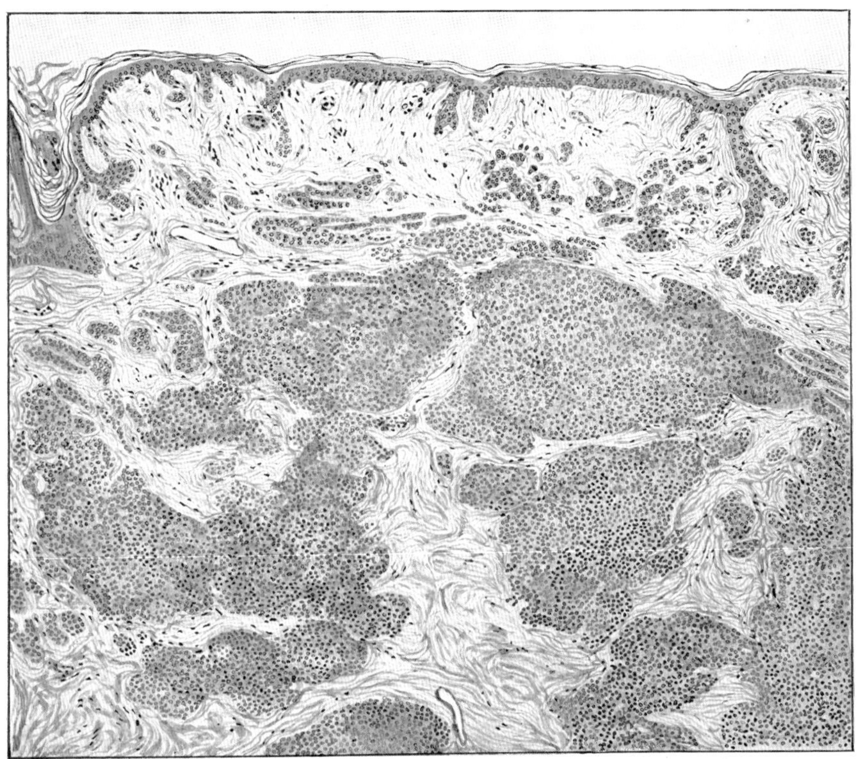

Fig. 505.—Non-pigmented nævus of skin of the shoulder. The papillæ of the corium are hypertrophied. Large masses of "nævus cells" lie in its deeper parts.

MELANOTIC SARCOMATA

These tumors cannot always be shown to have originated in a well-defined mole, and there are many cases in which the cutaneous manifestations remain inconspicuous while large internal metastases develop. Doubtless it could be said that the origin was really from some small mole in such cases, but in one which was seen in the Presbyterian Hospital recently there was only a bluish stain above the knee which could not be felt with the finger, and yet the adjacent inguinal lymph-nodes were greatly enlarged and the man actually coughed or spat up a piece of tissue, which on section showed the typical structure of a melanosarcoma. No autopsy was obtainable to reveal the position of the growth from which that piece came. Another case may be recalled in which a melanosarcoma apparently arose in a healing hæmatoma under the thumb-nail and caused death from numerous metastases some months after the first injury.

Usually it is possible to trace the black tumor-mass which develops in the skin to a preëxisting nævus at the same spot. That nævi are not essential is shown, however, by the growth of quite similar tumors from the choroid of the eye, from the brain and meninges, from the conjunctiva, the nasal mucosa, the adrenal, ovary, intestine (ampulla of Vater), the rectum, urethra, etc.

For those who hold to the ectodermal or epithelial origin of the tumors,

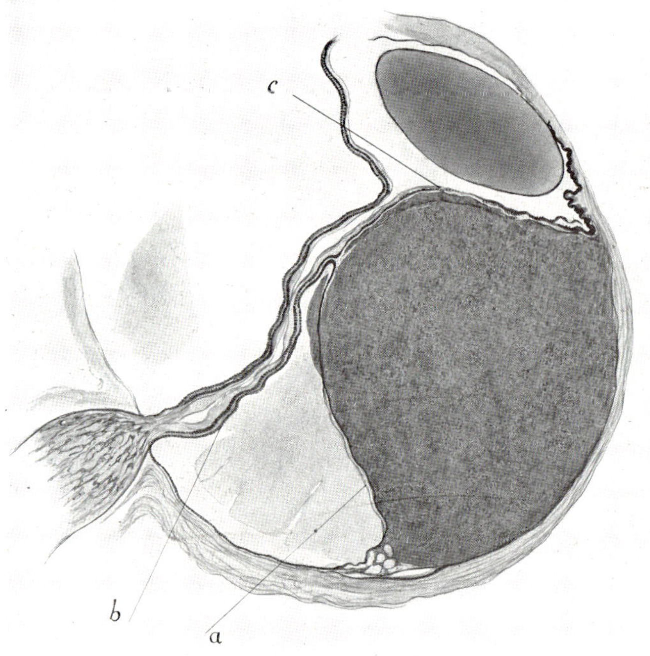

Fig. 506.—Primary melanoma of the choroid. There was relatively little pigment in this tumor. The retina is dislodged and stretches through the middle of the vitreous humor at *b*. The outer layer of the retina passes over the tumor at *a*.

it would seem that some of these sites could hardly be explained. Nevertheless, the invasion of ectodermal sympathetic cells in the adrenal is adduced to explain the tumors of adrenal origin, while in other cases the participation of displaced embryonic remains in the form of teratomata may afford a source of epithelial cells. It is not possible to form a definite opinion as to the true nature of the pigmented cells from the evidence now available. Naturally, there is no fundamental reason why mesodermal cells should not form pigment from materials supplied by the blood, although in general we are more accustomed to find the pigments of the body produced by cells of epithelial origin. Whatever is ultimately determined to be their true relation, it is clear that these cells do not merely receive pigment transferred to them from other cells, but maintain throughout their existence the ability to form pigment and transmit that ability to their offspring.

The melanosarcomata of the skin are composed of compact masses of cells which in section have an irregular polygonal form or are more often fusiform (*cf.* Fig. 49), although Ribbert shows that in fresh teased specimens they possess numerous long processes which are pigmented to their ends. The pigment is in fine granules and clumps and is yellowish brown or dark brown in color. Much of it is scattered free in the crevices of the tissue and is taken up by various phagocytic cells. The stroma is sometimes very

Fig. 507.—Melanoma. Multiple small metastatic nodules in the liver. The primary tumor was in the choroid of the eye.

delicate, but often coarse enough to divide the tumor into an alveolar arrangement.

In the eye these tumors spring from the choroid either as a flat, lamellar plate, or as a nodule which may be distinctly pedunculated. They grow up into the vitreous humor, pushing the layers of the retina before them, and finally filling the whole eye or bursting outward to invade the orbit (Fig 506).

In the other sites in which primary melanomata occur their mode of growth and histological structure are similar. Melanomata grow with great rapidity and spread their metastases by way of the blood-stream with extraordinary effect, producing secondary growths in great numbers in all the organs (*cf.* Fig. 48). These vary in size from minute groups of cells so small as to be visible only when they stand out by their black color against such a tissue as the white matter of the brain, up to enormous masses which occupy a great part of the liver. There are usually many nodules scattered in each organ, and in the case of the liver it is common to find hundreds of rounded tumors which are embedded everywhere in the tissue (Fig. 507). Most of these are very deeply colored, but some of them may be perfectly unpigmented. Frequently a single nodule shows both black and white portions. In the heart-wall one may find several coal-black nodules or a whole sprinkling of small black points.

In all these positions necrosis and disintegration of the tumor occur, and much of the pigment thus released is taken up by the endothelial cells and wandering phagocytes or remains scattered free in the crevices of the tissue. It seems to be carried in the blood-stream to the kidneys, and is decolorized in this transit, but appears again in its black form in the urine, especially after exposure to air. The pigment itself is one of the melanins, and contains sulphur, but no iron.

LITERATURE

Dalla Favera: Ziegler's Beiträge, 1903, xliii, 43.
T. C. Gilchrist: Jour. Cutaneous and Genito-Urinary Diseases, 1899, xvii, 117.
Ribbert: Ziegler's Beiträge, 1897, xxi, 471.
Geschwülstlehre, Bonn, 1904, 255.
Wolfrum: Ergebn. d. allg. Path., 1914, xvi, Ergnzbd., 660.
Kyrle: Arch. f. Dermatol. u. Syphilis, 1913, cxviii, 319.
Pinkus: Dermatol. Ztschr., 1908, xvi, 483.
Maclachlan: Jour. Med. Research, 1914, xxix, 433.
Winternitz: Johns Hopkins Hosp. Bull., 1909, xx, 314.

TUMORS OF ADRENAL ORIGIN (HYPERNEPHROMATA)

This is a group of tumors of such common occurrence as to be familiar to all pathologists, but yet so peculiar in their histological characters and location as to have given rise to differences of opinion with regard to their origin, which are even yet unsettled.

They are nodules of soft, opaque, yellow tissue, sometimes very small, sometimes growing to a great size, and situated in the adrenal gland, in the kidney, or just beneath its capsule, or in any one of many other positions, such as the liver, pancreas, retroperitoneal tissue, spermatic cord, epididymis, etc. The tumors may be multiple, and while the small multiple nodules appear to remain localized, the larger ones may exhibit an extreme malignancy, forming metastases in the lung, bones, and other distant organs.

Attention was directed to the probability of their origin from the adrenal by Grawitz, who referred those occurring in the kidney to the overgrowth of small misplaced masses of adrenal tissue embedded in the substance of that organ. It is found that accessory nodules of adrenal tissue are actually distributed quite widely in the body, and are found not only in the immediate neighborhood of the adrenal itself, or embedded in its cortex, but also in the liver, kidney, and in the other situations mentioned, broad ligament, spermatic cord, epididymis, etc. These are often of microscopic dimensions, may be present in considerable numbers, and are usually composed of tissue identical with that of the cortex of the adrenal. There are found occasionally accessory adrenals which contain medullary elements also, and a few have been described which were said to be composed entirely of medullary tissue. The most common are those in which cortical cells are arranged radially to form a small rounded nodule.

Such nodules appear not to grow to any great size. They contain the same abundant lipoids as the adrenal cortex, but do not produce adrenaline, since that is, of course, a function of the medulla.

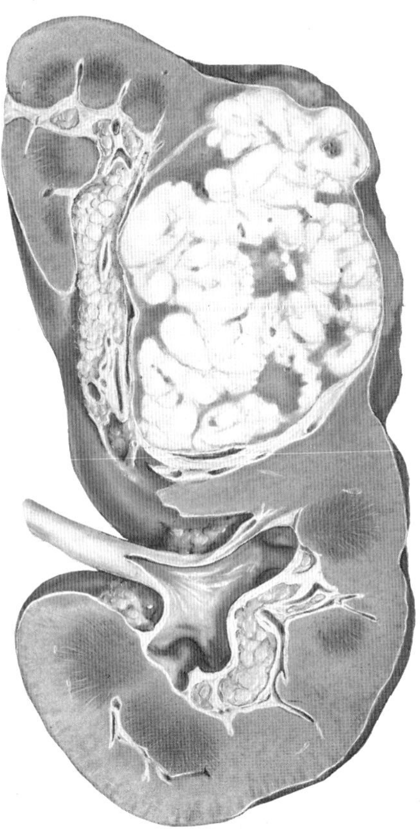

Fig. 508.—Hypernephroma embedded in the substance of the kidney.

The larger tumors are most commonly found embedded in the kidney, the tissue of which they push aside or destroy (Fig. 508). They usually grow in the cortex, bulging under the capsule, which they may perforate, but in many cases they extend through the pyramidal region so as to approach the pelvis. The best preserved part of the tumor is yellow or reddish-yellow, often interspersed with gray, translucent areas, but in practically every case there are found extensive areas of necrosis with wide-spread hæmorrhage, which gives the cut surface an extremely variegated appearance.

In the further course of their development these tumors metastasize sometimes by way of the lymphatic channels, but more often through the venous blood-stream. I have seen one case in which the lymphatics in the walls of the blood-vessels in the lungs were filled with the yellow tumor mass, in such a way that all these vessels stood out prominently as thick-walled tubes composed of a soft yellow material. In this case the primary transportation may well have taken place by way of the circulating blood, the filling of the pulmonary lymphatics being a secondary phenomenon. On the other hand, Oberndorfer, Ribbert, and others describe extraordinary invasions of the branches of the renal vein, with continuous extension of the tumor through the vena cava into the heart. We saw such a case at autopsy in which the main tumor was situated in the left kidney. The veins draining it were completely occluded by moulds of tumor tissue which extended to fill the left renal vein, and reached across to ramify in the right renal vein far into the right kidney. In the vena cava it proceeded upward, forming a cylindrical mass 3 cm. in diameter, which completely blocked and distended the vein up to a point just below the entrance of the hepatic veins. On looking down into the vena cava it could be seen as a rounded mass partly covered with fresh thrombi. Metastases were found in the lungs and in various bones, those in the skull being especially striking since their growth

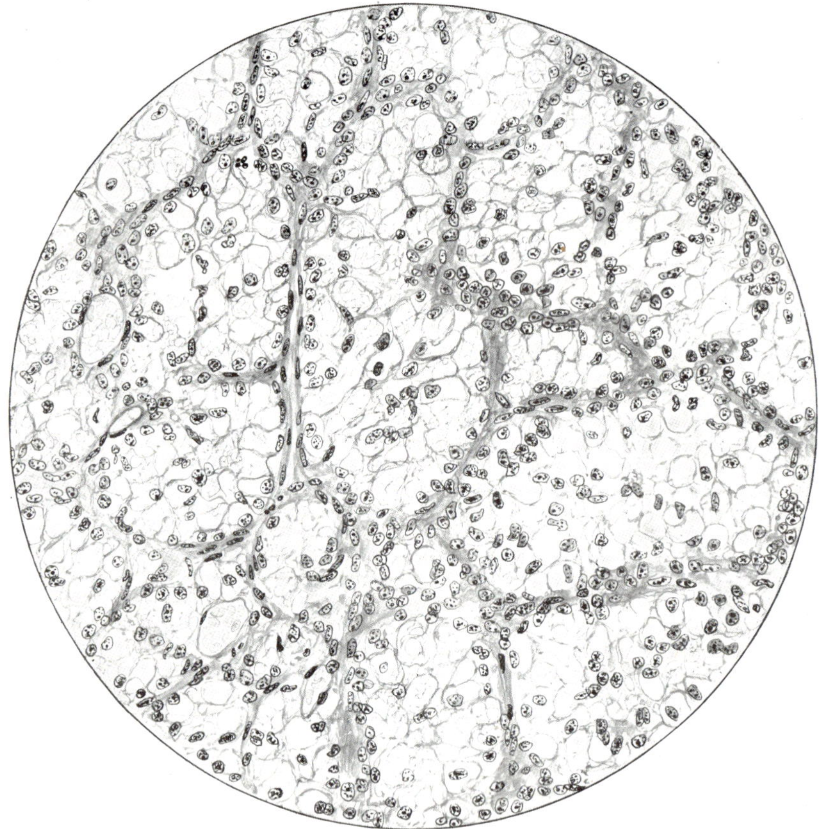

Fig. 509.—Hypernephroma showing characteristic large clear cells.

from the diploë was accompanied by the formation of sharp spicules of bone which projected about each nodule.

When studied microscopically, these tumors are found to present a great variation in structure, but those arising from the kidney resemble closely those derived from the adrenal itself. The most common microscopical picture is that in which wide strands of cells anastomose freely with one another and are cut at various angles (Fig. 509). These are supported by a delicate stroma with thin-walled blood-vessels. The cells are large, cylindrical, or cubical, and extremely pale and transparent, recalling in their appearance the cells of a growing plant tissue. Glycogen is found in these cells, together with abundant droplets of cholesterine esters and other lipoids, such as are normally found in the adrenal cortex. The resemblance of the tumor-cells to those of the adrenal cortex has always been emphasized, but it must be admitted that they are far more transparent than the cells of the gland. In many cases the tumor-cells are arranged not in strands, but as the lining elements of tubular spaces. These canals may anastomose widely or become distended into spaces of considerable size. Frequently they are filled with blood, which appears to be in a good state of preservation, so that the idea has arisen that these may be tumors in which the typical cells are really endothelial cells lining blood-channels, and that they should be regarded rather as endotheliomata. In other cases still the necrosis of the tumor tissue leaves nothing but mantles of cells about the blood-vessels, and these have been looked upon by some authors as peritheliomata. This peculiar condition has been mentioned elsewhere in connection with other tumors, and it was said that it seems quite wrong to assign to these remnants of tissue a name which suggests that they, as "perithelial" cells, had given rise to the tumor.

Not all these tumors are even as simple as this, for there are some in which large cavities occur and others in which the epithelial cells are thrown up into most complicated papillary folds which may almost fill the cavities. In these cases the cells are usually more granular and less like vegetable cells.

Since the assertion of Grawitz that such tumors, even when they occur in the kidney, arise from misplaced bits of adrenal tissue, there has been a great deal of discussion of their origin and true relations. Sudeck, Stoerck, and others contest their relation to the adrenal, and claim that there is strong evidence that they are really derived from the tissue of the kidney, and that they are renal rather than adrenal tumors. In the lack of any perfectly decisive proof it seems to me that their arguments are weak, and that the evidence which Grawitz himself brought forward to show their relation to the adrenals is stronger. These arguments, which deal with the lipoid and glycogen content, with the formation of spaces or lumina in the tumors, etc., may be read in the papers of Stoerk, Sisson, Sabolotnow, and others.

Wells has analyzed the lipoid content, and has found that it approaches that of the normal adrenal cortex and far exceeds that of other tumors. He could demonstrate no adrenaline-like substance in any of the tumors.

LITERATURE

Stoerk: Verh. d. Dtsch. Path. Gesell., 1908, xii, 123.
Grawitz: Arch. f. kl. Chir., 1884, xxx.
Sabolotnow: Ziegler's Beiträge, 1907, xli, 1.
Wells: Arch. Int. Med., 1909, iv, 291; Jour. Med. Research, 1908, xvii, 461.
Sisson: Ziegler's Beiträge, 1910, xlix, 476.
Davis: Arch. Int. Med., 1911, viii, 60.
Kostenko: Dtsch. Ztschr. f. Chir., 1911, cxii, 284.
Rosenfeld: Frankfurter Ztschr. f. Path., 1913, xiv, 151.

ENDOTHELIOMATA

The tumors so far discussed have been described as though they were composed of elements whose relationship to some tissue which gave them origin is so readily recognizable as to rouse no doubts. Further, they have been spoken of as though in every part they presented the same characteristic appearance. In many cases these things are true, and we have no hesitation in assigning a definite source for a tumor which is quite uniform in structure throughout, and whose cells are, as in the case of a fibroma or chondroma, obviously of the same general character as those of the tissue in which they develop. More emphasis should have been laid, however, upon the frequent admixture of other tissues, and especially upon the modifications which the essential tissue of the tumor undergoes. Thus nothing is commoner than to find, instead of a pure chondroma, an osteochondroma or a myxochondroma or a myxochondrosarcoma. In these cases it must be decided whether the tissues are of equal dignity in the tumor growth, or whether one or two of them represent metaplasia or degenerative changes in the other. In most of the cases already considered we have dealt with tissues so closely related that, as in the case of cartilage, bone, and connective tissue, we are not surprised to find one assuming the character of the other or giving rise to the other in its further growth. We realize that many of these changes are due to the infiltration of fluid or of mucin or to some other mechanical or chemical change which can produce an alteration in the appearance of the interstitial substance or of the cells themselves.

In spite of some difficult feats of tracing the cells to unfamiliar stages in the embryonic development of their parent cells, we have found it possible to feel pretty sure of the point of departure of the tumor elements. Of course, a rigid criticism might show that we are by no means possessed of proofs of these histogenetic relations, but, on the whole, there is so much evidence that the tracing seems safe enough.

There are, however, many tumors whose origin and histogenetic relations are difficult, if not impossible, to trace. They are never the familiar tumors which occur in dozens of cases in practically the same form and situation, but odd growths which appear in some unusual site or in tissues where any one of several origins might be assigned to them. In structure they are unlike any known tissue, and offer no suggestion as to their nature from the non-committal arrangement of their cells. Of course, it must occur to every one that in time these tumors will be recognized in spite of their lack of resemblance to known mature tissues, just as the neuroblastomata were finally recognized, although they had long been contemplated without understanding. But the stumbling-block is that a name has been discovered under which all these difficult tumors can be conveniently classed, and thus pigeonholed and withdrawn from further study. Every unusual tumor which lacks characters that will permit its ready recognition stands an excellent chance of being labeled endothelioma and relegated to oblivion.

Still more disturbing is the fact that certain well-known groups of tumors, such as the mixed tumors of the salivary glands, have been declared by some one to be endotheliomata, and have, therefore, been classed in that capacious group by every one. Happily, in that particular type of tumor there has been sufficient interest to bring forth further study with more accurate results.

In practically no case has the origin of a tumor from endothelium been proven. As Ribbert points out, the mere continuity of the tumor-cells with endothelium at the margin of the tumor is no proof of their identity. Borst has shown that tumor-cells may grow into lymphatic channels and cause the endothelial cells to proliferate, but that even when the proliferation is sufficient to close the channel, it is only a normal reaction to the presence of a foreign tissue and not a participation by the endothelial cells in the tumor growth. Ribbert thinks that proof of the endothelial nature of a tumor will require the study of that tumor at its inception, which is impossible.

Much confusion has arisen because of the uncertainty as to what should be called endothelium, and many different standpoints have been taken. All agree that the lining cells of blood- and lymph-vessels and the lining of the cerebrospinal spaces must be accepted as endothelium. Disputed tissues are the lining-cell layers of pleura, peritoneum, etc. According to the cœlom theory, these cells must be epithelial (hypoblastic and epiblastic) in origin. Some other characteristics, such as the possession of cilia, etc. make them seem more allied to epithelium, and indeed there are many now, including Ribbert, who regard the serosa cells as epithelial in nature and the tumors derived from them as epithelial tumors.

Even yet, in spite of all the work on the relation of the lymphatics to the connective tissue, much is written of the endothelial cells which line or partly line the indefinite lymph-spaces or crevices in the tissue, and what is written is used as a complete explanation of the origin of certain obscure tumors. Since it appears that the lymphatics are complete blind-ending tubes lined with endothelium, such tumors would have to be derived from their walls.

There is no reason that endothelial tumors should not arise from the endothelium of the lymphatics or blood-capillaries. No doubt they do and possibly some of the tumors described as endotheliomata really have this origin, but it is far from proven or even plausible in most cases, and in many the essential cells of the tumor, though flattened and stretched out, are easily shown to be epithelial cells. Indeed, in most of these tumors which arise in the skin, in the mouth, or nasal sinuses, in connection with bones, or in less characteristic situations, it is found that the tumor-cells are flattened, rather deeply staining cells, arranged in strands which anastomose and give off long-pointed processes which extend into crevices of the connective tissue. The cells do not resemble any normal type closely, and since no primary growth is found in any of the usual epithelial organs, and since further the cells stand out too distinctly from the stroma to be accepted as connective-tissue cells, it is rather feebly assumed that they must be endothelial cells. The proof is not much stronger than that, and is rather a process of exclusion than a positive tracing of a relation to endothelium. Even though every one must admit the possibility and even the probability of the existence of tumors derived from endothelium of the lymphatics, this kind of reasoning is most unsatisfactory.

In the following, the types of tumors which have been looked upon as derived from endothelium may be given briefly and discussed. It will be found that the evidence of their relation to endothelium is thought to be satisfactory in the cases of endothelioma of the dura, and in a very small number of tumors derived from capillary blood-vessels, but that in the others it is either disproven or very doubtful. New tumors are constantly being described in which an attempt is made to establish an endothelial origin, and the matter may soon reach a state of greater clearness.

Endotheliomata Derived from Lymphatic Endothelium.—Tumors of the skin are described by Borst and others as composed of nodular masses of rather dense tissue in which anastomosing strands of flattened smooth cells, sending off pointed processes, are embedded in connective tissue. Similar tissues are found elsewhere, and may be really endotheliomata or derived from much altered epithelium.

Cylindromata or tumors in which hyaline cylindrical strands or balls are interspersed with strands of flattened cells were described by Billroth, and have been much discussed in later years. They are usually tumors which occur in the mouth, near the salivary glands, or in the nasal sinuses, but may be found elsewhere. They are generally benign, but may metastasize. Histologically the cylindrical hyaline structures (which are not peculiar to these tumors, but may occur in sarcomata and carcinomata) are seen to be formed by modification of the connective-tissue stroma or of the walls of the blood-vessels (Fig. 510), although in some cases such hyaline masses appear to be formed in the middle of a strand of tumor-cells. The name is given on account of this anatomical peculiarity, and should not distinguish a special type of tumor. While it is difficult to decide upon the actual origin of the tumor-cells, Ribbert has brought strong evidence that they are *epithelial* and that they arise from the glands or surface epithelium of the mouth and nasopharynx.

Pleural or **peritoneal tumors** have given rise to much difference of opinion. They are apparently primary in the lining cells of the pleura or peritoneum, and can be distinguished from those which occur as metastases from primary tumors situated elsewhere. The latter are usually in the form of small lenticular or rounded nodules, which extend into the underlying lymphatic channels, while the primary tumors of the pleura are most commonly seen as thick white layers of dense tissue covering the lung and containing in the meshes of the connective tissue simple or very complicated arrangements of cells whose nature cannot be positively stated from a study of their morphology. There are some investigators who insist that they are derived from the endothelium of the underlying lymphatic channels, but the majority, including Ribbert, refer them to the serosa cella and consider them epithelial tumors. They may metastasize to lymph-glands or extend into the lung. Those arising in the peritoneal cavity are more likely to occur in nodular form. They too may invade, and, penetrating the diaphragm, spread over the pleura.

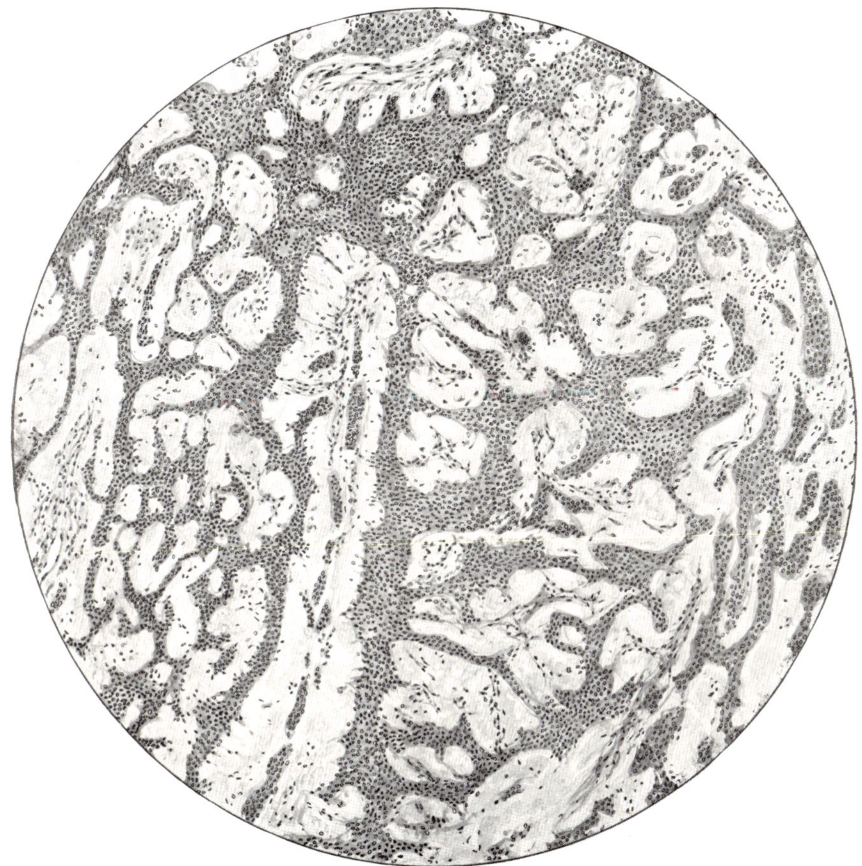

Fig. 510.—Cylindromatous tumor.

Endotheliomata of the Dura Mater.—There seems to be a general agreement of opinion as to the endothelial character of the lining of the dura. The cells of this lining are often thrown up into minute solid masses which can be recognized with the naked eye and which seem to foreshadow the possibility of tumor formation. Tumors attached to the dura and pressing into the surface of the brain are quite common. They may reach such a size as to compress the brain seriously and to cause death by occupying the limited space of the cranium. In one case we observed a tumor of the size of an egg lying on the convex surface of the cerebrum, in which it had pressed a deep groove for its own accommodation. This was a stalked growth hanging from the dura along the median longitudinal sinus. Others (as in Fig. 511) embed themselves deeply in the cerebral substance and may appear as though derived from the brain. They are sharply limited, however, and readily fall out of the depression in which they lie. Most of them appear in the neighborhood of the cerebellum and pons, and are sometimes called cerebellopontine tumors. They are not malignant and do not recur when removed. In section they are firm tumors which show a peculiar whorled arrangement, somewhat like that of a uterine myoma. This appearance is seen under the microscope to be due to the arrangement of

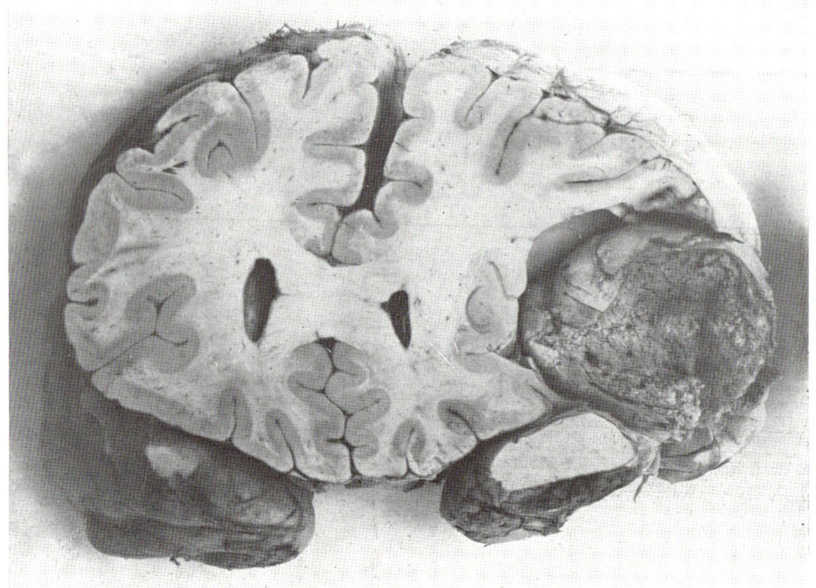

Fig. 511.—Endothelioma of the meninges lying in a deep depression in the surface of the cerebral hemisphere.

the flattened cells in strands which interlace, or in concentric arrangements (Fig. 512). Occasionally the flattened cells are closely wrapped around a central grain of calcified material, and this arrangement may be repeated throughout the tumor, giving rise to the so-called *psammoma*. Connective tissue may be associated with the "endothelial" cells and contributes a greater firmness to the tumor.

The term psammoma is another descriptive name, and is applied to any tumor which contains many tiny concretions or rounded grains of calcified material enwrapped in concentric layers of cells. Such tumors occur in the choroid plexus, in the hypophysis, in the pineal gland, and elsewhere in the body, as well as in the endotheliomata of the dura.

Tumors Derived from the Endothelium of the Blood-vessels.—A few tumors have been described which appear to represent this group, but they seem to be very rare. Borrman, for example, has described two tumors composed of long strands and channels composed entirely of endothelium and connected with the blood-capillaries. These he calls tubular capillary endotheliomata, and in so far as the relation to the capillary endothelium can be proved, the name is well chosen. Colmers has also described a tumor of the penis, metastasizing into the internal organs, which was composed of blood-channels lined by tumor-cells, which he regarded as endothelial cells.

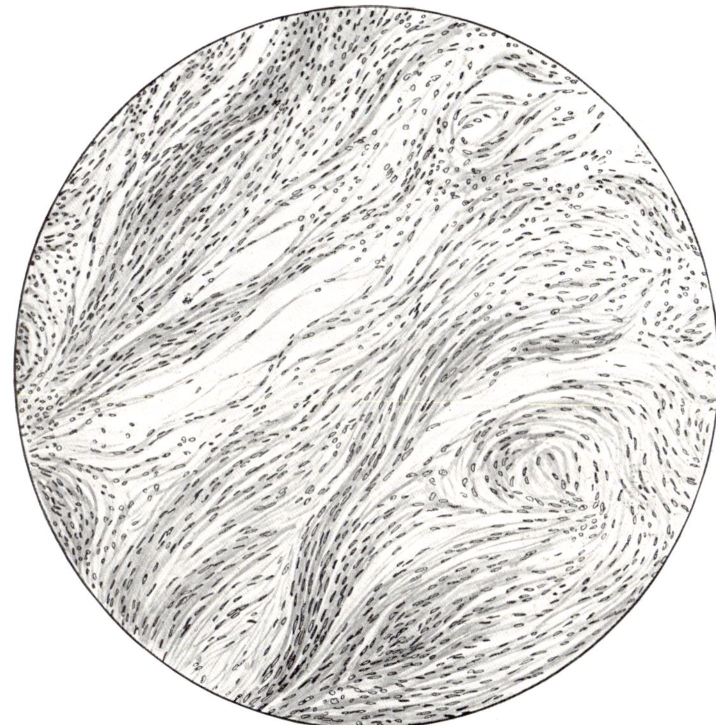

Fig. 512.—Meningeal endothelioma. The tumor is made up of long, fusiform cells arranged in whorls.

The endothelial cells were much changed in form, and greatly enlarged, and sometimes occluded the wide blood-channels of the corpora cavernosa into which they grew. B. Fischer describes another peculiar tumor situated in the liver, most of which it occupied. In the outlying parts of the many nodules this was seen to be a mere widening of the capillaries with thickening of the endothelium, but in the centre of each nodule the change in the endothelium became more striking, producing great widening of the capillary, often with occlusion and disappearance of the liver-cells. Most active blood formation was found to be going on in the capillaries of these areas, and one is led to speculate as to whether this may have been an exaggerated myeloid alteration rather than a tumor.

One tumor which I studied microscopically seemed to fall into this group. It was a pulsating mass in the region of the left scapula in a boy, and was incompletely removed at an operation, which had to be stopped because of the excessive hæmorrhage from the tumor. There was a recurrence which grew rapidly until the boy's death, when metastases were found in the lungs. In the metastases, as well as in the primary growth, the whole tumor was composed of delicate canals lined with high swollen cubical cells with very clear protoplasm, quite like those in a hypernephroma. Each canal was filled with blood, which seems to have been in circulation and to have given rise to the extensive hæmorrhages at operation. This tumor reminded us of a hypernephroma, and it is possible that it may have been a secondary growth, although no tumor was found in the adrenals or kidneys or elsewhere, except the pulmonary nodules, which were numerous and all about the size of peas.

"Perithelial" Tumors.—Many tumors have been described as composed of matted strands of blood-vessels, each of which is surrounded by a mantle of tumor-cells supposed to be derived from certain adventitial cells of the vessel-wall, the so-called perithelium. Such tumors have been named peritheliomata or perithelial angiosarcomata, and are said to be malignant growths metastasizing rapidly. It seems that the conception of perithelium is accepted passively by every writer and transferred from text-book to text-book. I have searched in vain for perithelium, or even for any clear description of it, and do not believe such cells exist. Of course, there are accompanying lymphatics in the walls of the blood-vessels, and there are the vasa vasorum, and it is conceivable that a tumor might arise from either of these. The cells described in such tumors have no resemblance to endothelium, but nothing can be concluded from that. In all the descriptions some mention is made of hyaline and necrotic changes in the stroma between the vascular strands, and this, it seems, affords the explanation of the appearance. Only those parts of a sarcoma remain alive which immediately inclose the blood-vessels, and hence become isolated in necrotic ground substance as mantles of cells around blood-vessels. There may be real peritheliomata, but it seems improbable, and I have not been able to find them.

LITERATURE

Borrmann: Ergebn. d. allg. Path., 1902, vii, 870; Virch. Arch., 1898, cli, Suppl., 151; *ibid.*, 1899, clvii, 297.
Monckeberg: Ergebn. d. allg. Path., 1906, x, 789.
Volkmann: Dtsch. Ztschr. f. Chir., 1895, xli, 1.
Hinsburg: Dtsch. Ztschr. f. Chir., 1899, li, 281.
Lubarsch: Ergebn. d. allg. Path., 1897, ii, 592.
Colmers: Ziegler's Beiträge, 1903, xxxiv, 295.
B. Fischer: Frankfurter Ztschr. f. Path., 1913, xii, 399.

CHAPTER L

TUMORS OF EPITHELIAL ORIGIN

Relation of epithelium to stroma. Papillomata: Origin from skin and mucosæ. Papillomata of bladder and ovary. Adenomata: Origin from skin, salivary glands, gastric and intestinal mucosæ, kidney, liver, adrenal, hypophysis, and prostate. Adenomata of the breast. Intracanalicular forms. Cystadenomata of ovary: Their origin and form; papillomatous types. Adenomata of the uterus.

In the tumors hitherto discussed cells evidently derived from the connective tissue or some other mesoblastic structure have in most cases formed the essential feature of the growth, although in every instance these have been supported and supplied with nutrition by a vascular connective-tissue stroma. It has been made clear that in these tumors, as in the growth of organs in the embryo or in the new formation of tissue in the healing of a wound, the supporting framework and the vascular supply are called for and made to serve the ends of the more important specific tissue. This becomes even more apparent in the case of the great group of tumors in which epithelial cells play the leading part in the constitution of the growth. Although there are some authors, such as Ribbert, who hold to the idea, expressed by Virchow, that the new-growth of epithelium is initiated by an atypical growth of the underlying connective tissue, the opposite view is maintained by the majority, and seems to me to be supported by far greater weight of evidence. Nevertheless it will be necessary to weigh this matter in each case, and in some it may be found difficult to decide.

Very convincing proof of the mastery of the epithelium seems to be furnished by those papillary epithelial tumors of the ovary which grow both from the inside and the outside of cysts in that organ. If minute clusters of the epithelial cells which cover the branches of these growths as they project into the peritoneal cavity are broken off and scattered over the loops of the intestine and on the surface of the other abdominal organs, they take root and grow, not merely into masses of epithelium, but into new branched formations which are supported by connective tissue springing from the peritoneal tissue, and supplied by branches of the blood-vessels of the organ on which they grow. Even if a bit of connective tissue be implanted with the group of epithelial cells, we must admit that the new blood-vessels and probably the new stroma are commandeered from the underlying tissues.

Although we may agree that epithelium growing so abundantly on a surface as to be forced up into folds demands a vascular stroma for each fold, and that epithelium growing in the form of a gland demands the formation of vascular connective tissue enough to surround it, there are instances in which the epithelium assumes a growth so rapid that it far outstrips the connective-tissue formation, and abandons the ordinary relation which it regularly bears to that tissue, in the formation of an organ or in the normal covering of a surface. Then the epithelial cells in solid strands push their way lawlessly into any crevice in the tissue. Even then, however, when muscle, organ tissue, or bone is destroyed by the advance of these cells, there is never formed any considerable mass of epithelium alone, but the connective tissue follows with its blood-vessels, though often in an irregular and inadequate way, and forms a support for the epithelium in its new position. Should the epithelial cells be set free in the lymph- or blood-stream and lodge in the capillaries of a distant organ, their multiplication in that new site is at once assisted by the ingrowth of fibroblasts and capillaries which quickly organize a stroma. These are the malignant epithelial tumors, and it is seen that the difference which exists between their structure and the more orderly form of the benign ones depends upon the headlong irregularity of their growth, with which the stroma can scarcely keep pace.

We may consider first the benign epithelial tumors, in which the relation between the epithelium and its stroma or supporting framework is maintained nearly as it is in normal tissues, and afterward the malignant or cancerous form, in which this relation is disturbed. It must be remembered, however, that the difference between a malignant and a benign tumor consists not merely in this morphological manifestation, but in the overwhelming energy of growth of the epithelial cells of the cancer against which the normal tissues can set up no effective barrier.

Benign Epithelial Tumors.—Those epithelial growths which maintain, at least in principle, the normal relations between epithelium and stroma fall into several groups, according to their general form, although these groups overlap in the sense that combinations or transitions from one form to another are found. The types are as follows:

A *papilloma* is a tumor of lobulated, branched, or papillary form, in which each fold or offshoot of the epithelial layer has a central core of connective tissue with blood-vessels.

An *adenoma* is a tumor composed of glands of tubular, acinous, or other form, embedded in a vascular stroma. Such a tumor may exist as a nodule in the substance of a solid organ, or it may project as a polypoid growth on a mucous surface. Since the glands are often without connection with the efferent ducts, many of them may become cyst-like. Indeed, there is no sharp line between these tumors and *cysts*, which may be multilocular or unilocular. Within such cysts the epithelium may be thrown up into papillary growths, so that a combination of cystoma or cystadenoma with papilloma occurs.

PAPILLOMATA

The term is applied on the basis of their form to tumors composed of branching, cauliflower-like, or finely lobulated growths of epithelium, with a stroma which branches to carry blood-vessels into each prolongation. Sometimes these branches are so small that only single capillary loops supply them with blood. Although this general principle of formation is carried out throughout the group, there are great differences in their form and consistence, which depend upon the character of the epithelium from which they rise, since those which occur upon the skin are usually rough and hard, while those growing from the mucous membranes in the interior of the body are more commonly very soft, with loose, œdematous stroma. In the skin, papillomata may appear anywhere on the surface of the body, but are somewhat more common on the face and in the anal and genital region, than elsewhere. They are often mulberry shaped on a short stalk, and rather soft, often more deeply indented, rough, and horny. These, especially in some cases in which they are situated on the penis or labia, may grow to a

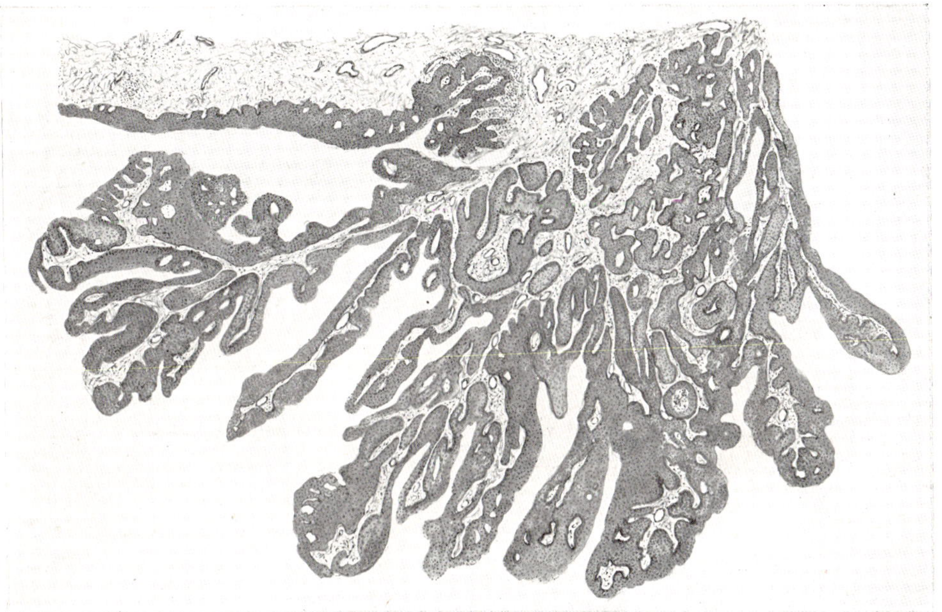

Fig. 513.—Papilloma of cheek.

considerable size. Being exposed to constant traumatism, they are frequently inflamed or ulcerated. Fig. 513 shows the structure of such a tumor which was found growing on the cheek, and corresponds almost exactly with the appearance of others found on the lips, margin of the anus, and elsewhere.

Less complex are the common warts, which are small papillomata, most frequently seen on the hands and composed of elongated papillæ covered with thick epithelium. In many of them the skin is merely thickened and deformed, although continuous, while in others the main mass of the wart seems to break through the surrounding skin, to protrude as a brush of fine, stiff, epithelium-covered papillæ. Section shows the continuity of the deeper layers of the epidermis with this papillary growth. In other cases the keratinization of the thick epithelial covering is so extensive that an actual horn-like outgrowth may be formed, and such horns, growing usually on the face or scalp, may reach a length of several centimetres.

Many pedunculated papillary tumors are pigmented or bear long hairs, and these on section are found to be made up largely of the peculiar cells described as characteristic of pigmented moles. They are, in fact, nævi which have assumed a papillary form, and although to this degree they are papillomata, the fact that they are only thinly covered with stretched-out epidermis and that the cells which take the initiative are nævus cells, and not epithelium proper, justifies the distinction. They are extremely common, and when not deeply pigmented, may resemble the ordinary papillomata very closely.

Besides these, there are many small, pedunculated fibromata which impose themselves as tumors resembling papillomata. They have been referred to in an earlier section, where their relation to the nerves was discussed. The fact that they are essentially new growths of connective tissue with only a thin covering of normal epidermis serves to distinguish them from the present group.

In the stratified epithelium which lines the mouth and nasopharynx papillomata spring up from the tongue, the nose, and elsewhere, which resemble those of the skin. Irritation and trauma may cause modification in the epithelium, so that the more exposed parts are denuded. Similar tumors are found in the larynx and trachea, often attached by stalks to the vocal cords, where, of course, they interfere greatly with phonation. These are fairly hard, and although in the trachea rising from cylindrical epithelium, may be covered with stratified epithelium.

In the urethra, vulva, and vagina similar growths occur. In these regions care must be taken to distinguish from true papillomata the flat and pointed condylomata, which are not tumors, but peculiar hyperplastic growths of epithelium caused by infection, with inflammatory reaction. The flat condylomata are of syphilitic origin, while the pointed or irregular ones are formed in the course of chronic gonorrhœa, chancroids, or other long-standing infectious processes about the genitalia. They even occur in pregnancy, and disappear after childbirth, although here the participation of an infection is not to be excluded. Apparently the gonococcus is not directly responsible for them. Such condylomata show on section (Fig. 514) an intensely inflamed tissue with distinct papillary new-formation of epithelium, so that without the clinical history it might be rather difficult to draw a sharp line between them and papillomata.

In the stomach and intestine papillomata occur, but they are by no means so frequent as the more polypoid glandular tumors, which will be referred to under Adenomata. This is probably because of the tendency of the cylindrical epithelium of the digestive tract to form tubular glands, rather than to throw itself up into papillary processes. Nevertheless, there are some such tumors which hang like great tassels in the cavity of the stomach, or less commonly in the colon. Those which I have seen in the stomach were associated with other tumors of a cancerous nature, but this is probably a coincidence. They are so soft and fragile that losses of substance frequently occur with hæmorrhage from the remaining surface.

The papillomata of the bladder are very similar in appearance, being extremely soft, tassel-like, stalked masses of thread-like papillæ which float about in water. They show in section a delicate stroma covered by thick, stratified epithelium, the surface layers of which are usually lost. From being caught in the urethral orifice in the contraction of the bladder the papillæ are often torn and portions are discharged in the urine, together with blood. These tumors tend to recur when they have been removed by

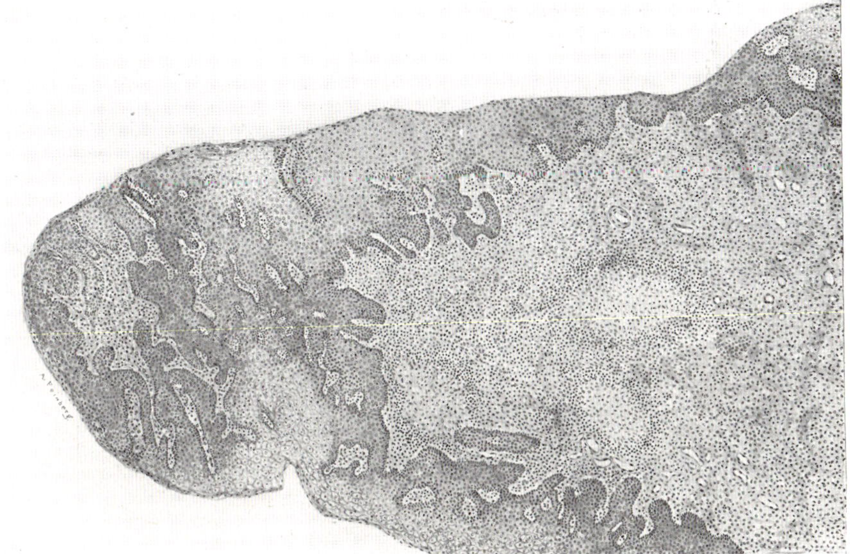

Fig. 514.—Acuminate condyloma from a case of chronic gonorrhœa.

operation, and in most cases, whether interfered with by operation or not, they finally invade and destroy the bladder-wall, revealing themselves as carcinomata. They should doubtless be regarded from the first as papillary carcinomata of the bladder.

From the surface of the ovary, and usually simultaneously from both ovaries, richly branching papillomatous tumors are found to grow, extending into the peritoneal cavity. They appear to arise from the epithelial covering of the organ, and are supported by the usual vascular stroma derived from the ovary. In their biological characters they resemble those which occur in the walls of ovarian cystadenomata.

In all these tumors the extensive growth of the epithelium, which casts it into folds and projecting papillæ, is, nevertheless, governed by a certain obedience to the normal laws of growth, which maintains a smooth line of demarcation between the epithelium and the underlying stroma. The whole tumor may become infiltrated with leucocytes during inflammation, and these cells wander readily from the stroma into the epithelium, but it is possible to trace round every projection and into each bay and indentation the distinct, regular line of separation between epithelium and stroma. The usefulness of a recognition of this line in diagnosis is realized daily. In a case observed recently there was a mass extending from the tonsil and pillars of the fauces downward on the epiglottis, in a man of middle age. Sections of an excised portion showed everywhere a typical papilloma with perfectly even, thick, stratified epithelial covering, uniformly marked off from the stroma. Doubts as to the nature of a tumor in that situation prompted the excision of another fragment, which in general showed the same structure, but at several points it was possible to see that an excessive and lawless growth of epithelium had burst the barrier, and had invaded the stroma in the form of long strands of cells. The malignant nature of the tumor was at once clear, and the diagnosis is being substantiated by the clinical course of the growth.

ADENOMATA

Epithelial tumors of glandular origin and retaining in general a gland-like structure are extremely common, and occur in practically every situation where there are glands. They may present themselves as nodules embedded in the substance of solid glandular organs, or as polypoid masses projecting on the surface of a mucosa. The stroma is sometimes dense and hard, often soft and gelatinous, so as to give the tumor a polypoid character. The epithelium-lined spaces may become enlarged to form cysts, and these may be partly occupied by papillary ingrowths of the same epithelium. It is as well to consider the cysts with the adenomata, since those cysts which are not modifications of these tumors are of a quite different nature, and are due either to obstruction and dilatation of the ducts of glands or to the congenital misplacement of embryonic tissues, under which headings they may be discussed.

Adenomata of the skin may arise from the sweat-glands or from the sebaceous glands. Such tumors are rare and must be distinguished from the vesicles which result from obstruction of the ducts of the sweat-glands and the so-called milia or comedones, which are due to the accumulation of sebaceous material in obstructed sebaceous glands.

In the digestive tract small adenomata may spring from the mucus-secreting glands, or occasionally appear in the salivary glands. The so-called *ranula* is a cystic tumor which forms in the frenulum of the tongue, and is derived from the sublingual ducts, especially from Nuhn's glands. In the salivary glands themselves there occurs not only a form of "cylindroma," but also and more frequently composite tumors containing several types of tissue. These may be discussed later.

In the stomach and intestine adenomata usually project or hang by a stalk as soft, polypoid tumors made up of abundant, irregular, and partly cystic glands, of much greater length than the normal glands, and embedded

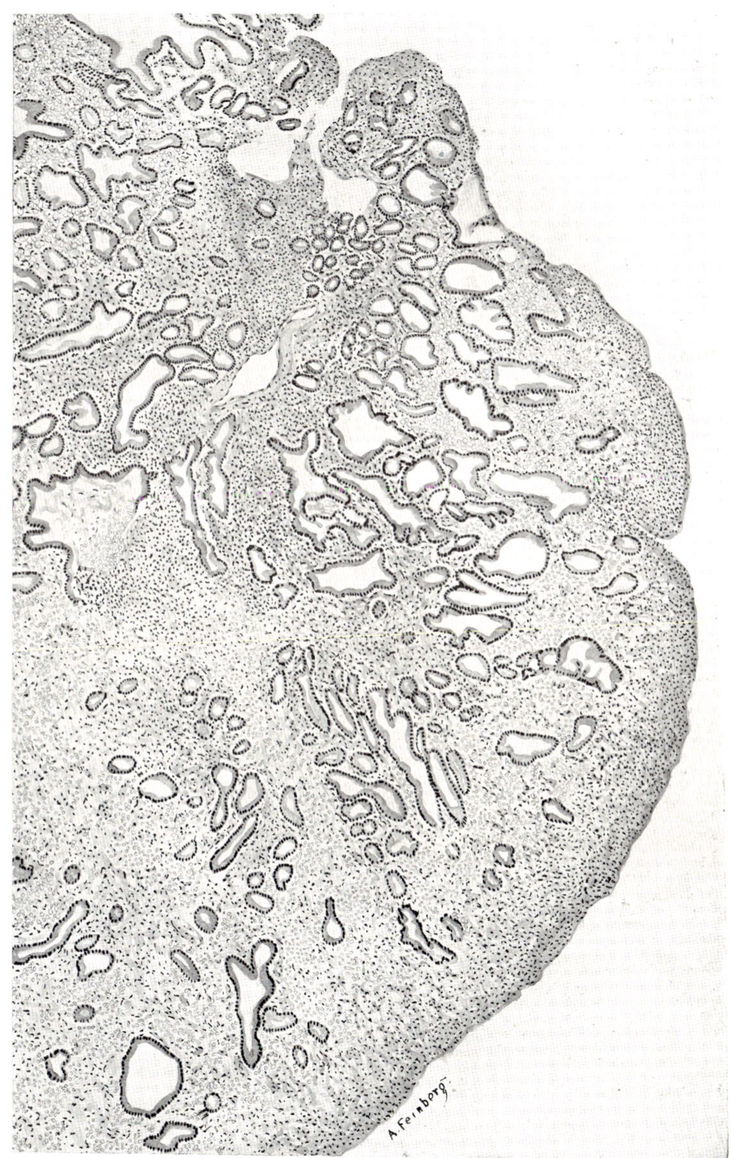

Fig. 515.—Tip of polypoid adenoma of the intestine.

in a loose stroma which, on account of the traumatism to which it is exposed, is constantly inflamed. Sometimes these polyps reach a considerable size, and may offer a certain obstruction, or be seized by the intestinal wall in its peristaltic contraction and dragged on into a lower part of the gut. In this process the wall of the intestine may be invaginated by the tension on the stalk of the tumor, and an intussusception started.

Microscopically, such adenomata are in continuity with the rest of the mucosa, but there is a sudden transition from the normal into the large distorted glands, lined with cylindrical epithelium, which may stain more deeply than the normal cells. The muscularis is not affected, but the submucosa is greatly thickened at this point and extends upward into the tumor (Fig. 515).

Polypoid adenomata are often multiple, and sometimes so numerous and so small as to give the intestinal mucosa a shaggy appearance. When they are larger (Fig. 516), they project into its lumen at every level as rounded, soft, velvety masses, varying in diameter up to one centimetre or more.

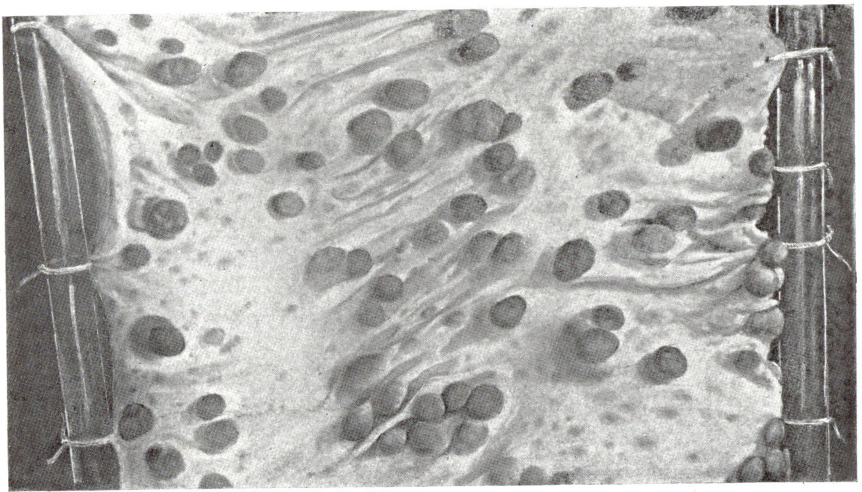

Figs. 516.—Multiple polypoid adenomata of the mucosa of the colon.

They must be distinguished from the irregular, polypoid masses of mucosa which are often formed at the margins of ulcers in the process of healing, or by the undermining of part of the mucosa in old dysentery. In the latter case the isolated mucosa breaks free at one end and hangs in the intestine as a polypoid mass.

Adenomata in the kidney are grayish-red nodules lodged in the cortex, usually small, but sometimes attaining a great size. They are composed of ramifying or twisted glandular or tubular epithelial structures in which the cells are much smaller than those of the convoluted tubules (Fig. 517). It seems probable that the tumor-cells are the offspring of cells destined to form kidney substance, but diverted to the formation of a tumor at a relatively early stage of development.

In the liver, as in other solid glandular organs, it is sometimes difficult to determine whether the nodular growths of the parenchyma of the organ should be looked upon as tumor formations, or as the result of a compensatory hyperplasia. It has been made clear in discussing cirrhosis of the liver that the destruction of a portion of the liver tissue causes the great overgrowth of the remaining fragments, so that the organ assumes a rough, nodular arrangement, in which the nodules are sometimes quite large.

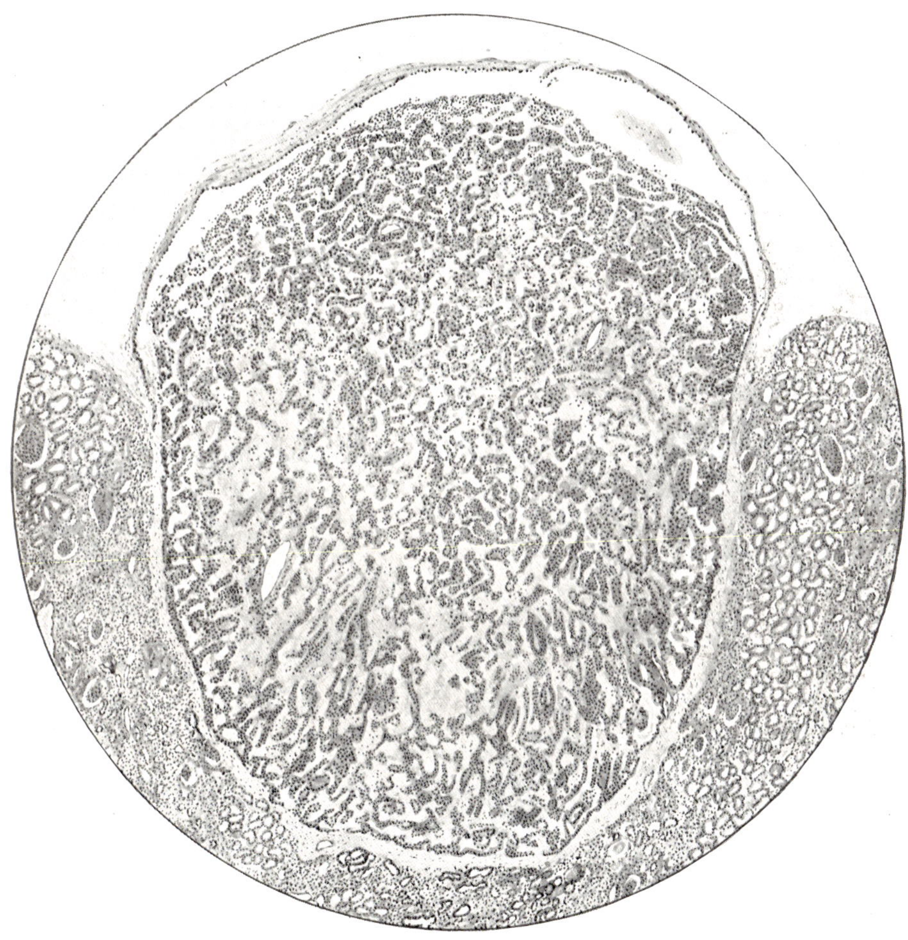

Fig. 517.—Adenoma of the kidney.

Microscopical study shows, however, that the strands of cells which make up these nodules, though disarranged from the normal order, are still in connection with the bile-ducts and actively functioning. It is probable that this is the nature of the circumscribed and irregularly arranged nodules of liver tissue which are sometimes found embedded in a liver which is otherwise almost normal looking. At least this explanation seems safest so long as the cells of the nodule closely resemble the normal liver-cells. Occasionally, however, there are seen nodules composed of irregular strands or tubules of cells which no longer stain as do the normal cells, and these must be regarded as adenomata representing less highly differentiated liver-cells or derivatives of the bile-duct epithelium.

The adenoma-like nodules of the cortex of the adrenal have been described elsewhere, and mention has been made of those of the thyroid. The thyroid adenomata are extremely common, and here again it is sometimes difficult to feel sure that we are dealing with actual tumors, and not with hyperplasia of the functioning gland. This is especially the case in the rather indistinctly outlined nodules of thyroid tissue in which the alveoli are distended with clear colloid and lined with thin, flat epithelium. In these cases the rest of the thyroid is frequently distended with colloid, in the same way, evidently, as the result of some abnormality in its function.

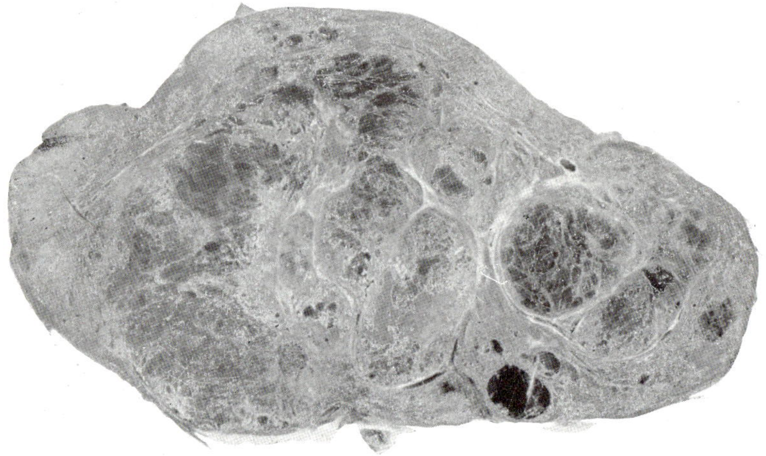

Fig. 518.—Adenomatous nodules in the thyroid. Some of these contain abundant colloid.

It is much easier to feel sure of the tumor character of the more common nodules which make up the bulk of the adenomatous or nodular goitres (Fig. 518), since they are sharply outlined and are composed of a quite abnormal tissue, in which the alveoli are often extremely small and lined with relatively large cuboidal cells. These cells occupy so much of the whole diameter of each alveolus that the lumen is often lost, and the tumor is found to be made up of narrow anastomosing strands or clusters of cells. Occasionally the larger alveoli contain distinct colloid secretion, but often there is none to be seen. The stroma is very abundant and becomes more conspicuous with the degeneration and disappearance of the alveoli, after which hæmorrhages and wide-spread necroses occur, followed by liquefaction of the tissue, with the formation of cyst-like cavities full of bloody or brown turbid fluid. Extensive calcification may occur in the walls of the cysts or in the substance of such adenomata.

Tumors of the *hypophysis*, composed of a gland-like growth of one or other of the elements of the organ, have been much studied of late, and have been mentioned in connection with acromegaly. They are most commonly composed of the chromophobe cells, which are arranged in solid strands or alveoli. Adenomata of the eosinophile cells have also been observed.

The adenomata of the prostate have been discussed elsewhere.

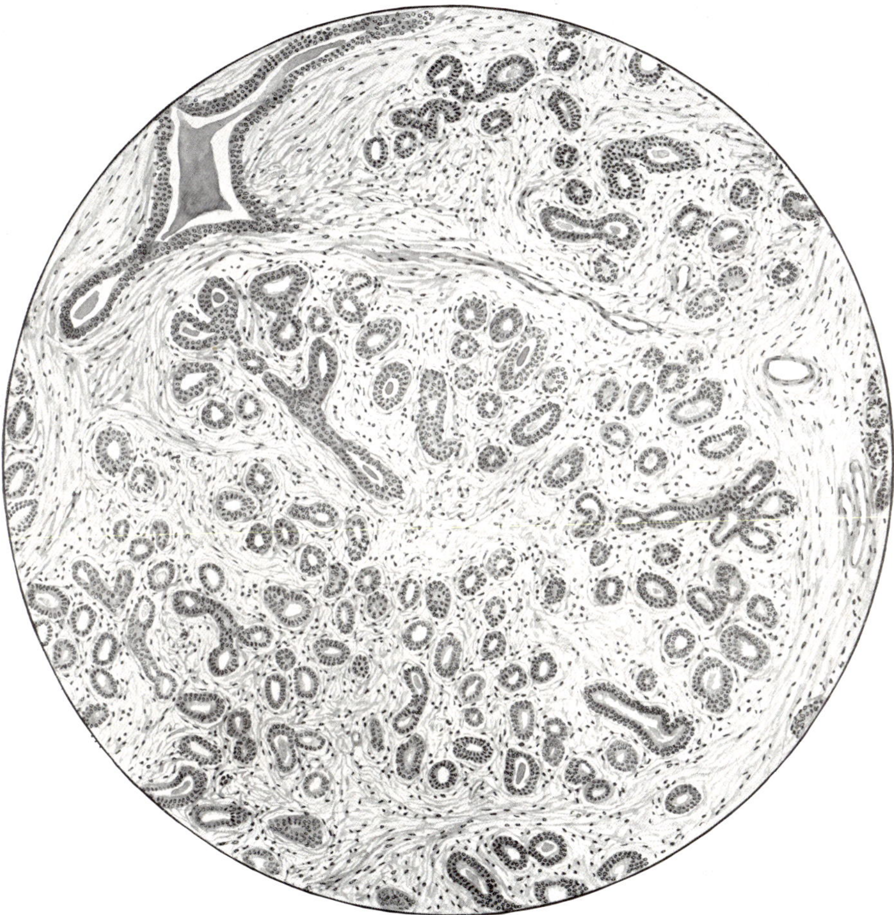

Fig. 519.—Adenofibroma of breast. The acini are very uniform in size, and are often lined with two layers of epithelial cells.

There remain the most common and important adenomatous growths, namely, those of the breast and the ovary.

The *adenomata of the breast*, often called adenofibromata on account of their dense stroma, are very common, and assume a great many different forms. They are benign tumors, limited in their outline, and growing expansively so that they can sometimes be shelled out of the remaining breast tissue. This is not always the case, and if they are examined in a section through the breast, they are found to appear as grayish-white, rather translucent nodules, or indistinctly localized areas of dense consistence. There is one group which in such a cut surface shows a peculiar structure, as though many small papillary or cauliflower-like masses were inclosed in cysts. These can indeed be partly turned out of such cavities, but are attached at some point by a stalk. They are the intracanalicular

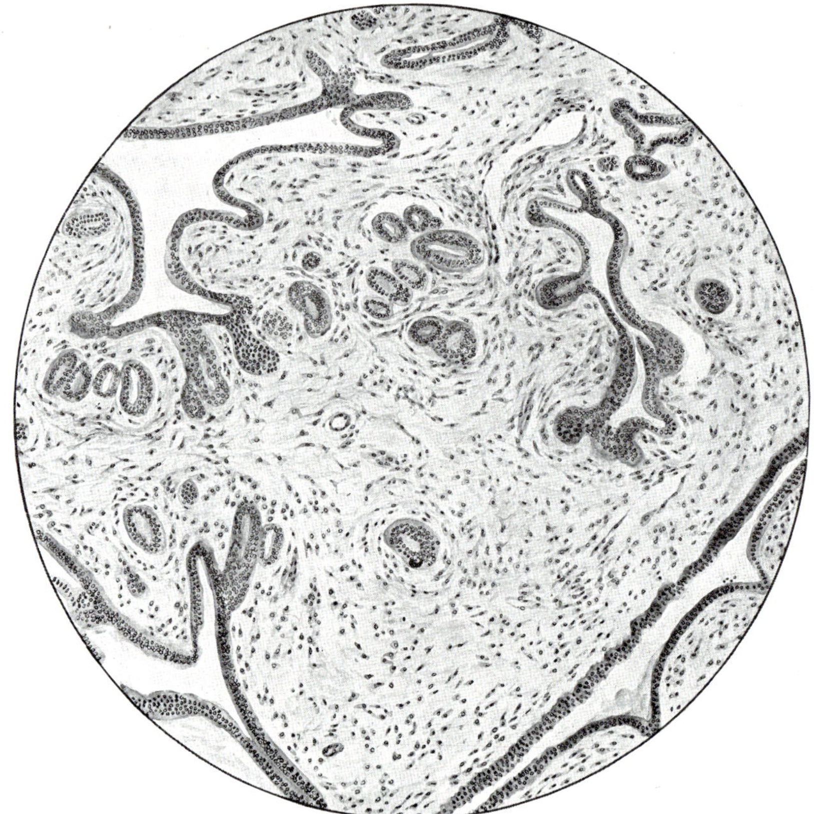

Fig. 520.—Adenofibroma of the breast. The epithelial structures resemble ducts in many places.

fibroadenomata, and their peculiar appearance will be recognized by the description of their microscopical structure.

The more homogeneous adenomata of the breast show on section many epithelial structures in the form of acini, canals, or small cysts surrounded by an abundant stroma which is usually rather lax immediately about the glands and denser in the broad intervening strands (Fig. 519). In some cases the whole stroma is cellular and rather œdematous, without any dense bands or areas of fibrous tissue. This is so, especially in the cases in which the epithelium-lined spaces have the character of long tubules (Fig. 520). In every case, whether the epithelial structures have the arrangement of acini or tubules or are in the form of cysts, the lining epithelium, which may be in two layers, is sharply bounded by a hyaline basement membrane. In some tumors this membrane is very broad and thick. When the cells are able to disregard the barrier and burst through to grow at large in the

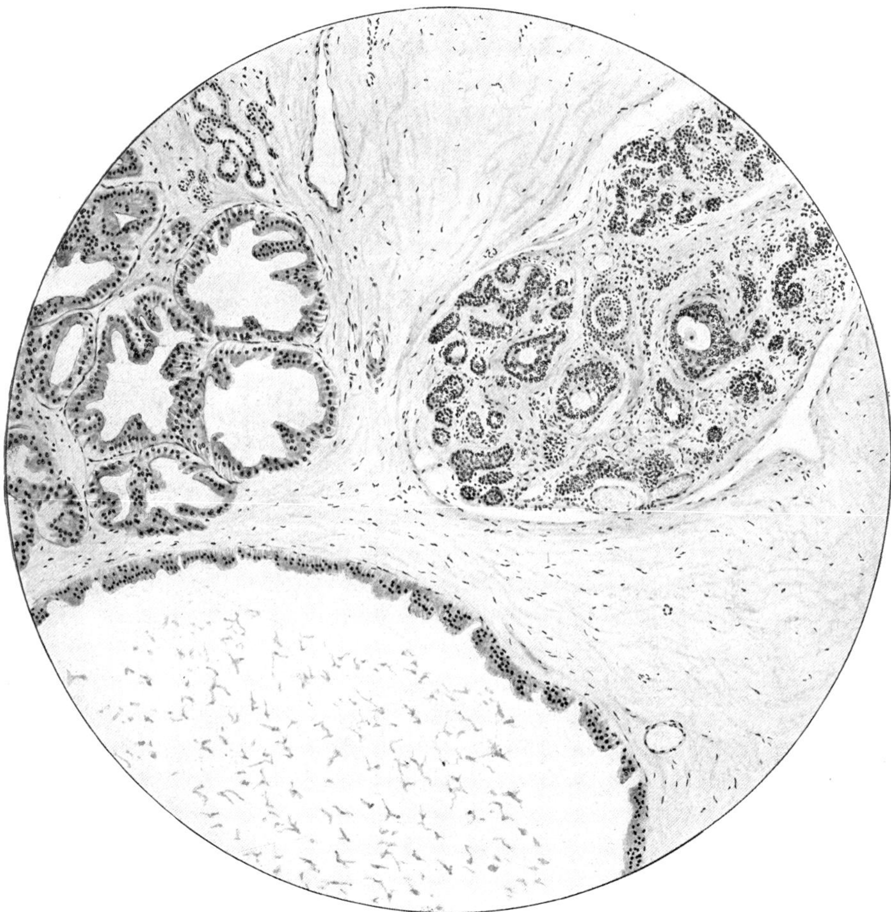

Fig. 521.—Adenoma of breast. Some of the acini are lined with high cubical or cylindrical epithelium, and such acini are sometimes dilated into cysts.

crevices of the stroma, the tumor must be recognized as a cancer. While it is not easy to show histologically that an adenoma can change its character and assume that of a carcinoma, the clinical history of these tumors gives much support to the idea that this change may occur.

The formation of cysts is of very frequent occurrence (Fig. 521), and although in most instances they never reach any great size, there are occasionally seen adenomata in which nearly the whole tumor is occupied by a cyst. Distinction must be drawn between the cyst formation in actual adenomata and the development of many minute cysts scattered diffusely through the breast in the so-called chronic mastitis, which will be described later. In the adenomata the cysts are found to contain clear fluid, or fluid rendered turbid by the presence of many desquamated cells, or blood-stained fluid which may become thick and deeply pigmented with blood-pigments. In some cases the cysts contain a butter-like material produced

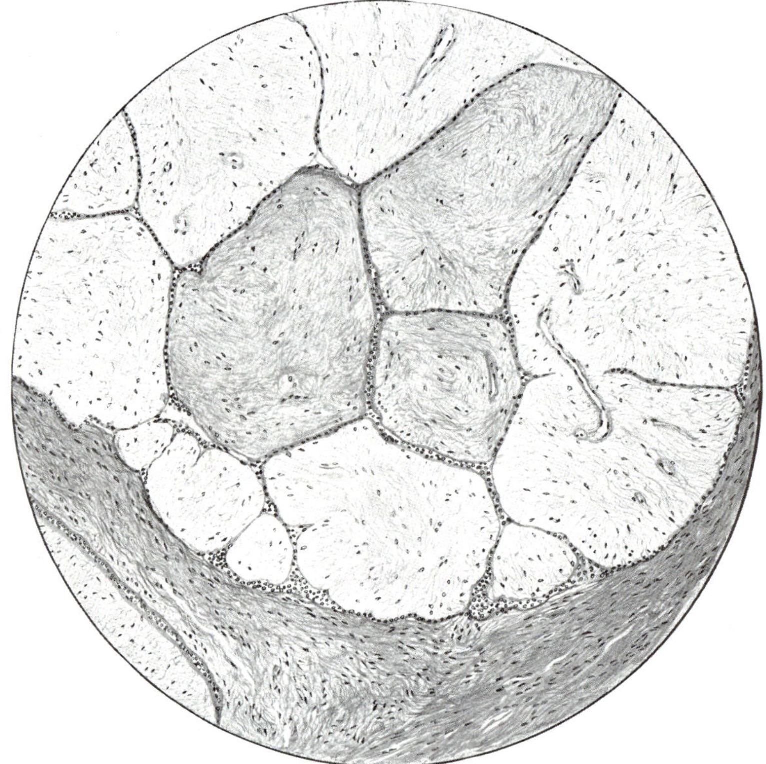

Fig. 522.—Intracanalicular adenofibroma of breast, showing numerous apparently free epithelium-covered masses packed together.

by the epithelium. The epithelium may be reduced to a thin layer of flattened cells, or it may be lost entirely. On the other hand, it is frequently proliferated and thrown up into folds and papillæ (*cf.* Fig. 521). Distinct papillomatous outgrowths may press into the cyst so as to fill it completely. Such intracystic papillomata are of quite frequent occurrence.

Intracanalicular Adenomata.—Closely related to these are the intracanalicular forms described above. In microscopic sections even the smaller epithelial structures may show the curious appearance in which isolated masses of connective tissue covered with epithelium lie packed together inside an irregular, epithelium-lined cavity or canal as though they were really free within the canal. The canal itself is thus reduced to a series of branching slits (Fig. 522). In truth these are sections of polypoid ingrowths which press into the cyst or canal and are cut at a point away from their stalks. Sections in another direction would show them as stalked polypoid masses. The question once more arises as to whether they are initiated by the growth of epithelium or by an excessive growth of connective tissue which pushes the epithelium into the cavity. In all probability it must be answered, as in the case of the papillomata, that the evidence is in favor of the primary activity of the epithelium. Such intracanalicular growths have a stroma which is loose and mucoid in the neighborhood of the glands; dense and firm in the intervening areas. The denser fibrous tissue stains red with eosin, while the mucoid tissue assumes a blue stain. On this account they are often called intracanalicular myxofibromata.

Cystadenomata of the Ovary.—In the *ovary* the epithelial growths are very commonly cystic. It is true that there are rare instances in which a papillomatous tumor springs from the surface of the ovary, and we shall see later that there are other solid ovarian tumors of a malignant character. The common adenomatous ovarian tumors are, however, cystic and are spoken of as *cystadenomata*. There are several varieties:

1. Simple ovarian cysts—the so-called hydrops folliculi.
2. Pseudomucinous cystadenomata.
3. Serous cystadenomata.

The division is not important since it is evident that it is based on no essential difference. The first type has long been supposed to arise from the Graafian follicles through mere accumulation of fluid in their cavities, and this view was supported by the finding of ova in the walls of the cysts (Rokitansky and others). Although rigorously upheld by Pfannenstiel, it has been practically abandoned by most writers since the work of Nagel, v. Kahlden, and others, who have shown that these cysts are not derived from Graafian follicles, but from ingrowths of the germinal epithelium of the surface of the ovary. v. Kahlden traced this clearly in many cases and showed that the ova seen by several investigators were really protoplasmic masses somewhat resembling ova, but produced by the epithelial cells, perhaps as a futile effort on the part of those cells to carry out the function for which they were originally intended.

The cystadenomata are also derived from solid or tubular ingrowths of the superficial germinal epithelium, and not from the Graafian follicles nor from the so-called Pflüger's cords, which are groups of ova and epithelial cells. They are frequently single, but often arise from both ovaries simultaneously and are formed of one large cyst or of a great number of smaller ones (simple and multilocular cystomata). At one time much attention was devoted to the chemical study of the contents of these cysts, and they were grouped on this basis although it is not a distinction of great importance. There are some which contain pseudomucin, a substance allied to mucin but easily split by boiling with acids so as to produce a carbohydrate which will reduce copper. This fluid may be slightly viscid or thick and gelatinous, sometimes dense enough to cut. I remember well one such cyst of enormous size from which, at operation, a whole tubful of yellowish brown, gelatinous, semifluid material was evacuated. The others, which may be called serous cysts, contain a fluid rich in albumin but not gelatinous and containing no glycoproteid.

The cystadenomata are sometimes quite small, and may at times push their way into the substance of the ovarian and broad ligament. Usually they occupy most of the substance of the ovary, which is spread out on the

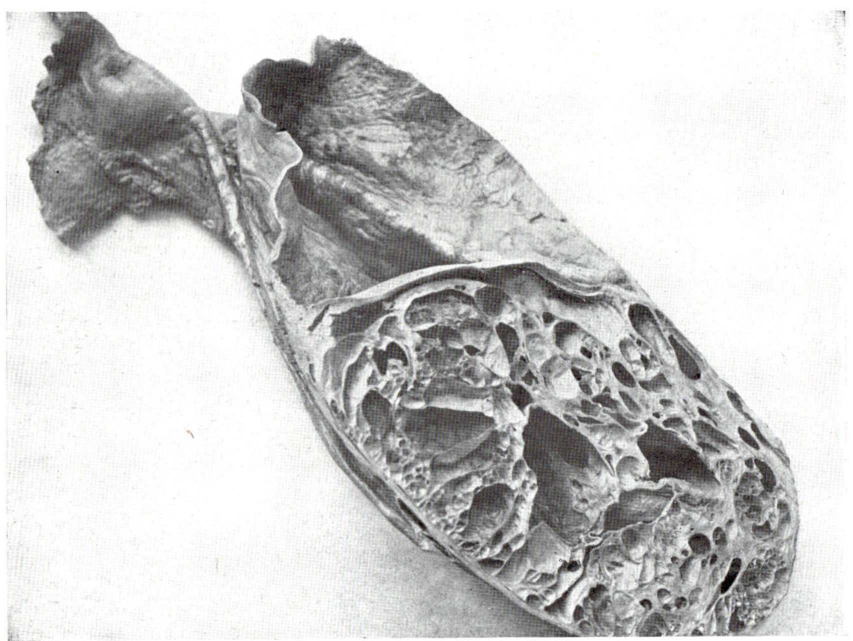

Fig. 523.—Large multilocular cystadenoma of the ovary. The Fallopian tube on that side is greatly elongated and stretched out over the tumor.

surface, and press up into the peritoneal cavity attached only by the stalk which contains the ovarian blood-vessels. In this way they may reach the most enormous size, producing a colossal distension of the abdomen where they are carried like a tremendous burden held in front. Their operative removal after the fluid is withdrawn through a cannula is often an extremely easy feat, since it consists merely in cutting through the stalk of the vessels.

The pseudomucinous cysts frequently develop many daughter cysts in their walls, or they may be definitely multilocular or composed of a great mass of small cysts (Fig. 523). These are lined with columnar or high cuboidal epithelium, which produces the fluid contents. They are by far the commonest of the cystadenomata (Fig. 524).

The serous cysts are also usually unilateral, but are very often multilocular, each small cyst being lined with high columnar epithelium which is often ciliated. We have recently observed, in two cases, bilateral multilocular ovarian cystadenomata composed of such small cysts that the very large tumors appeared to be almost solid. In such cases there is frequently a great accumulation of fluid in the peritoneal cavity.

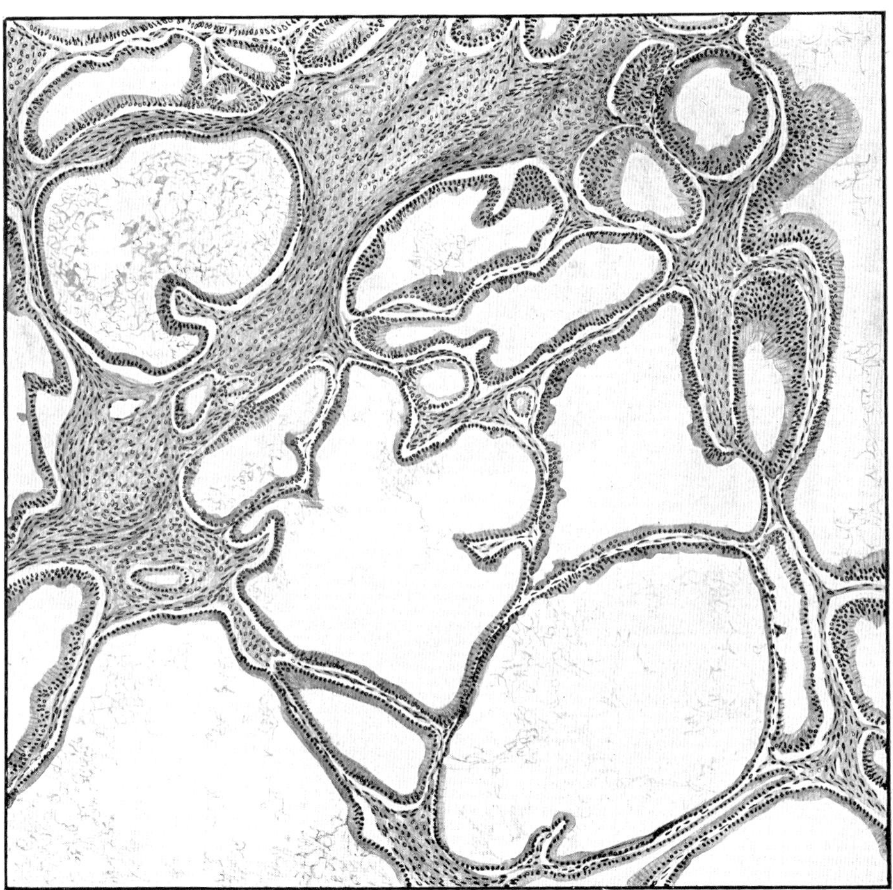

Fig. 524.—Multilocular cystadenoma of the ovary. The cysts are lined with high columnar epithelium.

Both pseudomucinous and serous cystadenomata may thus be multilocular, or in the form of a single cyst, although even then the remnants of broken partitions are usually evident. Both types show, as a rule, some infolding or papillary growth of their epithelium, and this may proceed to the formation of highly complex papillomatous ingrowths (Fig. 525). These are sometimes small and uniformly scattered over the wall; more often they arise from the wall in branching masses, leaving much of the lining smooth. Such masses may completely fill the cyst. The papillomatous growths may also appear on the outside of the cyst, so as to hang in the peritoneal cavity, and then they resemble the papilloma of the ovary already described. Fragments are broken off and swept into all parts of the peritoneum, where they adhere and grow, forming new papillomata wherever they lodge. This may take place, also, in the edges of an operative wound in the abdomen. In this sense the papillomatous cystoma partakes of the

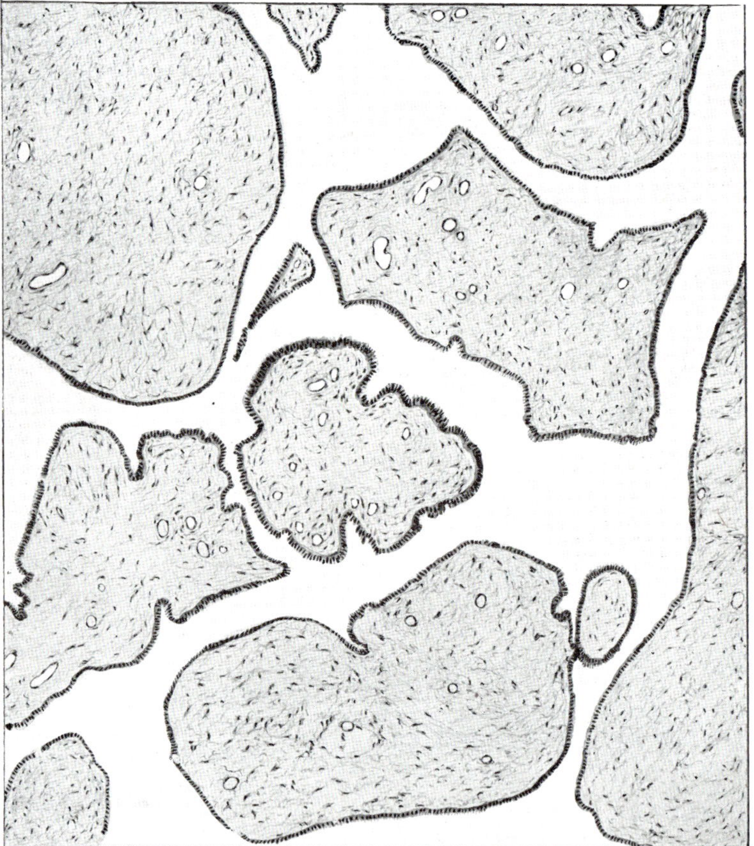

Fig. 525.—Portion of a papillomatous growth springing from the wall of an ovarian cystadenoma.

character of malignancy, but it goes no further and there are no metastases outside of the peritoneal cavity nor is there any destructive invasion of the underlying tissue. A somewhat analogous process follows the rupture of a pseudomucinous cyst, with extravasation of the contents into the peritoneum. The gelatinous material is spread everywhere over the wall and becomes partly organized by the upgrowth of granulation tissue. Some writers have thought that epithelial cells are implanted and continue the production of the pseudomucin, but the evidence for this is insufficient. The result is that the whole peritoneal cavity is lined with a thick, translucent layer, often spoken of as *pseudomyxoma peritonei*. A similar process may take place in connection with certain epithelial tumor growths of the appendix vermiformis.

Cysts of the *parovarium* are generally unilocular, thin walled, and filled with clear fluid. They are derived from the parovarian remnants which lie in the mesosalpinx and the cyst is found in that situation.

Adenomata of the Uterus.—From the uterine mucosa there are formed polypoid adenomatous growths comparable to those of the intestine. They are soft, broad masses, sessile on the mucosa of the uterus, and usually situated in or near one of the cornua, although they sometimes occur in the cervix and may contain small cysts. On section they are found to be composed of enlarged and distorted glands embedded in a cellular stroma.

LITERATURE

Aschoff: Ergebn. d. allg. Path., 1897, ii, 456.
Simpson: Jour. Med. Research, 1913, xxvii, 269.
Lincoln Davis: Annals of Surgery, 1906, xliii, 556.
Pfannenstiel: Veit's Handb. d. Gynäkologie, 1908, iv, 107.
Olshausen: Billroth-Lücke, Handb. d. Frauenkr., ii, 308.
Waldeyer: Arch. f. Gynäk., 1870, i, 252.
Seydel: Ergebn. d. allg. Path., 1901, vi, 805.
Williams: Johns Hopkins Hosp. Rep., 1892, iii, 1
v. Kahlden: Ziegler's Beiträge, 1900, xxvii, 1.

CHAPTER LI

CARCINOMATA

General characters, grouping. Flat-cell carcinomata. Epitheliomata of lip, skin, etc. Mode of growth and metastasis. Epitheliomata of tongue, tonsils, bronchi, œsophagus, gall-bladder, urinary bladder. Epitheliomata of the vaginal portion of the cervix uteri. Their frequency and importance. Adamantinomata. Basal-cell carcinomata. Their relatively benign character. Distribution, peculiar morphology. Relation to nævi. Other tumor assigned to this group. Analogous tumors of intestine and appendix.

General Characters.—The carcinomata or cancers are tumors composed essentially of epithelium, although they, like other tumors, are supported or surrounded by a vascular stroma, which they exact from the neighboring tissue. They are quite analogous to the papillomata and adenomata except in the fact that their epithelial cells are possessed of the enormous vigor of growth, which breaks through every barrier, and enables them to grow into new colonies when they are transported by the lymph- and blood-streams and lodged in distant organs. It is this character of malignancy which marks them out from other epithelial tumors, and even in the earliest stages gives them an anatomical form different from that of the benign growths. It is not possible with the means now at our command to distinguish with certainty a cell of the epithelium which has this exaggerated power of growth from a cell of the epithelium of a benign tumor or even a normal cell. But it is quite possible to distinguish these cells by their behavior, not only in the distribution of the tumor throughout the body, but in the minuter relations which, in microscopical section, the epithelial cells are seen to bear to the surrounding tissues. It is true that the cells themselves are usually different from normal cells, and in some cases extremely different. No doubt, in time we shall have a reliable morphological criterion by which we may say definitely that an isolated cell is a cancer-cell or a normal cell, but at present no such criterion exists, and we rely upon the arrangement of the cells and their relation, in their growth, to the surrounding tissues, because there are many instances in which the individual tumor cells look so precisely like the normal cells.

Practically the same distribution and architectural plan found in the papillomata and adenomata is repeated in distorted fashion in the carcinomata. We may, therefore, expect to find a great variety of cancerous tumors; nevertheless, by divergence from the original form, epithelial cells from the most widely different sources often approach a common nondescript type so that the tumors which they produce finally resemble each other.

We may distinguish the following groups of carcinomata:

1. *Squamous or Flat Cell Cancers.*—These arise in the skin, œsophagus, etc., or wherever there is stratified epithelium, and are commonly known as epitheliomata.

2. *Basal-cell Cancers.*—These arise chiefly in the skin, but analogous tumors are found elsewhere. They are relatively non-malignant and are the basis of the so-called *rodent ulcers.*

3. *Cylindrical-cell Cancers.*—These are analogous to the polyps or polypoid adenomata of mucosæ which have glands lined with columnar epithelium. They retain the tendency to form gland-like structures lined with cylindrical epithelium and are hence called *adenocarcinomata.*

4. *Cancers Derived from Acinous Glands.*—These are analogous to the solid adenomata and are the commonest cancers, since they include the cancers of the breast. In them the epithelium usually grows in solid strands. No very appropriate name has been given them and none is in common use. They are gland-cell cancers so non-committal in appearance as not to suggest a definite morphologically descriptive name. The term carcinoma simplex which was at one time applied to them is misleading and useless since they are in no sense more simple than the others. Of the various metamorphoses of these tumors which change their consistence or give them peculiar characters, almost constant enough to stamp some of them as another type of carcinoma, we shall speak later. The most striking of these is the formation of a gelatinous or colloid material either in the cells themselves, in cystic spaces lined by columnar cells, or in the stroma. Such *colloid cancers* fall readily enough into the different groups already given, but on account of this common peculiarity it might be tempting to class them together as a distinct type.

FLAT OR SQUAMOUS CELL CARCINOMATA

There is extraordinary similarity among these tumors from whatever point in stratified epithelium they arise. Those which spring from the skin show as a rule a greater tendency to keratinization than those derived from such epithelium as that of the œsophagus, but this is not invariably so and does not constitute a reliable distinction between the two.

Epitheliomata of the lip (Fig. 526) begin in persons of rather advanced age, most commonly in men, in the form of a slight scaly roughness with little or no underlying induration. After some slight traumatism which may cause the place to bleed, a crust forms, but there is no healing, and if it is pulled off, an ulcer is left upon which another crust forms. By this time thickening of the skin in that area is palpable. The growth of this thickened area proceeds until there is a considerable mass, which extends quite far into the substance of the lip. Usually there is repeated uncovering of a superficial ulceration, which quickly becomes overlaid with a dry crust, but it sometimes happens that this destruction of the surface is very slight indeed. On the other hand, the ulceration may go very deep and cause great distortion of the lip, hollowing out a great cavity which exposes the teeth. A firm nodule may be felt by this time in the position of the submental lymph-gland, and there may even be similar firm masses replacing the cervical lymph-glands. If operative extirpation of the primary tumor, together with the glands which may be involved, be delayed beyond the early stages, death follows after long delay, from the development of metastases in more distant organs, among which the liver is most prominent. As a rule, however, in all such neglected cancers which are allowed to metastasize, death is actually the immediate result of lobular pneumonia or other similar terminal infection.

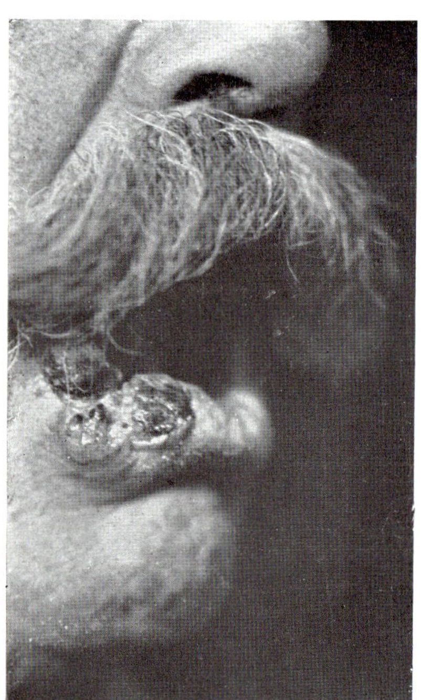

Fig. 526.—Epithelioma of lip with beginning ulceration.

When cut through, the tumor and its metastatic growths appear as grayish, translucent masses of tissue closely flecked with opaque yellow spots. These become more conspicuous as the tumor grows older and are scarcely to be found in the perfectly fresh margins where growth is proceeding. Slight pressure will express little masses or cylinders from the cut surface, and these are found to be composed of necrotic and keratinized cells.

Microscopical study of a section through an epithelioma of the skin (Fig. 527) reveals the existence of a mass of growing strands of epithelium which extend far down into the thickened dermis and subcutaneous tissue. These are solid columns of epithelial cells which frequently anastomose with one another and branch. They are several cells broad or may expand into much wider or bulbous masses in which there is evident a tendency to a concentric arrangement of the cells, which become more and more keratinized toward the centre. Sometimes these concentric horny masses are relatively large, and are often spoken of as cancroid pearls, cancroid being an old name for this type of epithelioma. All the stages in keratinization are seen plainly in passing from the outer layer of cells which lies next the connective tissue in toward the centre of such a pearl. The cells become thickly studded with black staining droplets of eleidin, which in turn fade as the nucleus and cell-body shrink into the horny scale of the innermost layers. The most extraordinary enlargement and deformities of the epithelial cells appear in such areas and all semblance of the regularity with which the process goes on in the normal skin may be lost.

The margin of the tumor is usually continuous with the normal skin—occasionally there is a break between the epithelial masses of the tumor and the edge of the normal epidermis, as though the tumor had burst up through the skin. When the two are continuous, there is not a perfectly abrupt transition, for the epidermis becomes thickened and sends down some rather irregular prolongations just before it joins the tumor. Even then it is quite possible that the epithelium of the tumor has healed to the epidermis after having burst up through it. It is not believed that the epidermis is converted into tumor tissue as the tumor spreads, but that all tumor epithelium arises from that which first began to grow. Therefore, the epidermis must

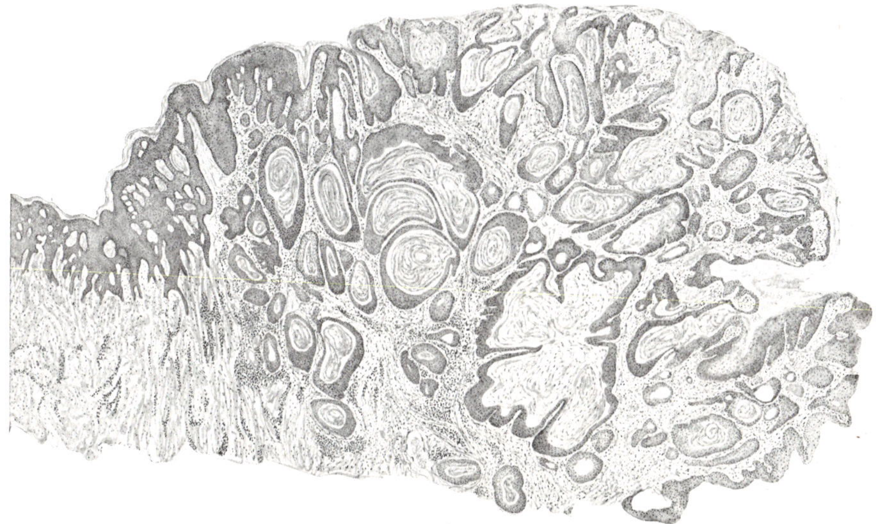

Fig. 527.—Epithelioma of penis showing atypical hyperplasia of adjacent epithelium and downgrowth of the tumor-cell strands.

be pushed aside or burst through in order to allow the tumor to grow. In the first case it might retain its continuity with the tumor throughout; in the second there must be a secondary healing together.

The stroma runs everywhere among the strands of cells, carrying blood-vessels. It is new tissue, of course, different in arrangement from the surrounding dermis and subcutaneous tissue, but in itself there is nothing peculiar to be seen. It has no recognizable tumor character, but is rather thickly infiltrated with polynuclears and especially mononuclear leucocytes or lymphocytes. It is encroached upon by the epithelial cells at every point, and if we follow the coarse strands downward, we find that at their termination they frequently narrow themselves to single rows of cells or even isolated groups of cells with advancing prolongations which are obviously insinuating themselves into crevices of the tissue (Fig. 528). In this way they invade not only the stroma, whose formation they have enforced, but also the deeper connective tissue and muscle. Any crevice or intercellular space is seized upon for their invasion, and they are by no means limited to the endothelium-lined lymphatic channels, although they also enter these. At the surface, where ulceration has taken place, the epi-

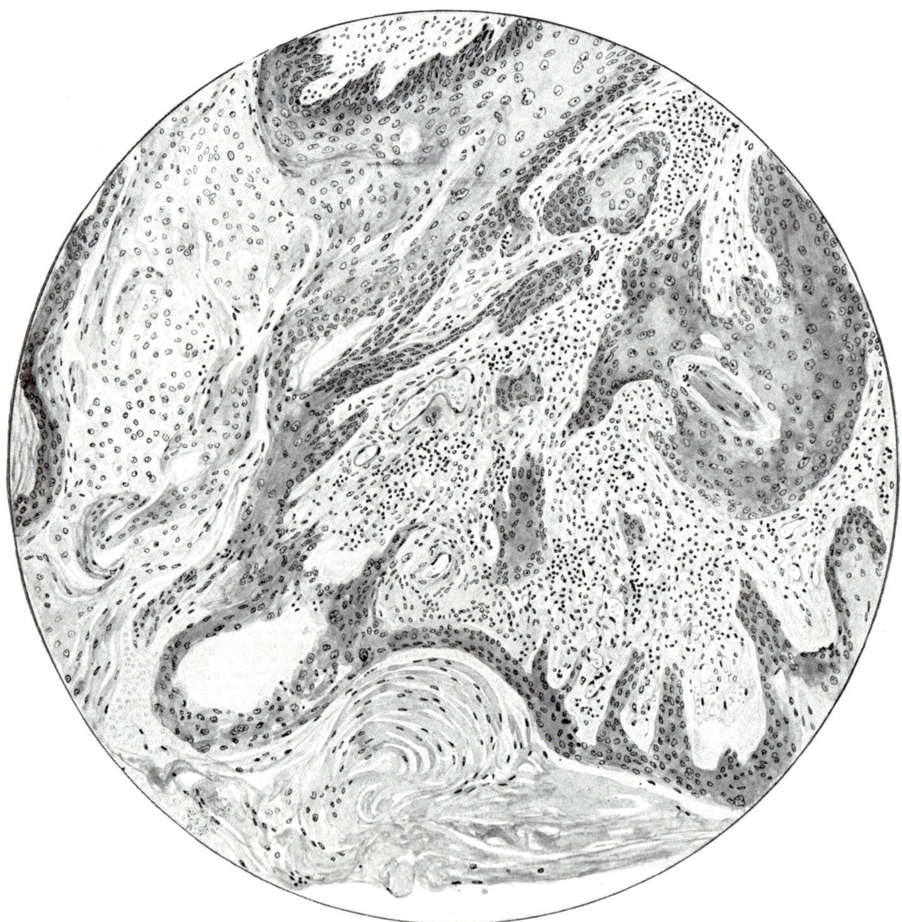

Fig. 528.—Portion from tumor (Fig. 527) more highly magnified, showing extensive keratinization, invasive growth of epithelium, and inflammatory reaction.

thelial strands are interrupted, and their broken ends exposed in the base of the ulcer or covered by an ordinary granulation tissue. Where the strands are intact, there may be excessively thick layers of keratinized or horny cells. In the deeper strands, too, instead of compact pearls, there are often found cavities lined with keratinized cells and filled with a soft débris of desquamated scales (Fig. 527).

The living cells of these strands are obviously unlike the cells of the normal epidermis in many respects, although since other conditions may produce similar morphological alterations, it is not possible to recognize them by these abnormalities as definitely cancerous cells. They are usually rather enlarged and polygonal, or irregular in outline, and are irregularly arranged with regard to one another. Their protoplasm takes a rather deep pink stain with eosin in many cases, and their nuclei seem especially rich in chromatin and consequently deep stained. There may be two or more nuclei in a single cell and the mitotic figures which are abundant may be irregular or multipolar. The cell strands are often invaded by leucocytes, and fragments of these cells may even be found embedded within the cancer cells. Other cell inclusions of various forms occur, and have been studied with great care, because it was thought that they might be parasites causing the growth of the tumor. These must be discussed later.

The most important point for consideration, however, is the relation of the tumor-cells to the adjacent tissue. They are not definitely and smoothly bounded by a line of demarcation from the connective tissue. Instead, it is constantly to be observed that the cells grow out irregularly at any point in the course of the strand, and push their way into that tissue in a way totally foreign to the normal epidermis. This process, which, as we have said, is most striking along the advancing margin of the tumor where it encroaches upon the underlying tissue, is the visible sign of the malignancy of growth which gives the tumor its peculiar character.

It has been said that the tumor-cells sometimes push their way into the lymph-channels, and it is probable that in doing this they are aided by a certain degree of amœboid activity, which they have been shown to possess in tissue cultures (Hanes and Lambert). In those channels they are swept along with the stream whenever they break loose, and lodge in the next lymph-gland, which acts as a sieve. There, instead of disintegrating and being devoured by phagocytes as other cells would be, they are often able to establish themselves in the lymph-sinus and grow rapidly, filling up all the sinuses between the lymph-cords and beneath the capsule of the gland with a solid injection of epithelial cells, or else spreading from the sinus in which they lodge to produce a nodule of tumor tissue which extends radially to occupy a large part of the gland. In this process the epithelium at once causes the formation of a new vascular stroma for its cells at the expense of the gland, and in its growth separates and destroys the normal tissue of the gland which it replaces. The structure of this new nodule is finally in every respect similar to that of the original tumor and all the processes of keratinization and other changes described for that situation are repeated here. This is true, too, for further metastases even when the renewed transportation of cells from the first metastasis gives rise to secondary or tertiary colonies in distant organs.

Epitheliomata may occur in many situations in the skin, although it seems that places at which two types of epithelium come together are rather predisposed to the development of these tumors. The lip, the edges of the nostrils, the eyelid, the penis and vulva, the margin of the anus are places where they most frequently occur. In the margins of old varicose ulcers they may develop, apparently stimulated or possibly even caused to grow by the long-continued irritation to which the skin in exposed in a site where it is continually endeavoring to grow and being as constantly frustrated.

Epitheliomata are by no means limited to the skin, but occur very frequently in mucosæ which are covered with stratified epithelium.

Thus such tumors may originate at almost any point in the interior of the mouth. Although they sometimes occur in the check or gums, epitheliomata of the tongue are far more common. They may occupy any situation from the tip to the extreme base of the tongue, and grow in such a

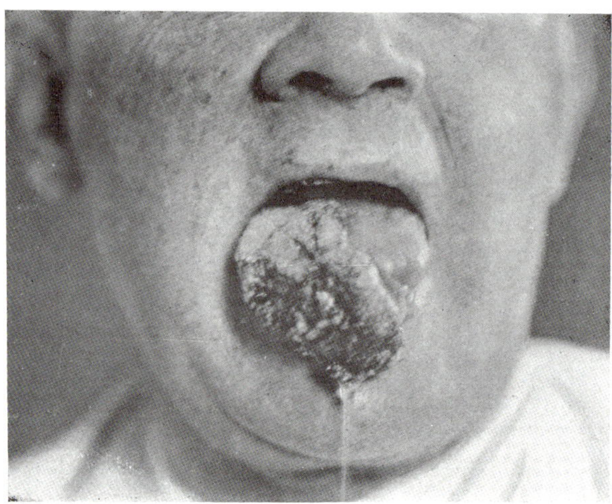

Fig. 529.—Epithelioma of tongue with ragged ulceration.

way as to form a dense mass extending far into its substance and becoming deeply ulcerated (Fig. 529). There is little or no keratinization, and the superficial layers readily become macerated. Metastases may appear in the regional lymph-glands and internal organs. In one case in which we found a great solid mass embedded in the root of the tongue, with only slight superficial ulceration, there were enormous nodular masses in the cervical lymph-glands throughout the whole chain, and other nodules in the liver. In another case in which the deeply ulcerated tumor had extended so as to approach the internal carotid artery, it finally eroded that vessel some weeks after a partial extirpation of the tumor tissue. A formidable hæmorrhage was stopped by ligature of the artery, but the man died ten days later. There were no metastases, but there was a large abscess in the cerebral hemisphere of that side. This case is cited merely as an example of the unexpected sequelæ which may complicate the course of a tumor of this kind, developed in the immediate neighborhood of important structures.

Epitheliomata may develop from the surface epithelium or crypts of the tonsils, and are often particularly destructive. Laryngologists meet with similar tumors involving the vocal cords, the arytenoid folds, or the epiglottis. They are quickly ulcerated, and lay bare the cartilages of the larynx after having destroyed the soft tissues. One case has already been mentioned in which a tumor assumed the form of a papilloma, although spreading over the arytenoid folds and epiglottis on both sides and extending to the pillars of the fauces. In most cases, however, the tumors are not elevated, but appear as flattened, rough thickenings of the tissue, soon hollowed out into ragged ulcers.

Tumors of the trachea and large bronchi are rare, and not ordinarily of the type of flat-cell epithelioma, as is natural from the fact that those canals are lined with cylindrical ciliated epithelium. Nevertheless in the substance of the lung tumors, which are definitely squamous, epitheliomata do arise from the branches of the bronchi. We have recently observed a whole series of these tumors of the lung, among which there were several instances in which a great cavity in the upper part of the lung was found on incision to be lined with opaque, yellowish-white, friable, crumbling tissue. In some of these the bronchus could be traced directly into the cavity, its walls becoming thickened by a great new-growth of the mucosa, which became continuous with the margins of the lining of the cavity. Microscopical sections show in these cases that most of the tumor is made up of strands of atypical stratified epithelium showing all the characters of those seen in the cutaneous cancers. The cells are held together by very distinct intercellular bridges (prickle cells) and undergo keratinization. In the bronchus one may trace the transition of cylindrical into squamous epithelium. It is perhaps an example of metaplasia which converts one kind of epithelium into another, although it is conceivable that some other explanation, depending rather upon embryonic displacement of cells destined to become squamous epithelium, might be offered instead. Dr. Adler has reviewed these tumors of the lung, and in his book it may be learned that there are many other types in which cylindrical cells play the important rôle. There are also some derived from the flattened alveolar epithelium, although their cells scarcely retain that form.

To return to the digestive tract, epitheliomata are common in the *œsophagus*, where they occur at almost any level, but most frequently opposite the cricoid cartilage, the bifurcation of the bronchi, and at the cardiac orifice of the stomach. Whether the explanations given for these traditional sites are satisfactory, must be left to the future to determine. It has been thought that the œsophageal mucosa at these points is irritated by passing food, since a certain projection into the lumen is caused by the firm structures which touch the outside.

The epitheliomata are usually broad, flattened masses which nearly encircle the œsophagus, and, by encroaching upon its lumen, obstruct it greatly. The starvation caused by this obstruction hastens the decline in health of the affected person. We have been repeatedly struck by the fact that the tumor may not extend all the way around the wall of the œsophagus, but leaves intact a narrow band of normal mucosa which joins the unaffected mucosa above and below the tumor. On section, the cut surface of the tumor is quite like that of other epitheliomata, except that it is perhaps less closely flecked with necroses. Nevertheless, ulceration does occur rapidly and at the same time the tumor extends through the muscular and connective-tissue coats. Usually adhesions of dense fibrous tissue form between the diseased œsophagus and neighboring structures, so that further growth of the tumor extends through the adhesions into those organs. Thus a main bronchus or the trachea may be invaded and perforated so that there is formed a definite fistula between the bronchus and œsophagus. In that case bronchopneumonia rapidly follows the leakage of œsophageal contents into the bronchus. The lung may be invaded directly, or an opening be formed into the pleural cavity. In rare cases the aorta or inferior vena cava are eroded and death may follow from hæmorrhage. Occasionally the tumor recedes in its growth and undergoes a partial healing, with the formation of scar tissue which contracts about the œsophagus, forming a narrow stricture. Metastases are found in the periœsophageal lymph-glands, in the lungs, in the liver, or in other more distant situations. I saw a case in which the tumor had invaded a pulmonary vein, producing infarcts in the kidneys and intestines and emboli surrounded by hæmorrhages in the liver and meninges. Another projected in the form of nodules into the lumen of the trachea, while there were secondary nodular growths in the parietal pleura. Microscopically these tumors, like those of the skin, grow in the form of solid branching strands of cells which readily invade the muscularis. They are rather less regular in form, and in the character of their nuclei, than the cells of the skin cancers and do not become keratinized. Nevertheless, the same concentric arrangements may be found with flattening and degeneration of the central cells.

The tumors of the *gall-bladder* are usually of the cylindrical cell type, but they may sometimes, as in the case of the lung, show themselves to be composed of squamous epithelium, a character which is maintained in all the metastatic nodules.

In the *urinary bladder* there appear papillomatous tumors which have already been described, and these, as it was then said, are probably from the beginning malignant in character and merely impose themselves for a time as benign growths. At the bases of the tassel-like papillomatous growths the thick stratified epithelium is found to invade the underlying tissue in the form of solid strands (Fig. 530). Usually after a time ulceration may destroy most of the papillomatous growth, leaving only a ragged area in the bladder-wall lined by rough masses of growing epithelium.

Another type of carcinoma of the bladder does occur, however, in which the wall is infiltrated and invaded widely without having lodged at any time a papillomatous growth. I saw one case, however, in which there were many small polypoid tumors scattered over the bladder-wall and concentrated

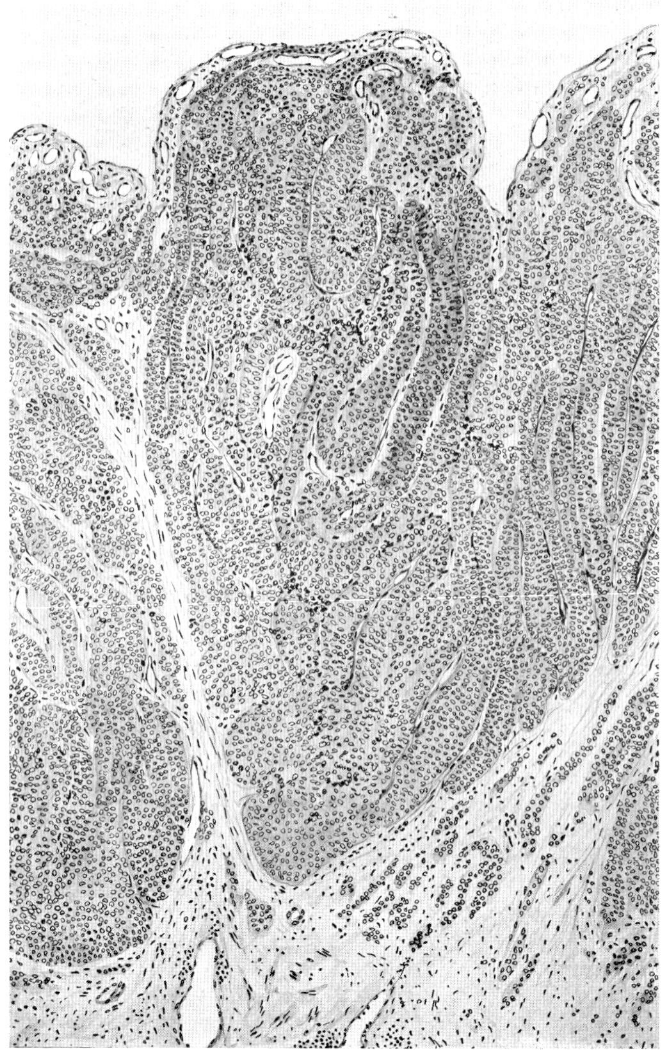

Fig. 530.—Papillomatous tumor of bladder, showing invasive growth of some strands of epithelial cells.

especially about one ureteral orifice. That ureter was greatly dilated and was lined with similar tiny papillomata which extended up into the pelvis of the kidney. It was difficult to be sure whether the primary growth was in the ureter or bladder. Single carcinomatous nodules sometimes occur in the *ureter*, causing its great obstruction, and giving rise to metastases in neighboring lymph-glands. In these one finds very delicate narrow strands of epithelial cells which no longer resemble closely the large cells of the typical epitheliomata.

The epitheliomata of the *cervix uteri* and adjacent vaginal wall are perhaps the most important of all, on account of their extreme frequency, their malignancy and rapid growth, and their fatal effects.

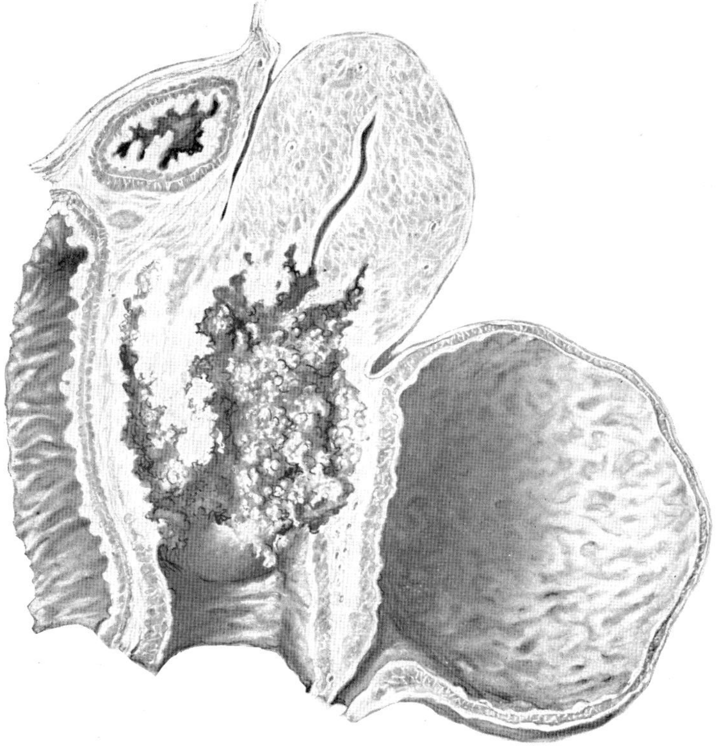

Fig. 531.—Epithelioma of vaginal portion of cervix uteri, invading uterine and vaginal wall. There is great ulceration, which approaches bladder and rectum without actually perforating them.

Another type of carcinoma of the uterus derived from the tubular glands of the body of the organ, and maintaining the character of an adenocarcinoma, will be described later, but it is of much less importance, since it is relatively rare and by no means so malignant.

These tumors (Fig. 531) develop in the portio vaginalis of the cervix uteri, near the line of transition of the stratified epithelium into the cylindrical mucosa, and appear at first as rough erosions with a surface which bleeds easily and is almost papillary in form. Growing into the substance of the cervix the tumor may surround the external os with a dense ring of friable epithelium. The further growth is usually accompanied by ulceration, which hollows out a funnel-shaped or irregular aperture. A longitudinal section of the uterus at this stage shows that much of the cervical wall is occupied by a gray, solid tissue with numerous opaque flecks of white. The growth stops abruptly above and gives place to the ordinary mucosa which lines the cavity of the uterus. Extension outside on the vaginal portion of the cervix and over the vault of the vagina is common, and later more of the vagina may be involved in the

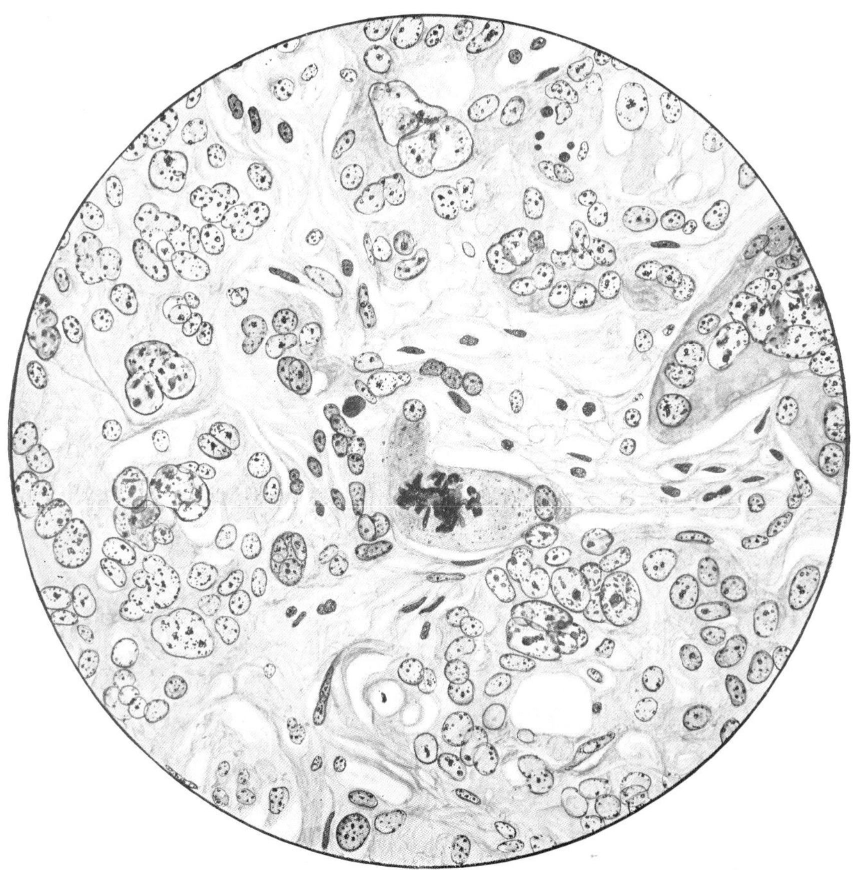

Fig. 532.—Epithelioma of cervix uteri with many multinucleated cells. In the centre there is an epithelial cell showing multipolar mitosis.

continuous growth. Metastases to the inguinal lymph-glands and later to those of the retroperitoneal region may occur at this stage, and there may even be nodules in the liver or lungs. The further growth of the tumor extends into the parametrium, forward into the wall of the bladder, and backward to involve the wall of the rectum. Ulceration takes place rapidly, and it is not uncommon to find a great, ragged perforation between the vagina and bladder or between vagina and rectum. I have seen one case in which, from such ulceration, bladder, uterus, and rectum all opened in common into a great ragged cavity. Infection of the bladder and ureters is sure to follow, and death may be immediately due to an ascending suppurative nephritis. The tumor is composed of thick, irregular strands of stratified epithelium, which is not keratinized, but in which the most extreme irregularities in the form of the cells may be observed. In one such case (Fig. 532) there were cells of all sizes, even including huge proto-

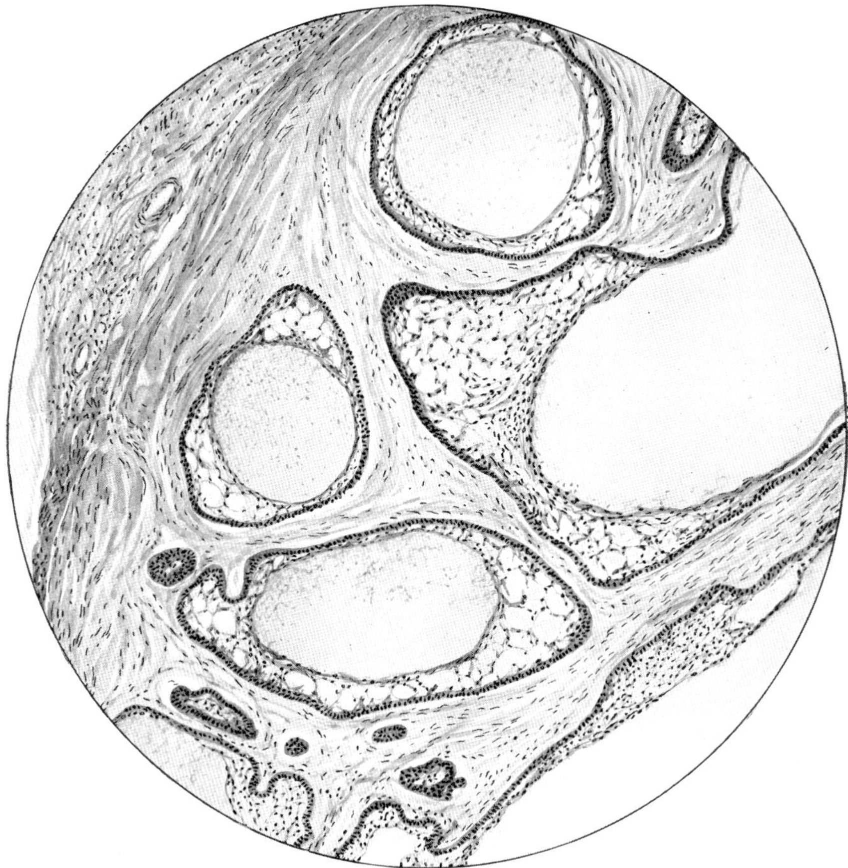

Fig. 533.—Adamantinoma. Each mass of cells presents a central cavity filled with fluid.

plasmic masses containing as many as 12 nuclei irregularly placed throughout the cell-body. Multipolar mitotic figures in which several centrosomes and achromatic spindles could be seen in relation to a very much branched arrangement of chromosomes gave the explanation of the formation of these multinucleated cells. Other tumors of this type are less atypical and merely present irregularly branching cords of cells, which ramify and spread freely in any direction to invade the uterine muscle. Necroses are frequent in such tissue, involving the broader bands of epithelial cells. The stroma which is formed in association with them is much infiltrated with wandering cells, and it may happen that, at the surface of the tumor, only those epithelial cells which are immediately around the blood-vessels remain alive and project as papillary remnants.

The remote metastases which may be in the peritoneum or omentum, in the liver, kidneys, etc., as well as in the regional lymph-glands, often reach a considerable size, although in the cases which I have seen they have been relatively small. They maintain the type of tumor tissue seen in the original growth.

Tumors which belong in this general class are the cancers of aniline workers, of chimney-sweeps, of betel chewers, and of those in whom x-ray burns have long persisted. It will be more useful to describe them in connection with the general discussion of carcinoma and other tumors.

Adamantine Epitheliomata or Adamantinomata.—These are rare tumors which develop in the substance of the jaw bone at the base of the tooth, and push their way out, displacing the tooth and causing the wasting away of the bone until they emerge as nodular, hard masses which may reach the size of a grape-fruit. The tumors, which are usually quite small, are derived, according to the general opinion, from the enamel organ, which is an epithelial structure at the base of the tooth concerned in the formation of enamel. Malassez regards them as derived from certain paradental remnants of epithelium, but the evidence for the other origin seems stronger.

The tumors are really benign, and should perhaps be considered in another place, but their morphology is much like that of an epithelioma. The strands of epithelium are broad and anastomose irregularly (Fig. 533). They are hollowed out centrally into cavities which are seen to be due to the gradual separation of the cells and the accumulation of fluid. The cells ramify somewhat, and are connected by very distinct intercellular bridges. The most peripheral cells abutting on the connective tissue are almost cylindrical in form. A characteristic appearance is produced by this arrangement, and it is very easy to recognize these tumors. The stroma is dense and fibrous and sometimes contains bone.

LITERATURE

Skin.—Janeway: Ztschr. f. Krebsforschung, 1910, viii, 403.
Dittrick: Amer. Jour. Med. Sci., 1905, cxxx, 277.
Penis.—Patterson: Univ. Penna. Med. Bull., 1901, xiv, 157
Œsophagus.—Sakata: Mitth. a. d. Grenzgeb. d. Med. u. Chir., 1903, xi, 634
Cummins: Proc. Path. Soc. Phila., 1908, xi, 44.
Tongue.—Küttner: Beiträge z. kl. Chir., 1898, xxi, 732.

BASAL-CELL CARCINOMATA

Krompecher has pointed out the fact that many of the tumors which grow in the skin and are distinctly derived from the epithelium are quite different in structure from the epitheliomata just described and quite as different in their biological characters. These comprise, in addition to many flattened irregular nodular masses, the so-called *rodent ulcers*, which have been long known to differ from the ordinary epitheliomata in that they are relatively benign and rarely show any tendency to metastasize rapidly. Krompecher regards these tumors as growths derived from the lowermost or basal layers of the epidermis, for which reason they show no tendency to keratinization or to pearl formation. Indeed, he is willing to ascribe certain tumors to the cylindrical or Malpighian layer, others to the rete layer with cuboidal cells, and the highly malignant epitheliomata to the more superficial or spiny layer. This seems open to question, and it is conceivable that, while the more innocent basal-cell cancers may, in truth, be derived from these lower layers, the malignant epitheliomata may represent a different biological alteration of any or all cells of the epidermis, so that their malignancy is not merely the effect of their being derived from a somewhat more differentiated layer of the same cells.

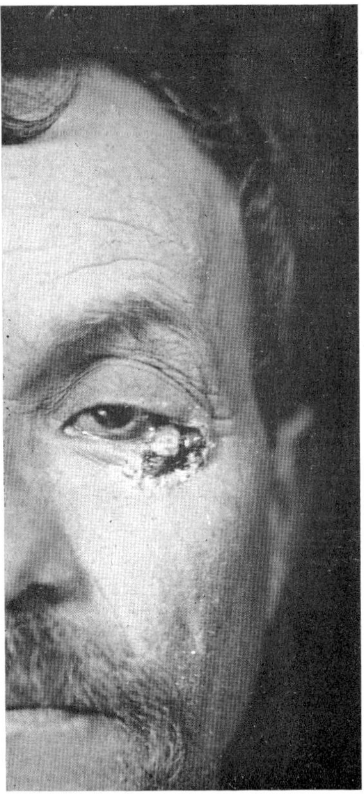

Fig. 534.—Basal-cell epithelioma or rodent ulcer of eyelid.

The basal-cell cancers appear most frequently on the face, being especially common in the upper part, about the forehead, the cheek, the nose, and the eyelids (Fig. 534). They are also to be found on the back or abdomen, or in any other region of the body, and it is to be observed that they do not, like the ordinary epitheliomata, arise at the margins of the skin and mucosæ, where complexities in development occur. Krompecher gives diagrams which show how they grow from the lower layers of the epidermis, forming masses of solid strands or complicated formations of ramified epithelial structures in which the cells maintain themselves in single layers. In these cases the superficial layer of the epithelium persists as a smooth sheet of cells, although occasionally it may dip down into the middle of each downgrowth of the basal epithelium.

On section through such tumors (Fig. 535) one is impressed with the fact that, in spite of the complexity of the downward-growing strands, all reach to about the same level. Further, it is seen that they are very sharply outlined against the stroma, and show little inclination to strew their cells into the irregular crevices of that tissue. Doubtless this morphological character is an expression of their benign type of growth. The cells are rather small and compact, with deeply staining nuclei and relatively scant protoplasm, which also takes a rather dark stain. There is little or

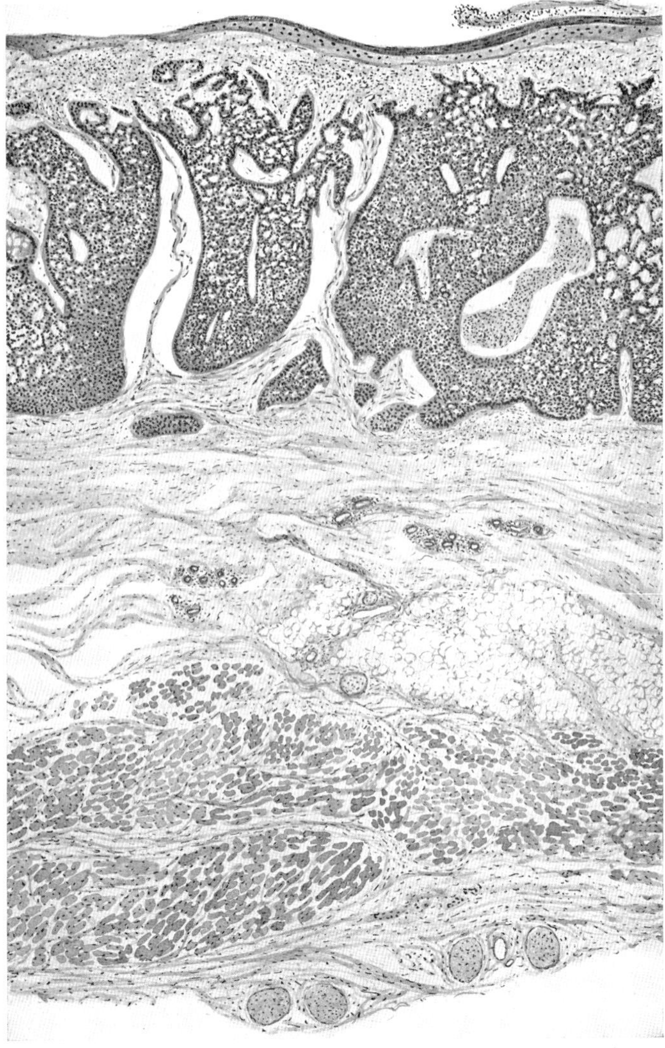

Fig. 535.—Basal-cell epithelioma of the skin, showing peculiar limitation of the downward growth.

nothing of the pallor, the inflation, and the nuclear irregularities which are so common in the cells of the more malignant epitheliomata. Necrosis and ulceration are common, however, and the tumors often present themselves as advancing ragged ulcers with only a very thin wall of tumor tissue.

Upon extirpation they show little tendency to recur, but even if there is a recurrence, it is exceptional to find metastases in the regional lymph-glands or in more distant situations.

It will at once suggest itself that the nævi bear a considerable resemblance to these tumors, since they are composed of small, compact cells which lie in the papillæ of the dermis, and are thought by many to be connected with the epidermis itself. It is true that, in nævi, the connection of the tumor-cells with the epithelium must be sought for with great care, and is frequently impossible to find, that the cells have little histological resemblance to those of the epithelium, and that their great tendency to form or to accumulate pigment in their cell-body marks them out from those of the basal-cell tumors. There the tumor-cell strands are everywhere continuous with the epithelium; they are not merely isolated groups of cells lying in the substance of the dermal papillæ: they are typically epithelial in character, and seldom contain any considerable amount of pigment. They have little energy of growth and rarely metastasize, while from the nævi there arise the most malignant of all tumors, the melanomata, which may scatter secondary nodules in thousands in every tissue of the body. Nevertheless, there are many who regard the nævi and the melanomata as tumors of epithelial origin, and Krompecher identifies them more or less closely with his basal-cell cancers. A decision is difficult in this matter, but it seems that there are sufficient points of distinction to warrant the separation of the groups. The tumors which were referred to as endotheliomata of the skin by Braun, and accepted as such by Borst, were mentioned under that heading as possibly derived from the endothelium of the lymphatic channels in the skin. Such tumors are, of course, possible, but Krompecher unhesitatingly ascribes to them an epithelial origin and regards them as identical with the basal-cell cancers. This identification he pushes further to include many tumors which arise from the glands which open upon surfaces of stratified epithelium, and even the mixed tumors of the salivary glands, which we shall discuss in the next chapter. He finds that basal-cell cancers arise in ovarian tumors, in dermoid cysts, and other tumors of teratomatous origin. This can, of course, never be contradicted, since those tumors have such manifold possibilities. Finally, the neuroepitheliomata of the retina described by Flexner, and later by Wintersteiner, seem to him to have similar characters.

In the intestine Krompecher describes no analogues of his tumors, but other authors have found curious carcinomata in the small intestine, usually occurring as multiple nodules, and often causing stricture or obstruction of the gut, which, from their structure and behavior, seem to resemble these basal-cell cancers quite closely. They are dense masses which partly encircle the intestine at several points or project into its interior and are made up of rather narrow strands of cells in a dense stroma. One tumor apparently of this character occurring in our material was called an intestinal adenoma. It is composed of broad, solid strands of cells, with rounded nuclei, which extend down into the muscularis and show little connection with the overlying mucosa. The cells of these strands are frequently collected into rosettes or interlacing strands, which look like tubules, but are solid and closely packed together to form the main masses. In this respect they remind one of the neuroepitheliomata. Similar tumors of relatively benign character are found in the appendix. There, too, the tumor tissue is composed of narrow, irregular, solid strands of small cells, in no place reproducing the crypts or glands of the appendix, as would be the case in an adenocarcinoma. Implantations in the peritoneum may occur, but metastases are rare.

In spite of the numerous papers which have appeared recently with regard to these tumors, it seems that there remains much to learn as to their relations.

LITERATURE

Krompecher: Ziegler's Beiträge, 1900, xxviii, 1. Der Basalzellenkrebs, Jena, 1903.
Bunting: Johns Hopkins Hosp. Bull., 1904, xv, 389.
Oberndorfer: Frankfurter Ztschr. f. Path., 1907, i, 426.
Burckhardt: *Ibid.*, 1912, xi, 219.
Dietrich: *Ibid.*, 1913, xiii, 390.

CHAPTER LII

CARCINOMATA (Continued)

Adenocarcinomata: General characters and distribution. Carcinomata of the stomach: polypoid, solid, and scirrhous forms. Their histology and mode of growth; metastasis. Colloid forms, their somewhat different mode of growth. Carcinomata of the gall-bladder and ducts; carcinomata of the pancreas, of the colon, of the prostate. Metastasis into bones from prostatic tumors. Adenocarcinomata of the uterus and of the ovary.

ADENOCARCINOMATA

From all mucosæ in which the epithelium is cylindrical in form, and from glands and ducts lined with cylindrical epithelium, there may be derived adenocarcinomata or cylindrical-celled cancers. These are malignant tumors which give rise to extensive metastases, often far larger than the primary growth. They maintain in irregular fashion the arrangement of tubular glands, transmitting this mode of growth to the primary metastases, but sometimes losing it in secondary metastases which arise from the transportation of cells from the primary ones. This modification of the architecture of tumors in secondary or tertiary metastases is not uncommon, and will be discussed later in a more general way.

While adenocarcinomata may thus appear in situations almost as numerous as those which form the point of origin of epitheliomata, there are certain sites which become important from the fact that they are so frequently the starting-point of these tumors—the stomach, the gall-bladder, and bile-ducts, the pancreas, the large intestine, the body of the uterus, and to a less extent the prostate and the bronchial mucosa. Of course, tumor tissue of this structure may also occur in teratomata, where there are abundant opportunities for its development. Except for the exaggerated energy of growth of their cells, they are quite comparable to the adenomata and polypoid glandular tumors.

Carcinomata of the Stomach.—The extreme prevalence of carcinomatous tumors of the stomach, their disabling effects, and fatal outcome cause them to occupy a very prominent place among tumors. There are many varieties, and many situations in the stomach may be occupied, so that the symptoms vary greatly. A cancer at the cardiac orifice, by obstructing the entrance of food into the stomach, may, like the epitheliomata of the œsophagus, result in starvation and extreme emaciation. A cancer in the fundus of the stomach or on any part of the wall away from the orifice may exist a long time without causing any symptoms, while such a tumor at the pylorus or encircling the pyloric ring is sure to cause stagnation of the gastric contents and dilatation of the stomach. Absorption of poisonous decomposition products must then occur, and the gastric juice loses its antiseptic qualities with the loss of its high content of hydrochloric acid, in place of which lactic acid often appears. Bacteria or moulds may thrive in considerable quantities in the accumulated material, particularly the large Oppler-Boas bacillus. Vomiting is frequent, and as a result of the drain of gastric juice or possibly of the absorption of toxic material, gastric tetany may appear just as it does when the pylorus is obstructed by the scar of an old ulcer.

The following types of cancer of the stomach are met with and are

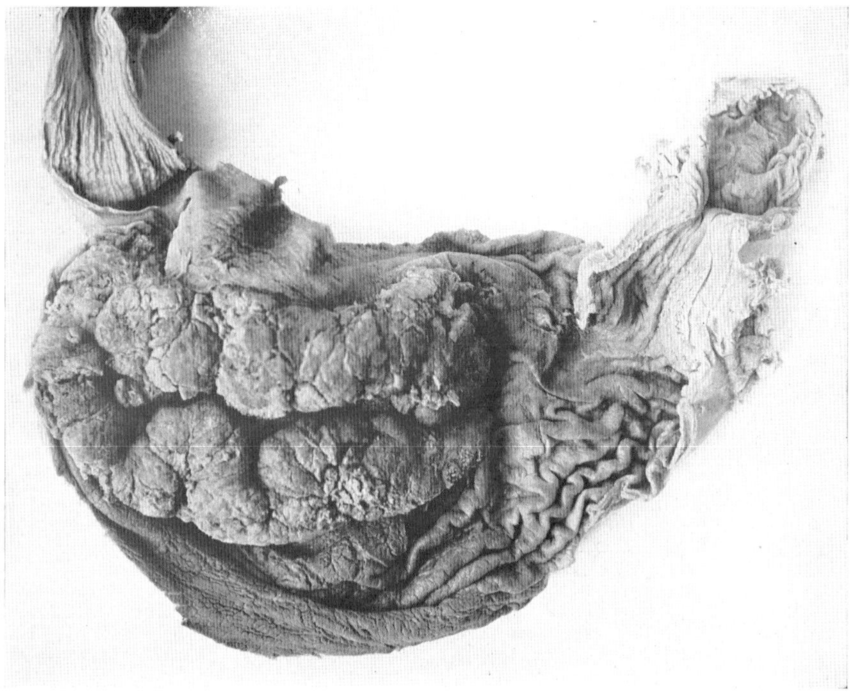

Fig. 536.—Large fungus-like carcinoma near fundus of stomach.

sufficiently different morphologically to fall into groups, although doubtless in principle they are alike.

Carcinomata about the cardiac orifice may be derived from the prolongation of the stratified epithelium of the œsophagus and may therefore have the anatomical characters of the epitheliomata. The others derived from the cylindrical epithelium usually maintain that type of cell, although in many instances in which fine strands of cells are found scattered through the musculature, the cylindrical character is lost.

Polypoid Carcinomata.—These occur anywhere on the stomach-wall and project into the lumen as broad, pedunculated, fungus-like masses, which are rather soft and easily torn or broken apart. In Fig. 536 there is shown an example of this type, in which the tumor is situated very near the cardiac orifice, and doubtless projected in front of it, without, however, causing any marked obstruction. Quite similar tumors are found near the pylorus. In this case there were no discoverable metastases, and it is my impression that these tumors do not form metastases so rapidly as do the other types. The normal mucosa passes upward to the overhanging edge and gives place to the most complex arrangement of gland-like structures lined with cylindrical epithelium. In places there appear to be papillomatous areas; in others through the whole depth of the tumor the tissue is made up of a delicate stroma, supporting wide and narrow ramifying tubular epithelial structures. There is surprisingly little downgrowth into the muscular wall in this case, but in others of the same type it is far reaching and destructive. Necrosis and sloughing of the exposed tumor is of almost regular occurrence.

Solid carcinomata of more sessile form are much denser than these fungating types. They, too, may grow anywhere in the stomach, but appear most frequently about the pylorus and the lesser curvature. Various stages may be found, from a beginning adenoma-like growth of small size to the huge, crater-like, excavated masses which occupy a great part of the wall of the stomach. I remember one such tumor as large as a child's head, composed of dense, elastic, yellowish-white tissue, which projected into the stomach and was hollowed out so that the cavity extended far into the liver, to which the outer surface of the stomach had become densely adherent. Ordinarily, such tumors are found as rounded or irregular ulcers with thick, elevated, rounded edges which can be felt to project a short distance beneath the adjacent mucosa (Fig. 537). One may pick up and move the mucosa almost as far upward on this ridge as its crest—beyond that, although the mucosa looks smooth and velvety for a short distance further, it is adherent and immovable. There follow a roughening and irregularity of the surface which then drops precipitously into the ulcer. On cutting through the margin of the tumor the transition of the normal mucosa into the greatly thickened epithelial mass of the tumor can be seen. Here as in the epitheliomata of the skin, the significance of this continuity may be questioned and it seems probable that in spite of the intermediate zone of modified mucosa, the unbroken epithelium may be maintained by repeated healing together. It is, however, possible that the normal mucosa is merely pushed back by the increase in size of the tumor. It does not seem probable that normal mucosa is converted into tumor as the growth advances.

It is rare to see a gastric carcinoma which is not ulcerated, although the tumor itself may be far larger than the area occupied by the ulceration. The cut surface reveals a white or grayish-white or yellowish tissue which interrupts the muscularis mucosæ, and passing through the submucosa, interrupts and penetrates the muscular coat of the stomach. At the margin the muscular coat may be traced for some distance into the tumor, and then it is found that the tumor has grown in thousands of fine strands between the fibres of the muscle, leaving it otherwise intact for a long time. In the subserous tissue it again becomes a solid mass. On the outer surface the site of the cancer is readily made out by the rigidity of the wall, and usually by the appearance of whitish, flattened nodules which cover the peritoneal surface. Dense adhesions to surrounding organs are very common, and the stomach is, in consequence, often kinked and distorted by being drawn up against the liver or pancreas. Metastatic nodules are usually found in the neighboring lymph-glands, which may be greatly

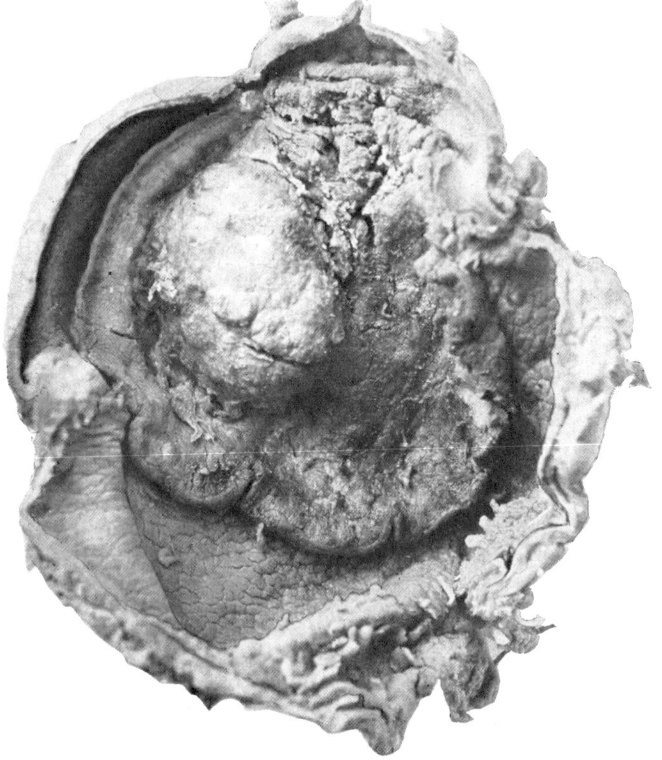

Fig. 537.—Carcinoma of stomach with ulceration and thickened, elevated margin.

enlarged. On section, they show a white tissue, usually with yellowish necrotic flecks in every way similar to that in the gastric wall. The omentum is studded thickly, in many cases, with minute nodules of the same tissue and is drawn up into a dense prismatic mass which lies transversely in the abdomen and can be felt through its wall. There may be more distant metastatic nodules in the peritoneum, but it is more common to find them rather limited to the region of the stomach. The occurrence of metastatic nodules in the liver is extremely frequent and these may reach a very great size and be very numerous. The most remarkable variation occurs in this respect, for while some large tumors show only a few small metastases, others of less extent are found to have given rise to enormous growths in the liver sufficient in number to occupy most of its substance. The occurrence of metastases in other situations will be referred to later.

It has long been thought that these tumors may develop in the edge of a round ulcer of the stomach, and there is much clinical and pathological evidence to support this view. The transformation of symptoms of long-standing gastric ulcer into those of a gastric carcinoma may not be very convincing, nor even the discovery of an ulceration in the middle of the tumor, with such induration of its base as to suggest the existence of a primary chronic gastric ulcer. But when the tumor develops on one side of a typical round ulcer, the conclusion is more difficult to escape. We

Fig. 538.—Dense carcinoma of stomach surrounding the whole pyloric region and narrowing the channel. There is diffuse infiltration of the whole thickness of the wall with the tumor-cells.

have seen two typical round ulcers of the stomach, in the margins of which carcinomatous growth of epithelium of unmistakable character was found, although in neither case had the tumor developed sufficiently to disturb the characteristic appearance of the ulcer.

Other solid gastric cancers grow as in Fig. 538, without such extensive ulceration and produce a great thickening of the mucosa and of the submucosa, infiltrating the muscle layer and the subserous tissue. Such a tumor does become ulcerated, but its earlier growth forms an extremely dense, resistant mass, which may completely surround the pyloric portion and render it quite rigid.

Occasionally there is found a peculiar thickening and induration of the whole stomach-wall, which causes it to shrink to a small size. There may be no prominent tumor nodule and little ulceration, but the mucosa is roughened and wrinkled, and not readily movable upon the underlying tissue. A section shows that the whole wall is infiltrated with a tumor in which the epithelial cells are relatively sparsely scattered in an abundant and dense stroma. This is the so-called diffuse *scirrhous carcinoma* of the stomach (Fig. 539).

Microscopically, various appearances are met with in these forms of more solid carcinomata. In most cases the normal mucosa, in approaching the tumor, becomes infiltrated with lymphocytes and other wandering cells, and its glands are lengthened and become tortuous, often with dilatation of the lowermost part. Nevertheless, they retain the smoothness of their

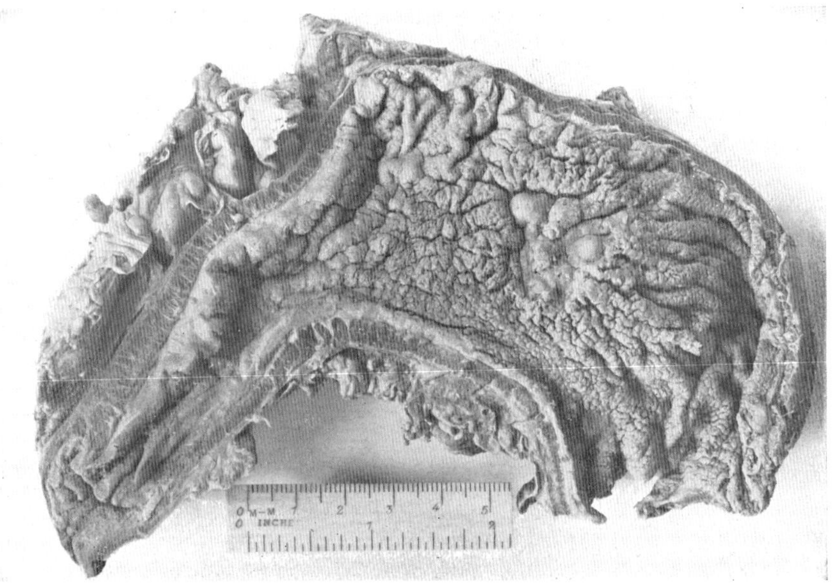

Fig. 539.—Scirrhous cancer with very slight ulceration occupying whole wall of stomach and causing its great contraction.

outline. Suddenly as the surface layer of the epithelium reaches the crest of the marginal ridge of the tumor, the whole arrangement changes and the cells themselves assume a different character (Fig. 540). The glands become exceedingly irregular, with numerous branches, or are greatly enlarged and partly or completely filled with epithelial cells. It is now very difficult to determine just how much of the epithelial mass belongs to each gland, for their identity as glands is lost, and instead there are ramifying cavities lined with several rows of cells among which are other cavities, or there are solid groups of cells. The cells lose their regular arrangement and to a great extent their uniform cylindrical shape. They no longer range themselves on a smooth basement membrane, but grow at will in any direction into the stroma. The sudden change from the moderately infiltrated and loose stroma of the mucosa, to the much denser stroma of the tumor which is thickly infiltrated with leucocytes, is very striking. Still, in other cases, the disarrangement of the glands in passing over from the mucosa into the tumor is by no means so great, and the whole tumor is

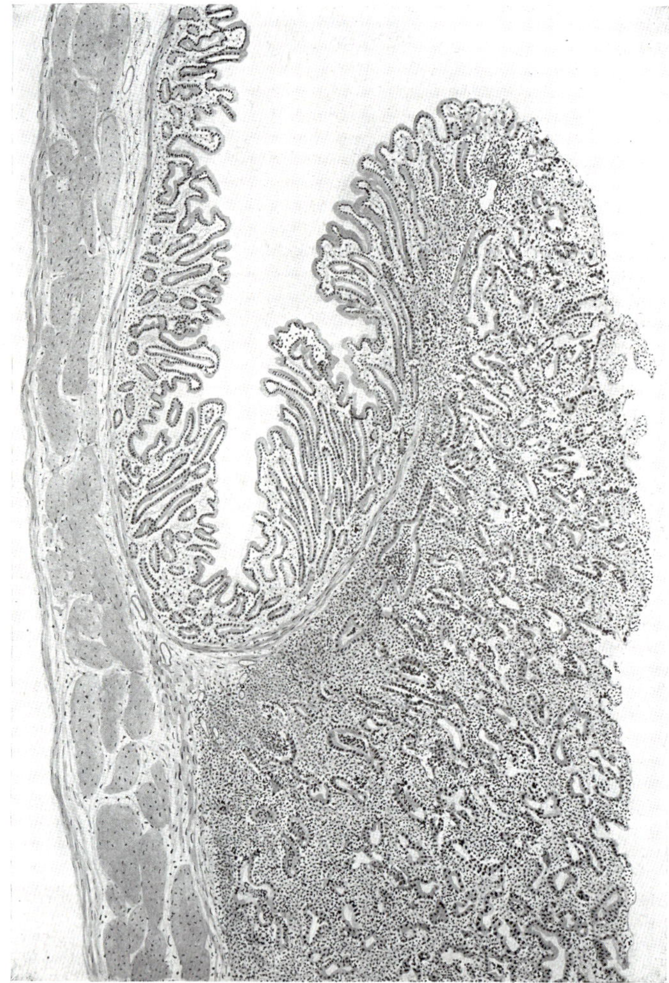

Fig. 540.—Carcinoma of stomach showing sudden transition of glands into the carcinomatous distortion.

found to be made up, even in its distant extensions through the muscle and into the subserous tissue, of long tubules which are coarse and deeply stained and variable in calibre, but which do not seem to fray out into the tissue, or to grow into more solid masses. At these extreme ends there is generally an indication of the invasive freedom of their cells. Usually, however, even in those in which the glandular or tubular arrangement is best preserved, there are parts of the tumor in which the tubules appear as solid strands with numerous spaces lined with cylindrical cells, which keep up the glandular appearance.

In the denser tumors, such as that shown in Fig. 538, it is common to find the glands of the mucosa, as one passes into the tumor, changing into extremely long narrow tubules which are lost in a dense and greatly thickened submucosa. Between these glands, the tissue is packed with

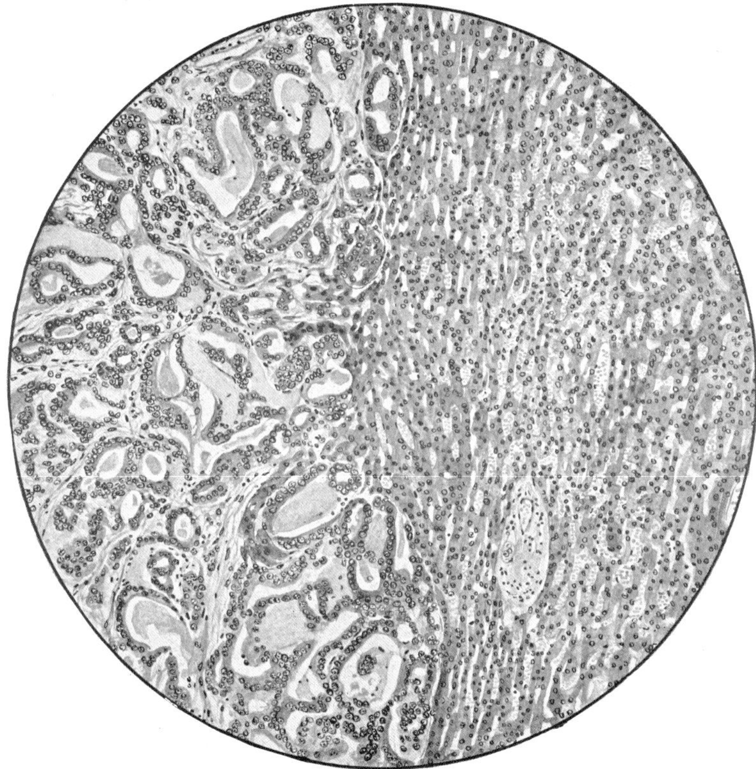

Fig. 541.—Margin of a secondary nodule in the liver derived from an adenocarcinoma of the stomach.

cells, many of which are clearly wandering cells, while great numbers are loose epithelial cells. It is difficult to trace the exact source of these cells, although they may sometimes be obviously derived from the lowermost ends of the glands. Deeper in the submucosa and far into the muscle they assemble themselves into more definite groups, which arrangement they retain wherever they are found. This is practically the character of the growth in the scirrhus cancers, in which very small solid groups of cells are set free from the ends of the glands, and grow into the submucosa. The extreme growth of connective tissue in response to this causes the mucosa, submucosa, and muscularis to become matted together into a leather-like mass, in which tumor-cell strands are sparsely scattered.

Occasionally there are observed several carcinomatous nodules projecting from the mucosa of the stomach, and the explanation is to be found in

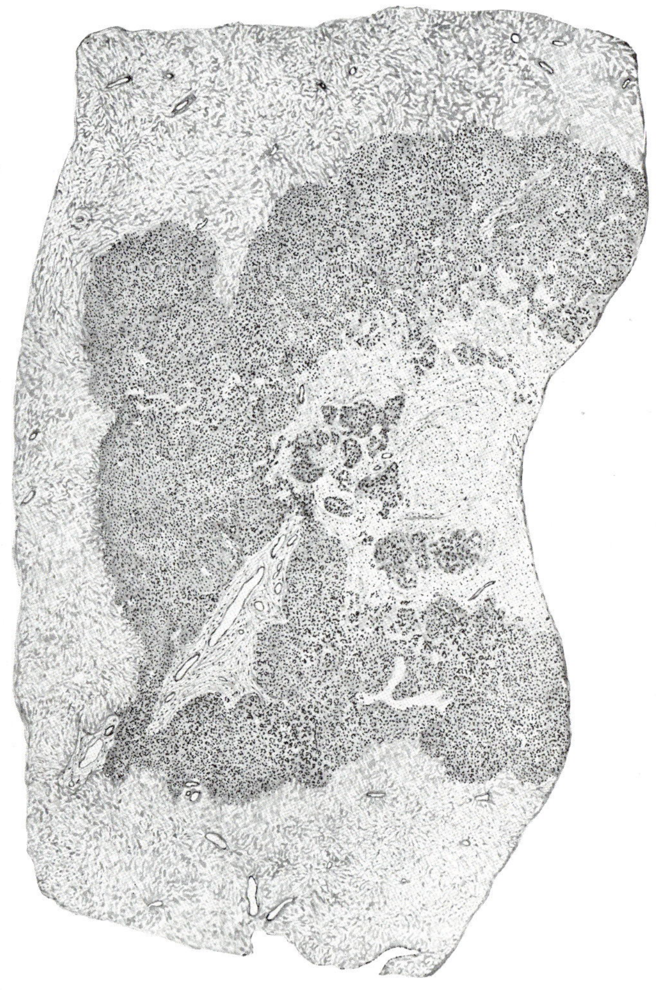

Fig. 542.—Metastatic cancerous nodule in the liver from a primary carcinoma of the stomach. The section shows the central necrosis and scarring of the tumor, with retraction and dell formation.

the fact that in these cases the network of lymphatic channels in the submucosa and in the subserous tissue is filled solidly with tumor-cells, which enter at the primary growth and grow along until they form a sort of injection of the whole network. The accessory nodules appear to be eruptions of tumor growth from those underlying lymphatics. This mode of growth was studied by Borrmann, whose illustrations correspond well with the condition found in several of our cases.

With regard to **metastasis** from the carcinomata of the stomach, a brief statement was made above. It is true that the adjacent lymph-nodes and the adjacent peritoneum are usually primarily involved, and also that numerous nodules are frequently formed in the liver (Fig. 541). These vary greatly in size and evidently in age, and while there are small,

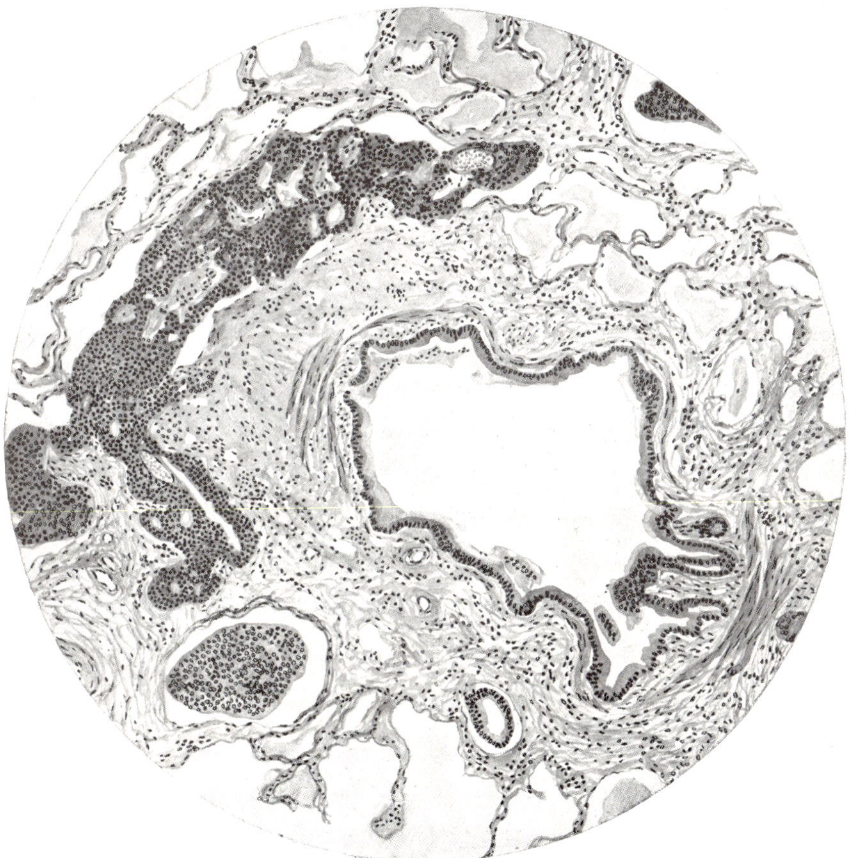

Fig. 543.—Invasion of lymphatics in the walls of a bronchus extending from pleural metastases.

translucent, grayish-white nodules of smooth, globular form, there are also very large masses of similar form, but showing the well-preserved tumor tissue only in their marginal portions. The whole central part of such nodules usually presents necroses, which may affect only small groups of cells here and there, so as to produce the familiar yellow flecks on a gray surface, or may be complete, so that nothing remains alive except the connective-tissue stroma. When the nodule lies at the surface of the liver, it at first presents a convex or flattened face, but with the liquefaction and absorption of this central necrotic part and the contraction of the stroma which remains behind, there comes a sinking of the centre. Every secondary cancer nodule of any age which projects from the surface of the liver shows this central depression, and on section the reason is plainly seen (Fig. 542). Doubtless insufficient blood supply is the cause of such necrosis. The nodules press upon the blood-vessels and bile-ducts and cause local areas of anæmia and chronic passive congestion, and also jaundice. The jaundice may be extreme, but it must be remembered that there are often opportunities for its production by the compression of the large bile-ducts outside the liver by the main tumor or by its intraperitoneal metastases.

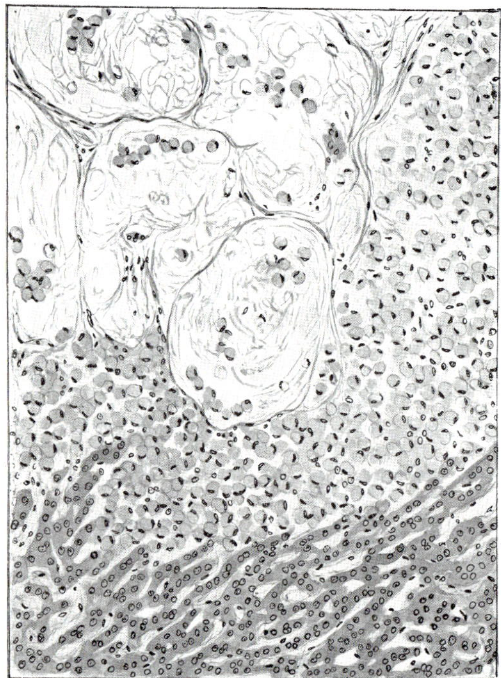

Fig. 544.—Colloid carcinoma of the stomach. Secondary nodule in the liver, showing the tumor-cells separated from one another, and each containing a globule of colloid.

The metastases are not confined to the abdominal organs, but are found in the pleural cavities on the costal pleura, or on the surface of the lung. There one observes peculiar minute, lenticular flecks of gray, translucent tissue, which look almost like tubercles. They are larger and flatter, however. On section, the lung is air containing, but is roughened by the projection of the interlobular septa, blood-vessels, and bronchi, all of which stand up a little from the cut surface as gray, translucent, rough ridges. This is due to the filling up of the lymphatics in the walls of vessels and bronchi and in the interlobular septa with an injection of epithelial cells (Fig. 543). Occasionally larger lymphatic trunks can be seen branching over the pleural surface, and made conspicuous by the grayish-white injection of tumor-cells. In other cases the secondary growths are in the form of button-like nodules on the pleura. In the lung itself the tumor may metastasize, with the formation of large, discrete nodules which push aside the tissue or, as in a case which we saw recently, with the production of a pneumonia-like process. Each alveolus over a large area of the lung was filled with tumor-cells, and since the alveolar walls and vessels were intact and undisturbed, the patch had almost exactly the appearance of a pneumonic consolidation.

Metastases in the brain, kidneys, spleen, and other organs occur, but are not especially common. Numerous metastases in the bones have been found, and I have seen one case in which these growths produced rarefaction with fractures of the bones.

Another form of carcinoma of the stomach which is peculiar in many of its characters is the *colloid cancer*. There are at least two types in which the accumulation of a gelatinous colloid material is found: one in which the glands or tubules of the tumor are made up of spaces in which the epithelial cells lie quite loose, are rounded or spherical, and contain each a large globule of clear fluid (Fig. 544); the other, in which the tubules are distended into cyst-like cavities lined with a single layer of cylindrical epithelium, and filled with glairy fluid (Fig. 545). The first of these appears as a diffuse thickening of the mucosa and of the whole wall of the stomach, with a gelatinous, yellowish, translucent tissue, which accumulates in soft nodules over the outer surface of the stomach and spreads quickly into adjacent glands and over the peritoneal surface. The second usually causes a far greater thick-

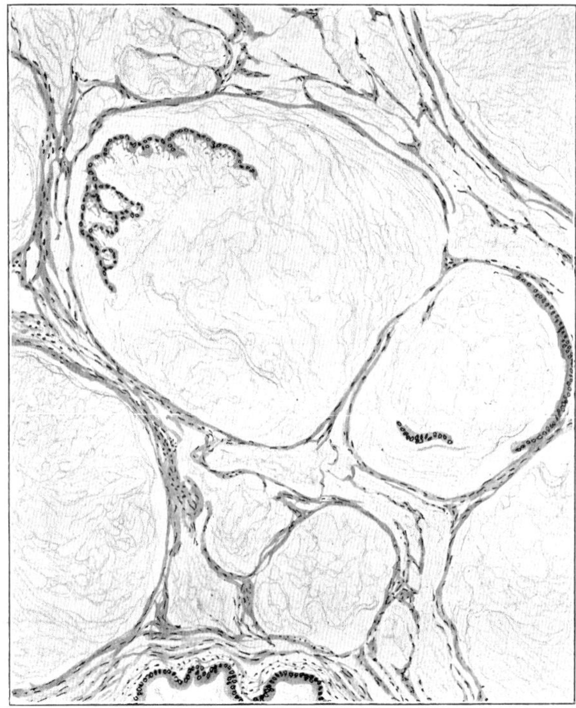

Fig. 545.—Colloid cancer of the stomach with large alveoli filled with colloid material and only partly lined with the remains of the epithelium.

ening of the stomach-wall, with a large ulcerated area in the mucosa and with great layers of new tissue on the outer surface (Fig. 546). The omentum is converted into a huge mass of friable gelatinous material, and the whole peritoneum may be lined with a thick layer of it. On cutting through any of this tissue the cavities filled with fluid are quite visible to the naked eye, so that this type was once called alveolar cancer. It has the appearance of sago pudding, and one may scrape off a tenacious glutinous fluid from the surface. In one case which I saw at autopsy all the abdominal organs and the parietal peritoneum were covered with a layer more than a centimetre in thickness, which was quite brittle, although fairly firm. It was so transparent that one could see the blood-vessels in its depth. Metastases, if they occur, have the same structure (Fig. 547), but while the tumor easily penetrates the stomach-wall and spreads implantations throughout the abdominal cavity, it is not strikingly capable of producing metastatic nodules in other organs.

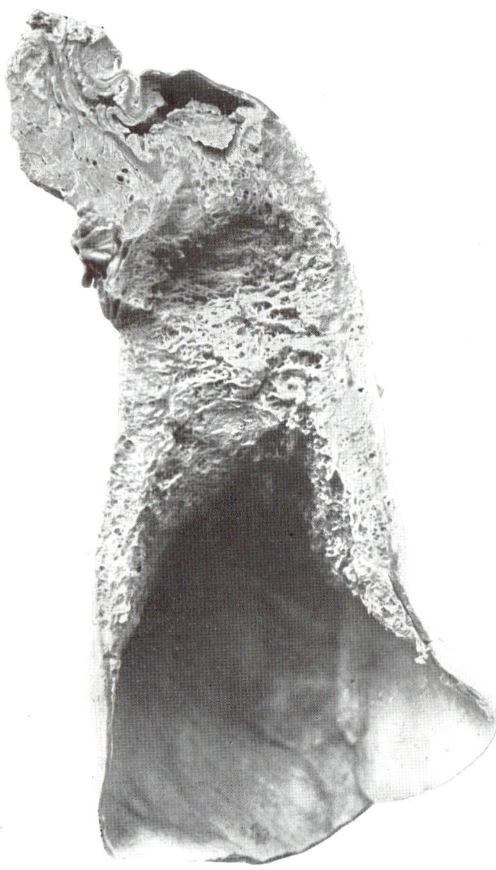

Fig. 546.—Colloid cancer of the stomach. There is great thickening of the stomach-wall, so that the pylorus is almost occluded. The colloid-filled alveoli of the tumor are visible to the naked eye.

Carcinomata of the Gall-bladder and Ducts.—These tumors may be described much more briefly since their general behavior resembles that of the adenocarcinomata of the stomach. It has been stated that epitheliomata may arise in the gall-bladder especially when there are incarcerated gall-stones there which have long caused irritation. One sees them sometimes accurately moulded round the gall-stones, and extending only so far as it lies in contact with the mucosa. Adenocarcinomata may spring from the mucosa of the gall-bladder even in the absence of inciting gall-stones, and usually metastasize quickly to the liver. As a rule, the primary tumor is

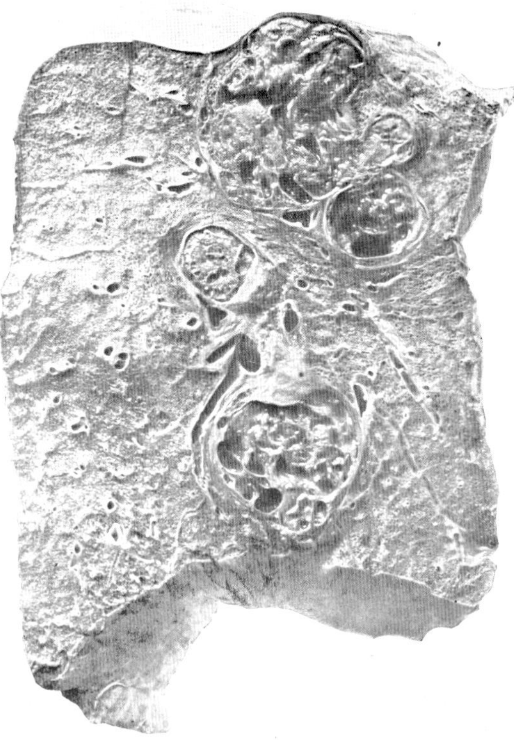

Fig. 547.—Secondary nodules in the lung from a colloid cancer of the stomach.

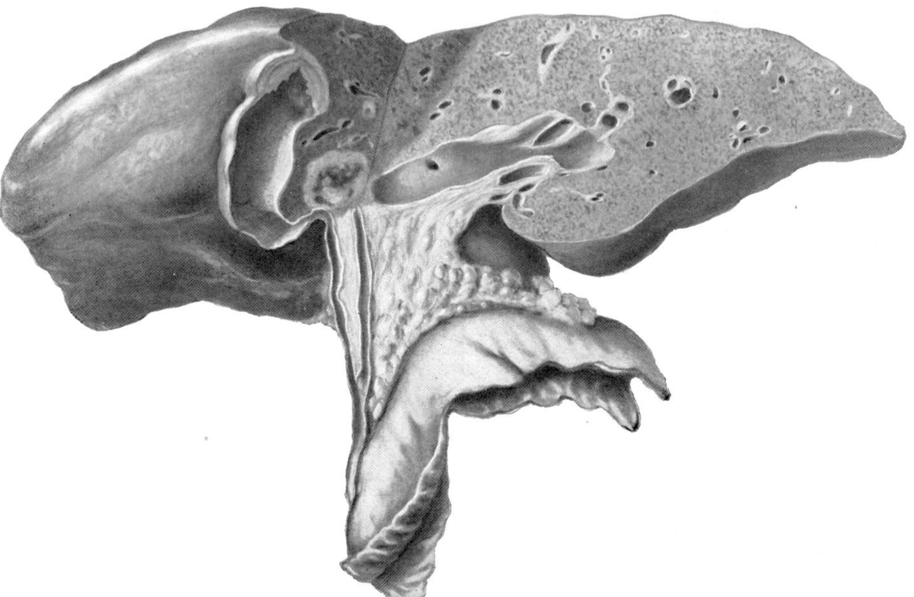

Fig. 548.—Adenocarcinoma of the fundus of the gall-bladder with metastases in the liver compressing and obstructing a large bile-duct and producing jaundice.

found to invade the liver in such a way that there is only a remnant of the gall-bladder wall which stretches over a large, ulcerated tumor mass embedded in the liver. Rupture of this into the peritoneum or into the adherent colon may occur. Metastases resemble those from the carcinoma of the stomach, and usually cause jaundice, occasionally, as in Fig. 548, by obstructing one of the larger ducts. Quite similar carcinomatous tumors may spring from the bile-ducts at any point, from the ampulla of Vater to the branches high in the liver. They often appear to be multiple in origin, although that is by no means certain. They almost invariably produce jaundice, which may be very deep. These tumors form a large proportion of the primary cancers of the liver and may grow to enormous masses in one or other lobe of the liver (Fig. 549).

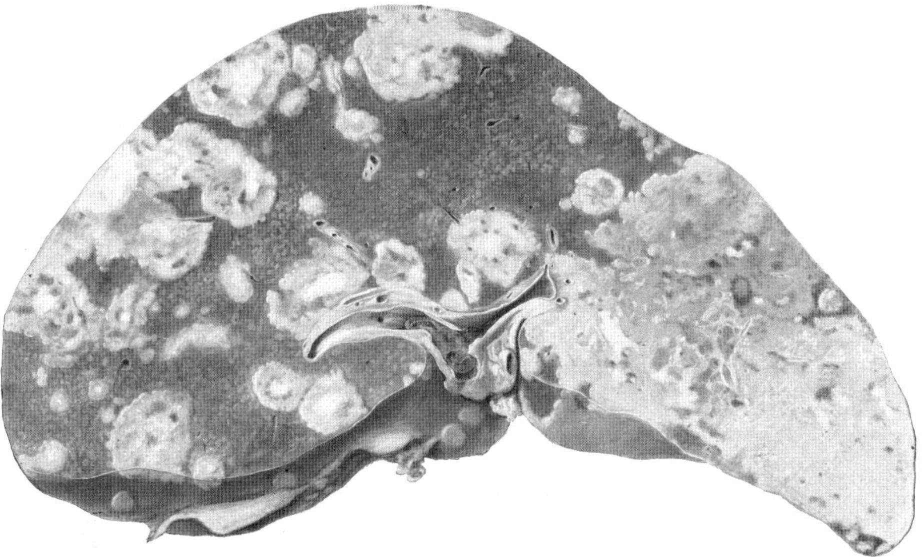

Fig. 549.—Primary carcinoma of liver springing from bile-ducts. Numerous secondary nodules in the liver.

Adenocarcinomata of the pancreas are most frequently situated in the head of the gland, near the duodenum, and form large, irregular masses invading and compressing the adjacent structures with various results. One or both of the pancreatic ducts may be compressed, and the pancreatic tissue drained by the obstructed duct becomes atrophic. The tumors have, as a rule, a complex tubular arrangement with high cylindrical epithelium. Metastases have the same distribution as in the carcinoma of the stomach.

Adenocarcinomata of the Intestine.—In the small intestine adenocarcinomata are quite uncommon if we except the multiple, relatively benign tumors which were described in connection with the basal-cell cancers. On the other hand, those of the *colon* are especially common, and therefore important. They may occur at the ileocæcal region (Fig. 550), or anywhere in the course of the colon or in the rectum. In nearly all cases the tumor springs up from the mucosa as a projecting mass which encroaches upon the lumen of the colon and usually encircles it. Great obstruction may be produced in this way, not only by the actual bulk of the mass, but more especially by the contraction of those tumors which, in their late stages, become extensively degenerated and scarred. In these cases the lumen of the intestine may be reduced to the diameter of a few millimetres, so that the contents stagnate above the obstruction, remain fluid, and escape continuously in small quantities. As stated in a previous chapter, muscular hypertrophy appears above the obstruction, often accompanied by ulceration of the mucosa.

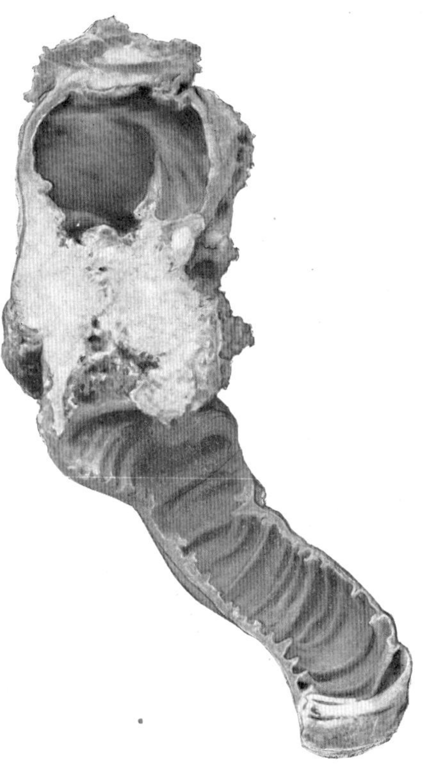

Fig. 550.—Adenocarcinoma at the ileocæcal valve causing almost complete obstruction.

The carcinomata of the colon are nearly always composed of irregular, tubular downgrowths of epithelium lined with high cylindrical cells (Fig. 551). In the deeper portions, these may, of course, become more atypical in appearance and more confused in their order, and groups of cells, with many cavities about which the palisade arrangement is held to, alternate with others in which the cavity is lined by several layers of cells (Fig. 552).

The intestinal wall is often penetrated by the growth, and extensive adhesions and excavations into adjacent organs occur. Regional metastases into neighboring lymph-glands are common, peritoneal implantations occur, and there are metastatic nodules in the liver in many cases, resembling closely those derived from tumors of the stomach. I recall one case in which there was a very small nodule of hard tumor tissue surrounding the colon and drawing it into an extremely narrow stricture. The whole mass was not more than 3 cm. in diameter, and yet there were many metastatic nodules in the liver, one of which reached the size of a man's head.

Carcinoma of the prostate is most commonly of the adenocarcinomatous type, although there are some cases in which the tumor-cells present themselves in broad, solid strands. The tumors are capable of penetrating into the bladder or into the rectum, with resulting ulceration and infection. Metastases are usually abundant in the lymph-glands of the pelvis and retroperitoneal tissue, in the liver, lungs, and other organs, but particularly in the *bones.* In two of our recent cases in which the primary growth was inconspicuous and microscopically showed the complex glandular arrangement of an adenocarcinoma, there were a few internal metastases, but on examining the skeleton, it was found that practically every bone was involved. The cancellous marrow of such bones as the vertebræ, sternum,

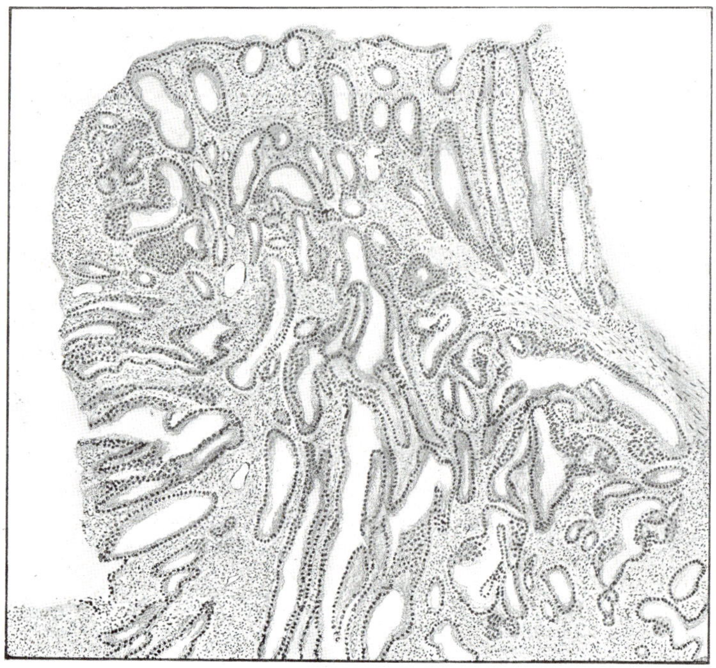

Fig. 551.—Margin of an adenocarcinoma of the rectum showing a transition from slightly modified mucosa to the tumor growth, which maintains a gland-like arrangement of the epithelium.

ribs, and clavicles was completely replaced by the tumor, which had stimulated an excessive new formation of bone, which was very dense and hard. In the long bones the marrow cavity was entirely filled with a yellowish, opaque, ivory-hard tissue, so that the bone seemed to be quite solid. It is so evident that much new bone is formed in such cases that these metastases are called osteoplastic. Microscopically it is found that every lamella of the cancellous bone is enormously thickened, and that the marrow spaces are correspondingly narrowed. All these spaces are filled with tumor tissue which completely excludes the marrow. The layer of osteoblasts is preserved in apposition to the bone, and it seems probable that the tumor exerts its osteoplastic effect by stimulating those cells to increased activity. Wide-spread necrosis, which involves a great part of such cancerous bone, seems to be of very frequent occurrence. The almost complete destruction of the bone-marrow leads to an extreme anæmia, and to efforts at blood formation in other organs, which have been referred to elsewhere in discussing osteosclerotic anæmia. The carcinomata of the prostate are well known for this peculiarity of metastasizing into the bones, a property which

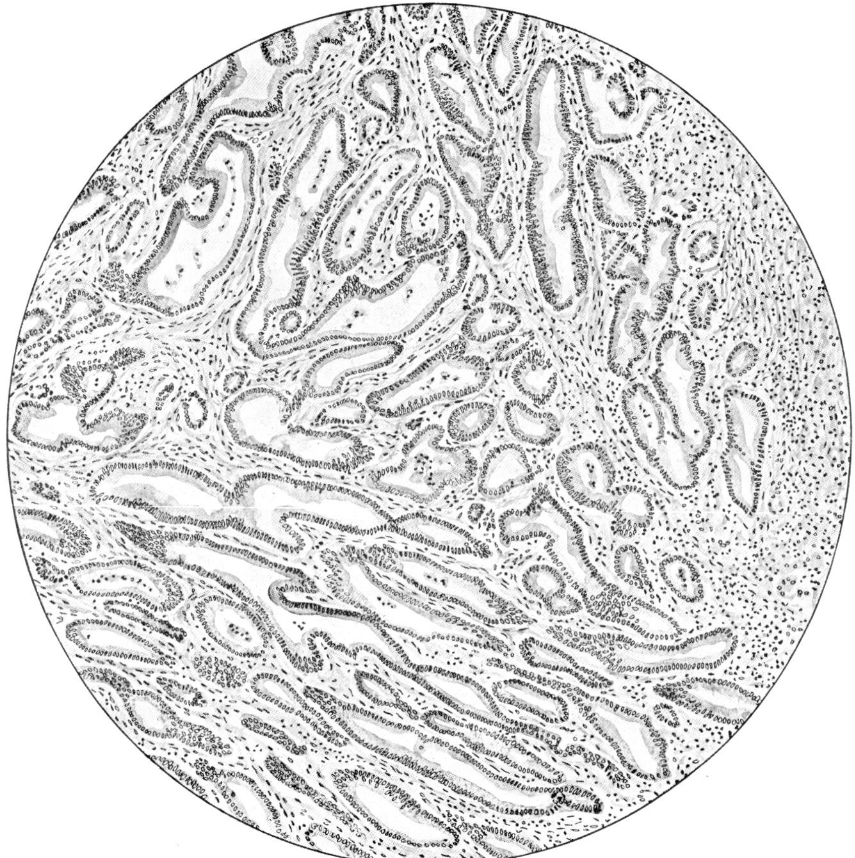

Fig. 552.—Adenocarcinoma of the rectum. Atypical gland-like growth.

is shared to some extent by the carcinomata of the breast, stomach, and thyroid.

Adenocarcinomata of the Uterus.—These tumors, already referred to in contrast with the epitheliomata of the cervix, are developed from the tubular glands of the fundus uteri or the more complex glands of the cervix. In some cases their growth seems associated with the previous existence of an adenoma of the uterus, but this is by no means a regular occurrence. Since they appear to grow rather slowly, many cases have been observed in which extirpation of the uterus was performed at a time when the carcinoma was still small (Fig. 553). In such a case the mucosa is found thickened and rough, with many papillary projections. The growth extends into the musculature, but for some time is fairly evenly outlined against it. Nevertheless, it is not long before the invasion of the musculature occurs by the downgrowth of some of the glandular elements which may be found deep in the uterine wall. Ulceration may occur, and the cavity of the uterus becomes enlarged by the excavation of the tumor in its wall. Even then the outer surface of the uterus may show no evidence of the presence of the tumor other than the enlargement.

Metastases are slow to form, and appear in the retroperitoneal lymph-glands. I have seen a few cases, however, in which the secondary growths

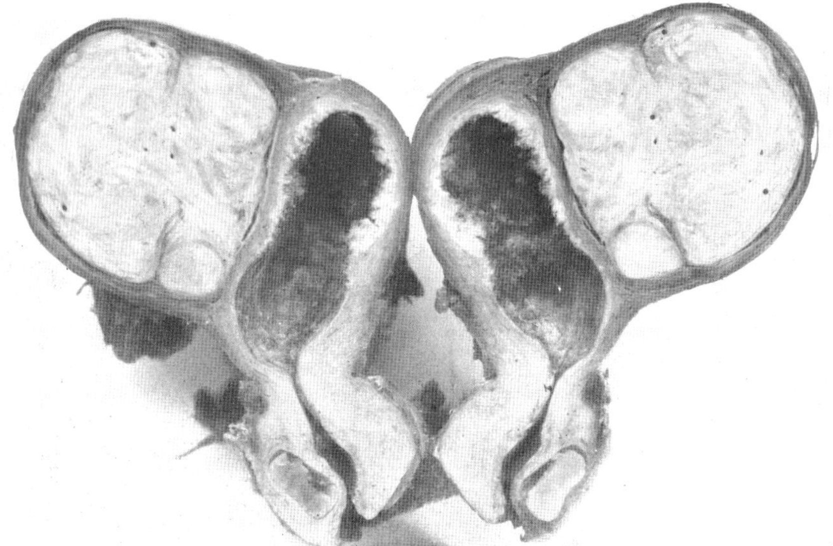

Fig. 553.—Adenocarcinoma of the uterus. The tumor is a mere ragged thickening of the mucosa at the fundus. There is a fibromyoma lodged in the substance of the uterine wall.

were very widely disseminated, involving the peritoneum, liver, and other organs. Microscopically, the tumor is made up of tubular epithelial growths resembling in all their complex modifications those already described for other adenocarcinomata, although seldom showing any such orderly columnar cells with globules of mucus as are usually found in the rectal carcinomata.

The tumor is to be sharply distinguished from the squamous cell epitheliomata of the cervix, not only through its histological characters, but through its original site, its mode and rate of growth, and its much slighter malignancy.

Adenocarcinomata in general, similar in character to these, develop in many other places, and mention may be made of the kidney, breast, ovary, and thyroid as points of origin.

Adenocarcinomata of the ovary are quite common, and assume many puzzling forms, sometimes appearing as solid tumors which may occupy both ovaries, and metastasizing widely into distant organs. The gland-like spaces in such a tumor are lined with cells which are very unlike the epithelial cells derived from the skin or mucous surfaces (Fig. 554). In other cases the tumor develops in a cystadenoma of the ovary and causes great

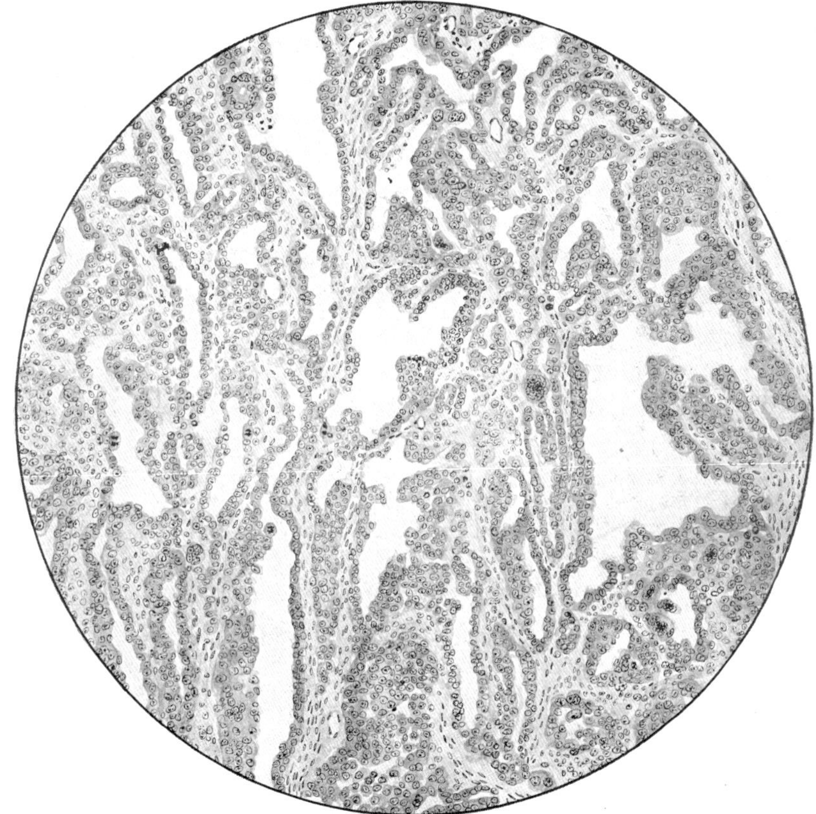

Fig. 554.—Adenocarcinoma of ovary. There are numerous mitoses in the epithelial cells and many multinucleated cells.

thickening of the wall of one or more of the cysts. These tumors are frequently colloid cancers, and even in their distant metastases maintain the power of forming blue-staining colloid material (Fig. 555). In one which we studied recently there was a huge cyst with thick walls which, on section, showed a sticky, gelatinous material in the substance of the walls. Metastases in the abdominal and retroperitoneal lymph-glands showed the tumor to be composed of small cysts lined with cylindrical epithelium, which was frequently thrown up into folds. The content of these cysts was, however, not like the colloid material mentioned above, but resembled the pseudomucinous content of some adenocystomata.

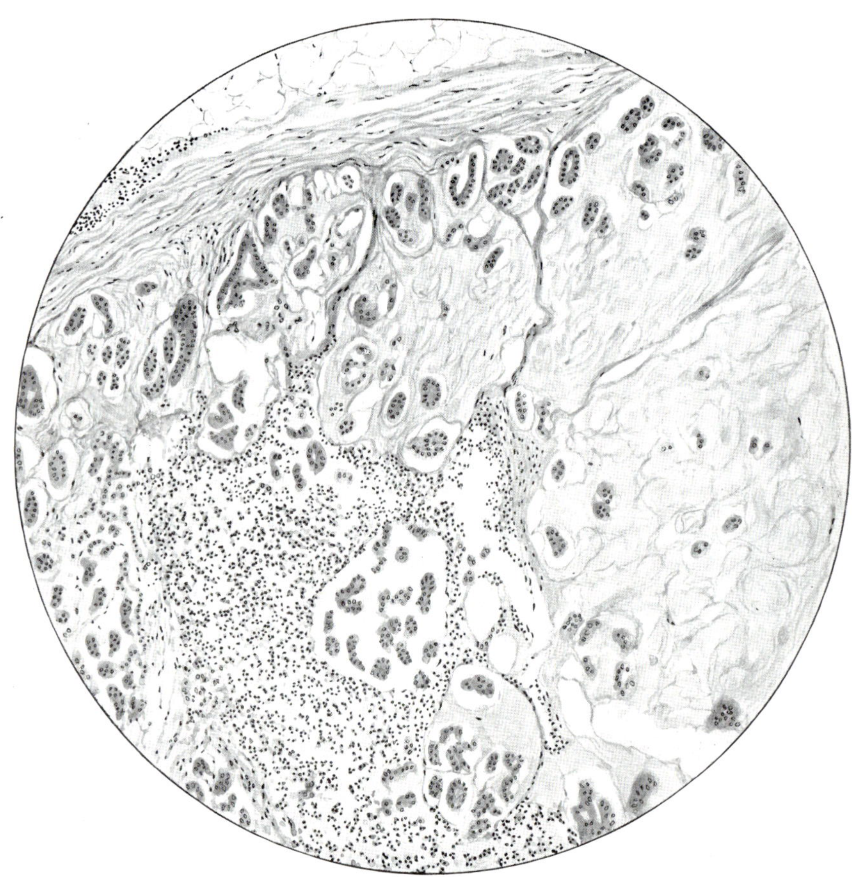

Fig. 555.—Metastasis in lymph-gland from colloid carcinoma of ovary. Many of the epithelial cells are seen to be isolated in the colloid material.

LITERATURE

Stomach.—Ebstein: "Magenkrebs," Volkmann's kl. Vorträge, 1875, No. 87.
Versé: Arbeiten a. d. Path. Inst. Leipzig, 1908, i, Heft 5.
Borrmann: Mitth. a. d. Grenzgeb. d. Med. u. Chir., 1901, Suppl. Bd. 1.
Lewis: Surg., Gyn. & Obst., 1914, xix, 757 (Pseudomyxoma).
Hauser: Cylinder-Epithel Karzinom des Magens, Jena, 1890.
Gall-bladder.—Laspeyres: Centralbl. f. d. Grenzgeb. d. Med. u. Chir., 1901, iv, 10.
Zenker: Deut. Arch. f. kl. Med., 1889, xliv, 159.
Miodowski: Virch. Arch., 1902, clxix, 117.
Uterus.—Hitschmann: Arch. f. Gynäkologie, 1903, lxix, 629.
Lehman: *Ibid.*, 1900, lxii, 439.
Cullen: Carcinoma of the Uterus, New York, 1900.
Pancreas.—Hulst: Virch. Arch., 1905, clxxx, 288.
Rectum.—Harrison Cripps: Cancer of the Rectum, London, 1890.

CHAPTER LIII

CARCINOMATA (Continued)

Gland-cell carcinomata: Carcinomata of the breast; epitheliomata, tumors derived from the acini (general form, mode of extension and metastasis, histology, relation to adenomata and chronic cystic mastitis, scirrhous forms), tumors derived from the ducts, colloid cancers. Carcinomata of the ovary; carcinomata of the thyroid; primary carcinomata of the liver with cirrhosis. Chorionic epitheliomata: Histogenesis of chorionic epithelium, its normal invasive growth. Hydatidiform mole. Chorionic epithelioma; gross appearance, metastasis, histology, and histogenesis; relation to corpus luteum.

GLAND-CELL CARCINOMATA

There is probably little justification for the separation of cancers derived from the cuboidal or polygonal cells of the solid glands from the others which have just been described, because the division is made on a purely morphological basis, and it is not always easy to distinguish them in this way. Nevertheless, the division is convenient and serves a useful purpose. Such tumors are extremely common in the breast. Elsewhere they play a less important part, but they are to be found in the thyroid, the liver, the ovary, the prostate, and in some other glands.

The Carcinomata of the Breast.—There is so great a variety of these tumors that the experience of any one is scarcely sufficient to cover the whole range. They are extremely common and fatal in their effects, and the efforts to extirpate them completely and to understand and frustrate their extension affords much work to the surgeon. It is difficult to make any short classification, but there may be distinguished the following:

1. Tumors of stratified epithelium, which are either those beginning in an eczema-like alteration of the nipple and adjacent skin (Paget's disease), or those which arise in the substance of the breast and are, nevertheless, composed of squamous epithelium (Troell and others).

2. Tumors Derived From the Cells of the Acini of the Gland.—These may be made up of abundant ramifying masses of cuboidal cells, with relatively little stroma, so that great, soft, cellular masses are formed (medullary cancer), or there may be less abundant cell strands, with a relatively greater amount of stroma, so that the tumor area is composed of firm whitish tissue, or finally the epithelial structures may be greatly reduced, so that only small groups and thin strands of cells are formed, embedded in a dense, scar-like mass of fibrous tissue (scirrhous cancer).

3. Tumors Derived From the Ducts and Their Branches.—These approach more nearly the cylindrical cell cancer, and are often in the form of tumor masses made up largely of tubular epithelial structures. There are usually cysts associated with this form, and these may have a thick lining of several layers of cells. There is another type, of relatively benign character, in which every section shows canals or cavities lined with a thick layer of many rows of irregular cells. These have been called adenocarcinomata by Halsted, and have also been referred to as comedo cancers, on account of the fact that cells can be squeezed out like the material from a comedo or blackhead in the skin.

4. **Colloid Tumors.**—Tumors derived from the epithelium of the acini, but presenting an extraordinary colloid or gelatinous metamorphosis of the stroma. Of these, the most important by far are those derived from the cells of the acini. The tumor appears as a hard nodule in the substance of the breast, and later often forms adhesions with the skin or causes a retraction of the nipple (Fig. 556). The extension to the skin may be followed by ulceration. A wealth of detail has been worked out by surgeons as to the mode of growth and extension, and an interesting series of observations has been made upon the more local spread by Handley. As described by Borrmann, in the spread of carcinoma of the stomach through the stomach-wall, there is in the breast a radiating growth of the carcinoma in the lymphatic plexus which extends outward in connection with the deep fascia. The lymphatic channels distended with tumor-cells become obliterated and disappear as the tumor growth passes outward, so that it is only in a zone, like the spread of a ringworm, that one finds these lymphatics actually filled with the tumor-cells. New nodules spring up into the skin from various points in their course, but by that time the channels much farther out are filled. In rare cases the skin of the whole chest-wall may be involved in a layer of cancer growth which ulcerates at many points (*cancer en cuirasse*).

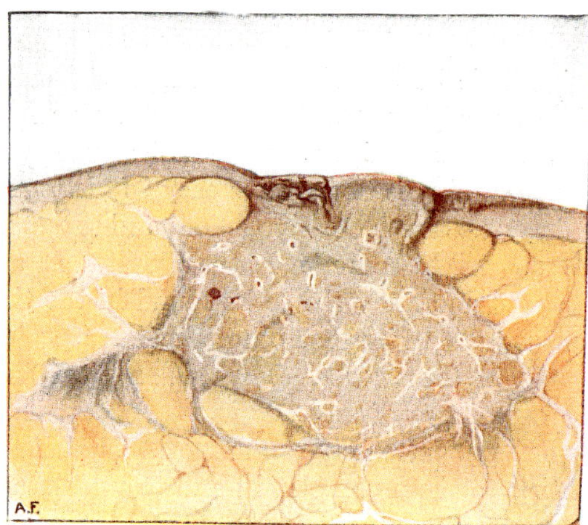

Fig. 556.—Carcinoma of the breast showing retraction of the nipple and limited invasion of the fat.

Handley's ideas as to the further spread into lymph-glands and distant organs are not so convincing.

It is known that in nearly every case metastatic nodules are formed in the axillary lymph-glands, and that somewhat later the subclavicular and cervical glands may be involved. Deep invasion through the pectoral muscles and extension along fasciæ at that plane are common, and one not infrequently traces extension through the intercostal muscles to the pleura and finally to the lung.

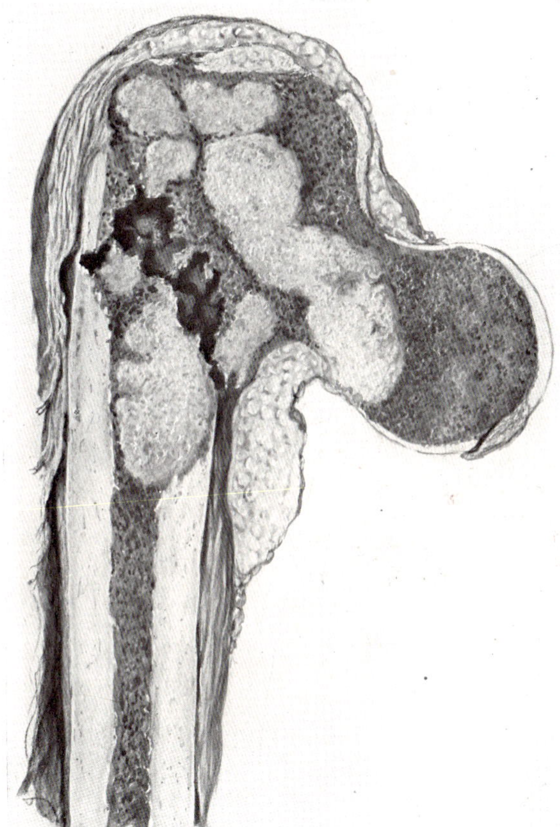

Fig. 557.—Secondary nodule from a tumor of the breast, involving upper end of femur, and producing a pathological fracture.

While extension thus occurs by way of direct growth through connective-tissue spaces and along fasciæ, as well as by continuous growth in the lymphatics or the transportation of isolated groups of cells in the lymph-stream to the axillary glands, there is also the possibility that further dissemination may occur by way of the blood-stream, and the metastases in the liver, bones (Fig. 557), ovaries, and other distant organs seem explicable only on this basis. Handley's statement that emboli of tumor-cells in the blood-vessels are destroyed by the formation of a thrombus may be true for the majority of tumor-cell emboli, but I think we have good evidence that it is not true for all, and that it is probably no such mechanical influence which destroys any of them. Out of great numbers of such emboli, it seems that almost all persist, but a few only take root and grow, producing the distant metastases.

Microscopically, these tumors are found to resemble rather closely in

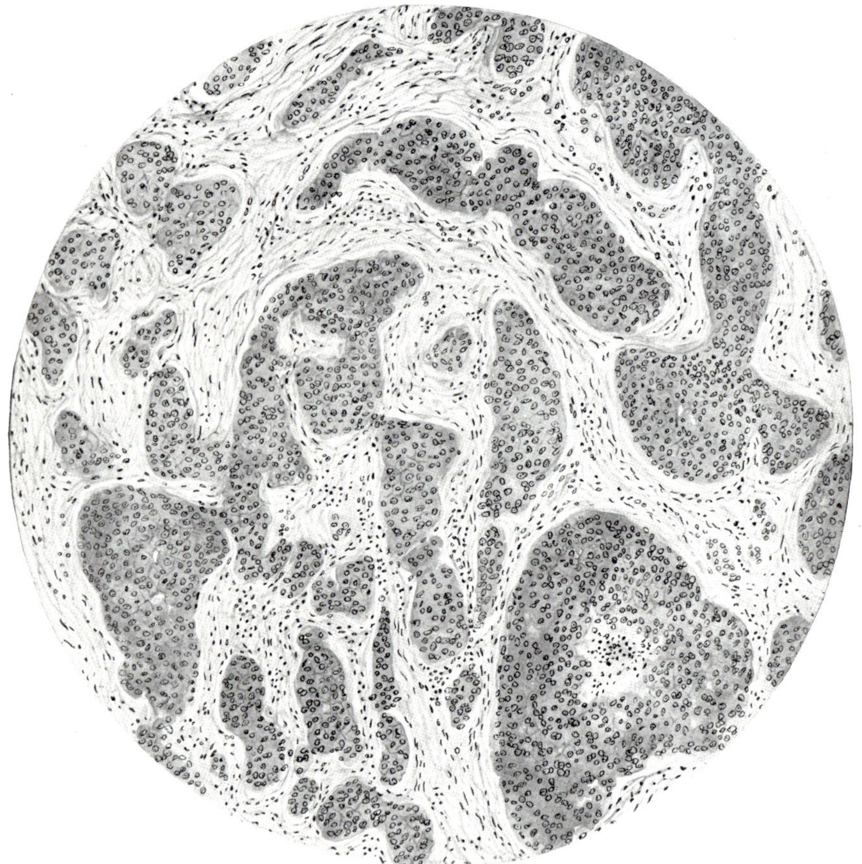

Fig. 558.—Medullary cancer of the breast with necrosis in some of the epithelial strands.

their general arrangement the softer forms of epithelioma, since they are composed of ramifying solid strands of epithelial cells which push their way into the crevices of the stroma. Their appearance is seen in Figs. 558, 559, 560. The striking feature in all is, of course, the unbridled growth of the cells, which is so energetic that no basement membrane can restrain them and they penetrate along the lines of least resistance everywhere.

An interesting point lies in their relation to the adenomata of the breast and to the so-called cystic mastitis of old people. It is not uncommon to find in sections of a breast tumor taken for diagnosis that the tissue has almost everywhere the appearance of a typical benign adenomatous growth. Indeed, it is surprising to learn how frequently those specimens which offer any difficulty in diagnosis are of this character. It is necessary then to determine whether in all places the epithelial strands and tubules maintain strictly their orderly form and their sharp outline which is produced

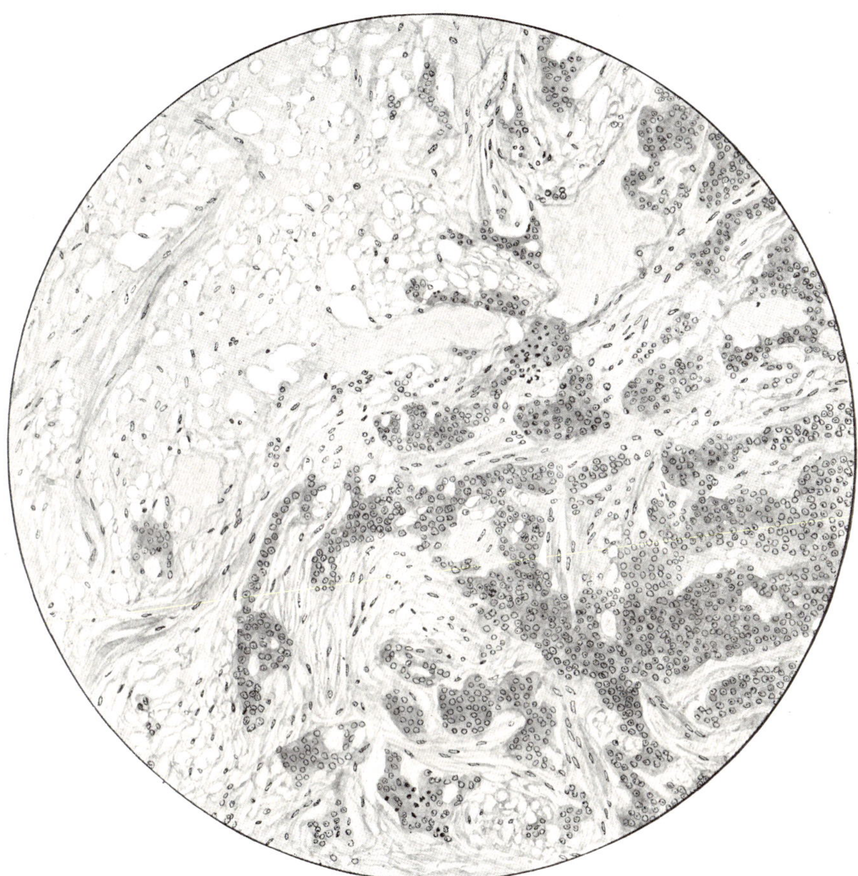

Fig. 559.—Carcinoma of the breast showing area of hyaline degeneration with advancing strands of epithelial cells.

by the basement membrane. In true innocent adenomata this basement membrane is often exaggerated, so that it appears as a broad, pink-staining hyaline membrane, which, of course, leaves no doubt as to the benign nature of that particular area of the growth. With the beginning of a cancerous growth, which one may often detect in very early stages, the cells evidently grow so rapidly as to burst through this membrane and spread rapidly without it. Their contact with the connective tissue immediately becomes far more intimate, and they are found lying loose, strewn in continuous or broken strands through the spaces in the stroma (Fig. 561). This seems to be the crucial test of carcinoma growth, for while the cells do assume an appearance different from that of the normal, it is not a change definite enough to afford any chance for a decision as to the carcinomatous nature of the tumor.

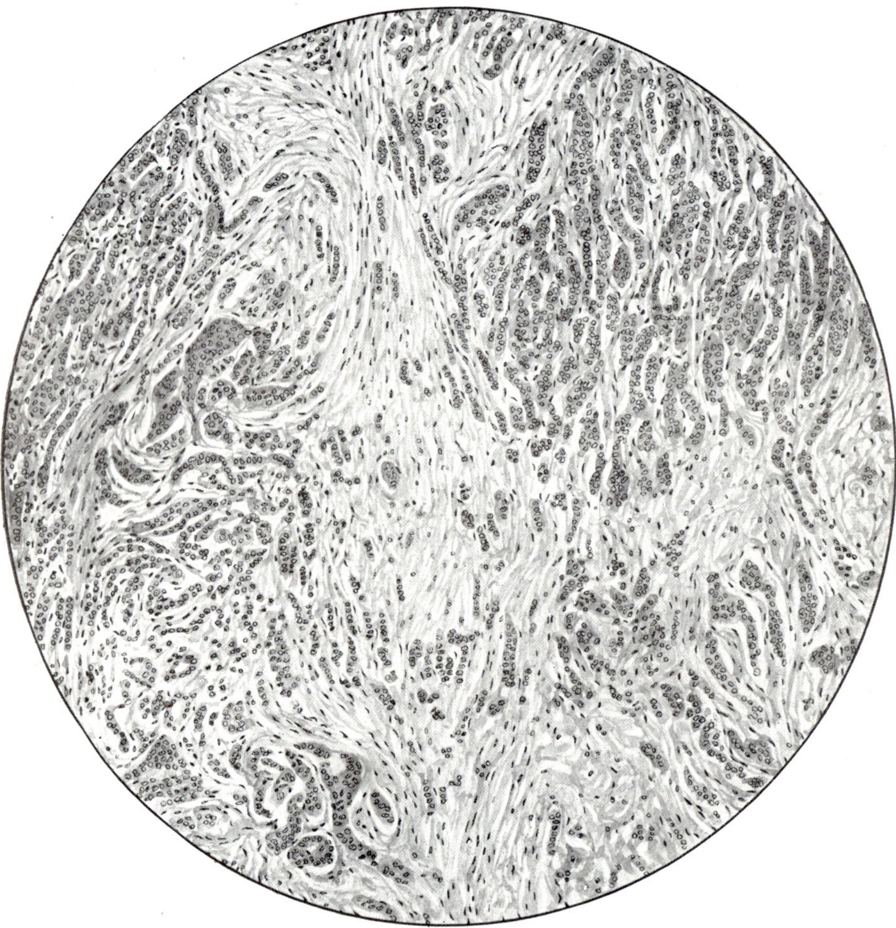

Fig. 560.—Carcinoma of breast. The epithelial cells are growing almost in single file into every crevice of the stroma.

In such cases it seems necessary to conclude that the carcinoma has developed from an adenoma, but there is no more difficulty in this assumption than in the more usual one that it develops from the normal epithelium of the gland.

Carcinoma growth seems especially common as a sequel of the senile hyperplasia with cyst formation, which is often referred to as *chronic cystic mastitis.* This condition comes on with the menopause or later, and leads to the formation of rather dense fibrous tissue throughout the gland, with hypertrophy of the acinous tissue into adenomatous structures, often with the formation of many cysts. It is not thought to be due to any infectious or traumatic injury, and the scarring is really a normal process at the time of menopause, but the formation of cysts, adenomata, and papillomatous growths must be considered as abnormal.

The *scirrhous* tumors, the arrangement of which is shown in Fig. 562, grow and metastasize much more slowly than do the softer forms, so that such a tumor may exist for many years without producing a fatal extension. Nevertheless Bloodgood finds, by statistical study of the hospital cases, that

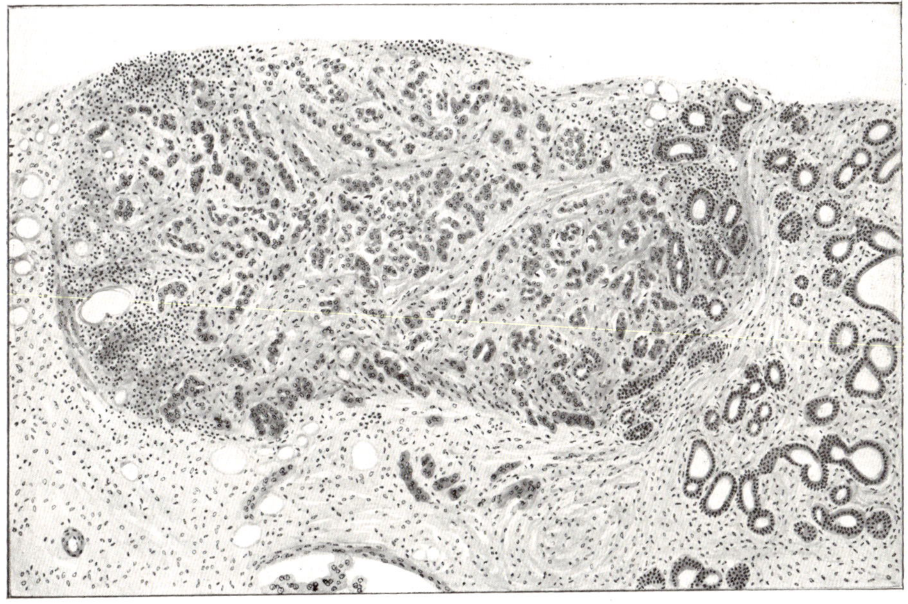

Fig. 561.—Development of a carcinomatous nodule in an adenofibroma of the breast. The invasive character of the carcinoma cells is apparent.

these are the most tenacious, and finally lead to the most unfavorable results.

The *adenocarcinomata* derived from the ducts or from adenomatous nodules are, in some instances, as in the form described by Halsted, relatively benign. My father extirpated such a tumor from each breast of an old woman who has survived many years without lymph-node metastases or local recurrence.

In other cases, however, there may be found a very large tumor mass composed chiefly of cysts filled with glairy fluid, and lined with high columnar or cubical epithelium. Between these are dense adenomatous masses. From the walls of such cysts an invasion may take its origin.

The *colloid* tumors are uncommon, but Lange collected 75 cases, and from their study learnt that metastases were rare, and that the tumors grow very slowly and are relatively benign (Fig. 563).

Carcinomata of the ovary may be primary or secondary. Although tumors distinctly secondary to mammary, gastric, or intestinal carcinomata have been found in this organ, their occurrence is rare and most of the ovarian

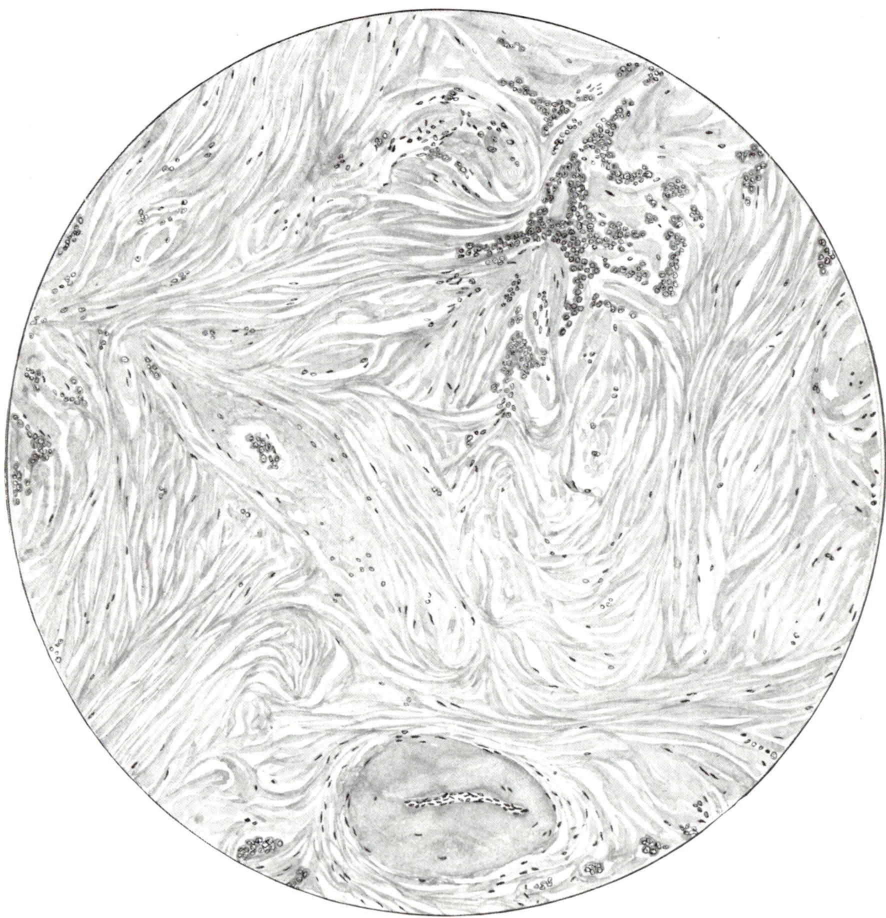

Fig. 562.—Scirrhous cancer of the breast. The epithelial cells are greatly reduced in number and scattered in an extremely dense hyaline stroma. The blood-vessels show thick hyaline walls.

cancers are primary. It is difficult to explain why they so frequently occur simultaneously in both ovaries. They are solid tumors, tumors combined with cystomata, or papillomatous growths, and almost every type of cancer observed elsewhere seems to be represented here. When the carcinoma is cystic or develops in connection with a small cyst, it may be surmised that the tumor began as a carcinoma. When, however, the malignant growth appears in the wall of a large cystadenoma of long standing, it must be supposed that its relation to the cystadenoma is analogous to that of the carcinoma of the breast to the adenoma within which it develops.

Metastases (Fig. 564) vary with the character of the tumor, and may be confined to intraperitoneal implantations in the papillary forms. In one which we studied recently both ovaries were replaced by cysts of about

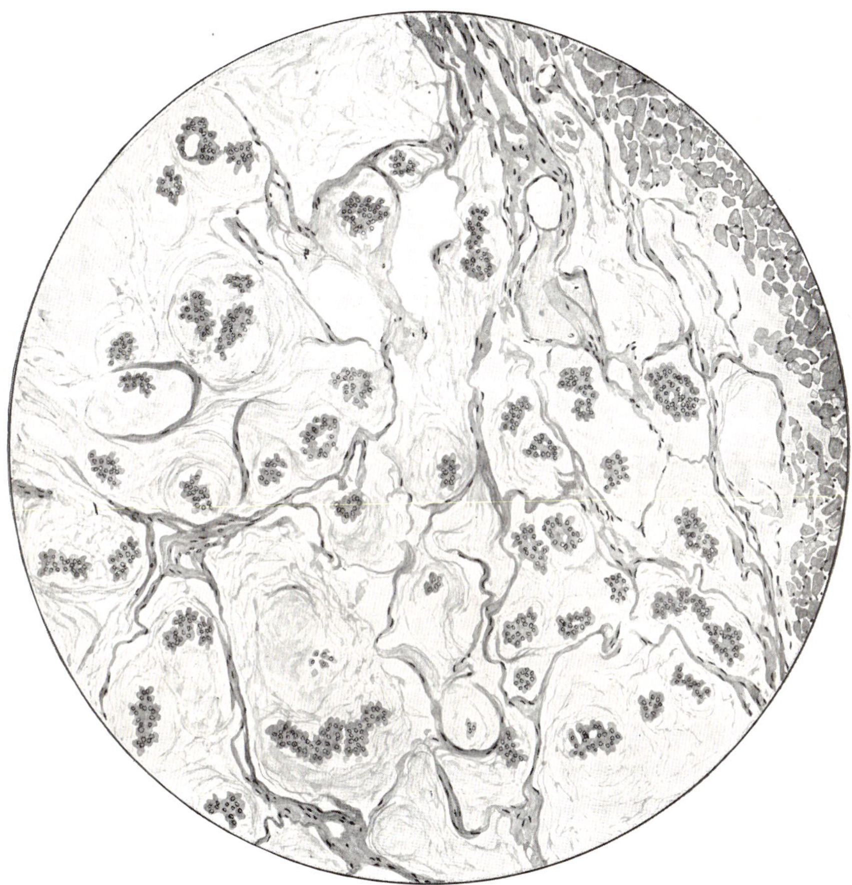

Fig. 563.—Colloid carcinoma of the breast. The colloid appears to be developed in the stroma in which the epithelial cells are isolated.

orange size, in the walls of which there were thick, yellow masses of solid tumor. There were metastases in the liver, and especially interesting was a continuous chain of white nodules along the round ligament extending into the substance of the liver. It is possible that further study may reveal an unusual method of invasion of the liver by extension along the lymphatics of that cord. Handley discusses a similar occurrence in connection with mammary carcinomata.

Krukenberg described as a form of sarcoma a tumor which is obviously carcinomatous and which often involves both ovaries. These nodules are rather dense and infiltrated with loosely arranged epithelial cells, each of which is swollen with a globule of colloid or gelatinous fluid. They are relatively benign growths.

The carcinomata of the ovaries, like the cystadenomata, are evidently

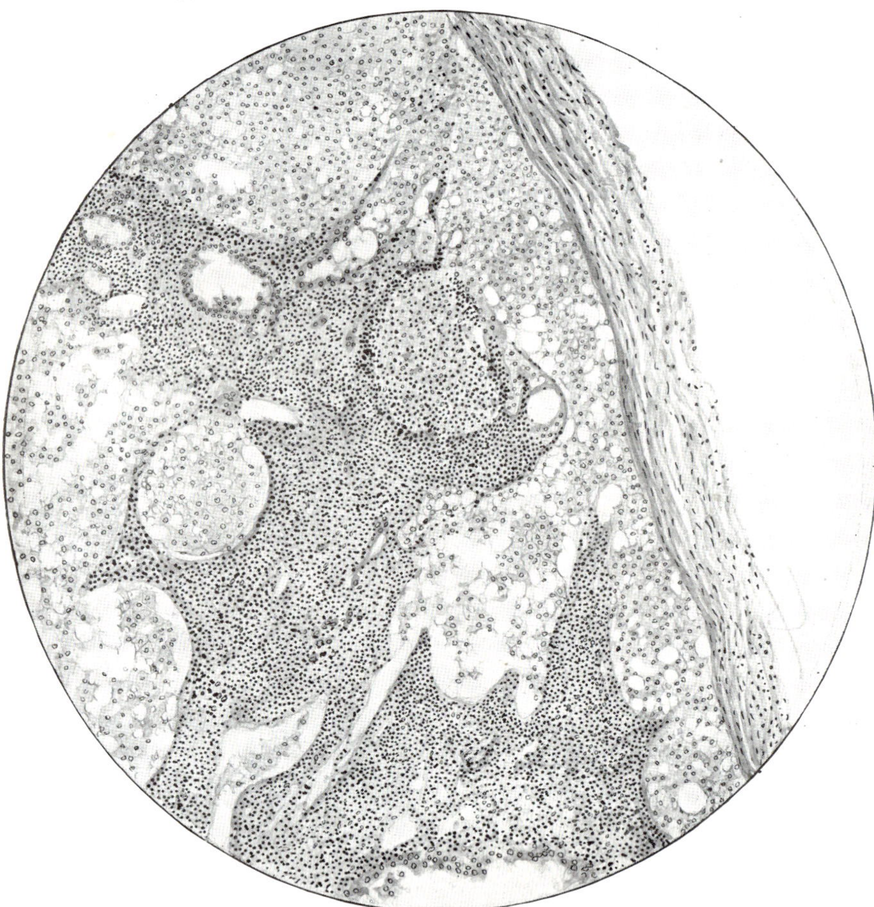

Fig. 564.—Metastasis from carcinoma of the ovary in an axillary lymph-gland. The lymph-sinuses are filled with epithelial cells.

derived from invaginations of the surface epithelium, although many other hypotheses have been offered as to their source. There seems to be no good evidence that they arise from the Pflüger's cords or from Graafian follicles.

Carcinomata of the Thyroid.—These tumors have been studied especially by v. Eiselsberg, Kocher, and Langhans, who find that they can distinguish several groups, among which a form of adenocarcinoma or proliferating struma is especially common. These occur as single nodules containing every transition between solid strands of cells and colloid-containing alveoli, closely resembling those of the normal gland. They are not very malignant, but occasionally metastasize in distant organs or bones. The second group, called by Langhans *carcinomatous struma,* has the arrangement in irregular solid strands of epithelial cells seen in many carcinomata of the breast. These quickly burst through the capsule of the gland and metastasize abundantly. *Metastasizing colloid struma* forms the third group, with numerous secondary nodules, composed of colloid-holding vesicles in which no striking morphological signs of its malignancy are to be seen. The tumors of the fourth group, named *alveolar large-cell struma,* are also malignant, and give rise to numerous metastases. They are composed of large cuboidal or cylindrical cells, arranged in small alveoli or in tubular or strand-like structures. The cells in these tumors are occasionally very large, with deeply stained nuclei. The other groups comprise the papillomatous tumors of the thyroid, in which branching processes grow into cysts or cavities in the thyroid, and squamous cell epithelioma, which may occur in the substance of the gland and must be ascribed to a congenital displacement of cells.

Primary Carcinoma of the Liver.—Reference has already been made to the cylindrical cell cancers of the liver which originate in the epithelium of the bile-ducts, and appear as solid white masses in the substance of the organ. There is another type quite different from this, which is so characteristic and constant in form that, once seen, it can never be forgotten or mistaken for any other tumor. This is the primary cancer which originates from the liver-cells themselves, and occurs in multiple nodules closely set throughout the whole liver. Whatever remains of liver tissue is profoundly scarred, as in the most advanced cirrhosis. The liver is greatly enlarged, and dark green or grayish, rounded nodules project everywhere. On section nearly the whole cut surface is occupied by these velvety green or gray rounded masses which stand up from the remaining liver substance (Fig. 565). There is usually quite deep jaundice, and often a terminal hæmorrhage from the rupture of some softened nodule which projects into the peritoneal cavity. There are no metastases, but branched emboli of tumor-cells may be found plugging the terminal twigs of the pulmonary artery in the lung. On opening the portal and hepatic veins masses of the tumor are often found projecting into the lumen of one or other of these veins.

Microscopically, it is found that the liver tissue between the nodules and in areas unoccupied by them presents the irregular masses of distorted liver-cell strands and the broad bands of collapsed framework and scar tissue, with numerous bile-ducts, which are seen in the ordinary nodular cirrhosis. The tumor nodules are composed of anastomosing strands of rather large cells, corresponding fairly closely with the liver-cells, but with larger nuclei rich in chromatin, and with swollen cell-bodies which take a rather deep stain. Great irregularities occur, and there are many huge cells with several nuclei. There is a tendency toward an arrangement in broad strands of cells separated by narrow capillaries, and in many places it is seen that these strands hang in the lumen of a blood-vessel, where they are surrounded by blood and everywhere covered with endothelium. It is extremely common to find blood-vessels thus packed with bunches of

Fig. 565.—Primary adenocarcinoma of the liver combined with cirrhosis. The figure shows two different cases, in each of which there were multiple nodules. The upper specimen shows especially well the invasion of the vein.

strands of tumor-cells which, on account of their endothelial covering, cause no thrombosis. The larger invasions of the branches of the veins seem to maintain this characteristic growth. Quite apart from the well-formed tumor nodules, there may be found in the cirrhotic liver tissue minute groups of tumor-cells recognizable by their abnormal form, but standing in direct continuity with the surrounding liver-cells, which they compress by their rapid growth. These seem to be beginning tumor nodules.

The multiplicity of these growths and their lack of power to form metastases have caused much speculation. They have been thought to arise simultaneously in many situations in the liver as the result of an overstepping of the bounds of what might be regarded as normal in the compensatory hyperplasia of the liver-cells in an advanced cirrhosis. Winternitz advanced the idea that they are really metastatic nodules, secondary to an original growth near the hilum of the liver, which invades the portal vein and scatters its cells through the whole liver. If such exquisite power of metastasis exists in the liver, it is difficult to understand why these same cells should be completely incapable of growing elsewhere, although they can be found as emboli in the capillaries of the lung in great abundance. It must be admitted that, whatever explanation is accepted, the behavior of this tumor is peculiar and unlike that of the other carcinomata.

LITERATURE

Breast.—Fr. Lange: Bruns, Beiträge z. kl. Chir., 1896, xvi, 1.
v. Winiwarter: Beiträge z. Statistik der Carcinome, Stuttgart, 1878.
Greenough and Hartwell: Jour. Med. Research, 1903, ix, 416.
Bloodgood: Kelly and Noble, Gynecology and Abdominal Surgery, 1907, ii, 180.
Halsted: Trans. Amer. Surgical Assoc. (Adenocarcinoma), 1898, xvi, 144.
Ovary.—Pfannenstiel: Veit's Handb. d. Gynäkologie, Wiesbaden, 1908, i. Hälfte, 177.
Glockner: Arch. f. Gynäkologie, 1904, lxxii, 410.
Thyroid.—Langhans: Virch. Arch., 1907, clxxxix, 69.
Th. Kocher: Deut. Ztschr. f. Chir., 1907, xci, 197.
Liver.—v. Heukelom: Ziegler's Beiträge, 1894, xvi, 341.
Travis: Johns Hopkins Hosp. Bull., 1902, xiii, 108.
Wegelin: Inaugural Dissertation, Bern, 1905. Virch. Arch., 1905, clxxix, 95.
Winternitz: Virch. Arch., 1913, ccix, 239.

CHORIONIC EPITHELIOMATA

In the study of the formation of the placenta there has never been complete unanimity of opinion as to the origin of the syncytial layer which covers the chorionic villi. The other cells which cover these villi and which are arranged in a more sharply defined layer (Langhans' cell layer) are universally recognized as the fœtal ectoderm, but for the syncytium, at least three ideas have been expressed: (*a*) That it is derived from the maternal uterine epithelium; (*b*) that it is a modification of maternal endothelium, and (*c*) that it belongs, like the Langhans' layer, to the fœtal ectoderm. The weight of evidence seems to be in favor of the last view.

During pregnancy there is normally a curious invasive growth of the chorionic villi into the uterine wall, and it is by no means uncommon to find masses of syncytium-like giant-cells with many nuclei lodged in the interstices of the muscle, quite deep down in the uterine wall. Indeed, such masses have been found to invade blood-vessels and to be carried as emboli into distant organs. Nevertheless, this invasive growth ends harmlessly, and the cells presently disappear from the tissue as though the body had some mechanism for destroying them when pregnancy is over.

Two curious abnormal conditions may arise during pregnancy which bring about a result quite different from the usual normal ending. One of these is the development of the hydatidiform mole, the other the growth and metastases of the chorionic epithelioma. In the case of the *hydatidiform mole* it is found that, when pregnancy approaches its termination, there may be expelled from the uterus, not a child with the cord and placenta, but a great mass of polypoid, gelatinous structures, which hang together like a huge bunch of grapes. There may be no fœtus at all, or the shrunken remnants of one, and the placenta is converted into the villous mole, which receives its name from its resemblance to the clusters of hydatids or cysts of the tænia larvæ which are sometimes seen. (Mole is used here in the old sense—mass.) Microscopically, these polypoid blebs are swollen chorionic villi enormously enlarged and covered with greatly proliferated epithelium. It is rare to see such a mass *in situ*, but in the uterus removed after the expulsion of the mole it is found that the villi grow into the uterine musculature and sometimes give rise to malignant, tumor-like extension and metastasis. Nevertheless, such invasive growth is by no means constant, and the woman may recover her health perfectly and even give birth to a second or third hydatidiform mole.

This has intimate relations, as will be seen, with the *chorionic epithelioma*. The pregnancy may be interrupted by the development of a hæmorrhagic tumor in the uterine wall, or after pregnancy is over such a tumor may develop even several months later. Curettings have the appearance of placental tissue, except that the cells are more profuse in these growths and are much better preserved than those found in curetted remnants of retained placenta. Still, it is only through determining the relation of the tissue to the uterine muscle, together with the alarming clinical symptoms of hæmorrhage, that a diagnosis can be made with any certainty. Frequently there is found a conspicuous hæmorrhagic tumor in the vaginal wall which will make the diagnosis clear.

With such partial removal of the tumor as is possible by curettage complete recovery occurs in some cases, and all traces of tumor growth disappear. In other cases the patient coughs up blood and bleeds from the uterus, and at the autopsy there is found a tumor invading the uterine wall and growing in metastatic nodules in the lungs, liver, brain, and elsewhere. The tumor in the uterine wall is a soft, ragged, intensely hæmorrhagic mass, variegated in color by gray or whitish areas, and by brownish patches in which the blood has undergone decomposition, with the formation of pigment. The metastases in the lungs are often round nodules, of about the size of a cherry, scattered abundantly through the organ. They, too, are deep red from hæmorrhage. There may be large, more ragged, and pigmented masses. In the brain the metastatic tumor may produce apoplectiform symptoms from hæmorrhage and compression.

Microscopically, these tumors are found to be made up almost entirely of broad, irregular, and ragged anastomosing strands of the two types of chorionic epithelium, in which the Langhans' cells can be readily distinguished by their smaller and more regular form, with pale or almost clear protoplasm, and fairly sharp cell outline, while the syncytial material spreads over them or forms solid areas of protoplasm which stains much more deeply, and in which numerous nuclei, often of great size, are embedded. The stroma and blood-vessels are inconspicuous or entirely lacking, since the tumor seems to grow into blood-channels, and everywhere the tissue is torn and disarranged by extensive hæmorrhages (Fig. 566).

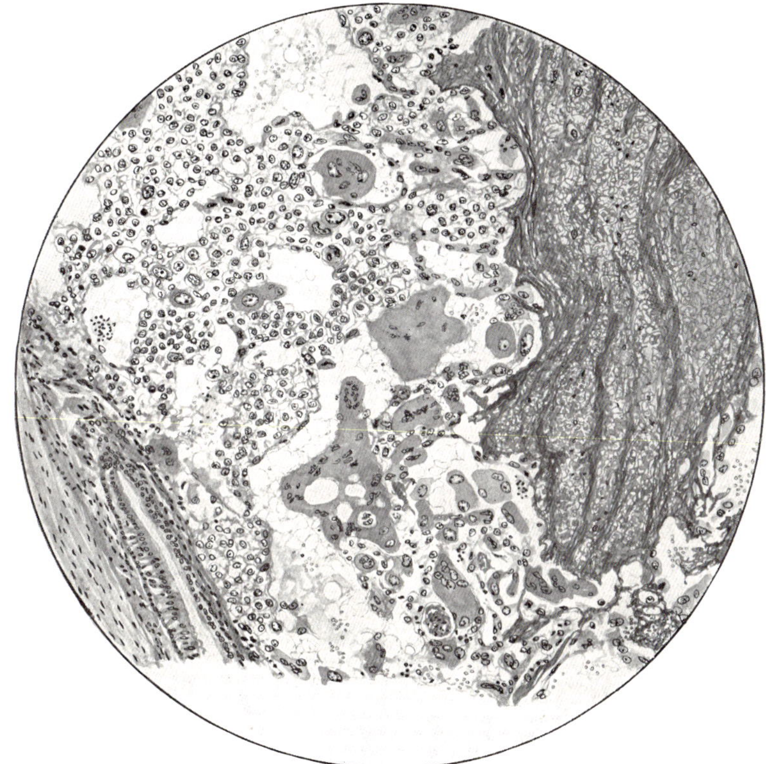

Fig. 566.—Chorionic epithelioma, metastatic nodule in the lung, showing Langhans' cells and syncytium.

It was thought for a long time that these tumors were of sarcomatous or endothelial nature, and that they had preceded pregnancy and were stimulated by it to more rapid growth. It was thought by others that they were derived from the decidua, and they were, therefore, spoken of as malignant deciduomata, but the work of Marchand cleared up the whole situation by showing clearly that none of these theories had any foundation, and that the tumor originates in the chorionic epithelium or fœtal ectoderm of the placenta, and that both layers of this epithelium are involved.

The tumors are especially interesting from the fact that a somewhat analogous growth and invasion of the chorionic epithelium occurs normally, and that an exaggeration of the development of the villi, often ending in the formation of a malignant tumor, is found in the hydatidiform mole. The fact that definite chorionic epitheliomata seem to retrogress sometimes and disappear completely is also peculiar, and has led to speculation (Fleischmann) as to whether there is some substance formed in the maternal blood at the end of pregnancy, which, like the experimentally produced syncytiolysin of Scholten and Veit, has the function of destroying the syncytial elements which remain buried in the uterine wall or lodged in distant organs. The failure of this substance might allow the unchecked development of the tissue into a destructive tumor, while its late formation might account for the disappearance of the tumor.

On the other hand, it is found that in a large proportion of cases the development of a hydatidiform mole or a chorionic epithelioma is accompanied by a peculiar enlargement of the ovaries, sometimes to the size of a large grape-fruit. This is due to the formation of numerous cysts, most of which are, like the cysts derived from corpora lutea, lined with several layers of yellow lutein cells. The well-known theory of Fraenkel and Born, according to which the corpus luteum is an organ of internal secretion controlling and forwarding the embedding of the ovum and the development of the placenta, is brought into play by Runge, Pick, and others as a ready explanation of this association. If there is a great overgrowth and excessive activity of the corpus luteum tissue, it may produce excessive growth of the chorionic villi over which its secretion is supposed to preside. Dunger reverses the idea and suggests that the excessive growth of the chorion requires the development of additional corpus luteum tissue. L. Loeb finds that irritation and injury of the mucosa of the uterus in guinea-pigs after coitus will, under certain conditions, produce very large growths of tissue, which he calls placentomata. In his papers he emphasizes the alteration in environmental conditions of the mucosa, and recognizes in these and other papers the importance of the influence of the corpora lutea.

The matter requires further study, and it seems to offer an extremely interesting border-line condition the comprehension of which might throw much light upon tumor growth in general.

LITERATURE

Risel: Ergebn. d. allg. Path., 1907, xi_2, 928.

Gaylord: Amer. Jour. Obstetrics, 1902, xlv, 465.

Marchand: Monatsschr. f. Geburtsh. u. Gynäk., 1895, i, 419. Ztschr. f. Geburtsh. u. Gynäk., 1895, xxxii, 405. *Ibid.*, 1898, xxxix, 173.

Fleischmann: Monatsschr. f. Geburtsh. u. Gynäk., 1905, xxi, 353.

Runge: Arch. f. Gynäk., 1903, lxix, 33.

R. T. Frank: New York Med. Jour., 1906, lxxxiii, 793.

L. Loeb: Arch. f. Entwicklungsmech. d. Organismen, 1911, xxxii, 67. Ztschr. f. Krebsforschung, 1912, xi, 259.

CHAPTER LIV

TERATOMATA; COMPOSITE TUMORS

Chorionic epithelium in tumors of the male. Teratomata. Early development of the ovum, potency of blastomeres. Their inclusion in the formation of double monsters. Formation of solid teratomata. Dermoid cysts. Cutaneous and branchial cysts. Cholesteatomata. Mixed tumors of salivary glands; of the kidney. Congenital cystic kidney. Mixed tumors of the breast and of the testicle. Chordoma.

In the last pages there has been given a description of the hydatidiform mole and of the chorionic epithelioma which may develop in connection with pregnancy, and it was pointed out that these are tumors of a more suggestively parasitic nature than the others which have been considered in previous chapters, since they are composed of the tissue of a different individual. This is not enough to shake our faith in the belief that the ordinary tumors are composed of the tissue of the same individual, but at least it causes us to reflect upon this question.

The existence of tumors morphologically identical with the chorionic epithelioma of women, but growing in the testicle of men, is especially calculated to rouse our interest in this question. These tumors belong to the composite type called teratomata, which contain tissue of many sorts, representing all of the three germinal layers, and give rise to metastases which are composed of Langhans' cells and syncytium. Chorionic epithelium occurs also in the tumors themselves, and may, indeed, be the only tissue found, in which case it is thought that the other types have been overgrown and obliterated by it. Scott and Longcope described a tumor of the testicle composed entirely of chorionic epithelium, and Frank had a similar case, but most of these tumors have contained a mixture of other tissues as well, which often resemble disorted organs in such a way as to suggest an abortive attempt at the formation of a fœtus.

Such a suggestion of the formation in a man's testicle of a fœtus with chorionic epithelium, however abortive, demands explanation, and numerous hypotheses have been put forward. Schlagenhaufer points out, first of all, the value of such an observation in settling the origin of the syncytial layer of the chorion. It must be derived from fœtal ectoderm, since in this situation there is no uterine mucosa to give it origin. He regards the tumor as an imperfect fœtus which has formed about itself fœtal membranes which spread into the tissue of the host, and metastasize to distant organs. Risel insists, however, that it is unnecessary to assume the formation of a chorionic membrane with villi, since the fœtal ectoderm can produce such chorionic epithelium easily enough.

Schlagenhaufer, finding that the tumors occasionally grow into large veins in polypoid clusters of translucent, grape-like bodies, suggested that this was analogous to the formation of a hydatid mole. I have studied one of the four or five tumors of this nature, and find that the villus-like

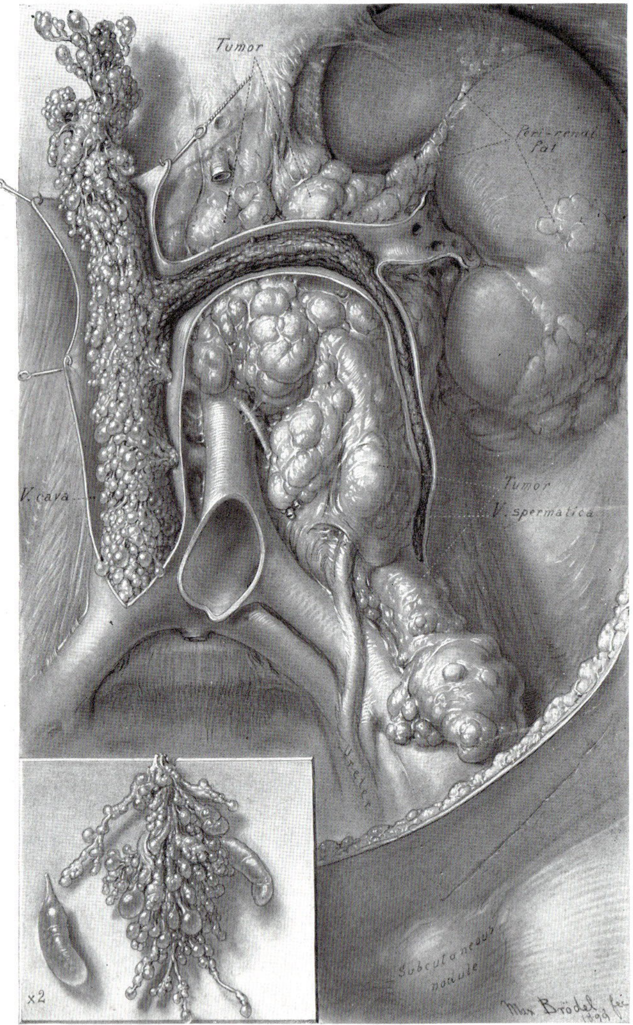

Fig. 567.—Teratomatous tumor of testicle invading vena cava through spermatic and renal veins. Hydatidiform, grape-like structures hang free in the circulating blood.

bodies (Fig. 567) are not covered with chorionic epithelium. It is, therefore, as Risel explains, only an accidental resemblance.

Teratomata.—While such fœtus-like tumors with chorionic epithelium are rare, there are others in which rudimentary, organ-like masses of tissue are mingled together as though in an unsuccessful attempt to form a fœtus, but without any development of chorionic elements. These are the solid *teratomata* or embryomata which are not very uncommon, and may occur in the

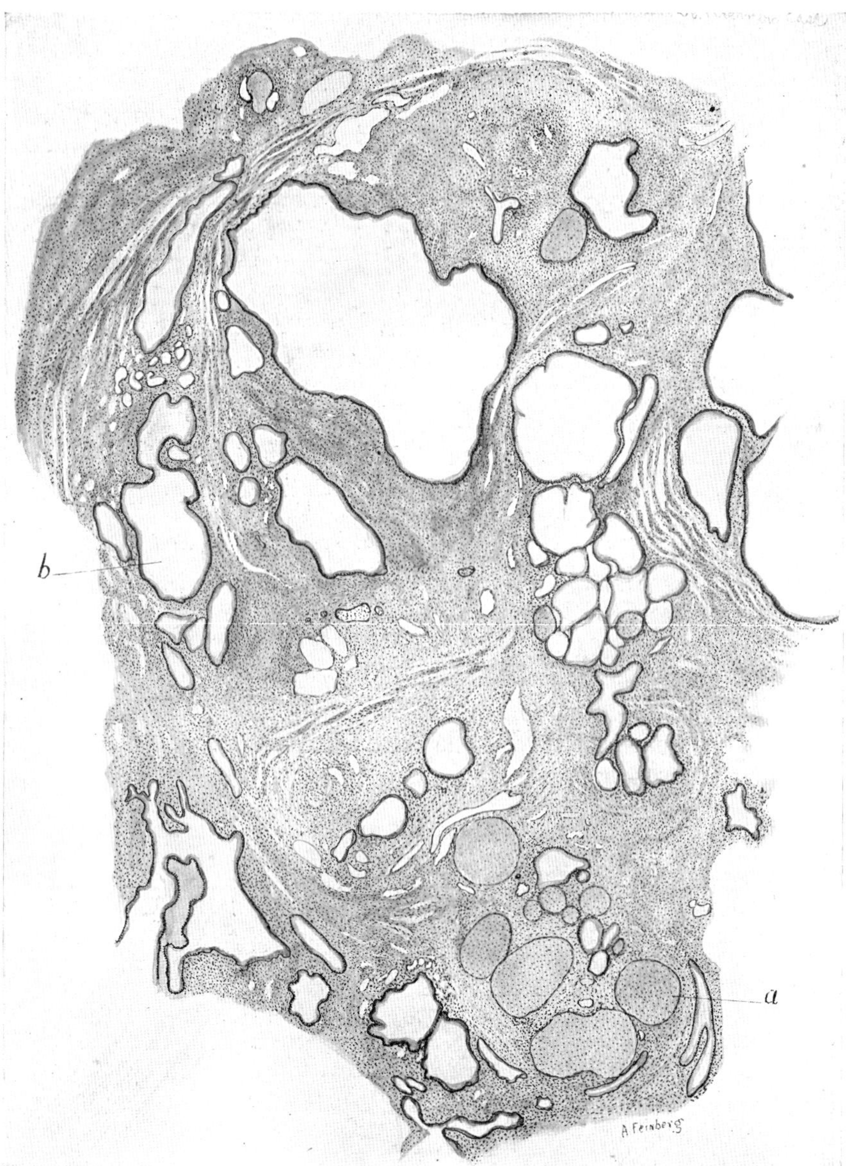

Fig. 568.—Teratoma of testicle with cartilage, (*a*) nerves, striated muscle, and cavities (*b*) lined with various kinds of epithelium.

ovary or testicle, or in almost any other situation in the body. They are especially frequently found at the poles of the body, springing from the roof of the mouth or from the sacrum, or, in somewhat different form, in the brain, in the orbit, in the mediastinum, or abdomen. Some of them project outwardly and are covered with skin, even presenting at times a vague resemblance to limbs or other parts of the body: others are completely inclosed within the body cavity, where they may be connected by a stalk with surrounding organs, or enveloped in a capsule.

Dissection of such masses shows that they are not like ordinary tumors, inasmuch as they are not merely composed of one type of tissue, but contain representations of all three germinal layers. There are structures of every degree of complexity, composed of skin and its appendages; malformed teeth are found sometimes in connection with bony structures, sometimes embedded in soft tissues. Misshapen eyes or masses of brain tissue, portions of intestinal mucosa or convoluted canals resembling the intestines alternate with cysts lined with epithelium difficult to recognize, and masses of cartilage or thyroid tissue (Fig. 568). There is no tissue which may not be represented, although liver and pancreas, testicle and ovarian tissue and chorionic epithelium are usually absent. Ganglion-cells are abundant, as a rule, embedded in a connective tissue which may assume almost any form. More detailed description of any one case would hardly repay us, because in the next a different set of tissues might be represented. But it is evident that the whole mass represents in some sense a frustrated attempt at the formation of a human body in which the whole plan has failed through the lack of the necessary parts, and the distortion and disarrangement of those which were available. It is obvious that, for an explanation, we must go back to the beginnings of embryonic development, in the hope that at some point a mechanism may be recognized by which it is possible for one individual or a rudiment of an individual to be inclosed within another.

In the beginning the ripening ova cast off some of their chromatin in the form of polar bodies, after which they are ready for fertilization. There are vague and unsatisfactory statements that the polar bodies may be fertilized by spermatozoa and undergo cleavage to a certain extent in insects, but not, so far as I can learn, in higher animals. Upon fertilization the ovum divides into two segments, and these again divide into two until there is a rounded mass of blastomeres. By invagination or gastrula formation ectoderm and entoderm are distinguished, and from them there is formed the mesoderm, which at first consists of two layers of cells, later dividing into the myotome and another mass which, by division, forms the middle plate, and the splanchnopleure and somatopleure, which enclose the cœlom. From the middle plate there arise the Wolffian body, the kidney, and the genital glands. The original Wolffian duct comes into very close relationship with the ectoderm at this point, a fact which is of interest in connection with the development of certain tumors.

The genital cells at first contain somatic material, but they lose this in the course of division and become purely sex cells at a very early stage. Since they retain their chromatin tenaciously they appear as deeply stained cells.

The power of development of the cells in each stage is of especial interest in any attempt to explain the formation of tumors. Much has been said of the possibility of the growth of the original sex cells, or of the ripening ovum, into differentiated tissues, but there is no real evidence that such parthenogenetic development can occur within the body, and any idea of internal fertilization in the tissues rests upon no support. There is no reason to deny the possibility of the fertilization and development of polar bodies, but although that idea has been put forward by Marchand, there is practically no evidence in its favor, and it has been pointed out that there may be multiple teratomatous tumors which could not be explained on this basis, since at most there are two polar bodies. The fertilized ovum is totipotent; that is, it is capable of giving rise to all the tissues of the body. So, too, are the first segmentation spheres, as is proven by the development of twins from a single ovum. These twins are always of the same sex, and resemble each other very closely—they are more nearly related than other brothers and sisters.

In later stages of segmentation the blastomeres remain multipotent or capable of producing several tissues, but probably not a perfect individual. Still later, the destiny of the cells becomes much more rigidly prescribed, and they are limited to the formation of certain tissues. When the germ layers are defined, elements from each of these layers have the power of producing ectoderm, entoderm, or mesodermal structures only, and are even more closely confined, according to their point of origin in the layer.

Nevertheless, it is obvious that there is a chance for the development of a mass of tissue of almost any degree of complexity from a blastomere, if we are willing to assume that it may become independent of the others at some stage in the segmentation. This idea involves the further assumption that this independently growing blastomere may remain attached to the main embryo, or become partly or completely surrounded by it in its growth, so as to be finally included in its body.

There is such abundant material illustrating every stage of attachment, inclusion, and final complete enclosure of one body in the other, that no assumption is required and the story is practically complete. It has been said that the complete separation of the first two segmentation spheres results in the so-called single ovum twins. The developing segments may, however, remain attached or fuse in the course of their development, as we see in the case of the well-known Siamese twins, and in hosts of other double monsters in which the two bodies are united by their sternal, sacral, or cranial regions. While these individuals seem to be more or less independent, there are important structures common to the two bodies, and other double monsters are not wanting in which the fusion becomes much more complete. When the isolated blastomere or group of blastomeres is derived from a somewhat later stage, so as to be incapable of producing a whole body, or when a totipotent blastomere in its development is outgrown by the other, there results a parasitic monster; that is, an incomplete individual attached to its brother or partly embedded in his body and deriving all its nutrition thence. Such an abortive individual may project in the form of incomplete arms or legs from the epigastric or pubic or other region of the host or "autosite." From this it is but a short step to the still more rudimentary organ masses, which are completely inclosed within the abdomen or thoracic cavity, and which, while maintaining a degree of independence, draw their blood supply from the adjacent tissues of the host. The solid teratomata, with their cysts and aimless organ rudiments, are practically of this nature. Of course, if the isolated blastomere and the main group of segmentation spheres begin to develop at the same time, we should expect the tissues of host and teratoma to appear to be of the same age or maturity, while if the isolated blastomere should remain stagnant during the growth of the host, it might be expected to produce by later growth a teratoma composed of embryonic tissues. It is said that this distinction can be made. No one has found and recognized such latent blastomeres, and the tissues of all teratomata are often so abnormal in appearance that it is difficult to judge of their maturity, so that this statement about the age of the growth is somewhat speculative.

It seems that the evidence in favor of the isolation of a blastomere as the origin of teratomatous tumors is incomparably stronger than that for any of the other modes of formation which have been suggested. With this explanation there is no difficulty whatever in understanding the localization of a teratoma in the testicle or in the brain, while with the others, which involve fertilization and development of ova, etc., insuperable obstacles are met with in many cases. With this explanation, too, there is no difficulty in comprehending the formation of teratomata of all degrees of complexity down to the simplest cysts, composed of only one or two types of tissue, whereas if they arose from fertilized polar bodies, primary sex cells, etc., we should expect in every case growths more closely simulating complete individuals. The formation of teratomata with chorionic epithelium becomes intelligible, since a blastomere in its development is like a growing embryo, capable of forming certain tissue, whatever its own situation. It becomes clear that there is a difference between the metastasizing chorionic epithelioma of women, and that which occurs in the testicle, in that the former is tissue of the offspring of the woman and belongs to another generation, while the latter belongs to the individual himself, and therefore is co-aëtaneous, or pertaining to the same generation.

The solid teratomata may grow to a great size, especially when they are enclosed in the abdominal cavity and attached to the retroperitoneal tissue or sacrum, but they are, as a rule, in themselves, quite benign masses with no capacity for unlimited growth. Nevertheless they produce extraordinary mechanical disturbances at times. I remember one case especially well in which a great mass appeared in the abdomen of a man and grew slowly. It was found impossible to extirpate it, and after some months he died with signs of the presence of a tumor in the lung. At the autopsy there was found a huge mass, inextricably entangled in the intestines, and springing from the retroperitoneal region. It contained convoluted, intestine-like channels and several large cysts, in the walls of one of which a carcinoma had developed. All the rest of the mass showed only an organ-like arrangement of tissues, and the metastases in the man's lungs were from this carcinoma. While it is true that the teratoma itself is benign, it is not at all uncommon to find the development of a distinct carcinoma at some point in its epithelium, exactly as we find it in the body in general.

Dermoid Cysts.—A simpler form of teratoma is that which is known as a *dermoid cyst*. These may occur almost anywhere, but are perhaps most common in the ovary, where there may be several. They are, as the name implies, composed essentially of derivatives of the ectodermal layer, but there is no line between them and the more complex teratomata—indeed, all dermoids on closer examination prove to have a more complicated structure than is apparent at first sight. A dermoid cyst is round or irregularly multilocular, and on incision is found to have a tough, hard wall and to be filled with a soft, greasy mass of granular, buttery consistency, in which there are often tangles of hair (Fig. 569). Sometimes the hair may be extremely long and abundant. It does not spring evenly from the whole wall, but has its roots in a thickened patch which is constantly present in the wall of such cysts (Willms). The thick area projects into the lumen of the cyst, and is sometimes very irregular and rough. It is covered with thick epidermis, and bears the roots of the hairs and an exaggerated array of sebaceous glands (Figs. 570 and 571). It is from these sebaceous glands that the buttery contents of the cyst are secreted. They may open in the hair-sheaths, but most commonly open directly into the cyst. There are sebaceous glands around the whole wall of the cyst, quite away from the hair-bearing patch. Opposite this patch the distal ends of the hairs may become buried in the wall and encapsulated by

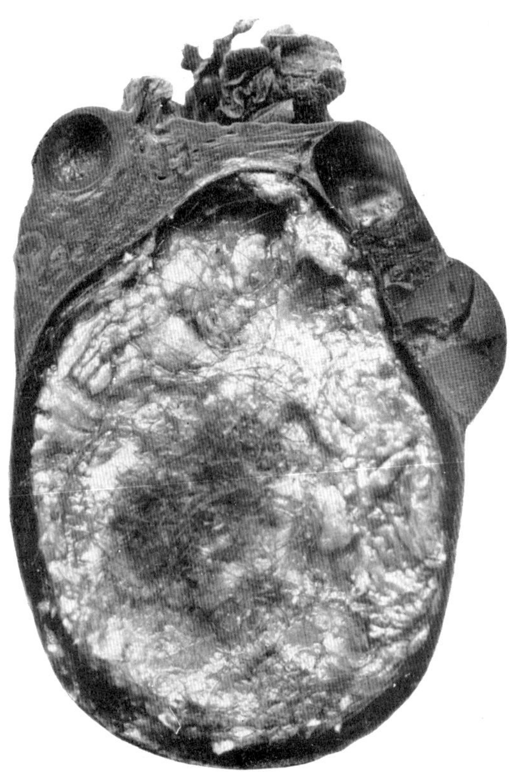

Fig. 569.—Dermoid cyst of ovary, showing sebaceous material and hair.

granulation tissue, so that they seem to have taken root there. In the mass of tissue which projects into the cavity there may be smooth muscle, like the arrectores pilorum, and fat and dense connective tissue. That these dermoid cysts verge on the more solid teratomata is seen from the fact that some of them have teeth in their walls often set in connection with a bony mass which lies deeper in the wall (Fig. 572). If there are pigmented rudiments of an eye or elements of the central nervous system, the approach to the complexity of the more solid teratomata is even closer. Willms points out the fact that most of the structures seen in dermoid cysts are such as might be developed from the head, that part of the embryo which develops most rapidly. Various degenerative changes occur

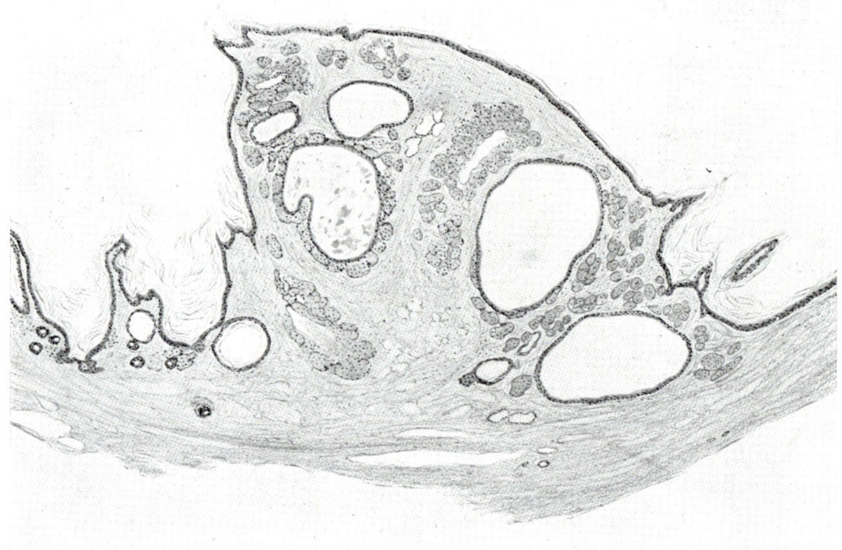

Fig. 570.—Wall of dermoid cyst, showing solid projection covered with epidermis. There are many hair and sebaceous glands on the surface.

in such cysts, the walls become calcified, their epithelium disappears and is replaced by granulation tissue, the sebaceous contents shrink and become solidified, and in some cases carcinomatous tissue develops in the wall.

Still simpler cysts occur in which the origin from a misplaced blastomere is not so evident. These are the wens or epidermoid cysts, which are found in the scalp, and are lined with stratified epithelium which grows in quantity and is desquamated into the interior to form a soft, flaky substance. They may perhaps be explained as displacements of ectoderm at a much later stage. So, too, with the atheromatous cysts or *branchial cysts*, which are developed from an imperfectly obliterated and isolated part of a branchial cleft. Either cylindrical or squamous epithelium may form their lining, and they sometimes grow in a ramifying way far up behind the ear and down into the neck. In one which we have recently studied the epithelial lining was very thick, and had desquamated enough of its cells to produce a soft, yellowish material like the caseous centre of a tubercle. They are hard to extirpate and tend to recur.

Cholesteatomata.—Another teratoid growth which may occur in the brain in connection with the meninges, or about the hypophysis, is a thin epidermal sac, which, from its abundant content of cholesterine crystals mixed with epidermal scales, is called a cholesteatoma. Such growths

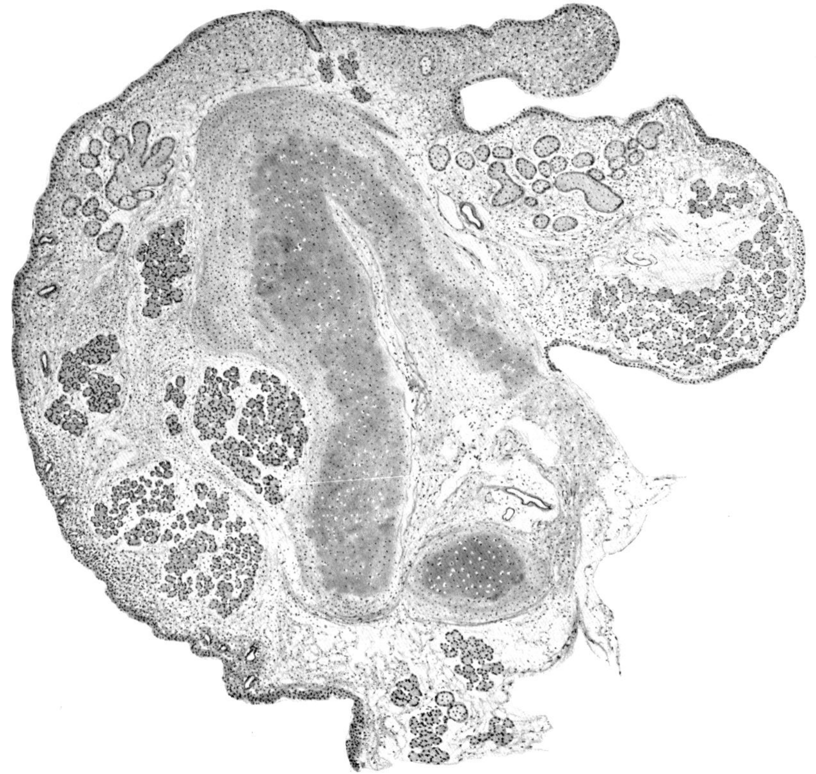

Fig. 571.—Wall of teratomatous cyst of the ovary. There is an epidermal lining with sebacous glands. In the deeper portions there is a mass of cartilage and structures resembling salivary glands.

which are lined with skin-like epidermis, and distended with desquamated epidermal cells, may occur in the orbit, or at times in the middle ear, where they do harm by occupying space.

Mixed Tumors.—This leads us to the composite or *mixed tumors*, which represent the teratomata derived from the isolation of cells already in an advanced state of differentiation, whose capabilities are therefore limited and pretty strictly determined. There is much dispute as to their nature and origin, but this explanation seems to me most acceptable and credible.

Such tumors are found in immediate connection with the salivary glands, in the kidneys in children, in the breast, in the testicle, and elsewhere, but it must not be supposed that they resemble each other in these different situations. All they have in common is the principle upon which they are formed.

Mixed Tumors of the Salivary Glands.—In their gross appearance these tumors resemble one another very closely—they are rounded or nodular,

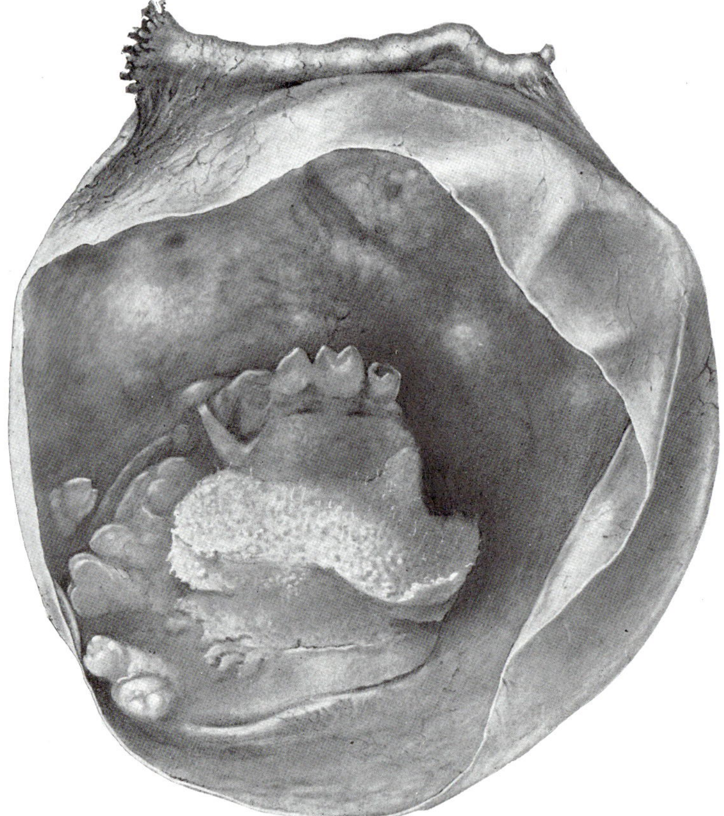

Fig. 572.—Teratomatous cystoma of the ovary, containing teeth and a tongue-like structure covered with hair.

elastic masses, which grow, as a rule, not in the gland, but in close proximity to it, being generally attached to its capsule. They spring in this way from the parotid or submaxillary, and may reach a very great size. On extirpation they may recur, but even then they run a benign course. On section such a tumor presents extensive, rather translucent, areas, with occasional patches of denser opaque tissue and rare points of calcification. Microscopically, the most varied appearances are seen (Fig. 573). The stroma is hyaline or like the matrix of cartilage; there may be true cartilage, mingled with dense fibrous tissue. Everywhere there are masses of cells arranged in tubules or cysts, or in long tapering strands which anastomose and finally fade into the crevices of the stroma. In some cases, but not in all, there are patches of this cellular tissue which are distinctly and unmistakably composed of stratified epithelium with concentric epithelial pearls. These were recognized by Landsteiner, who declared the tumors to be of

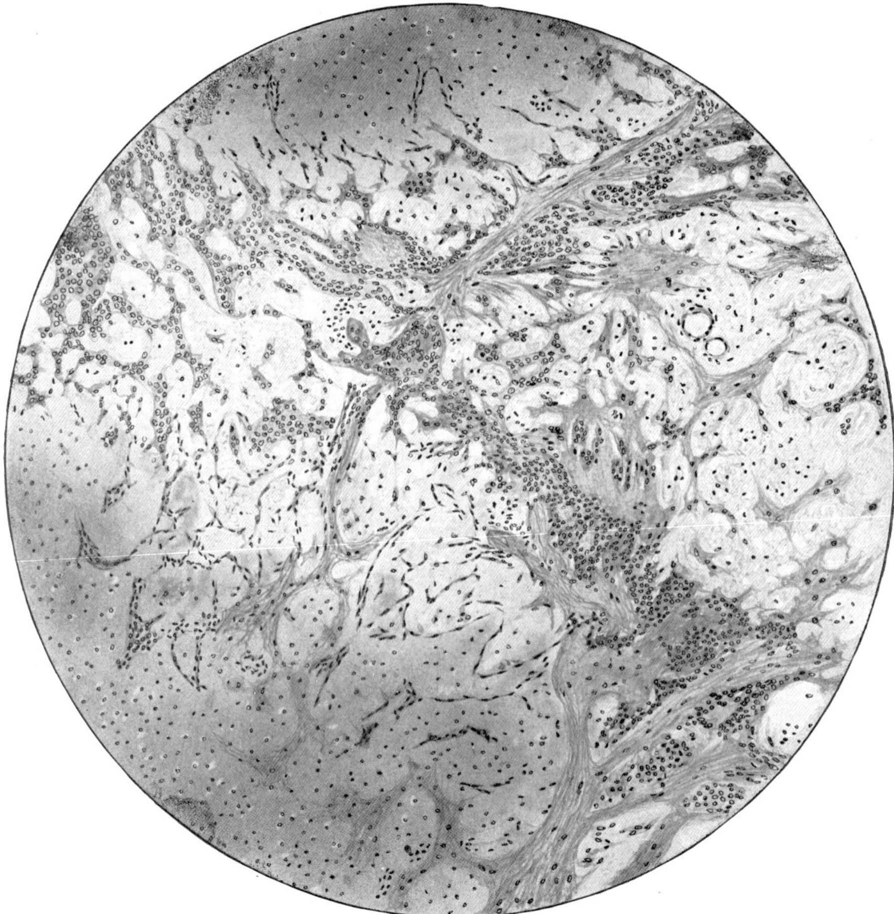

Fig. 573.—Mixed tumor of the parotid gland, showing cartilage and narrow strands of epithelial cells.

epithelial origin. Volkmann had studied many cases, and had decided that the narrow strands of cells were derived from endothelium, and indeed these parotid tumors make up a great part of the material for his monograph on endotheliomata. Krompecher thinks of them as basal-cell tumors. Marchand, Willms, and others regard them now as composite tumors, in which epithelium plays the most prominent part, and trace them to an origin analogous to that of the teratomata, except in that the embryonic rudiment is separated at a later stage.

Composite Tumors of the Kidney.—In infants and children there occur tumors of the kidney which grow to an enormous size, and metastasize into distant organs. They may appear as congenital growths in new-born infants, and are composed of a mixture of tissues in which cartilage, fat, smooth muscle, and myxomatous connective tissue, together with complex arrangements of epithelium, take part. Unlike the hypernephromata, they cause no hæmaturia, and are recognized by their growth to a great mass in the abdomen. Willms, Busse, Hedren, and others discuss their origin at length. While Busse thinks thay may be derived from the kidney, or at least from its embryonal rudiment, Willms places their origin farther back, in the middle plate, after its separation from the myotome. This tissue might well furnish all the elements which are found in such tumors. Striated muscle does not occur, and hence the myotome is not involved, but stratified epithelium does occur, and offers difficulties to Willms' view. Nevertheless the intimate relation of the anterior end of the Wolffian duct to the ectoderm—possibly a remaining trace of its old arrangement as a nephridial tube opening on the skin—may account for this epithelium.

The morphology of these tumors is so variable that no single description will apply. The student is referred to the paper of Hedren, in which the literature is reviewed and in which there are many illustrations. In general, the epithelial cells are small and are arranged in irregular, gland-like tubules, interspersed with solid cords.

Congenital Cystic Kidney.—There is no good place in which to mention this condition, since our knowledge of its nature is so unsatisfactory, and for that reason a brief space may be devoted to it here.

This is a peculiar affection of the kidneys which leads, during embryonic development, to the formation of cysts throughout both kidneys, and frequently to the formation of cysts in the liver as well. Most of the substance of the kidneys is occupied by these cysts, and there is extremely little functional tissue left between them. Yet such people may grow to adult life without knowing that there is anything amiss with their kidneys. In later life they may die of renal insufficiency after the injury of the scarcely sufficient tissue. In infancy the kidneys form huge masses of gelatinous cystic tissue, so large in one case which I studied that they had to be removed before birth was possible. This child was otherwise extensively malformed. Reconstruction (Meader) shows that the cysts may be in immediate relationship with the glomeruli, or may be developed in the first part of the convoluted tubule and connected by a narrow canal with the glomeruli.

Ribbert puts forth a theory that the cysts are caused by interference with the union of the glomerular part of the tubule with the other rudiment, which grows up from the ureter to join it. Hence the glomerular portion dilates into a cyst. The end of the ureteral portion may also become cystic. Others regard the whole process as an adenomatous growth, which it is said might account for the similar growth of cysts in the liver. It seems to me more plausible to base the change on anomalies of embryonic development.

In the adult the cystic kidneys may form two huge tumors occupying the whole abdominal cavity on each side (Fig. 574). At autopsy they are found to be no longer gelatinous, but made up of cysts about the size of a cherry or larger, filled with clear, or dark brown, or turbid fluid. Between these cysts, which are lined with low cubical epithelium, there are scattered normal tubules and glomeruli.

In infants one may occasionally see another type of cystic dilatation of the tubules which occupies the pyramid and leads to the fusiform widening of the conducting tubules.

Composite tumors of the breast are rare and are made up of stratified epithelium, together with various types of connective tissue. They are of less importance than the—

Mixed Tumors of the Testicle.—Perhaps these should not be referred to again, since they are undoubtedly of teratomatous character, but it is intended to emphasize the point that in many of these tumors, whether because of their late origin in the course of embryonic development, or because one tissue has outgrown the others, the structure is relatively

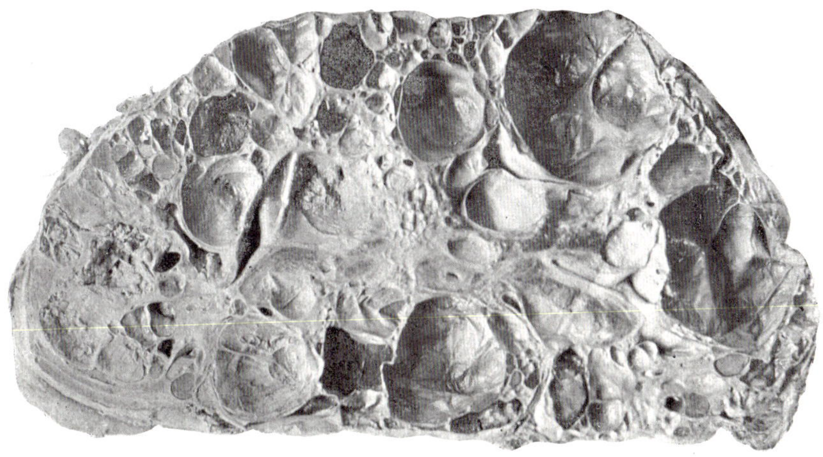

Fig. 574.—Congenital cystic kidney. Remnants of a pelvis are seen in the centre at the lower part of the figure.

simple. The most common tumor of the testicle is that in which in most parts the cells are uniform in appearance and are large round cells, arranged in irregular masses or strands, with a stroma which is infiltrated with lymphocytes (Fig. 575). These are commonly called round-cell sarcomata of the testicle, and possibly this is correct in some cases, but in many others there are transitions to other forms of tissue and admixtures of epithelium which indicate the more complex character of the tumor. Other tumors of the testicle contain cartilage and cysts. Their main tissue is arranged like epithelium, in complex, gland-like structures often resembling an adenocarcinoma. Still other more complicated forms occur, and we find ourselves once more approaching the solid teratomata. Still it is the rule for these testicular tumors that they grow with extreme malignancy, and extend into the spermatic cord and metastasize by way of the veins with great rapidity. In this respect they are unlike the ordinary teratomata, and we must assume that if they began as teratomata they have acquired the character of malignant tumors.

Chordomata.—Mention may be made here of a rather rare tumor which usually springs from the body of the sphenoid bone, and projects into the cranial cavity, compressing the brain and the cranial nerves. Similar tumors may arise from the sacrum and other parts of the vertebral column. They are shown to be malignant by their invasive mode of growth, which

Fig. 575.—Teratomatous tumor of the testicle composed largely of tissue like that of a round-cell sarcoma.

allows them to destroy the bone extensively and to penetrate into veins. Nevertheless, no metastases in other organs have been found. The tumor is lobulated, the lobules being composed of groups and strands of large and small cells in a homogeneous ground-substance which takes a bluish stain with hæmatoxylin. They are rich in glycogen. The work of various authors, and particularly that of Marchand's pupil, Nebelthau, has shown that these growths are derived from remnants of the chorda dorsalis.

LITERATURE

Chorionic Epithelioma of Testicle.—Scott and Longcope: Proc. Path. Soc. Phila., 1909, xii, 8.

Frank: Jour. Amer. Med. Assoc., 1906, xlvi, 248.

Chorionic Epithelioma of Testicle.—Schlagenhaufer: Verh. d. Dtsch. Path. Gesellsch., 1902, v, 209.
Risel: Ergebn. d. allg. Path., 1906, xi_2, 929.
Teratomata in General.—Seydel: Ergebn. d. allg. Path., 1901, vi, 858.
Willms: Die Mischgeschwülste, Leipzig, 1899.
Marchand: Missbildungen: Eulenberg's Realencyklopädie, 1897, xv, 503.
Dermoid Cysts.—Saxer: Ziegler's Beiträge, 1902, xxxi, 452.
Katsurada: *Ibid.*, 1901, xxx, 179.
Salivary Tumors.—Landsteiner: Ztschr. f. Heilkunde, 1901, xxii; Abth. f. path. Anat., 1.
Hinsberg: Dtsch. Ztschr. f. Chir., 1899, li, 281.
Wood: Annals of Surgery, 1904, xxxix, 57.
Mixed Tumors of Kidney.—Hedren: Ziegler's Beiträge, 1907, xl, 1.
Busse: Virch. Arch., 1899, clvii, 346.
Willms: *Loc. cit.*
Congenital Cystic Kidney.—Ribbert: Verh. d. Dtsch. Path. Gesell., 1900, ii, 187.
Busse: Virch. Arch., 1904, clxxv, 442.
Meader: Johns Hopkins Hosp. Bull., 1907, xviii, 354.
Mixed Tumors of Testicle.—Debernardi: Ziegler's Beiträge, 1908, xliii, 89.
Chevassu: Tumeurs du testicule, Paris, 1906.
Chordoma.—Jelliffe and Larkin: Ztschr. f. d. ges. Neurol. u. Psychiat., 1911, v, 590.
Wegelin: Atti del I Congresso Internaz. dei Patologi, Torino, 1911, 70.

CHAPTER LV

CLASSIFICATION OF TUMORS

THE only satisfactory classification of tumors would be on the basis of their ætiology. Since we know nothing of this, they are classed very much as animals or plants would be, on the basis of their most striking characters. The most fundamental available characteristics are: (1) The type of tissue which they resemble, and from which we suppose them to be derived; (2) the degree in which they diverge from the type, and the extent to which they have acquired the power of invasion and colonization, and (3) the form which the tumor assumes, that is, its architecture as a papillary, cystic, glandular, or solid growth.

In other words, we have tumors derived from one or more of the three germ layers, or more specifically from a tissue originating from one of these layers. They may be benign or malignant, and may grow in one or other of the many arrangements adopted by normal tissues, or in combinations or perversions of these forms. Rather than assume too accurate a knowledge of the ultimate derivation of the tumors, I have preferred to arrange them according to the general character of their tissues, both anatomical and biological, and their form.

Other classifications as given in the various text-books and treatises on the subject should be consulted. The following list is mainly for convenience in summarizing the various forms as they have been considered here. It is an arrangement, not a classification.

1. Benign tumors of connective-tissue character:
   - Fibroma.
   - Lipoma.
   - Chondroma.
   - Osteoma.
   - Xanthoma.
2. Tumors composed of tissue of muscular character:
   - Leiomyoma.
   - Rhabdomyoma.
3. Tumors composed of tissue of nervous character:
   - Neurocytoma, neuroblastoma, sympathoblastoma.
   - Ganglioneuroma.
   - Paraganglioma.
   - Glioma.
4. Tumors composed of blood and lymph channels—angiomata:
   - Hæmangioma.
   - Lymphangioma.

5. Malignant tumors of connective-tissue character—sarcomata:
   - Spindle-cell sarcoma.
   - Mixed-cell sarcoma.
   - Round-cell sarcoma.
   - Alveolar sarcoma.
   - Giant-cell sarcoma.
   - Osteosarcoma.
   - Myxoma.
6. Pigmented tumors:
   - Nævus.
   - Melanotic sarcoma or melanoma.
7. Tumor composed of tissue resembling adrenal cortex:
   - Hypernephroma.
8. Tumors thought to originate from endothelium—"endotheliomata":
   - Lymphangioendothelioma.
   - Cylindroma.
   - Pleural and peritoneal tumors.
   - Meningeal tumors.
   - Hæmangioendothelioma.
9. Benign epithelial tumors:
   - Papilloma.
   - Adenoma.
   - Cystadenoma.
10. Malignant epithelial tumors—carcinomata.
    - Flat-celled epithelioma.
    - Adamantinoma.
    - Basal-cell cancer.
    - Cylindrical-cell cancer or adenocarcinoma.
    - Gland-cell cancer.
11. Chorionic epithelioma.
12. Mixed tumors and teratoma.

CHAPTER LVI

GENERAL DISCUSSION OF TUMORS

General character of tumors; relation to tissues of host. Their independence of the laws governing the growth of normal tissues; consequent abnormal architecture and metabolism. Distinction between tumors and infectious processes. Nature of cells of tumors; specific relation to those of host; relation to embryonic stages of cell development; atypical character. Growth; implantation, extension, metastasis, recurrence. Contributory causes of tumor growth: injury and irritation (physical, chemical, parasitic; Rous' filterable tumor); internal secretions; malformations; disposition; senility; heredity.
Resistance and immunity.
Theories as to the ætiology of tumors: Theory of parasitic origin of tumors; theory of tumor growth as the effect of irritants; theories emphasizing a disturbance of equilibrium of tissues; Cohnheim's theory; Ribbert's theory; theories of tumor growth depending upon changes in the cells.

General Character of Tumor.—Up to this point we have considered the characters of tumors as though they were plants in a garden, observing their general structure and their mode of growth in individual cases. It is necessary now to make an attempt to learn whether there are common features in these respects, and whether we can discover the causes of their appearance and growth and of their peculiar relations to the host. Otherwise it must remain extremely difficult to give a definition of what a tumor really is.

It is clear from what has been said of all these tumors that they are composed of the tissue of the host. This was recognized by Johannes Müller, and in spite of Virchow's rather generous idea that carcinomata, as well as other tumors, might be formed in a connective-tissue matrix, Waldeyer insisted that the specific relation was closer and that cancers which are composed of epithelium could arise only from epithelium. After that the intimate relationship of each tumor to one form or other of normal tissue was looked for and usually found, although we are still puzzled to trace this relationship in many cases.

But if it is possible to feel sure that a given tumor is of epithelial or connective-tissue origin, or even that it belongs to the stratified or cylindrical epithelium, it is nevertheless equally certain that it does not resemble that tissue precisely.

The laws which govern the growth of normal human tissue and organs are very rigid. The form of the normal cells is so constant, and their relations to one another in the architecture of the organ so fixed, that we become familiar with their appearance, and instantly recognize any divergence from the accepted form. We know well too what changes occur in the morphology of normal cells as the result of variations in their functional activity, and, above all, we know the plan upon which they grow. Their reactions in all these respects, to a great variety of recognizable injuries and pathological disturbances, are very familiar, and we realize that under those circumstances the cells and tissues still obey the laws which govern their growth under normal conditions, and strive to restore as quickly as possible the forms and relations which have been established by ages of evolution.

In tumors we find the cells abnormal in form, in their relations to one another, and in their relation to surrounding tissues. They are abnormal in every functional activity, and in many cases in their increased vigor of growth. Great stress is usually laid upon this increased energy of growth, although in many tumors it is at a very low ebb, and in the most rapidly invading forms is not to be compared with that of the growing embryo.

The really essential difference between tumors and normal tissue is not the increased energy of growth, but the emancipation of the tissue from obedience to the laws which govern the growth of normal tissues. That this is closely related to the abnormality in the form of the cells is probable. It is as a direct expression of this complete lawlessness that the tissue produced by these cells has no regular architectural arrangement, that it never forms organs that could be of any possible use, and that it pays no regard to the rights of other organs, but bursts its way recklessly through their boundaries and their tissues, destroying their cells as it goes. Its behavior is like a complete disregard of international law, which has been established for the welfare of the whole world.

In the development of the body some people may hold that the equilibrium which is maintained between various tissues depends entirely upon the power of each to grow, but it is evident enough that a balance is maintained by a higher law than this, and that such an organ as the liver does not maintain a precise number of cells, because it has not the power to form more, but because the law of the general welfare demands that many, and no more. If some are destroyed, or if the general situation is changed, the liver will form more cells to restore precisely the balance. Hence even though it can be defined only vaguely, we are aware that there is a delicate but effective power which controls, possibly by way of the nervous system, the relations of tissues to one another. They are disciplined, and grow when they are required, but not of their own initiative.

It is far otherwise with tumors. No tumor of glandular character has a duct, nor have its glands any such arrangement that they could discharge a secretion. It is true that tumors of the organs of internal secretion may sometimes form a useful secretion, but one has the impression that this is a rare occurrence and inadvertent on their part. No tumors are known to be under the control of the nervous system. They seem to have no nerves except those accidentally enclosed in their growth and possibly vasomotor nerves in their blood-vessels. It is true that Young was able to demonstrate the nerve-fibres in a number of tumors by staining with methylene-blue, but he could not show that they really belonged to the tumor tissue, and, as far as I can learn, no one has been more successful. Tumors are not even subject to the normal conditions of nutrition, and withstand in the most surprising way starvation which causes the rest of the body to waste. A lipoma in a starving animal remains a plump tumor, distended with fat when all the other fat has disappeared. It is true that Moreschi found that, by starving mice inoculated with a tumor, he could inhibit its growth, but Rous found that if the tumor were well established, it continued to grow. In human beings the contrast between the appearance of huge cancerous growths in full progress, and extreme emaciation of the rest of the body, is often very striking.

Thus the isolation and independence of the tumor form the essential difference between its nature and that of the normal tissues. In virtue of this it behaves in such a way as to be, in nearly every instance, harmful to its host, either through occupying space and requiring nutrition, or by actually invading and destroying useful tissues. Since tumors are composed of human tissues, however, we cannot accept this inimical attitude as a natural thing as we would in the case of an animal parasite, and every effort has been directed toward learning why and how such independence has been attained.

Notwithstanding this general statement that a tumor is a growth of abnormal tissue which is largely independent of the laws governing and controlling the growth of normal tissues, it is often very difficult to decide what is, and what is not, to be called a tumor. Histological study often leaves us uncertain, and some growths are so sluggish that even a survey of their whole biological relations is hardly sufficient to inform us as to whether they have arisen as a response to some injury, or are really independent and transgressing the regulations which govern the normal tissues. Indeed, we not infrequently discover that something which has long been regarded as a tumor is really the slow product of a chronic infection, and Virchow's great book, Die krankhaften Geschwülste, is, perhaps intentionally, full of such examples. Tumors are simulated, on the one hand, by the reactions of the body to infection and injury, which often produce considerable masses of new and peculiar tissue; on the other hand, by malformations and displacements of tissue, with which, as has already been shown, their relations are especially intimate. Whether we can draw a boundary line to separate sharply the group of tumors from these is doubtful. It is relatively easy in the case of such typical malignant tumors as the carcinomata, but not easy when we consider such processes as Hodgkin's disease, leukæmia, leukosarcoma, lymphosarcoma, and round-cell sarcoma. In the case of *x*-ray burns, psoriasis, xeroderma, etc., it is not even easy to say when the normal reaction ceases and tumor growth begins; nor at the other extreme is it easy to determine when a mixed tumor becomes a teratoma, or where the term teratoma should be given up and reference be made to an imperfect or abnormal fœtus, or even to a twin brother.

It seems, however, that if we were able, in each instance, to decide accurately as to whether the normal laws of growth had been broken or not, we could outline sharply the whole group of tumors. The independence of tumors involves the progressive and unlimited character of their growth. They never reach any goal and are never complete, nor do their cells ever reach any stage comparable to maturity and functional perfection. The reaction to infection and mechanical or chemical irritation keeps pace with the injury; it exists only so long as the injury persists, and then, in complete obedience to the laws of growth and the regulation of the internal relations of the tissues, returns as quickly as possible to the normal. Misplaced embryonic tissues, no matter how complicated, proceed to the ordinary maturity of the tissue, and then remain as stationary as normal tissues. They are still abnormal and harmful to the host because they are out of place, but not because they are actively transgressing the law of the interrelation of organs. Of course, many teratomata show themselves ultimately to be malignant tumors, but these are instances in which a tumor has developed in the tissues of a teratoma and grown to invade the tissues of the host. Such a tumor grows usually from only one of the types of tissue which make up the teratoma, and is precisely comparable to a tumor which develops anywhere else in the host. So too after long irritation or infection the reacting tissue may reveal itself as a carcinoma, but it is a tumor which has freshly developed in pathological tissue, just as it might anywhere else. Far more often the reacting tissue does not give rise to a tumor growth.

If in such an obscure condition as Hodgkin's disease we were able to remove or destroy an infectious agent and to observe thereupon the immediate retrogression of the tumor-like nodules, we might conclude at once that they were not true tumors. Since we have not definitely recognized an infectious agent, we are not quite sure whether Hodgkin's disease is a tumor or not. How, then, one may well ask, can we be sure that cancers and sarcomata are not infectious processes, since we do not know their cause? We are *not* sure, and although every bit of evidence points to their being of a different character, we cannot be absolutely sure until some other cause of their growth is definitely demonstrated.

In this state of knowledge it seems best to hold to the one striking feature of tumor growth as contrasted with that of other tissue growth—its independence of the mechanical laws which govern the hereditary form of the body.

Of course, we must some day discover the cause of this alteration in the behavior of the tumor-cells, and it is conceivable that it may prove to be some parasite which accompanies or lives in the cells, perverting their course of life from that which is normal, and keeping them forever growing and dividing to produce new cells. It is difficult to imagine, however, what kind of parasite that could be. One may implant a carcinoma of a mouse into a normal mouse and from that, after it has grown, transplant a fragment to another mouse, and repeat this for hundreds of generations until the mouse from which the tumor was originally taken, and all its contemporaries and their offspring, have been dead for years of old age, and still the tumor-cells are alive and thriving with exactly the same anatomical and histological characters that they possessed at first. It is a kind of artificial immortality that seems to require only nutrition, and none of the reinvigoration which other living things usually gain from a sexual union with their kind. Nevertheless, it is not yet proved that unicellular organisms die after long periods of multiplication by fission without sexual conjugation, and Woodruff seems to hold that they may go on indefinitely in this way. Plants, such as banana trees, have in the same way been cultivated for hundreds of years from cuttings without any recourse to fertilization and seed planting.

We may pause here to review the general character of tumor growths before discussing the theories which have been proposed as to their causation.

GENERAL CHARACTERS OF TUMOR GROWTH

Tumors are composed of the tissues of the host, as has long been agreed, in spite of such efforts as those of Kelling, who attempted to prove that they are made up of the tissues of cows, pigs, or chickens which had been used for food. By the enormous amount of work which has been done in the last ten years in transplanting tumors from one animal to another it has been shown that their tissues are exquisitely specific and will grow continuously only in another animal of the same species. Thus a carcinoma of a white mouse will grow in another white mouse, but fails to reach any considerable size in a gray, or wild mouse, or in a rat, and finally undergoes retrogression. This explains easily the complete failure of those experiments in which it has been attempted to transplant human tumors to dogs, rabbits, and other animals. Even in monkeys such transplants have failed.

Resemblance to Normal Cells.—We have observed in previous chapters the extent of the resemblance of tumors to normal tissues both in appearance and in histological characters, and have realized that there are extreme variations, so that, while the cells of some tumors are almost precisely like the normal cells, even in their arrangement (thyroid tumors, etc.), others depart very widely from this form and become quite unrecognizable. We have learned that many tumors are composed of cells which seem to belong unquestionably to the same stage of development as those of the surrounding tissues, while others are made up of tumor-cells which have the morphology and arrangement, and possibly also the biological characters of the cells of some tissue in the early stages of its development. Examples of the latter condition are found in the neuroblastomata, in which cells belonging to an early stage in the development of the sympathetic nervous system persist in that stage, and multiply excessively to form a tumor, and in rhabdomyomata, which contain cells resembling embryonic muscle-cells. Nevertheless, I have never used the expression "return to an embryonic state" in speaking of such tumors as sarcomata, which are commonly spoken of as composed of "undifferentiated" or "unripe," connective tissue, because I do not believe that there is evidence to show that there is anything embryonic about that tissue. It is true that the cells are unlike the normal cells, but they do not especially resemble the connective-tissue cells of the embryo, and are often extremely unlike them. It seems far more plausible that they are cells so modified that their sole function is to reproduce themselves rapidly, for which reason they never assume the form of the normal cells, nor lie dormant in abundant intercellular substance. It is conceivable that they are cells which have, like the neuroblasts, never passed the embryonic stage of development, but this is a difficult explanation which is neither required nor supported by any facts. It does not seem at all probable that any cell of a mature animal can ever return to the embryonic condition. Even those cells of the blood-forming organs which continually produce new blood-cells, and the cells of the epidermis, which form new epithelial cells, are in no true sense embryonic cells. They have retained the function of becoming differentiated into one type of cell, but are even then far advanced from the condition of embryonic cells. The idea that cells may in tumor formation return to the embryonic state is based no doubt upon the desire to explain their new energy of growth, but this new character of their growth is not at all like that of embryonic cells. In the embryo, the cells pass through a definite development to become mature. If they grow rapidly, it is only in this respect that the cells of a tumor resemble them, because tumor-cells pass through no such regular development but merely continue to grow and divide. They do not approach the character of the embryonic cells, but assume a totally new character, in which they only roughly resemble the cells of the embryo in form and in the rate at which they grow. It is difficult enough to believe that embryonic cells can be isolated and remain latent for years embedded in the normal growing tissues, but far more difficult to believe that normal cells, once matured, can return to the embryonic state. For the former possibility we have proofs; for the latter we have no evidence whatever, so far as I can see.

Although we speak so easily of deriving tumor-cells from tissue of one type or another, we really depend largely upon their morphological resemblance for our proof of the relation. It is possible that we are often wrong in this, but, on the whole, the chance of error seems relatively slight.

Dependence upon Host for Nutrition.—Tumors, whatever the independence of their cells, are dependent upon their host for their nutrition. If the host dies, the tumor dies too. If a blood-vessel is plugged in a tumor, the area which should be supplied with blood becomes an infarct, just as it would in the kidney. Bashford has compared the mouse, in which a huge tumor larger than itself is growing, to a sort of nutritive machine engaged in feeding the tumor. Its heart hypertrophies to keep up the pumping of blood through the enormous mass of new tissue. Its liver and sometimes its kidneys enlarge. Price Jones found no great modification in the differential count of the bone-marrow of these animals, but states that there was great enlargement of the spleen. Studies of the vascular supply of tumors by methods of injection show that great numbers of blood-vessels run to the rapidly growing tumor—numbers far in excess of those which supply normal tissues. These are new formed at the demand of the growing tumor, and carry with them the supporting stroma of connective tissue. Bashford and his co-workers make much of the importance of the stroma, which they think is specifically adapted to each type of tumor. It is their belief that it is only in animals which respond by the production of an adequate stroma and blood supply that an implanted tumor can succeed in growing. Others lay much less stress upon the importance of the stroma.

When a tumor is implanted in a susceptible animal, its stroma and part of its specific cells undergo necrosis, but the surviving tumor-cells grow and are quickly invaded by a new stroma formed from the host, with new blood-vessels. It seems clear that the tumor-cells act as a dominant tissue, controlling and stirring up the development of the vascular stroma, practically as epithelial cells do in the development of an organ in the embryo. Subservient as this stroma is, it does not always remain so. Ehrlich and others have found that, after a time, when a carcinoma has been implanted, the stroma itself may assume the characters of tumor tissue, and grow vigorously as a sarcoma, oppressing and finally destroying the epithelial cells. Such a tumor, when transplanted, may continue its growth as a sarcoma, extorting now the new formation of another vascular stroma from its host.

Still, nothing has been observed as to the ingrowth of nerves into such a tumor, although this would seem to be a matter of the utmost importance. Little is written of the formation of lymphatic channels, although we know by injection experiments (Evans) that lymphatics are present in abundance in human tumors of many sorts.

Atypical Character of Tumor-cells-Adaptation.—All the tumor-cells are atypical in the ways mentioned. They are characterized not only by their powers of growth, but especially by their tendency to continue indefinitely to divide and produce new cells, regardless of any need or of any plan for the arrangement of these new cells or even of the existence of any space in which they can be lodged, and these new cells proceed in the same aimless way to produce others. That they are specifically related to animals of their own species is shown by their ability to grow indefinitely, in contact with the tissues of that species only. But the adaptation can be intensified by repeated transplantation into animals of the same species, for at first it is necessary to transplant a great number of pieces from a spontaneous tumor into as many mice in order to obtain one successful implantation. After that, however, with repeated transplantations the tumor acquires the power to grow in practically every mouse. This does not necessarily mean that it grows more rapidly, or more destructively, or to a larger size. It is merely a matter of adaptation to its surroundings, and whether we regard the cell as independently originating the growth, or as impelled by some parasite, the explanation of the adaptation must be the same.

FORM OF GROWTH, EXTENSION; IMPLANTATION; METASTASIS

The form of the growth is, as we have learned, extremely variable, and there are all gradations between tumors which surround themselves with a smooth capsule and grow expansively, and those which scatter their isolated cells like spray in every direction, or send out long threads of cells which insinuate themselves between the cells and fibres of the tissues, and even into the walls of blood-vessels and lymphatics. The former mode of growth usually appears in a benign tumor, the latter in a malignant tumor. These two forms are doubtless in large part the expression of differences in the rate and continuity of multiplication of the cells. The encapsulated benign form is far less exposed to the action of the cells and fluids of the organism than the spreading malignant form. Through this very fact the latter seems to become adapted to existence anywhere in the body, and is thereby aided in spreading and even in establishing colonies in distant organs.

As to the spread or extension, we have already described several forms.

Implantations.—In the older literature there were many descriptions of instances in which a carcinoma was thought to be transmitted by contact to another person. Some of these were cases in which, through intimate contact, as in the transfer of a genital carcinoma from husband to wife or the reverse, there was a semblance of probability, but in others, in which, for example, a nurse contracted a carcinoma of the breast from tending a patient with a similar carcinoma, there was unquestionably only a coincidence. Recent reports of such occurrences are rare. There are, however, instances of implantation of a tumor upon contiguous epithelial surfaces in the same individual, as, for example, the formation of a carcinoma of the vagina opposite the ulcerated surface of a carcinoma of the cervix uteri. These, too, seem questionable, and it is perhaps more probable that such tumors are really due to transportation by way of the lymph-channels, although theoretically there is no reason why some abrasion of the opposite mucous surface should not allow the implantation of cancer-cells.

Much more familiar is the implantation of the cells of a tumor in the raw edges of a wound made for the extirpation of the growth, with the development of nodules in the resulting scar. Even this is a rather uncommon occurrence, however. Within the body, the implantation of free fragments of tumor or tumor-cells is frequently seen in the peritoneal cavity and other serous cavities. It is especially common with papillomatous cystadenomata of the ovary and with colloid carcinomata, but it occurs also with various other tumors. Whether the nodules so often found on the surface of the lungs as growths secondary to a carcinoma, or sarcoma situated elsewhere are produced by implantation from the pleural cavity or by extension from the substance of the lung is rather difficult to tell. They occur as large, button-like nodules, or as smaller masses like beads, or even as tiny, flattened, confluent, or discrete thickenings of the pleura, and in every case they are continuous with growths of tumor-cells in the underlying lymph-channels. Sometimes these extend in the interlobular spaces or in the walls of blood-vessels or bronchi quite through the lung to the hilum, where the lymph-glands are generally involved. Thus it is possible that the tumor may have grown from the hilum or any part of the lung through the lymphatics to the surface, spreading out and developing there, and, indeed, in the absence of a tumor mass invading the pleural cavity this seems the more probable course. In other cases in which a tumor of the stomach or gall-bladder has distributed metastases on the under side of the diaphragm, the course of its extension to the pleural cavity and the surface of the lungs can be readily traced through the diaphragmatic lymphatics.

Extension.—The actual extension of an invasive tumor occurs, as we have seen, through the growth of strands of tumor-cells into the interstices of the surrounding tissue. These cells may become really isolated, but, as a rule, the strands or threads of cells maintain their continuity for a long time. With the widening of the strands the peripheral parts of the tumor become more condensed and the intervening normal tissue is destroyed. Frequently the advancing margin is much more compact, and the normal tissue is largely pushed aside and compressed, so that the tumor grows by the invasion of coarse projecting masses. In many instances these, as well as the finer strands, are guided by meeting with a dense fascia or other resistant tissue, and spread along its surface.

Far more commonly, however, the cells break through the walls of *lymphatic channels* and spread themselves like an injection mass along their lumina so as to fill them completely. This is particularly characteristic of the carcinomata, and has been studied carefully for such cancers as are of common occurrence (breast, uterus, etc.). Handley finds that the extension in carcinoma of the breast is through the plexus of lymphatic channels which accompany the fasciæ, and that these may become obliterated after the tumor has moved along their course. Thus in a wide halo around the tumor there are lymph-channels full of tumor-cells ready to grow into nodules or to wander farther, although the obliterated channels by which they reached that point are no longer visible. That this network of lymphatics in the deeper part of the skin and in the fasciæ may act in this way is shown by the numerous small tumor nodules which often appear in these regions, quite far from the original tumor. Handley, therefore, suggests that an extremely wide area of skin should be removed in order to extirpate the tumor completely.

Metastasis.—Even more familiar and common is the transportation of loose clumps of tumor-cells, or even single cells, by the stream of lymphatic fluid along the course of the channel until they are caught and held in the complex sinuses of a lymph-gland. Since the distribution of the lymphatics is well known, one may foretell easily which gland is likely to receive the first emboli of this nature. There the tumor-cells develop into a new tumor which gradually invades and replaces the tissue of the lymph-gland. Other emboli of the cells may pass to more distant lymph-glands, or the process may be repeated with the metastatic nodule as the source for new emboli. If such floating cells reach the thoracic duct, they may lodge in its walls and there grow, but they are far more likely to be swept on into the blood-stream, whence they are caught up in the capillaries of the lungs.

While such metastasis by way of the lymphatic channels is very common for carcinomata, it is somewhat less common for sarcomata and some other malignant tumors. These tend to grow in such a way as to penetrate the walls of the veins and discharge themselves directly into the blood-stream. Carcinomata do this also and it is by no means uncommon to find metastatic nodules which could be explained in no other way than by a transportation of the carcinoma cells by way of the blood. The invasion of sarcomata is frequently a very gross process, so that great masses of the tumor hang in the vein, or fill it completely. This is especially true of the hypernephromata, and we have already described a case in which the whole vena cava was filled with a tumor mass. The carcinomata primary in the liver exhibit the same tendency.

The transportation of liberated cells proceeds, of course, with the stream of blood, and we should expect to find them lodged, first of all, in the lungs. That this is commonly the case is shown by the development of numerous tumor nodules in the lung tissue, but it is quite common to find metastases only in the liver, or in some other organ in the systemic circulation. Of course, if the primary tumor is situated in the intestinal tract, it is easy to comprehend that the tumor-cells carried by the portal blood should lodge and grow in the liver, but in other cases we must assume that the floating cells have passed through the wide capillaries of the lung to reach the other organs, unless there are also large metastases in the lungs themselves from which a secondary embolism might occur.

Distribution of Metastases.—Numerous curious distributions of metastases occur, as when a neuroblastoma beginning in the adrenal gives rise to multiple secondary growths which are confined to the liver, or when a carcinoma of the prostate establishes practically all its secondary growths in the marrow of the bones. Virchow made the statement that in those organs in which tumors are commonly primary, metastases rarely occur, while primary growths are rare in those situations which seem to form the best soil for secondary nodules. Thus the stomach and uterus are common sources of primary tumors, but rarely the seat of metastases, while the reverse is true of the liver. Although this cannot be said to be universally true, it introduces the suggestion that certain tissues form an especially suitable ground upon which the tumor-cells may take root and thrive, and, further, that this is not the same for all types of tumors. Indeed, there are many tissues, such as the pancreas, thyroid, heart-wall, muscle, etc., which seem especially unsuited to support the growth of the tumor-cells, although these tissues must receive many emboli. There is no difficulty in accepting the idea that the tumor-cells may slip through the capillaries of the lungs, for in many cases they are not much larger than the blood-cells and ought to pass readily. It should be realized, however, that many emboli must pass into the organs and even into those most favorable to their growth, without ever developing into tumor-nodules. Instead, as M. B. Schmidt has shown, they are surrounded by minute thrombi and later destroyed.

The secondary growth may far outstrip in size the primary tumor: As a rule, it reproduces the histological structure of the primary nodule with considerable fidelity, so that one may often form an idea of the position of that tumor by examining the secondary growth. Nevertheless, as Hansemann points out, the metastasis tends to diverge further from the normal architecture than did the primary growth. A tertiary nodule, derived by metastasis from the secondary one, might show an even greater departure from the normal. Hansemann describes this as an increase in *anaplasia,* by which he means a peculiar divergence from the normal morphology and functional nature which is characteristic of tumor-cells and which is often associated with irregularities in the process of mitosis.

Nature of Metastasis.—The phenomena of metastatic growth show that the formation of a tumor in a distant organ depends upon the transportation of the cells of the original tumor to a new site, and the secondary nodule is seen to develop from these cells, and to reproduce the type of tissue which makes up the original growth. This is a totally different process from the metastasis which occurs in infections, in which we can recognize the causative agent, since there the infective agent alone is transported, and any nodule of new tissue which it may produce in the new situation is seen to be derived entirely from the tissue of the organ in which it lodges. It is the result of the reaction of those tissues to injury, and proceeds according to the well-known laws which govern the behavior of normal tissues when they act in unison to combat an injury. In the tumor-nodule one tissue opposes another—the local tissue antagonizes the immigrant tissue. If we assume that a parasite is the cause of the growth of tumor-cells, we have no evidence that it can exist without them, for we never find secondary tumors derived from the tissues of the organs in which they form. Since such hypothetical parasites must be so closely dependent upon the cells originally affected as to be practically an inseparable constituent of them, it is quite as easy to assume that the cells themselves take the initiative in the abnormal process.

Recurrences.—Tumors removed at operation may recur in the same place, or in the neighborhood, and from this it must be assumed that, in the field of operation, particles or cells have been left in the tissues which may grow again after the wound has progressed toward healing. This may be because the excision was not extensive enough to include in the extirpation all the prolongations of the tumor, or because, in the course of the manipulations, loose cells were strewn in the exposed wound surface. Regional recurrences which appear in the skin or deeper tissues at a little distance from the site of the original tumor are explained as growths from those lymphatics filled with tumor-cells which have been shown to radiate from the original growth.

CONTRIBUTORY CAUSES OF TUMOR GROWTH

It may be said in advance that nothing is known of the actual cause of tumor growth. Nevertheless, there are several things which must be seriously considered as bearing some relation to the development of tumors, since they have long been known to be intimately associated with the beginning of their growth, and have been regarded as predisposing or contributory causes. These are as follows: injury or irritation of physical or chemical nature with chronic inflammation; the effect of disturbances of internal secretions; malformations and displacements of tissue, and such general predisposing conditions as senility and inherited tendencies.

As causes of irritation, numerous parasites of all kinds have been described, but in no case has a definite causal relation been proven.

Injuries and Irritation.—Single severe injuries, such as blows or fractures, have frequently been followed by the development of a sarcomatous tumor, although rarely by a carcinoma. Thousands of such injuries have no such result, however, and it may well be questioned whether the connection is not an accidental one. Injuries which produce scars have sometimes resulted in a very striking way in the formation of a cancer in the scar. Thus a girl was burnt from shoulder to hip and recovered with a scar covering that whole area. Years later, a huge carcinoma appeared occupying the site of the scar (v. Bergmann).

Chronic or repeated mechanical irritation, the changes produced by light, *x*-rays, and radium, and by chemical irritants and bacteria, are more generally associated with the development of carcinoma. After explaining that they lead to chronic inflammatory processes and scar formation, which forms a transition between trauma and tumor formation, Borst summarizes the well-known examples of such tumors as follows:

Carcinoma occurs in the penis in cases of phimosis, in the tongue and cheek in association with the irritation of a carious tooth, in the mammary gland from pressure of a corset. There are the lip cancer of pipe-smokers, cancers of the gall-bladder, renal pelvis, and urinary bladder in connection with stone formation, the cancers of the ostia of the body and the normally narrow passages in the digestive tract, the occupational cancers, paraffin, tar, and chimneysweep's cancers, cancer of the bladder and kidney in aniline workers, pulmonary cancer of metal workers, workers in spinning mills and cigar factories, the carcinoma on the basis of chronic eczema (Paget's, Darier's diseases), on the basis of ulcerations (ulcer of leg, ulcer of stomach), carcinoma developing in fistulæ and scars, carcinoma following chronic endometritis, cystitis, chronic syphilis, and tuberculosis of the skin, cirrhosis of the liver, chronic nephritis, and various skin diseases, such as leucoplakia, hyperkeratoses, polyps, and condylomata.

In this heterogeneous collection the common principle appears to be the long-standing irritation which brings about inflammatory reaction, destruction and replacement of tissue, with distortion and disarrangement of cells. Nevertheless, since there are many more cases in which the same irritations never result in cancer formation, no one believes that they are an efficient cause of its development. No one has ever succeeded in producing a cancer experimentally by subjecting animals to such influences so that there must be another main cause which remains hidden.

B. Fischer found that the injection into the skin of Scharlach R or Sudan III, dissolved in oil, would, if the solution were injected with force, result in the production of an extraordinary tumor-like growth of epithelium. Others have confirmed this, and Helmholz was able to produce in this way a tumor composed of cartilage. With the absorption of the stain and the oil these growths gradually recede and disappear. They never form metastases.

Certain aniline bases had a similar but much less marked effect, and a 4 per cent. solution of ether in water was found by others to accelerate greatly and intensify the growth of tissues. Askanazy found that implanted embryonic tissue, if first treated with ether water, would grow into a large teratoma, more bulky than those which grew without this treatment. Loeb and others have pointed out that these are all lipoid solvents, and that their effect is in some way related to the existence of a lipoid capsule about each cell.

It has already been stated that carcinomata have been found to develop in the scars and eczematous areas produced by the action of x-rays and radium. No good explanation is offered for this, but it seems that this is the one method by which it might be attempted to produce malignant tumors by experimental means with some chance of success.

The part played by parasites has been studied at enormous length, and every conceivable sort of parasite has been described, both such as resemble known organisms, and such as have no resemblance to any recognized living thing. Bacteria of several sorts have been incriminated, and the *Micrococcus neoformans* of Doyen is perhaps the one most widely known. Blastomyces and yeasts have been cultivated from many tumors, and have been inoculated into animals with various results, sometimes producing tumor-like nodules. But none of these has stood before the ordinary tests which are applied to the recognition of the causal relation of bacteria in infectious diseases. Borrel has tried to show the intimate relationship between certain acarians, including the *Demodex folliculorum,* and epithelial tumor growth, and has insisted that, even though they may have no power in themselves to cause the growth of the tumor, they may transfer the unknown virus from one animal to another. The number of spontaneous tumors in mice kept in cages infected with these mites is very striking. Somewhat similar is the observation of Fibiger, who found that a type of flat-cell epithelioma of the stomach and œsophagus occurs in rats in which a peculiar nematode worm, a species of *spiroptera* which passes its larval stage in the cockroach, is found embedded among the cells of the tumor. Such tumors could be produced in normal rats by feeding with cockroaches containing the larvæ. Metastases are found in distant organs in which no nematodes or their eggs are discoverable. Fibiger thinks that the tumor is produced by the irritating action of some poison formed by the nematode, and states that this is the first instance of the experimental production of a metastasing tumor.

Analogous to this are the numerous observations of the development of carcinomata in the bladder-wall in Bilharzia infection, in the liver in infection with other trematodes (*Opisthorchis, Distomum Japonicum,* etc.), and in the neighborhood of cysticerci from tæniæ in various situations. Most interesting in this and other connections are the studies of Rous, who discovered a peculiar tumor of a hen which he was able to transplant to other hens of the same breed. The tumor in the course of repeated transplantation acquired an astounding power of growth and adaptation and could be successfully inoculated by the mere introduction into tissues of a needle which had been plunged into the growth. It was, then, possible to transplant it to fowl of other breeds. The tumor has the form of a sarcoma with long, spindle-shaped, and branched cells, and produces huge tumor masses in the connective tissues of the fowl. Most significant, however, is the fact that this tumor can be successfully transmitted by the inoculation of dried and powdered material, or even by the injection, into the tissues, of a clear, *cell-free* fluid, obtained by filtering a suspension through a Berkefeld filter. Naturally, there has been much difference of opinion as to whether this is a true tumor or the reaction of connective tissue to some extraordinary infection. The fact that it may be transmitted by a cell-free filtrate seems to indicate that it is caused by an extremely minute living organism.

Effects of Internal Secretions in Relation to Tissue and Tumor Growth.—There are many examples of the extraordinary growths of tissues which appear to be associated with activity of the organs of internal secretion, and most of these have been mentioned elsewhere. The growth of the breasts during pregnancy, of the antlers of the deer during the season of rut, of various transitory tissue masses in frogs and salamanders, and fishes during the analogous period, are instances in point. The theory of Fraenkel and Born, which is to the effect that the secretion of the corpus luteum is necessary to the proper progress of pregnancy, may throw some light on the development of malignant growths from the chorionic epithelium, since masses of persistent corpus luteum tissue are found in the enlarged ovaries in many of those cases. L. Loeb has even suggested that the internal secretion of the ovary or some of its derivatives has an influence upon the growth of mammary cancer, for mice castrated at an early age were found to develop cancer in far fewer cases than those not castrated.

Malformations.—The relation of tumor growth to malformation has already been discussed in describing teratomata, and will be referred to again in connection with theories of the causation of tumors. It is of interest here, as an example of the contributory causes of tumor growth, to recall the fact that malignant tumors frequently develop from one tissue of a teratomatous growth and metastasize alone, although in the absence of this specific change such teratomata are benign. The mere displacement and subsequent development of embryonic tissue does not lead to true tumor growth.

Disposition; Senility; Heredity.—We have some vague information with regard to these predisposing causes of tumor growth, but it is unsatisfactory. That there may be a constitutional tendency to the development of a tumor may easily be said, but it is, after all, a matter about which only a general impression can be gained. Hereditary transmission of tumor growth or rather of susceptibility to tumor growth should be accessible to more exact investigation. Bashford, in analyzing English statistics, concludes that there is no evidence whatever to show the existence of any such hereditary taint, and states that in his thousands of experimental animals there has been nothing to show that it occurs. Even when carcinoma animals were intentionally inbred, so as to increase the chance of inheritance, no larger number of spontaneous tumors was found than occurred in normal mice. Murray shows, however, in a later paper from Bashford's laboratory, that the incidence of spontaneous cancer is much higher in mice, whose immediate ancestors developed cancer, than in those in whose pedigree only remote ancestors were cancerous. Tyzzer found that the susceptibility of a parent mouse to inoculation with a certain tumor may be transmitted to its offspring even though the other parent be insusceptible, and Maud Slye, from a large experience with mice, states that spontaneous tumors occur in the offspring of those which have had tumors, in accordance with Mendel's law. Much remains to be learned in this matter.

The incidence as affected by age is more clearly recorded. It is a matter of general experience that carcinomata tend to appear in persons who have reached or passed middle age and are rare in young people. On the contrary, many sarcomata and those mixed tumors which sometimes occur congenitally, are more frequent in young people. It is possible that some of the contributory causes which favor tumor growth are really necessary in the case of cancerous tumors, for it is known that, while cancers originate in old persons and old animals which have long been exposed to those influences, young mice are far more susceptible than old ones to the artificial implantation of these tumors.

RESISTANCE AND IMMUNITY

Only the briefest outline of this subject can be given here, although an enormous amount of labor has been devoted to it in recent years.

Undoubtedly, many persons are highly resistant or incapable of harboring certain forms of tumor growth, although they may be susceptible enough to the growth and extension of another form. We have no way of determining this accurately, but we do know that when a tumor is already established in the body and is discharging into the circulation many emboli of its cells, most of these may be destroyed by the activities of the tissue fluids. Much light has been shed upon the question by the experimental study of tumors in animals. In mice, for example, malignant tumors which are transplanted from spontaneously developed nodules to normal mice fail to take at first, except in a very small percentage of the experiments. Later, with increasing adaptation to the conditions met with in the body of the mouse, the tumors, after repeated transplantation, acquire the power of growing in nearly every inoculated mouse. Nevertheless, there are some mice which show themselves refractory to the best adapted tumors. This is a natural immunity. If a mouse recovers spontaneously by destroying the tumor growth already begun in its tissues, or even if the tumor is completely extirpated after growing for a time there, it becomes immune and cannot be again inoculated successfully with that tumor. It is even immune with respect to other tumors, and Ehrlich has named this condition panimmunity. In this respect immunity from experimental tumors differs from the more specific immunity against infections. Even the inoculation of tissue or blood from another normal animal of the same species will confer an immunity from tumor inoculation. In all cases the immunity is dependent upon the inoculation of living cells, whether they be tumor-cells or those of the normal tissue. Ehrlich has offered an explanation of immunity which rests on the idea that a tumor requires for its growth a certain specific substance. He found that, by inoculation of a rapidly growing tumor, he could render impossible the growth of a second tumor, and, thinking that the first tumor had used up all this specific food substance, called this condition *athrepsia.* There have been many attacks on the validity of this theory, and it is not yet decided whether it will hold, since many investigators have found it possible to implant a second tumor in an animal already bearing one. The well-known zigzág transplantation from mouse to rat and back formed the strongest element of Ehrlich's proof. A mouse tumor implanted in a rat grows for a few days, but then regresses and dies, unless it be retransplanted into a mouse, where it once more thrives. Ehrlich thinks that the tumor must have lacked a particular food-stuff in the rat, necessary for its growth.

These principles have not been applied to any great extent to the study of human tumors, and little is known of the conditions of immunity in the human body.

Histological Character of the Immunity Reactions.—Several writers, among whom da Fano may be mentioned, have studied the histological reaction to the invasion of tumors and have found that lymphocytes and plasma cells are especially concerned in this reaction. Murphy and his associates have found, quite recently, that the susceptibility to tumor implantation is enormously increased by the destruction of the lymphocytes by exposure to the *x*-ray or by the administration of benzol. They look upon the accumulation of lymphocytes about a tumor, for this reason, as a protective or combative reaction. These views are supported by others of their experiments which show that an embryo in which no lymphocytes have yet appeared is extremely susceptible to tumor inoculation, while the implantation of a fragment of lymphoid tissue from an adult into the body of the embryo confers upon it a resistance practically equal to that of the adult.

THEORIES AS TO THE ÆTIOLOGY OF TUMORS

We are as yet quite ignorant of the actual cause of tumor growth. It is a question which has occupied the minds of pathologists and clinicians for many years, and theories in incredible numbers have been proposed. Some of these theories, put forward by men who had worked very intimately with tumors, have survived to this day, but it is rather discouraging to find that most of the modern theories are merely fantastic inventions of a philosophic character, proposed by men who do not seem to have lived with tumors, nor even to have been particularly familiar with them. They always introduce many new terms and a new classification of tumors, with specially constructed Greek names, and the whole merely adds to the confusion and reminds one of the writings of the scholastics of the middle ages. We are quite ignorant of the real cause of tumor growth, and therefore the theories may all be wrong. In the meanwhile, until the real cause is ascertained, we may learn along what lines these attempts at explanation have been made.

Theory of Parasitic Origin of Tumors.—The most obvious explanation would lie in the existence of a living organism, continually stirring the tissues to grow, but in that case it would, as we have explained, be necessary for the parasite to associate itself indissolubly with the cell, and accompany it in all its wanderings and divisions. No such minute organism has been found, and the gross parasites which have been described seem quite incapable of such subtle and constant relations, for it is not a reaction of any contiguous tissue that they provoke, but the irresistible growth of one sort of tissue, which wanders into new situations and maintains an independent existence. If there are parasites, we must be prepared to find them quite different from any which we now know, and capable of producing tissue reactions quite at variance with all the laws of normal growth and normal reaction to injury. They must be so included in the growing cells as to multiply with them and accompany them wherever they go, since otherwise it seems impossible that they could maintain their stimulating effect upon cells which had been transplanted to a distant organ. If the parasite never shows itself alone or through its effects on tissues in general, but only in this intimate relation with its own tumor-cells, it must remain difficult to distinguish it from an acquired quality of the tumor-cells themselves. There must be a different parasite for each of the many sorts of tumors, and every one of these parasites must have these characters of intimate affinity for the special cells which it chooses to stimulate. It must merge its ability to produce antibodies in the affected animal in that of the cells, since that immunity seems to be of cytotoxic character and not very specific. Lambert has shown that tumor-cells will grow *in vitro* in the plasma of an animal insusceptible to the growth of that tumor, but are injured or destroyed by the plasma of an animal immunized against it. Since a cytotoxic immunity can be produced against the implantation of the tumor by the introduction of normal tissues of an animal of the same species, the parasite must be killed, too, and must, therefore, have acquired the specific character of the cells. It really seems that it must have become identical with the cell.

Theories of Tumor Growth Based on the Effect of Irritants.—Numerous instances of tumor growth following upon irritation or injury with inflammatory reaction have been mentioned, and there has long been a desultory argument tending toward the emphasis of their importance as causes of tumor growth. Bashford lays stress upon the direct connection which is so often observed, and although it fails in most cases, it is very striking when it does occur. Only yesterday, while writing somewhat skeptically of this relation, a man aged seventy showed me his leg, which he had struck against a bath-tub some months before, producing an abrasion which had failed to heal. He had no suspicion that anything had happened except that it had not healed, but covering the site of the injury there was actually a rough, flattened tumor, which appeared to be of the nature of a basal-cell carcinoma. Most of these tumors appear after the irritation has existed a long time and has produced extensive inflammatory infiltration and reparatory changes in the underlying connective tissues, as well as in the epithelium itself. No one has succeeded in producing them experimentally, except perhaps by the use of x-rays or the introduction of certain gross parasites, and the question arises as to whether a predisposition through senile changes or otherwise may not be necessary for their initiation.

The idea of the influence of irritants recalls to our attention the whole question of the action of stimuli upon the growth of tissue, which has been so long discussed. Many investigators accept the existence of direct stimuli to growth, and bring forward numerous instances in the history of tuberculosis, syphilis, and a host of other infectious diseases and banal injuries. Others hold that the tendency to grow is roused only indirectly through functional needs, and Weigert has claimed that new-growth is essentially a reparatory process, attempting to make up for tissue which has been destroyed, thereby restoring the disturbed equilibrium of the tissues. In ordinary circumstances it is usually possible to explain the new growth of tissue as the effect of reparatory processes, even though in the cases of excessive growth it often appears that it is the response to repeated injuries which may affect the repairing tissue itself. Nevertheless, this explanation is complicated, and it is much easier to assume that injuries or irritants may directly stimulate the tissues to grow. In any case the new tissue remains subject to the general laws which govern the architecture of the body, and tends to return to the normal relations when the irritation ceases.

In the case of a tumor, a new element is introduced by the failure of the tissue to evince this general tendency to return to the normal relations after the irritation has ceased. The finality of its departure from the laws of growth is as though a train suddenly ran off the track, and careered through the neighboring streets and houses. Even though we accept the idea that irritation may directly stimulate tissue to grow, our explanation of the history of a tumor must really begin with its continuous independent and unlimited growth, which might be initiated, but not maintained in distant situations, by such irritants as are usually discussed.

Theories of Tumor Growth Depending upon Disturbance of the Equilibrium of Tissues.—So firmly established is the evidence of mutual support and restraint among the tissues, that many writers have sought, in a disturbance of this equilibrium, the explanation of the unlimited growth of tumors. Thiersch thought that, with senility, the energy of growth of the connective tissue failed, so that the epithelium could invade it and grow at will, while Waldeyer offered the reverse explanation, stating that the failure of the epithelium to maintain its ranks enabled the connective tissue to surround and isolate some of it, which then grew in its new situation. The inadequacy of these explanations is evident, and Hanseman pointed out at once the fact that tumors occur in the young and are especially malignant. Ribbert has pursued these ideas, explaining the ingrowth of epithelium as dependent upon primary changes in the underlying connective tissue, which becomes relaxed and infiltrated with leucocytes, so that it is exposed to the invasion of the epithelium, which it surrounds and isolates, thereby allowing unlimited growth through the disarrangement of equilibrium. The inflammatory infiltration of lymphocytes, upon which Ribbert lays stress, appears now to be the protective reaction which Murphy has shown to be so important in preventing the extension of tumors. While Ribbert's theory involves the primary activity of the altered connective tissue, it does not rest solely on that basis, but is related in certain ways to other theories, so that it must be referred to again.

Theories of Tumor Growth Depending upon Displacement of Embryonic Cells.—Cohnheim's Theory.—Another theory, associated especially with the name of Cohnheim, assumes that since certain tumors which occur congenitally are traceable to congenital maldevelopment, it is possible, or even probable, that a disarrangement of cells in the course of embryonic growth may lie at the root of tumor growth in general. Cohnheim's idea was that at some stage of embryonic life cells might become isolated while still possessed of great energy of growth and potentialities which would have carried them on to the development of some specific tissue of the body, had they remained in their normal connection with the rest of the cells of the embryo. These cells are conceived of as lying dormant among the growing tissues, and showing no tendency to unfold their own powers of growth during years. Then, when the other tissues have become organs of an adult man, and commonly late in the life of this man, the hidden group of cells, still endowed with embryonic vigor, begins to grow. Cohnheim did not think that these cells would begin their growth without some stimulus, but that, once started, they would exhibit a capacity for growth comparable only to that of the embryo.

Numerous criticisms have been made, of course. It is difficult to believe that such misplaced cells or groups of cells could remain latent for many years and still maintain their youthful vigor. Further it is known that when such displacements of tissue obviously occur, the cells tend to proceed through their allotted course of maturation and development, to produce finished tissue, rather than to continue as embryonic cells, although there are some teratomata in which the peculiar form of cells has been interpreted, rightly or wrongly, as embryonic. Since tumors may occur anywhere, and are frequently initiated by irritation, it is necessary to assume an extremely wide distribution of displaced cells if a group of them is to be ready wherever the irritation may act. While Cohnheim's theory may explain perfectly the teratomata and other growths which are obviously related to fœtal inclusions, it does not explain the malignant type of growth, since it does not explain why the cells of a tumor behave differently from those of an embryo, in that they continue to grow in the same atypical form and never proceed to anything resembling the end-product of tissue growth.

Ribbert's Theory.—Ribbert also assumes that the most important and indispensable basis for the origin of a tumor is the independence of a tissue germ, attained through isolation of the cells, through which the always adequate capacity for growth of the cells is liberated. Not every isolated group of cells forms a tumor, and those which do are dependent upon favorable conditions of development, nutrition, etc. The character of the tumor depends upon the type of tissue in the rudiment, its degree of independence, and its energy of growth at the time of its isolation from the surrounding cells. This isolation occurs most frequently in embryonic life, but may also occur in adults, and is produced by abnormal processes of growth. Another tissue may grow in such a way as to cut off a group of cells from its normal relations with its own tissue. The growth of the other tissue is in a sense a preliminary stage, which ends in the initiation of a tumor, when it has isolated a group of cells which act as the germ of the tumor. Tumor-cells are not biologically different from normal cells, and only the conditions under which they find themselves decide them upon tumor formation.

When Ribbert accepts in its general principle the Cohnheim theory, he modifies it by the statement that the isolation of the cells which are to produce the growth may occur in adult life, and that this isolation is brought about by the irregular growth of other tissues. Ribbert's other contention is that tumors are in a sense unicentric, that they grow out of their own material, invading the other tissue, it is true, but not infecting it or stimulating it to grow. He emphasizes particularly the statement that it is wrong to regard the growing margin of an epithelial tumor as a transitional zone between normal and tumor tissue, in which the normal tissue is being converted into tumor tissue. Instead, the tumor is entirely dependent upon its own dividing cells, which may burst through and upheave the adjacent epithelium or even heal together with it, but which do not convert it into tumor tissue. Borst and many others accept this statement, but Hauser and several more recent writers question its truth. It is well known that there is commonly a modification of the epithelium in the neighborhood of a primary epithelial tumor which resembles that at the edge of an old ulcer. The epithelial downgrowths between the papillæ may be exaggerated, and are surrounded by an exudate of lymphocytes. Whether this is capable of being shown to be a preliminary to actual conversion into cancer tissue remains to be determined. Lubarsch points out the fact that the epithelial tissue adjacent to a metastasis in an internal organ from an epithelioma of the skin is very much less distinctly changed than that which adjoins the primary growth.

Somewhat analogous to these theories which invoke the aid of the embryonic energy of growth are those more faintly expressed ideas which depend upon the possibility of a new fertilization. J. Loeb has shown that the eggs of some animals may be stirred to parthenogenetic development by the action of chemical substances. The disturbance of the lipoid sheath by some solvent, allowing the oxidative processes to go on, appears to be the mechanism concerned, and this explanation has been transferred to those experiments in which the introduction of scharlach oil, ether-water, etc., have stirred up a new growth of cells. There have, indeed, been efforts to show that an actual conjugation of adjacent cells may take place after a preliminary heterotypic division, with reduction of chromosomes to half their normal number (Farmer, Moore, and Walker). Such conjugation ought to confer a new impulse to growth, exactly as in the fertilization of the ovum. The idea is a most tempting one at first sight, but the proofs of the actual existence of this process have not been satisfactorily brought forward.

Theories of Tumor Growth Depending upon Changes in the Cells.—Hauser was among the first to insist that tumor growth could be explained only on the assumption of a profound change in the character of the cells of which it is composed. He speaks of new cell races, and recognizes especially their independence and their arrogance in overcoming other tissues and cells. Marchand, Beneke, and Ziegler hold somewhat similar views. Hansemann has elaborated the idea by attempting to define the character of this change in the cells, which he describes as *anaplasia*, an alteration in the cell not always easily recognizable by its form, but consisting in changed histological characters which allow it to proliferate rather than to functionate. This, in its more intense degrees, is accompanied by changes in form and arrangement of the cells, and is associated with atypical or asymmetrical mitoses. Anaplasia is not the cause of tumor growth, but the term is descriptive of the changes which occur in the cells. Borst, recalling the infinite complexity of the process of distribution of parental characters to all the cells of the developing body, regards the change in the cells which leads to tumor growth as due to some irregularity in the formation of their "idioplasm," which one-sided development does not necessarily incapacitate them for an ordinary function in the ranks of other cells, but leaves them capable of independent and atypical growth. Schwalbe adheres to this idea, which he expresses differently, inasmuch as he speaks of congenital pathological abnormality of the cells, or cell malformation.

It was said in the beginning that we do not know the cause of tumor growth, and it seems quite unprofitable to attempt new theories except on the basis of adequate new facts. Those at our disposal have been so well pondered over that the newer theories prove to be merely the invention of new terms to express the old vague ideas.

Nevertheless, I must express my own impressions of what has been learned and written of tumor growth without advocating any new theory. We have a fairly clear conception of the laws of normal growth from the beginning to the end of life. Those laws apply equally well to the growth of the embryo and to the growth of the adult. Tumor growth does not obey these laws, but transgresses them in every direction. It seems idle, therefore, to attempt its explanation by assuming that embryonic cells persist and grow in the adult body. That may explain teratomata very well, since they are essentially finite growths that obey the normal laws, as well as they can with their incomplete tissues and in their cramped situations. But it does not explain the growth of tumors.

On the other hand, we are quite familiar with the effects of every sort of injurious influence in disturbing temporarily the normal growth of tissue, and can formulate general laws for these effects which are found to be always respected. But tumors do not respect them at all. For that reason I have written of tumor-growth separately from all the rest of pathology as a thing apart, not to be dealt with according to the laws of reaction of normal tissues. Although we discuss every sort of injury as a possible cause of their growth, we cannot conceive of one which would have this result without assuming some abnormal character in the tissue itself. No known injury can elicit such a reaction in normal tissue, and it must be a parasite of a totally unimagined kind which could do it.

We are left with the impression that there is somehow produced a sudden, profound, and permanent change in the character of the cells themselves, and that other tissues which are invaded or form the stroma are affected by their activity; but although we realize this irrevocable change, we cannot assign a reason for it, nor even tell precisely in what structural alteration it may be recognized.

LITERATURE

Only such treatises as are of general character and give further references to the literature are given here:

Virchow: Die krankhaften Geschwülste, Berlin, 1863–1867.

Borst: Die Lehre von den Geschwülsten, Wiesbaden, 1902. Würzburger Abhandlungen, 1906, vi, 221. (Excellent paper.) Ziegler's Beiträge, 1910, xlix, 638. Aschoff: Pathol. Anat., 1913, i, 51.

Ribbert: Geschwülstlehre, Bonn, 1904, with Supplements. Das Carcinom des Menschen, Bonn, 1911. (*cf.* Orth, Ztschr. f. Krebsforsch., 1913, xiii, 566, for a criticism of this work and Ribbert's theories.)

E. Albrecht: Verh. d. Dtsch. Path. Gesellsch., 1904, viii, 89. Monatsschr. f. Geburtsh. u. Gynäk., 1904, xx, 123.

v. Dungern and Werner: Wesen der bösartiger Geschwülste, Leipzig, 1907.

Israel: Berl. kl. Woch., 1900, xxxvii, 608, 644, 667.

Schwalbe: Verh. Naturh. Mediz. Verein zu Heidelberg, 1906, N. F. viii, 337.

M. B. Schmidt: Verbreitungswege der Karzinome, Jena, 1903.

Apolant and Ehrlich: Genese des Carcinoms, Verh. Dtsch. Path. Gesellsch., 1908, xii, 3.

Versé: Problem des Geschwulstmalignität, Jena, 1914.

Lubarsch: Pathol. Anat. u. Krebsforschung, Wiesbaden, 1902.

Wolff: Lehre von der Krebskrankheiten, Jena, 1911.

Da Fano: Ztschr. f. Immunitätsforschung, 1910, v, 1.

Murphy: Jour. Exp. Med., 1913, xvii, 482; 1914, xix, 513; 1915, xxii, 204.

Rous: Jour. Exp. Med., 1910, xii, 696; 1911, xiii, 397; 1912, xv, 119, etc.

Apolant: Ztschr. f. allg. Physiologie, 1909, ix, 63, Ref. (Review of experimental work.)

Hansemann: Anaplasie, bösartigen Geschwülste, Berlin, 1893–1897.

Borrel: Problème du Cancer, Paris, 1907. Bull. Inst. Pasteur, 1907, v, 206. Ann. de l'Inst. Pasteur, 1909, xxiii, 97.

Fibiger: Ztschr. f. Krebsforschung, 1913, xiii, 217.

Herxheimer and Reinke: Ergebn. d. allg. Path., 1910, $xiii_2$, 356; 1913, xvi_2, 1.

Bashford and others: Publications Imperial Cancer Research Fund, 1904–1912.

Woglom: Studies in Experimental Cancer, Crocker Research Fund, New York, 1913.

Levin, Lambert, Hanes, and others. MacCallum, General Introduction: Experimental Studies in Cancer, Crocker Research Fund, N. Y., 1912.

INDEX

Note.—Page references to illustrations appear in *italics*. In cases where there are several references to discussions of the same subject, the more important references are printed in **heavy type.**